William A. Andrews, Faculty of Education, University of Toronto
T.J. Elgin Wolfe, Faculty of Education, University of Toronto
Robert S. Hedges, Clarkson High School
Adel Kamel, Stouffville District High School
John R. Percy, Department of Astronomy, University of Toronto

SCIENCE 10
An Introductory Study

PRENTICE-HALL INTERMEDIATE SCIENCE SERIES

SERIES EDITOR:

William A. Andrews
Professor of Science Education
Faculty of Education, University of Toronto

Science: An Introductory Study 9
—Student Text
—Teacher's Guide

Science: An Introductory Study 10
—Student Text
—Teacher's Guide

Discovering Science 9

Discovering Science 10

Prentice-Hall Canada Inc., Scarborough, Ontario

Canadian Cataloguing in Publication Data

Main entry under title:

Science, an introductory study 10

(Prentice-Hall intermediate science series)
For use in schools.
Includes index.
ISBN 0-13-794629-5

1. Science. I. Andrews, William A., date II. Series.

Q161.2.S342 1988 500 C88-094150-2

Prentice-Hall Inc., Englewood Cliffs, New Jersey
Prentice-Hall International, Inc., London
Prentice-Hall of Australia Pty., Ltd., Sydney
Prentice-Hall of India Pvt., Ltd., New Delhi
Prentice-Hall of Japan, Inc., Tokyo
Prentice-Hall of Southeast Asia (Pte.) Ltd., Singapore
Editora Prentice-Hall do Brasil Ltda., Rio de Janeiro
Prentice-Hall Hispanoamericana, S.A., Mexico

ISBN 0-13-794629-5

Project Editor: Julia Lee
Production: Pamela Russell
Illustrator: James Loates and Associates
Composition: Q-Composition
Cover photo: H. Armstrong Roberts Inc./Miller Comstock Inc.

5 6 96

Printed and bound in Canada

Policy Statement

Prentice-Hall Canada Inc., Secondary School Division, and the authors of *Science: An Introductory Study 10* are committed to the publication of instructional materials that are as bias-free as possible. This text was evaluated for bias prior to publication.

The authors and publisher of this book also recognize the importance of appropriate reading levels and have therefore made every effort to ensure the highest degree of readability in the text. The content has been selected, organized, and written at a level suitable to the intended audience. Standard readability tests have been applied at several stages in the text's preparation to ensure an appropriate reading level.

Research indicates, however, that readability is affected by much more than word or sentence length; factors such as presentation, format and design, none of which are considered in the usual readability tests, also greatly influence the ease with which students read a book. These and many additional features have been carefully prepared to ensure maximum student comprehension. "To the Student" (page **ix**) describes those features. Further information is in the Introduction of the *Teacher's Guide*.

Contents

Acknowledgments

The authors wish to acknowledge the staff and associates of Prentice-Hall Canada Inc. for their dedication and their skillful coordination and production of this text under difficult timelines. In particular, we extend our thanks to Catherine Leatherdale, David Peden, Julia Lee, and Pamela Russell. We also thank Steve Lane for his assistance in the planning and development of this text.

We wish, further to thank the many teachers who consulted with us in the developmental phase of this text. Among these people, Jim Boutlier of Clarkson Secondary School made special contributions. Our thanks also to the people who volunteered to serve as models in the photographs. In particular, we wish to acknowledge the assistance of students from the classes of Donna Moore at David and Mary Thomson Collegiate Institute, students from the classes of Rob Hedges at Clarkson Secondary School, and students from the classes of Adel Kamel at Stouffville District High School. We are grateful for the photographs that these people and those mentioned in the photo credits provided in order to make our book more appealing and useful.

Our thanks are extended, once again, to James Loates and Associates for their attractive and accurate artwork. Finally, we extend a special word of appreciation to Lois Andrews for her skillful and dedicated preparation of the final manuscript and index as well as for her editorial and managerial assistance.

W.A. Andrews
Editor and Principal Author

To the Student

Welcome to *Science: An Introductory Study 10*! We hope you will enjoy this course and learn many interesting and useful things. This book has two main aims. One aim is to provide you with knowledge about the world around you. The other aim is to give you experiences in using the scientific method of inquiry. In order to achieve these aims, this book is divided in a logical fashion into nine parts.

Introduction
Unit 1 Interactions
Unit 2 Organisms and Their External Environment
Unit 3 Organisms and Their Internal Environment
Unit 4 Heat
Unit 5 Magnetism and Electricity
Unit 6 Applied Chemistry
Unit 7 Waste Management
Unit 8 Astronomy

The Introduction is designed to reacquaint you with the scientific method of inquiry. Although there are many scientific methods, there is a common underlying pattern of logical thought and action in every scientific study. The Introduction presents that pattern and shows you how it can be used to investigate some interesting problems. You also use this pattern again and again throughout this text. Our intent is that you become so comfortable with this pattern that you can approach problems in a manner similar to that used by scientists. We also want you to understand what science is, and to be aware of its usefulness and limitations. Often in our daily lives we encounter problems that can be solved best by using the scientific method. Learn it well!

The eight units of this book include material from many branches of science. Units 1 to 3 deal with biology, Units 4 and 5 with physics, Unit 6 with chemistry, Unit 7 with environmental science, and Unit 8 with astronomy. As you can see, you will get a taste of several sciences. This will help you choose the senior science courses you wish to study in later years. It will also help you explain many of the interesting and important things around you. For example, before the end of this course you will be able to answer questions such as these: How can we help save endangered species? Can we harvest forests in such a way that wildlife living there will not be harmed? How do animals find their way during migration? How do earthworms breathe? How fast is your reaction time? How does heat get from one place to another? How do insulation and thermopane windows help prevent heat loss from a home? How is soap made? How do storage cells and batteries work? How can we decrease the amount of waste we produce? What is a star made of?

Yes, you will find answers to questions like these as you work your way through this book. But, of most significance, we hope that as a result of this course, you will begin asking questions about the world around you. If that happens, this course will have been successful.

How To Use This Book

This book contains more information than can be studied in one year. Your teacher will select those chapters and sections that will be most useful to you and your classmates. You will study the topics in this book through activities and through narratives. Activities are experiments carried out in the laboratory. They give you practical experience in using the scientific method. Scientists, however, do not simply conduct experiments; they also read a great deal. Therefore, this book includes narratives, or reading sections, which contain important information and explain concepts developed in the activities.

Science: An Introductory Study 10 was written to make the learning of science interesting and clear. The following features help make learning easier. To get the most out of this text, you should keep them in mind.

1. Reading Sections

Each chapter has some reading sections. Read them carefully. They provide the basic information that you need to do the activities. They also summarize and explain activities and provide interesting examples from the world around us.

Always do the questions in the *Section Review* at the end of a section. They aren't difficult. You can find the answers to all the questions in the section. Finding these answers will help you understand what you have read.

2. Laboratory Activities

Always read the procedure before you begin the activity. Then follow the steps carefully. Pay special attention to any ***CAUTION***. Finally, try all the *Discussion* questions. They are generally of two types. Some are included to help you find out if you understand the activity. Others are included to show you how to apply what you learned to problems from everyday life.

3. Chapter Contents and Objectives

Each chapter begins with a table of contents that provides an overview of the reading and activity sections in the chapter. Each chapter opening also contains a list of the chapter objectives. Read both of these carefully before you start the chapter. This will give you both a feeling for what the chapter is about, and an indication of what your teacher expects you to learn.

4. Chapter Highlights and Key Terms

Every chapter ends with a list of the main points of the chapter called *Chapter Highlights*. Always read them. If you don't understand some of them, ask your teacher for help. A list of *Key Terms* is also included at the end of each chapter. If you don't remember the meanings of some of these terms, you should read about them again. (Consult the Index at the back of the book. The number in bold black type indicates the page on which an explanation of the term is found.)

5. Special Features

This text has three special features that will help you decide if you might be interested in a career in science.

- **Careers** are descriptions of science-related careers and the preparation you must make for these careers.
- **Biographies** are stories of the life and work of some Canadian scientists who are, today, making important contributions to science.
- **Vistas** are descriptions of exciting areas of science that are currently attracting considerable attention.

6. End-of-Chapter Questions

Each chapter concludes with four types of questions:

- **Recognizing the Concepts**. These multiple-choice items test your ability to recognize the main ideas and concepts of the chapter.
- **Understanding the Concepts**. These short answer items are designed to help you see how well you understand the main ideas and concepts.
- **Applying the Concepts**. These questions give you an opportunity to use the knowledge you have gained in the chapter. Usually they deal with practical applications that are interesting, challenging, and useful.
- **Investigations**. The end of each chapter also includes what we call investigations. These are further classroom activities, home projects, self-directed experiments, library research projects, field studies, and so on. In these items we give you only an idea to get you started. The rest of the time you are on your own, solving problems the scientific way.

W.A. Andrews
Editor and Principal Author

INTRODUCTION

This introduction is designed to refresh your memory about the nature of science and its importance to all of us. It also reviews the scientific method and shows you how this method can help you in your daily life.

Fig. I-1 You have used the scientific method before.

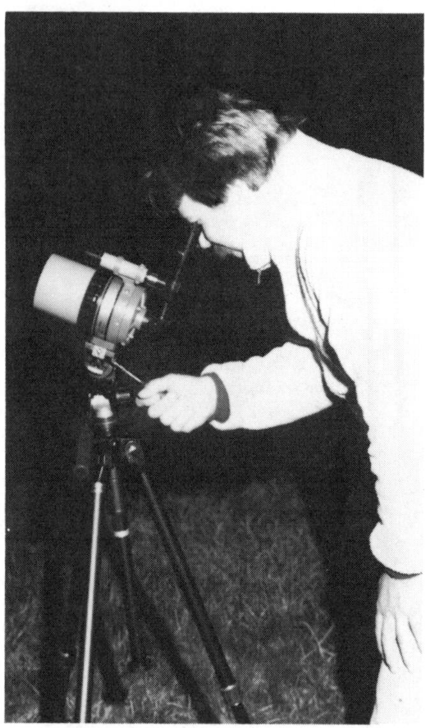

Fig. I-2 Astronomy is a science. What does it have in common with other sciences?

What Is Science?

In your science course last year you encountered at least four sciences: physics, chemistry, biology, and environmental science. The same four sciences and a fifth one, astronomy, are dealt with in this book (Fig. I-2). What do they have in common that allows all of them to be called science? In what ways do they differ?

Every science has two main parts. First, it has a body of knowledge. For example, certain facts, theories, models, laws, and other information make up the science of zoology (the study of animals). A different set of facts, theories, models, laws, and other information make up the science of chemistry. The sciences, then, differ in the subject matter with which they deal.

The second part of every science is the method used for discovering and using knowledge. This method is much the same for all sciences. Therefore it is called the **scientific method**. Most scientists agree that there is no one scientific method that all scientists follow rigidly in all their studies. Yet, most scientists also agree that, over the long run, a general pattern is followed in most scientific work. You used the scientific method last year. It will be reviewed later in this introduction.

Fig. I-3 This store sells many makes of bicycles. How would you decide which one to buy?

Why Study Science?

Why study science? If you hope to become a scientist, you know the answer. You have to learn basic science like that in this book before you can learn more advanced science. However, you likely learned another reason last year. There are often times when you can use science, either its content or its method, in your daily life. And you will usually be glad that you did. As consumers we have to make choices every day. What is the best toothpaste to buy? What bicycle is the best buy for under $500 (Fig. I-3)? Which VHS video tape is the best buy? What zoom telephoto lens should I buy for my camera?

How do you make such choices? It certainly isn't easy! The advertisements on radio and television don't help. Everyone's product seems to be "the best". Newspaper advertisements aren't much better. The advertisements aren't necessarily false, but in many cases they can be misleading. However, they won't be misleading to people who think before they buy, particularly if they think scientifically. If you think and act scientifically before you buy, you will do most of these things:

- Question the claims of manufacturers.
- Collect data on the products you plan to buy.
- Set up and do any experiments that you feel are necessary.
- Record the results you get (or the data you found). Use data tables to make comparisons easier.
- Draw a conclusion regarding the best buy.

Let's now look at some examples that will remind you how important it is to think and act scientifically.

Buying VHS Video Tapes

If you visited five different stores and asked which VHS video tape was the best buy, you could get five different answers. How, then, do you make a choice? Clearly, data organized in tabular form would help you compare the tapes. If you had the proper equipment, you could collect your own data. Of course, you don't have such equipment. However, the tapes have been tested by independent organizations. Most of the data in Table I-1 are from these tests. The price is the result of our own investigation.

Table I-1 Comparing VHS Video Tapes

			Video		*Audio*	
Brand	*Average price*	*Warranty (months)*	*Colour noise*	*Signal retention*	*Bandwidth*	*Dynamic range*
Brand A	$ 7.50	6	1	1	1	1
Brand AA	10.95	36	1	2	1	2
Brand B	13.50	3	1	1	3	1
Brand C	11.75	3	2	1	3	2
Brand D	12.60	none	2	1	4	2

Notes:

1. The *numerals* are from this scale: 1 2 3 4 5
   Best ⟷ Worst
2. *Colour noise* includes unwanted visual information such as "snow", streaks, and blobs of colour.
3. *Signal retention* is a measure of how long the recorded image will last on the tape.
4. *Bandwidth* is the range of audio frequencies the tape can record (from deep bass to high treble).
5. *Dynamic range* is the range between the loudest and softest sounds the tape can record.
6. We have omitted the names of the tapes since prices and characteristics do change with time.

Fig. I-4 Many makers of video tapes put tape characteristics on the package. Read this information as well as independent test results.

Now, which tape would you buy (Fig. I-4)? The answer is clear, isn't it? Brand A received the top rating in all categories and is much cheaper than the others. Incidentally, Brand AA is made by the same firm that made Brand A. Brand AA is advertised as the top-line tape of that company. Yet it fails to match Brand A in two categories and costs $3.45 more. It does have a longer warranty, but it does not perform as well as Brand A does.

A scientific investigation of video tapes helps you select the best tape and save money. All you need to do is, first, question the claims of the manufacturers. (As we found out, what they say is not always correct.) Then you simply collect data, either by yourself or from independent sources, and organize it in a data table. You can see how easy it is to draw conclusions after that.

Fig. I-5 A 70-200 mm zoom lens is ideal for many types of outdoor photography. Here it is being used to photograph a squirrel in action.

Buying a Telephoto Zoom Lens

A telephoto lens that zooms from about 70 mm to about 200 mm is ideal for sporting events, portraits, and some wildlife photography (Fig. I-5). But a visit to a camera store will reveal a bewildering array of lenses with varying prices and features. How do you select the best lens? Do you believe the manufacturers' claims? Do you follow the advice of the salesperson? Or do you conduct a scientific investigation? You should, of course, study data from the manufacturers. You should also ask the advice of experts in the store. But nothing is more helpful than a scientific investigation like the one we just went through for video tapes. Table I-2 shows part of the data collected in such an investigation. All the lenses are in the 70–210 mm zoom range. The prices are values we obtained in our investigation.

Before you begin to study the data, a photographer in your class will explain these terms: zoom lens, telephoto lens, aperture range, sharpness, flare, and distortion.

Table I-2 Buying a Telephoto Zoom Lens

Brand	*Price*	*Aperture range*	*Mass (g)*	*Sharpness*	*Flare*	*Distortion*
Brand A	$165	f/3.5–22	624	2	2	2
Brand B	529	f/4.0–22	822	1	1	3
Brand C	99	f/4.5–22	539	3	2	4
Brand D	285	f/3.8–22	709	4	4	4
1 2 3 4 5 Best ⟷ Worst						

Which lens would you buy? Certainly not Brand D! It is the second most expensive, the second heaviest, and the worst performer. For the price, Brand C isn't bad. But it is a slow lens (f/4.5) and requires more light than any of the others. Brand B is a good lens, except it costs over three times as much as Brand A and is a slower and much heavier lens than Brand A. Though it beats Brand A in two categories, it has more distortion. Everything considered, Brand A is probably the best buy. The studies from which we obtained these data give still more information that would help you make a selection the scientific way.

Why Should You Study Science?

Hopefully these two examples have shown you two good reasons for studying science. First, when you study science you learn to think and act scientifically. The examples have shown that, if you do this, you will often make better decisions in your life. Second, when you study science, you will learn information that will help you understand the world around you. Likely you have already discovered a third reason for studying science—it's fun!

The Scientific Method

The people who tested the video tapes and telephoto zoom lenses used the scientific method. We suggested that you, too, should use this method as a way of thinking and acting. You will be using the scientific method throughout this course and, hopefully, in your daily life.

There is no one method that all scientists must use in their studies. However, most scientists tend to follow a general pattern that has six main steps. The steps are:

1. Recognizing a problem;
2. Collecting information on the problem;
3. Making a hypothesis;
4. Doing an experiment;
5. Observing and recording results;
6. Making a conclusion.

Let us review these steps by seeing how the scientific method was used to solve two interesting problems:

- How do migrating birds find their way?
- How do rattlesnakes track their wounded prey?

How Do Migrating Birds Find Their Way?

The universe is full of mysteries. It is the job of scientists to explore those mysteries and try to solve them. Let's see how the scientific method was used to investigate the mystery of bird migration.

The Arctic Tern: Migration Champion

Fig. I-6 This bird migrates about 40 000 km each year. That is about the distance around the earth at the equator.

The Arctic tern makes one of the most remarkable and longest journeys of all migratory species (Fig. I-6). Some Arctic terns nest in eastern Canada north of the Arctic Circle. They begin their autumn migration by flying across the Atlantic Ocean to the west coast of Europe. They follow this coast to the west coast of Africa and then fly southward to their winter range. This range can extend right to the Antarctic Circle. An Arctic tern probably sees more daylight in its lifetime than any other animal. Its summer days in the Arctic are 24 h long and its winter days in the Antarctic are almost as long. However, in order to experience these long days the tern must fly great distances each day. To do this, it frequently flies at night. How does it find its way over such long distances, often over water, and often flying at night?

Some Background Many studies have shown that some birds rely on **natural landmarks**. That is, they follow familiar routes along river valleys, past a mountain, across a peninsula, and so on. But many birds obviously do not do this. In one experiment a bird called a shearwater was taken from its nesting colony in Britain and released in Boston, about 5000 km away. In 12.5 d the bird was back on its nest in Britain! How did this bird start from a place it had never seen, fly across an unknown ocean, and locate its nest among countless thousands on a small island off the coast of Britain? Clearly this bird has uncanny navigational skills. What are they?

Scientists have discovered that the **sun** plays an important role in the navigation of daytime migrants. And the **stars** are equally important for nighttime migrants. But two questions still remain unanswered. First, before a bird can use either the sun or stars as navigational aids, it must know exactly where it is relative to other points. How can it know this? Second, how does the bird navigate when clouds obscure the sun and stars? Let's see how the scientific method was used to answer these two questions.

1. Recognizing a Problem

The ability of birds to navigate in the absence of any visible clues has aroused the curiosity of many scientists. (Aren't you curious too?) This curiosity led to the statement of the problem: *How do migrating birds know where they are, and how do they find their way when landmarks, the sun, and the stars cannot be seen?*

2. Collecting Information on the Problem

The first step in trying to solve the problem is to find out everything important that has been done on this problem. In this case, a search of the literature revealed numerous experiments that show how birds use landmarks, the sun, and the stars in navigation. However, the literature contained only one clue that helped solve the problem. One scientist reasoned that birds may have some internal compass that keeps them on the proper course. The scientist dissected the heads of some birds and found iron-rich tissues. This is the clue that led to the hypothesis.

3. Making a Hypothesis

Using this clue, scientists made up a hypothesis, or a possible solution, for the problem. This hypothesis said: *Birds locate their position and find their way without visible aids by using the earth's magnetic field.* Every hypothesis is just an educated guess. Some come to the scientist as a burst of genius. But most are derived by the scientist after a literature search. In any case, a hypothesis must be tested by an experiment.

4. Doing an Experiment

Many experiments have been done to test this hypothesis. In one experiment a scientist released several homing pigeons near a large deposit of magnetic iron ore. The birds lost their way. However, once they had flown clear of the deposit, they found their way and resumed the correct course. A control population of homing pigeons was released the same distance from "home" but away from the magnetic deposit. All these birds immediately took the correct path home.

Fig. I-7 Why is the control vital to this experiment?

In another experiment tiny magnets were fastened to the heads of some homing pigeons (Fig. I-7). Pieces of a non-magnetic metal with the same mass as the magnets were fastened to the heads of an equal number of homing pigeons. All the pigeons were released. None of the pigeons carrying magnets arrived home. All the others arrived.

5. Observing and Recording Results

Experiments like these were repeated many times in many locations. All the scientists made careful observations and recorded them. These data were often published in journals so they would be available to other researchers.

6. Making a Conclusion

After analyzing the data, scientists concluded that *birds locate their position and find their way without visible aids by using the earth's magnetic field*. The iron deposits in the birds' heads are used like you would use a compass to find your way. When you study this magnetic field in Chapter 14 you should be able to see why they made this conclusion. In this case the conclusion supports the hypothesis. In many cases this is not so. Do you remember what scientists do when the conclusion and hypothesis do not agree?

Scientific experiments like this often open the door to new problems. One obvious problem that arises here is this one: How do birds use the built-in compass that they appear to have? That is, how does this compass work?

Fig. I-8 The rattlesnake strikes its prey and then lets it run away. Later, though, the snake will find the prey. How?

Another mystery that scientists have solved using the scientific method is a rather curious behaviour of the rattlesnake. Let's follow this mystery through from problem to solution.

1. Recognizing a Problem

Observers have long noted that rattlesnakes catch their prey as follows. The coiled snake waits until its prey, often an unsuspecting rodent, comes within striking distance. Then the rattler strikes out, and its fangs inject a poisonous venom into the prey (Fig. I-8). This venom does not kill instantly. It is surprising, therefore, that the rattler now releases the prey and lets it run away! The snake waits long enough for the venom to kill or at least immobilize the prey. Then it follows the trail of the wounded animal and gets its meal. The rattler can follow the wounded prey at night, even though it cannot see all that well in daylight. Here, then, is the problem: *How does a rattlesnake track its wounded prey?*

2. Collecting Information on the Problem

As is usually the case, the first step in solving a problem is to do a literature search. The following information, related to the problem, was collected during such a search:

- A rattlesnake's eyes are sensitive only to visible light.
- A rattlesnake has a heat-sensing organ under each eye. These organs can detect heat radiating from homeothermic (''warm-blooded'') animals. As a result, they help the snake locate and strike its prey. However, they cannot help it track the prey several metres.
- A rattlesnake's tongue detects certain odours. You may have seen a snake flicking its tongue. The tongue brings odours back into the mouth.
- A rattlesnake will not track an unbitten animal.

Using this information, scientists were able to form a hypothesis. Before you read on, what do you think it is?

3. Making a Hypothesis

Rattlesnakes do not track their wounded prey by sight or with their heat sensors. And, rattlesnakes will only track prey they have bitten. As a result, an educated guess, or hypothesis, could be: *A rattlesnake follows the odour of its own venom to track and locate its wounded prey.*

4. Doing an Experiment

As is usually the case, the hypothesis helps direct the scientists' work. That is, it suggests the experimental approach that should be taken. In this case, the scientists need to do an experiment to see if the snake's venom leaves an invisible trail that the snake can follow by smell. The venom, then, is the independent variable in this experiment. The behaviour of the snake is the dependent variable.

To test the hypothesis, scientists dragged a dead mouse that had been bitten by a rattlesnake along a curved path. When the snake was released near this path, it moved exactly along this path, tongue flicking as it sampled the odours in the air. Of course, this experiment needs a control. Its function is to make sure the snake is responding to the venom odour and not something else. Therefore a dead mouse that had not been bitten by a rattlesnake was dragged along a similar curved path. Though the snake still flicked its tongue, it did not follow the path.

5. Observing and Recording Results

This experiment was repeated many times, in different locations, and with different snakes. The data were recorded in a table to make it easier for scientists to keep track of and analyze the data. See if you can set up a data table for this experiment.

6. Making a Conclusion

After analyzing the data, the scientists concluded that the hypothesis was correct. Therefore they made this conclusion: *A rattlesnake follows the odour of its own venom to track and locate its wounded prey.*

Like the migration experiment described earlier, this one also opens the door to further experimentation. A rattlesnake's venom contains many substances. Is it just one of these or a combination of them that a rattlesnake senses and follows? How would you design an experiment to find an answer to this new problem?

Fig. I-9 Do you remember testing leaves for the presence of starch during photosynthesis experiments last year?

More About Science

How Science Grows

After scientists have arrived at a conclusion, they usually do more experiments to check the conclusion. If the experiments do not support the conclusion, the original hypothesis may have to be changed. It may even have to be discarded. Then the whole process must start over again. Sometimes, though, the experiments do not support the hypothesis because something is wrong with the experiments. Perhaps the experimental procedure needs to be redesigned. Or, perhaps the observations and measurements were not accurate enough. When a scientist's results do not agree with the original hypothesis, the scientist usually reexamines the design of the experiment. The scientist then makes a new set of observations to see if the fault lies with the hypothesis or with the experiment.

If many experiments support the conclusion, the scientist may make up a theory. A **theory** is a list of postulates (assumptions) that the experimenter makes up to explain the results. For example, suppose a scientist has done many experiments that show plants die without light. She may next develop an explanation of why this is so. That explanation could include postulates such as these: Light provides the energy needed for certain chemical reactions in plants. Light energy is converted to chemical potential energy in plants (Fig. I-9).

The experimenter would likely do further experiments to test and refine this theory. Sometimes those experiments lead to the abandonment of the theory. Often, though, they lead to refinements in the theory that suggest new problems, new hypotheses, and new experiments. *This is how scientific knowledge grows.*

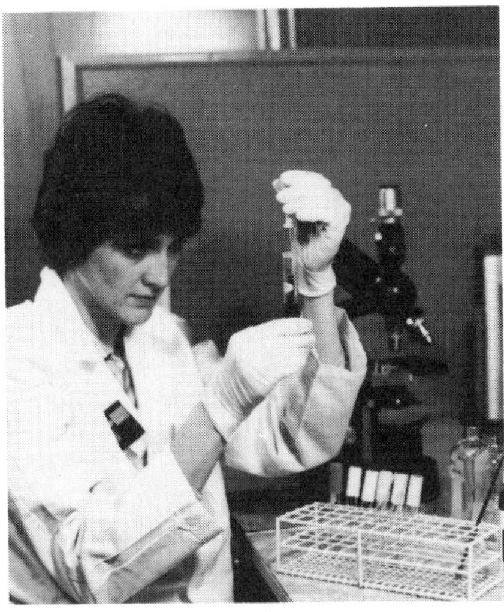

Fig. I-10 This molecular biologist is doing research that involves changing the genetic makeup of bacteria. The purpose is to develop a greater understanding of genes and the ways in which they can be manipulated. This research could eventually provide industries with knowledge and skills that they need to produce useful products like pharmaceuticals. Therefore industries provide grants to scientists such as this one.

Science and Technology

The main driving force behind **science** is the desire to know and understand the things around us. In contrast, **technology** is driven by the desire to solve specific problems or to achieve specific results. The two are connected in this way: Science develops principles, laws, and theories. Then these are used in technological developments. For example, science developed the principles used in rocketry—the principles of combustion, the principles of aerodynamics, and so on. Then technology used these principles to build space vehicles that had specific roles to play like the exploration of the moon.

Clearly, technology benefits from science. But science also benefits from technology. First, the prospect that scientific work may some day lead to a technological advance often generates funds to support that work (Fig. I-10). Second, technology develops new techniques and equipment that science can use. Third, technology provides a practical means of testing scientific principles and theories.

Fig. I-11 Science has developed the understandings we need to greatly reduce acid rain. Given the necessary funds, technology can build the equipment to do this. However, we must make the value judgment that we are willing to pay increased taxes to help to reduce this problem. Are you willing? This group is debating this matter.

Science and Value Judgments

While science provides us with answers to many questions, it cannot answer all questions. It can only answer those that can be explored using the scientific method. For example, science has provided us with a knowledge of the nature of the atomic nucleus. Then technology used that knowledge to develop the nuclear bomb. Science did not make the decision to use our knowledge to build nuclear weapons. The decision was a human one, based on values and judgments quite apart from science. In this case, politicians and the military realized that nuclear weapons could bring a speedy end to World War 2.

Science can, however, help us make value judgments by forecasting the consequences of our actions. For example, scientists who are familiar with the effects of radiation have teamed up with atmospheric physicists and others to predict an end to life on earth if we have a full scale nuclear war. We can, of course, ignore scientific predictions. Science cannot make us do something we do not want to do. The decision to start or not to start a nuclear war is a human decision based on values, not a scientific decision. Value judgments remain the responsibility of each one of us and the society in which we live (Fig. I-11).

Religion and philosophy deal with values and provide answers to many questions that science cannot answer. They do not use the scientific method to produce their answers, nor can the scientific method be used to test their conclusions. However, this does not make their answers incorrect.

Theories, Models, and Black Boxes

Science is often described as the interaction between experiment and theory. A scientist does some experiments and makes up a theory to explain the results. If the theory does the job, the scientist may use it to predict the results of

Fig. I-12 Scientists often spend more time at a desk developing theories than they do in the laboratory doing experiments.

further experiments (Fig. I-12). The results of those experiments often suggest changes to the theory. The changed theory may be used to predict still further experiments. This cycle goes round and round (Fig. I-13). Each time the cycle is completed, the scientist usually has a better understanding of whatever is being studied. And, as we said earlier, it is this cycle that is responsible for the growth of scientific knowledge.

In your science course last year, you encountered several theories. The two main ones were the particle theory and the atomic theory. You will also be developing and using theories in this course. Earlier in this introduction we described briefly what a theory is. Now, let's examine the term more thoroughly.

A **theory** is a list of postulates (assumptions) that are made up to explain phenomena. That is, a theory consists of statements made up by someone to explain experiments, natural happenings, or even things the person read about. The postulates may or may not be true. The confidence you can have in them depends on the experimental evidence that led to their invention and on how well they have been tested. A theory is usually developed and refined as follows. (Think about how this development parallels the scientific method described earlier.)

- A person's curiosity is aroused by a phenomenon or series of phenomena. This person wonders why things happened as they did (Step 1 of the scientific method).
- This person collects and studies the results of experiments related to the phenomenon. He or she may do the experiments or use the results of others (Steps 2 to 6 of the scientific method).
- The person makes up a theory to explain the results or conclusion.
- The person does further experiments to test the theory.

A theory, then, has two main uses. It explains the results of some experiments and it predicts the results of further experiments. In other words, it keeps taking the experimenter through the scientific method.

What Is a Model?

A theory can normally be described in one or more of four ways. Such descriptions are called **models**. A model may be a word description, a mathematical

Fig. I-13 The interaction of experiment and theory

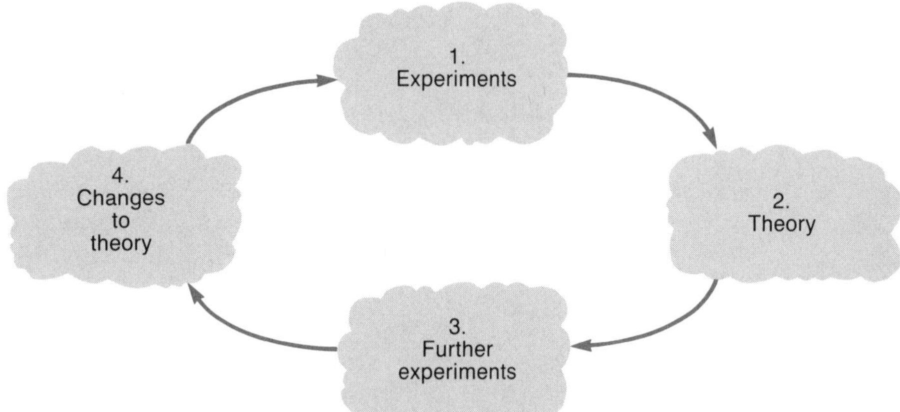

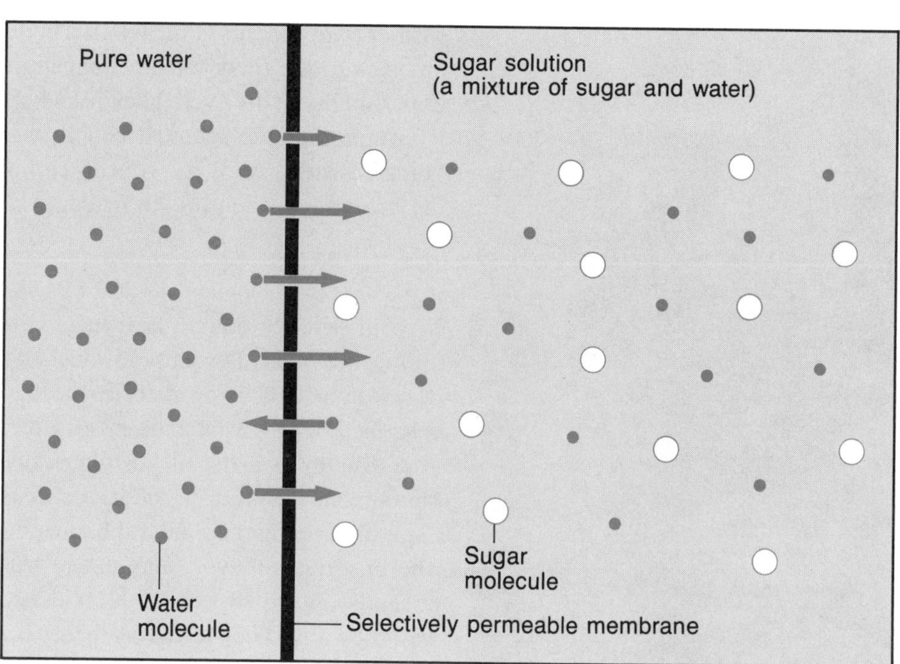

Fig. I-14 A diagrammatic model of osmosis

Fig. I-15 Building a physical model of osmosis

equation, a diagram, or an actual physical model. In any case, a model gives you some kind of mental picture that helps you explain things.

A Model for Osmosis Last year you studied osmosis, the diffusion of water through a selectively permeable membrane. A **word model** for osmosis might explain how the pore size of the membrane allows some types of molecules to pass through but not others. For example, water molecules can pass through dialysis tubing but sugar molecules cannot. A **diagrammatic model** might show these ideas as in Figure I-14. If you were given some tennis balls, golf balls, and some bricks, could you build a **physical model** to represent osmosis (Fig. I-15)?

Scientists have developed several **mathematical models** for osmosis. One mathematical model includes this equation: $P = cRT$, where P = the osmotic pressure, c = the concentration of the solution, T = the temperature and R = a constant. Study Figure I-16 for a moment. You may recall from last year that a pressure builds up in the "cell" as water diffuses in. According to this equation, that pressure, called the osmotic pressure, will increase if the concentration of the solution in the "cell" is increased. Based on your experiments last year, does that make sense?

Fig. I-16 A pressure builds up as water diffuses into the "cell".

Models for Black Boxes Many things can only be studied by making indirect observations. That is, they cannot be observed directly. Therefore much remains unknown about them. Scientists call such things **black boxes**. The word "black" suggests the unknown, or something that can't be seen. A black box, then, is anything that can be studied only by indirect observations. As you study the black box, you begin to form a mental picture of what is in the box. In other words, you form a model for the black box. Generally speaking, the more experiments you do, the better your model becomes. Here are two examples to illustrate how one forms models for black boxes.

Fig. I-17 Is a computer a black box for you? For whom would it not be a black box?

Fig. I-18 Spacecraft have provided direct observations of the surface of the cloud cover of Jupiter. How do we find out what is in the atmosphere and below it?

Example 1: The Computer as a Black Box A computer is a black box for most of us (Fig. I-17). We have never seen inside it. We don't know exactly what is in the computer. Therefore we don't know exactly how it works. However, if you use it for a time, you can learn some things about the inside of the computer. Following the instruction manuals, you can perform certain operations. As you do so, you may discover such things as the computer's storage capacity, the nature of the software packages stored in it, and the paths followed to perform certain tasks. The more you work with the computer, the more you will learn about how it works. In fact, you may build up in your mind an image of how the computer works. But all your observations have been made indirectly. You haven't actually seen what is inside the computer. Until you take a course where you study the interior parts and their functions, the computer remains a black box to you.

Example 2: Jupiter as a Black Box When astronomers look at Jupiter with a telescope, they see only the surface of Jupiter's cloudy atmosphere. No one has seen under those clouds. As far as we know, Jupiter may not even have a solid surface. In 1973 and 1974, the Pioneer 10 and 11 spacecraft gave us a closer look at that cloud surface. A better look came in 1979 when Voyagers 1 and 2 sent back over 33 000 photographs of that surface and Jupiter's satellites. However, all these spacecraft trips were flybys. They did not enter the atmosphere of Jupiter to sample it or to look below the atmosphere.

These flybys provided direct observations about the cloud cover of Jupiter and about other features, like moons, outside the cloud cover (Fig. I-18). For example, the photographs show giant bolts of lightning flashing through Jupiter's atmosphere. They also show something never seen before with telescopes—a thin flat ring circling Jupiter. If we assume that a camera "sees" things much as a human eye does, these are direct observations.

Other instruments on the spacecraft collected indirect observations that have greatly increased our knowledge about Jupiter. These instruments measured such things as the radiation coming off various parts of the planet and changes in the gravitational and magnetic fields from place to place. These observations, added to those already obtained from earth, allow astronomers to describe Jupiter in this way: Jupiter is 318 times more massive than earth. It has a diameter of 143 000 km and is much less dense than earth. Its gravitational attraction is very high. If you weigh 70 kg on earth, you would weigh about 175 kg on Jupiter! Jupiter radiates more heat into space than it receives from the sun. It must, therefore, have a very hot core. Jupiter may be composed almost entirely of hydrogen and helium. However, these gases are probably compressed to a liquid state in Jupiter's interior. There may be a small rocky core at the centre of the planet. Methane and ammonia gas are also present in the atmosphere.

No one went to Jupiter and collected samples of the atmosphere for analysis. No one has seen under the atmospheric cloud. Yet we know much about Jupiter from indirect observations. Before the spacecraft flybys, astronomers had a model for the nature of Jupiter. That model was changed and improved after the flybys. And it will continue to be changed and improved as further indirect observations are made. However, the exact nature of Jupiter under the cloud cover will remain a black box until actual exploration occurs.

Fig. I-19 Are you ready now to use the scientific method and other "tools" of science?

Scientists, Theories, and Models

As you have seen, scientists often use theories and models. They do experiments and then make up a theory to explain the results. Then they use the theory to predict the results of further experiments. This usually refines the theory and makes it better. Eventually the scientists want to make their theories clear to others. To do this, they develop verbal (written), pictorial (drawn), mathematical, or physical models to illustrate their theories (Fig. I-19).

Career: *SCIENCE WRITER*

HELP WANTED: SCIENCE WRITER

Daily newspaper requires person to research and write articles on astronomy, environment, medicine, and other scientific topics.

Do you like both science and creative writing? If you do, a career as a science writer may interest you. Science writers are employed by newspapers and magazines to write scientific articles. They are also employed by television and film companies to write scripts for scientific documentaries and science fiction dramas. Some employers may hire full-time science writers. Others may employ freelance writers who work for several different companies.

A B.Sc. degree in science would be a good preparation for this career. Of course, this means that you must do well in secondary school science. Your communication skills are just as important. Therefore, take as many English courses as you can in secondary school and university. You must also have good library research skills and the ability to interview scientists effectively.

UNIT 1 Interactions

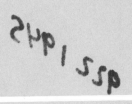

CHAPTERS

1. **Biotic and Abiotic Environmental Factors**
2. **Matter and Energy in Ecosystems**
3. **Populations, Communities, and Biomes**
4. **Human Influences on Ecosystems**

Recent surveys show that most Canadians care deeply about the environment. We treasure clean air and clean water. We want to protect our forests, fields, lakes, streams, wildlife and parks. However, caring and wanting are not enough. We have to act. We must work individually and as a society toward the goal of an environment that is healthy for humans and other living things. In order to work effectively, we need to understand the principles that govern the ecosystems we want to protect. Also, we need to know how to put that knowledge into action.

This unit will help you develop the ecological knowledge and skills you need in order to help solve and prevent problems that threaten the natural world.

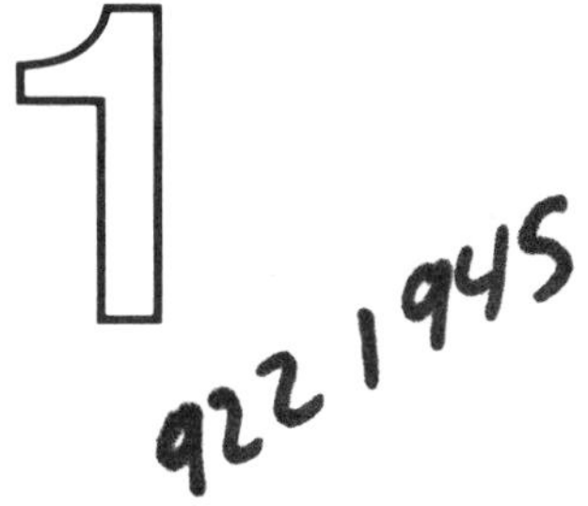

Biotic and Abiotic Environmental Factors

CHAPTER CONTENTS

CHAPTER OBJECTIVES

After completing this chapter you should be able to:

1. Describe and apply the ecosystem concept.
2. Set up and explain a classroom ecosystem.
3. Define and illustrate the major biotic components of ecosystems.
4. List and describe the major abiotic factors in ecosystems.
5. Conduct an investigation of the ecology of an indoor pond.
6. Participate in the planning and implementation of a field trip.

Every living thing on earth interacts with other living things and with its non-living environment—air, water, and soil, for example (Fig. 1-1). You are no exception. Can you think of ways you depend on other living things? In what ways are other living things affected by you? How do you depend on your non-living environment? And in what ways do you affect it?

As you might imagine, the answers to questions such as these are important. We cannot possibly look after the living and non-living things around us if we do not understand how we interact with them and how they interact with one another. The science of ecology explores such interactions. In this chapter you begin your investigation of this exciting and important branch of science.

Fig. 1-1 The mule deer is the characteristic deer of the foothills of the mountains of western Canada. This deer thrives in areas dominated by brush and open forest. As a result, its numbers have increased as mountain forests have been cut. What species might benefit when deer numbers increase? What species might suffer?

Fig. 1-2 This ecologist is designing a study on the sand dunes of the Lake Huron shore at Port Elgin, Ontario. Her particular interest is the interaction between certain fungi and their environment. These fungi are part of the sand dune ecosystem.

1.1 The Ecosystem Concept

Most ecologists find that their work is more meaningful if they design their experiments around the ecosystem concept (Fig. 1-2). You will likely discover the same thing when you do the activities and field trips in this unit. The word "ecosystem" is probably not new to you. It has been in general usage in our society for several years. However, because the ecosystem concept is such an important one, we want to make sure you understand it well. Therefore, after we have reviewed some basic terms of ecology, we will outline this concept for you. Then, in the next section, you will build a model ecosystem that you can study.

What Is an Ecosystem?

The most widely accepted definition of **ecology** is that it is the study of the relationships of organisms with their environments and with each other. An organism's environment includes such factors as water, oxygen, carbon dioxide, soil minerals, light, humidity, temperature, and wind. Such *non-living* factors are called **abiotic** factors. An organism's environment also includes all the *living* things, or the **biotic** factors, around it.

Imagine a place where biotic and abiotic factors are interacting—a pond, for example. If you could draw a line around this place and isolate it, you would have an ecosystem. Simply stated, an **ecosystem** is an interacting system that consists of groups of organisms and their non-living environment (Fig. 1-3). We say "simply stated" because there are no isolated units in nature. You can draw a line around a pond if you wish. But that won't keep rain and air out or birds and frogs in. In the long run, everything interacts with everything else. Nature knows no boundaries. However, in spite of this limitation, the ecosystem concept is still a useful one, as you will see.

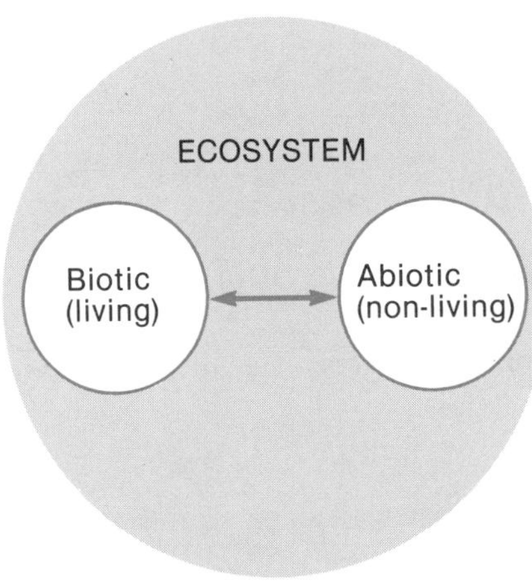

Fig. 1-3 An ecosystem has two interacting parts: biotic and abiotic.

The Size of an Ecosystem An ecosystem can range in size from the entire earth to a puddle or a handful of soil. There are no fixed limits to the size of an ecosystem. Any community of living things interacting with its environment forms an ecosystem. A woodlot is an ecosystem. So is a lake, a city park, a meadow, a pond, an ocean, and the whole Arctic tundra. Even a classroom aquarium is an ecosystem.

A Model for an Ecosystem The most important thing to remember about an ecosystem is that *all* its parts are interrelated. Each part is affected by all the other parts. Therefore, if one part is changed in any way, all the other parts will be changed also. Figure 1-4 is a diagrammatic model for an ecosystem. As this model suggests, climate is the overriding factor which determines the general nature of an ecosystem. For example, if the climate is always dry and hot, the soil will likely be sandy. And the plants, animals, and other life will be organisms which are adapted to desert conditions.

The arrows in Figure 1-4 represent the possible connections between the parts of an ecosystem. If, for example, the plants in an ecosystem change, the

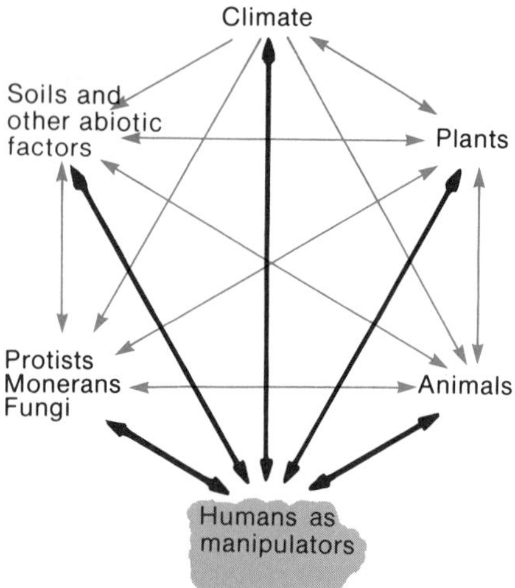

Fig. 1-4 Each part of an ecosystem, biotic or abiotic, is affected by the other parts. Most natural ecosystems have their parts shown here.

soil, animals, and all other factors will change. The chain of events that occurs when one factor in an ecosystem is changed is usually long and complex. But these events are certain to happen.

Extension

Test your understanding of this ecosystem model by answering these questions:

- What are some "other abiotic factors" which could be placed in Figure 1-4?
- Trace the chain of events which could occur if cattle were introduced into a natural meadow ecosystem and overgrazed it.
- Humans are animals, so we fit into the "Animals" slot in this model. Why do you suppose there is another slot for humans labelled "Humans as Manipulators"?
- Trace the chain of events which could occur if soil erosion was extensive in a field.
- Trace the chain of events which could occur if a lake received excess plant nutrients because human sewage entered it.

Section Review

1. a) What is ecology?
   b) Distinguish between biotic and abiotic factors.
2. a) Define the term ecosystem.
   b) What is the main fault with this definition?
3. a) Discuss the size of an ecosystem.
   b) Draw a diagrammatic model for a generalized ecosystem.
   c) Describe this model in a paragraph.
4. Suppose a roadside is sprayed to kill all plants but grass. Use the ecosystem model to trace the consequences of this action.

Fig. 1-5 This model ecosystem was set up by one of the authors in 1968. Since then, the top has been removed only on a few occasions to replace fish that failed to reproduce before they died of natural causes. No food has been added and the bottle has never been cleaned out. How do you suppose this ecosystem has functioned for so long?

1.2 Activity: Making a Classroom Ecosystem

In this activity you will build a model ecosystem so you can see first-hand how an ecosystem works. The basic principles you learn here also apply to natural ecosystems such as lakes, ponds, and forests. See how many of these principles you can discover.

Depending on the amount of space available in your classroom, you may work as a class to set up just one large ecosystem or work in groups to set up several smaller ones. You and your family might enjoy having one of these in your home, too (Fig. 1-5).

Problem

What are the basic parts of an ecosystem? How does an ecosystem work?

Materials

large bottle or jar with top (at least 3–4 L)
table lamp with 60 W bulb
khuli loach or another plant-eating fish
strands of an aquatic plant (3 or 4)
pond snails (8–10)
clean gravel and/or sand

Procedure

a. Place sand or gravel in the jar to a depth of 2–3 cm.
b. Fill the jar with water. If you use tap water, let the jar stand with the top removed for 48 h. This lets the chlorine leave the water.
c. Add a few strands of an aquatic plant. Any submerged aquatic plant will do. *Cabomba* (fanwort) and *Ceratophyllum* (hortwort or coontail) do particularly well in closed ecosystems.
d. Add 8–10 pond snails to the water.
e. Place a khuli loach in the water. You may use one or two small guppies instead of the khuli loach. Or you could use both types of fish.
f. Put the top on the jar and seal it tightly.
g. Place a table lamp with a 60 W bulb in it close to the jar, as shown in Figure 1-6.

Fig. 1-6 A model ecosystem for your classroom. Where do the plants, fish, and snails get their nutrients? Why is light needed? Why don't the animals die with the top on? How is this ecosystem like a lake or pond?

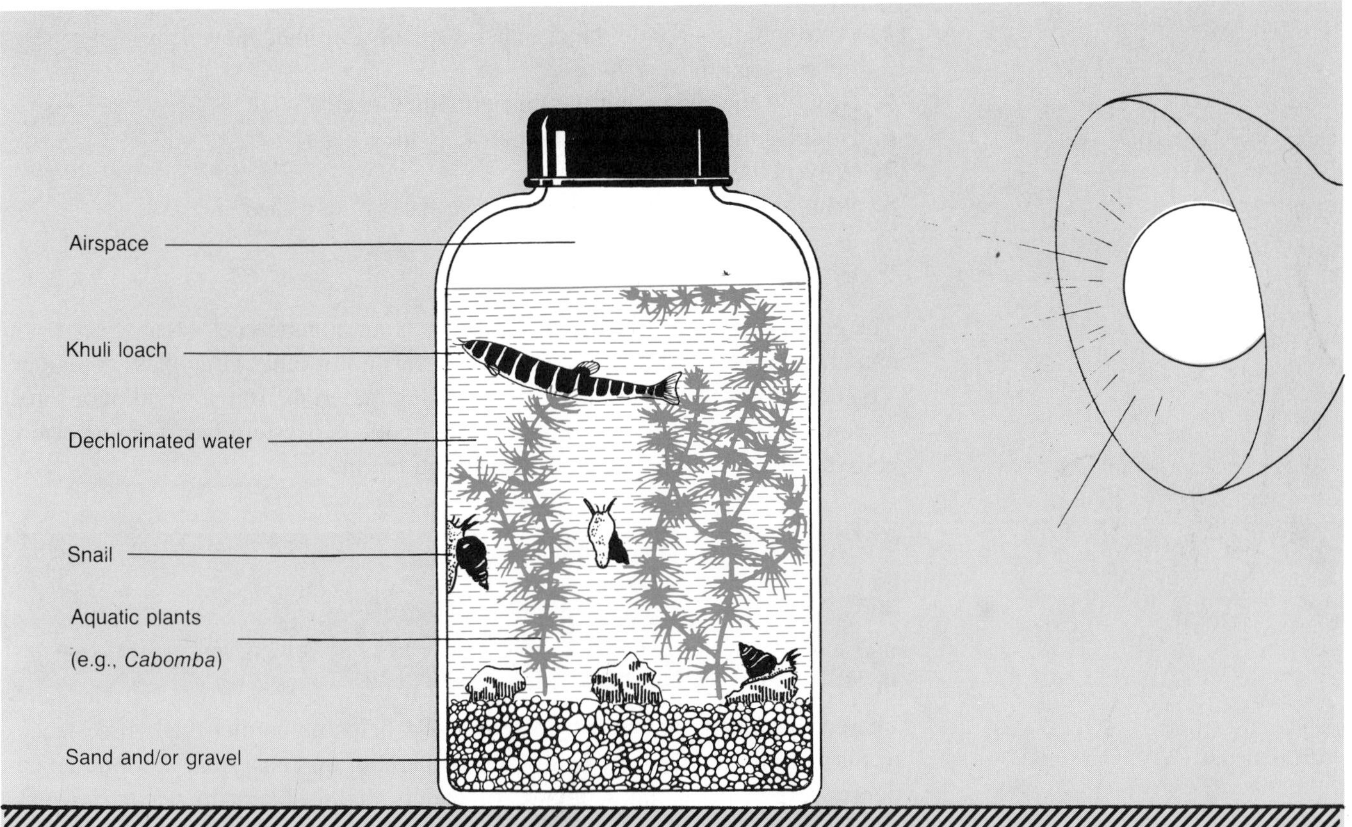

h. Place the set-up in a location away from windows and other places where light and temperature conditions change greatly during the day.

i. Leave the lamp on 24 h per day or place it on a timer that provides at least 16 h of light per day. Do not depend on your memory to turn the light off and on!

j. A healthy ecosystem of this kind will have a pale green colour in the water. This colour is caused by algae. They develop from spores present on the plants and animals. Algae are important in the ecosystem. They provide both food and oxygen for the animals. Move the light closer if the water does not develop a green colour after a few days. Move it further away if the green becomes intense.

k. Observe your ecosystem closely from time to time for several months. Make careful notes of any changes that occur.

Discussion

Many days may pass before you can answer all these questions. In the meantime, you will read on, using knowledge gained from this model ecosystem to help you understand some basic ideas and concepts of ecology.

1. Your ecosystem is called a *closed* ecosystem. How does it differ from a natural ecosystem?
2. Why do you think we used a closed ecosystem for this activity?
3. From what source do the plants and algae get carbon dioxide for photosynthesis?
4. From what source do the organisms (plants, animals, and algae) get oxygen for respiration?
5. How do the plants get the nutrients they need?
6. How do the animals get the nutrients they need?
7. Why is the light required?
8. What do you think will happen if a fish or snail dies?

Extension

The ecosystem you made in this activity is an aquatic ecosystem. See if you can make a **terrestrial ecosystem** in a terrarium or other large glass container. You could build a woodland aquarium using materials from a woodlot or forest in your area. Or you could build a more exotic ecosystem like a desert or bog ecosystem. Research this well before you begin.

1.3 Applying the Ecosystem Concept

The ecosystem model shown in Figure 1-4 helps us predict the consequences of our actions. By remembering that all parts of an ecosystem are interdependent, we can trace the sequence of events that is likely to occur if we do something to an ecosystem. This section uses two issues, clear cutting of forests and recreational use of lakes, to illustrate this idea.

Fig. 1-7 The shrubs and perennial weeds that have grown here for many years are being cut down to encourage grasses to grow. Now the area will support more cattle. What other species could benefit from this action? What species could suffer?

Humans and Ecosystems

Humans are animals. Therefore, like other animals, we fit into the "Animal" slot in the model in Figure 1-4. However, unlike other animals, we change ecosystems in dramatic ways (Fig. 1-7). We manipulate ecosystems as shown by the black arrows. For example, we remove the natural grasses from a meadow and replace them with a grass we want, such as wheat. We replace deer, woodchucks, and other grassland animals with cattle and sheep. We kill fish we don't want in lakes and replace them with desirable sport species such as trout. We change the structure of streams to produce trout habitat. Yet such changes may make life impossible for other species. We till the soil and fertilize it so it will grow what we want. We use herbicides to kill plants we don't want. We cut trees from mountain slopes to build homes, pool decks, and saunas. We even change the climate by polluting the air.

All these things are not necessarily "bad". Humans do have to eat and have a place to live. We need farms and recreation. Sometimes, though, the *way* we do these things is "bad". We often do not consider the ecological consequences of our actions. Let's look at two major societal issues from an ecosystem perspective. Then you will see that we can still use ecosystems without destroying them.

Issue 1: Clear Cutting of Forests

Suppose that a lumber company completely cleared a forested area of trees. We call this **clear cutting** (Fig. 1-8). What effects would this have on the forest ecosystem? The trees would no longer add humus to the soil since they could no longer drop leaves onto the ground. Snails, slugs, earthworms, fungi, and bacteria thrive on leaf litter and humus. Therefore their numbers would

Fig. 1-8 This clear cut area was once a dense stand of coniferous trees. What are the ecological consequences of this action? Could the negative consequences be reversed?

Fig. 1-9 This forest was selectively logged just 2 years before this photograph was taken. Mature hardwoods were cut and skidded out after freeze-up. This minimized damage to the forest floor. The decay of branches and twigs, combined with the decreased competition for light and space, will increase the growth rate of the remaining trees. The old timber roads have become excellent trails for hiking and cross-country skiing.

decrease. Some species might vanish completely. Animals that feed on these organisms would be affected. Soil might erode because the leaf canopy would no longer be present to absorb the energy of a heavy rainfall. If the soil were washed away, many plant species would disappear. The animals that eat these plants would move away or die of starvation. Plants that require shade and moisture, such as ferns, would die. In fact, direct sunlight would kill most of the forest floor plants.

On the other hand, many species of plants that require sunlight might then be able to grow in this area. These include grasses, goldenrods, and asters. Shrubs and tree species that could not grow in the shade of the forest might appear. New insect populations might be established. And bird species that feed on these insects might appear. Mammal species, such as white-tailed deer, might increase in numbers. The trash formed by unused tree parts would form habitat for small animals. Then, when it decays, the trash would revitalize the nutrient pool of the soil.

Clearly, the changes which would occur because of clear cutting are not all "bad". Also, economics often dictates that an area be clear cut. Further, some forest species like Jack pine will not normally regenerate unless they are clear cut. Yet other forests, like a maple-beech-oak forest, can be successfully logged by **selective cutting** (Fig. 1-9). Clear cutting does change the forest ecosystem, perhaps forever. Therefore it is important to evaluate cutting proposals ecologically before cutting proceeds. Continue this evaluation of clear cutting by answering the following questions:

- What could a lumber company do to lessen the impact of clear cutting and help to restore the original ecosystem?
- How might clear cutting affect nearby ecosystems like a stream or lake?
- What could our society do to lessen the need for clear cutting in areas where it is not desirable?

Fig. 1-10 What effects could recreational use of a lake have on the lake ecosystem?

Issue 2: Recreational Use of Lakes

Many of us like swimming, boating, cottaging, water skiing, and fishing (Fig. 1-10). Such recreation is important to the physical and psychological well-being of humans. But, according to the ecosystem concept, we cannot use a lake for recreation without having some effects on that ecosystem. What might those effects be?

In order to make swimming more pleasant, aquatic plants are often removed from the margin of the lake. When this is done, some fish species lose their spawning habitat. Also, fish lose some of their food supply, since many of the insects which they eat live among the aquatic plants.

Cottages on a lake can add nutrients to the lake, if septic systems are too close to the lake or if they are improperly maintained. Human sewage and wash water contain nitrates, phosphates, and other plant nutrients. These can increase the growth of algae and plants in the lake. Up to a point, this is good. These organisms add oxygen to the water and provide food and habitat for animals. But if the algae and plants become too dense, they eventually begin to die in large quantities. The decay of these dead organisms robs the water of oxygen, and fish die. Also, excessive growth of algae and plants inhibit boating, swimming, and other human activities. So, in the long run, no one wins if we pollute a lake.

As you can see, human activities do affect a lake. However, if the ecology of the lake ecosystem is understood and respected, the effects need not overwhelm the lake. Continue this evaluation of recreational use of lakes by answering the following questions:

- How could one access a lake for swimming without removing marginal vegetation?
- How could we make sure that cottages do not pollute lakes?
- What impacts could motorboats have on the ecology of a lake? How could these impacts be lessened?

Extensions

1. Obtain information on clear cutting from the Ontario Ministry of Natural Resources. Evaluate the information from an ecological perspective.
2. Obtain the booklet ''Cottage Country'' from the Ontario Ministry of the Environment. Evaluate, from an ecological perspective, the septic tank system, privies, chemical toilets, incinerator toilets, and composting toilets.

Section Review

1. What is meant by ''Humans as manipulators'' in Figure 1-4?
2. Use Figure 1-4 to help you predict the sequence of events which could occur if a hillside was sprayed with herbicides to kill unwanted weeds and shrubs.
3. **a)** What is clear cutting?
   b) What negative effects can clear cutting have?
   c) What positive effects can it have?
4. Trace the sequence of events which could occur if human wastes were allowed to escape into a lake.

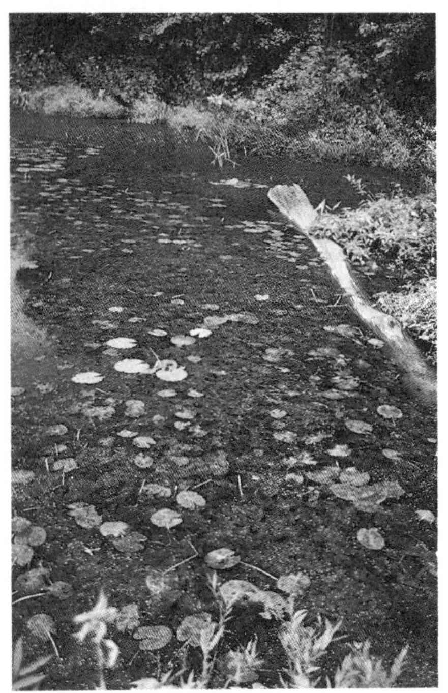

Fig. 1-11 What are the biotic and abiotic components of this pond ecosystem?

1.4 Structure of an Ecosystem: Biotic Aspects

As you know, an ecosystem has two main parts, a **biotic** (living) part and an **abiotic** (non-living) part. The pond in Figure 1-11 is an ecosystem. Its biotic part includes all the living things in the pond—plants, animals, fungi, protists, and monerans. It also includes animals such as racoons and herons that visit the pond on occasion to feed. Its abiotic part includes all the non-living factors that influence it—the temperature, the oxygen concentration, the phosphate concentration, the nature of the bottom, and others. This section deals with the major biotic aspects of ecosystems. The next section covers the abiotic factors.

Habitat The **habitat** of an organism is the place where it lives. For example, the habitat of a lake trout is clean cool water. The habitat of a sunfish is the warm weedy shallows at the edge of a lake. The habitat of an earthworm is organically rich soil. The habitat of a porcupine is the branches of trees. And the habitat of a prickly pear cactus is dry sandy soil. Habitats may overlap. For example, a trout may on occasion visit warm water to feed on small fish. As well, a sunfish may swim into cool water to escape a predator.

Niche The **niche** of an organism is its total role in the community. For example, the niche of a beaver in a small stream is to feed on plants, to dam the stream, to become food for wolves, to be bitten by deer flies, and so on. The niche of a wolf is to feed on beavers and other small animals, to be bitten by blackflies and deer flies, to fertilize the soil with its urine and feces, and many other things.

Comparing Habitat and Niche Many people confuse habitat and niche. This may help you remember the difference. Think of the habitat as the "address" of the organism and the niche as the organism's "occupation" or "job".

The niche of an organism decides its main habitat. For example, the niche of a savanna sparrow is, in part, to feed on meadow insects (Fig. 1-12). Therefore the habitat of savanna sparrows is often the fence rows that separate farmers' fields.

Fig. 1-12 The savanna sparrow frequents meadows and other open spaces in the countryside. How does its niche determine its habitat?

Competition If two species have the same habitat and similar niches, they will compete with one another. For example, both red-winged blackbirds and yellow-headed blackbirds live in the marshes of western Canada. Both species have similar niches. For example, they have similar diets and both prefer to search for food on tall aquatic plants. Clearly, then, they will compete if they both try to use the same part of a marsh as a habitat. Often competition causes one species to leave the habitat. In this case, however, both species can remain in the same marsh. The yellow-headed blackbirds occupy the deep areas, while the red-winged blackbirds occupy the shallow areas near the shore.

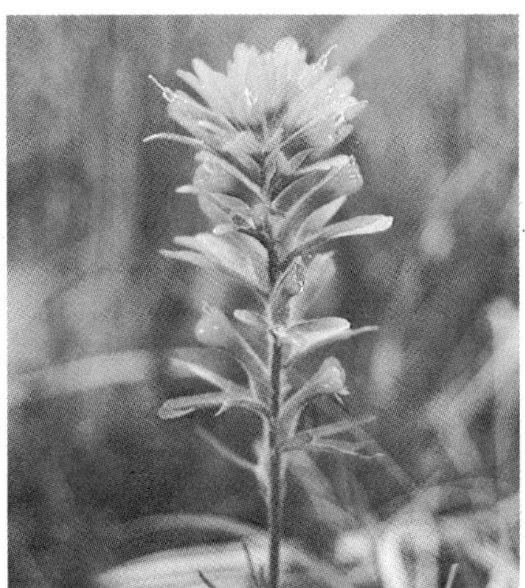

Fig. 1-13 This plant, the Indian paintbrush, is one of the few producers in one wet, sandy area near Sarnia, Ontario.

Fig. 1-14 This particular woodchuck dug its burrow next to a farmer's garden. In a few days it had eaten all the peas and beans in the garden—ample evidence that it is a herbivore!

Fig. 1-15 This fox was searching for mice in a meadow when this photograph was taken. Mice are herbivores. (They eat plants, including their seeds.) Therefore the fox is a first-order carnivore. Later, this fox was observed eating blackberries. What is it then?

The red-winged blackbirds arrive first in spring. They set up territories that cover much of the marsh. Then the yellow-headed blackbirds arrive and begin to set up territories in the deeper areas. The red-winged blackbirds now contract their territories to the shallow areas of the marsh. If a marsh has no red-winged blackbirds in it, the yellow-headed blackbirds expand their territories into the shallow areas. By splitting up a marsh in this way, the birds avoid competing in the same habitat.

Major Biotic Parts of Ecosystems

All organisms in an ecosystem depend on one another in many ways. Few, if any, ways are more important than those that provide food. Therefore organisms are often classified on this basis. There are three main categories: **producers**, **consumers**, and **decomposers**. Let's see what these are.

Producers All life depends directly or indirectly on producers. Plants, many protists, and many monerans are producers. They contain chlorophyll and, as a result, can carry out photosynthesis. That is, they store some of the sun's energy in sugar, starch, and other molecules. They make, or *produce*, their own food—hence the name **producers** (Fig. 1-13).

Organisms that produce their own food are also called **autotrophs** (''self-feeders''). The trees of a forest, the corn in a field, the algae in a lake, and the cattails in a marsh are all producers, or autotrophs.

Consumers Some organisms cannot make their own food. They must feed on, or *consume*, other organisms. Therefore they are called **consumers**. Most consumers are animals that feed on plants or other animals. Consumers are also called **heterotrophs** (''other feeders'').

Animals that feed directly on producers are called **first-order consumers** or **herbivores** (''plant-eaters''). Beavers feed on aquatic plants and tree bark; woodchucks feed on grasses and other plants (Fig. 1-14). Therefore both beavers and woodchucks are herbivores. Deer, rabbits, and cattle are other common herbivores.

Animals that eat other animals are called **carnivores** (''flesh-eaters''). Wolves, polar bears, sharks, trout, and mink are carnivores. Those carnivores that feed on herbivores are called **first-order carnivores**. A fox is a first-order carnivore when it eats a mouse (Fig. 1-15). A wolf is a first-order carnivore when it eats a deer. And you are a first-order carnivore when you eat chicken, beef, or pork. (Technically, you would have to do your own killing.) First-order carnivores are also called **second-order consumers**. Why is this so?

Those carnivores which feed on first-order carnivores are called **second-order carnivores** (and also **third-order consumers**). If a trout eats small fish that ate herbivorous insects, the trout is a second-order carnivore. Then, if you or a bear ate the trout, you or the bear would be a **third-order carnivore** (**fourth-order consumer**). However, you and the bear would be second-order carnivores if the trout that you ate had fed on plant-eating fish only.

How many of these feeding levels exist? Some ecosystems have five or more orders of carnivores. All ecosystems, however, have what are called **top carnivores**. What do you suppose this means (Fig. 1-16)?

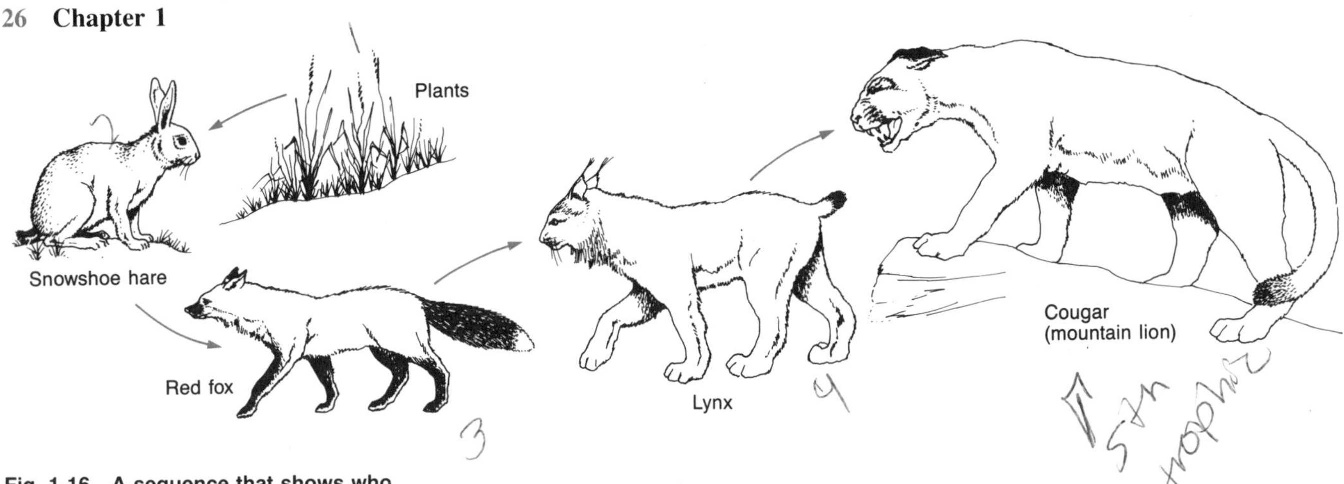

Fig. 1-16 A sequence that shows who eats whom is called a food chain. In this unusual food chain, the cougar is top carnivore. The chance of this particular food chain occurring is less than one in a thousand. Food chains normally do not have this many steps. For example, both lynx and cougars are more likely to eat snowshoe hares directly than to get their food as shown here. Why do you think it is generally an advantage for animals to feed in short food chains?

Some animals are both herbivores and carnivores. For example, the red fox does not just eat rabbits, mice, and birds. It also eats fruits and seeds it finds in the meadows and woods. In fact, during the summer and fall some foxes eat little else except plant material. Even the grizzly bear eats plant material. When it first emerges from its den in the spring, it usually grazes on grasses and digs up plant roots. In the summer it, like the fox, dines on a variety of berries and other fruits. Animals which are both herbivores and carnivores are called **omnivores** (''all-eaters''). Are you a herbivore, carnivore, or omnivore?

Carnivores which feed on live animals are called **predators**. The animals that are eaten are called **prey**. The egret in Figure 1-17 is a predator; the animals it eats are the prey. The bald eagle is, at times, a predator that preys on living fish. However, bald eagles that live along the seacoast eat mainly dead fish cast up on the beach by the waves. Animals that feed on dead animals or plants are called **scavengers**. Snails, crayfish, crows, and vultures are also scavengers. An animal may be a carnivore for one meal and a scavenger for the next. For example, a wolf may kill a deer and eat part of it one day. Then it may return to the kill and feed on the remains for several days afterwards.

Have you ever seen a dead fish, a slice of bread, or any other animal or plant covered with a fuzzy grey growth? This growth is a fungus. It is feeding on the dead organism. Though you cannot see them, bacteria will also be feeding on that organism. Fungi and bacteria that feed on dead organisms (both plant and animal) are called **saprophytes** (Fig. 1-18).

Fig. 1-17 The great egret nests only in the southern parts of Ontario. This large, graceful bird was hunted in the early 1900s to obtain feathers for hats. This hunting almost reduced this egret to extinction. Laws now protect it. This predator wades through marshes and along lakes, ponds, and streams. What do you suppose its prey are?

Decomposers All ecosystems contain **decomposers**. These organisms are mainly bacteria and fungi such as yeasts and moulds. They break down (decompose) and feed on non-living organic matter such as dead plants, dead animals, and animal wastes. When could decomposers also be called saprophytes?

All organisms eventually die, and all animals produce wastes. If decomposers were not present, ecosystems would soon clog up with wastes and dead organisms. But decomposers perform an even more important function than eliminating organic matter. As they break down or feed on the organic matter, they release nutrients into the environment. These nutrients can then be used again to help producers grow. For example, decomposers break down the leaf litter in a forest. Nutrients are then released from the leaves into the soil, from

Fig. 1-18 *Amanita virosa*, the "destroying angel". This mushroom, though harmful to humans, is beneficial to many trees in our northern woods. It feeds on dead organic matter in the soil and, as a by-product, supplies the trees with essential nutrients like nitrogen and phosphorus. Scientists believe that many, if not most, of the trees in Algonquin Park would die without this relationship with fungi.

which they are absorbed by tree roots.

The moulds that often grow on bread and fruits are also decomposers. They break down the bread and fruits as they feed on them. Some of the nutrients in the bread and fruit become part of the moulds. Other nutrients are released into the environment.

Trophic Levels

As you have seen, all life depends, directly or indirectly, on producers. Either consumers eat producers or they eat other consumers. You have also seen that feeding relationships are linked together in **food chains**. Each step in a food chain is called a **trophic level**, or feeding level. Therefore grass is said to occupy the first trophic level, or the trophic level of producer. Animals which eat grass occupy the second trophic level, or the trophic level of herbivore. And animals which eat herbivores occupy the third trophic level, or the trophic level of first-order carnivore (Fig. 1-19).

Bear in mind that most animals feed at more than one trophic level. For example, the cougar in Figure 1-16, page 26, occupies the fifth trophic level. If, however, it fed directly on snowshoe hares, it would occupy the third trophic level. What trophic level have you occupied so far today?

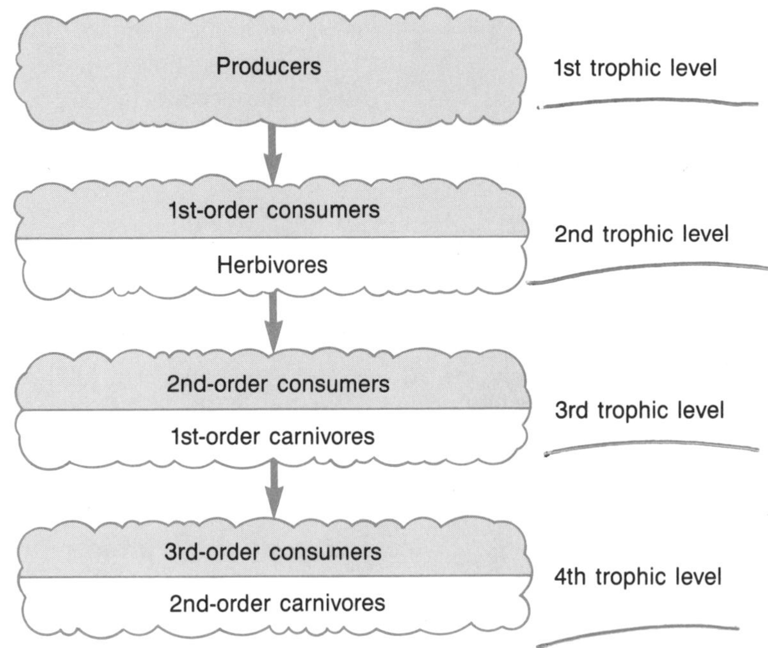

Fig. 1-19 What trophic level would you occupy if you ate a dish of cornflakes? a piece of steak? a fish which had, in turn, eaten a herbivorous fish?

Food Chains and Food Webs

Food Chains As you read about trophic levels, you learned that organisms are linked together in feeding relationships called **food chains**. Many food chains follow the pattern shown in Figure 1-20. That is, they begin with producers that are eaten by herbivores that, in turn, are eaten by carnivores. However, some food chains begin with dead plants or animals. Examples are a crayfish feeding on a dead fish in a lake and an earthworm eating humus-laden soil. Yet, in a sense, even these food chains began with producers. The

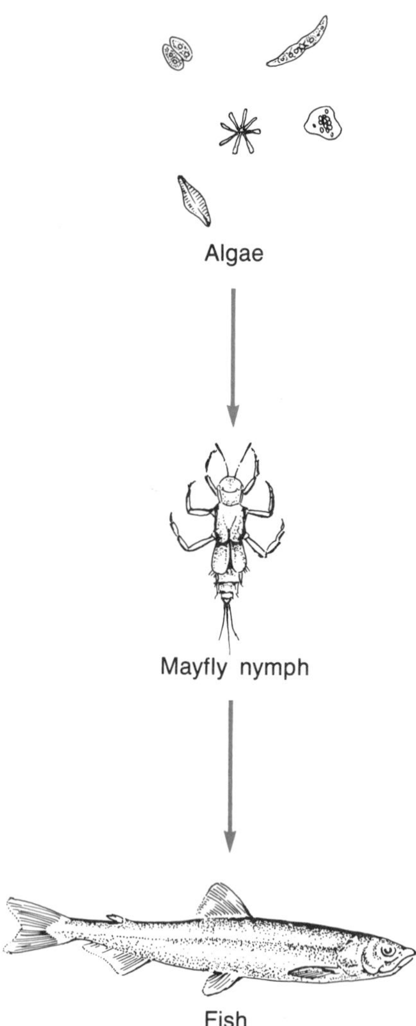

Fig. 1-20 An aquatic food chain. The algae are producers; therefore they get the energy they need from the sun. The mayfly nymphs eat algae and, in turn, are eaten by fish.

fish, when it was alive, was in a food chain that began with a producer. The fish may have eaten smaller animals that had eaten algae or plants. And the humus being fed upon by the earthworm was once mainly living plants.

Many food chains have just three trophic levels:

Producer → Herbivore → First-order carnivore

Some examples are:	grain →	mouse →	fox
	clover →	rabbit →	wolf
	grass →	grasshopper →	bird
	corn →	cattle →	human
	algae →	mayfly →	fish

Food chains with more trophic levels than three simply have more predator-prey relationships. Though these exist, they are not as common as shorter food chains. You saw one of these longer chains in Figure 1-16, page 26. Though this food chain can and does exist, it is uncommon. Snowshoe hares are much more abundant than any other animals in the food chain. This fact and others make it easier for both lynx and cougars to prey on them instead of feeding as shown in the diagram. What might some of the other factors be?

Figure 1-21 shows another food chain with five trophic levels. Again, this food chain occurs, but not as often as other food chains involving the same animals. Why might hawks choose to feed directly on grasshoppers, frogs, and mice instead of eating snakes which had eaten these other animals?

Food Webs As you know, most animals feed in more than one food chain. A certain species of plant can be eaten by several species of animal. Also, a certain species of animal can eat several types of food. Since organisms are often in more than one food chain, the food chains in an ecosystem are connected. The connected food chains are called a **food web**. Figure 1-22 shows a simple aquatic food web. Follow the arrows in this food web to find out what eats what. How many food chains can you identify? Can you name the trophic level of each organism?

Ecological Pyramids

Pyramid of Numbers As you may have guessed, food chains usually proceed from very small organisms to larger and larger ones. Therefore the number of organisms at each trophic level tends to decrease as you move along the food chain. In other words, many small producers feed fewer larger herbivores that, in turn, feed still fewer and larger carnivores. Such relationships are often represented by a **pyramid of numbers** (Fig. 1-23).

Not all pyramids of numbers have such a regular shape. In fact, some aren't pyramids at all! Think about the hundreds of mould organisms that feed on a dead fish. What will this "pyramid" of numbers look like?

Although the pyramid of numbers is simple, it is not used much by ecologists. That is because it treats all organisms only in terms of numbers. It ignores differences in size. Yet to a hungry fish, size is important. One stonefly

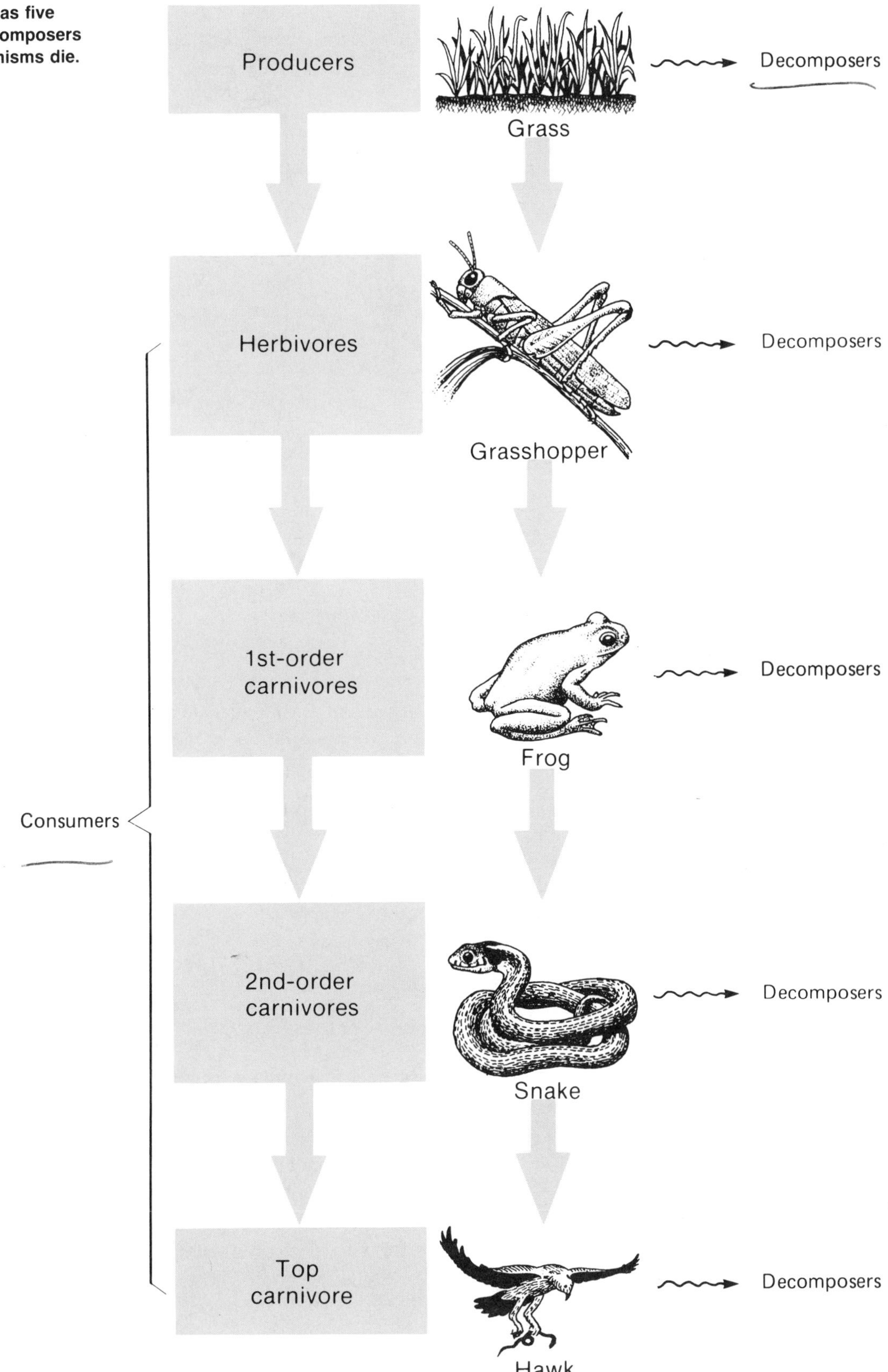

Fig. 1-21 This food chain has five trophic (feeding) levels. Decomposers feed at all levels when organisms die.

Fig. 1-22 An aquatic food web

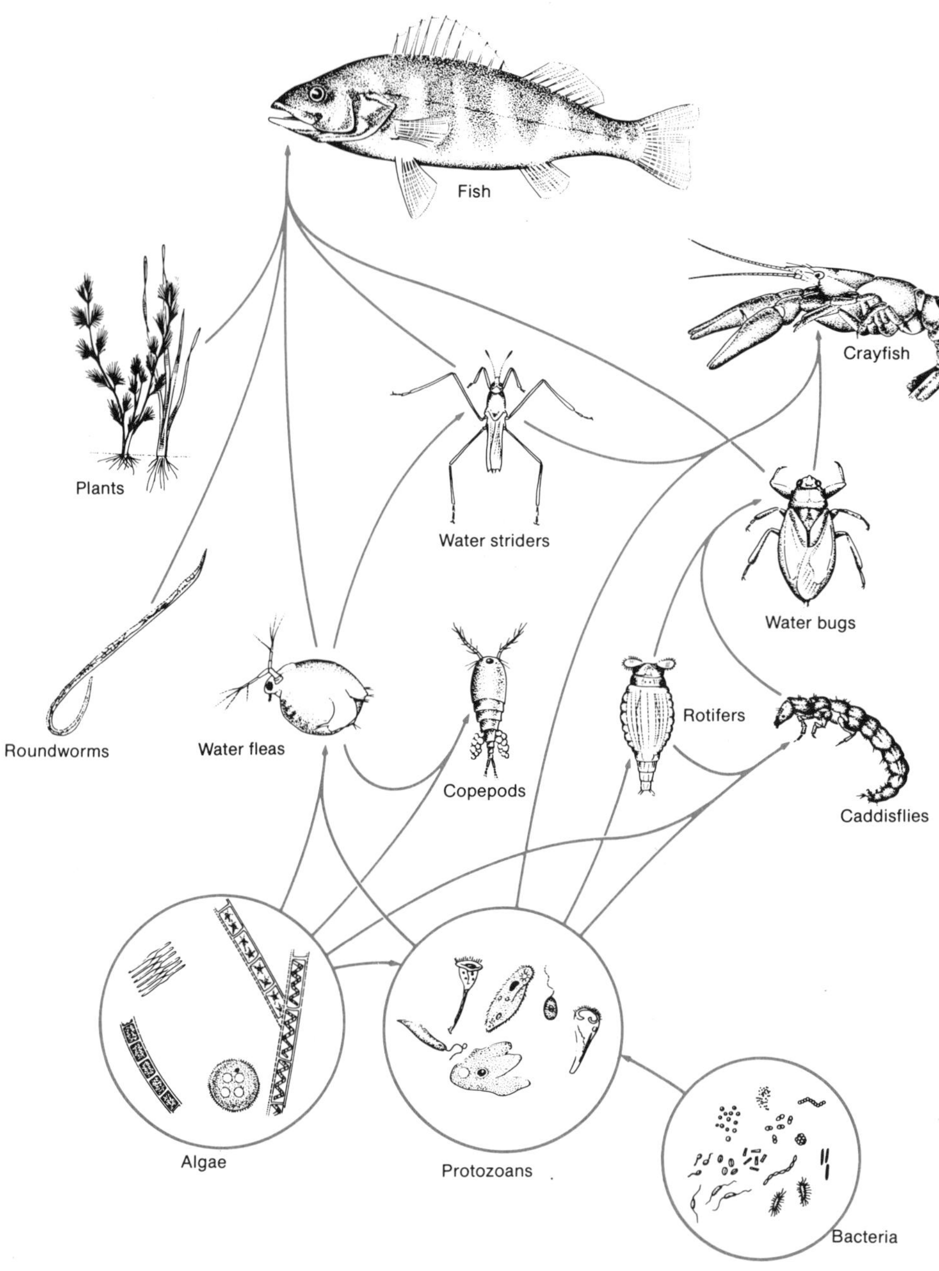

2nd-order carnivore	1 fish
1st-order carnivores	7 stoneflies
Herbivores	35 mayflies
Producers	11 500 diatoms (small algae)

Fig. 1-23 A pyramid of numbers that represents feeding relationships at the edge of a lake

with a mass of 1.2 g makes a better meal than one mayfly with a mass of 0.4 g.

Pyramid of Biomass To avoid the fault in the pyramid of numbers, ecologists often use a **pyramid of biomass**. Each trophic level in this pyramid shows the biomass (total mass of the organisms) at that level. Figure 1-24 is a pyramid of biomass for a food chain of which you may be a part:

grain → chicken → human

Chickens eat grain and humans eat chickens. About 30 g of grain are needed to form 10 g of chicken. Yet that 10 g of chicken will form less than 1 g of human.

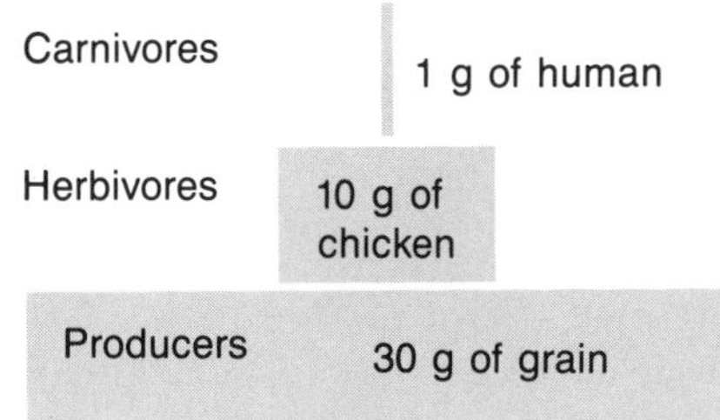

Fig. 1-24 A pyramid of biomass. Note how the mass decreases as we move along the food chain.

It makes much more sense to talk about *masses* of organisms at each trophic level than about *numbers* of organisms. After all, the important thing for a trout is the total mass, not the number of stoneflies it eats. (In like manner, you probably don't care *how many* potatoes you eat for dinner. Rather, you care about the *total amount*, or mass, of potato. One big potato may feed you better than three small ones.)

There is just one small problem with pyramids of biomass. They imply that equal masses of all organisms have equal energy contents. For example, they imply that 1 g of rabbit and 1 g of mouse are equivalent foods for a fox. This is not so. Different types of tissues have different energy contents. The most noticeable difference occurs between plant and animal tissue. An organism can usually obtain about 20% more energy by eating 1 g of animal than by eating 1 g of plant.

Pyramid of Energy The most useful pyramid then is one which shows energy instead of masses or numbers. All animals need energy to live. Some eat plants to get this energy. Other animals eat animals to get their energy. The more easily animals get the energy they need, the better. Therefore the efficiency with which energy is passed along the food chain is more important than either the numbers of organisms or their biomasses. Ecologists today direct most of their attention toward **pyramids of energy** (see Fig. 2-4, page 47). You will learn about these in Section 2.1, page 46.

Section Review

1. **a)** Distinguish between habitat and niche.
   b) What happens if two species with similar niches move into the same habitat?
   c) Describe the habitat of the snails in your classroom ecosystem.
   d) What is the niche of the snails in that ecosystem?
2. Organisms in an ecosystem can be classified into three main categories. What are they?
3. **a)** What is a producer?
   b) Name five producers.
   c) Why are producers also called autotrophs?
   d) Name the producers in your classroom ecosystem.
4. **a)** What are consumers?
   b) Explain why consumers are classified as first-order, second-order, and so on.
   c) How do herbivores, carnivores, and omnivores differ?
   d) What is a top carnivore?
   e) Name the consumers in your classroom ecosystem. What do they eat?
5. **a)** Distinguish between predator and prey.
   b) Can foxes be both predator and prey? Discuss.
6. **a)** What are scavengers?
   b) Name five scavengers.
7. **a)** What is a saprophyte?
   b) Name two groups of organisms that are saprophytes.
8. **a)** What are decomposers?
   b) Give two reasons why decomposers are important.
   c) How do you know your classroom ecosystem contains decomposers?

9. a) What is a trophic level?
   b) What other name is given to the second trophic level?
   c) What numerical trophic level do third-order carnivores occupy?
10. a) What is a food chain?
   b) Complete the following food chains:
      - In a meadow: grass → crickets → . . .
      - In a forest: saplings → deer → . . .
      - In a lake: algae → microscopic animals → . . .
      - In a woodlot: acorns → squirrels → . . .
      - In a garden: seedlings → earthworms → . . .
   c) List the possible food chains in your classroom ecosystem.
11. a) What is a food web?
   b) List five food chains that begin with algae in Figure 1-22.
   c) Draw the food web for your classroom ecosystem.
12. a) Distinguish between a pyramid of numbers and a pyramid of biomass.
   b) Why do ecologists direct most of their attention toward pyramids of energy?

A

B

Fig. 1-25 A riffle (fast) area (A) and a slow area (B) of the Maitland River in southwestern Ontario. What differences can you see? What other differences likely exist? The two areas are only 50 m or so apart.

1.5 Structure of an Ecosystem: Abiotic Factors

In Section 1.4 you read about the biotic aspects of ecosystems. In this section you will look at the abiotic aspects. As you read this section, think about the interaction of the biotic and abiotic components of ecosystems.

Aquatic Ecosystems

Freshwater aquatic ecosystems can be divided into two main types—flowing waters and standing waters.

Flowing Waters We commonly use words like river, stream, brook, and creek to describe flowing waters. Ecologists call them all **streams**.

Life in a stream is affected by many abiotic factors. Among these are the temperature, the speed of the water, the nature of the bottom, the oxygen concentration, and the pH. For example, a fast section of a stream will likely be cool, have a cobble bottom, and have abundant oxygen. In contrast, a slow section of the same stream will likely be warmer, have a sandy or muddy bottom, and have less oxygen (Fig. 1-25). It may also have rooted plants in it. Why will these not likely be present in the fast section?

The cobble bottom, cool water, and abundant oxygen of a fast stream make an ideal habitat for stoneflies and mayflies. These, in turn, are food for trout which also prefer cool, highly oxygenated water. In contrast, a slow stream supports few or none of these.

Standing Waters There are just two main types of standing waters that are wholly aquatic, **ponds** and **lakes**. Others that you may have heard of—bogs, swamps, and marshes, for example—are partly terrestrial. In fact, they are

A

B

Fig. 1-26 The two main types of standing waters are ponds (A) and lakes (B). How are they alike? How are they different?

commonly called **wetlands**. There is not a sharp distinction between ponds and lakes. However, a pond is usually defined as a body of water in which light can reach the bottom at all places. In contrast, light cannot reach the bottom in the deeper regions of lakes. In general, then, ponds are smaller and more shallow than lakes. You can see in Figure 1-26 some of the results of the difference in depth.

Life in a lake or pond is affected by many abiotic factors. Among these are temperature, light, depth, nature of the bottom, oxygen concentration, and pH.

Terrestrial Ecosystems

Five main abiotic factors affect organisms in terrestrial ecosystems. They are **temperature**, **moisture**, **wind**, **light**, and **soil conditions**. Think about a meadow that is adjacent to a woodlot (Fig. 1-27). How do these ecosystems usually differ in the five abiotic factors? What evidence have you seen that these differences in abiotic factors promote differences in biotic factors?

Adaptations of Organisms

Each species of organism has a **range of tolerance** for each abiotic factor in an ecosystem. This range depends on the abiotic factor and on the organism. When the range is exceeded in either direction, the species suffers. Within each range of tolerance there is an **optimum point** at which the species lives best. Obviously conditions cannot be optimum all the time for all species of organism. In fact, most organisms spend most of their lifetimes at conditions which are less than optimum. Therefore those organisms with the broadest tolerance to all factors generally survive best and have the widest distribution. We say that these organisms have the best **adaptations** to their environments.

Some adaptations are **structural**. For example, stonefly nymphs that live under rocks in fast streams are streamlined in shape. Also, they have muscular

Fig. 1-27 How do the abiotic conditions of a meadow differ from those of a woodlot nearby?

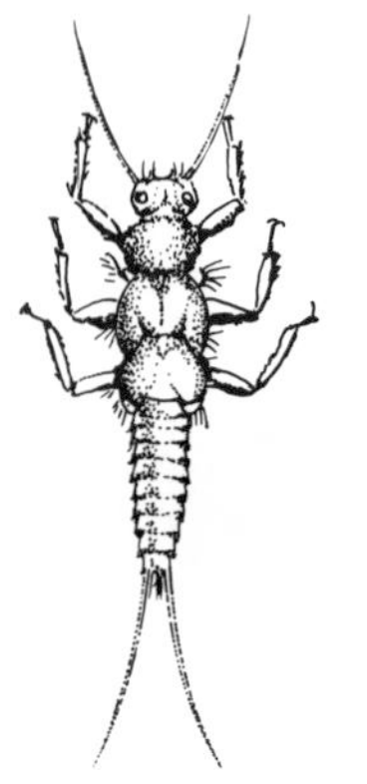

Fig. 1-28 The stonefly is adapted to fast water. How?

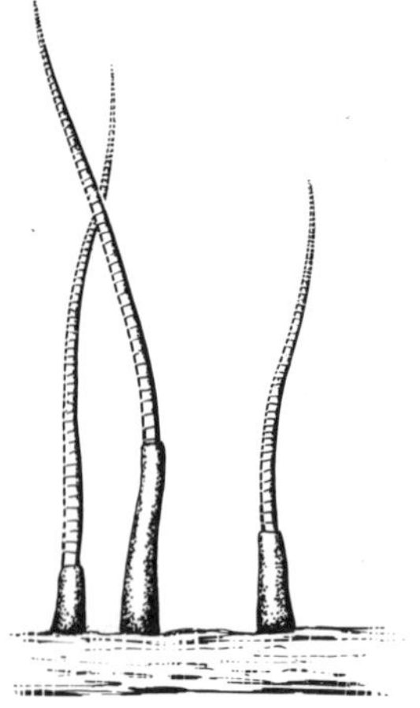

Fig. 1-29 The sludgeworm is adapted to a muddy bottom habitat. How?

legs and hooks on their feet (Fig. 1-28). In contrast, sludgeworms are adapted to the bottom ooze of ponds, lakes, and slow streams. They have no adaptations for holding on in fast water. Instead, they are adapted to the muddy bottom. They build a tube in the muddy bottom material and feed head-down in this tube (Fig. 1-29). To capture oxygen in this low-oxygen environment, they rotate their "tails" through the water. These adaptations of sludgeworms are called **behavioural**. Why is this a good choice of terms?

Section Review

1. a) List five abiotic factors that affect life in a stream.
   b) Compare the abiotic conditions in a fast and slow stream.
   c) Use an example to illustrate how the abiotic conditions can determine the organisms which can live in a stream.
2. a) Compare a pond and a lake.
   b) What is a wetland?
   c) List six abiotic factors that can affect life in a pond or lake.
3. a) List the five main abiotic factors that affect organisms in terrestrial ecosystems.
   b) Compare these five abiotic factors for a meadow and a nearby woodlot.
4. a) Give the meaning of each of these terms: range of tolerance, optimum point, adaptation.
   b) Distinguish between structural and behavioural adaptations.

1.6 Activity: Investigating the Ecology of an Indoor Pond

In preparation for this activity, your teacher and a few members of your class will visit a pond to collect the materials needed to set up the indoor pond. Then, a few times during the next few weeks you will be given a few moments to investigate the ecological relationships in the pond. In the last section you learned that all organisms are adapted to their habitats. This ecological relationship will be the focus of this activity. You will also watch for changes in the pond community as time passes.

Problem

How are pond invertebrates adapted to their habitats? How does a pond community change with time?

Materials

large aquarium
biotic and abiotic materials from a pond
identification guide for pond organisms

pails (3)	probe	light
dip net (large)	small beaker	fish food
hand lens	aquarium pump	dip net (aquarium)

Procedure A Collecting the Materials

CAUTION: For safety reasons the trip to the pond must be supervised by your teacher or another adult.

a. Visit a pond with 2 or 3 large pails and a dip net. The whole class need not go on this trip. However, one member of the group that does go should report to the rest of the class on the location and method of sampling.

b. Collect the following from the pond:
- at least 10 L of pond water
- submergent aquatic plants such as *Elodea* (Canada waterweed), *Ceratophyllum* (coontail), *Cabomba* (fanwort)
- duckweed and algae
- invertebrates swimming in and on the water
- invertebrates living on submergent plants and in the bottom ooze. Be sure to include several snails.
- bottom ooze, sand, and gravel
- two or three small pond minnows. Do *NOT* collect other vertebrates such as frogs and turtles. They cannot be cared for properly in a classroom pond. (*Note:* A few guppies will do well in this ecosystem.)

Fig. 1-30 This "pond" was set up several years ago. The community of living things in it has changed over the years and is still changing. How will yours change?

Procedure B Setting Up the Indoor Pond

Now you are ready to put the materials together to form a small pond (Fig. 1-30). Remember that you are making an ecosystem. Therefore it will require interacting biotic and abiotic components. The biotic component must include producers, consumers, and decomposers. Discuss the set-up thoroughly as a class before you begin. The following suggestions should help ensure a healthy ecosystem:
- If you wish to add tap water to top up the aquarium, let it stand for 1–2 d to dechlorinate.
- Most of the bottom material should be sand and gravel. Too much bottom ooze can cause problems. You should add some, however, to ensure that decomposers are present, and to provide a habitat for sludgeworms, planaria, and other bottom organisms.
- Slow aeration will help maintain a productive ecosystem.
- Keep the aquarium away from direct sunlight and sources of heat. Steep temperature changes are harmful.
- Feed the fish sparingly. Why?

Procedure C The Ecological Studies

Note: All of you cannot crowd around the aquarium at once. Therefore all of you won't be doing this activity at the same time.

a. Make a full-page copy of Table 1-1 in your notebook.

b. Capture an invertebrate with the small beaker or dip net.

c. Leave the invertebrate in water in the beaker. Identify it using the book(s) provided by your teacher. Put its name in your table.

d. Look for other invertebrates of the same species in the aquarium. Note their habitat (bottom ooze, vegetation, surface, open water, sides of aquarium, etc.). Record the habitat in your table.

e. Look at the invertebrate in the beaker with a hand lens. Note and record structural adaptations.

f. Observe the behaviour of this invertebrate and similar ones in the aquarium. Note and record behavioural adaptations.

g. What advantages do these adaptations appear to give the organism? Record these in your table.

h. Repeat steps (b) to (g) for the number of invertebrates suggested by your teacher.

i. Share information with your classmates to develop food chains and webs for the pond. Make detailed notes on the **community structure** (the species present and their relative abundance). You can record relative abundance as abundant (a), frequent (f), occasional (o), and rare (r).

j. Examine the aquarium a week later and, if possible, a few weeks after that. Each time, repeat your study of community structure.

Table 1-1 Adaptations of Pond Invertebrates

Organism	Habitat	Adaptations		Advantages to organism
		Structural	*Behavioural*	

Discussion

1. How is this ecosystem similar to and different from the model ecosystem you set up in Activity 1.2?
2. Your table should be complete for the number of invertebrates suggested by your teacher. Discuss any aspects of it that you find puzzling with your classmates and teacher. Reference books could also be consulted.
3. Describe and account for any observed changes in community structure.

Extension

Monitor the pond ecosystem on a weekly basis for the remainder of the year. Write a report on the changes in community structure over that period of time.

1.7 Planning a Field Trip

You will be going on a field trip shortly. This section will help you with the planning that should precede the field trip. The field trip we have chosen to outline in Section 1.8 is a terrestrial one. Your teacher may choose to conduct an aquatic field trip. In both cases, the preliminary planning and general approach are the same. The equipment, procedure, and, of course, the organisms and their environments will differ.

Organizing Your Group

Most field work requires the cooperative effort of 5 or 6 people if the work is to be completed in a reasonable time period. Your teacher will place you in a group with 4 or 5 others. Your group should now meet and distribute special tasks as follows:

Special Task	*Function*
Group leader	responsible for overall performance of the group
Equipment manager	prepares a list of the equipment, instructs others in its use, and ensures that it is all returned to the school undamaged
Data collector	ensures that all data are recorded in appropriate tables
Identification coordinator	maintains the "library" of identification materials and ensures that organisms are properly identified
Safety officer	prepares a list of group members; ensures that the group stays together; ensures that safety regulations are followed

Planning the Study

The special tasks just outlined should ensure that your group works effectively and safely. Of course, all of you will have to do scientific studies as you perform these special duties. Therefore your group should now examine the field trip in Section 1.8, page 38 (or the special instructions provided by your teacher). Discuss the field trip, basing your discussion on questions such as these:

- What is the central purpose of the field trip?
- How can we direct our work toward this central purpose?
- Does it matter if we cannot identify some organisms? What will we do if we can't identify some?
- How can we do the study without harming the area and the life in it?
- Would a photographic record be helpful?
- What data sheets do we need?
- How can we get the work done safely and efficiently?
- How can we ensure that the special tasks get done?
- How can we make sure that everyone gets a chance to do some of the scientific work?
- What predictions can we make regarding expected findings?
- What kinds of information will we record in our data tables?

Section Review

The notes you make during your group meeting are your write-up.

Fig. 1-31 A wide variety of plants makes an old-field community an exciting place to study ecological relationships. Why is this so? This site was a vegetable garden just three years ago.

1.8 Field Trip: Ecological Relationships in a Meadow, Park, or Other Greenspace

For this field trip you will visit a meadow, park, conservation area, abandoned field, roadside ditch, or some other greenspace. A suitable site will likely exist within walking distance of your school. The ideal site is an old-field community—an area that has been unmown for several years. The dominant plants will be grasses, asters, goldenrods, thistles, milkweed, and so on (Fig. 1-31). The greater the variety of plants, the better. You may wish to recommend a site that you know of to your teacher.

At the site you will search for organisms, both plant and animal. You will investigate each organism closely, emphasizing its ecological relationships.

Problem

What organisms are present at the site? What are their ecological relationships?

Materials

clear plastic jars with tops (5)
hand lens
white tray
garden trowel
sweep net (or kitchen sieve)
Field Guides for identification of plants and insects

Fig. 1-32 A sweep net dislodges invertebrates from the plants.

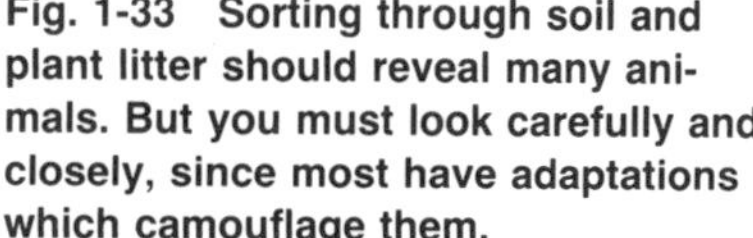

Fig. 1-33 Sorting through soil and plant litter should reveal many animals. But you must look carefully and closely, since most have adaptations which camouflage them.

Procedure

a. Make 3 full-page copies of Tables 1-2 and 1-3.

b. Look at each type of vegetation closely. If you can identify it, put its name in both of your tables. If you can't, make a sketch of it. Now, complete both tables for each plant.

c. Sweep a certain type of vegetation (e.g. goldenrod) with the sweep net (Fig. 1-32). If you have no sweep net, a kitchen sieve will do. Transfer the animals you catch to jars. Study them through a hand lens. Put their names (or sketches) in your tables. Then complete both tables for each animal.

d. Repeat step (c) for several other types of vegetation.

e. Use the trowel to collect some topsoil and plant litter. The top 4-5 cm will do. Put this in the white tray and spread it out. Then search for animals (Fig. 1-33). Study them closely with the hand lens. You may wish to put them in jars to examine them more easily. Put their names (or sketches) in your tables. Then complete both tables for each animal.

f. Examine the area for decomposers and/or evidence that decomposers are present. Make a record of your findings.

g. Release all animals near their habitats when the study is complete.

h. Look for evidence of human impact on this ecosystem. Record it.

Table 1-2 Study of a Greenspace

Name or sketch of organism	*Habitat*	*Niche*	*Trophic level*

Table 1-3 Adaptations of Organisms

Name or sketch of organism	*Adaptations*		*Advantages to organism*
	Structural	*Behavioural*	

Discussion

1. Write a half-page report that supports this statement: "Organisms are adapted to their habitats."

2. List as many food chains as you can for this ecosystem.

3. Create a food web for this ecosystem.
4. What larger animals may be involved in the food web of this ecosystem? Cite any indirect or direct evidence of this involvement.
5. What roles do the producers play in this ecosystem? What would happen if all plants but the grasses were killed with herbicides?
6. Predict what would happen if the most abundant herbivore species were eliminated.
7. How do you know decomposers are present?
8. Evaluate the impact of humans on this ecosystem.
9. Evaluate this statement: "The greater the diversity of organisms, the more stable an ecosystem will be."

Extension

Perhaps time and circumstances permit your class to do a more involved field trip than this. If so, we suggest you incorporate the measurement of abiotic factors into the study. A field trip of this type is outlined on page 165 of *Investigating Terrestrial Ecosystems*, Prentice-Hall Canada Inc., 1986.

Chapter Highlights

1. Ecology is the study of the relationship between organisms and their environments.
2. The ecosystem concept can be used to predict the effects of human actions on ecosystems.
3. The biotic structure of an ecosystem can be described in terms of habitats, niches, trophic levels, food chains, and food webs.
4. Ecological pyramids can be used to represent trophic levels.
5. A wide range of abiotic factors interact with biotic factors in an ecosystem.
6. A change in one variable in an ecosystem will change many other variables.
7. Every organism is adapted to its habitat.

Key Terms

abiotic
adaptation
autotroph
biotic
carnivore
clear cutting
community structure
competition
consumer
decomposer
ecology
ecosystem
food chain
food web
habitat
herbivore
heterotroph
niche
omnivore
predator
prey
producer
pyramid of biomass
pyramid of energy
pyramid of numbers
range of tolerance
saprophyte
scavenger
selective cutting
trophic level

Recognizing the Concepts

Each of the following statements or questions is followed by four responses. Choose the correct response in each case. (Do not write in this book.)

1. The trees of a woodlot, together with all the other biotic and abiotic components of the woodlot, make up a(n)
   a) habitat **b)** food chain **c)** niche **d)** ecosystem
2. The grasses of a meadow occupy the trophic level of
   a) herbivore **b)** habitat **c)** producer **d)** prey
3. Trout feed on insects, worms, and small fish. Trout, in turn, are food for some mammals. Leeches and lampreys often parasitize trout. Dead trout make plants and algae grow. This description is *best* called a partial description of the trout's
   a) habitat **b)** niche **c)** ecosystem **d)** trophic level
4. A skunk eats living grubs and worms. It also eats fruits of some plants. It even eats garbage. The skunk is best described as a(n)
   a) omnivore **b)** herbivore **c)** carnivore **d)** scavenger
5. A hawk swoops down from the sky and kills and eats a rabbit. This hawk is a
   a) scavenger **b)** decomposer **c)** prey **d)** predator
6. Consider this food chain:
   algae → small animals → minnows → trout → humans
   The trout in this food chain are
   a) top carnivores
   b) second-order carnivores
   c) third-order carnivores
   d) first-order carnivores
7. Studies show that, for every square metre of surface area, a lake has 150 g of producers, 16 g of herbivores, and 4.5 g of carnivores. These data can be used to draw a
   a) food web
   b) pyramid of numbers
   c) pyramid of biomass
   d) pyramid of energy

Understanding the Concepts

1. Explain why a lake can be called an ecosystem.
2. Distinguish between niche and trophic level.
3. **a)** Distinguish between a consumer and a decomposer.
   b) Under what circumstances would a predator be a first-order consumer?
   c) Distinguish between a scavenger and a saprophyte.
4. Name the trophic level of each organism in this food chain:
   algae → water fleas → minnows → trout → bear
5. Draw a pyramid of numbers for this food chain:
   grass → rabbits → wolves → fleas
6. Why must all ecosystems have decomposers?
7. Complete the following food chains:
   grass → woodchuck → ______ ; tree → caterpillars → ______ ; ______ → deer → wolf; aquatic plants → ______ → fish.

8. Write the food chains that are in the food web in Figure 1-22.
9. a) How is a grasshopper structurally adapted to life in an open meadow?
   b) What behavioural adaptation does a goldfish display when the oxygen content in its aquarium gets too low?

Applying the Concepts

1. a) If hunters shot all the deer in a forest, what changes might occur in the forest?
   b) If hunting were totally banned in the forest, what changes might occur?
2. Parts of southern Ontario in the Niagara Peninsula and along the Lake Erie shore contain Carolinian forest. This means that, because of a warm climate, these areas have organisms typical of those that live in the Carolinas of the southeast United States. Among these organisms are trees found in few other places in Ontario—sycamore, sweet gum, and tulip tree, to name a few. Some foresters have argued that the mature trees of these species should be logged out. In addition to providing income to landowners, such logging will open up the woods and allow younger trees to grow better. Use the ecosystem concept to prepare an argument for or against this proposal.
3. Select five foods that you ate during your last three meals. Draw the five food chains that include those foods and you.
4. Light is an important abiotic factor in ponds, lakes, and very slow streams. It is not an important abiotic factor in fast streams. Why is this so?
5. Examine the photographs of skulls in Figure 1-34. What trophic level did each of these animals occupy? How do you know?
6. a) What kinds of decomposers would you expect to find in a municipal landfill site that receives mainly household garbage?
   b) Why should such a site be located and managed in such a way that run-off from it cannot escape to underground or surface waters?

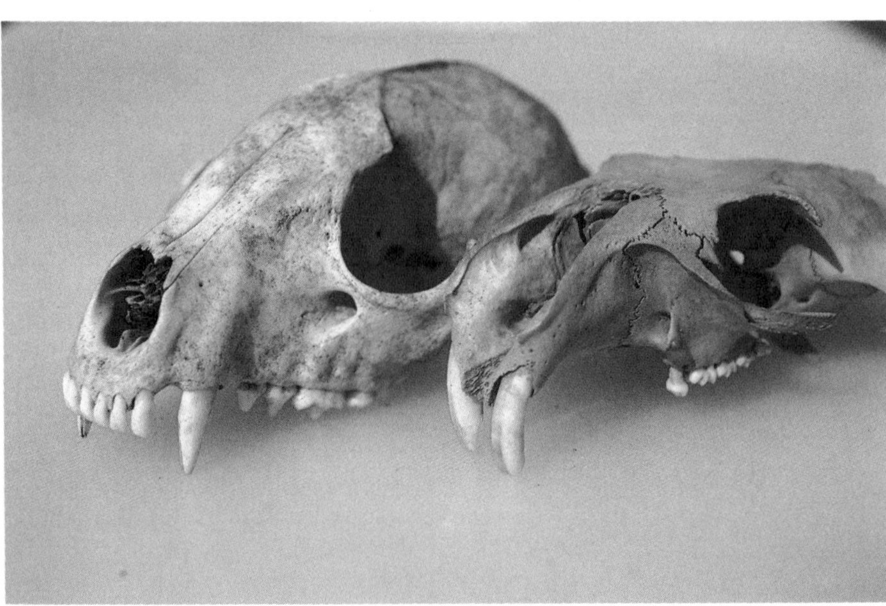

Fig. 1-34 What trophic levels did these animals occupy?

7. When cattle are allowed to graze in the grasslands and savannas of Kenya, the numbers of large carnivores like lions usually decrease in the grazed areas. Why is this so?
8. **a)** Design an animal that would have ideal structural adaptations for life in fast water.
   b) What behavioural adaptations would make life even easier for this animal?

Investigations

1. Go on a hike to a nearby park or other greenspace. Make notes on the habitat and niche of at least five animals. (Binoculars would be helpful.) Write a report on your findings. Photographs of the habitats could be included in your report.
2. Obtain a copy of a masterplan for a provincial park from the Ministry of Natural Resources. Analyze the management proposals in this plan from an ecosystem perspective.
3. Design and do an experiment to show the effects of moisture on seed germination and seedling growth.
4. Consult books in the library to find an example of mutualism not described in this book.
5. Make a poster of a food web with at least 10 organisms in it. Use pictures from magazines or take your own pictures or draw them.
6. Write a short paper on a parasite that causes a human disease.
7. Identify an ecological problem in the area in which you live. Analyze its causes and effects, and propose possible remedies. The ecosystem concept should be central to your arguments.
8. Research the objectives of a conservation organization such as the Conservation Council of Ontario, the Ontario Forestry Association, the Sierra Club of Ontario, the Wildlands League, or the Federation of Ontario Naturalists (Fig. 1-35).

Fig. 1-35 The Federation of Ontario Naturalists is one of Ontario's premier conservation organizations. What happens in this building and in the Federation's outreach program?

Biography

Frank Glew: Outdoor Educator

Frank Glew is the Coordinator of Outdoor Education for the Waterloo County Board of Education. He began his teaching career in a one-room school in Waterloo County. For the first several years of his teaching career he worked part-time on a B.A. degree at Wilfrid Laurier University, specializing in English and Biology. Glew says that this eduation in both English and Biology has been invaluable in his teaching career. Frank also worked for two years in an elementary school in Tillsonburg where he taught science and physical education to Grade 7 and 8 students. It was this combination of subjects that got Frank interested in teaching outdoor education.

Frank Glew next moved to Etobicoke in Metropolitan Toronto where he taught science for three years at a senior elementary school before becoming a science consultant. He then served as head of the science department at a secondary school in Etobicoke, where he was responsible for curriculum development from Grade 9 to Grade 12.

Frank's interest in outdoor education increased to the point where he finally moved back to Waterloo County to become a consultant in outdoor education. He held this position for 15 years before being appointed coordinator of outdoor education.

In order to do his job better, Frank pursued a M.S.Ed. degree, with an emphasis on environmental education, at Northern Illinois University. He is currently working on a Ph.D. degree in environmental education at Columbia University in New York.

Frank says that he likes his job because it allows him to share his love of the outdoors and his respect for all life with others. He also likes the challenges the job offers and the opportunities to make decisions.

2 Matter and Energy in Ecosystems

CHAPTER CONTENTS

CHAPTER OBJECTIVES

After completing this chapter you should be able to:

1. Describe the paths of energy and nutrients through an ecosystem.
2. Outline the water, carbon, and nitrogen cycles.
3. Investigate the effects of excess nutrients on ecosystems.
4. Recognize various types of succession.
5. Evaluate human impact on ecosystems using your knowledge of succession.

In Chapter 1 you looked at the *structure* of ecosystems—their biotic and abiotic parts. However, you did not learn how ecosystems *function*. This chapter provides that knowledge.

All living things need matter and energy. Matter is needed to make new cells and to repair worn-out parts; energy is needed to "power" life processes such as movement and growth. How does energy get into an ecosystem? How does it reach every organism in the ecosystem? How does matter get into an ecosystem? And how does each organism in the ecosystem get the matter it needs? In short, how does an ecosystem function (Fig. 2-1)?

Fig. 2-1 The ecosystem on Baffin Island in Canada's north has functioned for thousands of years without help by humans. How does it get the matter and energy that it needs?

Fig. 2-2 Activity abounds in natural ecosystems. How do the organisms get the energy they need for this activity?

2.1 Flow of Energy in Ecosystems

Perhaps you have spent a few quiet moments by a lake or walking through the woods (Fig. 2-2). If you have, you probably noticed the constant activity of the organisms around you. The seemingly endless energy of birds may capture your attention most. However, in the spring and summer you certainly cannot miss the activity of insects, particularly mosquitoes and blackflies! Beyond these organisms you see, countless others fill the air with their sounds.

Activity is the essence of life. In order to have activity, energy is needed. Let's see how organisms get the energy they need.

Energy from the Sun to Top Carnivores

All the energy used by living things comes, in the first place, from the sun. Producers store some of the sun's energy in the foods they make by photosynthesis. They use some of this food for their own life processes. The rest is stored. Herbivores get their energy by eating producers, while carnivores get their energy by eating herbivores or other carnivores. In this way the sun's energy is passed along the trophic levels of food chains from producer to top carnivore.

Energy Flow Is One-Way

The passing of energy along a food chain is not very efficient. A great deal of energy is lost at each trophic level. As an example, consider the following food chain:

diatoms → mayflies → fish

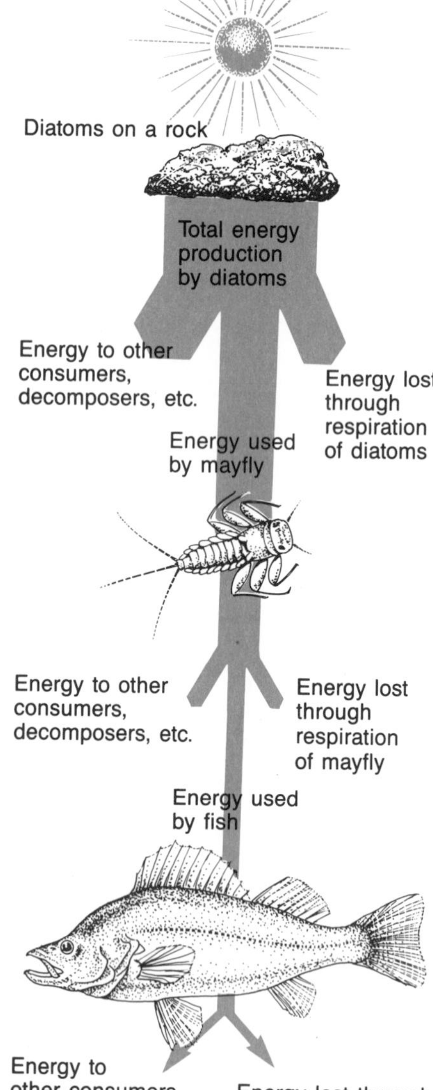

Fig. 2-3 This common food chain of our lakes and streams shows the energy flow characteristics of any food chain, aquatic or terrestrial.

Follow Figure 2-3 as you read on. The diatoms, through photosynthesis, store some of the sun's energy in foods. Much of this energy is lost as heat through respiration by the diatoms. However, when the mayflies eat the diatoms, the mayflies get some of the stored energy.

Like the diatoms, the mayflies lose much of the energy they took in through life activities such as respiration. When the fish eats the mayflies, the fish gets some of the energy stored in the mayflies. It does not get all this energy, however. For instance, parts of the exoskeletons of the mayflies cannot be digested by the fish.

The fish also loses much of its acquired energy through life activities such as respiration. Parasites and decomposers also use some of the fish's energy. In the end, little energy remains to be passed onto higher trophic levels.

As Figure 2-3 shows, **energy is gradually lost along a food chain**. Much of this energy leaves the food chain as heat. It cannot be recaptured by any organisms in the food chain. It is lost forever to that ecosystem. Thus **energy flow is one-way along a food chain. For an ecosystem to keep operating, energy must always enter it from the sun**.

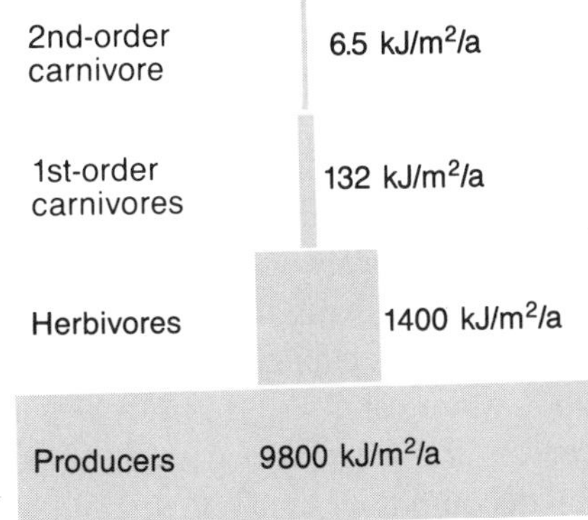

Fig. 2-4 A pyramid of energy for a lake. Each numeral represents the *total* energy flow at that trophic level in kilojoules per square metre of surface per year.

Pyramid of Energy

In Section 1.4 you saw that there are three kinds of ecological pyramids: pyramids of numbers, biomass, and energy. The most important of these is the **pyramid of energy**. How well an ecosystem functions depends on how well each trophic level captures energy and passes it on to the next level. This is much more important than the numbers of organisms or their sizes (biomasses).

Since energy is lost along a food chain, all pyramids of energy look like the one in Figure 2-4. They taper off to almost nothing. Each level in this pyramid represents the total energy flow at that level. This includes the energy tied up in the formation of new cells and the energy given off by respiration.

An Issue: Energy Flow and Humans

We are as dependent as any other organism on the flow of energy through ecosystems. Our very existence depends on it. However, we have the ability to control energy flow and divert it for our own use. For example, we can destroy a natural ecosystem like a grassland or forest and replace it with a grain crop that will yield more energy for us. As the human population increases, more crops will be needed to meet the larger food demands. Therefore more natural ecosystems will be destroyed. Fewer habitats will be available for organisms. As a result, some species may eventually become extinct. However, alternatives do exist. What are they? What can *you* do to promote them?

Extension

Sit down with a small group of your classmates and share and debate your answers to the two questions that were just asked.

Section Review

1. Distinguish between the structure and functioning of an ecosystem.
2. Describe the path of energy from the sun to top carnivore in a food chain.
3. Describe how energy is lost along a food chain.
4. What is meant by the phrase "energy flow is one-way in an ecosystem"?
5. Account for the shape of a pyramid of energy.
6. From an energy perspective, why do humans often destroy natural ecosystems?
7. Describe the flow of energy in the classroom ecosystem you built in Section 1.2.

2.2 Flow of Matter in Ecosystems

Nutrients: The Elements of Life

An ecosystem needs more than energy in order to function. It also needs matter. The matter is used by organisms in the ecosystem for life processes such as growth. Most ecosystems need over 20 elements. Among these are nitrogen and oxygen. Just the plants in most ecosystems need 16 elements. Because these elements are so important to living things, they are called **nutrients**.

Nutrient Cycles

In Section 2.1 you learned that energy is lost along a food chain. Little or no energy is left at the end of the food chain to be recycled to the producers. However, this is not the case for nutrients. Nutrients flowing through the food chain are returned to the producers. Let's see how this happens.

Producers get their nutrients from the soil, water, and air. Herbivores get these nutrients when they eat the producers. Carnivores also get the same nutrients when they eat the herbivores. Then decomposers break down animal wastes and dead organisms. This releases the nutrients back into the soil, water, and air so producers can use them again. In this way, **nutrients are recycled through an ecosystem**. The path each nutrient follows is called a **nutrient cycle**. Figure 2-5 compares energy flow and nutrient recycling in an ecosystem. Study this comparison closely.

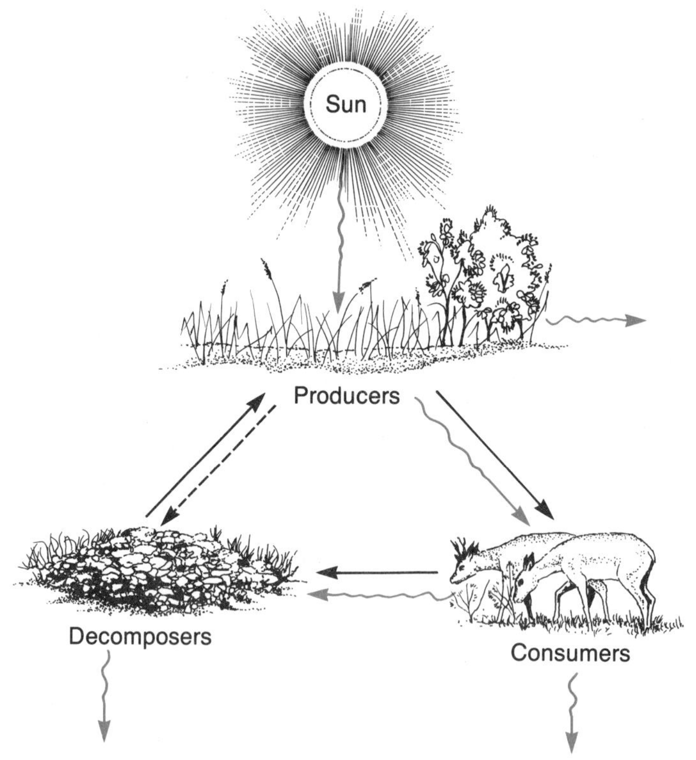

Fig. 2-5 Energy and nutrient flow in an ecosystem. The coloured arrows show the direction of energy flow. Note that energy is lost at each level. The black lines show the path of nutrient flow. Note that nutrients complete the cycle while energy does not. The broken arrow represents both energy and nutrient flow to decomposers as they break down dead producers.

An Issue: Nutrient Flow and Humans

Many lakes are in trouble because we have added nutrients to them and upset the natural recycling process. These excess nutrients are, in part, fertilizer run-off from farmers' fields and city lawns. However, human sewage and animal wastes from farm feedlots are the main contributors of nutrients. Sewage treatment plants dispose of treated sewage in streams or lakes. And manure at feedlots is often left exposed to the rain, allowing nutrients to be dissolved

Fig. 2-6 Nutrients leach from wastes at feedlots and wash into nearby streams. Such leaching can be prevented. How?

and washed to nearby streams (Fig. 2-6). Eventually the nutrients end up in lakes. If the lakes are not adequately flushed, the nutrients build up. How will this affect the lake? (Study Figure 2-5 for an answer.) What positive effects can excess nutrients have? What negative effects can they have? What should be done about this problem? What can *you* do?

Extension

Sit down with a small group of your classmates and share and debate your answers to the four questions just asked.

Section Review

1. Why are some elements called nutrients?
2. a) Describe the path of nutrients through an ecosystem.
   b) Why do we call this path a nutrient cycle?
3. How do humans often upset the natural nutrient balance of lakes?
4. What evidence do you have that nutrients are being recycled in the classroom ecosystem you built in Section 1.2?

2.3 Some Nutrient Cycles

You learned in Section 2.2 that nutrients are recycled. This section describes two nutrient cycles to show you more clearly how that recycling occurs.

The Water Cycle

The hydrogen and oxygen atoms in water are nutrients that organisms need. Clearly there is no problem obtaining these nutrients in aquatic ecosystems. However, they are sometimes in short supply in terrestrial ecosystems. The overall cycling of water in nature involves both aquatic and terrestrial ecosystems and the air above them. Let's see how this occurs.

Water vapour enters the atmosphere through **transpiration** from vegetation. (Transpiration is the loss of water through pores in the leaves of plants.) It also enters the atmosphere by evaporation from bodies of water and the soil (Fig. 2-7). In the cool upper atmosphere this vapour condenses, forming clouds. In time, enough water collects in the clouds to cause precipitation. When this occurs, some of the water falling on the ground runs along the surface of the ground to a stream, pond, or other body of water. This water is called **surface run-off**. Some of the water also soaks into the ground by a process called **percolation**. Some water percolates down to the bedrock. Then it becomes **ground water** and gradually runs back to lakes and other bodies of water.

Some of the water in the soil moves up to the roots of plants by **capillarity**. The roots absorb the water. This is how most plants get the hydrogen and oxygen they need. Animals can obtain water by eating plants or by eating other animals. Of course, they can also obtain water by drinking it directly from a body of water. When plants and animals die, they decompose. During this process, the water present in their tissues is released into the environment.

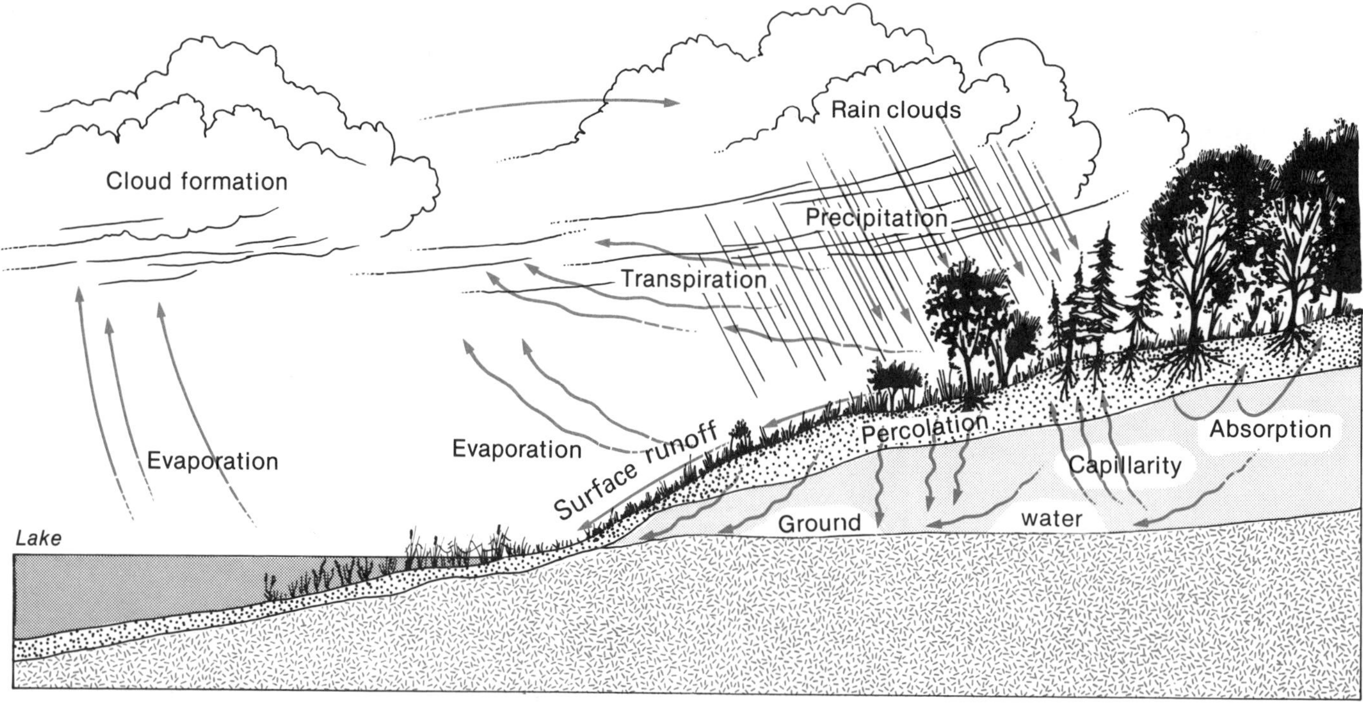

Fig. 2-7 The water cycle. Try to trace the possible paths of a water molecule from a cloud, through an ecosystem, and back to a cloud again.

The Carbon Cycle

Carbon is another nutrient that all organisms need. In fact, it is the basic building block of all living things. Like water, carbon moves through an ecosystem in a cycle (Fig. 2-8). Here is how the cycle works.

Carbon is present in the atmosphere as carbon dioxide. Producers (plants and algae) use it to make food. Now the carbon is in the producers. Herbivores eat the plants, and carnivores eat the herbivores. Now the carbon is in animals. Both plants and animals respire. Their respiration returns carbon dioxide to the atmosphere. Decomposers break down dead plants and animals as well as animal waste. This, too, returns carbon dioxide to the atmosphere.

Some organic matter does not decompose easily. Instead, it builds up in the earth's crust. Petroleum and coal were formed from the buildup of plant matter

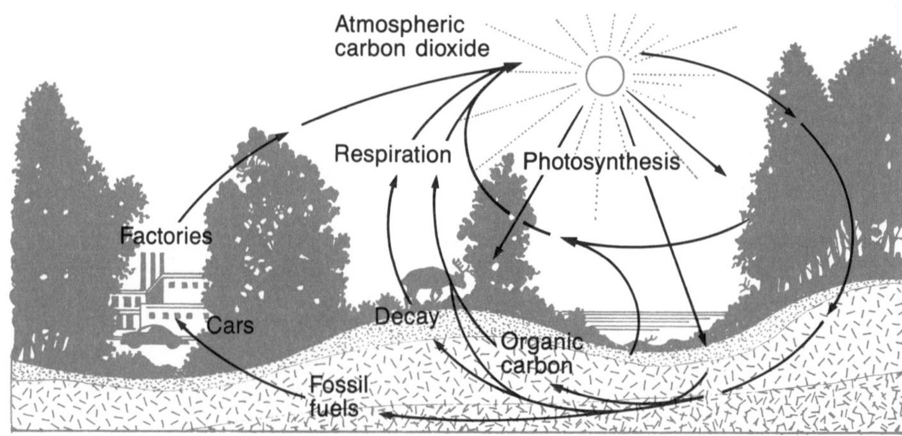

Fig. 2-8 The carbon cycle. Try to trace the possible paths of a carbon atom from the atmosphere, through an ecosystem, and back to the atmosphere again.

millions of years ago. At one time, the carbon cycle was almost a perfect cycle. That is, carbon was returned to the atmosphere as quickly as it was removed. Lately, however, the increased burning of fossil fuels has added carbon to the atmosphere faster than producers can remove it.

The cycle just described occurs on, in, and above the land. A similar cycle also occurs in aquatic ecosystems such as lakes and oceans. In fact, water (mainly in the oceans) holds over 50 times as much carbon dioxide as the air.

Summary of the Structure and Functioning of Ecosystems

An ocean, pond, forest, desert, park, alpine (mountain) meadow, and your classroom ecosystem don't look much alike. Yet they are all ecosystems. Therefore they have a common structure. They also function in the same basic way. You learned about the structure of ecosystems in Chapter 1 and about how they function in this chapter. Let's list those things ecosystems have in common.

- Most ecosystems have the same three biotic parts: producers, consumers, and decomposers. The actual species will, of course, differ from ecosystem to ecosystem.
- A highly interdependent relationship exists between the biotic and abiotic parts of an ecosystem.
- Energy flow in ecosystems is one-way. Energy is gradually lost along food chains. Little or none is recycled to producers. Therefore energy must always enter the ecosystem from the sun.
- Most ecosystems need the same 20 or so nutrients. These nutrients are recycled within each ecosystem.

Section Review

1. Two nutrient cycles are discussed in this section. For each cycle, do the following in your notebook:
  a) State why the cycle is important.
  b) Give a point-form description of the cycle.
  c) Make a simple sketch of the cycle.

2. Make a summary of the four things most ecosystems have in common.

2.4 Activity: Investigating Nutrient Flow in an Aquatic Ecosystem

In Section 2.2 you were asked to think about the effects of excess nutrients on a lake. This activity gives you a chance to test your thoughts.

Nutrients pass through cycles in ecosystems. They move from producers through consumers and then are returned to producers by decomposers. Also, the nutrients in dead producers are recycled to producers by decomposers. As a result, a balance usually exists in an ecosystem. That is, some of each nutrient is in the producers, some of it is in the consumers, and some of it is in the free state, ready to be absorbed by producers.

What do you suppose would happen to an ecosystem if we added extra nutrients in the free state? How might this affect the cycles; the producers; and the consumers?

In this activity you will make a simple aquatic ecosystem. Then you will add some lawn fertilizer to it. This fertilizer contains three main nutrients, nitrogen, phosphorus, and potassium. After you have made your prediction, proceed with the activity.

Problem

How will excess nutrients, particularly those present in lawn fertilizer, affect an aquatic ecosystem?

Materials

wide-mouthed jars, with a capacity of at least 2 L (2)
pond water (2 L)
pond snails (6)
strands of *Ceratophyllum, Cabomba, Elodea*, or other aquatic plant, each about 10–20 cm long (6)

Procedure

a. Fill both jars with pond water. You could get this from the aquarium you set up in Section 1.6.
b. Add half the aquatic plant to each jar.
c. Add 3 pond snails to each jar.
d. Label one jar "Control". Label the other jar "Experimental" (Fig. 2-9).

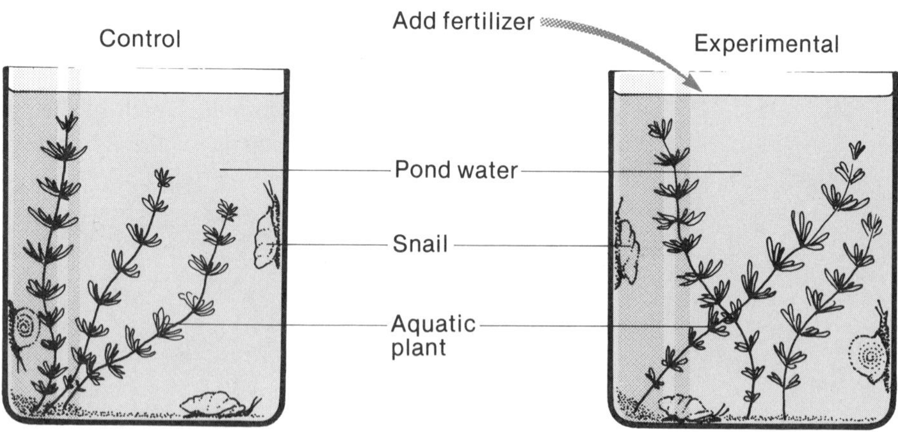

Fig. 2-9 How will fertilizer affect the experimental jar?

e. Dissolve a *small* pinch of lawn fertilizer in water. Then add the solution to the experimental jar.
f. Place the jars, side by side, in a bright location.
g. Observe the jars each day for 2–3 weeks. Make notes on changes in the appearance of the aquatic plant, the snails, and the rest of the ecosystem.

Discussion

1. What are the producers in your ecosystems?
2. What are the consumers in your ecosystems?
3. a) What important invisible organisms are in your ecosystems?
   b) What is their role?
4. What is the purpose of the control?
5. Why are the jars placed side by side?
6. a) Describe the changes the fertilizer caused in your ecosystem.
   b) Explain these changes.
7. Explain why sewage and fertilizer run-off can cause plant and algal growth in lakes.

Extensions

1. The ecosystems in this activity were kept simple in order to make the interpretation of the results easier. Repeat the experiment with more complex ecosystems. For example, you can add duckweed and algae as producers and sideswimmers and fish (guppies) as consumers.
2. Examine the label on a bag of lawn fertilizer. What nutrients does the fertilizer contain? Research the functions of each of these nutrients.

2.5 Succession on Sand Dunes

At first glance, ecosystems may appear stable or unchanging. However, they do change with time. You have probably noticed that a vacant lot, left untouched, does not remain in its original state for long. It may have started out with bare soil. But it soon becomes overgrown with grasses and weeds. As time passes taller weeds dominate the shorter ones. In a few years shrubs may appear. Several years later small trees may begin to colonize the area. If you could camp out under one of these trees for a few hundred years, you would witness one of nature's most remarkable phenomena—**ecological succession**. What is succession? Why does it occur? The most striking and clearly defined example of succession occurs on sand dunes. Therefore we will use the sand dune environment to explain succession.

Fig. 2-10 The sand dunes at Pinery Provincial Park near Grand Bend, Ontario are among the most famous in North America. Other famous dunes occur at Sand Dunes Provincial Park in Prince Edward County. Smaller dunes occur at many sites along the Great Lakes. Vacationers are attracted by the beauty and mystique of the dunes. Scientists are attracted by their uniqueness.

Sand dunes commonly form on the leeward side of large lakes (the shore toward which the wind blows). They also form on ocean shores. Some of the most famous dunes in the world occur around the Great Lakes (Fig. 2-10). Wave action piles sand on the beach where the sun and wind dry it out. Then winds blow the sand inland. This often creates large mounds of sand called **sand dunes**.

Such an area is a harsh environment for any organism. Some of the harsh conditions are:

- lack of moisture
- few available nutrients
- shifting sands
- high day temperatures

Fig. 2-11 Marram grass is a common sand grass on many dunes.

- intense light
- strong winds
- low night temperatures

In spite of these conditions, some organisms do establish communities on sand dunes. And, as you know, their presence changes the environment. The changed environment then supports different organisms. These organisms, in turn, change the environment again. And on it goes.

This interaction of biotic and abiotic factors makes a sand dune a region of change. Let us take an imaginary trip through time to see exactly what happens. Imagine that you are sitting on a sand dune. It has no life on it, other than you. This dune is located on the shore of one of the Great Lakes. You are going to sit there for several hundred years and watch succession occur.

Stages in Succession on Sand Dunes

The Pioneer Stage As time passes, some dead organic matter (leaves, twigs, fish) is sure to be swept onto the dune. This small amount of organic matter enriches the sand. Now patches of sand grass, a **pioneer plant**, begin to grow around you (Fig. 2-11). This hardy plant is well-adapted to the dry conditions of a sand dune. It has an extensive root system that absorbs the small amount of water available. This root system also anchors the plant in the shifting sand. The plant's narrow leaves bend against the force of wind-driven sand. The sand grass stabilizes the dune with its large branching root system. Also, it traps drifting sand, making the dune even larger. Most sand grasses propagate by sending underground stems (rhizomes) through the sand.

Fig. 2-12 This juniper, an evergreen, often invades dunes around the Great Lakes. How is it adapted to the dune environment?

The Shrub Stage As sand grass dies, humus is added to the soil. This changed soil can now support plants which need more nutrients and water. A shrub called sand cherry often becomes established at this stage. You may even notice evergreen shrubs such as junipers around you (Fig. 2-12). Like sand grass, junipers have large branching roots. As well, they hug the ground as protection from the winds. Other adaptations to the dune environment include a thick cuticle on the leaves (needles) and narrow leaves. Why are these an advantage to the juniper?

The Cottonwood Stage Next, cottonwood trees (poplars) begin to shoot upward among the shrubs. These trees soon become the **dominant plants** in the area. As a result, they are called the **index plants** of this stage in succession. The shade cast by the shrubs and cottonwoods provides welcome relief to you from the scorching sun. It also helps the soil hold its moisture longer. Decaying leaves add further organic matter to the soil. Ants and beetles move busily among the sand grass plants. Birds feed on sand cherries and juniper berries. The digger wasp, an **index animal** of the cottonwood stage, burrows into the sand at your feet. You notice that the sand's colour is darker. This is because of the added organic matter.

The Pine Stage The enriched soil now enables pine seedlings to become established in the area. Eventually they become the dominant plants. Thus they are the index plants of this stage in succession. As the pine trees develop, they

Fig. 2-13 Look closely and you can see oak leaves from the oak stage of succession and pine needles from the remaining pines. These leaves slowly add humus to the soil. The dry conditions inhibit decay. Do you know why?

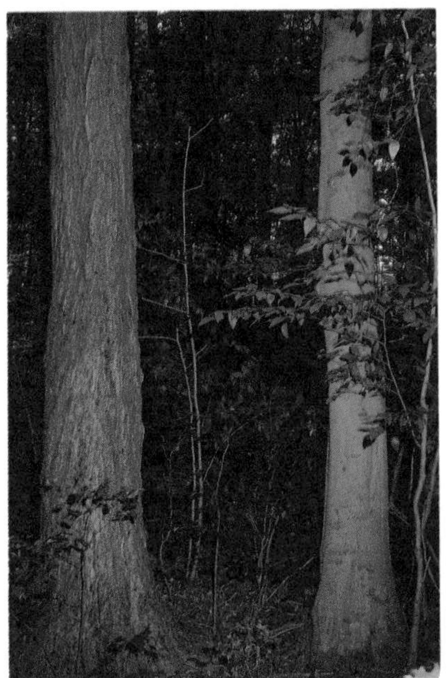

Fig. 2-14 The climax forest in much of southern Ontario is dominated by maple and beech trees. The beech tree is the one on the right with smooth grey bark.

drop needles about you. The soil becomes still richer. But now, a strange thing happens. Pine trees are sun-loving plants but the large pine trees cast a dense shade on the soil. As a result young pine trees do not receive enough light to develop. The pine trees have changed the environment so much that their own species cannot become established in the area. As adult trees mature and die, no young pines replace them.

The Oak Stage Black oak seedlings grow well in the environment created by the pines. They need the added shade, moisture, and soil nutrients. They also need the protection from strong winds that the pines offer. Therefore, if a squirrel or blue jay drops an acorn from a black oak into the pine forest, it will germinate and grow. Eventually black oaks dominate the area. However, the trees are not very large nor are they closely spaced. This is because nutrients and water are still in short supply. This stage may remain for centuries while the black oaks slowly add humus to the soil through fallen leaves, bark, and branches (Fig. 2-13).

As further humus accumulates, red and white oaks invade the area. They grow well in the shade of black oak trees, whereas young black oaks do not. After many years, still more shade-tolerant trees invade the area—ash, basswood, and hickory.

The Climax Stage Oak, ash, basswood, and hickory cast a shade too dense for their young to survive. But young maple and beech trees are very shade-tolerant. They thrive in this environment. After a long period of time, they dominate the area (Fig. 2-14).

Unlike other species, young maple and beech trees can develop in the shade of the parent trees. As a result, the community becomes self-perpetuating. This means young trees are always ready to replace dead ones *of the same species*. Such a self-perpetuating community is called a **climax community**.

A climax forest seldom consists of just maple and beech. Occasional oaks, basswoods, and even pines may tower among the maples and beeches. Other species such as black cherry and ironwood may be present. And, in moist areas, hemlock, an evergreen, joins the climax community.

In some dune areas of Ontario, succession has not yet passed the oak stage, even after one or two thousand years.

What Is Succession? You have seen a hot, dry, bright environment change to a cool, moist, shady environment. You have also seen a **plant succession** occur from pioneer grasses to climax forest. An **animal succession** accompanied the plant succession. The ants and digger wasps of earlier stages were gradually replaced by earthworms, new insect species, millipedes, centipedes, and snails. Toads, salamanders, and a host of mammals and birds appeared.

Now, let us return to the original questions: What is succession? Why does it occur? In summary, living things change their environment. In doing so, they sometimes make the environment less favourable for themselves. But they also make it more favourable for another community of plants and animals. Each stage in succession, except the climax, brings about its own downfall. **Succession**, then, is the gradual replacement of one community of living things by another.

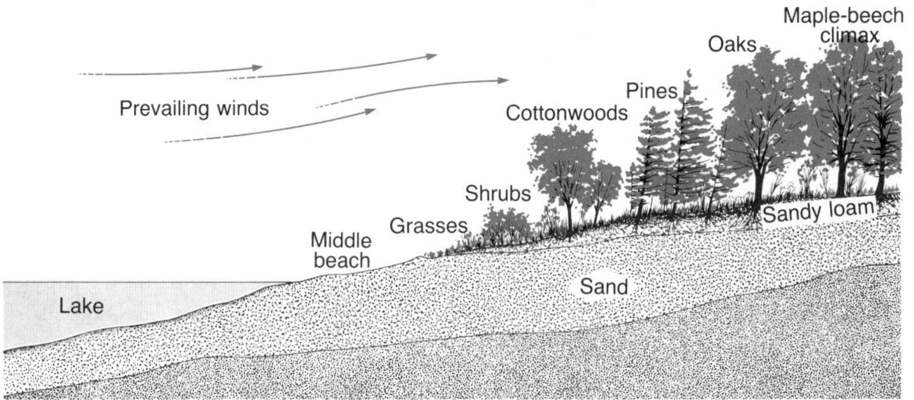

Fig. 2-15 Succession on a sand dune in the Great Lakes region

As succession continues, species diversity, population numbers, and niche availability increase. Also, total biomass and organic matter increase. All of these add to the complexity of the ecosystem. This complexity makes the ecosystem more stable. Many plant and animal species mean more food webs will be formed. Thus there is less chance of the entire community collapsing if one species disappears.

Obviously you cannot wait in one spot for hundreds of years to observe succession. But you don't have to. In many dune areas you can see all stages in a few minutes. Simply start at the water's edge and walk inland (Fig. 2-15).

As a dune enlarges and becomes covered with plants, a new dune forms closer to the water. Then, as it becomes covered with plants, a still younger dune forms between the second dune and the water. Meanwhile the original dune has advanced further in succession. This process can happen again and again. As a result, a young dune with few or no plants exists closest to the water. The next dune inland will be further on in succession. And the next dune will be still further on. Thus you can see all the stages of succession by walking from the water's edge inland.

Section Review

1. Give the meanings of the following terms: pioneer plants, dominant plants, index plants, index animals, climax community.
2. List, in order, the index plants of a sand dune succession.
3. **a)** Why does a plant succession occur on dunes?
   b) Define succession.
4. **a)** Why is complexity important in an ecosystem?
   b) What factors add to the complexity of an ecosystem?

2.6 Types of Succession

You have seen, using sand dunes as an example, that succession is the gradual replacement of one community of living things by another. Such replacement occurs in places other than sand dunes. It occurs in fields and forests, on rocks, in ponds and lakes, on a rotting log, and in many other places. The succession in each of these differs in some ways from succession in the others. We can classify those differences as types of succession. Let's see how this is done.

Fig. 2-16 Mt. St. Helen's in Washington state erupted in 1980. Virtually all life where this photograph was taken in 1986 was killed. The ground was covered with volcanic ash. Note how succession has brought a variety of plants back to the area.

Primary Succession Succession that begins in an area that has not supported life within recent geological times is called **primary succession**. A sand dune succession is of this type. So too is the succession on bare rock and on volcanic ash (Fig. 2-16).

You have probably seen rocks covered with plants. But have you ever wondered how the plants got established on the rocks? The pioneers of succession on bare rock are **lichens**. The first lichens to colonize a rocky surface usually appear as finely textured coloured patches that are difficult to remove by hand (Fig. 2-17). These lichens send hyphae (root-like organs) several millimetres into the rocky surface to obtain nutrients. They do this by secreting acid onto the rock. This action starts the breakdown of the rock. A leaf-like lichen often joins the succession at this early stage. Weathering (the freeze-thaw cycle) helps the lichens break up the rock.

Pioneer mosses usually invade the area next. They grow in clumps which help develop the soil by trapping wind-blown earth and organic matter. Soil continues to build as mosses and lichens die and decay.

Fig. 2-17 Lichens are the pioneers of succession on rocky surfaces.

Lichens like *Cladonia*, reindeer moss, may now appear (Fig. 2-18). These lichens are accompanied by larger mosses. These larger plants trap still more wind-blown material. Also, their great bulk quickly builds up the organic portion of the soil. Ferns often appear at this stage if the area is moist. Then seed-bearing plants, usually hardy annual weeds and grasses, begin to grow in the area. Biennials and perennials follow. Among the perennials are grasses. By now the soil can be up to 30 cm deep on the rock. Sun-loving shrubs like the sumac can grow in this soil. They provide the environment needed by the seedlings of sun-loving trees such as poplars and white birch.

Once sun-loving trees have become established, a succession of trees follows. In the Great Lakes region this succession often resembles that of sand dunes. It may not, however, reach the maple-beech climax stage. That's because maple and beech are not native species in all parts of the country where succession begins on bare rock. This succession is most common on the Canadian Shield in northern Ontario.

Fig. 2-18 This succession has taken decades, maybe even hundreds of years, to reach the stage where *Cladonia* dominates.

Secondary Succession Succession that begins in an area that once supported life is called **secondary succession**. An abandoned field or a forest destroyed by fire or lumbering will undergo this type of succession. Secondary succession is generally more rapid than primary succession because soil is already present. Also, some forms of life are already in the area. Let's see how this type of succession progresses.

Imagine that you have just cultivated a garden or field. It is completely weed-free. Then suppose you decided not to plant this garden or field after all. You are just going to let it sit untouched. What will happen?

All of us know that, in a matter of weeks, or just days, weeds will invade the garden. These **pioneers** are usually grasses and annual plants such as pigweed, ragweed, sow thistle, and lamb's quarters. Later in the season these will be joined by biennial and perennial plants such as dandelions and thistles. Often perennial grasses such as quack grass dominate the area. The area could

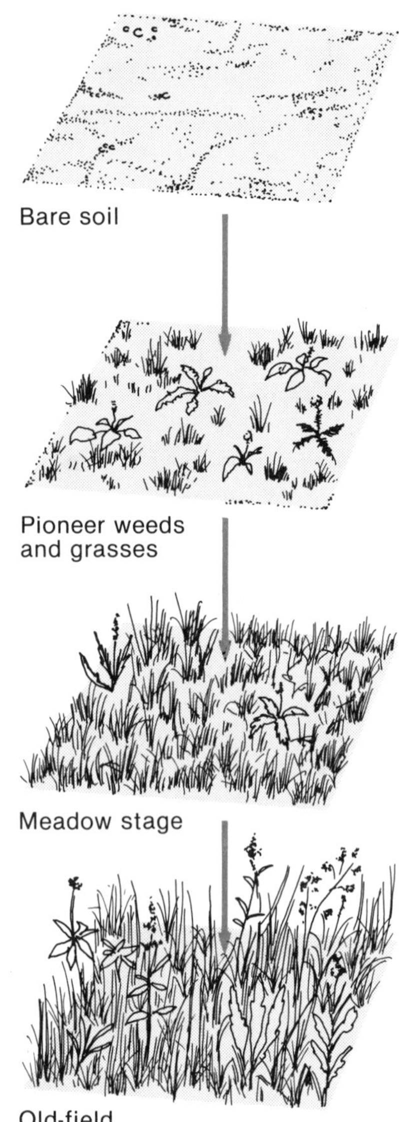

Fig. 2-19 Formation of an old-field community

stay in this grassy or **meadow stage** for two or three years. Usually, though, it quickly moves into a stage called an **old-field community** (Fig. 2-19). This community is dominated by biennials and perennials such as goldenrod, milkweed, asters, fireweed, cinquefoil, yarrow, and wild carrot.

Sun-loving shrubs appear in the old-field community as soon as the tall plants provide the needed environment, usually a year or so after the old-field community is established. Among the sun-loving shrubs are sumac, red osier, dogwood, and ninebark. Then sun-loving trees invade the area. Hawthorn, a shrubby tree, and apple often dominate. Soon after, however, poplars and birches move in. Then the succession follows a path similar to that on sand dunes or bare rocks. A climax forest of maple and beech may eventually stand where once there was a field or garden.

Succession in Ponds and Lakes All the examples of succession we have discussed so far have been terrestrial. However, succession also occurs in standing waters (ponds and lakes) and in wetlands. For example, an entire pond or lake goes through primary succession just like a field does. Let's trace this process.

Imagine that you have just dug a very deep pond. Since the pond is quite deep, sufficient light cannot reach the bottom to promote plant growth. Thus the bottom consists of nothing but the parent earth material. This is the first stage in pond succession. It is called the **pioneer stage**, or **bare-bottom stage**.

As the years pass, run-off from the land and the decay of dead organisms add soil to the bottom of the pond. The pond gradually becomes more shallow. Eventually it is shallow enough that green plants can grow on the bottom. These submergent or underwater plants soon cover the bottom. Among these are *Chara* (stonewort), *Elodea* (Canada waterweed), *Ceratophyllum* (coontail), and *Cabomba* (fanwort). This stage in succession is called the **submergent vegetation stage**.

Over the years, the decay of these plants adds further humus to the bottom of the pond. In time, the pond is shallow enough that *floating-leafed* plants such as the water lilies can grow. These plants, in turn, make the pond still more shallow. Now it can support the growth of emergent plants such as cattails, rushes, and sedges. Such plants are called emergent because part of them sticks out or emerges from the water. This stage in succession is called the **emergent vegetation stage**. The pond is now called a **reedswamp**.

The decay of emergent vegetation fills the pond still further. Now no large open expanse of water remains. The reedswamp has changed into a **marsh**. As the "islands" of land become drier, shrubs may begin to grow on them. The marsh has changed into a **carr**. As the land becomes still drier, trees may begin to grow. The carr has become a **swamp**.

Given enough time, any pond or lake should fill in completely. However, the process of succession does not stop at this point. A whole series of terrestrial plant communities will continue the process. You read about this earlier.

You do not need to stand by a pond and watch it for hundreds of years to see the stages in succession. A pond is generally deepest near its centre and gradually becomes more shallow towards the edge. Therefore you can usually see the first three stages of succession if you look at the pond along a line that runs from the deepest spot to the edge (Fig. 2-20).

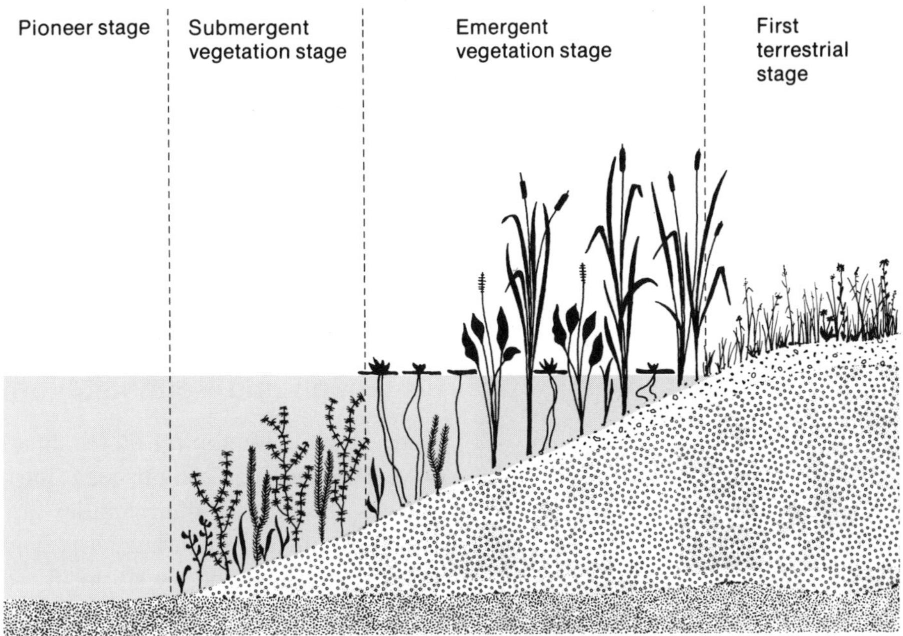

Fig. 2-20 Stages in pond succession

The preceding description emphasized plants. That's because they are the most obvious organisms present and, as well, because they dominate the succession. However, a succession of animals parallels the plant succession. For example, the tiny algae of the pioneer stage are matched by microscopic animals. The submergent plants are matched by gill-breathing animals (mayflies, dragonflies, and so on) that live on them. And the emergent plants are matched by animals that are adapted to a life that is partly terrestrial and partly aquatic, just like the plants. Frogs, snakes, and turtles are examples.

Section Review

1. a) What is primary succession?
   b) Why are lichens effective pioneers in a succession on bare rock?
   c) Describe how soil is made on bare rock.
   d) Outline the succession that occurs on bare rock.

2. a) What is secondary succession?
   b) Why does it proceed more rapidly than primary succession?
   c) Outline the succession that occurs from bare soil to climax forest.

3. a) Distinguish between autotrophic and heterotrophic succession.
   b) Classify each of the following as autotrophic or heterotrophic succession:
   - succession on bare rock
   - succession on a fallen log
   - succession on a sand dune
   - succession in a clear cut forest area
   - succession in a rotting carcass

Extension

Continue to monitor successional changes in the indoor pond that you set up in Section 1.6, page 34. This investigation could be continued until the end of the year.

2.7 Applying the Concept of Succession

Succession is a natural process. That is, it is part of the way ecosystems function. It makes sense, therefore, for us to keep succession in mind as we utilize natural resources. This section outlines a few examples which show how we can use our knowledge of succession to prevent disruptive environmental changes and to help the environment recover from harmful activities.

Protection and Rehabilitation of Sand Dunes

Some of the communities on the dunes around the Great Lakes took thousands of years to become established. But thoughtless humans can destroy them in minutes. Sand dune communities are very fragile because the topsoil is not very thick. If it is disturbed, it is quickly blown away by the strong winds or washed away by a heavy storm. It may be fun to drive a trail bike, mountain bike, dune buggy, or other off-road vehicle over sand dunes. But this is certain to destroy the dune communities. Even climbing up through a dune community can destroy it (Fig. 2-21). You should always stay on the trails when you are walking among sand dune communities.

Once a "blowout" has occurred, hundreds of years may pass before natural succession restores a dune community like the original one. However, our understanding of succession makes it possible for us to speed up this process. For example, marram grass can be planted on bare dunes (Fig. 2-22,A). Poplars and pines can be planted where sufficient nutrients remain to support their growth (Fig. 2-22,B). Many hundreds of years of succession can be bypassed by stabilizing the dunes in this way.

A

B

Fig. 2-21 A trail through the dunes (A) can result in a "blowout" that destroys in minutes what took nature thousands of years to establish (B).

A

B

Fig. 2-22 Countless thousands of marram grass plants have been planted to accelerate succession at Pinery Provincial Park (A). If conditions permit, succession can be accelerated still further by planting poplars and pines (B).

Fig. 2-23 These pines were planted 15 years ago on this marginal farmland. They were seedlings about 20 cm tall at that time.

Reforestation of Marginal Agricultural Land

Ontario has some of the world's finest agricultural land. However, we are also farming a great deal of marginal land. This is hilly land or land with poor soil that probably should never have been cleared of trees. But it was. Now much of it is eroding and is no longer useful as agricultural land. However, it can still grow trees. How do we restore the forest on such land?

We can let this land sit idle. If we do, it will likely go through secondary succession (see page 57). And in two or three hundred years a mature maple-beech forest will likely cover the area. Or, we could give succession a helping hand by planting trees on the area. Even though the final species we want may be maple, we cannot simply plant maple seedlings in the area. (Do you know why?) Instead, we must plant early successional species like the pines in Figure 2-23. In 15 or 20 years, the thinning of such a plantation can yield pulpwood, fence posts, firewood, and other marketable products. Subsequent thinnings take place about every 10 to 15 years after that. Each time the wood can be sold. As the pines are thinned, hardwoods like oak, ash, and maple will seed into the area. The area is now well on its way to becoming a valuable climax forest. And, because of human intervention, this has happened many decades before it otherwise would have happened.

Sustained Yield Forestry

In Farm Woodlots Most farms in Ontario have a woodlot, or hardwood bush, on them. Studies have shown that farmers can often make more money off a hectare of well-managed woodlot than they can off a hectare of corn in the same time period. As a result, more and more farmers are beginning to "crop" the woodlots on their farms. What is the proper way to do this?

Fig. 2-24 G.W. Martin Logging Ltd. is actively involved in sustained yield forestry operations in the hardwood forests of Haliburton and Hastings Counties and other parts of Ontario. This forest can be logged again in about 15-30 years.

Most farm woodlots are in the climax stage of succession. Therefore mature maple trees can be selectively logged from the woodlot without seriously disrupting the ecology of the woodlot. The climax stage of succession is self-perpetuating. Therefore, unless the logging opens up large areas in the woodlot, the logged maples will be replaced by maples and beeches. This process can be repeated whenever maple trees reach the appropriate size, hence the name **sustained yield forestry** (Fig. 2-24). If, however, remnant pines and oaks were removed from a climax woodlot, you would not likely see those species again in that woodlot. Why?

In Northern Forests Sustained yield forestry is not quite as simple in the coniferous forests of northern Ontario. These forests consist of very dense stands of conifers, mainly black spruce, white spruce, tamarack, balsam fir, and jack pine. These trees grow so close together that it is impossible to go in and selectively harvest trees (Fig. 2-25). As a result, some areas are often **clear cut**. That is, all the trees are harvested from an area. Generally speaking, clear cutting is seen by the public as a poor forestry practice. Certainly there are countless examples of the misuse of clear cutting. Hillsides have been denuded, exposing the soil to wind and water erosion. And vast tracts of cleared forest have been left, untended, to follow a successional path back to forest.

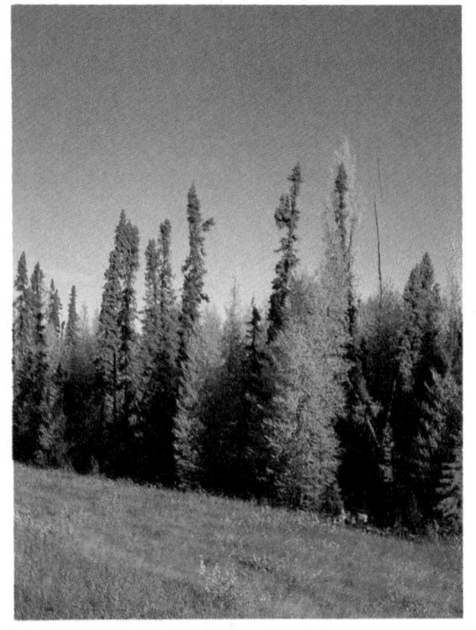

Fig. 2-25 Note the closeness of the trees in this coniferous forest.

However, forestry practices are changing. Cleared areas are replanted with suitable conifer species to hasten succession back to coniferous forest. Hillsides, lakeshores, and river valleys are usually not harvested. And strips or clumps of trees are left to reseed the area. Unfortunately these trees, exposed to the winds, are often uprooted. The fallen trees provide a different environment, and succession may, therefore, take a different course.

Producing Wetlands for Wildlife

Over the past several years, populations of some species of waterfowl have been declining across the country. One factor responsible for this decline is loss of habitat. For example, marshes have been drained to produce farmland. The Ontario Ministry of Natural Resources has been working with groups like Ducks Unlimited to replace the lost wetlands. Marginal farmland in low-lying areas is purchased. Then a system of dykes is established to permit the regulation of water flow and levels. By doing this, succession is accelerated and maintained at the stage which supports the widest variety of waterfowl and other animals (Fig. 2-26).

Fig. 2-26 The Hullett Wildlife Area in Huron County consists of 2200 ha of wetlands and uplands. It has become home for a wide variety of animals and provides recreation for humans—birdwatching, canoeing, hiking, hunting, and cross-country skiing.

Section Review

1. **a)** Describe the possible causes of a blowout on a sand dune.
   b) How can recovery from a blowout be accelerated?
2. Describe the procedure used to reestablish forest on marginal agricultural land.
3. **a)** Describe sustained yield forestry in a farm woodlot.
   b) How can recovery from clear cutting be hastened?
4. How is succession accelerated and controlled in wildlife management areas?

Chapter Highlights

1. Energy flow in ecosystems is one-way; energy is not recycled.
2. Nutrients are recycled in ecosystems.
3. Humans can upset the natural nutrient balance in ecosystems.
4. Succession is the gradual replacement of one community of living things by another.
5. We can use the concept of succession to manage, protect, and rehabilitate ecosystems.

Key Terms

carr
clear cutting
climax community
dominant plant
energy flow
index animal
index plant
marsh
nutrient
nutrient cycle
pioneer plant
primary succession
pyramid of energy
reedswamp
secondary succession
succession
sustained yield forestry
swamp

Recognizing the Concepts

Each of the following statements or questions is followed by four responses. Choose the correct response in each case. (Do not write in this book.)

1. Herbivores get their energy
   a) directly from the sun
   b) from plants
   c) from carnivores
   d) from decomposers
2. A homeowner left the grass clippings on the lawn when it was mowed. She discovered that the lawn needed less fertilizer than it did when she collected the clippings. This is because
   a) energy flow is one-way
   b) energy must enter the lawn ecosystem from the sun
   c) the clippings help retain water
   d) nutrients are recycled
3. The nutrient that is the basic building block of all living things is
   a) oxygen **b)** hydrogen **c)** nitrogen **d)** carbon
4. The owner of a swimming pool returned from a holiday to find the water in the pool green. An extensive growth of algae, called an algal bloom, had occurred. The owner added an algicide (algal killer) to the water but did not clean the pool filter. In a few days the green colour was gone. However, in a few more days it returned. The algae returned mainly because
   a) nutrients were recycled in the pool
   b) energy flow is one-way in the pool
   c) nutrients entered the pool from the air
   d) the carbon cycle is no longer perfect

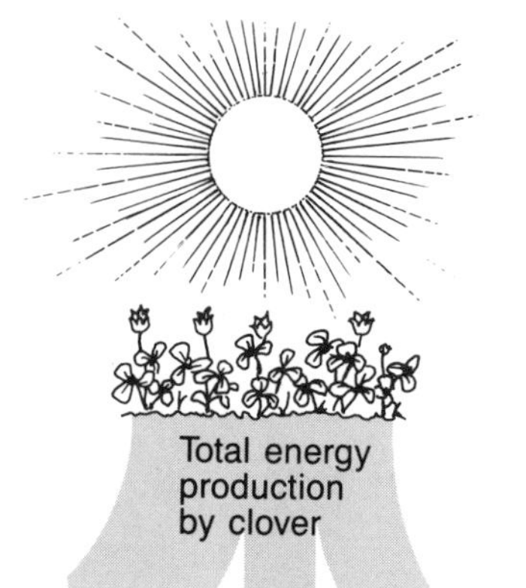

Fig. 2-27 An energy flow diagram

5. Where is primary succession likely to begin?
   a) in an abandoned field **b)** on volcanic lava **c)** where a forest has been clear cut **d)** in a freshly dug garden
6. An index tree of an early stage in succession is
   a) maple **b)** oak **c)** hemlock **d)** poplar
7. An old-field community is usually dominated by
   a) trees **b)** shrubs **c)** grasses and annual plants **d)** biennial and perennial plants
8. Selective cutting is least likely to upset ecological balance in a woodlot dominated by
   a) maple **b)** oak **c)** pine **d)** poplars

Understanding the Concepts

1. Study Figure 2-27 closely. Then describe in writing what it tells you.
2. An oxygen cycle exists in nature. Ecologists often consider it along with the carbon cycle. They call the result the **carbon-oxygen cycle**. Why does it make sense to do this? (Look back to Figure 2-8, page 50.)
3. **a)** List the possible sources of excess nutrients in the Great Lakes.
   b) Why do they often cause abundant algal growth (''algal blooms'')?
4. **a)** List, in order, the stages in a secondary succession in your area.
   b) Why do earthworms and other soil invertebrates become more abundant as succession proceeds?
5. Explain why a maple-beech forest is called a climax community.
6. **a)** Distinguish between primary and secondary succession.
   b) Defend the choice of the words ''primary'' and ''secondary''.
7. **a)** Why is a blowout more likely to occur on sand dunes than on an abandoned farm?
   b) Why can't oaks and maples be planted in a blowout to help rehabilitate the dune?
8. Why do foresters need a knowledge of succession?
9. Why are ecosystems in an advanced stage of succession more stable than those in earlier stages?

Applying the Concepts

1. It has been suggested that to make the best use of food on this crowded planet, we should all become herbivores. In other words, we would no longer eat cattle, pigs, and fowl. Instead, we would eat the plants that these animals would normally have eaten—grains, soybeans, and so on. What do you think of this idea? Why?
2. If the filter is not working properly, an aquarium containing fish and snails often develops an algal bloom (an extensive growth of algae). This can be recognized by a green colour. Why does the algal bloom occur?
3. What would happen to a pond ecosystem if all the decomposers died? Why?
4. The manager of a conservation area was observed removing the submergent vegetation from a small pond. When asked why he was doing this he replied, ''. . . to get rid of the unsightly weeds and make the pond cleaner.'' What do you think of his answer? Why?

Fig. 2-28 Setting up a mini-pond (A). The photograph (B) is of a mini-pond set up about 20 years ago. Note the soil that has formed.

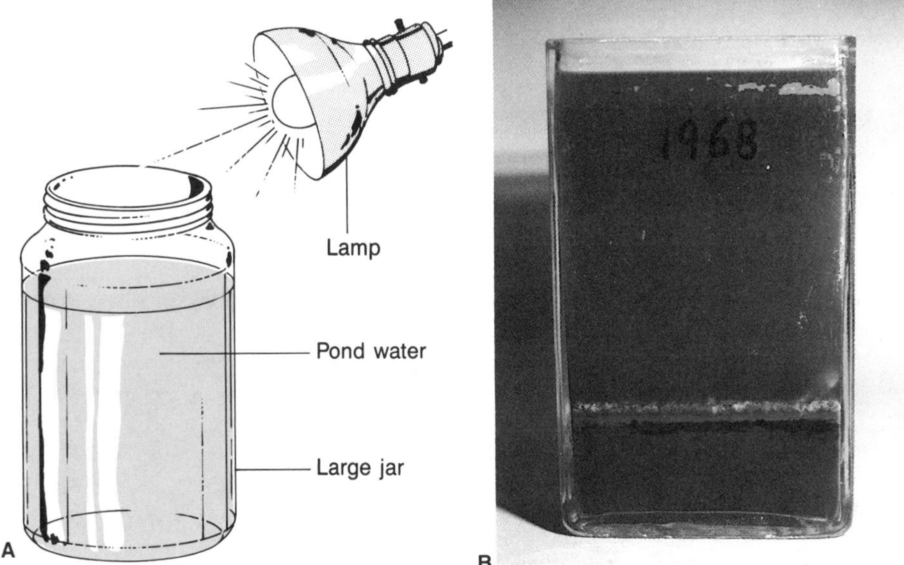

5. a) Some users of recreational vehicles want access to sand dunes. They say that the dunes are not of much use if they can't be used for recreation. What would you reply to these people?
   b) What kind of activities would you permit in sand dunes? How would you regulate these activities to protect the dunes?
6. Imagine that you have bought an abandoned field. The soil in the field is fairly sandy. You would like to have a pine-oak forest in the area within 40 years. How would you proceed?
7. Ontario has many maple syrup bushes. In order to maximize syrup production, most trees except maple are removed from these bushes. What danger does this practice present?

Fig. 2-29 You should see the start of secondary succession in just a week or two.

Investigations

1. Find out if your municipality allows sewage effluent to run into a river or lake. Has this affected water quality? Is the water quality getting better or worse? What are the plans for the future? If you feel conditions warrant improvement, write to the appropriate person(s) explaining your position.
2. Consult an advanced ecology text to find out about bog succession. Write a report on your findings. Diagrams would be a helpful addition.
3. Put a large pan or bucket of tap water outside. Observe it carefully for several weeks. Describe any evidence of succession which you observed.
4. Research the value of wetlands for agriculture.
5. Make a mini-pond in a large jar (Fig. 2-28,A). This is just a miniature version of the indoor pond described in Section 1.6, page 34. Omit the fish and aeration. Monitor and record successional changes in this pond for several months. You could do this at home (Fig. 2-28,B).
6. Try this if you can find a square metre or so of land that can be dug in your yard at home or at school: Dig the area thoroughly, break the lumps, and remove all plants. Then visit this plot every two weeks for as long as time permits. Make a careful record of the secondary succession that occurs (Fig. 2-29).

3 Populations, Communities, and Biomes

CHAPTER CONTENTS

CHAPTER OBJECTIVES

After completing this chapter you should be able to:

1. Distinguish among the levels of organization studied by ecologists.
2. Describe and demonstrate natural population growth.
3. Demonstrate competition.
4. Analyze predator-prey data.
5. Interpret population data.
6. Identify and research major Canadian biomes.

Organisms never live in isolation. They usually live with other organisms of the same species and they are usually intermingled with organisms of other species (Fig. 3-1). Because these organisms live together, they interact. Therefore they become a subject for study by ecologists.

This chapter explores the various levels of organization in which living things are involved—populations, communities, biomes, and the biosphere. Your work will range from the investigation of populations of microscopic organisms in a beaker to the study of ecological relationships in the tundra and other large land masses of Canada.

Fig. 3-1 This prairie dog, photographed in southern Saskatchewan, does not live alone. It lives in a colony with other animals of the same species. It also lives among other species of living things, both plant and animal. These include predators such as coyotes, foxes, and hawks.

3.1 From Individual to Biosphere

No individual organism lives completely on its own. It may live with other individuals of the same species to form a population. Several populations may live together in a community. Several communities may make up a biome. And several biomes occur in the biosphere. These five terms—individual, population, community, biome, and biosphere—are called **levels of biological organization** (Fig. 3-2). Ecology deals largely with the latter four levels. Let's look more closely at their meanings.

- A **population** is a group of individuals of the same species, living together in the same area. A pond has many populations in it. Look closely at Figure 3-3. You can see the white water lily population and, perhaps, the populations of other plants. This pond also has a bullfrog population, a sunfish population, a dragonfly population, a yeast population, and many others.

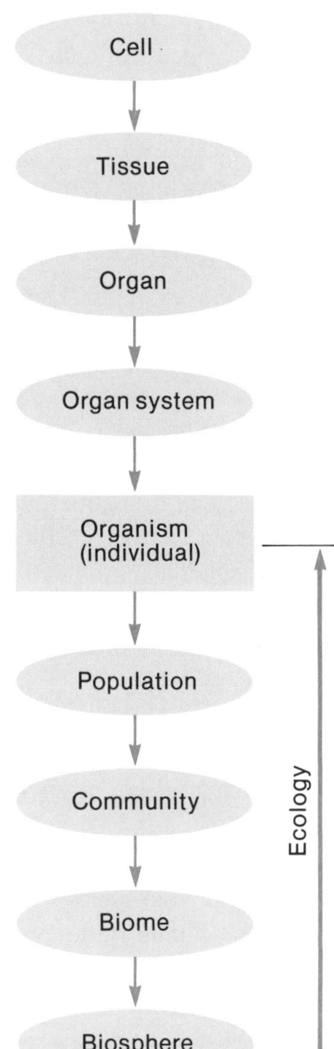

Fig. 3-2 Levels of biological organization. In your science course last year you saw how cells are organized into tissues, tissues into organs, organs into organ systems, and organ systems into organisms or individuals. Biological organization doesn't stop there. It continues through 4 more levels—the topic of this section.

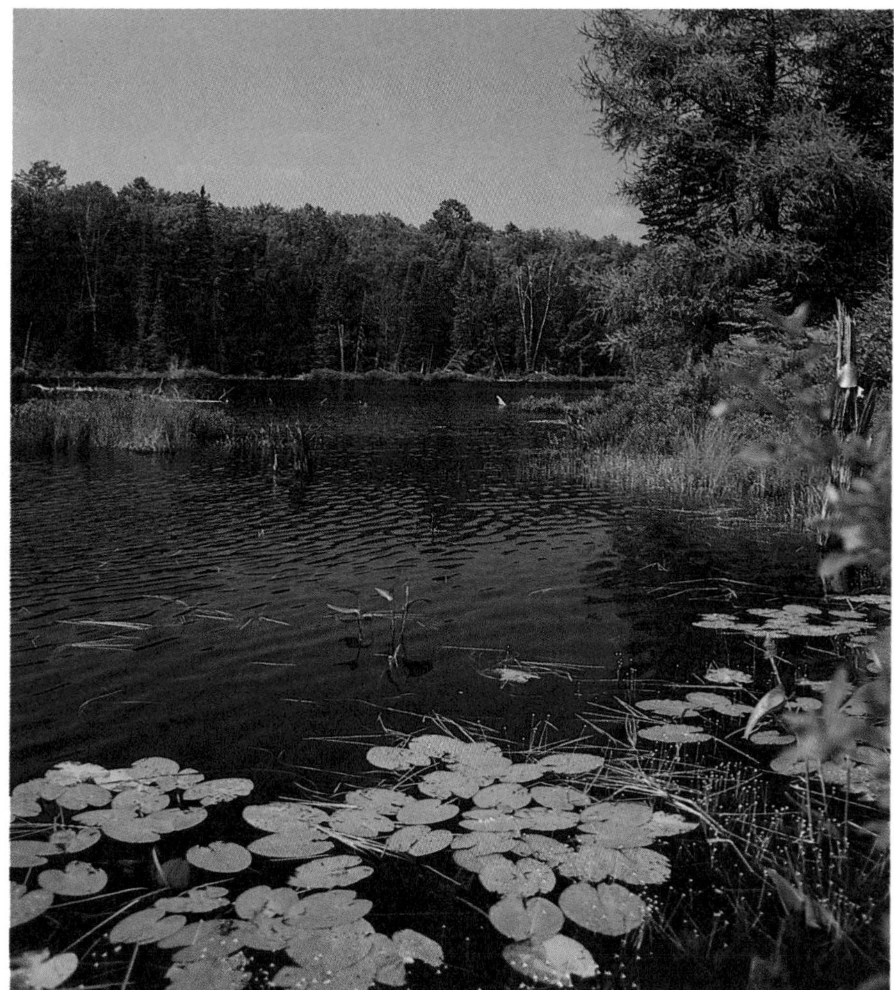

Fig. 3-3 This pond contains populations of numerous species of plants, animals, and other living things. How many populations can you name that likely live in a pond?

- A **community** is *all* the living things in an area. In other words, a community consists of several populations. The pond in Figure 3-3 is a community. This pond community has many populations other than the ones identified above. How many can you name?
- A **biome** is a large geographic area with a characteristic climate. The coniferous forest that stretches across northern Canada is a biome; so is the tundra of Canada's Arctic region. Canada has just seven main biomes. The whole earth has only thirteen main biomes.

  A biome consists of several communities. For example, among the communities that make up the coniferous forest biome are lake communities, pond communities, bog communities, and upland forest communities.
- The **biosphere** is the region on earth in which all life exists. Organisms live in the lower part of the atmosphere. They live in almost all bodies of water on earth. They also live on the surface and in the first metre or two of the soil. This thin layer on the earth, from the lower atmosphere to the bottom of the oceans, makes up the biosphere.

  It is convenient to think of the biosphere as being made up of biomes—the coniferous forest biome, desert biome, tundra biome, and grassland biome, to name a few.

Section Review

1. a) List, in order from smallest to largest, the four levels of biological organization that ecologists most often deal with.
b) Define each of those four levels.
2. List ten populations you might find in the woods in your area.
3. List five communities you might spot if you went hiking in the mountain biome of western Canada.

3.2 Activity: Graphing a Bacterial Population Growth Curve

This is a "dry" activity, one in which you don't collect your own data but, instead, use the data of others. In this case you will graph and interpret data from a study in which the growth of a bacteria population was investigated.

Problem

What is the shape of a bacterial population growth curve? Why does it have that shape?

Materials

graph paper

pencil

Procedure

a. Study Table 3-1 closely. These data were obtained by a scientist as follows: A suitable nutrient medium was inoculated with a small number of a certain species of bacterium. The resulting culture was incubated at the optimum temperature for this organism. Every hour the number of bacteria in a drop of the culture was counted. (A sampling method was used, so the scientist did not actually count every bacterium.)

b. Graph the data in Table 3-1. Put the time in hours on the x-axis and the population number on the y-axis.

c. Examine your graph. Mark the following regions on it:

- region of slow but progressive population growth
- region of rapid population growth
- region of population decline
- region of population stability

Table 3-1 Growth of a Bacterium Population

Time (h)	Population number	Time (h)	Population number
0	150	11	6600
1	190	12	6100
2	380	13	5500
3	700	14	5300
4	1450	15	5400
5	3000	16	5600
6	5600	17	5500
7	7000	18	5300
8	7600	19	5400
9	7650	20	5500
10	7400		

Discussion

1. Account for the region of slow growth.
2. Why does the growth rate eventually increase a great deal?
3. What factors may be responsible for the peaking and subsequent decline in numbers?
4. Interpret the right-hand portion of the curve.
5. This population could eventually crash to zero. Why?

3.3 Population Growth in Natural Populations

A **population** is a group of individuals of the same species living in the same area. The bacteria referred to in Section 3.2 are a population. The muskrats

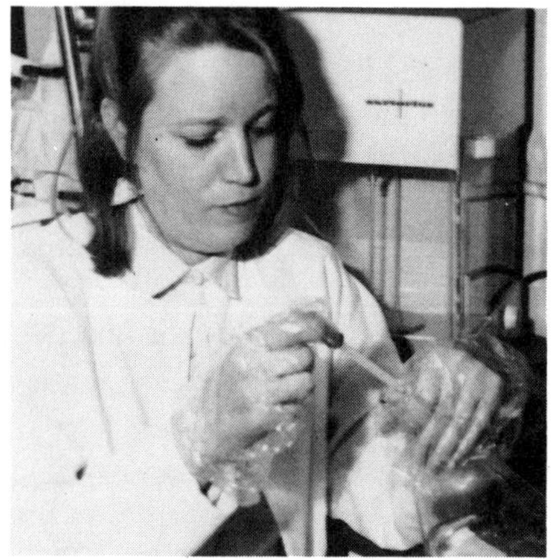

Fig. 3-4 Yeast cells are often used for population studies. These cells multiply rapidly. Therefore results are obtained quickly.

in a pond and the deer in a meadow are both populations. The poplar trees in a woods are a population, and the humans in a city are a population.

The numbers present in the first four populations—bacteria, muskrats, deer, and poplar—are controlled by the laws of nature. What are those laws? And how do these laws control population growth? Human populations appear, at this time, to be beyond control by the laws of nature. Are they? We will look at this in Chapter 4. But first, let us look at how the growth of natural populations is regulated.

Population Growth Curves

Many scientists have studied population growth. One of these did her experiments with yeast cells (Fig. 3-4). She started a yeast culture by putting a few yeast cells in a suitable medium. Then she counted the yeast cells in a certain volume of medium every 5 h for a total of 25 h. Then she graphed the results. This gave the **population growth curve** shown in Figure 3-5. Note that this graph has three main regions:

- Region A—The population size increases slowly.
- Region B—The population size increases more rapidly.
- Region C—The population size levels off and stays constant.

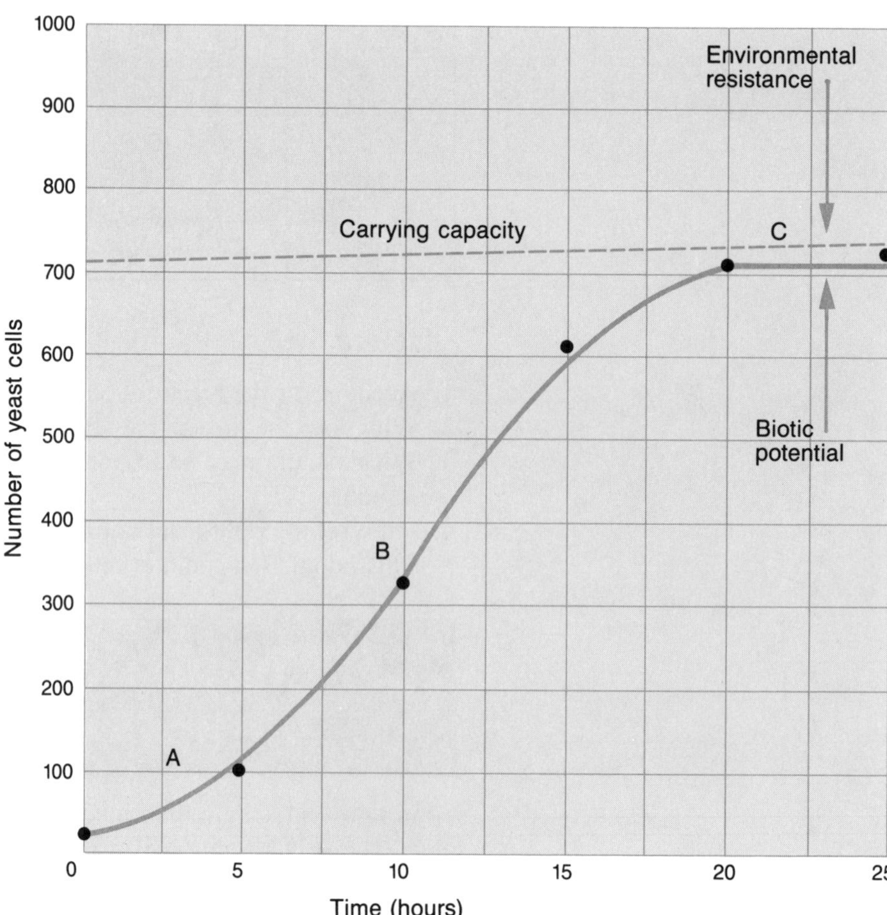

Fig. 3-5 A simplified population growth curve for a yeast population. This graph has been "smoothed out". Normally, population growth overshoots the carrying capacity, then decreases to it. Also, the numbers fluctuate above and below the carrying capacity.

Most natural populations follow a growth curve like this one. Now let's look at some explanations.

Factors Affecting Population Size

Biotic Potential and Environmental Resistance In Region A the population size increases slowly. This is because the number of "parent" yeast cells is very low.

In Region B the population size increases more rapidly. This is because there are more and more "parent" yeast cells to make new cells.

In Region C the population size levels off and stays fairly constant, though it does fluctuate up and down somewhat. Why is this so? All species have a tendency to reproduce. This tendency is called the **biotic potential**. The biotic potential tends to increase the population size. However, other factors work against that tendency. These factors are called the **environmental resistance**. As the graph shows, population size levels off when the environmental resistance balances the biotic potential. The ecosystem is now said to be at its **carrying capacity**. What factors do you think make up the environmental resistance?

Birth Rate, Death Rate, and Migration Here's another way of looking at factors that affect population size. There are three main factors that affect population size in an area:

- birth rate
- death rate
- migration

The **birth rate** tells us how fast new individuals are being added to the population. The **death rate** tells us how fast individuals are dying in the population. And **migration** tells us how many **immigrate** (move into) or **emigrate** (move out of) the area. When the three are combined, we get an idea of how fast the population is growing.

Several factors affect the death rate: overcrowding, lack of shelter, disease, fighting, environmental pollution, shortage of food, human activities, and predators.

The same factors tend to affect the birth rate. For example, some make the parents less healthy and, as a result, fewer healthy young are born. Some of the same factors also affect migration. Animals tend to immigrate to less crowded areas where there is food. Or, if you like, animals emigrate from crowded areas where there is fighting and little food.

Section Review

1. What is a population growth curve?
2. Explain these terms: biotic potential, environmental resistance, carrying capacity.
3. Account for the shape of a natural population growth curve.
4. Describe how birth rate, death rate, and migration can affect population size.

3.4 Activity: Investigating Population Growth in the Laboratory

In this activity you will establish a population of paramecia, a common protozoan. Then you will study the growth of this population, seeking data comparable to that for bacteria in Section 3.2 and yeast in Section 3.3. When you have the data, you will graph the population growth curve and interpret it.

Problem

What does the population growth curve for paramecia look like?

Materials

graduated cylinder (100 mL)
jar or beaker (50 mL)
dropper
culture of paramecium
marking pen
dechlorinated water
wheat or rice grains (3)
microscope
microscope slides (2)
cover slips (2)
pipette (5 mL)
methyl cellulose (5%)

Procedure

a. Place the grains of wheat or rice in the jar. Then add about 40 mL of water. This mixture forms the food supply for bacteria which, in turn, is the food of the paramecia.

b. Place a mark on the side of the jar to show the water level. Each day, replace evaporated water by topping up the jar to this mark. Use water that has been dechlorinated by letting it stand for 48 h.

c. Examine a sample of the paramecium culture using a microscope at low power. This is to ensure that you know what paramecia look like (Fig. 3-6). Return the sample to the culture jar.

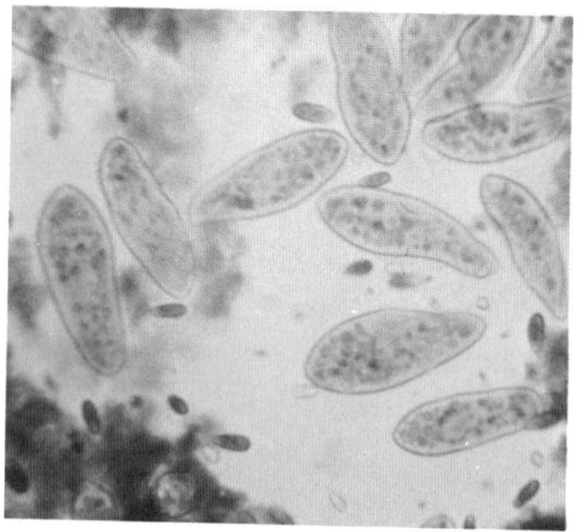

Fig. 3-6 Paramecia are single-celled highly motile organisms.

d. Gently stir the culture to mix it thoroughly without harming the paramecia. Then promptly withdraw a 5 mL sample using the pipette. Add this sample to your jar. Gently stir to distribute the paramecia through the water.

e. Gently stir the contents of your jar. Then promptly fill the dropper with the contents.

f. Put one drop on a microscope slide and add a cover slip. Empty the dropper back into your jar.

g. Count the number of paramecia in the drop, using the microscope at low power. If the paramecia move too rapidly to permit a reasonably accurate count, add one drop of 5% methyl cellulose solution. This immobilizes the paramecia without harming them.

h. If possible, wash the paramecia off the slide and back into the jar.

i. Repeat steps (e) to (h) at least 3 times. Average your results.

j. Record the data, the number of paramecia in each trial, the average number, and the appearance of the contents of the jar in a suitable data table.

k. Store the jar in a dark cupboard at room temperature.
l. Every 2 d repeat steps (e) to (k). Record your results. Continue this for about 3 weeks, if possible.
m. Graph your data to prepare a population growth curve. *Note*: The data in Sections 3.2 and 3.3 were obtained by scientists under almost ideal conditions. Don't expect your results to be exactly like theirs.

1. Why must you top up the jar to the same mark each day?
2. Why must you stir the contents of the jar before taking a sample for counting?
3. How many major regions can you recognize in your graph? Account for each region.

3.5 Activity: Investigating Competition Among Plants

Competition is rivalry among organisms for light, nutrients, and other resources. There are two kinds of competition, intraspecific and interspecific. **Intraspecific competition** is rivalry among members of the *same* species. **Interspecific competition** is rivalry among members of *different* species. What do you think will happen if plants of the same species are so crowded that they compete for light, minerals, and water? What do you think will happen if plants of different species compete?

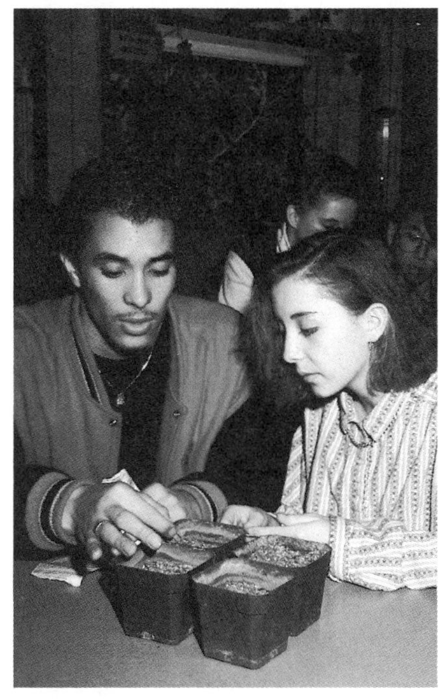

Fig. 3-7 In each case the seeds are to be evenly spaced.

Problem

How does competition affect plants?

Materials

radish seeds
leaf lettuce seeds
small pots (4)
potting soil
water

Procedure

a. Make up hypotheses in response to the two questions asked in the introduction.
b. Fill all 4 pots with potting soil and tamp it down lightly.
c. Label the pots, 1, 2, 3, and 4.
d. Place seeds on the surface of the soil in each pot as instructed in Table 3-2 (Fig. 3-7).
e. Cover the seeds lightly with soil and tamp it down gently.
f. Water the pots. Maintain a regular watering schedule to avoid overwatering and the complete drying out of the soil.
g. Place the pots in a bright location.
h. At regular intervals (e.g. every 3 d), record data that will permit you to draw conclusions that address the hypotheses. The height and thickness of

the stem, the number and sizes of the leaves, and general plant vigour are some suggestions. Use a data table.

Table 3-2 Investigating Competition

Pot number	*Seeds*	*Spacing*
1	5 radish	evenly distributed
2	10 radish	evenly distributed
3	20 radish	evenly distributed
4	10 radish and 10 lettuce	mixed and evenly distributed

Discussion

1. Describe and account for the effects of intraspecific competition.
2. Describe and account for the effects of interspecific competition.
3. What advice do you have for home gardeners as a result of this activity?
4. Over a long period of time, intraspecific competition may actually strengthen a species. Why?

A

B

Fig. 3-8 The snowshoe hare (A) is prey for the lynx (B).

3.6 Case Study: Investigating a Predator-Prey Relationship

In this case study you will investigate one of the most famous sets of data ever collected on a predator-prey relationship. The data come from very thorough records kept by the Hudson's Bay Company over many years. Though old, these data demonstrate the classic predator-prey relationship.

Lynx, a cat of the boreal forest, prey on snowshoe hare (Fig. 3-8). In some areas, hare provide over 70% of the lynx diet. As a result, the population growth curve of the lynx should show a relationship to that of the hare. What do you think that relationship is?

The data on this relationship are in Table 3-3. Study them carefully as you answer the questions that follow.

Questions

1. Graph these data on the same sheet of graph paper. Put the year on the x-axis and the population numbers on the y-axis. Use a different colour for the growth curves of hare and lynx.
2. **a)** These population growth curves are said to fluctuate. What does that mean?
   b) How many years are there in one fluctuating cycle of the hare population?
3. What factors may be responsible for the unusual number of hare in 1895?

Table 3-3 Population Numbers of Hare and Lynx by Year

Year	Hare numbers	Lynx numbers	Year	Hare numbers	Lynx numbers
1895	85 000	48 000	1918	5 000	5 000
1900	18 000	6 000	1921	52 000	11 000
1903	65 000	18 000	1924	78 000	28 000
1905	40 000	61 000	1927	18 000	42 000
1908	28 000	28 000	1930	4 000	5 000
1909	25 000	4 000	1933	22 000	18 000
1910	51 000	10 000	1934	86 000	32 000
1912	70 000	32 000	1936	15 000	40 000
1915	30 000	42 000			

4. a) Why does the hare population number fluctuate?
   b) Why does the lynx population number fluctuate?
   c) Describe and account for the relationship between the two population growth curves.
5. We say that a good predator-prey relationship keeps the two populations "in balance." What does this mean?
6. a) Lynx skins are quite valuable today. What would happen if trapping regulations were abolished and all the lynx in a large area were killed?
   b) Are trappers likely to kill all the lynx in an area, even if regulations were abolished? Discuss.

A

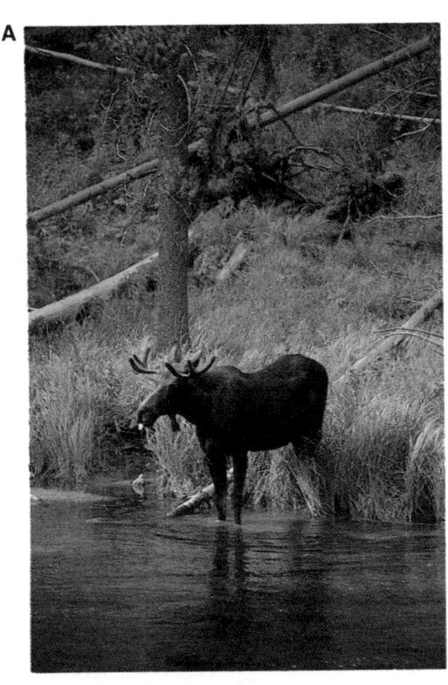

B

Fig. 3-9 The moose (A) is prey for the timber wolf (B).

3.7 Case Study: Do Moose Need Wolves?

Here is a more recent set of data on a predator-prey relationship for you to analyze.

The moose population on an island sanctuary was about 1000 animals in 1974. The 300 km² island was characterized by dense areas of spruce forest and bogs. There were no natural predators of the moose. Wildlife managers thought the growing moose population would eventually become too large, outgrowing the carrying capacity of its ecosystem. Already a number of moose were dying each year from a combination of winter exposure and starvation. Other factors could be involved as well.

The managers decided that the moose population must be controlled, so it would not overshoot the carrying capacity and end up crashing. In 1975 they decided to fly in 10 wolves. Wolves are natural predators of moose (Fig. 3-9). Wolves are best described as opportunistic feeders. That is, they will prey on whatever the opportunity provides. Often this means that the wolves kill the weakest individuals, such as the old, the diseased, and the very young calves. Such moose are the easiest to get. Although wolves also capture some stronger moose, a healthy moose in its prime can usually fend off its attackers. Therefore wolves can help to strengthen a herd of moose as well as control its numbers.

The results of this natural predation program are shown in Table 3-4.

Table 3-4 Wolf and Moose Population Changes on an Island Sanctuary (1975–84)

Year	Wolf population	Moose population	Moose offspring	Predation	Starvation and winter kill	Population change (moose)
1975	10	1132	478	223	97	+158
1976	13	1290	543	304	148	+ 91
1977	17	1381	690	384	267	+ 39
1978	23	1420	736	453	269	+ 14
1979	27	1434	754	596	271	−113
1980	30	1321	663	628	101	− 66
1981	33	1255	620	746	39	−165
1982	25	1090	526	543	3	− 20
1983	21	1070	535	487	0	+ 48
1984	21	1118	549	498	0	+ 51

Questions

1. Graph the changes in the wolf and moose populations for the nine-year study period. Plot time on the x-axis and population numbers on the y-axis. Use a different colour for each population.
2. What would likely have happened to the moose population if a few more wolves had been introduced in 1975? Would this have been better for the ecosystem? Explain.
3. Why did the wolf population decrease after 1981?
4. In which year was moose mortality due to starvation and winter exposure the highest? Using your data and knowledge of ecology explain why so many moose died.
5. Assume hunters were allowed to kill half the wolf population in 1980. There would be only 15 wolves left. Predict what might have happened to the moose population as a result.
6. Is wolf predation on this island effective at limiting moose numbers? List other factors which could limit a moose population on this island.
7. How did the size of the moose population influence the number of wolves on the island? What other natural factors would limit the wolf population?
8. You should notice a time lag between the population changes of wolves and moose in your graph. This is what usually happens between predators and their prey populations. Suggest why such a time lag occurs.

9. To maintain a healthy prey population, the predator:prey ratio is of great importance. Explain this statement.
10. If the moose population on the island is to remain stable at 1132 individuals and the number of moose offspring in 1985 is 550, how many moose would 25 wolves have to eat in a year? (Assume predation is the only limiting factor.) Calculate the average number of moose per wolf per year. *Note*: This calculation is just an approximation, since predation is not normally the only limiting factor for prey populations.
11. Could hunting have been used, alone or with wolf predation, to achieve a stable moose population? Discuss.

3.8 Major Biomes of Canada

Introduction to Biomes

Since a biome has a characteristic climate, it also has a characteristic climax community. The boreal coniferous forest of northern Canada is an example. It has a characteristic **climate**—cold and wet. This climate, in turn, creates a certain **climax community** consisting of organisms that are adapted to that climate. This community is most easily recognized by its dominant vegetation. For example, the boreal coniferous forest is dominated by conifers like black spruce (Fig. 3-10). They thrive in this cool moist climate.

Canada has just seven major biomes—tundra, boreal coniferous forest, temperate deciduous forest, grassland, mountain, chaparral, and temperate rain forest. Study Figure 3-11 to see where these occur. The United States has the same seven biomes plus three more. In the whole world there are just thirteen main biomes.

Fig. 3-10 The boreal coniferous forest is dominated by black spruce in most regions. These trees can be identified by the dense clump of short branches at the top.

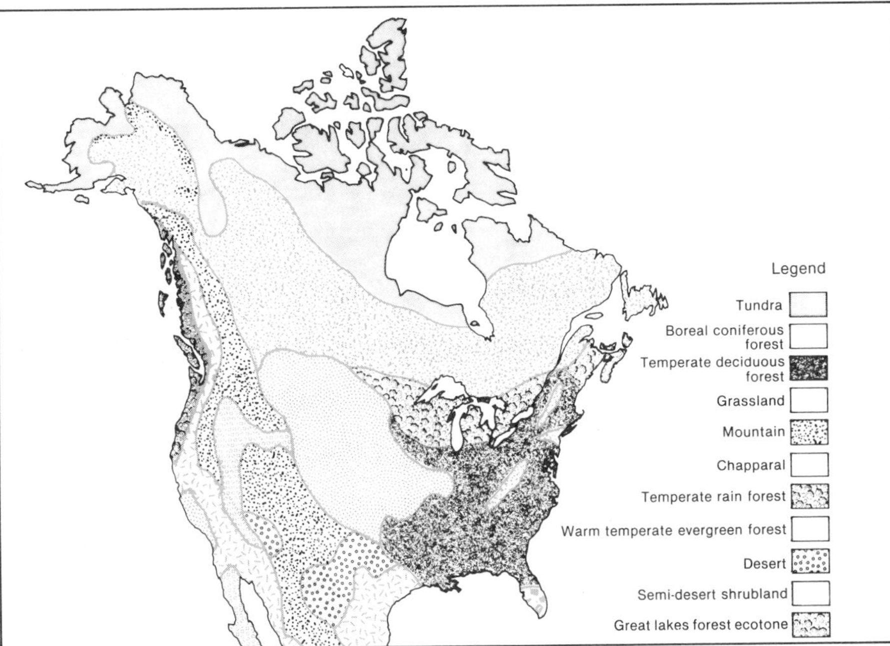

Fig. 3-11 The major biomes of Canada and the United States. How many occur in Canada? How many occur in Ontario? Which one do you live in? Which ones have you visited? The Great Lakes forest ecotone is a transition zone between the boreal coniferous forest and the temperate deciduous forest. Most of Ontario's population is in this zone.

There are zones between biomes in which one biome blends into another. Some ecologists call these zones lesser biomes. Others call them **ecotones**. Most people in Ontario live in the Great Lakes forest ecotone (see Figure 3-11). In this ecotone the boreal coniferous forest biome and the temperate deciduous forest biome blend together. That's why this area has a mixture of coniferous and deciduous trees.

The remainder of this section gives *brief* descriptions of the abiotic and biotic characteristics of six of the main biomes of Canada. The main function of these descriptions is to provide an overview of the biomes to assist you with the selection of your research topic for Section 3.9.

The Tundra Biome

The **Arctic tundra** is a vast treeless plain that stretches beyond the northern forests to the edge of the Arctic ice cap. In places the plain is broken by sandhills and even mountains (Fig. 3-12).

Abiotic Factors The tundra climate is cold, windy, and dry. Even the wet summer months have only about 2.5 cm of precipitation. In the winter there is little snowfall, but the snow is constantly blown around. Therefore one gets the impression that snowfall is heavy. The tundra is often called a frozen desert.

This area has 24 h of daylight in midsummer. And, in midwinter, it has 24 h of darkness. Winter lasts nine months. The spring thaw and Arctic summer are crowded into three months. In fact, the growing season is only about 60 d.

The soil thaws only to a depth of a few centimetres to half a metre. Below this lies the **permafrost**, soil that never thaws. This frozen layer is 600 m deep in spots. It prevents proper drainage of spring meltwater. As a result, vast marshy areas form on the land. Such areas are called **muskeg**.

Fig. 3-12 Here in the Pangnirtung Fiord on Baffin Island, the tundra plain is surrounded by spectacular mountains.

A

B

Fig. 3-13 Willow herb (A) and Arctic poppy (B) are two of the colourful herbs that carpet the tundra for a few short weeks in the summer.

Temperature limits the variety of organisms in the tundra. As a result, food chains and food webs are simple, and adaptations are easy to spot.

Biotic Factors Lichens, mosses, grasses, and herbs dominate the tundra vegetation (Fig. 3-13). A few stunted woody shrubs such as birches and willows grow in lower areas. Even 100-year-old shrubs are less than 1 m tall. Their southern relatives are large trees.

Most tundra plants are **perennials**. They must grow for several seasons in order to store enough energy to flower. Also, most Arctic plants reproduce by **vegetative propagation**, since seeds have little chance of germinating in the tundra soil.

Most tundra animals are white in the winter. Among these are the Arctic hare, grey wolf, lemming, Arctic fox, and ptarmigan. These animals change to darker colours during summer for better camouflage (Fig. 3-14).

Arctic animals are protected from the cold by an insulating layer of fat. They also have air pockets trapped within long, dense fur or feathers. These provide further insulation. Many animals beat the winter cold by migrating. For example, the Barren Ground caribou move southward to the tree line, and geese fly south to the ocean marshes.

Any tundra visitor will tell you that the most common animals are blackflies, mosquitoes, and deer flies. However, the most important animal may be the lemming. This small rodent is a herbivore. It forms a key link in many Arctic food chains and webs. It is eaten by the Arctic fox, weasels, bears, wolves, and birds of prey such as hawks and the snowy owl.

The Boreal Coniferous Forest Biome

Fig. 3-14 The Arctic hare is commonly white in the winter. Note how well its summer colours blend with the background of lichens and mosses.

Moving south from the tundra, one meets clumps of dwarf trees, scattered in sheltered nooks. Finally one reaches a distinct **tree line**. This is the edge of the **boreal coniferous forest**. This vast coniferous (cone-bearing) forest stretches across Canada. Parts of it occur in all provinces, the Yukon, and the Territories (Fig. 3-15).

Abiotic Factors Average monthly temperatures are higher than the tundra's. The growing season varies from 60 to 150 d. Summer days are shorter but warmer than they are in the tundra. Most important, the ground thaws completely. The winters are less severe and shorter. Snowfall is heavier, but total precipitation is still low.

During the last ice age, glaciers gouged depressions in the land. These filled with water, forming the countless lakes, swamps, and bogs of the northern woods.

Decomposers work slowly in the cold wet soil. Thus **peat** (partly decayed organic matter) is common throughout the woods.

Biotic Factors **Coniferous trees**, or **conifers**, dominate the northern boreal forest. These cone-bearing trees include black spruce, white spruce, jack pine, white pine, and tamarack. All but the tamarack are **evergreen**. In other words, they keep their needles during the winter.

Fig. 3-15 The great northern woods abound with lakes, swamps, and bogs.

Fig. 3-16 The wolverine is a fast predator of the boreal forest.

Fig. 3-17 The crossbill has a strong curved bill for cutting through the cone scales. Its tongue then reaches the seeds inside.

Conifers are well-adapted to the poor soil, low temperatures, and limited rainfall. Their leaves are reduced to needles. These needles have a waxy outer skin that reduces water loss. The needles can also withstand freezing.

The evergreens form a dense canopy all year round. Thus little light reaches the forest floor. As a result, the common plants on the forest floor are ferns and mosses. Lichens are also common. And fungi such as mushrooms serve as decomposers among the fallen needles.

Boreal animals must survive the long, cold winter. The ground is frozen and the snow presents some problems. Foxes, wolves, and moose are common. They have thick winter fur. The snowshoe hare is also well-adapted. It turns white and has large tufts of fur on its feet that serve as snowshoes. The wolverine preys on the hare. It has spreading toes that let it run swiftly over the snow (Fig. 3-16).

Moose, too, are adapted for dealing with deep snow. They wade through it on stilt-like legs. Or, if it gets too deep, several moose get together and trample it down. Then they can reach tree shoots, brush, and twigs. Those same long legs serve the moose well in the summer. Moose wade in lakes and marshes where they browse on aquatic plants.

As in the tundra, the most common animals are insects. Blackflies, mosquitoes, and deer flies attack anything with blood. Moose stand neck-deep in water to escape them. Other insects attack trees. Outbreaks of spruce budworm and larch sawfly have wiped out vast areas of trees in many parts of Canada. Parts of scenic Cape Breton have been almost denuded of trees.

Small birds called warblers are common in the boreal forest. They feed largely on the abundant insects. Seed-eating birds are also common. They have specially adapted beaks for getting seeds from the cones (Fig. 3-17). Blue grouse and spruce grouse feed directly on the needles of the conifers. These needles contain little nutrient. Therefore these birds must eat constantly during the winter.

Fig. 3-18 In the autumn, the maples, oaks, and poplars add a spectacular blaze of colour to the landscape.

Fig. 3-19 The red fox is a resourceful feeder. It will eat just about any small animal it can catch. It also frequently feeds on plant material.

Fig. 3-20 The grassland biome is flat in some places and rolling in others. The best of the flat land is used to grow wheat. Cattle graze on the rolling land along with pronghorn antelope and other herbivores.

The Temperate Deciduous Forest Biome

The **temperate deciduous forest** occurs on the southeast edge of the boreal forest. Only the southern parts of Ontario and Quebec are in this biome. However, as Figure 3-11 shows, most of the southeastern United States occurs in it. This biome is recognized by its temperate (moderate) climate and deciduous trees (trees that drop their leaves in the winter).

Abiotic Factors Average annual precipitation in this biome is 75 to 125 cm. This precipitation falls fairly evenly through four distinct seasons. The climate is moderate, and the growing season is as long as six months.

The winters are short, but they are cold enough to greatly reduce growth and photosynthesis. Trees in this biome lose their leaves in the winter to conserve water. These leaves decay rapidly on the forest floor, resulting in soil rich with humus.

Biotic Factors Because the soil is rich, much of this biome has been cleared for farming. Little of the original forest remains. Where it does, it is dominated by sugar maple, beech, and oak (Fig. 3-18). The southernmost areas have hickory, sycamore, and other Carolinian species. The rich soil of the forest floor supports a wide variety of ferns, mosses, and wild flowers.

Tree dwellers abound in the deciduous forest. Squirrels, chipmunks, tree frogs, and woodpeckers are examples. They find shelter and food among the trees. All such animals are well-adapted to a life in trees.

Unlike conifers, deciduous trees are a rich source of food for animals. The buds and twigs store a great deal of food. Deer feed on the leaves, buds, fruit, and seeds of trees and shrubs. Rabbits, mice, and other rodents eat bark and small plants.

Carnivores include owls, hawks, weasels, and large mammals like bobcats. Some mammals, like racoons, skunks, and the red fox, are omnivores (Fig. 3-19). They eat many types of food, both plants and animals. The red fox, for example, feeds on mice, large insects, fish, eggs, berries, and even grass.

The rich soil supports a host of organisms. Just one square kilometre of soil litter can have over 120 species of invertebrates—spiders, insects, millipedes, centipedes, earthworms, and many others.

The Grassland Biome

As Figure 3-11 shows, the **grassland biome**, or **prairies**, is a small part of Canada. It is much more extensive in the United States. Nonetheless, Canada's grassland biome grows a significant part of the world's food supply and is home to a wide diversity of plants and animals.

Abiotic Factors The grassland biome is within the same latitudes as the temperate deciduous forest. Therefore its seasons and energy supply (from the sun) are similar. However, the grasslands have a much lower precipitation. The annual rainfall is only 25–75 cm. This is enough to grow many grasses, but it is too low for tree growth (Fig. 3-20).

Fig. 3-21 Cinquefoil (A) and cone-flower (B) are two common flowering plants of the grassland biome.

Prairie soils are among the most fertile in the world. Grasses decay quickly. As a result, a deep layer of humus covers the prairies.

Biotic Factors The difference in rainfall produces three distinct types of grassland. Moderate rainfall makes the eastern prairies a **tall grass zone**. Further west, the drier central grasslands support **mid grasses**. And in the dry western plains, **short grasses** grow.

Tree growth is limited to stream valleys and low mountain ranges. Cottonwoods (poplars) are the most common trees. A wide variety of colourful flowering plants can be found among the grasses (Fig. 3-21).

Grassland animals have many interesting adaptations to open country. Grazing animals like pronghorns have eyes located well above the snout. This enables them to watch for predators while grazing. Smaller mammals, like the ground squirrel, stand up on their haunches to see over the grass (Fig. 3-22). Others, like kangaroo rats, hop up and down to watch for enemies.

There are few trees to provide hiding places in the grasslands. Therefore animals rely on speed, burrows, and camouflage to escape enemies. Pronghorns, for example, can reach 100 km/h. Jack rabbits, using 8 m leaps, can go 70 km/h! Ground squirrels and prairie dogs escape into burrows. Other animals have learned to stand still in the grass and rely on camouflage for protection.

Insects are common in the grasslands. There are over 100 species of grasshoppers alone. The large number of insects and seeds attract a wide variety of birds.

Fig. 3-22 This position helps the ground squirrel see its predators. Unfortunately (for the ground squirrel), it also helps predators see the ground squirrel.

Mountain Biomes

Mountain biomes are small in area when compared to other biomes. Yet they are an interesting and important part of the landscape in British Columbia, Alberta, and the Yukon. The plural is used in this instance because the mountains do not belong to just one continuous block of land.

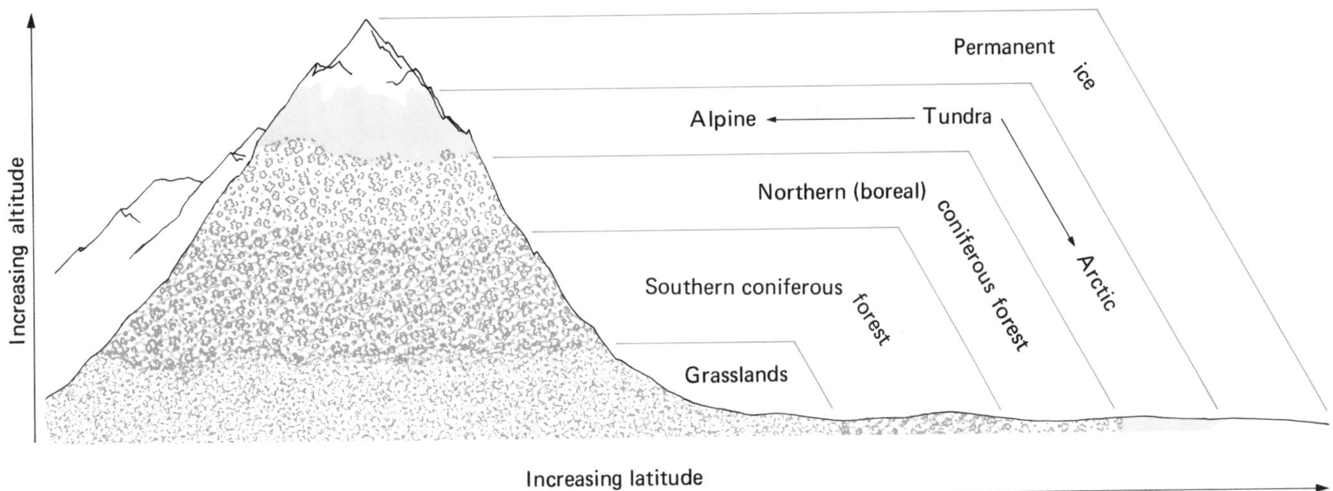

Fig. 3-23 If you climb a tall mountain you will walk through ecosystems that generally resemble the biomes you would walk through if you walked from the Saskatchewan grasslands to the North Pole.

Abiotic Factors A change in altitude can affect the environment as much as a change in latitude. As altitude increases, the temperature drops about 1°C for every 150 m. Also, wind speed increases at higher altitudes. And, the soil is thinner near the tops of mountains since erosion has carried the soil down.

These gradual changes in temperature, wind, and soil create ecosystems on the mountain that resemble the biomes we have discussed so far in this chapter. Figure 3-23 compares the mountain ecosystems to the biomes.

Biotic Factors Forest creeps up most mountain slopes to the **timberline**, the uppermost limit at which trees can survive (Fig. 3-24). Above the timberline is the **alpine tundra**. In higher mountains there may be a permanent **snow belt** above this.

As in the Arctic, alpine tundra plants are small and stunted. To survive the cold and wind, alpine growth hugs the ground. Lichens, mosses, and a wide

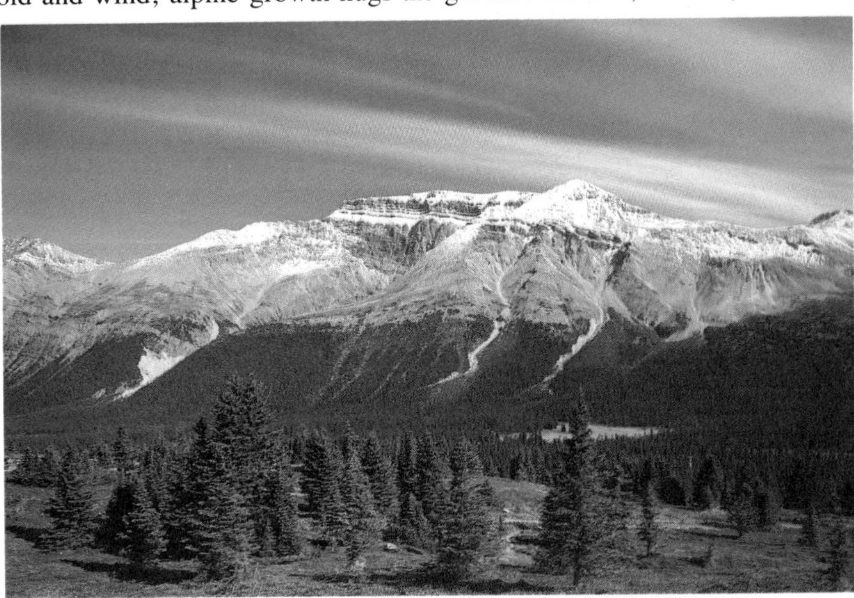

Fig. 3-24 The timberline marks the upper limit of tree growth. Beyond this lies the alpine tundra.

Fig. 3-25 Bighorn sheep descend from the peaks into the valleys when weather conditions and scarcity of food necessitate this move.

variety of flowering plants can be found in alpine meadows. The species and adaptations are similar to those in the Arctic tundra.

Alpine and Arctic wildlife share many of the same adaptations. Both have many species that change colour for camouflage. Both have species that hibernate. And both have species with body coverings that are well-insulated to conserve heat. Also, both have species that migrate to warmer regions in the winter. Arctic animals must migrate hundreds of kilometres. However, alpine animals like bighorn sheep need only walk down the mountain (Fig. 3-25).

The Temperate Rain Forest Biome

Look back to Figure 3-11. Note the strip along the Pacific coast that begins in Alaska, runs south through British Columbia, Washington, and Oregon, and ends in California. This unique forest of giant conifers lies between the Pacific Ocean and the coastal mountains. It is called the **temperate rain forest biome** (Fig. 3-26).

Abiotic Factors This coniferous forest is quite different from the boreal coniferous forest you read about earlier. The trees are much larger and growth is more rapid. Also, the plants that grow under the trees are more numerous and luxuriant in growth. These differences are mainly due to the unique climate of the coast—abundant moisture, high relative humidity, and moderate temperatures.

The winds along the coast are prevailing westerlies. They moderate the climate, resulting in average monthly temperatures from a low of 2°C to a high of 18°C. The soil is frost-free for a period of 120 to 300 d.

In winter, the westerly winds pass over the warm Japanese Current. As a result, the winds become laden with water. When these winds move inland, they strike the coastal mountains. The mountains force the winds to rise. In the higher, colder atmosphere, the water in the air condenses. Then it falls as rain or snow. Some areas of this forest receive as much as 635 cm of precipitation a year!

In summer, the prevailing winds shift to the northwest. These winds are cooled by the northern seas. As a result, the colder air masses carry little water. But they do cause heavy fogs. The fogs soak the forest canopy. The water then drips from the canopy to the forest floor. These heavy fogs add 130 cm or more of water to the soil each year.

Fig. 3-26 Giant conifers dominate the temperate rain forest.

Biotic Factors Three abiotic factors nourish the evergreen giants of the temperate rain forest. The same three factors promote a rich growth of ferns, mosses, and other shade-tolerant plants on the forest floor. These factors are

- an abundance of moisture
- a high relative humidity
- a moderate (generally warm) temperature

The most characteristic of the plants of this forest are the dominant trees. There are five main species of giant conifers:

- Sitka spruce
- western hemlock
- western red cedar
- Douglas fir
- redwood

Sitka spruce occur throughout this biome from Alaska to California. They often grow to a height of 60 m and a diameter of 1.8 m. Some even grow larger. Western hemlock, slightly smaller trees, also grow throughout this biome. Western red cedar occur mainly in British Columbia, Washington, and Oregon. These trees, like the Sitka spruce, can top 60 m and can have a diameter of up to 2.4 m. Douglas fir grow throughout the biome. These trees can reach a height of 75 m or more, with a diameter of up to 2.4 m. The real giants, however, are the redwoods. These grow mainly in a strip about 700 km long, through Oregon and California. They commonly grow over 80 m tall, with a diameter of 3 m. Occasional trees have reached 105 m!

Section Review

1. Why does a biome have a characteristic climax community?

2. **a)** Name the seven main biomes of Canada.
b) What important ecotone exists in Ontario?

3. For each of the six biomes described in this section, do the following in your notebook:
a) State its location in Canada.
b) Outline its important abiotic features in point-form.
c) Describe two or three examples to illustrate how organisms in that biome are adapted to the abiotic factors.

3.9 Activity: Researching a Canadian Biome

Section 3.8 gave you brief descriptions of six main Canadian biomes. The seventh, the **chaparral**, occurs in British Columbia, mainly in the rain shadow of the western coastal mountains (see Figure 3-11). You are to select one of these biomes and research it thoroughly in the resource centre. Appendix C gives helpful information on how to conduct your research. You may also want to view filmstrips and other visual aids that the resource centre has. Watch the television guide for programs dealing with the biome you have chosen. This is a major term project and should result in a paper of at least 3000 words, or about 10 double-spaced typed pages. Photographs or your hand-drawn art-work could be used to illustrate your paper.

Organize your paper under the following headings:

- **Location in Canada**
  Describe where the biome occurs in Canada. You may wish to refer to its location in the United States and elsewhere.
- **Abiotic Factors**
  Provide a detailed description of the climate, light conditions, and soil conditions of the biome.
- **Biotic Factors: Vegetation**
  Describe the dominant vegetation of the biome, emphasizing how the plants are adapted to the unique abiotic factors.

- **Biotic Factors: Animals**
  Describe several of the characteristic animals of the biome, emphasizing how they are adapted to the vegetation and abiotic factors.
- **Human Impact on the Biome**
  Describe the importance of the biome to humans, problems we have caused or may cause in the future, and conservation measures undertaken. You may wish to recommend further conservation measures.

Chapter Highlights

1. Ecologists deal mainly with four levels of biological organization—population, community, biome, and biosphere.
2. An ecosystem reaches its carrying capacity when the environmental resistance balances the biotic potential.
3. Birth rate, death rate, and migration affect population size.
4. Competition can influence the size and vigour of individual organisms.
5. Canada has seven main biomes—tundra, boreal coniferous forest, temperate deciduous forest, grassland, mountain, temperate rain forest, and chaparral.
6. Each biome has a characteristic climate and a characteristic climax community.

Key Terms

biome
biosphere
biotic potential
birth rate
boreal coniferous forest
carrying capacity
community
competition
death rate
emigrate
environmental resistance
grassland biome
immigrate
interspecific competition
intraspecific competition
migration
muskeg
permafrost
population
population growth curve
temperate deciduous forest
temperate rain forest
timberline
tundra biome

Recognizing the Concepts

Each of the following statements or questions is followed by four responses. Choose the correct response in each case. (Do not write in this book.)

1. All the bullfrogs in a pond are best called a(n)
   a) population **b)** community **c)** ecosystem **d)** organism
2. All the plants in a forest are best called a
   a) forest ecosystem
   b) forest plant ecosystem
   c) forest plant population
   d) forest plant community

3. An ecosystem is at its carrying capacity when the environmental resistance balances the
   a) birth rate
   b) death rate
   c) biotic potential
   d) migration rate
4. Which of the following is an example of interspecific competition?
   a) Tomatoes planted close together produce small fruit.
   b) Weeds crowd out vegetables in a garden.
   c) Blue jays fight among themselves at a bird feeder.
   d) White pine trees in a plantation grow more slowly than single trees nearby.
5. Which one of the following best describes the tundra climate?
   a) cold, windy, and dry
   b) cold, windy, and wet
   c) cold, calm, and dry
   d) cold, calm, and wet
6. The most concentrated foods of the temperate deciduous forest are
   a) leaves and grasses
   b) bark
   c) twigs
   d) buds and seeds
7. The grasslands have a climax vegetation of grasses mainly because of
   a) low and irregular precipitation
   b) hot short summers
   c) long cold winters
   d) moderate rainfall and temperature

Understanding the Concepts

1. Identify each of the following as a population, community, or biome.
   a) the deer in a meadow
   b) all the corn plants in a field
   c) all the organisms in a forest
   d) the brook trout in a stream
   e) the prairies of Canada
   f) the polar bears on Hudson Bay
2. Distinguish between a community and an ecosystem.
3. Name five populations you could find in a wooded area near your home.
4. Why do seed companies normally print on the package the spacing at which you should plant vegetable seeds?
5. Explain what has happened in the population that has the growth curve shown on page 88 in Figure 3-27.
6. Why do conifers often dominate drier areas of the temperate deciduous forest?
7. Which provinces of Canada have some grasslands?
8. Compare Arctic and alpine tundra as habitat for birds.

Applying the Concepts

1. Do you think the world has a carrying capacity for the human population? Defend your answer by discussing the biotic potential and the environmental resistance of the biosphere.

Fig. 3-27 A population growth curve

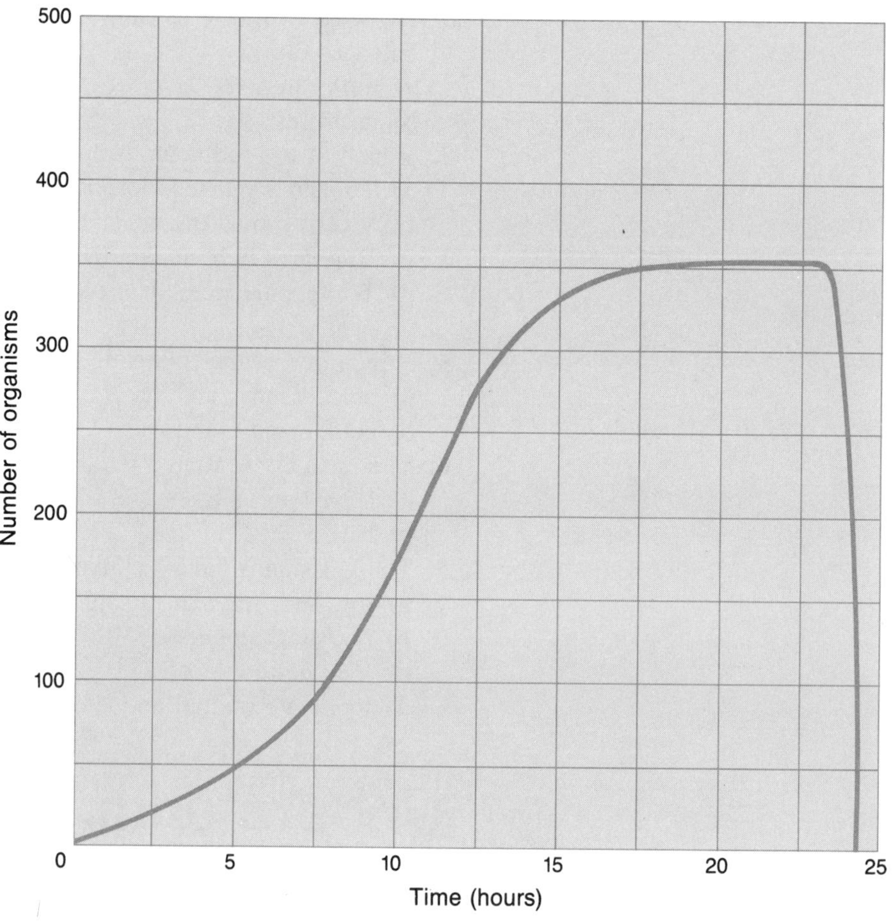

2. a) What kind of competition occurs between the grasses and the weeds in a lawn?
   b) Without human help, the weeds often out-compete the grasses. Why is this so?
   c) Other than killing the weeds, what could you do to give grasses a competitive edge over weeds in a lawn?
3. a) Why is it an advantage for a tundra plant to be an evergreen?
   b) What major problems would a gardener have trying to grow vegetables in the Arctic during the summer?
   c) Design an ideal Arctic mammal. Describe its shape, size, body covering, and other special adaptations.
4. Poplar trees often colonize burned or cut areas of the boreal coniferous forest. Why is this so?
5. In some parts of Canada, wolves are shot to prevent them from killing moose, bighorn sheep, elk, and other large herbivores. The main reason for this killing is to provide more big game for sport hunters to shoot. What do you think of this "wolf management" program? Defend your position.
6. Within 100 km or so of many urban centres, dogs are major predators of deer. They are very effective predators when the snow has a crust on it.
   a) How do you think the dogs arrived in deer country?
   b) Why are they so effective when the snow is crusty?

c) If you were in a position to take action, what would you do to lessen this slaughter?

7. The giant conifers of the temperate rain forest are disappearing at an alarming rate. Make a list of things city dwellers could do to help conserve these trees.

Investigations

1. Snow geese are important to tundra vegetation. Nutrients leach from the land into ponds and lakes. The snow geese return these nutrients to the land. Find out how they do this.
2. Research travel arrangements from your home to a high Arctic community (Fig. 3-28). What is the cost? How long is the trip? What is the route? What will food and accommodation cost per day?
3. Use a map of Canada and Figure 3-11 to find out how far you would have to travel to visit the *nearest* example of tundra, boreal coniferous forest, temperate deciduous forest, and grassland.
4. Jack pine is called a fire successional species for the boreal coniferous forest. Find out what this means.
5. The spraying of boreal forest with chemicals that kill spruce budworm has become a very controversial issue. Some people say the spraying is necessary to protect the forest. Others say the spraying harms humans, wildlife, and the ecology of the forest. Research both sides of this issue and summarize your findings in a 500-word report.
6. Obtain from the Ontario Ministry of Natural Resources its official policy on the management of privately-owned woodlots. Evaluate this policy.
7. Select one of the following grassland animals and find out why it has been brought to the verge of extinction. Then find out what, if any, conservation measures have been taken to protect it—swift fox, kit fox, prairie dog, black-footed ferret, prairie chicken.

Fig. 3-28 This is part of the village of Pangnirtung on Baffin Island in the eastern Arctic. Regular flights visit this village and most other Arctic communities.

Career: *WILDLIFE MANAGER*

HELP WANTED: WILDLIFE MANAGER
Ministry of Natural Resources requires wildlife manager to direct a deer management program in an agricultural area. B.Sc. in wildlife management required.

A wildlife manager's job may be broken down into three major areas: evaluation, preparation of a management plan, and implementation of the plan. To show you how these three areas function, let us imagine that the deer population of an area is to be managed so that maximum sport hunting may be allowed.

During the evaluation phase, the manager seeks answers to questions such as these: What is the present population size? Has it been increasing or decreasing? What is the optimum population size? In what condition is the habitat? Is there adequate shelter and food? What role does predation play in population control? What is the optimum number of deer that could be harvested per year? How serious is poaching in the area?

Next the manager prepares a detailed management plan. It answers questions such as those above and proposes ways to achieve suggested targets. Then, during the implementation phase, the wildlife manager works with a team to improve the habitat, establish and enforce hunting regulations, and monitor the results.

To be a wildlife manager you need a minimum of a B.Sc. in wildlife management and a liking for the outdoors. In secondary school take all the science you can and spend some of your spare time reading about wildlife and investigating it in the field.

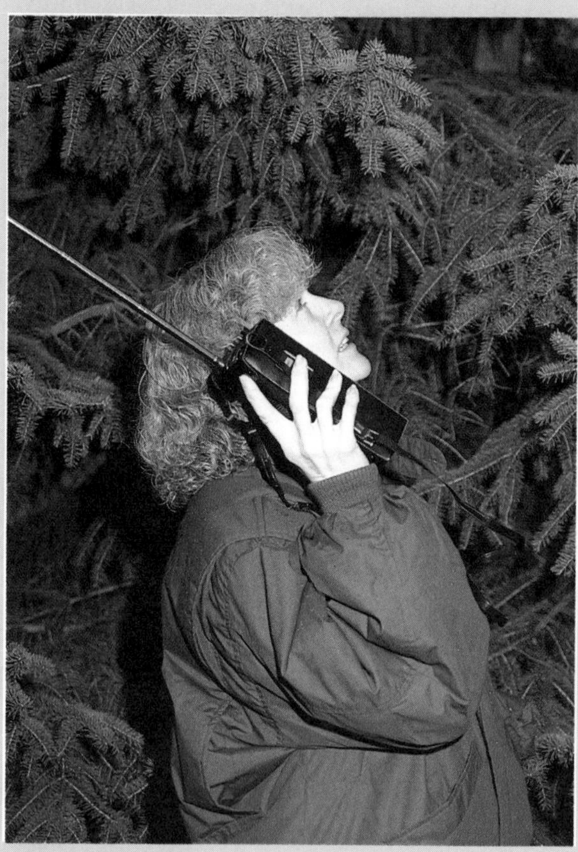

4 Human Influences on Ecosystems

CHAPTER CONTENTS

CHAPTER OBJECTIVES

After completing this chapter you should be able to:

1. Describe human population growth.
2. Demonstrate the importance of doubling time in population growth.
3. Evaluate future options for the human population.
4. Evaluate objectively major human impacts on ecosystems.
5. Participate effectively in an environmental hearing.

Most of us want productive forests and farms (Fig. 4-1). We want our streams and lakes well-stocked with fish. We want abundant wildlife in the countryside. We want clean air and clean water, and we are concerned about acid rain. We hope that our mineral resources like petroleum, iron, and copper won't run out.

We know that we are an integral part of the ecosystem in which we live. We will forever depend for our very existence upon an environment that gives us non-toxic food, clean water, oxygen, and the raw materials we need to build homes, make clothing, and provide other necessities. But we are faced with a dilemma. Our activities, over the long run, seem to be harming the environment. Why is this so? Can we have a better environment now and still have all our wants met? Can we be sure that natural resources will be around in the future to meet our needs?

Fig. 4-1 Ontario's farms and Canadian farms as a whole are among the most productive on earth. But have we achieved that productivity at a cost to the environment? Can we sustain that productivity and still have healthy ecosystems around agricultural areas?

In Chapters 1, 2, and 3 you gained the knowledge needed to explore such questions from an ecological perspective. You also had some opportunities there to practise the evaluation of environmental issues. This chapter extends those opportunities to some major environmental matters of importance to Canadians.

We have not tried here to cover all issues or to cover all aspects of the issues we have chosen to deal with. Our purpose in writing this section is to open your eyes to the fact that environmental problems do exist and to show you that you can help solve and prevent them.

4.1 The Need for Ecosystem Management

Fig. 4-2 When this log cabin was built 125 years ago, the environmental effects probably went unnoticed. Is that true when homes are built today?

There was a time when Canadians could use our natural resources just about any way we wanted. Our numbers were low enough that we could cut trees to build homes, kill any animals we needed for food, dump wastes in the woods or streams, and it made little difference (Fig. 4-2). The environment could absorb these impacts. Since the effects were not too noticeable, we became careless in the way we treated the environment. Forests were treated as though they were endless. Rivers were treated like giant sewers. Fish and wildlife were treated as inexhaustible sources of food and sport.

Over the years we developed patterns of resource use that were based on these early experiences. Our population gradually increased in numbers but the way we treated our resources did not change accordingly. We have now reached the point at which our old patterns of resource use are no longer acceptable. The natural environment cannot cope with the demands we place on it. It needs our help.

We have two options for helping the environment: We can decrease our demand for resources or we can manage the resources to meet our demand. Of course, we can also do both—decrease the demand so management need not be as great. Many Canadians have already chosen the first option. They live more simply, drive less, recycle domestic wastes, grow some of their own food, and shun commercial products that pollute. However, society as a whole has followed the second option. We are managing our resources to maintain or increase present productivity. After all, many Canadians depend, directly or indirectly, on natural resources for their employment. Forestry, agriculture, mining, and tourism employ millions. And secondary industries based on these employ further millions. We need the productivity of these industries. We need their products and the employment they give.

This raises a question: How can resource-based industries maintain productivity and, at the same time, have a low impact on the environment? In some cases they probably can't. But in many cases they can. The key to sound use of our resources is **ecosystem management**. The resource is managed to maintain productivity. However, management decisions are made on the basis of the ecosystem concept. Both we and the resources are in the same ecosystem. The well-being of one depends on the well-being of the other. You will get some insights into ecosystem management in later sections of this chapter.

Section Review

1. Explain the historical reason for our over-exploitation of natural resources.
2. What options do we have for helping the environment?
3. What would happen if we significantly decreased our use of natural resources?
4. What is ecosystem management?

4.2 Human Population Growth

Most ecologists agree that the size of the human population has a great deal to do with the world's environmental problems. A few million people spread over the earth would have little impact on the natural environment. But hundreds of millions, concentrated in small areas, can have a profound impact. This section examines human population growth so you can get an idea of what that impact can become in the future.

You should realize, of course, that the lifestyle in certain countries is the factor that impacts most on the environment, rather than numbers of people. For example, most Canadian families have at least one car. Iron, aluminum, and other metals must be mined to make the car. Petroleum is used to make much of the interior and to run the car. The car pollutes, demands roadways, and becomes garbage some day. Most people on earth do not have a car. Therefore this major burden on the environment is non-existent for most people on earth.

Human population growth is controlled by most of the same factors that control other populations—disease, overcrowding, shortages of food, and fighting. Centuries ago these factors kept population numbers in check. Life expectancy in Europe was only 9 or 10 years in the 1500s. The death rate was high. Disease and wars killed many. As a result, few people were alive to reproduce.

In recent years, however, the death rate has decreased. Better health care, technology, and modern agriculture are the main reasons. These factors have lowered the environmental resistance. As a result, population numbers are increasing at an alarming rate. Table 4-1 shows the population numbers of the world since the year 0. These are graphed in Figure 4-3. What forms of environmental resistance might stop this rapid growth?

Table 4-1 Human Population Growth

Year	*Number of people*	*Years for doubling to occur*
0	250 000 000	
1650	500 000 000	1650
1850	1 000 000 000	200
1930	2 000 000 000	80
1976	4 000 000 000	46
⋮ Projection	⋮	⋮
2010	8 000 000 000	34

Fig. 4-3 Human population growth

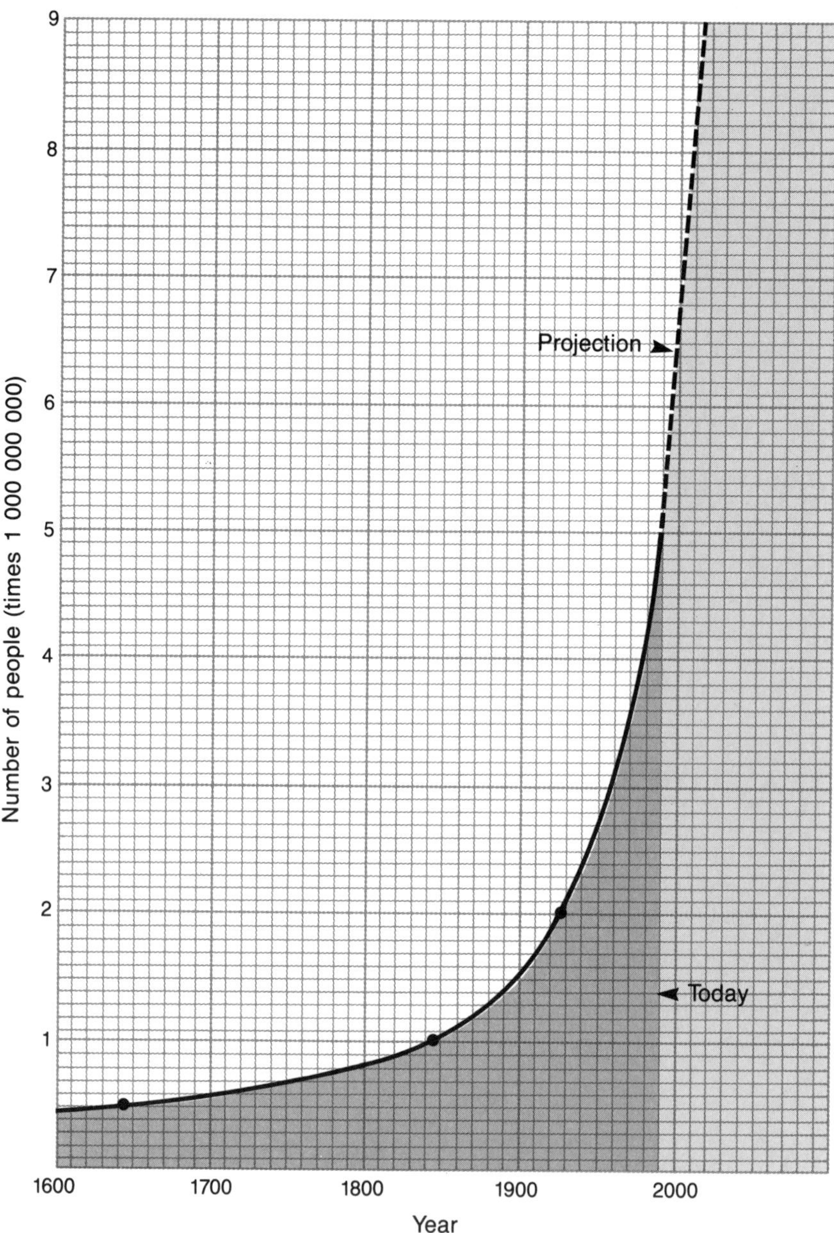

Section Review

1. What factors have lowered the environmental resistance in the human population since 1500?
2. Approximately how many people are on earth today?
3. In 1850 the earth's population was 1 000 000 000 people. Another 1 000 000 000 were added in the next 80 years. Copy Table 4-2 into your notebook. Then complete it using Figure 4-3.

Table 4-2 Years Needed to Add a Billion People

Number of people	*Years needed to add another 1 000 000 000 people*
1 000 000 000	—
2 000 000 000	80
3 000 000 000	
4 000 000 000	
5 000 000 000	
6 000 000 000	
7 000 000 000	
8 000 000 000	

4.3 Activity: Simulating the Rate of Human Population Growth

Figure 4-3 gives you a good idea of how fast the earth's human population is growing. However, this activity should give you an even better idea. In this activity the jar represents the earth. You are to simulate the growth rate of the human population using these rules:

1. Each bean represents 250 000 000 people.
2. Each second of time represents 10 years.

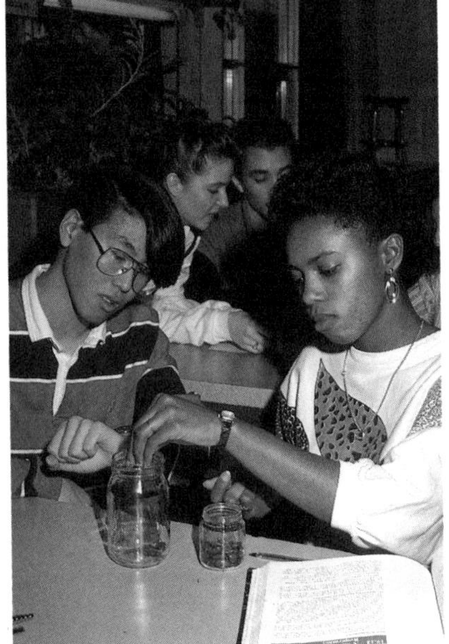

Fig. 4-4 This simple activity should give you a feeling for the rapidity of the growth of the earth's human population.

Problem

Can you simulate the growth rate of the human population?

Materials

beans (about 40) watch (with seconds) jar

Procedure

a. Copy Table 4-3 into your notebook. Study the table closely to figure out how we arrived at the numerals in the last two columns. Then complete the last two columns.

b. Place 1 bean in the jar (Fig. 4-4). This bean represents 250 000 000. That's the number of people on earth in the year 0 A.D.

c. Wait 165 s, then add 1 bean. The 165 s represents 1650 years. That's the time taken for the population to double to 500 000 000 (represented by 2 beans).

d. Wait 20 s, then add 2 beans. How many years does this represent? The jar now contains 4 beans. How many people does this represent?

e. Continue this process using the numbers you calculated for the table.

Table 4-3 Human Population Growth Rate

Year the population doubled	Number of people	Doubling time	Number of beans in jar	Time you have to put beans in jar
0	250 000 000	—	1	
1650	500 000 000	1650 years	2	165 s
1850	1 000 000 000	200 years	4	20 s
1930	2 000 000 000	80 years		
1976	4 000 000 000	46 years		
2010	8 000 000 000	34 years		

Discussion

1. What is meant by **doubling time**?
2. What happens to the doubling time as the years go by?
3. Describe what you learned in this activity about the growth rate of the human population.

4.4 The Future of the Human Population

The population of the earth is now increasing at the rate of about 250 000 people/d. To accommodate these people could require adding a city the size of London or Windsor, Ontario to the earth every day! Or they could be accommodated in five cities the size of North Bay or in six or seven cities the size of Chatham or Belleville. They could be spread more evenly in 30 or 40 towns the size of Goderich, Port Elgin, or Gravenhurst. Or they could be housed in countless tiny shacks around big cities, in earthen mounds in deserts, in tents in refugee camps, in packing cases in streets, . . . or in no home at all.

This 250 000 people/d amounts to about 90 000 000 people per year, or over three times the population of Canada. The doubling time for the earth's population is now about 34 years. Suppose it stayed at that level. Then in about 400 years *every bit* of land on earth would have densities of people as great as in the world's largest cities. And in about 850 years there would be about 120 people for each square metre of land and water! It is clear that this cannot and will not happen.

What Will Happen?

Human population growth must level off soon. Otherwise there will be little room for people and no room to grow their food. How might this levelling occur?

The growth rate can only be lowered by changes in the birth rate, death rate, or both. History shows that three major factors have increased the death rate. These are starvation, war, and disease. Some experts feel that these factors will affect the death rate more and more as the years go by. That is, they tell us that we can expect more and more people to die from starvation, wars, and disease.

The same factors, of course, affect the birth rate. The birth rate drops during famines. It also drops during wars because families are separated. And diseases can lower the birth rate. So, if we do nothing, these natural factors may level off our population growth. This is not a pleasant thought, is it? Who wants to grow up in a world where the population is governed by famine, disease, and wars? But there is an alternative. Let's look at it.

Zero Population Growth

Suppose each family had only two children. Then, in the long run, population growth would level off. That is, there would be no population growth. This is called **zero population growth**.

Suppose everyone on earth agreed today to aim for zero population growth. That doesn't mean that the earth's population would stay at its present 5 000 000 000. About half the people on earth haven't had their children yet. Also, these people would have their children while they and perhaps even their parents are still alive. Therefore the earth's population would still continue to grow for 30 or 40 years. It would level off at about 8–10 000 000 000 people. Most scientists agree that, with sound ecosystem management, the earth can support that many people. In other words, that is the carrying capacity of the earth.

Food for the Future

How can we feed more people, even if we stay below the carrying capacity? Even now millions starve to death every year, and about three-quarters of the people in underdeveloped countries don't get enough to eat. They get enough to stay alive, but their bodies are weak and they get diseases easily.

Most experts agree that the earth will have increasingly more famines in this decade and in the years to come. There have already been some major famines, mainly in countries in Africa and Asia. Often crops are being grown on marginal farmland. Even in a normal crop year the people barely get enough to eat. A drought, flood, hot spell, or cold spell can reduce the harvest. If this happens, many people will not get enough to eat.

History shows that people will starve to death during famines, even though other countries like ours have surplus food. Today farmers in Canada and the United States cannot sell all the food they can grow. Yet millions in other countries are dying of starvation. And hundreds of millions go to bed hungry every single day.

Why does this happen? Most of the reasons seem to be political. It costs money to help other countries. Therefore helping others would raise our taxes, and governments that raise taxes too much may not stay in power very long. Some governments at the receiving end cause problems, too. They insist on distributing the food, but their distributing systems are poor. Therefore the starving often do not get the food.

Canada does have an active foreign aid program. But the amount we spend is small compared to what we spend on any one of highways, weapons, holidays, cigarettes, or alcohol. The world spends about $2 000 000 000 a day on armaments. Poverty, starvation, and disease could be wiped from the face of the earth if even a fraction of that money was used for health care, food production, and education. For example, just one or two days of the military budget could feed, clothe, and educate about 1 000 000 starving children for 10 years. Or it could educate 100 000 000 people so they could become self-sufficient in agriculture, in education, and in medicine. It seems that most countries on earth can always find the money to fight wars. But we never seem to be able to find enough to help others. We will, though, find enough when we really want to.

Disease and War

Disease and war are two more factors beyond starvation that could limit human population growth. A giant plague such as an AIDS epidemic could sweep across the earth. Also diseases that hardly affect us could kill millions of poorly fed people. But experts don't think diseases will play a big role in limiting human population growth. Modern medicine can control most diseases.

We all know what a nuclear war could do, and the threat is always there. But no one wants this as a method of population control.

What Do We Do?

You have seen that four main factors can limit human population growth. These are starvation, disease, war, and birth control (Fig. 4-5). The first three are cruel and undesirable. The last one would be effective; however, there are

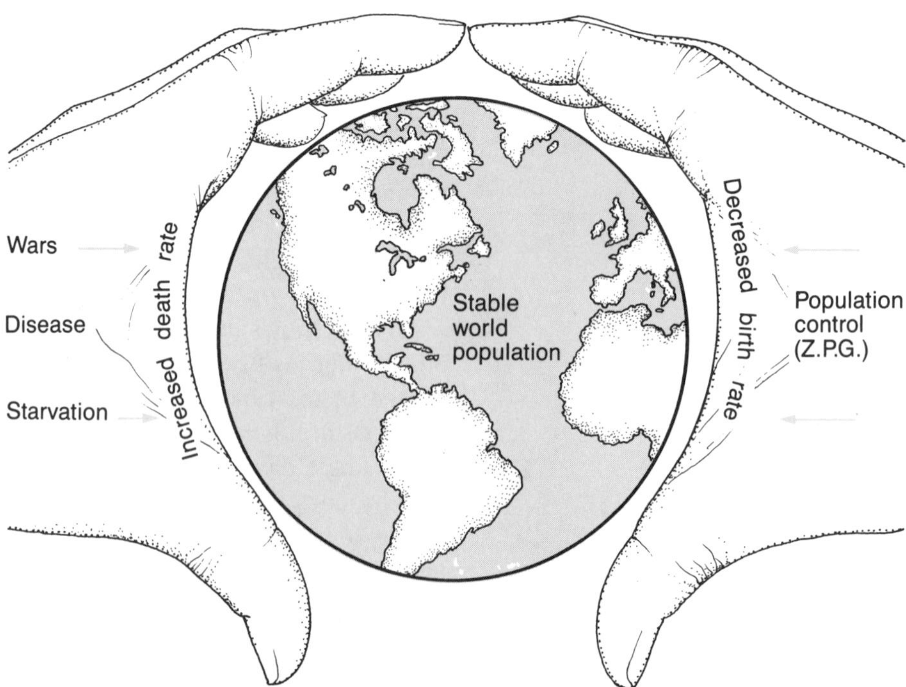

Fig. 4-5 What are the options for achieving a stable population on earth?

problems. For example, it will be difficult to get people to limit families to just two children. What, then, do we do? We know that families in well-educated and well-fed populations tend to be small. Perhaps our best solution, then, is to help other countries with food and education. The following is a list of possible things Canada could do. Discuss them with a group of your classmates.

- Help provide food NOW for starving people.
- Help other countries become self-sufficient in agriculture.
- Continue to develop new strains of crop plants that grow well in other countries.
- Help other countries with irrigation projects.
- Help other countries with education projects. People must be able to read and write to work together to solve population problems.

Section Review

1. Describe the present increase in the earth's population.
2. What three factors have historically increased the death rate?
3. What is zero population growth?
4. What problems often prevent countries with surplus food from feeding starving populations in other countries?
5. List and evaluate the four main factors that can limit human population growth.

Extension

Five suggestions were given as possible things Canadians could do to help control the world's population growth. Discuss these with a small group of your classmates. Then write a critical analysis of the suggestions.

Fig. 4-6 These hardwood logs will be sawed into lumber to make furniture and to build homes.

4.5 Managing Our Forests and Woodlots

Overall Importance of Forests

Forests like those in northern Ontario have long been a major resource in Canada. They provide firewood for heating and cooking. They produce lumber for building homes and furniture (Fig. 4-6). They are a source of pulpwood for making paper. They yield foods such as fruits, nuts, and sugars. And, more recently, they have become popular places for recreation—camping, hiking, and nature walks (Fig. 4-7).

Fig. 4-7 These campers followed abandoned logging roads to reach this idyllic campsite.

Forests also help prevent rapid run-off of water. This, in turn, lessens soil erosion, helps prevent flooding, and helps keep water quality high in streams. And forests are the habitat for a wide variety of plants and animals. Forests also play a role in forming the microclimate of an area. In fact, large forested areas can greatly affect the climate of a whole continent and, perhaps, the entire earth.

Economic Importance of Forests

Forests are very important to the economy of Canada. In recent years the forest industry contributed over $23 000 000 000 to the Canadian economy per year. Canada now produces about 14% of the world's timber and other forest products. This is the third largest share in the world. And Canada is the world's leading exporter of forest products. Much of these exports goes to the United States. This provides Canada with a $15 000 000 000 annual trade surplus. Over 250 000 000 trees are cut each year to keep Canada's forest industry going.

About 300 000 people are employed directly in the Canadian forest industry, including loggers, sawmill workers, pulp and paper employees. Another 700 000 people have jobs that depend directly on the forest industry: newspaper employees, home builders, and furniture builders. Canada's population is near 25 000 000. Of this number, about 10 000 000 are employed (most of the rest are children and young adults still in school). Therefore, about 1 working Canadian in every 10 depends on forestry. In British Columbia this ratio jumps to 1 in every 4. As you can see, if the forest industry is in trouble, the national economy will suffer as well.

The Present Condition of Our Forests

The seemingly endless supply of trees in Canada has encouraged over-exploitation and improper management. In fact, a Science Council of Canada report says that the forests have degenerated to a dangerous point. Wastage is great. One estimate suggests that to get the 250 000 000 trees marketed each year, over 3 000 000 000 are cut. In other words, only 1 of every 12 trees cut is used. The others are cut and left to rot. Perhaps they are too small, hard to get at, damaged, or not quite perfect. Regardless of the reason, the waste is great.

Fig. 4-8 Campfires have a certain attractiveness and, at times, are needed for warmth. However, a good portable stove is much safer in the northern woods, particularly during dry periods.

Fires destroy about six times more forest than loggers cut each year. Careless users of the forest cause much of this loss through discarded cigarette butts and improperly set and extinguished campfires (Fig. 4-8). Insect pests also cause great damage. In the 1970s the spruce budworm alone defoliated 75 000 000 ha (750 000 km^2) of forest in Ontario, Quebec, and the Maritimes. This area is almost equal to the land area of Ontario. And recent studies suggest that acid rain is affecting growth and regeneration of forests.

What Can Be Done?

There are currently from 20 000 000–25 000 000 ha (200 000–250 000 km^2) of logged but unreforested land in Canada. And Canada's forests are reduced a further 1 000 000 ha (10 000 km^2) each year by poor management. This is an area about equal to the size of Prince Edward Island. A first step, then, is to replant more actively and effectively and to cut more carefully. (See Section 2.7, page 62 for comments on clear cutting.)

A second step is to reduce losses by fires. Prevention is much more effective than trying to put out fires once they start. You should know the fire regulations before beginning a camping trip in the forest. You should also know how to make a safe campfire. (Generally, the safest campfire is a small portable stove.)

And people who smoke should be *absolutely certain* that butts are extinguished. (It would be safer if they did not smoke.)

A third step involves better pest control. Some pesticides seem to be effective against major insect pests. But they can also pollute streams, kill wildlife, and affect human health. The trend today is toward **integrated pest management**. This method uses lower amounts of pesticide along with other control measures. Among these other methods are:

- Thinning of the forests through controlled burning and cutting. Pests seem to thrive in the thick forests which have developed since forest fires have been better controlled.
- Development of resistant tree species. Cut areas of forests can be replanted using species which are resistant to major diseases.
- Biological controls. Forests are sprayed with bacteria, fungi, and other organisms which control the pests.

Fig. 4-9 This plantation is growing on agricultural land that was taken out of production because it was unprofitable as farmland.

A fourth step is to recycle wood products such as newspapers. If we recycle, fewer trees will have to be cut from our forests. Finally, **tree farms** could be used to supply more of our pulpwood (Fig. 4-9). Species have been developed which are large enough to cut for pulpwood in about 5 years. These should be more actively planted as crops on marginal farmland.

Canada must move toward **sustained yield forestry**. In such forestry, the government and industry ensure that cut trees are replaced. Further, cutting is done in such a way that there will always be a supply of marketable trees. Overall, Canadian forest management techniques lag behind those of the United States, Sweden, and Norway. Sweden, for example, has only one-quarter of the forest land Canada has. But it produces two-thirds as much wood product. In recent years, Canada's share of the world pulp market has dropped from 70% to 30%. Clearly a strong effort is needed to revitalize the forest industry. This effort will have to be guided by well-trained foresters. Canada now has only one forester for every 500 000 ha of forest. This ratio is one for every 14 000 ha in countries like Sweden and Norway.

Fig. 4-10 This plantation of white pine is being pruned by the landowner to encourage straight knotless growth. The Ministry of Natural Resources provided advice on the timing and techniques to use. In 30 or 40 years these trees will provide valuable lumber. In the meantime, what is the value to the landowner and the environment of this plantation?

Woodlots

Almost every farm in southern Ontario has a woodlot. However, in many prime agricultural areas, less than 5% of the land area is forested. Nonetheless, an encouraging trend is occurring. Poorer agricultural land is being taken out of production and planted in trees. Such **tree farms** are usually managed well by the Ontario Ministry of Natural Resources or, in some cases, the landowners (Fig. 4-10). In most cases, the objective of the owner is to make money. As a result, tree farms are often planted to a **monoculture** (one species), and they often specialize in fast-growing **hybrid species**.

Woodlots, whether they be natural or tree farms, are of great importance ecologically, economically, and socially. They provide wildlife habitat and soil protection. They act as ground water recharge areas. They help moderate climatic extremes. They are sources of wood and wood products. They are prime sites for recreation. And they add greatly to the beauty of the countryside. For these and other reasons, woodlots must be protected and improved.

Because of poor management (often no management), woodlots are not making the contribution they could make. Proper thinning could greatly increase timber production from woodlots. In many areas, the woodlots need to be expanded to make a noticeable contribution. Extensive replanting needs to take place. For example, trees need to be planted along fence lines to protect crops and soil from the winds. And trees should be planted along all creeks and rivers to reduce erosion and increase water quality.

Section Review

1. List the diverse uses of forests.
2. Summarize the economic importance of Canadian forests.
3. Describe the present condition of Canada's forests.
4. List and describe five things Canadians can do to ensure a continued supply of trees.
5. **a)** What is integrated pest management?
   b) What advantage does it offer?
6. **a)** What is sustained yield forestry?
   b) Evaluate Canadian forest management.
7. Describe the values of farm woodlots and tree farms.

4.6 Agricultural Practices

One in five people in Ontario is involved directly or indirectly in agriculture. The central purpose of agriculture is to get the most food possible out of the land at a price consumers will pay. Canadian farmers have achieved this purpose well—but at a cost to the environment. Let us look at the kinds of agricultural practices that can cause problems and see what many farmers are doing about them.

Tillage Practices

Farmers have traditionally used the moldboard plough, and most still do (Fig. 4-11). On some types of soil there are no alternative methods of ploughing

Fig. 4-11 The moldboard plough turns the soil completely over, burying the plant debris that protected the soil from wind and water erosion.

that are satisfactory. But in any case, excessive tilling, particularly if it bares the soil, is a major cause of **soil erosion**. The loss of soil due to erosion amounts to 12 t per hectare every year in Ontario. The soil that erodes is the topsoil, the most productive layer. This soil took thousands of years to form. Yet, in cash crop areas (wheat, corn, barley, beans, and soybeans), where losses are usually greatest, topsoil is being washed and blown away at the rate of 1–2 cm a year. In the prairies, wind erosion has reduced crop yields by as much as 30% on higher ground. All told, soil erosion costs Canadian farmers $1 000 000 000 a year in lost income due to decreased production. Clearly soil erosion is a serious problem.

What can be done to stem the tide of soil erosion? Many farmers say that if they try to use conservation methods, they will go bankrupt. They would have to buy new machinery and, at the same time, take land out of production. But other farmers have already taken action. They have abandoned the deep-cutting moldboard plough in favour of **conservation tillage** implements that do not turn the soil over. These implements leave a residue of plant material on the surface which helps prevent erosion and conserve moisture. If you think about it, this is a good example of ecosystem management. The soil is being left much like it would be under natural circumstances—with plant debris lying on the top. Conservation tillage normally involves fewer passes over the field. This saves money in both fuel and wear and tear on machinery.

Many farmers are using other soil conservation methods such as crop rotation, strip-farming, contour tillage, and shelterbelts of trees. During **crop rotation** the same crop is not grown on the same land for more than a year or two at a time. The crops are rotated to add organic matter to the soil and to keep the land covered more of the time. Both of these lessen erosion losses. **Strip-farming** is practised extensively in the prairies. Instead of cultivating large expanses of soil, the soil is cultivated in strips. The uncultivated land, with its plant cover, catches soil that is eroding from the cultivated land. In **contour ploughing**, the contours of the land are followed, instead of ploughing up and down hills. You can probably imagine how this lessens erosion (Fig. 4-12). **Shelterbelts** of trees were planted extensively around fields when wind

Fig. 4-12 Contour ploughing involves ploughing across the slope of a hill instead of up and down.

Fig. 4-13 Spruce trees make an excellent shelterbelt to protect a homestead or a field from the wind.

erosion became a serious problem in the 1930s (Fig. 4-13). Most of these were removed in the 1960s and 1970s as farmers switched to larger equipment and larger fields. But today, many farmers are replanting those shelterbelts with the assistance of local Conservation Authorities. All told, soil conservation methods are not in widespread use in Canada. But a rapidly growing number of farmers are practising them.

Irrigation

Irrigation of the land has become popular in many areas. It greatly increases crop yields. It also allows new crops to be grown where they couldn't be grown before. But it can also drain too much water from wildlife habitats and it can increase the salt content of the soil. This **salinization**, as it is called, can eventually kill crops. Excessive irrigation can also increase soil erosion.

Pesticides

The use of **herbicides** (weed killers) is widespread. Their use has greatly increased crop yields. It also reduces the amount of tillage needed. But often this method of weed control is used alone, without other methods such as crop rotation. If this is done, soil structure (the proper particle size) can be destroyed. Then soil losses through wind erosion increase.

The use of **insecticides** (insect killers) is also widespread. Their use, too, has greatly increased crop yields. But insecticides can have negative effects on the fish and wildlife that feed in food chains involving the target species.

Fertilizers

Commercial (inorganic) fertilizers are widely used to increase crop yields. They are needed to maintain the productivity of these foodlands. But often they are used as the *only* method of adding nutrients to the soil. If this is done, the soil structure gradually breaks down. And, once again, soil erosion increases.

Organic matter is needed to maintain soil structure. Some farmers add it by putting animal wastes on the soil. Others plant legumes such as alfalfa. This plant adds both organic matter and nitrogen.

1. Why does the moldboard plough, or any form of excessive cultivation, lead to soil erosion?
2. a) What is the principle behind conservation tillage?
   b) Explain how each of the following can lessen soil erosion: crop rotation, strip-farming, contour ploughing, and shelterbelts.
3. State the good and bad features of each of the following: irrigation, pesticides, fertilizers.

Biography

Greg Andrews: Farmer

Greg Andrews farms near the village of Blyth in southwestern Ontario. He specializes in the raising of pigs up to a mass of about 20 kg. At this mass the pigs are sold to other farmers who feed them until they are ready for market.

By today's standards, Andrews' farm is small—about 60 ha. However, it is a very productive farm, since he practises many of the conservation techniques described in Section 4.6. Manure from the pigs and from a herd of 60 beef cattle enriches the soil with organic matter. Crop rotation lessens soil erosion and small machinery reduces soil compaction.

How did Greg Andrews prepare to be a farmer? While he was a student in East York (Metropolitan Toronto) schools, Greg spent his summers getting practical experience on the farm. Then, when he graduated from secondary school, he attended the Centralia College of Agricultural Technology. He graduated from this college in two years with a diploma in Agriculture Business Management. Greg says that his secondary school science was vital in his success at the college and in farming. It helps him understand soil tests, fertilizer requirements, feed ratios, building ventilation, machinery operation, and many other aspects of farming.

Greg says that farming is hard work and doesn't pay very well. But he also says: "How many city people have endless green fields, woods, and streams for a backyard? And how many city people can go cross-country skiing just about every day in the winter?"

4.7 Fish and Wildlife Conservation

Why Are Wildlife Managed?

The term **wildlife** means, literally, all the wild animals in an area. However, biologists who manage this resource often use the term to mean just mammals. This resource is, too often, managed just for those species that are worth money to us. These tend to be species we want to kill for one of three reasons—food, furs, and fun. We call these the three F's of wildlife management. Because of this emphasis in wildlife management, many wildlife biologists classify mammals as food species, fur bearers, and game species (Fig. 4-14). People in parts of Canada kill animals for food. The deer and moose they shoot may be their only meat for the year. This is called **subsistence hunting**. A few people in our country kill animals to get furs for their own clothing. Most furs, however, are shipped to domestic and foreign markets to be used by the fashion industry. And some people kill animals for the challenge and pleasure of the hunt. This is called **sport hunting**.

A great deal of money can be made out of killing animals. Hunting permits and hunters bring in millions of dollars. The black bear hunt, alone, brings about $40 000 000 a year into the Ontario economy. Therefore our provincial government tends to manage the countryside to create more of the species we want to kill. Recently, though, more attention has been given to other species by the government. People are beginning to realize that other species have a right to live on this earth. They also realize that every time a species disappears,

Fig. 4-14 The deer (A) is both a food and game species. So is the black bear (B) (if the hunter eats it). The raccoon (C) is a fur bearer.

A

B

C

our ecosystem becomes more fragile. We are part of the ecosystem; therefore our existence depends on the existence of the other species in it.

Habitat Destruction

Conservation is not simply a matter of protecting animals from hunters and trappers. It is true that hunting and trapping have harmed many species. Indeed, they have made some species extinct in the past. However, hunting and trapping are now carefully controlled by our government. Thus these activities should no longer endanger animal species. In fact, evidence indicates that, for some species, controlled hunting and/or trapping actually benefits the species. Can you see why?

The most serious problem for wildlife is, most likely, **habitat destruction**. We have replaced natural habitats with cities and farms. Cottages dot the countryside, and roads crisscross all parts of the country. Human activities are everywhere. Some animals adapt well to the changed environment. Deer, for example, are much more numerous since we have cleared the land of trees. And racoons love the city. But most wildlife need their natural habitat.

The Ontario Ministry of Natural Resources uses money from hunting licences to improve the habitat for wildlife and to ensure that regulations are obeyed. Also, organizations like the Ontario Federation of Anglers and Hunters are quite active in habitat preservation and restoration. So, of course, are many people who do not hunt. Working together, hunters and non-hunters can ensure abundant wildlife for the future. Hunters and non-hunters often get involved in bitter disputes about sport hunting. There's nothing much wrong with that provided both parties understand one thing: sport hunting is essentially a moral issue, not a biological one. We must not let disagreements deter us from providing a diverse and healthy environment for wildlife.

Fish and Birds

Like wildlife, the fish and birds that get the most attention from wildlife biologists are generally those we want to kill. Streams and lakes are managed for trout and other sport fish. And marshes are managed for ducks and other game birds.

Fortunately, the habitat that is good for game species is often good for a host of other species. However, habitat destruction is taking place faster than management can replace it. Water pollution kills many species of fish. And the draining of wetlands has forced birds into smaller and smaller areas. Action is needed now to prevent further habitat destruction.

Section Review

1. **a)** What is wildlife?
   b) What is the focus of wildlife management?
2. **a)** List two main benefits to society of sport hunting.
   b) Evaluate the statement: "Sport hunting is essentially a moral issue, not a biological one."
3. What benefit comes to other animals when habitat for wildlife, fish, and birds is managed for game species?

4.8 Water Quantity and Quality

As you might well imagine, the oceans are vital to life on this earth. They are a major link in the water cycle that replenishes our fresh water supplies. The algae of the oceans add oxygen to the atmosphere and remove carbon dioxide. The oceans yield needed protein in the form of fish for countless millions of people. In fact, many Canadians rely on the fishing industry for their employment. You are likely more familiar with freshwater ecosystems. These are the lakes, ponds, and streams that are so abundant in Ontario. This section concentrates on them since they, large or small, are vital to all of us.

Water Quantity

First, let's look at water quantity, or the amount of water. Freshwater ecosystems provide us with drinking water and water for irrigating food crops. They provide habitats for fish we can eat. They provide places of recreation. They also help return water to the atmosphere to keep the water cycle going.

Without water, life on earth would cease to exist. Your body is almost 80% water. Lettuce, cabbage, and tomatoes are over 90% water. Eggs and lean beef are about 75% water. In fact, all plants and animals contain large amounts of water in their tissues. Unless they live in the oceans, they must get this water from freshwater sources.

Of vital concern to humans today is the need for water to produce food. Growing just 1 kg of wheat requires 600 L of water; 1 kg of rice 2000 L; 1 kg of meat 25 000 to 60 000 L; 1 L of milk 9000 L. A single corn plant absorbs over 200 L of water from the soil in one growing season.

Industry also uses large amounts of water. At least 500 000 L of water are needed to make one car (Fig. 4-15)!

Fig. 4-15 It took about half a million litres of water to make this car. Doctors recommend that you drink about 8 glasses of water a day. That's roughly 2 L. At that rate, it would take you 700 years to drink the amount needed to make a car.

Each of us uses directly or indirectly about 9000 L of water a day. This includes water for drinking and bathing as well as a share of the water used by agriculture and industry. In 1900 each person in Canada used only 2400 L. Industrialization and irrigation of farmland have caused the increase.

Since the earth has so little fresh water, care must be taken not to use large amounts needlessly. Global studies show that humans are now removing fresh water from the land faster than the water cycle can replace it. In Canada we use about twice as much water as the water cycle returns. Every time we want more water, we pump it from a lake or river or we drill a new well. Sooner or later a limit will be reached. Some scientists say that, within a few years, we will no longer be able to find all the fresh water we need. Perhaps it would be more accurate to say the fresh water we *want*.

This situation is causing some concern in North America. In a country such as India that is short of food, has a large population, and a low average rainfall, the situation is desperate. In an attempt to find more water to grow more food, India drilled about 80 000 wells in just one year. In the same year it installed about 250 000 pumps to bring water from lakes and rivers. How long can this continue?

Water Quality

A scientist at the Canada Centre for Inland Waters at Burlington recently estimated that a glass of water from Lake Ontario probably contains:

- 10 000 000 000 000 000 000 chloride ions (a component of salt)
- 100 000 000 000 molecules of chemicals formed due to the chlorination of sewage
- 10 000 000 000 molecules of cyanide from industrial processes and mining operations
- 10 000 000 000 molecules of solvents used by industries
- 4 000 000 000 molecules of freons (chemicals used in refrigeration devices and some aerosol cans)
- 1 000 000 000 molecules of wood preservatives
- 500 000 000 molecules of PCBs
- 100 000 000 molecules of chemicals that resulted from the burning of coal
- 10 000 000 molecules of insecticides
- 10 000 molecules of dioxin

Dioxin, PCBs, and some of the other substances are known carcinogens (cancer-causing agents). However, before you become too alarmed, you should realize that they are a very small portion of the glass of water. It contains about 10^{25} molecules of water. (That's a 1 with 25 zeros after it.) Recent evidence does suggest, however, that people living near the Great Lakes have a greater incidence of cancer. The drinking water may be the reason or part of it. Therefore concern is justified, as is a demand for a cleanup. Incidentally, the water in many other parts of Ontario is not much cleaner (Fig. 4-16).

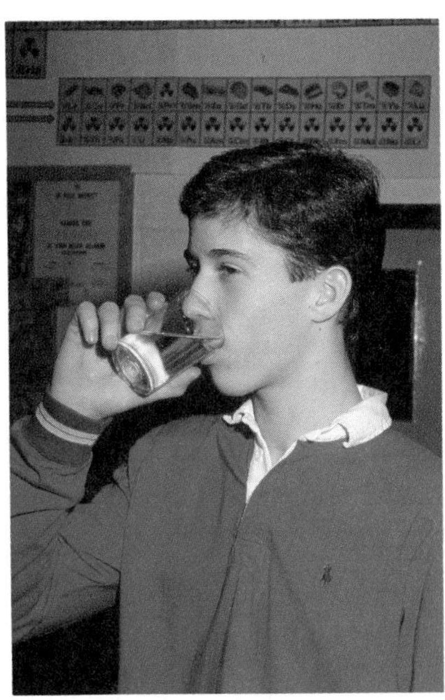

Fig. 4-16 Do you know what you are drinking? Where did it come from? What kinds of pollution run into your drinking water source? If you don't know the answers to these questions, you owe it to yourself to find them.

The chemicals we just listed come mainly from industrial processes, mining operations, farm run-off, domestic sewage, and air pollution. These and other wastes are described and evaluated in Unit 7. At this point we simply want to say that our freshwater ecosystems have been used for a long time as dumps for domestic sewage, industrial wastes, and agricultural wastes. Though much more care is being taken now, we will have to live with mistakes from the past. Our government has shown a determination to greatly reduce all forms of water pollution. With public support, including a willingness to pay higher prices for consumer products, we can have much cleaner water. Are you willing to pay?

Section Review

1. Present a case for the importance of freshwater ecosystems to us.
2. What is the difference between finding the amount of fresh water we need and the amount we want?
3. Why should we conserve fresh water?
4. Why should we be concerned about the quality of our drinking water?
5. Why does the government need public support if it wishes to greatly reduce water pollution?

4.9 Acid Deposition

A chapter on human influences on ecosystems would not be complete without a discussion of acid deposition. This may well prove to be the most serious form of pollution humans have created. Fortunately, it can be reduced markedly. The technology exists, public support for a reduction exists, the government is demanding action, and some industries are beginning to react. But before we get into this further, we should clear up some terms. Almost everyone has heard of **acid rain**. This is the name given to this form of pollution when it was first discovered that acids were coming down out of the sky dissolved in rain. Then someone discovered that snow, mist, fog, and other forms of precipitation could also be acidic. Therefore the name was changed to **precipitation**. More recently, it was discovered that acids from smokestacks could be deposited on the earth quite independently of precipitation. Therefore the name was changed to **acid deposition**.

Sources of Acid Deposition

The main sources of acid deposition are:

- smelters which extract metals from sulfur compounds
- power plants which burn coal or fuel oil
- vehicles
- homes and industries which burn fuel oil or coal for heating purposes

Collectively these sources produce two gases, sulfur dioxide and nitrogen dioxide. These gases are both acidic. Also, they dissolve in water to form acids, namely sulfuric acid and nitric acid. When the gases themselves or the acids fall on the earth, they are called acid deposition.

Rain that has not been affected by these acids is still acidic. In fact, its pH can be as low as 5.6 due to the carbonic acid formed when carbon dioxide in the air dissolves in the rain. However, rain in Ontario often has a pH as low as 3.5 or 4.0. That's around 100 times more acidic than "ordinary" rain. Most often the winds that bring this acidic deposition to Ontario come from the Ohio Valley, an industrial region of the United States. However, our own power plants, cars, and industries contribute, too. And they send acid deposition to parts of the United States. Acid deposition is clearly a transborder problem.

Effects of Acid Deposition

The effects of acid deposition are not well understood. However, evidence is accumulating that suggests acid deposition is responsible for many serious environmental problems. Let us examine some of these.

Effects on Aquatic Ecosystems As you may know, southern Ontario sits mainly on basic bedrock (limestone and dolomite). In contrast, northern Ontario sits on the Canadian Shield which consists mainly of granite and other siliceous rocks that are acidic (Fig. 4-17). This means that lakes in southern Ontario tend to be basic and lakes in northern Ontario tend to be acidic. As a result, when acid deposition enters southern lakes it gets neutralized. However, if it enters northern lakes, it makes them more acidic. The excess acid can kill adult fish and other aquatic life. More often this acid disrupts reproductive cycles and prevents young fish from being born. The acid also dissolves heavy metals such as lead, mercury, and cadmium from the rocks. These can kill aquatic organisms and contaminate food chains of which we are a part.

When snow melts in the spring, a sudden discharge of acidic water enters lakes. Over a period of a few days a lake can receive 1000 times the acid it would get during a heavy rainstorm. This **acid shock**, as it is called, can have disastrous effects, even on basic lakes. Because of acid deposition, countless lakes in northern Ontario are devoid of fish. Scientists fear that many more will be in this state in the near future.

Effects on Terrestrial Ecosystems The effects of acid deposition on terrestrial ecosystems are less well understood. However, research is gradually gathering some frightening evidence. First, the acids appear to damage the leaves of trees and crops. This damage reduces leaf area and, therefore, reduces photosynthesis. As a result, growth of the plants is retarded. Second, the acids can damage the roots of plants. This is particularly likely if the soil is already acidic, as it is on the Canadian Shield. The acids can also prevent the uptake of crucial nutrients by the roots or cause the uptake of harmful substances. Also, the acids may kill fungi in the soil that are responsible for returning to the soil nutrients that plants need.

Scientists are not sure whether acid deposition is, alone, responsible for the death of trees and other plants or whether it works in conjunction with something else. However, evidence is beginning to suggest the latter. For example, maple trees, already stressed by tapping for maple syrup production, appear to be dying at a much more rapid rate than those not tapped. Also, trees that are well-fertilized seem to be able to withstand acid deposition. Further, trees in marginal soils and older trees appear susceptible. One thing is quite clear: Maple trees and other trees have suddenly started to die off at an alarming rate (Fig. 4-18). It is also clear that acid deposition is involved in some way.

Fig. 4-17 This area is dominated by acidic bedrock. Therefore the lakes are highly susceptible to acid deposition.

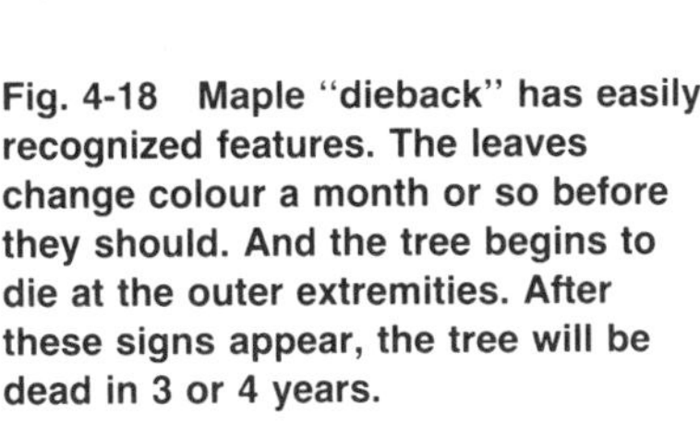

Fig. 4-18 Maple "dieback" has easily recognized features. The leaves change colour a month or so before they should. And the tree begins to die at the outer extremities. After these signs appear, the tree will be dead in 3 or 4 years.

What Can You Do?

Ontario has recently begun to move rapidly to stem the tide of destruction due to acid deposition. Several industries have voluntarily cut back on emissions. Others are under government control orders to do so. Our cars now have better catalytic converters to remove more nitrogen dioxide. Research is being done to find out more about the causes and prevention of damage. So we are on our way to coping with this problem.

You can help by supporting the government in its control orders. Write a "thank you" note to the premier and your member of parliament whenever they take a stand against acid deposition. Also, prepare yourself to pay more for consumer products. It costs money to clean up emissions from smokestacks and cars. Finally, you can support our federal government and groups like the Acid Rain Coalition in their efforts to convince our American neighbours to join us in this fight against acid deposition before it is too late.

Section Review

1. Distinguish among acid rain, acid precipitation, and acid deposition.
2. List the main sources of acid deposition.
3. Summarize the effects of acid deposition on aquatic ecosystems.
4. Summarize the effects of acid deposition on terrestrial ecosystems.
5. Make a list of things you can do to fight acid deposition.

4.10 Activity: Conducting a Simulated Environmental Hearing

Environmental hearings are becoming a popular way of coping with controversial environmental issues in Ontario. For example, hearings were conducted when Ontario Hydro was selecting a route for transmission lines from the Bruce Nuclear Power Station. Hearings were also held when the Ontario Waste Management Corporation was selecting a site for its hazardous waste disposal facility. And hearings are often held to evaluate major forestry projects, highway developments, and so on.

During such a hearing, individuals and groups of individuals appear before a hearing panel. They present their cases for or against the project. The hearing panel receives both oral and written submissions and arrives at a decision. This decision is usually passed on to some regulatory body as a recommendation.

Since hearings are becoming a common way of allowing the public to be heard, we thought you should get some experience with them. In this activity your class will select an issue and conduct a simulated public hearing. The following steps and suggestions should help you with your planning:

a. Appoint five people from your class to be the **hearing panel**. This group

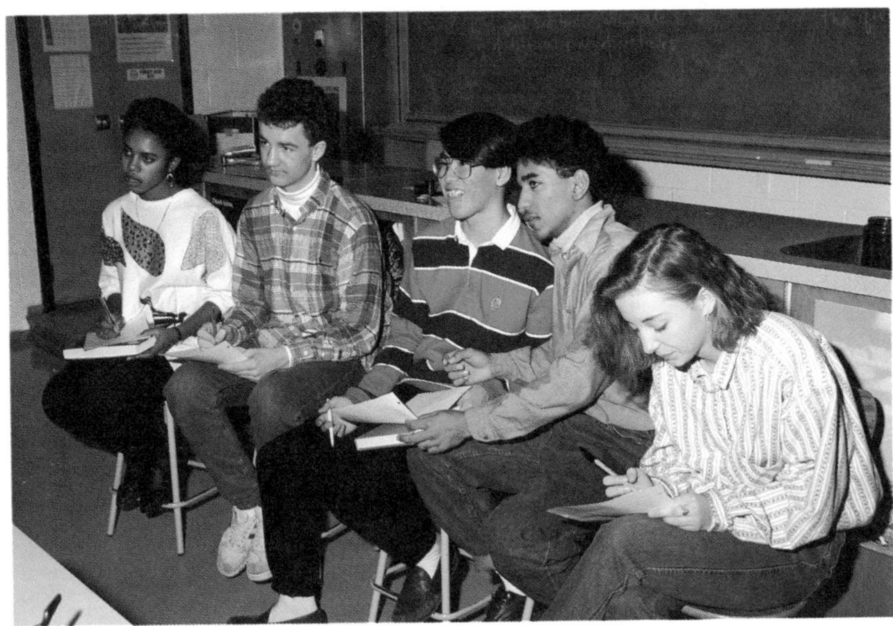

Fig. 4-19 The hearing panel could position itself at the front of the room, with the chairperson in the centre.

will listen to the presentations, receive written presentations, and make a decision regarding the project proposal. The hearing panel should elect a chairperson (Fig. 4-19).

b. Select a controversial environmental issue as the topic of the hearing. If possible, select one that is of current interest to the people of Ontario and/or Canada. Here are some suggestions:
- The building of a pipeline through the tundra to bring petroleum from the Arctic Ocean to southern refineries by way of the Mackenzie River Valley.
- The use of supertankers to transport petroleum from the Arctic Ocean to southern refineries through the straits between Canada's northern islands.
- The building of an international airport on prime agricultural land.
- The building of a new subdivision on prime agricultural land.
- The location of a landfill site (''garbage dump'') in a township that is next to a large city that has run out of places to put its garbage.

c. Assign roles to members of the class who are not on the hearing panel. These roles could include:
- representatives of the company making the proposal
- appropriate government officials
- representatives of various environmental groups
- citizens who will be immediately affected by the proposal
- people from companies which could benefit by supplying materials for the project
- local people who could benefit indirectly from the project

d. Research your role and the necessary background knowledge thoroughly. For example, you cannot present a case against the building of a pipeline through the tundra unless you understand how it could affect the permafrost, caribou migration routes, aboriginal people, and so on.

e. Prepare your paper. Plan for a 5 min oral presentation, and leave your written paper with the hearing panel.

f. Listen to all points of view carefully. Evaluate the hearing panel's conclusion. Now evaluate the effectiveness of your presentation.

Chapter Highlights

1. Ecosystem management allows ecosystems like forests to meet our needs without seriously disrupting their ecology.
2. Human population growth appears to be out of control.
3. Zero population growth is the best option for controlling the world's population growth.
4. Canada must attain sustained yield forestry to protect the forests and jobs.
5. Soil erosion is our main agricultural problem. It can be decreased by proper soil management.
6. Wildlife management, done on an ecosystem basis, can meet both the needs of wildlife and the wants of humans.
7. Habitat destruction is probably the most serious factor affecting fish, wildlife, and birds.
8. Canadians should have greater concern for water quantity and water quality issues.
9. Acid deposition may be our most serious environmental problem.
10. Environmental hearings are a democratic way to approach environmental issues.

Key Terms

acid deposition
acid shock
conservation tillage
doubling time
ecosystem management
habitat destruction
herbicide
insecticide
integrated pest management
irrigation
monoculture
soil erosion
sport hunting
subsistence hunting
sustained yield forestry
zero population growth

Recognizing the Concepts

Each of the following statements or questions is followed by four responses. Choose the correct response in each case. (Do not write in this book.)

1. According to Figure 4-3, the number of people on earth in 1900 was about

a) 2 000 000 000 **c)** 1 000 000 000
b) 1 500 000 000 **d)** 2 500 000 000

2. According to Figure 4-3, the number of people on earth will reach 7 000 000 000 in the year

a) 2000 **b)** 2010 **c)** 2020 **d)** 2100

3. Sustained yield forestry involves
   a) no management of the forest
   b) selective cutting only
   c) management of the forest on an ecosystem basis
   d) cutting of the forest with no thought to the future
4. Conservation tillage lessens soil erosion because it
   a) involves crop rotation
   b) uses strip farming and contour ploughing
   c) doesn't disturb the soil
   d) leaves plant debris on the soil surface
5. The most serious factor affecting wildlife today is probably
   a) habitat destruction
   b) trapping
   c) subsistence hunting
   d) sport hunting
6. Acid deposition has the most serious impact on
   a) the Great Lakes
   b) lakes located in limestone bedrock
   c) lakes located in siliceous bedrock
   d) lakes in southern Ontario

Understanding the Concepts

1. Explain why sustained yield forestry is a good example of ecosystem management.
2. Explain why the doubling time of the earth's population keeps decreasing with time.
3. Why will a residue of plant material on the soil lessen soil erosion?
4. What connection do you see between habitat destruction and the increasing human population?
5. Explain why acid deposition is a transborder problem.

Applying the Concepts

1. Is there an upper limit to ecosystem management beyond which the ecosystem would begin to suffer irreversible harm? Illustrate your answer with an example.
2. Canada has a fairly low population growth rate. What factors are responsible for this?
3. Some people have suggested that we solve our population problems by colonizing the planets. Evaluate this suggestion.
4. Write a letter to Ontario's Minister of Natural Resources that makes a reasoned plea for sustained yield forestry.
5. What dangers do you see in the creation of monoculture tree plantations?
6. City people demand cheap food and, as a result, may be partly responsible for soil erosion. Why is this so?
7. Imagine that you are the government official in charge of forest policy for Ontario. What major policies would you try to implement?

8. Some duck populations are decreasing at an alarming rate, yet these species can be legally shot. What do you feel about this? Why?
9. Many of the chemicals in our drinking water can be removed during water purification. Most, however, are not. Why do you suppose this is so?

Fig. 4-20 Plan your interview well before you begin. What questions will you ask? How will you record the results? How will you ask the questions?

Investigations

1. Find out which five countries have the most serious food shortages.
2. Find out which five countries have the most rapidly growing populations.
3. Interview five people about zero population growh. Write a report on your findings.
4. Interview five people to see if they would like to see money diverted from armaments to the world's problems. Write a report on your findings.
5. Find out about careers in forest management. Write a report on your findings.
6. Interview a sport hunter about his/her sport. Evaluate your findings on the basis of the ecosystem concept.
7. Find out what poaching is. What problems does it cause? Who does it? Why do people poach? How can it be stopped?
8. Get the Ontario government's policy statement on the management of privately-owned woodlots. Evaluate it from an ecosystem perspective.
9. Interview five people about the water quality of a local freshwater ecosystem. Summarize and evaluate your findings (Fig. 4-20).
10. Research the effects of acid deposition in a specific ecosystem such as a maple forest, high-altitude spruce forest, or trout-bearing lake.

Career: *SOIL CONSERVATIONIST*

HELP WANTED:
SOIL CONSERVATIONIST

The Ministry of Agriculture and Food requires a B.Sc. graduate in agriculture with a specialty in soil science to conduct studies of soil erosion and to advise farmers on corrective measures.

Soil erosion is a serious problem on many Ontario farms. In some areas crop yields have fallen dramatically because of the loss of topsoil. Fortunately, wise soil management can bring this problem under control.

At the request of a farmer, the local office of the Ministry of Agriculture and Food will send out an expert to investigate an erosion problem and recommend practices to lessen it. This expert, often called a soil conservationist, will normally have a B.Sc. degree in agriculture with an emphasis in soil science. The University of Guelph offers excellent preparation for this career. The soil conservationist prepares a soil conservation plan that may recommend reduced tillage, crop rotation, windbreaks, grassed runways, reforestation, or another alternative land use.

If you wish to contribute to the protection of our soil resources, study all the science, mathematics, and English you can in secondary school. Then enroll in the above-mentioned university program. The provincial and federal governments, forest companies, and private consulting firms all employ soil conservationists. Some banks do, too. Why would they do that?

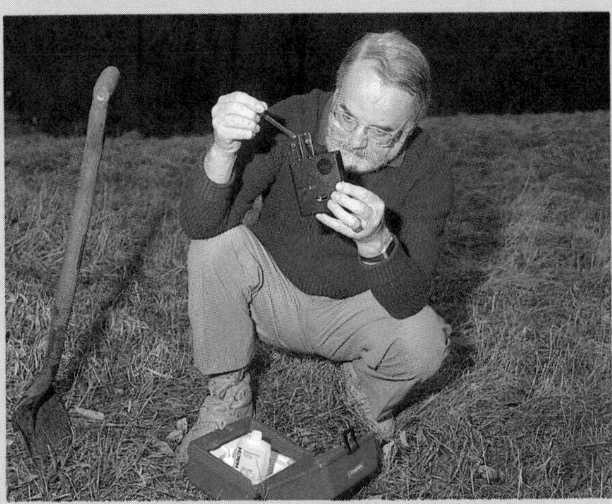

VISTA

THE TERMITE CONNECTION

Would you believe that an insect which seems to do nothing but eat wood may be changing the earth's climate? Well, some scientists think so. Here's the story:

Methane gas is commonly called marsh gas or natural gas. When it is released into the air, it gradually reacts with oxygen to form carbon dioxide. Carbon dioxide is known to contribute to the "greenhouse effect"—the gradual warming of the earth. This warming may melt the ice caps, flooding coastal cities. It may also cause disruptive climatic changes. Indirectly, then, methane can cause global problems. Now, what is the **termite connection?**

Until about 1980, scientists thought that marshes, rice paddies, landfill sites, and cattle were the main sources of methane. Then an American chemist, Pat Zimmerman, showed that termites are major contributors. A mound like the one shown here contains two or three million termites. Each one ingests cellulose. (The plant material that it eats is made of cellulose.) Then symbiotic microbes in its gut digest the cellulose, just as microbes in the stomach of cattle do. A by-product of this digestion is methane. Zimmerman estimates that termites release 150 000 000 t of methane into the air each year.

Clearly, termites are a significant source of methane. And, unfortunately, they are a growing source. Most people do not like termites because they destroy homes. However, we should remember that they play an important ecological role in nature. They break down the cellulose in fallen trees and make nutrients available for new plant growth. They thrive where there is fallen wood in a warm, damp environment. As a result, their numbers are growing wherever tropical rain forests are being cut. In fact, their numbers increase as much as ten-fold in such areas.

Currently there is about half a tonne of termites for every person on earth! That may be enough to change the climate of the earth. But are the termites the real culprits?

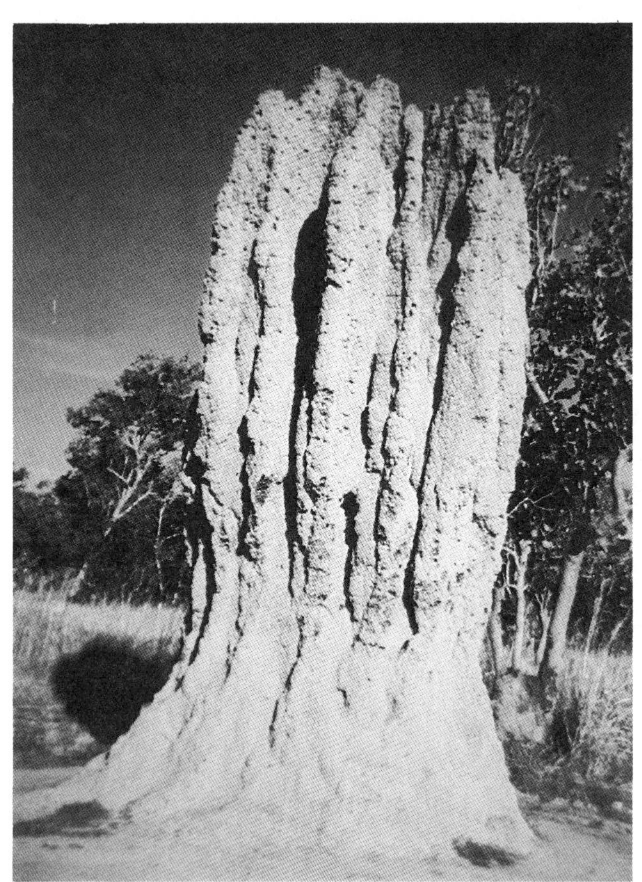

UNIT 2 Organisms and Their External Environment

CHAPTERS

One of the things all organisms have in common is that they are adapted to the environments in which they live. Most of the time, an organism's external environment is "friendly". It provides a habitat, suitable temperature, nutrients, and a place to eliminate wastes. But sometimes it can be quite hostile. Sudden changes in temperature, moisture, or other environmental factors can threaten the survival of an individual, a group of individuals, or even an entire species. As a result, an organism must constantly monitor its environment and be able to respond to any threatening changes it senses.

This unit begins with a brief survey of the classification of living things to set the stage for the study of specific organisms. Then the unit focuses on how certain protists and animals sense and respond to their environments. Special emphasis is given to the ways in which organisms are adapted to survive in their environments.

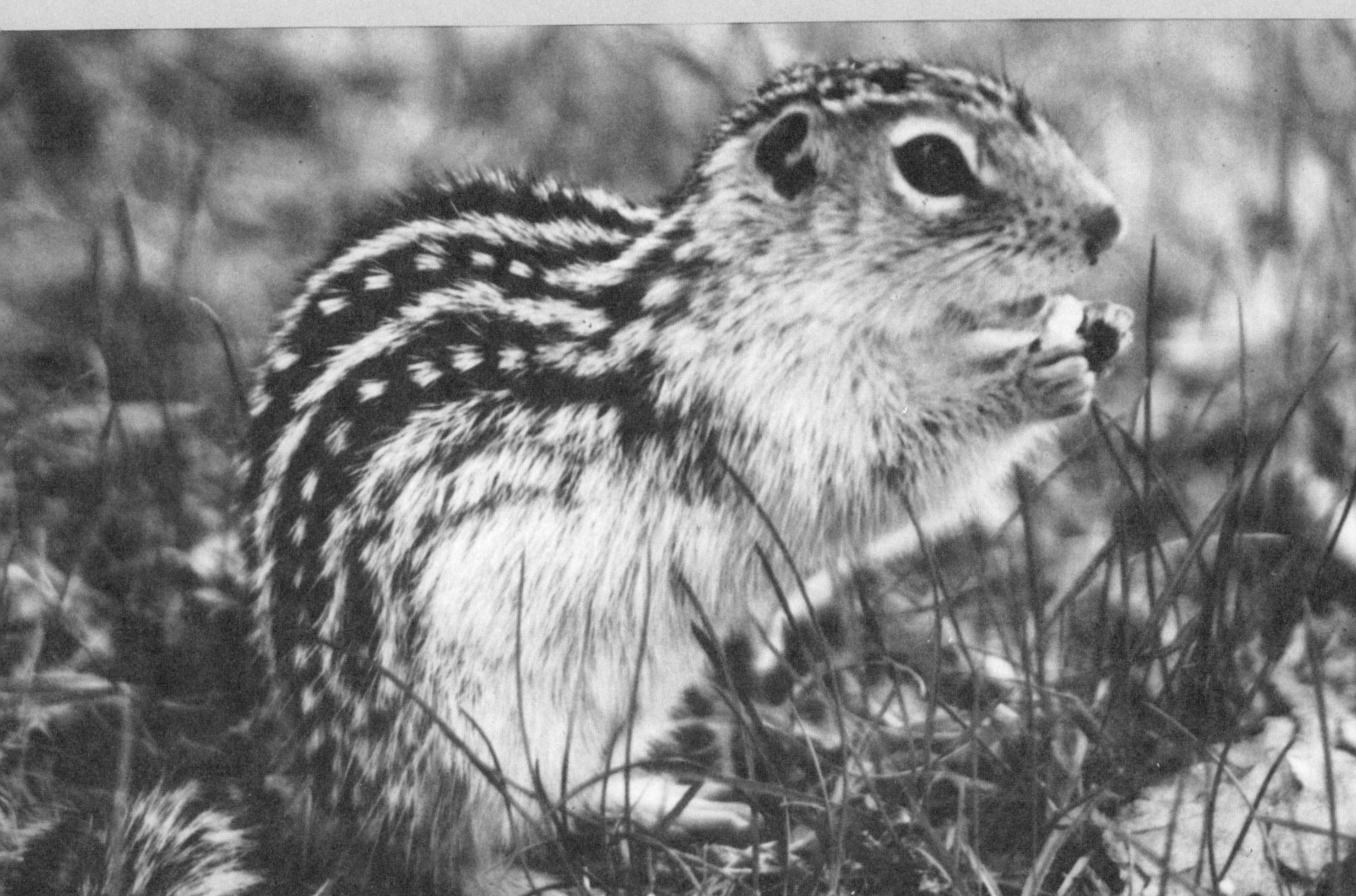

5 The Diversity of Organisms and Their Environments

CHAPTER CONTENTS

CHAPTER OBJECTIVES

After completing this chapter, you should be able to:

1. Describe the diversity of life on earth.
2. Name species using binomial nomenclature.
3. Recognize the seven main classification groups.
4. State the unique characteristics of the organisms in each of the five kingdoms.
5. Use a dichotomous key to identify organisms.
6. Illustrate and account for the adaptations of organisms to their environments.

What is it? This is the most common question people ask when they are on a hike with a biologist. Why do people want to know the name of an organism? How can you find out what its name is? How are organisms named (Fig. 5-1)? And, more important, how are they classified so we can keep track of what they are?

Fig. 5-1 What is it? If you say "frog", you could confuse many people because there are hundreds of species of frogs on earth. But if you answer "*Rana catesbeiana*", most people on earth can look this animal up in a book written in their own language and see exactly what you mean. Where did this strange name for a bullfrog come from? Why is it useful?

In order to get the most out of Chapters 6 to 10, you need to know how organisms are named and classified. You likely studied this in an early science course. Therefore this chapter simply reviews the key ideas. Be sure to discuss any difficulties with your teacher.

Fig. 5-2 This is *Eurycea bislineata*, commonly called the two-lined salamander. It thrives in moist, mature woodlands in eastern North America. If you were a biologist, you couldn't write a paper pleading a case for the protection of this animal's habitat if the animal didn't have a name.

5.1 Naming Living Things

Biologists have identified and named about 1 500 000 different kinds, or **species**, of organisms world-wide. Most biologists agree that this may be less than 5% of the total number of organisms. In fact many biologists feel that there may be as many as 80 000 000 species of organisms on earth! Every day new species are discovered and named. Most of these are being found in the tropical rain forests by biologists who work there among loggers. These discoveries must be exciting to **taxonomists** (biologists who name and classify organisms). Unfortunately, many of these species will be extinct before anyone else sees or even hears of them. Some ecologists think that the cutting of the tropical rain forests could make over 1 000 000 species extinct in the next 10–20 years and another 1 000 000 extinct during the following two or three decades.

Why bother naming things, you may ask, if they are going to go extinct anyway? To ecologists, identification is just the first step in protecting an organism. Once it has been named and classified, its ecology can be studied. Then recommendations can be made for its preservation (Fig. 5-2).

What Is a Species?

Earlier we referred to species as being "different kinds of organisms." This statement invites a question: How different must organisms be to be different species?

Fig. 5-3 Are these dogs "similar in structure"?

Linnaeus's Definition The first successful attempt to name species scientifically was made by a Swedish botanist, Carolus Linnaeus (1707–1778). He defined a **species** as a group of organisms that were very similar in structure. This definition was sufficient to allow Linnaeus and his students to identify and name the 50 000 or so organisms known at that time. It proved not to be sufficient, however, to allow us to classify the vast number of organisms known today. The reason is that the definition still invites the question: How similar? At first glance, many dogs do not appear to be "very similar in structure" (Fig. 5-3). In fact, they appear less similar than, for example, a German shepherd dog and a grey wolf. Yet modern-day taxonomists classify all dogs as the same species, but dogs and wolves as separate species. Let us look at their basis for doing this.

A More Recent Definition Extensive research over many decades led biologists to the following definition of a species:

- The organisms must be similar in structure (just as Linnaeus had said).

- The organisms must interbreed under natural conditions.
- The offspring must be fertile (able to produce offspring).

What this definition really says is that genetic similarities are more basic than physical appearance in determining how closely related organisms are. In fact, taxonomists today use genetic tests when they are naming and classifying new organisms. You will have to wait until a later course in biology to see how they do that. (Of course, you could choose to find out for yourself in the meantime!)

This definition does not permit biologists to name all species accurately. However, it does work for most common species. For example, all breeds of dogs can and will interbreed under natural conditions. (An exception occurs when differences in physical size make mating impossible). Further, the offspring of this interbreeding are fertile. However, dogs and wolves do not interbreed under natural conditions. They have been known to interbreed when a dog enters wolf territory (an unnatural condition) and when a wolf enters a dog's territory (also an unnatural condition). Normally, however, interbreeding does not occur.

A thoroughbred horse and a zebra will not, in the wild, mate and produce offspring. Thus, though they look similar in structure, they are not the same species. A thoroughbred will, however, interbreed with a donkey. The offspring is called a mule. A mule is almost always sterile. That is, it cannot produce offspring. Therefore, the thoroughbred and donkey are separate species.

How Are Species Named?

The system of nomenclature begun in the eighteenth century by Carolus Linnaeus is used today in almost all countries. When Linnaeus was doing his work, scientists did all their writing in Latin. As a result, Linnaeus used Latin words to name species. His system is quite simple. He gave each species a name that consists of two words. As a result, this system is called **binomial nomenclature**. Table 5-1 shows the scientific names of some common species.

Table 5-1 Examples of Binomial Nomenclature

Common name	*Scientific name*
Human	*Homo sapiens*
Dog	*Canis familiaris*
House cat	*Felis domesticus*
Sugar maple tree	*Acer saccharum*
White pine tree	*Pinus strobus*

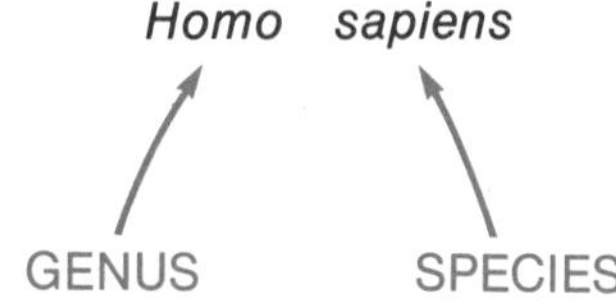

Fig. 5-4 Binomial nomenclature uses two words, a genus and a species name. The term means, literally, "naming with two names".

The first word of each scientific name is called the **genus** and the second word is called the **species**. Note that the genus begins with a capital letter and the species does not. Note, too, that both the genus and species are printed in *italics*. If the use of italics is impossible (as in your notebook), then the genus and species are underlined. Therefore *Homo sapiens* and Homo sapiens are the correct forms for writing the scientific name of humans (Fig. 5-4).

A **genus** (plural **genera**) is a group of species that are similar. For example, dogs, coyotes, and grey wolves are in the same genus, *Canis*. However, they are not similar enough to meet the definition of species. As a result, they have different species names, as Table 5-2 shows.

Table 5-2 Three Animals in the Same Genus

Animal	*Species name*
Domestic dog	*Canis familiaris*
Coyote	*Canis latrans*
Grey wolf	*Canis lupus*

Why Use Scientific Names?

Fig. 5-5 The mule deer often has a white tail. Does that mean it is a white-tailed deer?

You may be saying by now: Why do we need these difficult Latin names? Why can't we just call a deer a deer, a beaver a beaver, and a maple tree a maple tree? You can, if you are sure everyone knows exactly which organism you mean. But this is not always the case. For example, the animal in Figure 5-5 is a **mule deer**. It is the characteristic deer of the foothills of the mountains in western Canada. The mule deer often has a white tail. The deer that you see here in Ontario is the **white-tailed deer**. It, as the name clearly indicates, also has a white tail. Therefore, a person not familiar with these deer could be confused if you use the name white-tailed deer. The scientific name of the mule deer is *Odocoileus hemionus* and that of the white-tailed deer is *Odocoileus virginianus*. Therefore, if you say ''*Odocoileus virginianus*'' (if you can say it!) instead of ''white-tailed deer'', there will be no confusion. Anyone anywhere can look that name up in a book and know exactly which animal you mean.

Fig. 5-6 Bigleaf maple is better called *Acer macrophyllum*. Why?

Here is a second example. The leaf in Figure 5-6 was collected in British Columbia. It is from a tree called the **bigleaf maple**. The shape of the leaf is almost exactly the same as that of our familiar **sugar maple**. How, then, do you make it clear to someone who doesn't know these trees well that this leaf is from the British Columbia tree and not from a sugar maple with large leaves? You simply say it is from *Acer macrophyllum*. Now people can look it up in a tree book and know they are reading about the right tree and not about the sugar maple, *Acer saccharum*.

Scientific names need not be used all the time. However, they must be used when it is important to let others know exactly what species you mean.

Section Review

1. **a)** How successful have biologists been at naming the organisms on earth?
   b) Why is taxonomy important in the protection of species?
2. **a)** Define a species.
   b) Explain why all dogs are classified in the same species.
3. Describe the system of binomial nomenclature.
4. Defend the use of scientific names.

5.2 Classifying Living Things

As you learned earlier, there could be as many as 80 000 000 species on earth. Of these, over 1 500 000 species have been identified and named. How can biologists keep track of such a bewildering number of organisms? How can we name these organisms when no known language has as many words in it as there are species? You have already learned the answer to the second question—we use binomial nomenclature. Now let's look for an answer to the first question.

The Need for Classification

Humans have been classifying living things for thousands of years. The earliest humans probably classified organisms as plant or animal. They may have further classified the plants as harmless or poisonous and the animals as harmless or harmful. This system of classification is, of course, still used today. We classify Boston ivy, a vine that you may have seen growing on buildings, as harmless, and poison ivy as poisonous. We classify rattlesnakes as harmful and gartersnakes as harmless. Such classification systems are clearly useful to us.

Biologists have long recognized the need to classify living things in a more scientific way. It is very difficult to remember the characteristics of thousands of organisms. Therefore biologists group together, or classify, organisms that have similarities. Then remembering is much easier. Let's see how they do this.

The Main Classification Groups

To classify an organism, biologists first place it in a **kingdom**. As you may know, most taxonomists today use a **5-kingdom system**: Monera, Protista, Fungi, Plantae, Animalia. Therefore, if biologists were classifying you, they would place you in the kingdom Animalia. You have now been grouped with countless thousands of animals—snails, worms, spiders, elephants . . .—that share certain characteristics with you. Next, biologists would place you in a **phylum**. The name of your phylum is Chordata. You are now grouped with just those animals that have a notochord. This is a fibrous structure that runs down the back of all chordates when they are embryos. It is the axis around which your spinal cord developed.

Next, biologists would place you in a **class**. The name of your class is Mammalia. You are now grouped with those animals that have hair on at least part of their bodies and suckle their young. Then you would be placed in an **order**, in your case, the order Primates. You share this order with monkeys, baboons, apes, chimpanzees, orangutans, and a few other species. Then you would be placed in a **family**, in your case, the family Hominidae. Humans are the only living species in this family. Now you would be placed in a **genus**, in your case *Homo*, and given a **species** name, *Homo sapiens*. You share the family Hominidae and the genus *Homo* with a number of extinct human organisms. Among them are the species *Homo erectus* and *Homo habilis*.

Like you, each species must be classified into seven main classification groups. Each group is called a **taxon** (plural **taxa**). The seven main taxa are arranged in this sequence:

Kingdom
Phylum (or Division)
Class
Order
Family
Genus
Species

Note that the term "division" appears with the taxon "phylum". This term is often used instead of phylum for plants. Table 5-3 shows the seven taxa for some common organisms.

Table 5-3 Classification of Some Common Organisms

Taxon	Human	Gorilla	Dog	Golden Eagle	Housefly	Red Oak	Amoeba
Kingdom	Animalia	Animalia	Animalia	Animalia	Animalia	Plantae	Protista
Phylum or Division	Chordata	Chordata	Chordata	Chordata	Arthropoda	Anthophyta	Sarcodina
Class	Mammalia	Mammalia	Mammalia	Aves	Insecta	Angiospermae	Rhizopoda
Order	Primates	Primates	Carnivora	Falconiformes	Diptera	Fagales	Amoebida
Family	Hominidae	Pongidae	Canidae	Accipitridae	Muscidae	Fagaceae	Amoebidae
Genus	*Homo*	*Gorilla*	*Canis*	*Aquila*	*Musca*	*Quercus*	*Amoeba*
Species	*sapiens*	*gorilla*	*familiaris*	*chrysaetos*	*domestica*	*rubra*	*proteus*

Generally becoming less like humans →

As you can see from Table 5-3, the taxa include fewer and fewer species as you move from kingdom to species. However, gorillas, dogs, eagles, and houseflies are all in the same kingdom. But houseflies do not share the same phylum with the other four species. Only gorillas and dogs share the class Mammalia with us. And only gorillas are in the same order as humans. From the family taxon down, humans are alone.

Further Taxa As more and more information is gathered about organisms, biologists need more than the seven main taxa. For example, there are more than 100 breeds of dogs—German shepherd, terrier, hound, collie, to name a few. All can interbreed freely. Thus they are all the same species, *Canis familiaris*. How, then, do we name them scientifically so that they can be distinguished from one another? We simply add a taxon called **subspecies**. Using this taxon, a German shepherd becomes *Canis familiaris inostranzewi* and a terrier is *Canis familiaris polustris*. When required, further taxa such as subphylum, superclass, and variety are added.

Section Review

1. a) Give an example which shows that people have likely always classified living things.
   b) Why do biologists classify living things?
2. a) List the seven main taxa, in order from the most inclusive to the least.
   b) If several species are in the same class, what other taxa will they also share?
3. Why are taxa, other than the seven main ones, required?

5.3 The Five Kingdoms of Organisms

Until a few decades ago, most biologists classified all organisms into just two kingdoms, Plantae and Animalia. In this 2-kingdom system, bacteria were classified as plants and amoebas as animals. Today, however, most biologists use the **5-kingdom system**:

- Kingdom Monera (bacteria and blue-green algae)
- Kingdom Protista (sarcodinans, ciliates, flagellates, and some algae)
- Kingdom Fungi (slime moulds, moulds, yeasts, and mushrooms)
- Kingdom Plantae (some algae, mosses, ferns, conifers, and flowering plants)
- Kingdom Animalia (sponges, worms, . . . humans)

The remainder of this chapter gives you the general characteristics of these five kingdoms and their main phyla.

Kingdom Monera

The kingdom Monera is divided into two phyla:

- Phylum Schizophyta (bacteria)
- Phylum Cyanophyta (blue-green algae)

Of the 3100 known species of monerans, about 1600 species are bacteria and 1500 are blue-green algae (Fig. 5-7). Compared to other kingdoms, the number of species in this phylum is small. And the organisms themselves are certainly small. But their numbers are enormous—they are the most numerous living things on earth. And their importance is great. They may also be the oldest living things on earth. Fossils that look like monerans have been found that are over 3 000 000 000 years old!

Monerans live just about everywhere—the tops of mountains, the depths of the oceans, in the Arctic, in hot springs, in fresh and salt water, on rocks. Just what are they? What do bacteria and blue-green algae have in common?

Characteristics of Monerans

1. All monerans are one-celled. The cells may occur singly or in groups. When cells group together, they may form a colony. Such forms are said to be **colonial**. They may also form a chain of cells called a filament. Such forms are called **filamentous**.

A

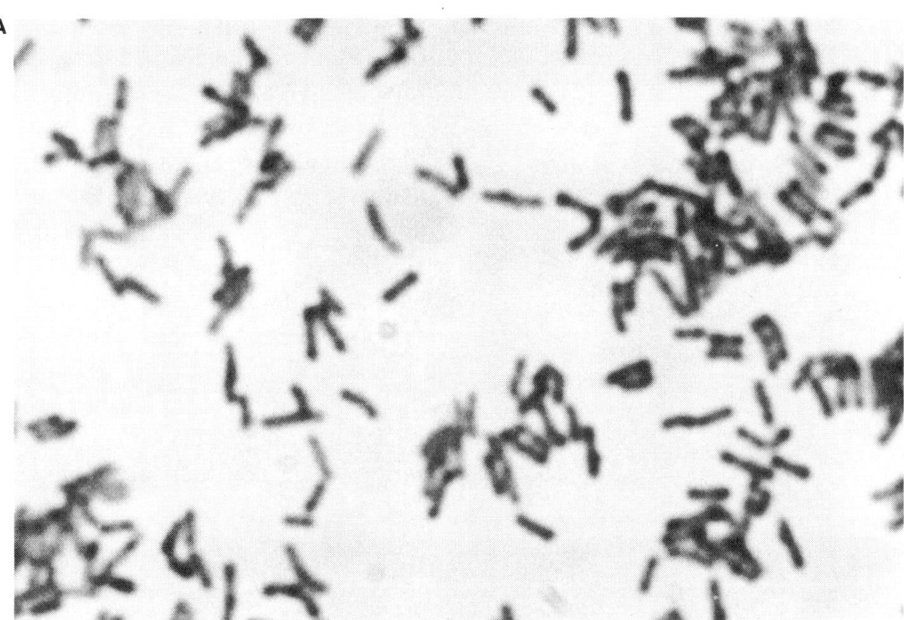

B

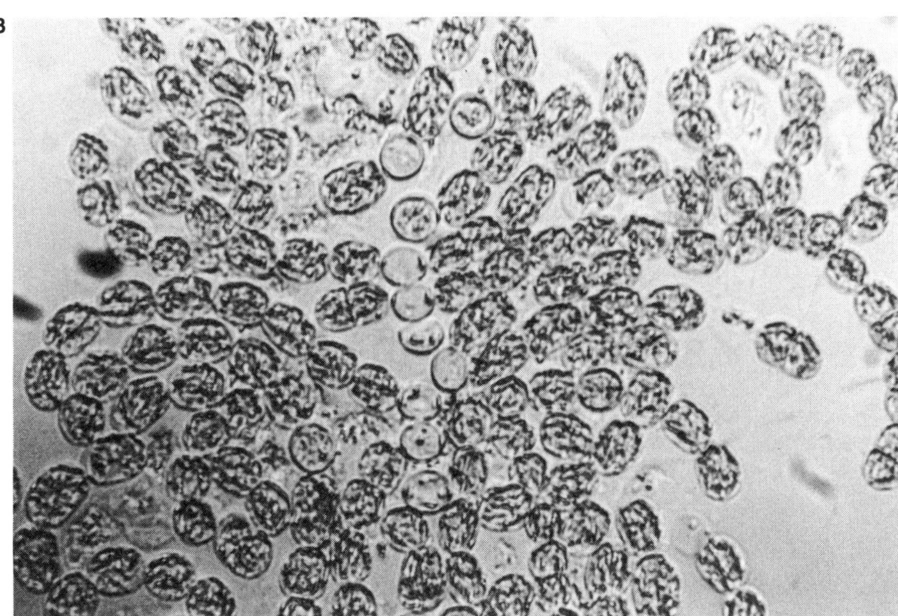

Fig. 5-7 Bacteria (A) and blue-green algae (B) make up the kingdom Monera.

2. The cells of monerans lack a true nucleus. They do not have nuclear membranes. Therefore nuclear material such as DNA is spread throughout the cell.
3. The cells of monerans lack internal membranes. In addition to lacking nuclear membranes, monerans also lack other internal membranes. They have no membranes to enclose cell organelles. As a result, they lack membrane-bound organelles such as mitochondria and plastids.
4. The cells of monerans have rigid cell walls with a unique composition. The cell walls of both bacteria and blue-green algae contain substances that are not found in the cell walls of any other organisms.

5. Moneran cells often secrete a slime coating. This jelly-like coating protects the cells. It also helps to hold colonies and filaments together.
6. Most monerans reproduce only by asexual means. Sexual reproduction occurs in only a few species. Most species reproduce by **binary fission**.
7. Many monerans can form spores. Under adverse conditions such as extreme temperature or dryness, many monerans form **spores**. These have very thick walls to protect the contents from the adverse conditions.

Blue-green algae contain chlorophyll. As a result, they are **producers**. They produce food through photosynthesis and, as a result, are the foundation of many food chains. As they photosynthesize, they also produce oxygen. As you can see, these organisms are vital to other life forms on earth.

Though some bacterial species are harmful to other organisms, most are beneficial. Possibly the most beneficial are those species which function as **decomposers**. They help break down organic wastes and recycle nutrients through ecosystems.

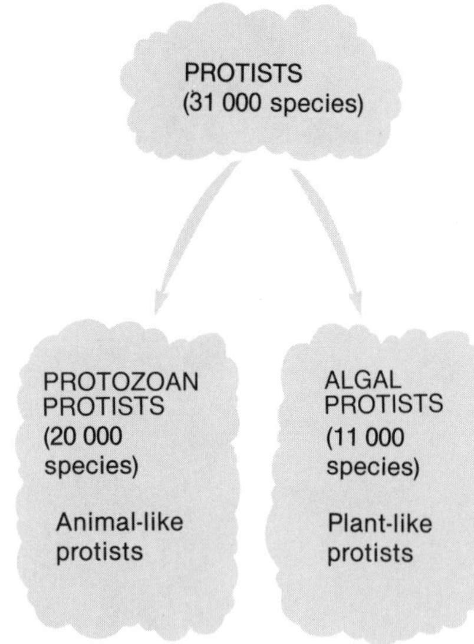

Fig. 5-8 All protists can be classified into two sub-kingdoms: the protozoan protists and the algal protists.

Kingdom Protista

Protists are simple organisms, but not as simple as monerans. Like the monerans, they are one-celled and they live in water or in a wet land environment. But unlike the monerans, most protists have a nucleus and organelles. They are the second simplest of the five kingdoms. There are two kinds of protists, **protozoan protists** and **algal protists** (see Figs. 5-8 and 5-9). Let's look briefly at the general characteristics of these two sub-kingdoms.

Characteristics of Protozoan Protists Protozoans are important to us in many ways. Some are food for small animals and, in this way, they support food chains of which we may be a part. Other protozoans break down sludge in sewage treatment plants. Others break down and recycle dead organic matter in ponds and lakes. Unfortunately, some species cause deadly diseases. Malaria is an example.

A

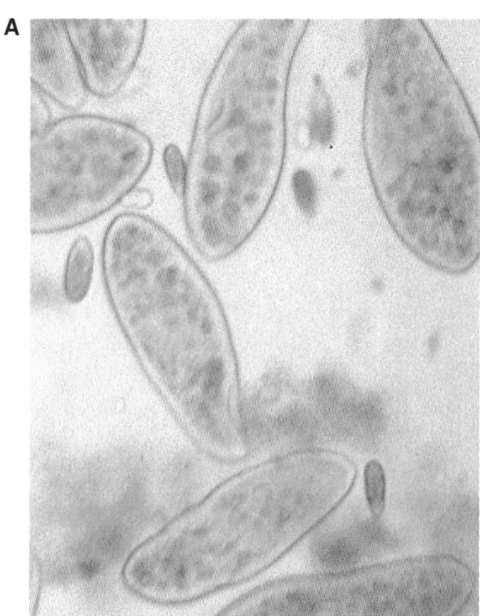

B

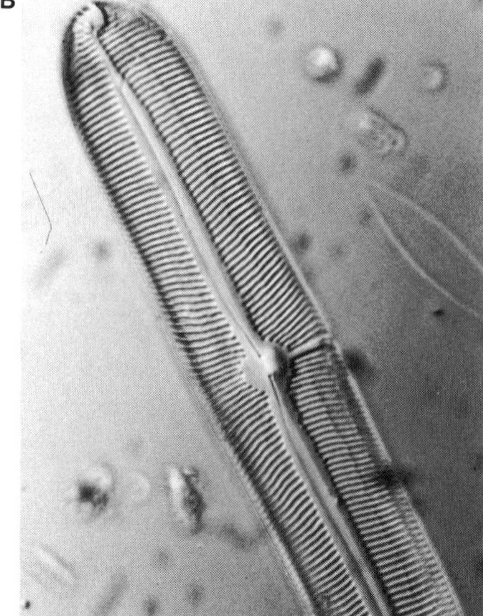

Fig. 5-9 The paramecium (A) is a protozoan protist and the diatom (B) is an algal protist. Can you see how they differ?

Fig. 5-10 Protists may move with pseudopods (A), cilia (B), or flagella (C).

A

B

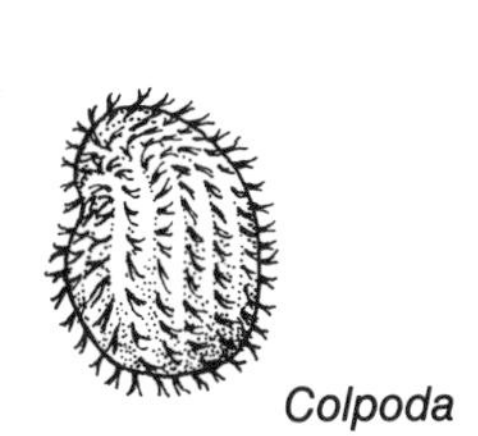

C

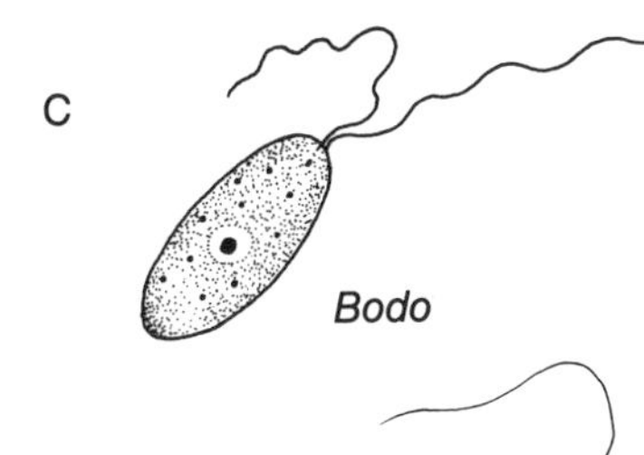

Protozoans used to be considered the simplest animals. In fact, the word *protozoan* means "first animal". However, they are no longer classified as animals. The following characteristics suggest why it is best not to classify them as animals.

1. Protozoans are one-celled. Some of these cells, however, live together in colonies.
2. A few species can change shape. However, most have a definite shape.
3. Most protozoans have a nucleus and some organelles.
4. Most protozoans can move. They use **pseudopods** (false feet), **cilia** (tiny hairs), or **flagella** (whip-like tails), depending on the species (Fig. 5-10).
5. Protozoans reproduce by binary fission, or splitting into two parts. Some species can reproduce sexually. That is, genetic material is exchanged between two cells.
6. Protozoans are consumers. They feed on bacteria, yeasts, algae, other protozoans, and dead organic matter.
7. Most protozoans are microscopic. Some are only 2 μm (micrometres) long. Most are less than 250 μm long. A few are over 3 mm long and can be seen without a microscope.

Characteristics of Algal Protists The algal protists differ widely in form and function, yet they have much in common.

1. All are one-celled, but sometimes these cells occur in colonies.
2. Practically all contain chlorophyll.
3. All live in water or in wet terrestrial environments.
4. All have nuclei and membrane-bound organelles.

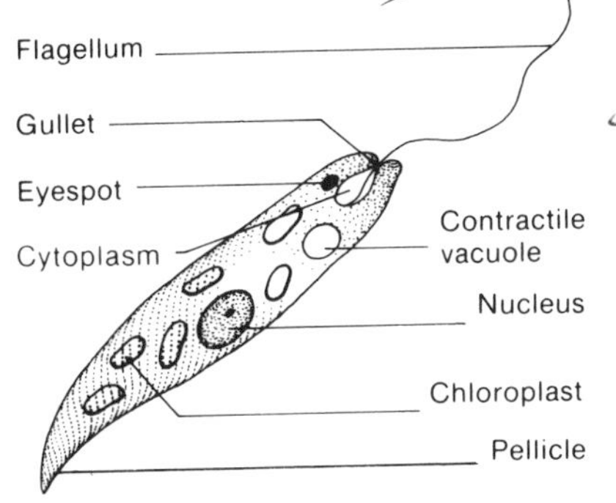

A. The coloured flagellate, *Euglena*

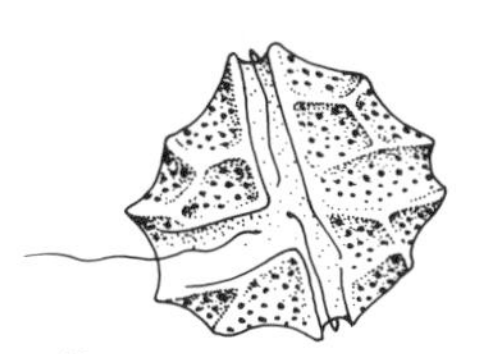

B. The dinoflagellate, *Peridinium*

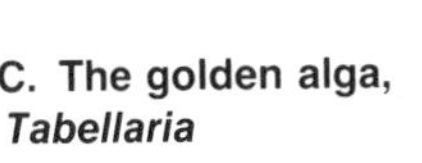

C. The golden alga, *Tabellaria*

Fig. 5-11 The three main types of algal protists

Coloured Flagellates There are about 11 000 species of algal protists. Of these, about 500 species are **coloured flagellates** like *Euglena* shown in Figure 5-11,A. These organisms occur in almost all freshwater environments and some species occur in salt water. Several species, like *Euglena*, thrive in polluted water where they often multiply at a rapid rate. Sometimes the water turns bright green because of all the algal protists. Such a state is called an **algal bloom**. In some cases the water turns red or brown because of *Euglena's* eyespots which are red. Coloured flagellates are active swimmers, propelling themselves with one or two whip-like **flagella**.

Dinoflagellates About 1000 species of algal protists are **dinoflagellates** (Fig. 5-11,B). These organisms are common in both freshwater and saltwater environments. They are particularly common in warm ocean waters. Dinoflagellates are the second most important algae in the world. They are the first step in many ocean and lake food chains. As a result, they help produce many of the fish we eat. In addition, they add oxygen to the atmosphere as they photosynthesize. Dinoflagellates propel themselves with two flagella. Many species bloom easily. In some blooms there are 20 000 000 dinoflagellates in just one litre of water! The water often turns reddish during such blooms. As a result, these blooms are often called "red tides". They are common along all the shores of North America. Sometimes these blooms produce deadly toxins that kill fish and make shellfish such as oysters inedible.

Shelf fungus

Mushroom

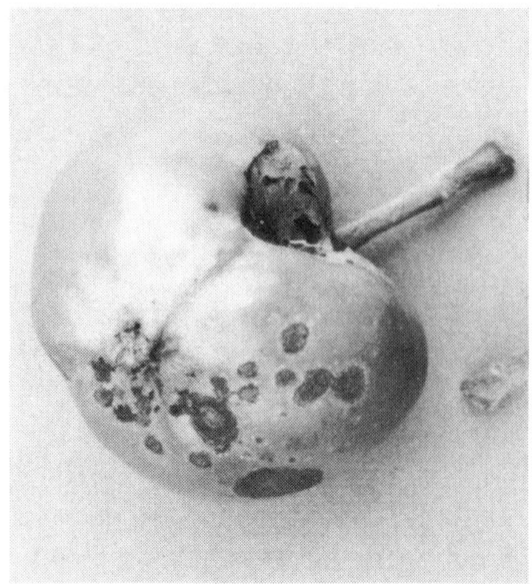
Apple scab

Fig. 5-12 Three common fungi. How are they alike? How are they different?

Golden Algae The remaining algal protists, about 9500 species, are golden algae, and most golden algae are **diatoms** (Fig. 5-11,C). Most diatoms have no method of locomotion. However, they rank as the most important of all algae. In fact, they are among the most important of all living things. They are the first step in many food chains in the oceans and, as a result, help to produce much of our food. They also make much of the earth's oxygen. Like coloured flagellates and dinoflagellates, diatoms drift with the currents. Such small drifting organisms are called **plankton**. Those which are plant-like, as algal protists are, are called **phytoplankton**. Those which are animal-like are called **zooplankton**.

Diatoms occur in all types of water and in wet terrestrial environments. When diatoms die, everything decays except their cell walls which are made of silica, a glass-like material. This material settles to the bottom of the lakes and oceans. Over the years it forms a deep layer of fine solid called **diatomaceous earth**. We now mine this substance from areas that used to be lakes and seas. It is used for filtering sugar, gasoline, and water. It is also used as an abrasive in polishing preparations and as an insulating material.

Kingdom Fungi

Figure 5-12 shows three fungi which are likely familiar to you. However, they are just three of the 80 000 known species of fungi. Collectively, fungi rank among the most important organisms on earth. Figure 5-13 lists the common types of fungi in each of the six phyla. If you think about the organisms in these lists, you may see why fungi are so important.

Characteristics of Fungi

1. All fungi lack chlorophyll. As a result, they cannot make their own food, but must get it from an outside source. Some fungi are **parasites**. They get their food from *living* organic matter such as apples, grains, and even humans. The remaining fungi are **saprophytes**, or decomposers. They get their food from *non-living* organic matter such as dead plants, dead animals, and animal wastes. Fungi feed by secreting enzymes into the food. The enzymes break the food into small particles. These are then absorbed by the fungus and used for nutrition.
2. Most fungi are made of **hyphae**, each **hypha** being a hair-like structure. The hyphae often appear as separate tiny hairs as they do in moulds. Sometimes they are woven together to form a fleshy mass, as occurs in mushrooms.

Fungi live in almost all environments but are found most frequently in moist, organic-rich areas. They live in water, on dead trees, on soil, on living plants, and even on animals, including humans. Fungi must have organic matter to survive. That organic matter may be a dead tree, a slice of bread, an orange, or a human foot.

Fungi as Decomposers Many fungi function as decomposers. That is, they break down non-living organic matter. What they do not use for their nutrition is returned to the soil for green plants to use. Unfortunately, not all decomposer action is so useful. Fungi also decompose foods, leather, cloth, wood, and paper.

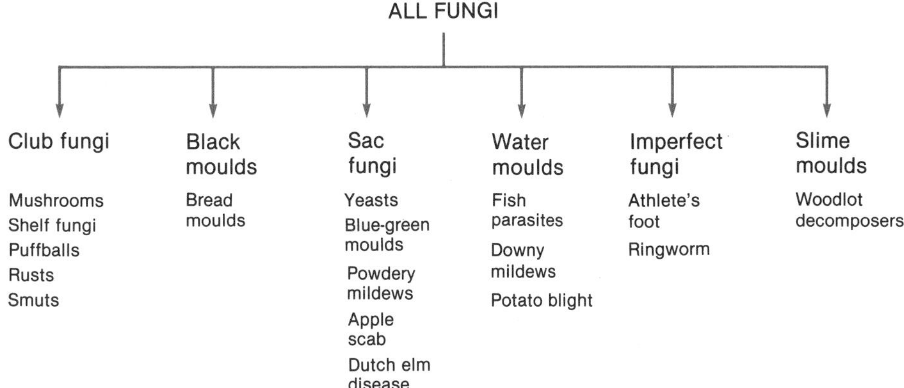

Fig. 5-13 The six main phyla of fungi

Fungi as Parasites Many serious diseases of plants and animals are caused by parasitic fungi. For example, most grain crops (corn, wheat, oats, barley) can be attacked by fungi. Also, cattle, horses, and even humans can be attacked by the ringworm fungus.

Use of Fungi Many fungi—mushrooms, puffballs, morels, truffles, and yeasts—are edible. Also, many cheeses owe their special flavour and colour to moulds. Yeasts are widely used in the baking and brewing industries. Other fungi play key roles in the synthesis of certain antibiotics, vitamins, and other important compounds.

Kingdom Plantae

Over 300 000 species of organisms are classified in the plant kingdom. This number is growing every day as newly discovered tropical species are named. (Why do you suppose most of the newly discovered species are in the tropics?) Table 5-4 lists the ten phyla into which plants are classified. (*Note*: Some botanists use the term "division" instead of "phylum".)

Plants differ widely in structure. Some, like a few of the algae, are small and simple (Fig. 5-14,A). Others, like some trees, are the largest living things on earth (Fig. 5-14,B). However, regardless of size, most plants share some common characteristics.

A

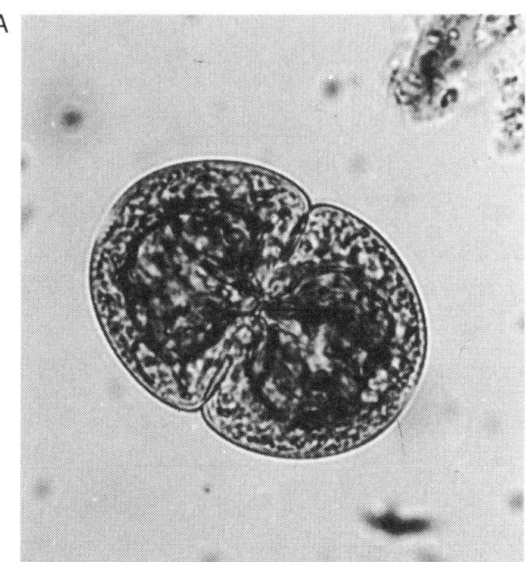

B

Fig. 5-14 A microscope must be used to see plants like the green algae called desmids (A). In contrast, the giant sequoias of California are the largest organisms on earth (B). The largest living sequoia is 90 m tall and 33.8 m in circumference at the base! The coastal redwoods in California are the tallest trees, some being over 115 m tall. In Canada, our largest trees are Douglas fir, western red cedar, and Sitka spruce. They grow in the temperate rain forest of British Columbia. The largest Douglas firs reach 100 m in height and 15 m in circumference at the base.

Table 5-4 The Main Phyla of the Plant Kingdom

Common name of the phylum (division)	Number of species
Green algae	6 000
Red algae	2 500
Brown algae	1 500
Stoneworts	100
Mosses and liverworts	24 000
Club mosses	1 100
Horsetails	30
Ferns	10 000
Conifers	550
Flowering plants	250 000

Characteristics of Plants

1. Plants are made of cells. Some simple plants are one-celled, but most plants are made of many cells. These cells are sometimes alike, but in most plants they are specialized for different functions.
2. The walls of plant cells are made of cellulose. This tough material keeps the cells rigid and protects their contents.
3. Most plant cells contain the green pigment chlorophyll. It is usually found in small organelles called **chloroplasts**. Chlorophyll allows plants to capture light energy from the sun and store it as chemical energy in the cells. This process is called **photosynthesis**.
4. Most plants are anchored in place by roots or other structures.

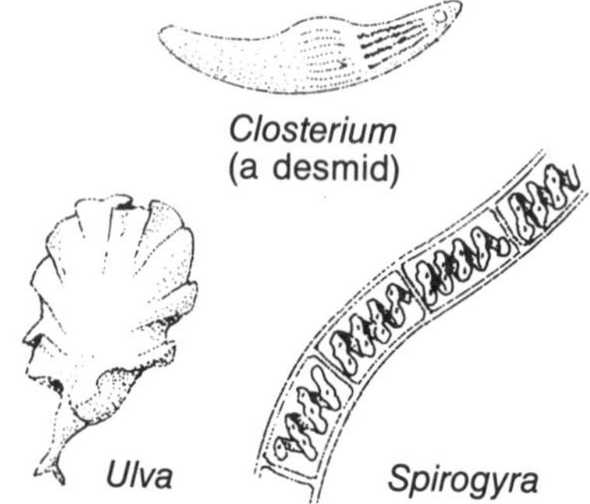

The Main Phyla of Plants

Green Algae

Some green algae exist as a single cell. Others are many-celled and some of these are made of long chains of cells. Most green algae look green because of the chlorophyll in their cells. Some types grow in freshwater streams and lakes. Others prefer the salt water of the oceans.

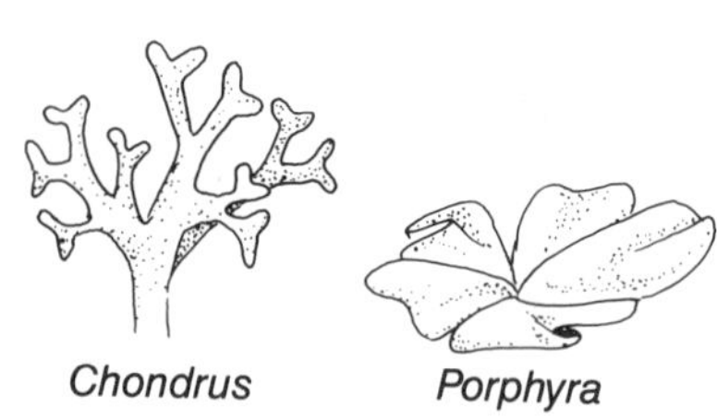

Red Algae

Red pigments in the cells of these plants make them appear red or brownish in colour. Chlorophyll is also present, but its green colour cannot be seen. Red algae may be one-celled or many-celled. Some are very branched and feathery. Most grow in warm ocean waters, where they may be attached to the rocks near the shore, or floating. They are often called **seaweeds**. Some species are harvested by people in North America, Europe, and Japan for food and other products. One substance that comes from red algae is used as a thickener in ice cream, toothpaste, and chocolate milk.

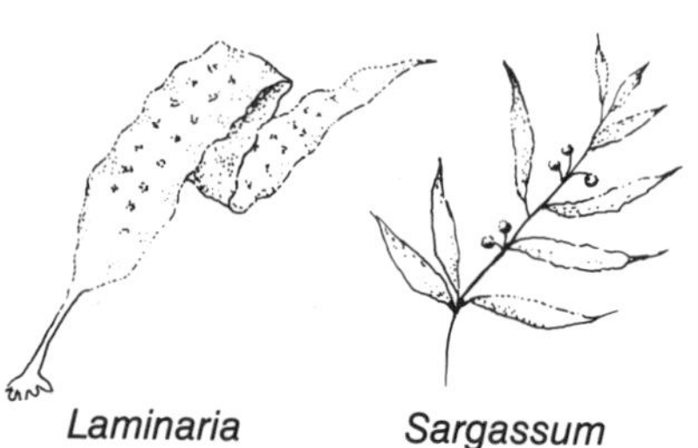

Brown Algae

Brown algae are called seaweeds too. The large ones, which may reach 30 m long, are known as **kelps**. They usually grow attached to rocks in cold oceans. Their cells contain brown pigments as well as chlorophyll.

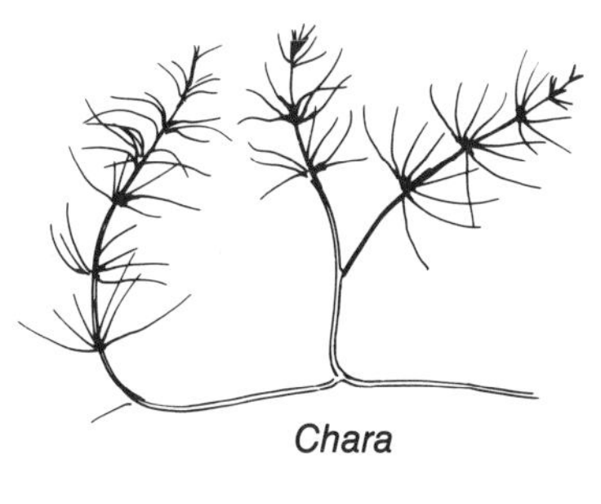

Chara

Stoneworts

Stoneworts are strange plants that live in freshwater streams and ponds. The main shoot has many circles of short branches on it. The plants are anchored to the mud or sand. Stoneworts often feel quite gritty to touch because they are usually covered with pieces of lime.

Mosses and Liverworts

Mosses and liverworts usually grow in damp, shady places on rocks or soil. They are small greenish plants that are rarely more than 20 cm in height. This is because they have no conducting tissue to carry water very far up from the ground. The plant body may be leafy in appearance, or flat and leathery. Biologists believe mosses were the first plants to grow on land.

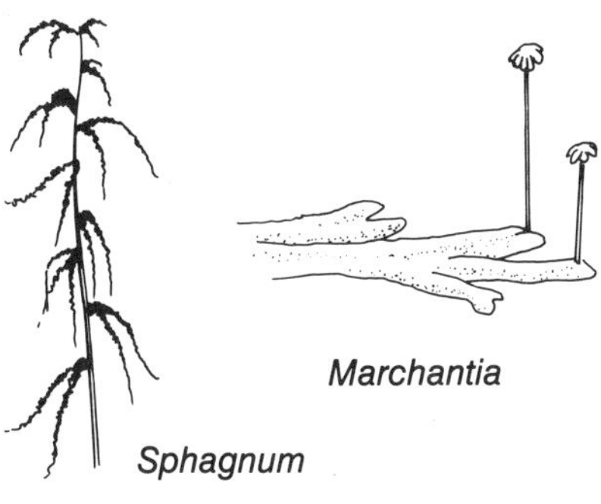

Marchantia

Sphagnum

Club Mosses

These are small leafy plants that spread by horizontal stems which run along the surface of the ground, or just underneath it. The upright shoots are less than 40 cm tall and are **evergreen**. Some of them have club-shaped cones at the tips of the shoots which contain **spores**. The spores are released into the wind. When they land in a suitable place, they grow into new plants.

Club mosses grow in shady moist places. Some are bushy and look like tiny pine or cedar trees. For this reason, they are called ground pines and ground cedars.

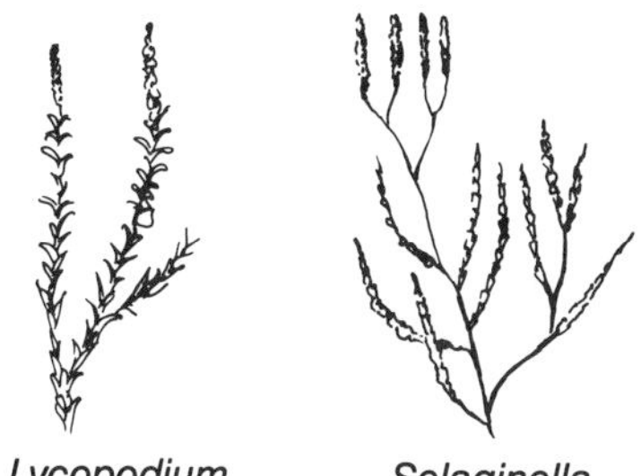

Lycopodium lucidulum

Selaginella

Horsetails

Horsetails grow in clumps near lakes and streams, and in damp fields and ditches. Most are about 20 cm to 50 cm tall. Horizontal stems that grow underground send up hollow, jointed shoots. The shoots often have circles of soft, feathery branches (resembling a horse's tail, perhaps!). In the spring, the tips of some shoots develop cone-like structures. These release spores for reproduction.

Horsetails feel gritty to touch because their cells contain a hard substance called **silica**. (Sand has silica in it). The pioneers used these gritty branches to scour (clean) out pots and pans. Thus, horsetails are also known as ''scouring rushes''.

Equisetum hyemale

Ferns

Most ferns grow in shady moist places such as forests and the cracks between rocks. They are leafy plants that are usually less than 1 m tall. A few tropical ones, known as ''tree ferns'', are much larger.

Ferns often have underground stems that send up new leaves every spring. The leaves are usually divided into many leaflets. On the backs of some of the leaves are tiny spore cases. They release spores into the air. The spores grow into new plants when conditions are right.

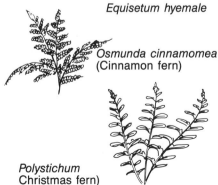

Osmunda cinnamomea (Cinnamon fern)

Polystichum Christmas fern)

Conifers

''**Conifer**'' means cone-bearer. All conifers are woody trees and shrubs. They reproduce by **seeds** that develop inside **cones** on the branches. The leaves of conifers are usually very small and evergreen. They may be needle-like or scale-like.

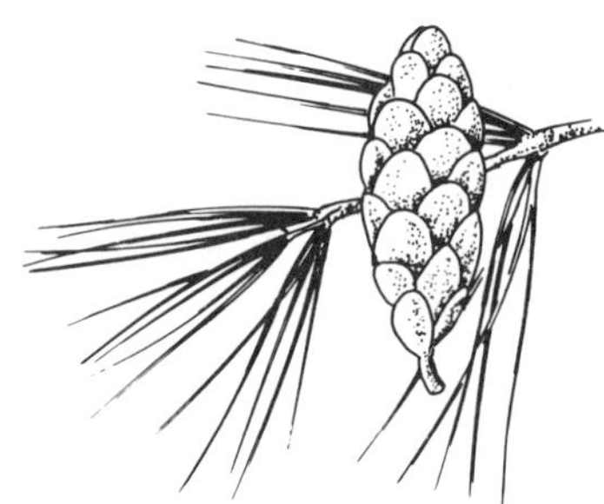

Pinus strobus
(White pine)

Arisaema
(Jack-in-the-pulpit)

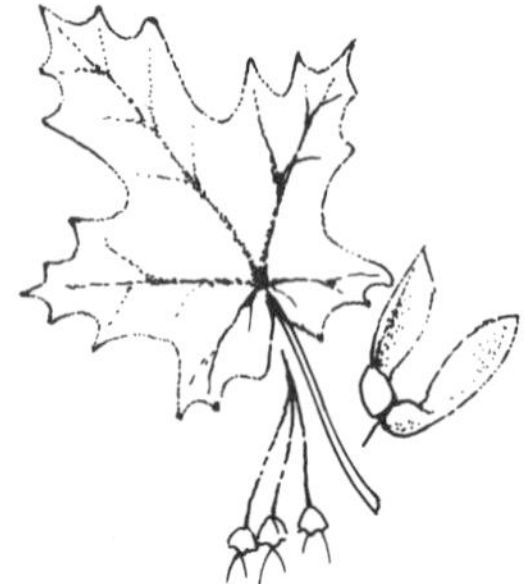

Acer saccharum
(Sugar maple)

Pines, spruces, cedars, and firs are conifers. Forests of them cover large areas of Canada. They are very valuable for their lumber, pulp and paper, and resins.

Flowering Plants

This large phylum includes a wide variety of trees, shrubs, and soft-stemmed plants. All of them produce some kind of flower. The flowers may not be very noticeable, but they develop into **fruits** that contain one or more **seeds**.

Any tree that is not a conifer is a flowering plant. For example, maples, oaks, beeches, and willows are flowering plants. So are grasses, vegetables, water lilies, milkweeds, and poison ivy. Most human food plants are flowering plants too.

Kingdom Animalia

Over 1 200 000 species of organisms have been classified in the animal kingdom, and millions still remain to be discovered and classified. Most of the undiscovered ones are probably insects, spiders, and other arthropods. And most of them likely live in the tropics. Table 5-5 lists the nine main phyla of animals. What do all these animals have in common?

Table 5-5 The Main Phyla of the Animal Kingdom

Common name of phylum	*Approximate number of species*	*Example*
Sponges	4 500	Bath sponge
Cnidarians	9 500	Jellyfish
Flatworms	6 500	Tapeworm
Roundworms	10 000	Hookworm
Molluscs	75 000	Clam
Segmented worms	10 000	Earthworm
Arthropods	1 000 000	Housefly
Echinoderms	5 000	Starfish
Chordates	46 000	Human

Characteristics of Animals

1. Animals are made of many cells. These cells are specialized to form different tissues. In most animals, the tissues are grouped into organs and the organs are grouped into organ systems.
2. Animal cells contain specialized parts such as a nucleus.
3. Animal cells are covered by a cell membrane. They have no cell walls; therefore, they tend to be flexible.
4. Animals get their energy by eating other organisms. Some animals are herbivores, others are carnivores, and still others are omnivores.
5. Most animals can move from place to place.
6. All animals reproduce sexually. That is, a **male gamete (sperm)** unites with a **female gamete (egg)** to form a **zygote**. The zygote develops into

an **embryo**, and the embryo eventually becomes a mature animal. A few animal species can also reproduce asexually. A new animal grows on the parent one, by a process called budding.

The Main Phyla of Animals

Sponges

About 4500 species of animals are classified as **sponges**. These are the simplest animals. The cells of sponges are grouped together; however, they do not form true tissues. The body has many canals in it, through which water flows.

Sponges have no organs. Also, they have no movable parts or appendages. Most species have an internal skeleton made of silicates (glass-like substances), limestone, or proteins.

Sexual reproduction occurs in all species. As well, some sponges reproduce asexually by budding. Some species have both sexes in the same animal. Others have separate sexes.

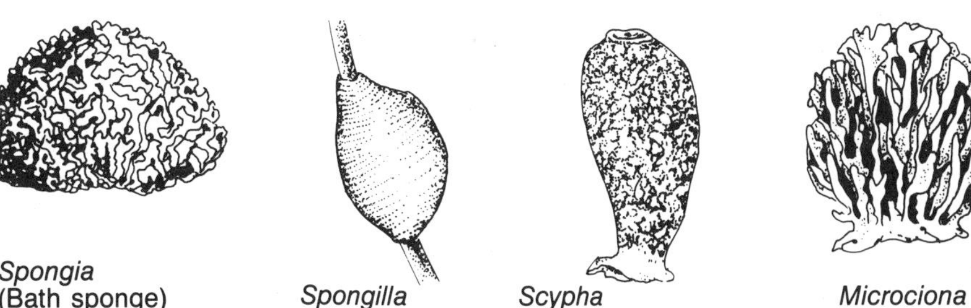

Cnidarians

About 9500 species of animals are classified as **cnidarians**. These include hydras, jellyfish, corals, and sea anemones. Cnidarians have a mouth which is surrounded by tentacles. The tentacles deliver food to the mouth. Digestion occurs in a large body cavity. Then undigested solids are expelled through the mouth.

Some cnidarians, such as jellyfish, swim or float in the water. Others, like corals, live attached to some object or to each other.

These animals have no circulatory, breathing, or excretory systems. They have a few nerve cells in the body wall, but no organized nervous system.

Reproduction may be asexual (by budding), or sexual. Some species have both sexes in the same animal. Others have separate sexes.

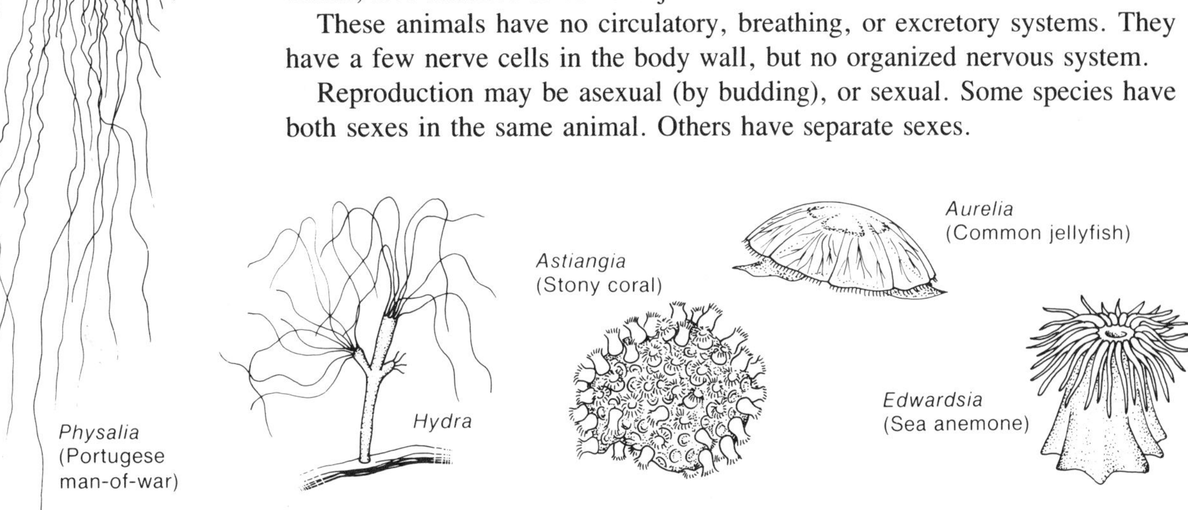

Flatworms

About 6500 species of animals are classified as **flatworms**. These include planaria, tapeworms, and flukes. Tapeworms and flukes are parasites that feed on the tissues of other animals. Planaria are free-living, inhabiting ponds, lakes, and other wet environments. As the name suggests, these worms are flat. Also, they have no segments (body divisions) like an earthworm does.

Flatworms have a simple digestive system. Like cnidarians, they have a mouth but no anus. Food enters and wastes leave by the same opening. Flatworms have a simple nervous system. However, they have no skeletal, breathing, or circulatory system.

Sexual reproduction occurs in all species. Most flatworms have both sexes in the same animal.

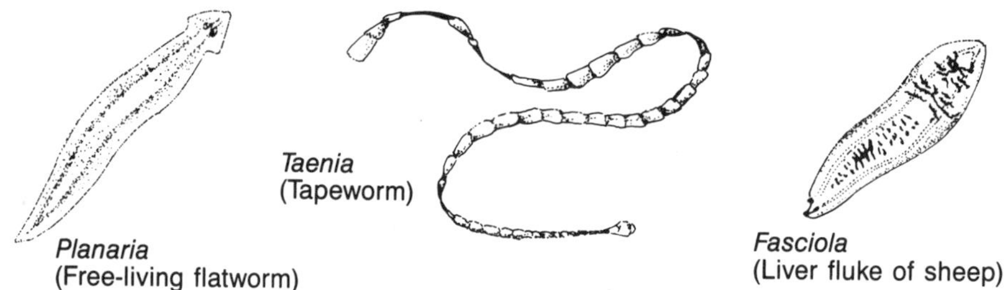

Roundworms

About 10 000 species of animals are classified as **roundworms**, or **nematodes**. Some of these are scavengers, which feed on decaying organic matter. However, most species are parasites. Some are parasites of plants, others are parasites of animals. In fact, over 30 species can live in humans.

Roundworms are small, most being from 0.5 mm to 1 mm long. A few are as long as 1 cm. As the name suggests, these worms are round. Also, they have no segments like an earthworm.

Roundworms have a complete digestive system. That is, it begins with a mouth and ends with an anus. Some species have simple excretory systems. Also, the nervous system is well-developed.

Sexual reproduction occurs in all species, and most species have separate sexes. The male is usually smaller than the female.

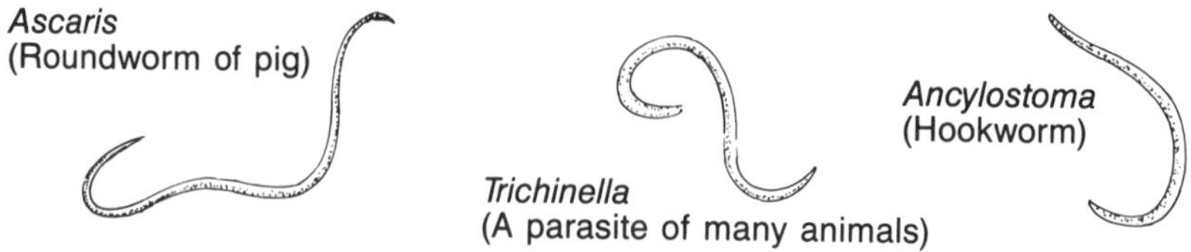

Molluscs

About 75 000 species of animals are classified as **molluscs**. They make up the second largest phylum of animals. Among the molluscs are clams, snails, whelks, conchs, oysters, and octopuses.

Molluscs have a soft body which is often enclosed in a shell. The shell is very small or missing in some species like the octopus.

Most species have a well-developed head region. All have a ''foot'' on the underside that is used for crawling, burrowing, or swimming.

The digestive system is complete. The circulatory system has a heart and a few blood vessels. Breathing occurs through gills, the skin, or a simple lung. Excretion occurs through one or more simple "kidneys". The nervous system has organs for smell, taste, touch, and sight.

Sexual reproduction occurs in all species. Most species have separate sexes.

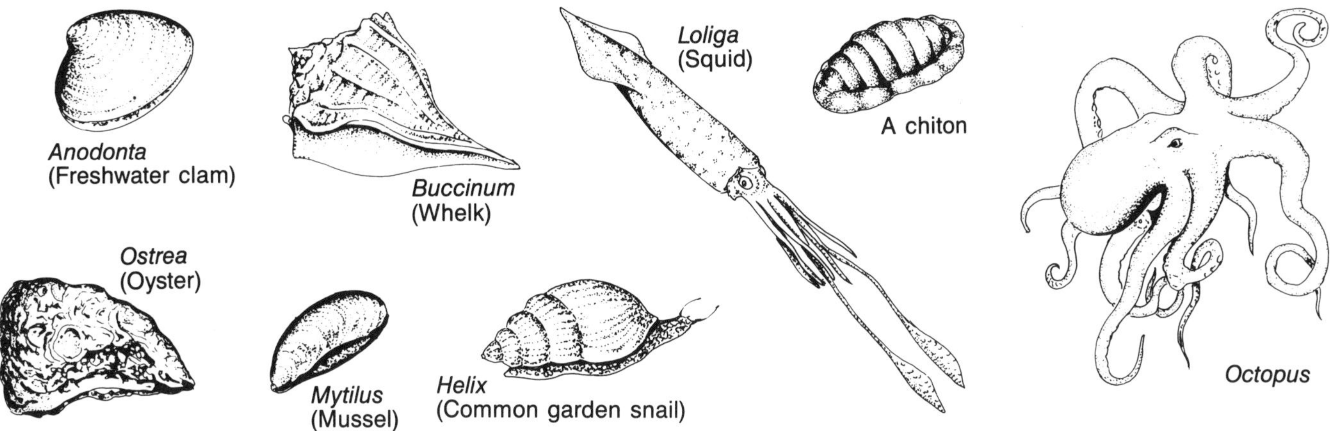

Segmented Worms

About 10 000 species of animals are classified as **segmented worms**. The most familiar segmented worms live in the soil. You have likely seen several species of earthworms. However, most segmented worms live in water. Some saltwater species reach a length of 1 m. Giant Australian earthworms are over 3 m long! As the name suggests, all these worms have their bodies divided up into segments.

The digestive system is complete and the circulatory system is well-advanced. Blood circulates through blood vessels, with the help of five pairs of "hearts". The blood contains hemoglobin to carry oxygen.

In most species, breathing occurs through a moist skin. Some marine species have gills. Excretion occurs through simple excretory organs. The nervous system is well-advanced. It is a central nervous system with a simple "brain" and a main nerve cord. It also has sensory organs for touch, taste, and detection of light.

Sexual reproduction occurs in all species. Most species have both sexes in the same animal. But a few have separate sexes.

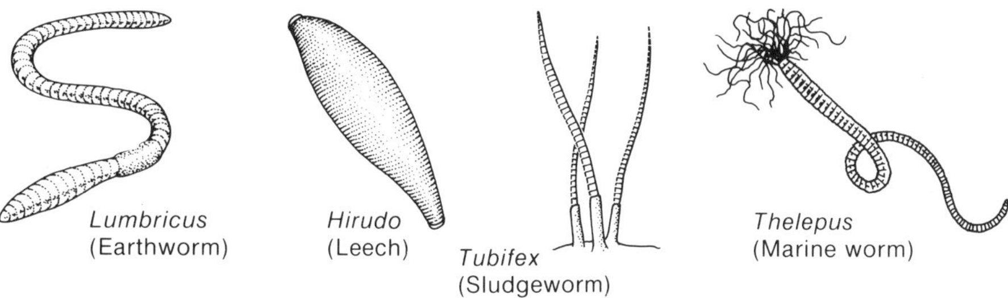

Arthropods

About 1 000 000 species of animals are classified as **arthropods**. They make up the largest phylum of animals. In fact, most animals are arthropods. The name arthropod comes from two Greek words, *arthros*, meaning "joint" and *podos*, meaning "foot". Arthropods do have jointed feet. In fact, all their appendages (legs, wings, antennas, mouthparts) are jointed.

The arthropod phylum includes crustaceans such as shrimps, crayfish, lobsters, crabs, and barnacles. It also includes insects, spiders, scorpions, millipedes, centipedes, and a host of other animals.

Arthropods have three body divisions: head, thorax, and abdomen. They also have a hard **exoskeleton** (outer skeleton). Sometimes only two body divisions can be seen, since the head and thorax are joined.

The digestive system is complete. The mouth has specialized mouthparts. The circulatory system is open. That is, the blood does not travel always within blood vessels. Instead, it is pumped by a long heart through vessels into large spaces where it bathes the organs and tissues.

Aquatic arthropods breathe by means of gills. Land species use trachea (air tubes). Still others use their body surface. Excretion occurs through simple excretory organs. The nervous system includes a "brain" in the head and two nerve cords. Among the sensory organs are antennas, compound eyes, and simple eyes.

Sexual reproduction occurs in all species. The sexes are separate. And, the males and females often look different.

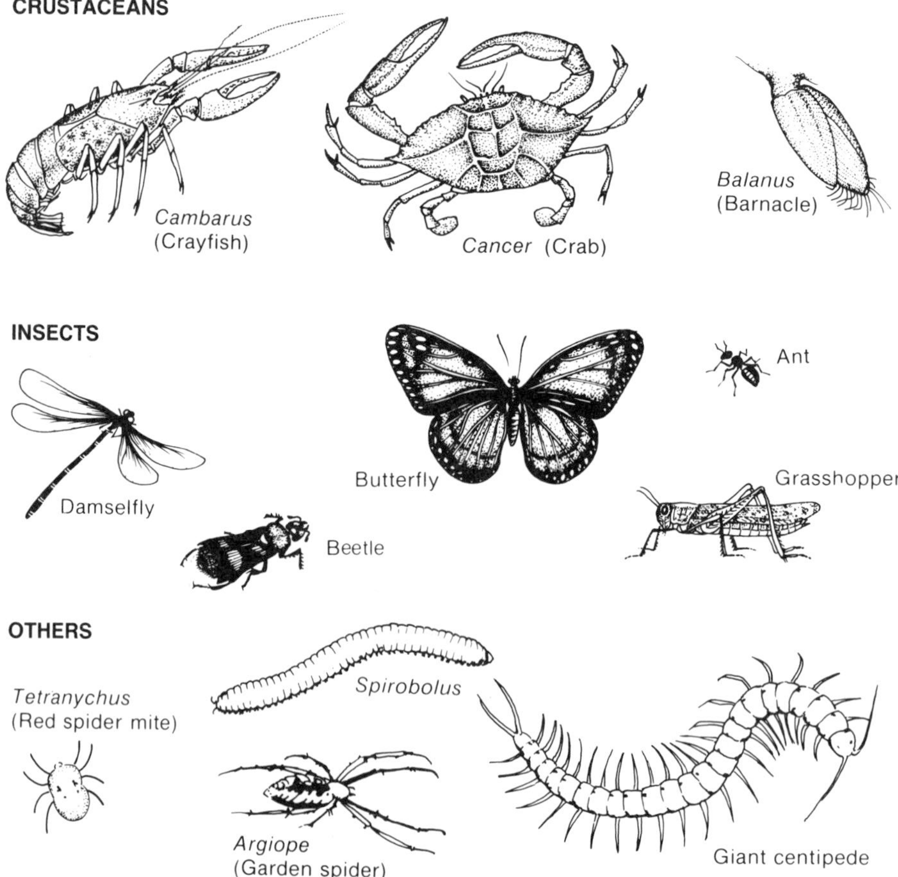

Echinoderms

About 5000 species of animals are classified as **echinoderms**. Among these are starfish, brittle stars, sand dollars, sea urchins, and sea cucumbers. All echinoderms live in salt water.

Echinoderms have five-part bodies that radiate out from the centre like spokes on a wheel. Each part usually has projections called "tube feet". These are used in locomotion, feeding, and breathing. The body is covered by a thin skin, under which is a hard **endoskeleton** (inner skeleton).

The digestive system is complete. Breathing is by tiny gills on the body surface and by the "tube feet". The circulatory and nervous systems are simple.

Sexual reproduction occurs in all species. Most species have separate sexes.

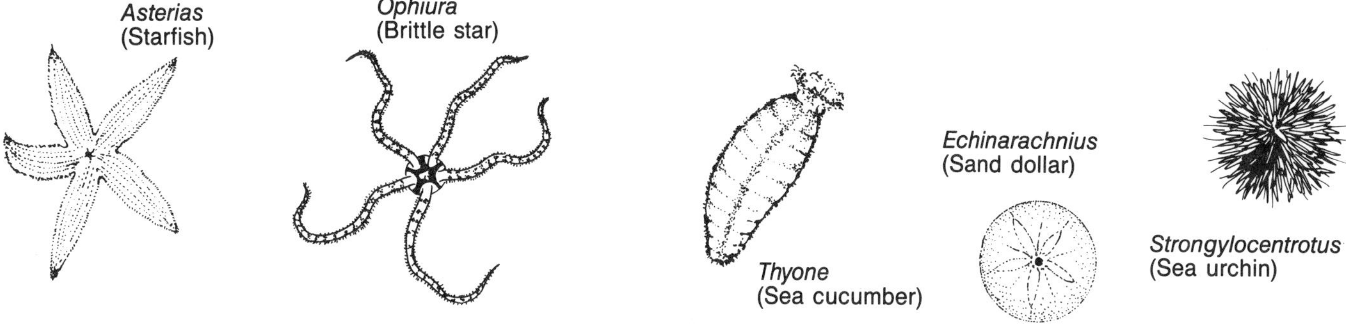

Chordates

You belong to one of the 46 000 species that make up the **chordates**. Most chordates are **vertebrates**. They have a **vertebral column** which is made up of many bones called **vertebrae** (singular: **vertebra**). Vertebrates have a **nerve cord**, or **spinal cord**, on the back of the body. It is protected by the vertebral column. The brain is at one end of the nerve cord.

There are six main classes of vertebrates in the chordate phylum: cartilaginous fishes, bony fishes, amphibians, reptiles, birds, and mammals.

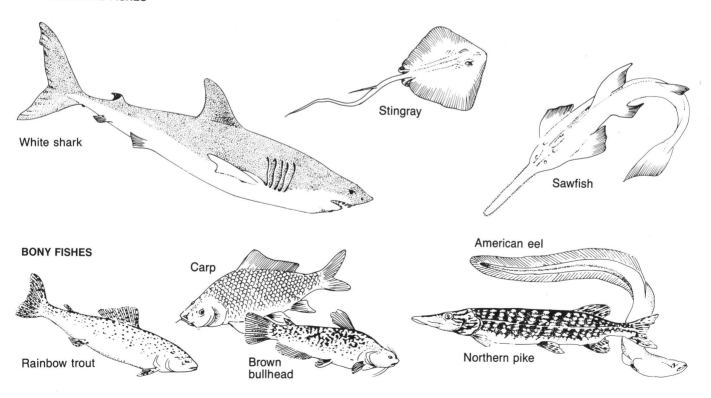

CARTILAGINOUS FISHES

White shark
Stingray
Sawfish

BONY FISHES

Rainbow trout
Carp
Brown bullhead
American eel
Northern pike

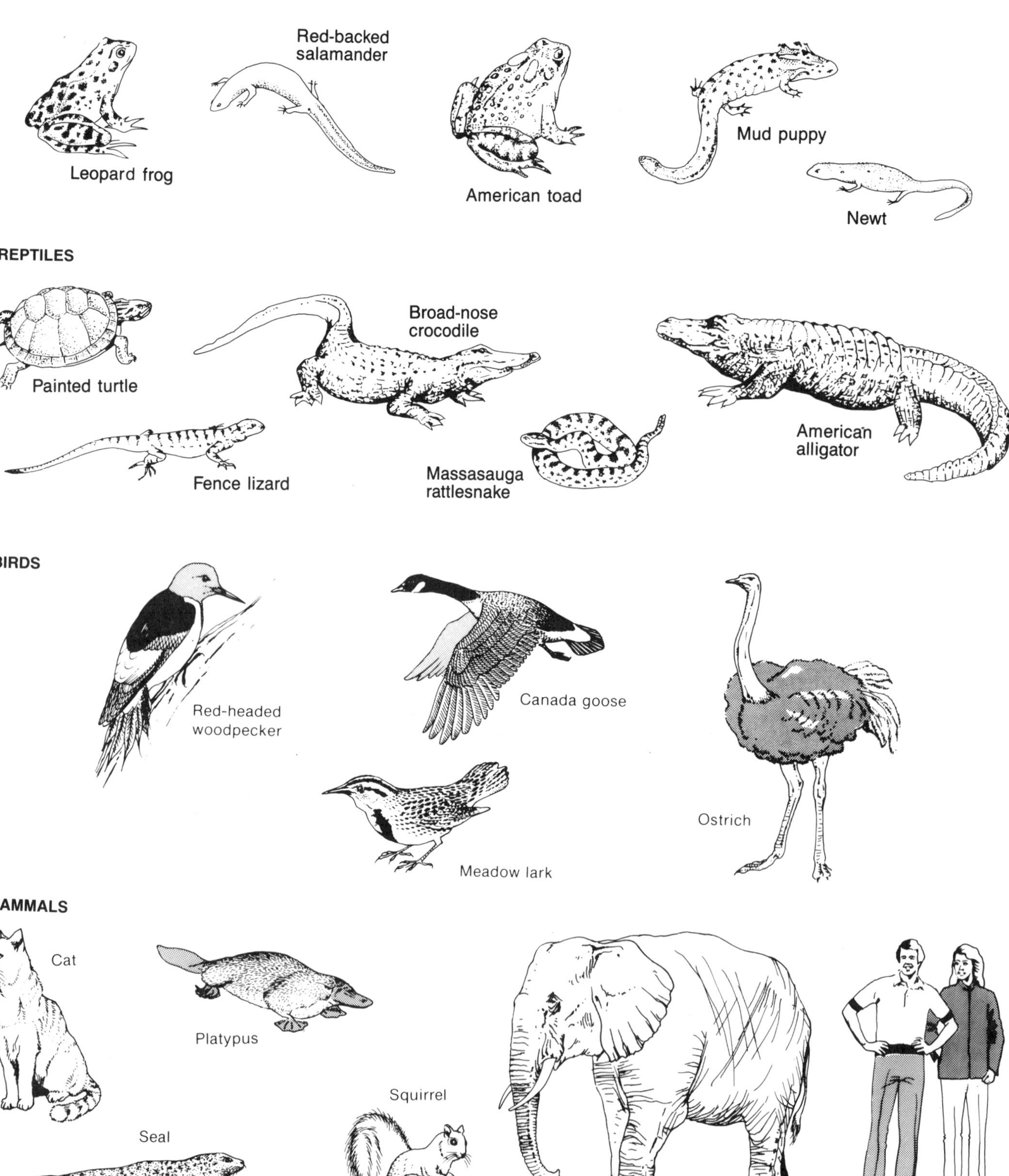
AMPHIBIANS
Red-backed salamander
Leopard frog
American toad
Mud puppy
Newt
REPTILES
Broad-nose crocodile
Painted turtle
Fence lizard
Massasauga rattlesnake
American alligator
BIRDS
Red-headed woodpecker
Canada goose
Ostrich
Meadow lark
MAMMALS
Cat
Platypus
Squirrel
Seal
Elephant
Human

Section Review

1. List the five kingdoms of living things in order from simplest to most complex.
2. a) What phyla make up the kingdom Monera?
   b) What do all monerans have in common?
   c) In what ways are monerans important to ecosystems?
3. a) What two sub-kingdoms make up the kingdom Protista?
   b) List the characteristics of the organisms in each of those sub-kingdoms.
   c) Distinguish among coloured flagellates, dinoflagellates, and golden algae.
   d) Explain each of these terms: plankton, phytoplankton, zooplankton, diatomaceous earth.
4. a) What do fungi have in common?
   b) In what ways are fungi important to ecosystems?
5. a) What characteristics are shared by most plants?
   b) What characteristics are shared by most animals?

Note: Make sure that you read about the main phyla of plants and animals. You will use this information in the next section.

5.4 Activity: Classifying Organisms from All Five Kingdoms

Your teacher has prepared several stations around the room. At each station is an organism. It may be a moneran, protist, fungus, plant, or animal. Some, of course, are under microscopes. Can you find out which kingdom the organism is in? Then can you decide on its phylum and, perhaps, other taxa?

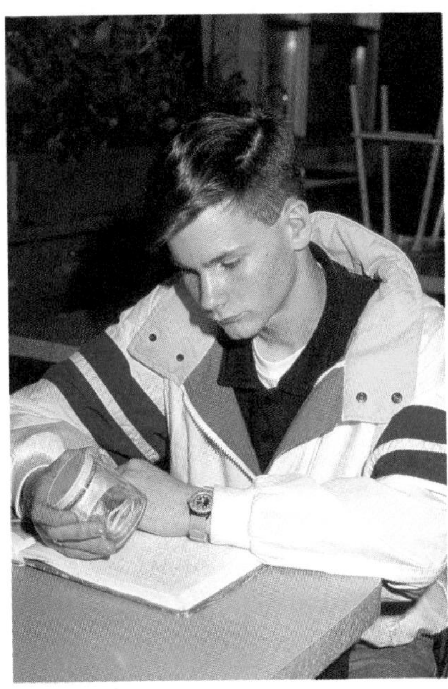

Fig. 5-15 Close examination and the use of Section 5.3 should let you classify the organism to kingdom and phylum.

Problem

What type of organism is at each station?

Materials

organisms from all kingdoms and many phyla
microscopes
identification guides

Procedure

a. Copy Table 5-6 into your notebook. Make it a page long.
b. Select a station and write its number in your table.
c. Study the organism closely (Fig. 5-15). Use Section 5.3 and, if necessary, identification guides provided by your teacher, to complete the table for that organism. Decide, first, which kingdom the organism is in. Then decide on its phylum. If time permits, try to classify it even further. Be sure to record your reasons for classifying the organism as you did.
d. Repeat steps (b) to (c) at the remaining stations.

Table 5-6 Classifying Organisms

Station number	*Kingdom*	*Phylum*	*Other taxa*	*Reasons for your classification*

Discussion

The completed table is your write-up for this activity.

5.5 Activity: Classifying Aquatic Invertebrates

It is relatively easy to decide which kingdom an organism is in. But it gets progressively more difficult to place the organism in a phylum, class, order, family, genus, and species. However, scientists have developed a systematic

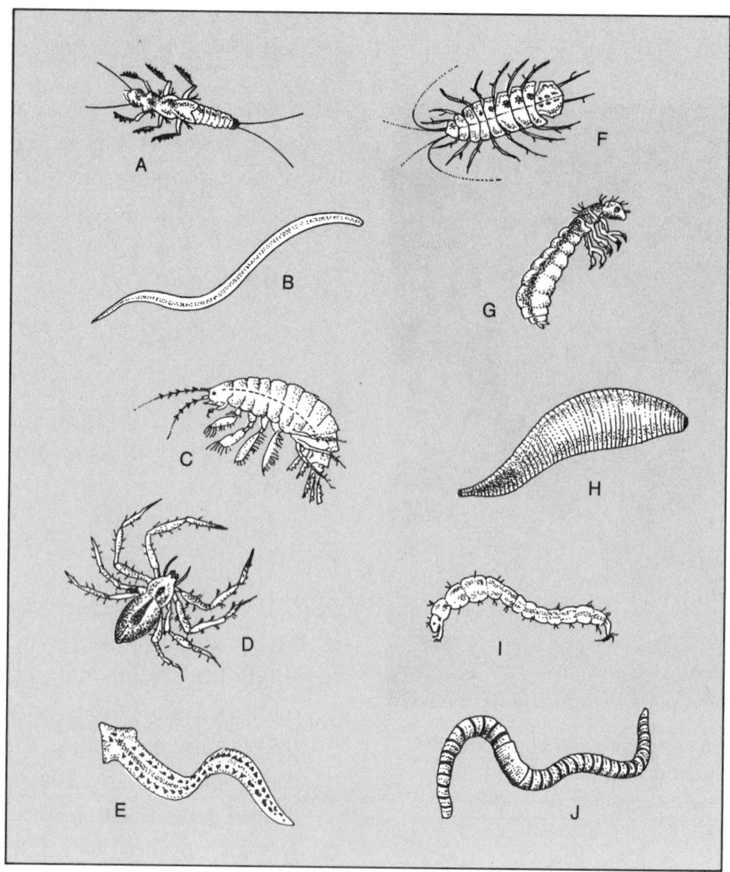

Fig. 5-16 Can you classify these aquatic invertebrates using the dichotomous key?

way of doing this. They have made up what are called **dichotomous keys**. As the "*di*" in the name suggests, this key works by giving you *two* choices at each step.

Figure 5-16 shows ten aquatic invertebrates. The following key will let you identify some of them only as far as phylum. Most, however, can be identified to class and some as far as order. To identify them to family, genus, and species, you would need a much more complex key. Your teacher will help you key out one organism to show you how the key works. The purpose of this activity is to let you discover how useful dichotomous keys can be. Your teacher may choose to give you actual specimens to use along with the diagrams.

Key to Aquatic Invertebrates

1a	Legs present	go to 2
1b	Legs absent	go to 5
2a	3 pairs of legs	class Insecta (insects) (except Diptera)
2b	More than 3 pairs of legs	go to 3
3a	4 pairs of legs	class Arachnida (spiders and mites)
3b	More than 4 pairs of legs	class Crustacea: go to 4
4a	Body flattened top to bottom	order Isopoda (sow bugs)
4b	Body flattened sideways; swims on its side	order Ampipoda (scuds)
5a	Has a head	order Diptera (flies)
5b	Does not have a head	go to 6
6a	Does not have body segments	go to 7
6b	Has body segments	go to 8
7a	Body round	phylum Nematoda (roundworms)
7b	Body flat	phylum Platyhelminthes (flatworms)
8a	Has suckers at both ends	class Hirudinea (leeches)
8b	Has no suckers	class Oligochaeta (bristleworms, sludgeworms)

5.6 Organisms and Their Environments

Response to Environmental Stimuli

All living things are able to respond to certain **stimuli** or changes in their environment. A dog comes when you whistle. A fly moves when you try to swat it. A *Mimosa* plant folds its leaves in response to darkness, touch, and heat. A plant in a window turns its leaves toward the light. Earthworms seek out moist soil containing decaying vegetation (Fig. 5-17). In all these examples a **stimulus**—sound, touch, heat, light, moisture—causes a **response** by a living thing. A living thing's response to a stimulus is called **irritability**.

Fig. 5-17 An earthworm removed from the soil immediately returns to it. If given a choice, the earthworm will eventually end up in moist, organic laden soil. Why?

Irritability is valuable to animals in many ways. It helps them obtain food and avoid predators. It is most highly developed in those animals that have nervous systems and keen sense organs such as eyes, nose, and ears.

Plants usually respond slowly to stimuli because they lack sense organs, muscles, and other parts needed for a quick response. However, they usually respond to light by turning their leaves toward it. They also respond to gravity by sending roots downward into the soil. Many homeowners have discovered, to their dismay, that poplar and willow trees often respond to the presence of water around a home by clogging the water drains with roots.

Even single-celled organisms such as amoebas show irritability. They respond to touch, light, heat, and other environmental stimuli.

Responses to stimuli must be coordinated if they are to be effective. Even simple organisms have many parts and each part must do the right thing at the right time if the proper response is to be carried out. For example, when you call a dog to supper, stimuli will be received by one or more of the eyes, ears, and nose. The responses to these stimuli must be coordinated within the dog before it can respond properly. Some muscles must contract; others must relax; digestive juices must be secreted. A system of **nerves** and a system of chemical regulators called **hormones** coordinate these responses in a dog and many other animals. In plants, only hormones are involved in the coordination of responses.

Organisms respond to stimuli by changing their relationship to it. For example, a dog usually comes when you whistle. It changes its location in response to the stimulus. Such responses, which often occur in definite patterns, are called **behaviour**. Remember that behaviour must begin with the organism. A ball rolling down a hill is not showing behaviour. It is simply being pulled along by the force of gravity. However, a dog that responds to a whistle creates a change in its relationship to its environment. Your whistle does not pull the dog to you.

Adaptation to the Environment

As you have just learned, organisms show irritability; they respond to changes in their environment. These changes include temperature, moisture, light, availability of food, and the presence of predators. Often the changes are sudden. For example, a storm might bring unusual amounts of water to an area. In this case an animal might respond by seeking shelter on higher ground. If its food supply in an area is suddenly destroyed by fire, an animal might respond by moving to a new area.

In contrast, other changes occur over a long period of time. The climate of an area may gradually change over thousands of years, or soil may gradually build up on a rocky landscape. Some organisms may no longer be able to survive in that area because they are not suited to the new conditions. They can either leave the area, or they can change so that they are suited to the new conditions. The first option can be done quickly. However, basic change in an organism can occur only over many generations.

Change occurs as a result of a characteristic called **variation**. Offspring always differ in some ways from one another and from their parents. These differences are called variations. Most variations do not affect an organism's chances of survival. For example, the fact that your hair is a different colour from your parents' will not likely affect your chances of survival. However, now and then a variation occurs that does give an organism a better chance of surviving in a changing environment. Suppose that the climate of an area is changing and deeper snow is produced each winter. Clearly, a variation that produced longer legs in a deer would increase that deer's chances of surviving in that area (Fig. 5-18). If this variation is passed on to the offspring of that deer, they, also, would have an increased chance of survival. Gradually the only deer to be found in the deep snow area may be the long-legged types. The others would have moved away or died. The process by which a certain type of organism becomes better suited to survive in its environment is called **adaptation**.

Keep in mind that organisms do not change in order to survive in a changing environment. The deer in our example did not grow long legs because they needed them to survive in the deep snow. Organisms do not change to survive; they survive because they change.

Fig. 5-18 Long legs may increase the deer's chances of survival in deep snow. However, its narrow hooves do not. Why? White-tailed deer probably evolved in areas of the United States where snow is uncommon. Only in recent times did they migrate north to snowy regions. Of what advantage are long legs and small feet to a deer in, say, Virginia? Millions of years from now, what might the legs and feet of our white-tailed deer look like? Why?

The long legs of deer are known as a **structural adaptation** to the environment. Countless generations likely passed before this adaptation appeared in its present form. This adaptation increases the survival chances of the species in many ways. Can you name some of these?

When a deer is frightened, it darts for the cover of the brush or forest and remains motionless. This is a response to a stimulus. However, since deer almost always respond in this way, this response is called a **behaviour**. It, too, probably developed over countless generations. This behaviour increases the survival chances of the species as well. As a result, it is called a **behavioural adaptation**.

Terrestrial organisms must cope with a wide range of abiotic factors—temperature, moisture, light, wind, and soil conditions. They must also cope with diseases, predators, and other biotic factors. In like manner, aquatic organisms must cope with a wide range of abiotic and biotic factors. Section 1.5, page 32, gave you some examples of how species are adapted to their environments and how they cope with changes. You may wish to read that section again.

Section Review

1. Explain each of these terms: stimulus, response, irritability.
2. What is behaviour?
3. a) What is variation?
   b) Why does variation usually require many generations?
4. a) What is an adaptation?
   b) Distinguish between a structural and a behavioural adaptation.

Chapter Highlights

1. About 1 500 000 species have been classified, but millions remain to be discovered and classified.
2. Organisms of the same species can interbreed to produce fertile offspring.
3. Species are named using binomial nomenclature.
4. The main classification groups are, in order: kingdom, phylum (division), class, order, family, genus, species.
5. The 5-kingdom system uses these kingdoms to classify organisms: Monera, Protista, Fungi, Plantae, Animalia.
6. Dichotomous keys can be used to classify organisms.
7. Organisms show behavioural and structural adaptations to their environments.

Key Terms

adaptation
algal protist
Animalia
behaviour
behavioural adaptation
binomial nomenclature
class
coloured flagellate
diatom
diatomaceous earth
dinoflagellate
endoskeleton
exoskeleton
family
Fungi
genus
Monera
order
phylum
phytoplankton
plankton
Plantae
Protista
protozoan protist
response
species
stimulus
structural adaptation
subspecies
taxon
taxonomy
variation
zooplankton

Recognizing the Concepts

Each of the following statements or questions is followed by four responses. Choose the correct response in each case. (Do not write in this book.)

1. Binomial nomenclature names species using
   a) the genus and species names
   b) the family and genus names
   c) the phylum and species names
   d) the family and genus names
2. All breeds of house cats have the species name *Felis domesticus*. Which one of the following statements is *not* true about cats?
   a) All breeds of cats can interbreed under natural conditions.
   b) All breeds of cats are biologically similar in structure.
   c) When certain breeds of cats interbreed, the offspring are infertile.
   d) All breeds of cats are in the same family.
3. Three dog-like animals have the scientific names *Canis familiaris*, *Canis latrans*, and *Canis lupus*. These animals are:
   a) all of the same species
   b) in the same genus but in different species
   c) in the same genus but in different families
   d) in the same family but in different genera
4. Look back at Table 5-3, page 125. The two organisms most closely related to a dog are:
   a) golden eagle and housefly
   b) human and golden eagle
   c) human and gorilla
   d) gorilla and golden eagle
5. An organism is one-celled, lacks a true nucleus, and lacks internal membranes. This organism is a
   a) protist
   b) very simple plant
   c) fungus
   d) moneran
6. A single-celled organism contains chlorophyll and moves using a flagellum. This organism is likely a
   a) diatom
   b) coloured flagellate
   c) dinoflagellate
   d) microscopic animal
7. Which one of the following statements about fungi is not true?
   a) Some fungi are parasites; others are saprophytes.
   b) All fungi are decomposers.
   c) Some fungi can make their own food.
   d) Some, but not all, fungi are made of hair-like structures called hyphae.
8. Cows on a dairy farm normally line up at the milking parlour in the same order each milking time. This is best described as a(n)
   a) response b) stimulus c) behaviour d) adaptation

Understanding the Concepts

1. Distinguish between the terms genus and species.
2. Defend the use of scientific names when an accurate identification is necessary.

3. List the seven classification taxa in order of descending size. If three species are in the same order, what other taxa will they share?
4. Using the 5-kingdom system, state the kingdom in which each of the following organisms would be found: human, maple tree, bread mould, cat, duck, giant kelp (a seaweed), sphagnum moss, grasshopper, Kentucky bluegrass, housefly, diatom, cholera bacterium, spider, amoeba, mushroom.
5. a) Distinguish between phytoplankton and zooplankton.
   b) Protozoans which move with flagella are often called colourless flagellates. What organelle do they lack that coloured flagellates have? What advantage do coloured flagellates have over colourless flagellates?
6. Explain how fungi help recycle nutrients through ecosystems.
7. Algae occur in three of the five kingdoms. Identify these three kingdoms and give an example in each case.
8. Distinguish between a response and a behaviour.

Applying the Concepts

1. a) Four members of the dog family, Canidae, are the red fox (*Vulpes fulva*), the Arctic fox (*Alopex lagopus*), the coyote (*Canis latrans*), and the wolf (*Canis lupus*). Which two animals are more closely related? How do you know?
   b) Is a red fox or wolf more closely related to a domestic dog? How do you know?
2. a) Dogs and cats are in the same order, Carnivora. What other taxa do they share?
   b) What taxa do you share with dogs and cats?
   c) What order are you in? Why do you think you are in a different order from dogs and cats?
3. a) Some protists can be classified as producers and others as consumers. Explain why this is so.
   b) Look at the drawing of *Euglena* in Figure 5-11, page 129. How would you classify this protist? Why?
4. To many people a sponge looks more like a plant than it does an animal. Defend its classification as an animal.
5. Make a dichotomous classification key that someone else could use to identify ten of this year's new cars.
6. Most birds of prey, such as hawks, have sharp hooked beaks and long curved talons (claws). How do you suppose these adaptations came to be?
7. Use your knowledge of adaptation to explain why clear cutting of tropical rain forests will make numerous species extinct.

Investigations

1. Get a dichotomous key for coniferous trees from your teacher. Use it to identify five conifers in your area.
2. A horse (*Equus caballus*) and a donkey (*Equus asinus*) will interbreed. But, as you can see from the names, they are not classified as the same species. Find out why this is so.

Fig. 5-19 How is this animal adapted to its environment?

3. Find out how our North American lifestyle is connected with the clear cutting of tropical rain forests.
4. Classification systems with more than five kingdoms have been developed. Research one of these to find out how the five kingdoms we have used were divided to create more kingdoms.
5. Select any vertebrate animal. Research how it is adapted to its environment (Fig. 5-19).

Career: *BIOLOGICAL PHOTOGRAPHER*

HELP WANTED:
BIOLOGICAL PHOTOGRAPHER

Biological supply house seeks photographer to produce black-and-white and colour photographs of plants, animals, and microscopic organisms. Darkroom provided.

Photographers with a knowledge of biology are often employed to illustrate textbooks, trade books, journals, and technical reports. As you can see by looking through this text, some of these photographers are nature photographers—they photograph plants and animals in their natural habitats. Other biological photographers take pictures of organisms through light microscopes using a process called photomicroscopy. Still others photograph specimens with an electron microscope to produce electron micrographs which reveal cellular detail.

To be a biological photographer you should take several courses in secondary school science, particularly in biology. After graduation from secondary school you can enter a degree or certificate program in Photographic Arts at a university or community college. When you apply for admission to such a program, you may be asked to supply a portfolio of your photographs. Therefore you should begin that collection now. A B.Sc. in biology would be a distinct employment advantage.

6 Sensing the Environment

CHAPTER CONTENTS

CHAPTER OBJECTIVES

After completing this chapter, you should be able to:

1. Explain why organisms need sensory systems.
2. Explain why other animals do not rely on vision and hearing in the same way humans do.
3. Explain how animals detect their environments.
4. Describe the role of the central nervous system in sensing the environment.
5. Explain why large animals need more complex nervous systems.
6. Describe the uses we can make of animal and technological sensory equipment.

In order to survive, a successful organism must respond to its environment. To do this, all organisms need **receptors** (sense organs) to detect change. All of an organism's receptors form its **sensory system**. In this chapter you will study the interesting ways in which organisms use their receptors to monitor their external environment (Fig. 6-1).

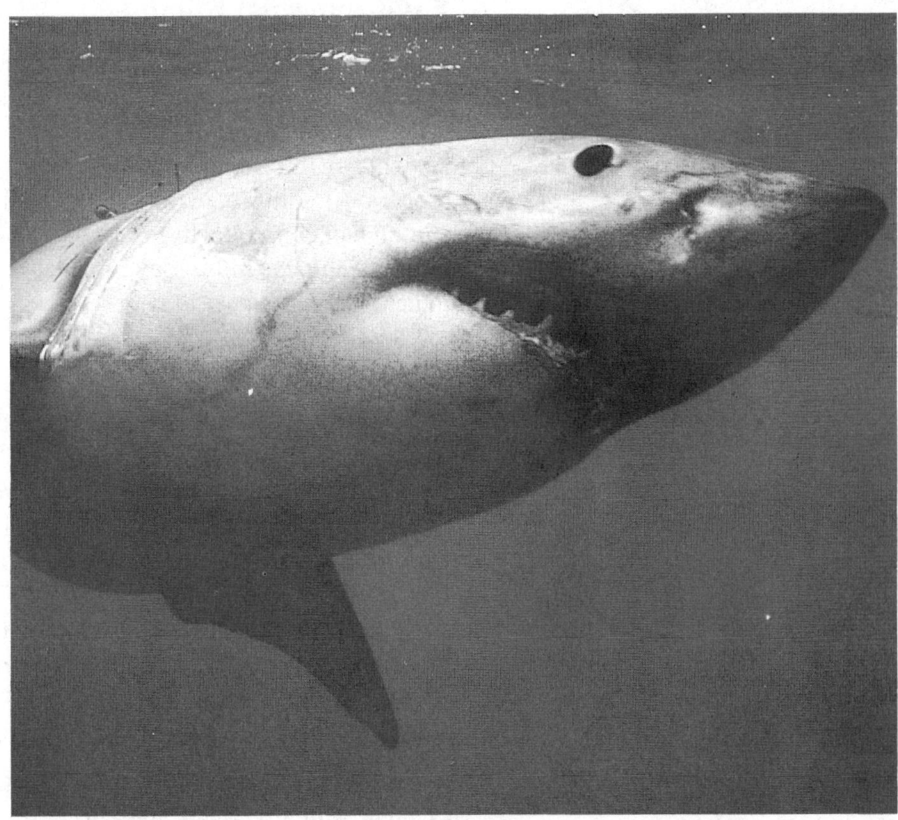

Fig. 6-1 If you moved into this organism's environment, it would detect your presence long before you could see each other. How would this animal detect you? What possible responses might it have to your presence?

Fig. 6-2 Protists such as these detect many kinds of stimuli. How do these organisms respond to such stimuli?

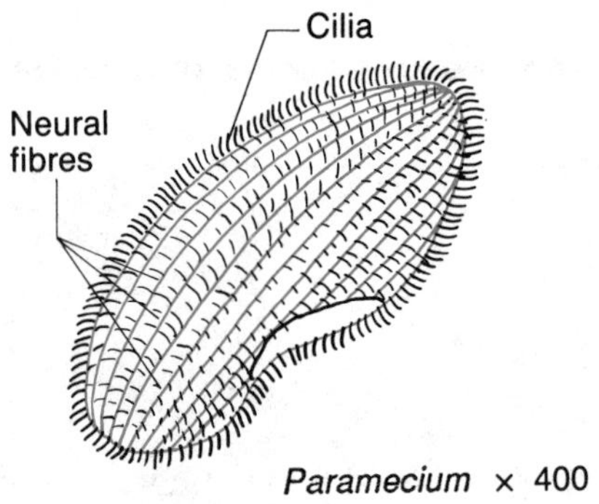

Paramecium × 400

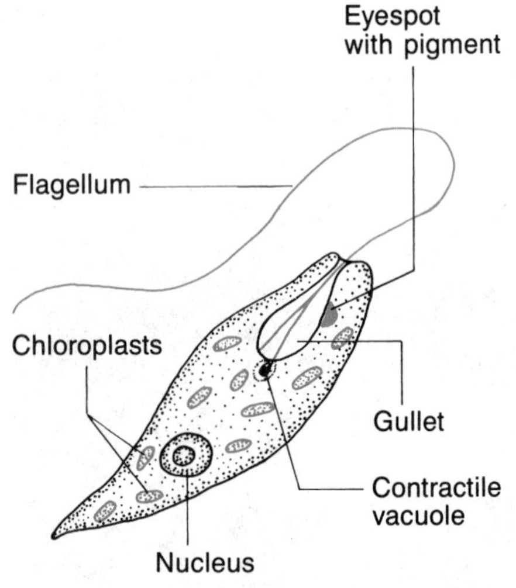

Euglena × 1000

6.1 Why Do Organisms Have Sensory Systems?

Every organism has needs such as food, water, and a space to live in. Most organisms need a means of avoiding predators. They also have to adjust their lifestyles to changes in seasonal climate. To be able to meet all these needs, every successful organism must detect its environment. If an organism fails to detect what it needs, it dies.

Consider this example. A microscopic protist called a **paramecium** lives in ponds along with frogs, herons, and cattail plants (Fig. 6-2). Lacking eyes, neither the cattail nor the paramecium can see the herons. Even if they could, such information would be useless to these organisms. Herons do not eat paramecia or cattails. On the other hand, frogs *must* detect a heron's presence and respond appropriately to avoid being eaten.

What would happen if the frog and the paramecium were to switch their sensory systems? Obviously, the frog would soon be consumed by an undetected predator. But the paramecium would also die from starvation or exposure. The frog's senses were not designed to detect food and shelter that is suitable for a paramecium.

To be successful, then, an organism must have a sensory system that collects *appropriate* and *significant* information about its environment.

Environmental Stimuli

Any change in the outside environment that changes the behaviour of an organism is called a **stimulus** (plural: **stimuli**). The change in behaviour produced by the stimulus is called a **response**. Different living things do not respond to the same stimuli. (Think of the frog and paramecium collecting food or avoiding predators.) But all living things respond to some kind of stimuli and consequently are said to be **irritable**. **Irritability** is a characteristic of living things. In biology, ''irritable'' does not mean ''bad-tempered'' but, rather, ''responsive''.

Response to Stimuli

Different kinds of living things do not respond in the same way to the same environmental stimulus. For instance, if a nail is hammered into a tree, the tree responds but it may take many years before the response can be observed. Suppose, though, that you accidentally stepped on the same nail with your bare foot. Your response would be quite different from that of the tree, even though the stimulus was identical.

Since organisms respond in different ways, we classify these responses into types which you will study in more detail in the next chapter.

Coordinating Senses and Responses

All organisms must have some means of linking the senses and responses together. Otherwise no appropriate response can occur. Organisms like you rely on a **nervous system** for this vital communication. However, there are other means for such communication besides nerves. We will investigate some of them in the next section.

Section Review

1. Why must organisms sense their environments?
2. Distinguish between a stimulus and a response.
3. What kinds of stimuli do you respond to?
4. What is the main function of the nervous system?

6.2 Simple Sensory Systems

The Sensory Systems of Single-celled Organisms

Single-celled organisms such as protists are not large enough to have complex sensory systems like yours. Sense organs such as eyes and ears require many specialized cells. Instead, protists possess **neural fibres** as shown in the paramecium in Figure 6-2. These fibres gather information about the area in which paramecia swim and direct the response to any stimuli. For instance, bumping a solid object produces a response: back up, change direction, and swim forward again. If the neural fibres are severed, the paramecium cannot coordinate the movements of its response organelles called **cilia**.

Euglena, also in Figure 6-2, has a photosensitive organelle called an **eyespot** near its anterior (front) end. There is also a red pigment spot that *Euglena* uses to shade the eyespot by turning its body. Thus *Euglena* not only detects light but also detects the direction of light as well. Why would this information be important to *Euglena*? (*Hint*: Look at the other kinds of organelles in this cell.)

Even though they are single-celled, these protists can detect a surprising number of other kinds of stimuli. A paramecium, for example, will swim *towards* a weak acid region (a **positive taxis**) but *away* from a salty region (a **negative taxis**). It also shows a positive taxis towards one electrode in an electric field. It can even detect temperature differences, showing a preference for water at 24°C to 28°C. You will investigate some protist senses in Section 6.3.

Such simple systems have many limitations. Because these organisms are so small, the receptors are not specialized enough to pick up detailed information. A brain is not necessary because there is not enough sensory information to require one.

Network Systems: The Sensory Systems of Multicellular Organisms

Unlike paramecia, multicellular organisms must communicate from cell to cell. To do this, multicellular organisms have specialized cells: one kind detects and another kind responds. There must be a communication link between the **receptor cells** and the **effector (response) cells**. For instance, if the receptor

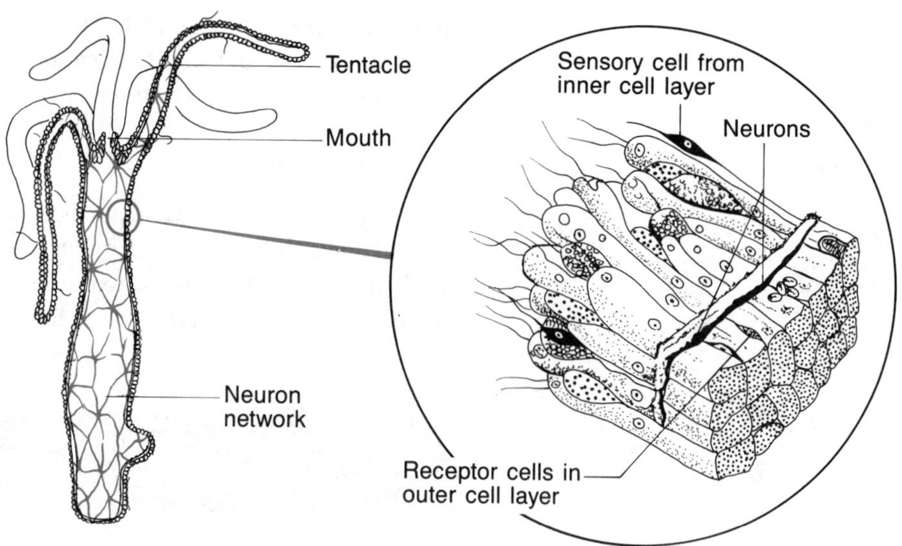

Fig. 6-3 A network of connected nerve cells allows this hydra to transmit information about its environment to all cells. Obtain some live hydra and observe how they respond to various stimuli.

cells in your eyes see an oncoming car and do not communicate to the effector cells in your legs, then you will certainly get hit.

Perhaps the simplest sensory and communication system is present in hydra (Fig. 6-3). In this animal, sensory cells pass messages along to effectors. As a result, more than one cell can be involved in a coordinated response to an environmental stimulus. In effect, hydra have simple **nerves** or **neurons** (communication cells). This type of nervous system is called a **network system**. Note that hydra do not have a central information processing area (brain). A brain is not necessary for this animal.

A network system has a drawback. Stimuli must be strong or persistent in order for the animal to respond. This is because information from a single receptor cell "gets lost" as it gets passed from cell to cell. Effector cells are not activated unless the stimulus is strong and persistent.

Section Review

1. **a)** What kinds of stimuli can protists detect?
   b) How do they respond to each?
2. **a)** What is an effector cell? a nerve cell?
   b) Why do multicellular animals have nerve cells while protists do not?
3. What is a taxis? Give an example of a positive and a negative taxis.
4. What advantage does a network system give to animals such as hydra?

6.3 Activity: Protist Senses and Responses

Even though protists lack specialized sense organs like yours, they can detect a surprising number of environmental changes. In this activity, you will test a variety of protists to determine how they respond to certain stimuli.

Problem

What stimuli do protists detect?

Materials

cultures of *Euglena, Stentor, Paramecium*
black card
scissors
tape
thin wire
microscope slides (2)
petri dishes (2)
cover slips (2)
droppers (2)
microscope
vinegar
salt
AA, C, or D dry cell

Procedure A Response to Light

Fig. 6-4 How do protists respond to light? How quickly do they respond? A desk lamp may be used to illuminate the cultures from above.

a. Cut two pieces of black card just large enough to fit under a petri dish and two smaller pieces to cover half of a petri dish.
b. In a location that is well lit from above, place two empty petri dishes on top of the two larger black cards.
c. Fill one dish with a culture of *Euglena* and the other with a culture of *Stentor*.
d. Put the lid on each dish. Then cover half of each dish with the smaller cards (Fig. 6-4).
e. Observe the two cultures after 5 min, 1 h, and 1 d. Record where the organisms are found.

Procedure B Response to Acidity

a. Obtain a culture of *Paramecium*.
b. Prepare a wet mount using one drop from the culture on a slide. Cover the drop with a cover slip.
c. Put the slide on your microscope and focus on the paramecia using low power. Avoid strong light since this overheats and kills protists.
d. Place a drop of vinegar at the right edge of the cover slip using the dropper.
e. Observe the direction of movement of the paramecia. Remember what you see in the microscope is backwards.

Procedure C Response to Salinity

a. Repeat the ''response to acidity'' procedure using about 5 grains of salt instead of vinegar. *CAUTION: Do not let salt or salt water contact any part of your microscope.*

Procedure D Response to an Electric Field

a. Prepare a microscope slide as shown in Figure 6-5, using wire, tape, and a small dry cell. *CAUTION: Do not touch the wires together after connecting them to the dry cell.*
b. Mount the slide on the microscope stage so that the ends of the two electrodes are in the field of view on low power.

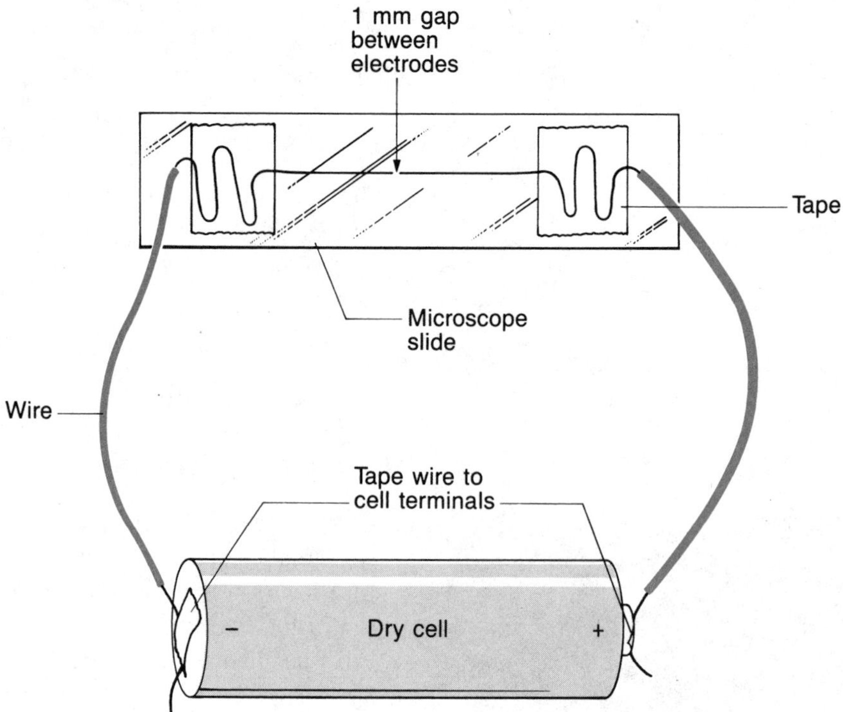

Fig. 6-5 A few loops of wire will help hold the electrodes (the ends) about 1 mm apart. Connect the wires to the dry cell last.

c. Place a drop containing paramecia over the two electrode ends. Cover with a cover slip.

d. Observe the location and direction of movement of the paramecia for a few minutes.

Discussion

1. a) Compare *Euglena* and *Stentor* in their response to light. Include mention of the rates of their responses.
   b) How would you separate a mixed culture of these two protists?

2. a) How do paramecia respond to weak acids?
   b) Bacteria produce acids as part of their digestive process. How might this account for the response of paramecia to the acid stimulus?

3. a) How do paramecia respond to salt?
   b) Concentrated salt solutions are called **hypertonic**. Such solutions will draw moisture out of cells. How might this account for the response of paramecia to the salt stimulus?

4. Which electrode attracted the paramecia, positive or negative? If paramecia have an electrostatic charge, is it positive or negative?

5. Describe how each species of protist moves. Draw a diagram of each protist showing the parts used and direction of motion.

Extension

Design and conduct experiments to test the response of amoebas to these same stimuli. Amoebas do not swim. Instead, they move along the bottom of the container.

Fig. 6-6 Stepping on a sharp object causes a message to be sent to the CNS by the sensory neurons. Interneurons relay the message simultaneously to the brain and to the effector neurons. The effector muscles in the leg move the leg away from the stimulus.

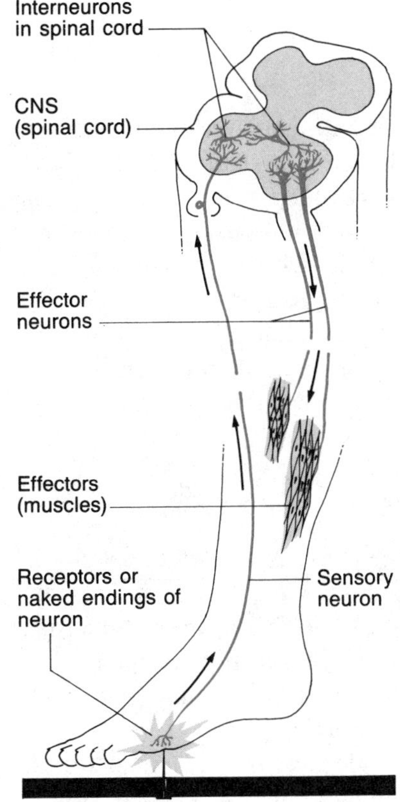

6.4 Complex Sensory Systems—Invertebrates

The Central Nervous System

Animals that are larger than hydra display a number of significant structural changes. First, such animals have more cells. This means they can have more receptors and a greater variety of effector organs. Second, the nerve cells are greatly improved over those in hydra and can transport information much faster. Finally, larger animals use an information processing centre called a **central nervous system (CNS)** to coordinate responses to stimuli.

The use of a central nervous system in detecting and responding to stimuli necessitates a change in the structure of the whole sensory system. Instead of receptor cells communicating directly with effector cells (as in hydra), a larger organism needs two sets of special cells to carry messages. One set (**afferent nerves**) carries messages from the receptors to the CNS and another set (**efferent nerves**) carries instructions back to the effectors. These nerves are made of cells called **neurons**. The receptor cells can be called **sensory neurons**. The CNS sends a message back to the response (effector) organs by **motor neurons**. A motor neuron stimulates the response organs, causing locomotion. The CNS contains many neurons called **interneurons**. These act as "relay switches" between incoming and outgoing messages (Fig. 6-6).

While all large animals have a central nervous system, the abilities and location of that system are quite different. Figure 6-7 shows the nervous systems of a planarian (a freshwater flatworm reaching 2 cm in length), an earthworm, and a grasshopper. Let's see how these compare.

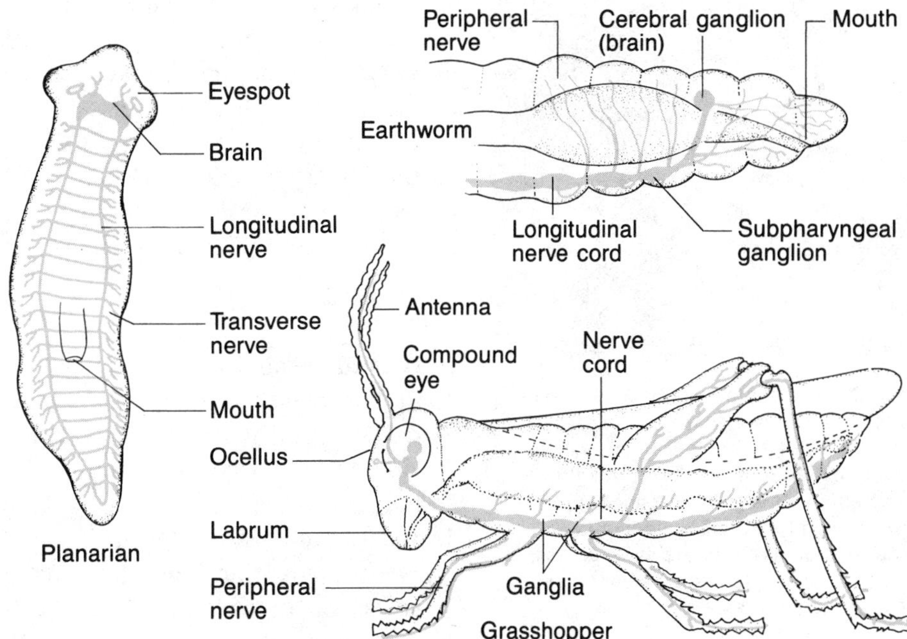

Fig. 6-7 As animals become larger and capable of gathering more sensory data, their nervous systems must increase in size and complexity.

The Nervous System of Planaria

A planarian has a pair of longitudinal nerves running the length of its body. These connect to finer transverse nerves which, in turn, connect to the sensory neurons. The anterior (front) ends of these longitudinal nerves are enlarged clusters of nerve cells called **ganglia** (singular: **ganglion**). This pair of ganglia is the planarian's crude brain. Two clusters of light-sensitive neurons are also located near the front of the animal. These clusters are primitive eyes. These spots cannot focus as your eyes do. However, they are capable of detecting light intensity and direction.

The Nervous System of Earthworms

Earthworms also have a pair of longitudinal nerves running along the ventral (lower) part of the animal, forming its central nervous system. They also have a cluster of four ganglia that forms a brain at the anterior end. Each segment has a pair of smaller ganglia as well as three pair of finer **peripheral nerves**. These segmental ganglia coordinate nervous activity within each segment. The brain coordinates overall activity. The earthworm also has long specialized neurons or "giant fibres" which run through its longitudinal nerves. One long neuron transmits information faster and better than many short connected neurons. Communication speed is very important as organisms become large. Why do you think this is so?

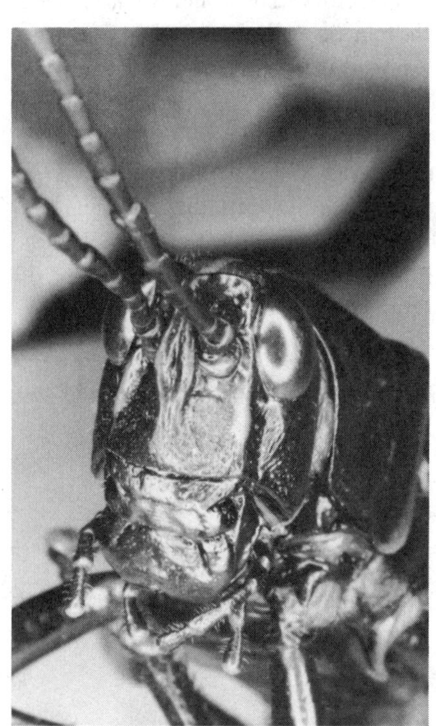

Fig. 6-8 Grasshoppers have two compound eyes, each made of hundreds of facets. They also have three simple eyes that are only sensitive to light. The antennas are smell (olfactory) receptors. To handle the complex information collected by these specialized receptors, the grasshopper needs a larger brain than worms have.

The Nervous System of Grasshoppers

Grasshoppers also have a pair of ventral nerve cords connected to ganglia in the head. Peripheral nerves connect to this central nervous system at a number of ganglia. Note how large the brain is compared to that of the two worms. This is partly because of the additional sensory information available. For example, the grasshopper has well-developed eyes and antennas (Fig. 6-8). The brain has a special ganglion just for visual (optic) stimuli.

The grasshopper has well-developed "ears" located on the abdomen near the rear legs. Other insects have their "ears" in different places. For example, mosquitoes have them on their antennas and crickets have them on their legs. Insects have more giant fibres than worms. As a result, their nerve communication is faster and more efficient. Why do you think this is necessary for insects such as the grasshopper? Insects also have more body parts to move and coordinate. Can you explain why their central nervous systems are larger?

Section Review

1. How are central nervous systems different from network systems?
2. a) Distinguish between afferent and efferent neurons.
b) Distinguish between sensory and motor neurons.
3. How are the nervous systems of hydra, planaria, earthworms, and grasshoppers similar? How are they different?
4. What advantage do "giant fibres" have over short neurons?
5. What relationship is there between brain size and the number of sensory and motor organs of the animal?

6.5 Complex Sensory Systems—Chordates

The Structure of Chordate Nervous Systems

The most advanced nervous systems are found in the phylum to which you belong: Chordata. Chordates do not have a pair of ventral longitudinal nerves. Instead, the nerves and ganglia are fused (joined) into one long cord called the **spinal cord**. It is found on the dorsal (upper or back) surface of the body. In most chordates, it is surrounded by pieces of bone called **vertebrae** (singular: **vertebra**). As in simpler animals, the brain and spinal cord are called the central nervous system and the remaining nerves are the peripheral system (Fig. 6-9). Chordate brains are larger than insect brains. They also have a number of distinct regions (Fig. 6-10).

The major difference among the brains shown in Figure 6-10 is the size of the cerebrum. In mammals and birds, the optic lobes are part of the cerebrum. In humans, the cerebrum is so large that it covers the other brain sections. The folds in the human brain produce a larger surface area for special kinds of interneurons called **association neurons** or **grey matter**. These association neurons are responsible for memory, reasoning, personality, and imagination.

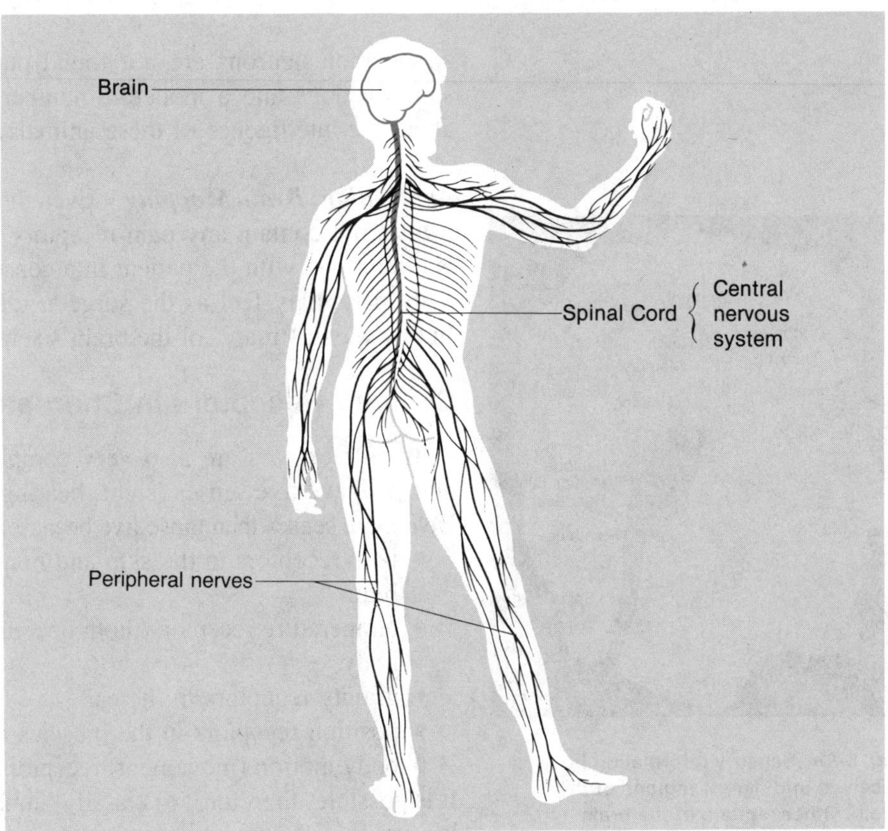

Fig. 6-9 The human central nervous system (coloured) and peripheral nerves (black)

Fig. 6-10 Diagrams A to D show four chordate brains as seen from above. Diagram E shows a side view of the human brain. Note how small the cerebrum is in fish and how large it is in humans. Note also that the left half of the human brain is slightly larger than the right. This is normal for right-handed people since the left half controls the right side of the body.

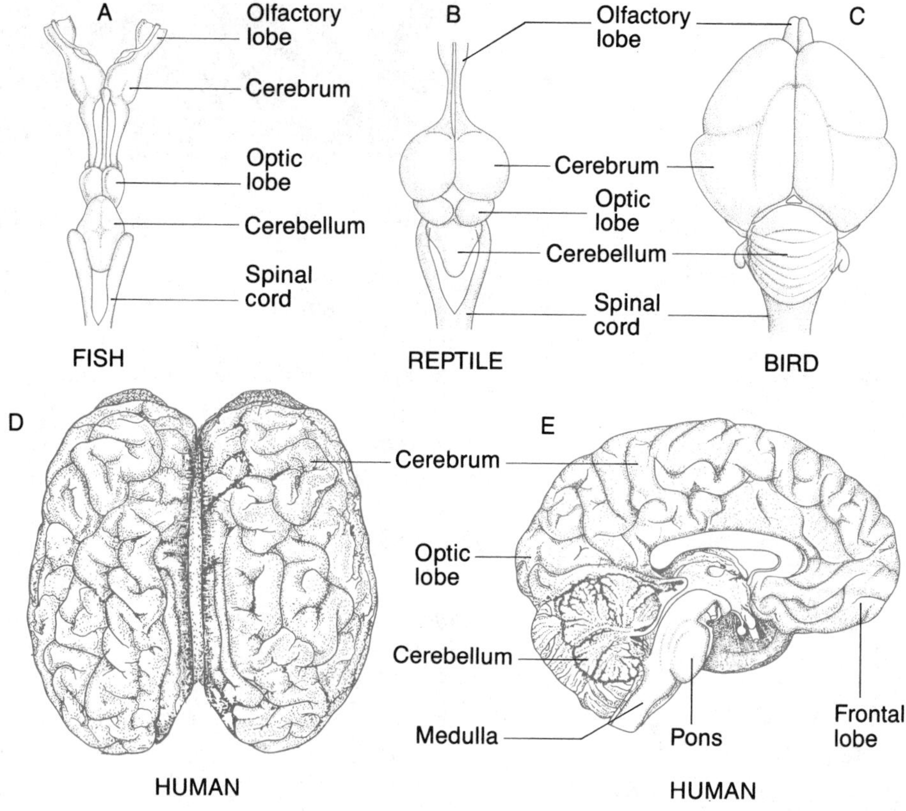

Association neurons are not found outside the chordate phylum. There are some in dogs and a moderate number in monkeys. What does this suggest about the intelligence of these animals?

Application: Brain Mapping Even though the cerebrum is a mass of neurons, it does not contain any pain receptors. For this reason, human brain surgery is often done with the patient in a conscious state. Patients can describe what body parts they feel as the surgeon touches various parts of their cerebrum. In this way a ''map'' of the brain's sensory sections can be made (Fig. 6-11).

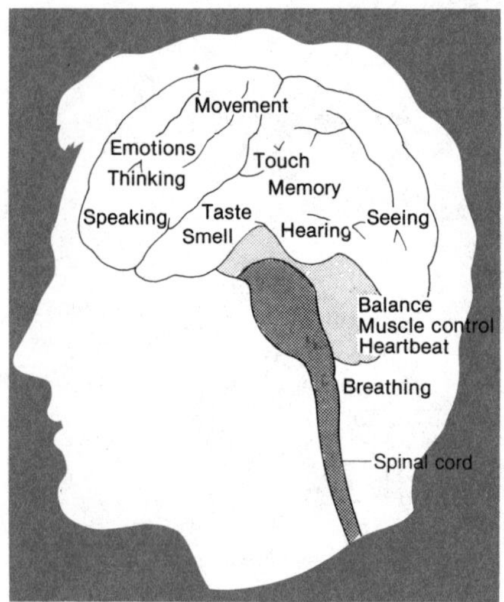

Fig. 6-11 Sensory information is received in different regions of the brain. Other regions of the brain control responses.

Sensory Receptors in Chordates

Sensory receptors are also very complex in chordates. We usually say that humans have five senses (sight, hearing, smell, taste, and touch). In fact, you have more senses than those five because of additional kinds of sensory receptors:

- pain receptors in the skin and in all internal organs except the lungs and brain
- temperature receptors (both heat and cold) in the skin and throughout the body
- gravity receptors in the ear
- position receptors in the muscles and skin
- body motion (movement) receptors in the ear and throughout the muscles

It is possible, therefore, to classify human senses into eleven categories: sight, hearing, smell, taste, temperature, pressure, balance, pain, gravity, body position, and body movement.

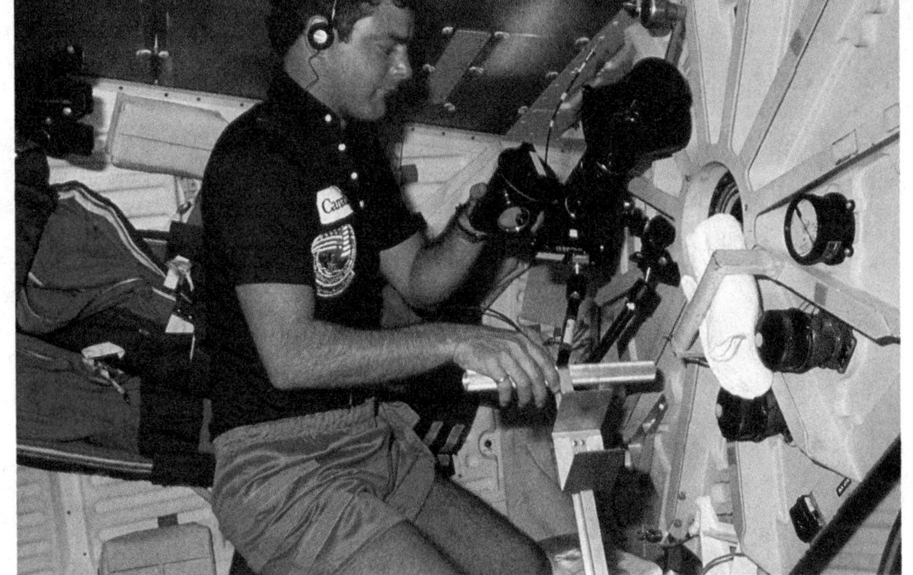

Fig. 6-12 **Astronauts must learn how to accommodate for the loss of many senses in space.**

Sensory receptors can be classified as **exteroceptors** or **interoceptors**, depending on whether they collect external or internal stimuli. Since this study unit deals with the external environment, we will concentrate on the exteroceptors.

Receptors can also be classified by the type of stimuli that each responds to. **Chemoreceptors** detect certain chemicals. **Mechanoreceptors** detect pressure, pain, stretch, position, movement, and vibration. **Photoreceptors** detect light. **Thermoreceptors** detect heat and cold. **Electroreceptors** for detecting electrical charges are not found in humans but are common in aquatic organisms from protists to fish.

Application: Receptors in Space Astronauts encounter unexpected difficulties with their sensory systems while in space. For example, the water content of the body is controlled by position receptors which are ''fooled'' by the lack of gravity. As a result, astronauts retain extra water in space, giving them a puffy or obese appearance. Lack of gravitational stimuli also causes the loss of bone calcium. Extended space travel may produce astronauts whose leg bones will not support them.

Mechanical work in space is extremely difficult because the position receptors in other muscles don't work either. The sensation is like having all of your limbs go to sleep. Imagine working in a bulky space suit (no touch, limited vision, no balance) and not knowing where your hands or feet are! Astronauts must spend hundreds of hours learning new ways to do simple tasks in the absence of gravity-dependent senses (Fig. 6-12).

Section Review

1. How does the structure of chordate nervous systems differ from that of invertebrate systems?
2. What are association neurons? What organisms have these?
3. How can we determine what function is controlled by a particular section of the brain?
4. What senses do humans have? What ones do we not have?
5. What are the five kinds of sensory receptors?
6. What senses do we lose in the absence of gravity? How does this hinder work in spacecraft?

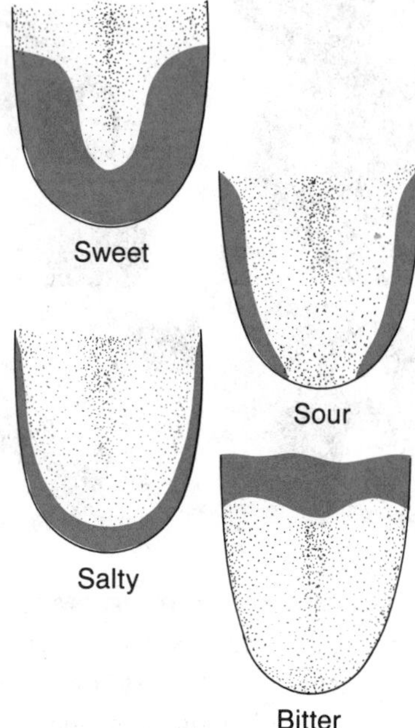

Fig. 6-13 Tastebud distribution. Try to verify these diagrams using sugar, lemon, salt, and tonic water solutions. Take a cotton swab, dip it in one solution, and dab it on your dry tongue. Can you taste sugar at the back of your tongue? Can you taste bitter tonic water at the tip? Can you taste salt at the back and sour in the centre?

Fig. 6-14 A male moth uses olfactory receptors to locate a mate by her odour. The receptors are on the large antennas. Can you explain why these receptors are extremely sensitive to the female odour but much less sensitive to other smells?

6.6 Chemoreceptors

It is difficult for humans to imagine what life would be like without sight and hearing. However, the absence of these senses doesn't hinder many other organisms. These organisms have developed other sensory abilities such as chemoreception to a very high degree. Each animal relies on one or two types of sensory receptors to collect most of its information. These are called **primary senses**. Your primary senses are sight and hearing. Many other animals rely heavily on different senses. What do you think the primary senses are for a snake? a worm? a grasshopper?

What Are Chemoreceptors?

Chemoreceptors are responsible for two senses (taste and smell) as well as certain kinds of irritation. As an example, imagine how your eyes react when you cut up an onion. Or, how does a broken blister feel if salt is put on it? These irritating substances and many others are detected by chemoreceptors. Note, however, that these skin receptors do not identify the irritant. Instead, they just indicate that some kind of irritation is occurring. Almost all animals have chemoreceptors of this type.

In contrast, the chemoreceptors of the tongue and nose are specialized enough to identify the irritants. One sniff identifies an onion and one taste identifies salt.

Taste Receptors

Taste receptors or **tastebuds** in humans detect the sensations of sweet, salty, sour, bitter, and water. Other tastes are formed by combinations of these five sensations. Your taste receptors are all on your tongue (Fig. 6-13), but other organisms have them elsewhere. Arthropods have taste receptors on their antennas and on external mouthparts called palps. Flies even have tastebuds on their feet! Aquatic organisms have these receptors on their skins. Can you explain the locations of these chemoreceptors in other organisms? How do these locations help the organism survive?

Olfactory (Smell) Receptors

Olfactory (smell) receptors detect a much wider range of chemical stimuli. The chemicals must be dissolved in water before they can be detected. For aquatic organisms, this is no problem. For terrestrial creatures such as you, the chemicals must dissolve in the moisture at the top of the nasal cavity where the olfactory receptors are located.

Olfactory receptors are much more sensitive than taste receptors, not only in humans but in other animals as well (Fig. 6-14). Many organisms, from protists to mammals, rely on their sense of smell as their primary sense for locating food, finding mates, and communicating with others. Even an intelligent animal like a dog uses the odours on fire hydrants and lampposts to detect the presence of other dogs. Each dog adds its own "calling card" to the collection by urinating. The importance of smell for a chordate may be estimated by the relative size of the brain's olfactory lobe. In fish, the lobe is large; in humans it is small.

Olfactory receptors contribute to your sense of taste. At your next meal, try tasting your food while holding your nose. What happens to the taste sensation? The same thing happens when you have a cold. How do you explain these observations?

Section Review

1. What are your primary senses?
2. Of your two kinds of chemoreceptors, which is more sensitive? How do you know?
3. Name two organisms that are more dependent on their chemoreceptors than you are.

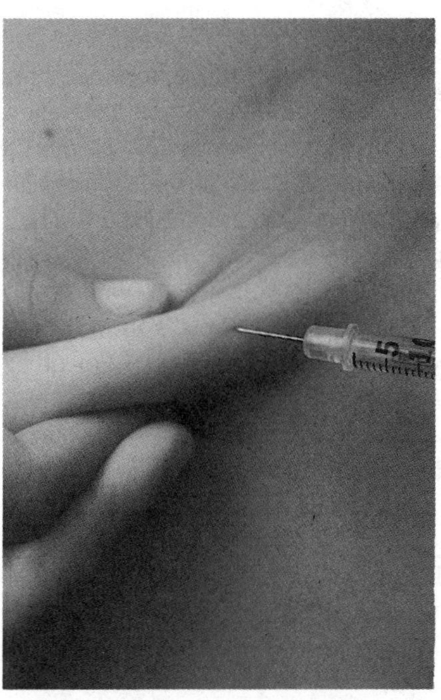

Fig. 6-16 A diabetic quickly learns to locate injection sites where there are few pain receptors. Which regions of your skin contain the fewest pain receptors? Can you devise a simple test using the touch of a pin?

6.7 Mechanoreceptors

Your skin and other organs are full of receptors that detect **pressure**, **pain**, and **stretch**. A microscopic examination of your skin shows a number of receptors, each designed to detect one kind of stimulus (Fig. 6-15). These receptors are not equally distributed on the body surface. For example, pain and pressure receptors are abundant on the fingers, hands, and face. They are less abundant elsewhere (Fig. 6-16).

Nocturnal (active at night) animals and those living at great depths in the oceans use sensitive touch and pressure receptors to help detect their environment. For such animals, hairs, whiskers, and similar "probes" are more important than eyes. Can you explain why?

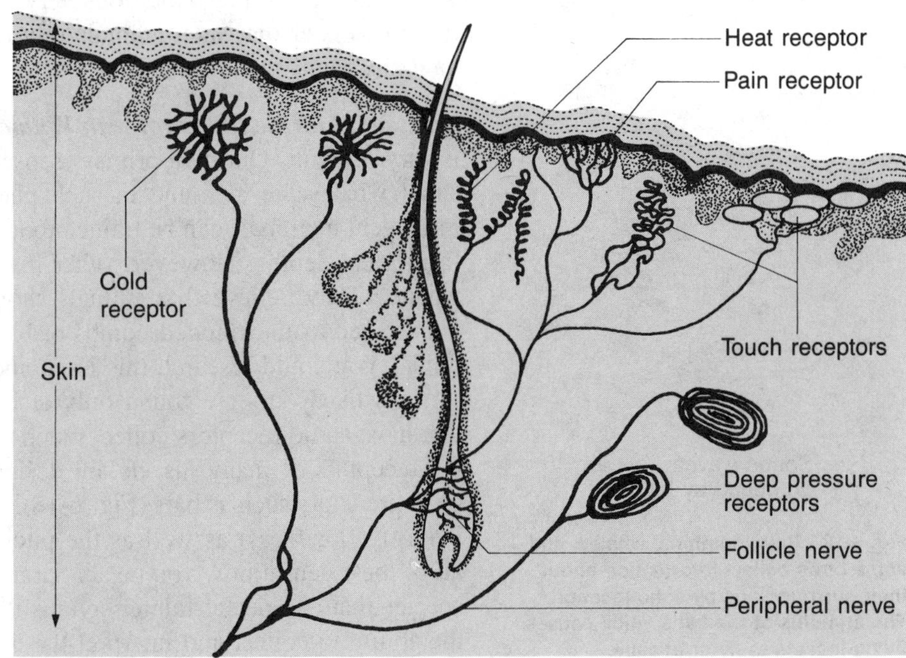

Fig. 6-15 Your skin contains mechanoreceptors for touch, pressure, and pain. The nerve at the base of each hair follicle detects hair movement. The skin also contains thermoreceptors for heat and cold.

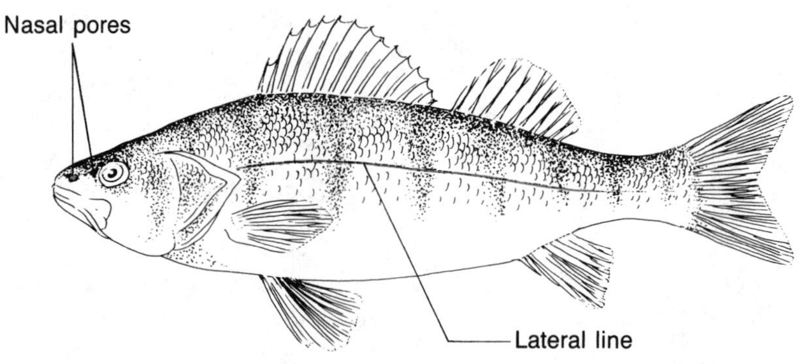

Fig. 6-17 The lateral line detects sound vibrations travelling through water. The fish can detect a wide variety of sounds, giving it enough information to "see" its environment by sound. Submarines imitate fish by using sonar to "see" objects underwater.

Audioreceptors

Audioreceptors (vibration receptors) are special pressure receptors used for hearing. Although it may seem unusual to us, most animals do not have ears. Instead, they detect sounds in other ways. For instance, earthworms emerge from their tunnels on damp summer nights to mate. Their skin receptors can detect the ground vibrations caused by an approaching animal's feet. They quickly retreat into their hole if that animal comes too close.

Fish can also hear without ears. They have vibration sensitive organs along their **lateral lines** (Fig. 6-17). For many fish, the lateral line is the primary sense organ. In effect, a fish hears the location, size, and movement of other animals.

Dolphins and whales (both mammals) go one step further: they emit sounds and detect the echo using pressure receptors in their heads. Experiments with blindfolded dolphins show that these animals can locate, identify, and even tell the texture of objects using sound alone. Other experiments show that large whales talk to each other underwater at distances up to 200 km apart! Ocean water transmits sound vibrations very well but is a poor transmitter for light. It's no wonder that such animals rely on a better sense than vision to gather vital environmental stimuli.

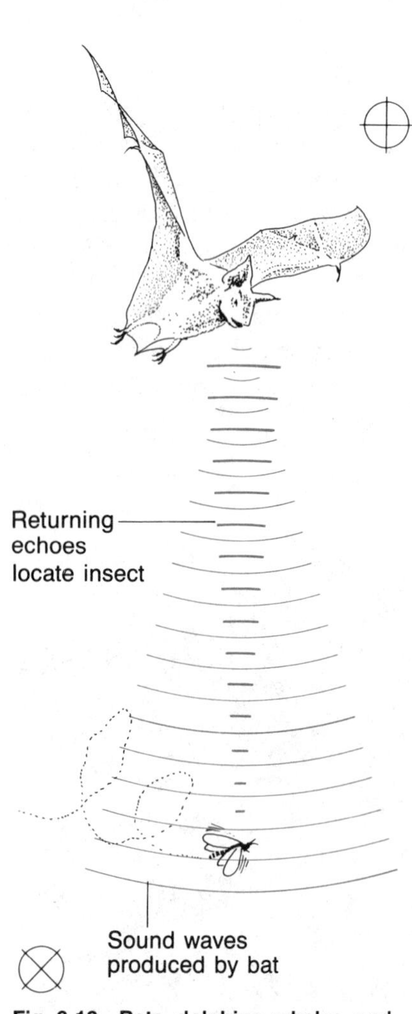

Fig. 6-18 Bats, dolphins, whales, and some birds collect information about their surroundings by echo location. The stimulus of the bat's voice causes flying insects to fly erratically, attempting to avoid capture.

An Issue: Marine Retrieval with Whales Locating objects lost under the sea is very difficult. Our own primary senses are useless in dark, silent water. But small whales are at home in such places. Scientists have found that these intelligent mammals can be trained to locate and even retrieve valuable objects from great depths. However, other marine biologists are upset at this use of whales. They believe that animals should not be used to recover dangerous goods such as unexploded bombs or barrels of toxic chemicals. What do you think? You could research this issue and report to the entire class.

Ears like yours are found only among mammals and birds. Invertebrates that have audio receptors collect much less detailed information. For instance, the receptors of many insects are designed to hear only the sounds of mates or of predators such as bats (Fig. 6-18). Your ears detect the presence of sound intensity (loudness) as well as the pitch and tone of that sound. To interpret all of these sensations, you need a large auditory brain centre. There are other species that can detect fainter sounds than you can hear. However, few have the ability to collect and interpret the detail and quality of airborne sound the way your nervous system does. Clearly, hearing is one of your primary senses.

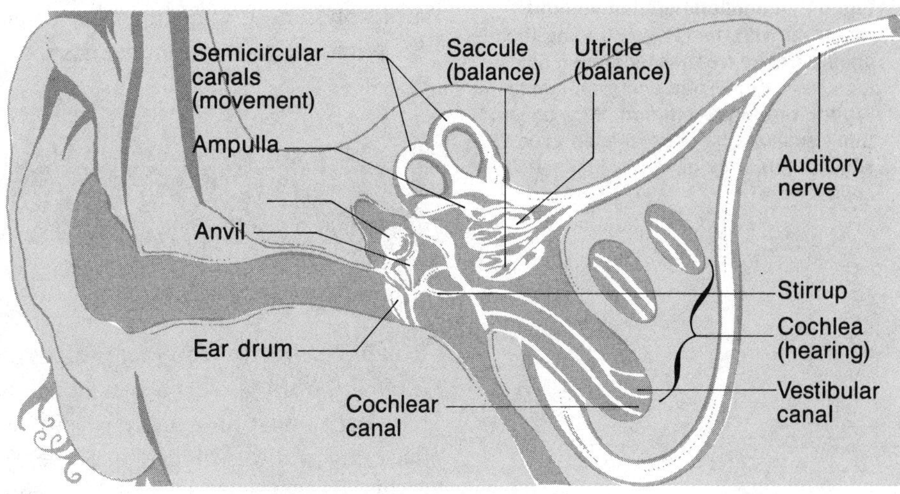

Fig. 6-19 The human ear contains receptors for hearing, balance, and movement.

Equilibrium and Motion Receptors

Equilibrium receptors help to control balance or body equilibrium. They are found in many different animals. Your equilibrium receptors are located in your ears (Fig. 6-19). Two hollow sacs, the **utricle** and **saccule**, contain sensory hair cell neurons on their inner surface. Also inside these sacs are tiny ear stones called **statoliths**. These are made of the same material as bone. When you are upright, gravity pulls the statoliths against the receptors at the bottom of the sacs. However, if you change position, the statoliths stimulate a different set of sensory cells. Thus, you can detect up and down, no matter what body position you are in (Fig. 6-20).

Crayfish have a similar organ which is discarded and replaced each time it sheds its exoskeleton (molts). However, the newly-molted crayfish must replace the statoliths using grains of sand. An interesting experiment was conducted using newly-molted crayfish that were given iron filings instead of sand. Later, when a magnet was placed above these crayfish, they responded by turning over on their backs. Can you explain why?

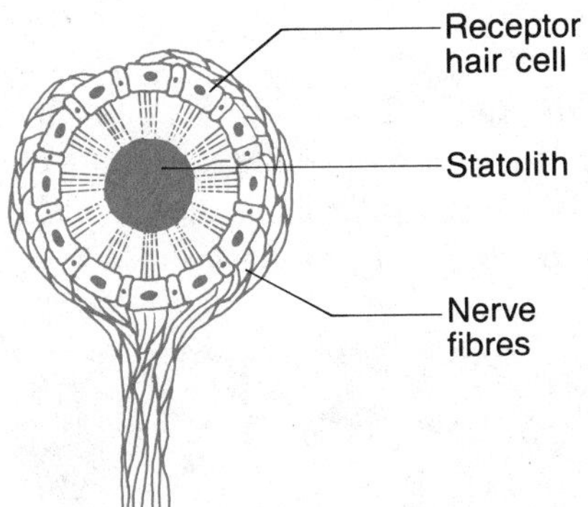

Fig. 6-20 An ear stone or statolith stimulates sensory hair cells only in the downward direction in this equilibrium receptor organ.

Motion receptors are also found in the ear. These consist of three hollow tubes connected to the utricle and lined with sensory hair cells. The tubes, called **semicircular canals**, are filled with fluid. As the head is turned in any direction, the fluid in one or more of the canals moves and stimulates the sensory hair cells. As long as the fluid keeps moving, you "feel" motion.

Each tube is at right angles to the other two, so that movement in all directions is detectable. However, your body's familiar motions are in the horizontal direction. If you stand on a ship in rough seas or take a roller coaster ride at an amusement park, the other less familiar canals are heavily stimulated. Your body responds by giving you motion sickness, possibly to make you stop.

Section Review

1. What kinds of sensations are detected by mechanoreceptors?
2. What kinds of specialized receptors are used to detect vibration?
3. Explain why vision is not a primary sense for most aquatic animals.

Fig. 6-21 Scallops are active ocean molluscs with many eyes ringing their shells. Unlike freshwater clams, scallops have numerous enemies, including the predatory starfish. Why do you think scallops have developed eyes while clams only have photosensitive cells?

4. Explain how your inner ear detects both balance and movement.
5. What causes motion sickness?

6.8 Photoreceptors

Types of Photoreceptors

You have already seen that protists can detect and respond to light. Some, like *Euglena*, even possess a specialized photosensitive organelle called an eyespot. Similarly, most animals have photosensitive cells. In some complex animals these are well-developed into eyes. The earthworm has no eyes, but experiments show that it seeks dark conditions using photoreceptors on its back. Starfish have light sensitive cells on their feet. Molluscs such as clams have similar cells near the opening in their shells. Some molluscs have even developed simple eyes. For example, the common scallop has thirty-two simple eyes (Fig. 6-21).

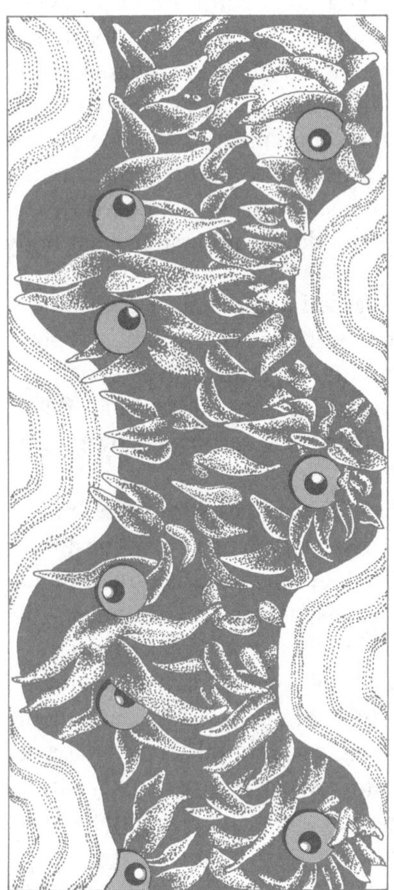

What is an eye? It is an organ with a lens that concentrates light on photoreceptors. This use of a lens enables an animal to form an image using light. An image gives the animal some additional information about the size, shape, colour, and motion of objects around it.

Compound Eyes

Compound eyes are found in arthropods (Fig. 6-22). Each facet is a lens that focuses light onto a cluster of receptors called a retina underneath the facet. In effect, an insect has hundreds of individual eyes joined together to make one compound eye. Predatory insects such as dragonflies have up to 60 000

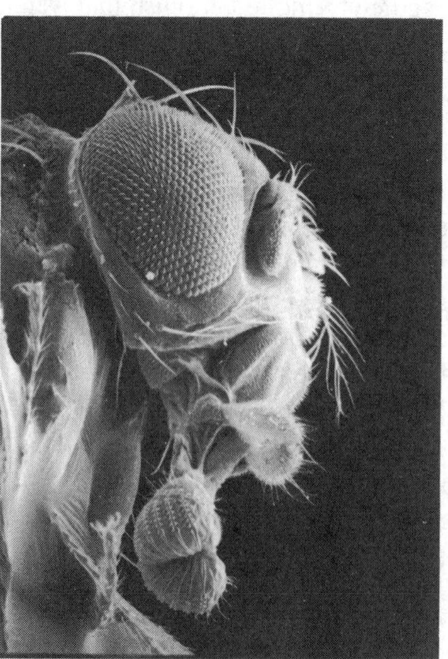

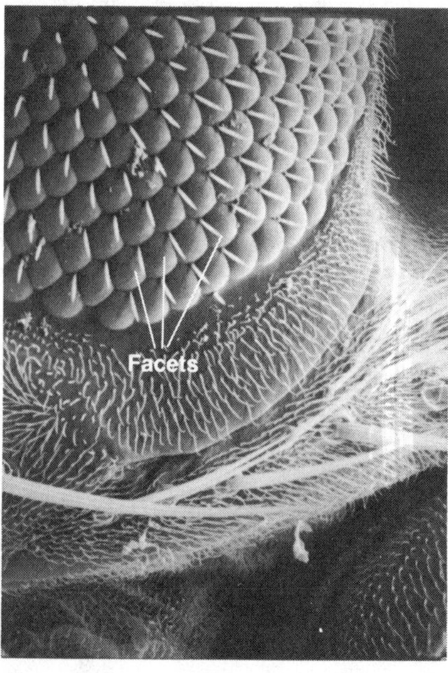

Fig. 6-22 The compound eye of a fruit fly magnified 75 × and 375 ×. What mechanoreceptors do you see?

Fig. 6-23 The dragonfly relies on vision to detect flying insects. Note how the size and location of the compound eyes permit this animal to see in almost all directions simultaneously.

facets. Dragonflies catch other insects like mosquitoes in the air. Can you explain why a dragonfly has such huge eyes (Fig. 6-23)?

Compound eyes can detect motion much faster than our eyes can. However, the images they form are blurred. As a result, they are not as good as yours for distinguishing details such as shape and colour. Experiments on arthropods show that they do not see all colours that you do. Some can see wavelengths that you cannot detect: ultraviolet.

Some insects including the grasshopper have some simple eyes called **ocelli** (singular: **ocellus**), usually located between the compound eyes. Spiders lack compound eyes but have eight ocelli.

Lensed Eyes

This type of eye is found in chordates and some predatory molluscs such as octopi and squid. Each animal has one pair. Instead of facets, these eyes have an internal **lens** that can adjust the focus (Fig. 6-24). There is also an **iris** that adjusts the amount of light reaching the sensitive **retina** where the sensory neurons are located. In the human eye these neurons are of two shapes: **rods** for dim light vision and **cones** for colour vision and bright light. Each human eye contains about 125 000 000 rods. These are located mostly around the edges of the retina. About 6 500 000 cones are located near the **fovea** which has the keenest vision. It is interesting to note that you can see an object better in dim light if you don't look directly at it but just to one side instead. Can you explain why?

There are no rods or cones on the retina at the base of the **optic nerve**. As a result, this spot is called the **blind spot**. You can verify the presence of a blind spot by closing your right eye and focusing your left one at the "T" in Figure 6-25 at a distance of 10 cm from the page. Move your head away from the page slowly while continuing to stare at the "T". At some distance (usually

Fig. 6-24 The human eye with a detached section of retina. Each cone detects one of the primary colours: red, green, or blue. Other colours are detected by your brain as various combinations of these three.

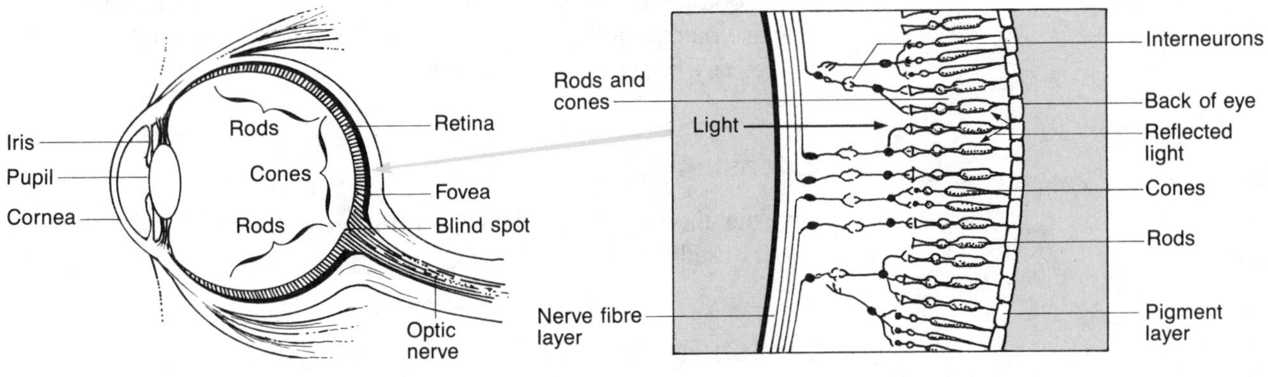

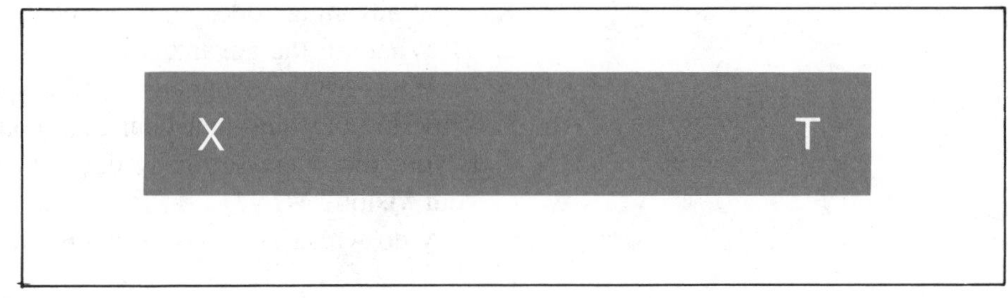

Fig. 6-25 Use this figure to find your blind spots.

less than 30 cm) the ''X'' will disappear when its image is focused on the blind spot. With the right eye open the ''T'' should disappear while you focus on the ''X''.

Colour Vision

Colour vision is believed to be better in humans and apes than in other animals. Colour detection depends on the presence of a number of visual pigments called **rhodopsins** made from protein and vitamin A. Most animals use only one kind of rhodopsin. Therefore they can see only one colour. Primates like you use a number of different rhodopsins, giving you a wider range of colours. Each pigment works best for a particular environment. For example, fish and tadpoles use one particular kind of rhodopsin for aquatic vision. However, as the tadpole develops into an adult frog, it switches pigments to one better suited for terrestrial vision.

Application: Vitamin A in World War 2

You have likely heard that you can improve your vision by eating lots of vitamin A (found in vegetables such as carrots). This inaccurate belief was ''invented'' by the Allied forces during World War 2 as a way of hiding a technological advance from the Axis forces. Aircraft designers had discovered that the bright dials in a bomber cockpit interfered with the pilot's ability to see targets at night. They found that the dials could be made much dimmer but just as readable if they used coloured light instead of white. There was an immediate improvement in the pilots' accuracy which the Axis forces certainly noticed. To cover up the real reason which would be copied in the Axis aircraft, the Allies circulated a story about feeding their pilots lots of carrots to give them good night vision. Unfortunately, most people still believe the story. As long as you obtain the daily recommended dose of vitamin A, your vision will not get any better by eating more.

Extension

Find out the colours used in the instrument panels of cars. Why are these colours used?

Section Review

1. What advantage does an eye have over a cluster of photoreceptors?
2. **a)** What are the advantages and disadvantages of compound eyes?
   b) What are the advantages and disadvantages of lensed eyes?
3. Why do you think that your eyes contain many more rods than cones?
4. If your diet were seriously deficient in vitamin A, what would happen to your vision? Why?
5. Why do we say that vision is one of our primary senses?

6.9 Electroreceptors and Thermoreceptors

Electroreceptors

Electroreception is the detection of electric fields. The contraction of any muscle produces a tiny electric current and field. Some aquatic animals have receptors to detect these fields and thereby sense the presence and movement of other organisms. It is difficult for humans to understand this ability because we have no electroreceptors.

Paramecia are thought to detect electric fields because they migrate towards a negative electrode. Primitive fish such as sharks have many electroreceptors. One fish, the electric eel, has developed the ability to *produce* a very strong electric field. It can deliver up to 400 volts to stun its prey.

Thermoreception

Thermoreception is the detection of temperature. Each species of organism operates best at a certain temperature called its **optimum temperature**. For your internal organs, the optimum temperature is 37°C. As a **homeothermic** (''warm-blooded'') animal, you maintain that temperature constantly.

Like you, every organism has an optimum temperature. However, unlike you, most other animals are **poikilothermic** (''cold-blooded'') and must depend on their environment to adjust their temperatures to optimum. **Thermoreceptors** or temperature receptors are absolutely essential for this task.

You have separate heat and cold receptors in your skin (see Figure 6-15). Most other animals have single temperature receptors located on the external surface, antennas, and mouthparts.

Rattlesnakes and other **pit vipers** have a pair of heat sensitive pits to detect their warm-blooded prey (Fig. 6-26). A blindfolded rattler will locate and strike at a light bulb when it is turned on. Can you explain why? What advantage does a rattler have over its prey (mice) when the two organisms are hunting for food at night?

Application: Sensing with High Technology

We have invented many devices to extend our senses and pick up stimuli that would otherwise be undetectable. We *can* detect electric fields—our communication equipment depends on this. We ''sense'' heat using infrared film. We employ telescopes and microscopes to see things our eyes alone cannot detect. Electronic ''sniffers'' probe airport luggage for explosives or narcotics.

Extension

What high-tech sensors have you seen? How do they work? Research a particular device that is designed to extend our human senses. You will find several examples in your science laboratory.

Fig. 6-26 Sensitive thermoreceptors in pit vipers detect warm prey such as mice. A snake's tongue collects odours for the chemoreceptors on the roof of its mouth.

Section Review

1. a) How can electroreceptors detect other organisms?
   b) Why are electroreceptors better than eyes in an underwater environment?
2. a) What is the difference between poikilothermic and homeothermic organisms? Which are you?
   b) Of what survival advantage are thermoreceptors?
   c) How do thermoreceptors help an organism survive?

6.10 Activity: Investigating Earthworm Senses

Like all animals, earthworms detect and respond to changes in their environment. What abiotic factors do you think earthworms detect? How do they respond?

Problem

What abiotic conditions do earthworms detect and respond to?

Materials

shallow tray
rich organic soil
water
earthworms (5)

one or more of:
sand
light source
soda water
baking soda solution
cold packs (2)

Procedure

a. Copy Table 6-1 into your notebook.

Table 6-1 Earthworm Ecology

Abiotic factor	*Predicted behaviour of earthworms*	*Experimental result*
Soil organic content		
Soil acidity		
Light intensity		
Soil moisture		
Soil temperature		

b. Complete the column in Table 6-1 titled "Predicted behaviour of earthworms". Think about where you have seen earthworms and about the following questions as you do so. If earthworms are given a choice, will they select

1. sandy or rich organic soil?
2. acidic, neutral, or basic soil?
3. a light or dark area?
4. water-logged, dry, or moist soil?
5. warm, hot, or cold soil?

c. Your class has been divided into 5 groups for this activity. Join the group to which you were assigned.

Soil Organic Content Group

d. Put moist sand to a depth of 5 cm in one half of the tray (Condition A in Figure 6-27).

e. Put rich organic soil to a depth of 5 cm in the other half of the tray (Condition B in Figure 6-27). The soil should have the same "wetness" as the sand.

f. Place the 5 earthworms in the centre of the tray.

g. Note the locations of the earthworms every 3 min for 15 min. Record the average of your results in your table.

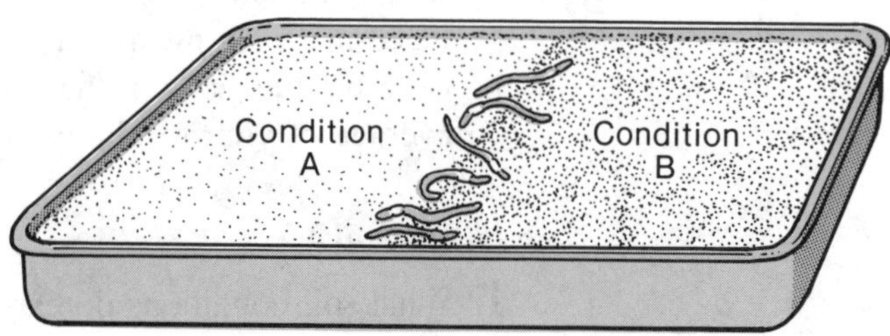

Fig. 6-27 What abiotic conditions do earthworms detect and respond to?

Soil Acidity Group

d. Put rich organic soil to a depth of 5 cm in the tray.
e. Moisten one half of the soil with soda water, an acid (Condition A in Figure 6-27).
f. Moisten the other half of the soil with baking soda solution, a base (Condition B in Figure 6-27). Make sure this half is moistened the same amount as the other half.
g. Place the 5 earthworms in the centre of the tray.
h. Note the locations of the earthworms every 3 min for 15 min. Record the average of your results in your table.

Light Intensity Group

d. Put rich organic soil to a depth of 5 cm in the tray.
e. Cover half of the tray with dark paper (Condition A in Figure 6-27).
f. Put a bright light over the other half of the tray (Condition B in Figure 6-27).
g. Place the 5 earthworms in the centre of the tray.
h. Note the locations of the earthworms every 3 min for 15 min. Record the average of your results in your table.

Soil Moisture Group

d. Put *dry*, rich organic soil to a depth of 5 cm in one half of the tray (Condition A in Figure 6-27).
e. Put *moist* (but not soggy), rich organic soil to a depth of 5 cm in the other half of the tray (Condition B in Figure 6-27).
f. Place the 5 earthworms in the centre of the tray.
g. Note the locations of the earthworms every 3 min for 15 min. Record the average of your results in your table.
h. If time permits, repeat this experiment using soggy soil instead of dry soil for Condition A.

Soil Temperature Group

d. Put rich organic soil to a depth of 5 cm in the tray.
e. Place a cold pack at 0°C or below in the soil at one end of the tray (Condition A in Figure 6-27). Make sure this pack was in a freezer overnight.
f. Place a cold pack at about 40°C in the soil at the other end of the tray (Condition B in Figure 6-27). Make sure this pack was in 40°C water for several minutes.
g. Place the 5 earthworms in the centre of the tray.
h. Note the locations of the earthworms every 3 min for 15 min. Record the average of your results in your table.

Discussion

1. What soil conditions do earthworms seem to prefer?
2. Why did you use as many worms as possible in each group?
3. What types of sensory receptors do you know worms have as a result of your experiments?

4. Suppose you wanted to catch some earthworms. What could you do to get them to leave their burrows?

Extensions

1. Design and conduct an experiment to demonstrate whether or not earthworms can detect gravity.
2. Design and conduct an experiment to demonstrate the sensory abilities of another animal, such as mealworms, snails, millipedes, or sow bugs.

6.11 Activity: Testing Human Senses

How well do your senses work? Are your classmates able to detect the same stimuli equally well? Can your senses be tricked? Is there variation in the distribution of mechanoreceptors on your skin? You will have lots of fun seeking answers to these and other questions about your own senses.

There are too many sensory tests available to completely describe them here. Commercially-available test kits with instructions can be used. We recommend the following:

For Vision

an Eye Chart
Ichikawa Colour Blindness Kit (Fig. 6-28)
Visual Perception Kit (demonstrates depth perception and binocular vision)
Binocular Vision Kit
Peripheral Vision Test Kit

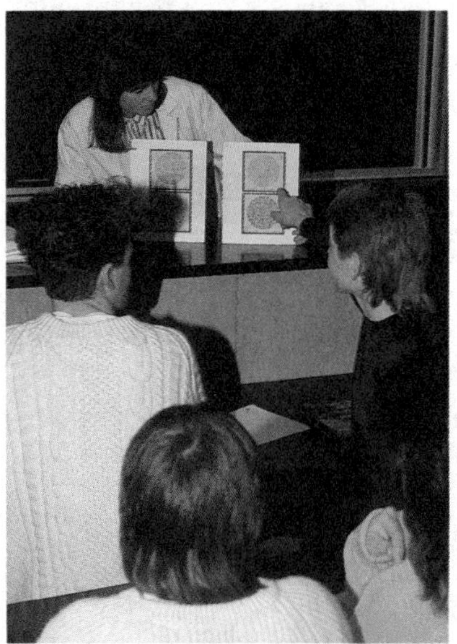

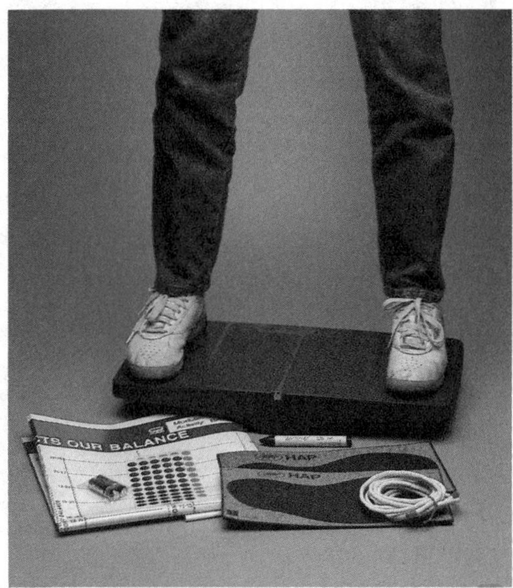

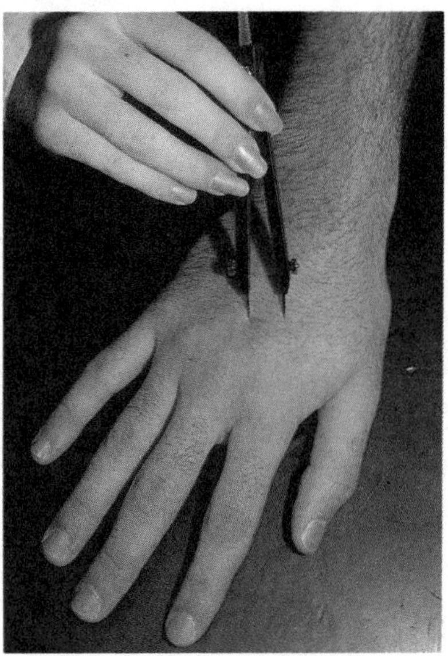

Fig. 6-28 Numerous testing devices are available to investigate your own sensory receptors.

For Smell, Taste, and Skin Mechanoreception

Human Senses Experiment Kit (demonstrates a "taste map", odour fatigue, and four mechanoreceptors)
Taste Discrimination Kit (demonstrates sensitivity to the four known taste sensations)

For Equilibrium

Balance and Movement Kit (Fig. 6-28)

Each kit measures one or more senses. Alternatively, you can design your own experiment. Here are some problems that you could try on your own:

- Can the thermoreceptors in your hands be fooled into "detecting" a stimulus improperly?
- How close together are your touch receptors on various parts of your skin surface (Fig. 6-28)?
- Can all people taste a chemical called PTC?

For each experiment that you conduct, follow the scientific method and record all information. Prepare a proper report at the completion of those parts of this activity that you took part in.

Chapter Highlights

1. Sensory systems are essential for an organism's survival.
2. Different organisms have different kinds of sensory systems.
3. Central nervous systems are necessary to handle large quantities of sensory information and to coordinate responses.
4. Animals use five kinds of sensory receptors: chemoreceptors, mechanoreceptors, photoreceptors, electroreceptors, and thermoreceptors.
5. Humans have eleven senses.
6. Humans extend their own senses by using other animals with better senses or by building "high-tech" sensors.

Key Terms

afferent nerve
association neuron
central nervous system
chemoreceptor
efferent nerve
electroreceptor
equilibrium
homeothermic
interneuron
irritable
mechanoreceptor
motor neuron
nerve
network
photoreceptor
poikilothermic
receptor
response
sensory neuron
sensory system
stimulus
taxis
thermoreceptor

Recognizing the Concepts

Each of the following statements or questions is followed by four responses. Choose the correct response in each case. (Do not write in this book.)

1. Which of the following are primary senses in humans?
   a) sight and smell **c)** taste and hearing
   b) sight and hearing **d)** touch and taste
2. Aquatic (water) organisms are most likely to detect environmental stimuli by
   a) electroreception and hearing **c)** touch and vibration
   b) sight and taste **d)** echo location and heat
3. Which of the following senses does *not* use mechanoreceptors?
   a) hearing **b)** equilibrium **c)** touch **d)** temperature
4. Which of the following types of receptors is *not* found in humans?
   a) olfactory receptors **c)** electroreceptors
   b) photoreceptors **d)** thermoreceptors
5. When threatened, octopi release black ink that paralyzes chemoreceptors. What type of organism is an octopus likely escaping from when it uses ink?
   a) a predator that ambushes its prey (e.g. a moray eel)
   b) a stationary carnivore (e.g. an anemone)
   c) a fast surface predator (e.g. a barracuda)
   d) a slow bottom hunter (e.g. a grouper)

Understanding the Concepts

1. Distinguish between afferent and efferent neurons.
2. The nerve networks in *Hydra* use short neurons but the nerve cords in larger animals use giant fibre neurons. Why do these latter neurons work better?
3. Distinguish among sensory, motor, and interneurons.
4. Why is a central nervous system necessary for large animals?
5. Humans usually say that they have five senses, but we have indicated eleven. Which of these eleven were classified as "touch" in the five-sense classification? Which of these eleven were not included at all?

Applying the Concepts

1. The largest organisms on earth are trees. Even though they have many cells, they lack nervous systems entirely. Why are such systems missing from these giant organisms?
2. Different responses to the same stimulus can be used to separate animals, as you saw in Activity 6.3. Explain how the following devices take advantage of differential responses to affect only one group or species of organism:
   a) an electric bug light/trap
   b) a silent dog whistle
   c) shark repellant

3. a) Female mosquitoes use chemoreceptors in their antennas to detect and follow high levels of carbon dioxide gas. Explain why the ability to do this is an advantage to mosquitoes.
   b) Design a mosquito trap that makes use of the mosquito's sensory ability.
4. If you were to redesign the human sensory system to enable it to detect all stimuli, what additional stimuli would you want to collect? Why?
5. Why are you able to see objects more clearly in dim light when you do not look directly at them?
6. How do blind people overcome their lack of vision when reading a book? How do deaf people overcome their lack of hearing when communicating with others? Refer to receptors in your answers.

Investigations

Fig. 6-29 Devices such as these improve our ability to sense our environment.

1. Find out how astronauts are taught to perform tasks in the absence of gravity. What receptors are relied on when the position receptors do not work?
2. Some researchers are concerned about our exposure to electric fields from appliances and electrical transmission lines. Since our bodies do not detect electrical fields, we have no sensations. However, we may still suffer damage. Find out what damage scientists think is being done to us. How strong a field do they feel causes damage?
3. All organisms are unable to sense **ionizing radiation**. Find out what ionizing radiation is. Why are we concerned about it? How do we detect it? Why has it recently become an issue?
4. Write a report describing the development of the mammalian ear. What parts of the body did it develop (evolve) from?
5. We use hundreds of devices to extend our senses. A few of these are shown in Figure 6-29. Write a report about one instrument, explaining how it improves our sensory perception and how we use the instrument to our advantage.
6. Recent research suggests that some animals may be able to detect magnetic fields. Write a report discussing magnetoreception. How would this sensory ability help certain animals?

Biography

Maureen Higgins: Specimen Production Supervisor

Maureen Higgins is the production supervisor of the live specimen department at a major Canadian biological supply company. If you use living protists, animals, or plants in your school, the chances are good that she cultivated these for you.

Higgins began working as a technician after she graduated from high school. She was given on-the-job training raising protists. After three years with the company, she now supervises the entire live department. Schools, colleges, and universities throughout the United States and Canada rely on her department to grow and deliver high-quality living study materials.

Growing protists is difficult. Each species prefers a certain set of conditions: pH, light intensity, minerals, and food supply. All of these must be maintained at optimum levels. Large protists feed on smaller ones and bacteria, all of which must be grown under controlled conditions year-round. Even protists have to have their "cages" changed so that they don't die in their own metabolic wastes. Maureen's biggest challenge is in keeping large populations of these organisms free from infection, parasites, and contamination. She maintains multiple cultures of each species as a backup.

VISTA

X-RAYS, CATS, AND NMRS

Extending our senses by using technology is one of our favourite ways of gathering new information. Microscopes, radiotelescopes, and other devices—simple and complex—have extended our knowledge about our external environment. But we have always had difficulty with our internal environment, that is, our own bodies. Recent developments have extended our primary senses to "see" inside ourselves.

Radiation and radioactive materials have been very useful in internal medicine. Strong ionizing radiation passes through our body tissues but is absorbed in different amounts by different kinds of tissue. **X-rays** (a type of ionizing radiation) easily pass through skin, muscle, and other soft tissue, but are partly blocked by bone and metal. Thus a picture of part of your body taken with x-rays instead of visible light detects bone damage or hard foreign objects.

X-rays have two problems: they do not show most abnormalities in soft tissues, and they are invasive. That is, they cause tissue damage because of their high energy. To partly solve the first problem, technologists developed a machine called a **Computerized Axial Tomography Scanner** or **CATS.** X-rays are fired at a patient from a number of angles simultaneously. The non-absorbed radiation is fed into a computer which produces a two-dimensional picture. This picture shows soft tissues much better than a simple x-ray. However, it still uses invasive radiation. CATS are also expensive to buy and operate.

Very recently, a similar scanner has been developed called the **Nuclear Magnetic Resonance Scanner** or **NMRS.** It uses radio waves (see Figure 25–7, page 576) which have very low energy and are completely non-invasive. It produces better soft tissue pictures than CAT scanners. For the first time, doctors are able to "see" a patient's internal organs without surgery or tissue damage! Compare the NMRS picture to the x-ray photograph. With proper funding, it is hoped that every hospital will have at least one of these scanners soon.

Humans have developed many other devices to extend our senses, with new ones being invented all the time!

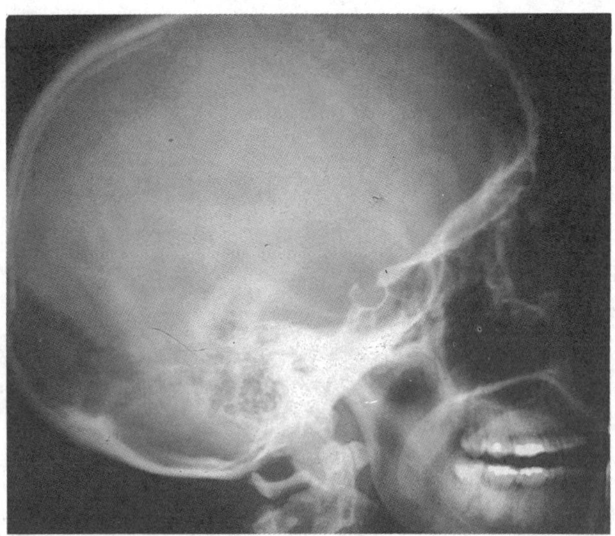

X-ray image

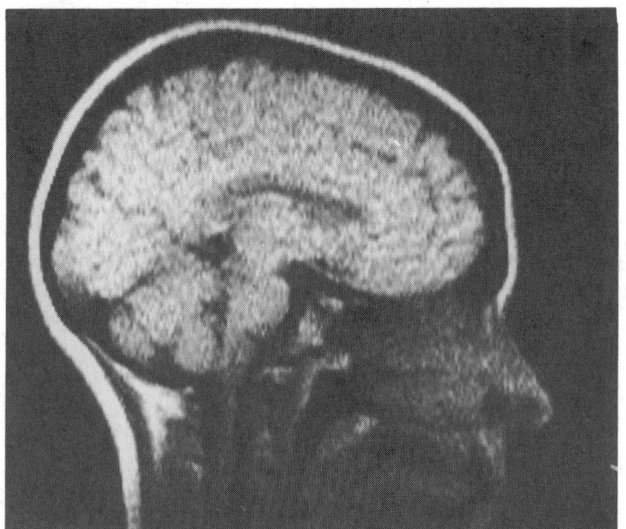

NMRS image

7 Responding to the Environment: Psychobiology

CHAPTER CONTENTS

CHAPTER OBJECTIVES

After completing this chapter you should be able to:

1. List the types of responses organisms use and describe examples of each.
2. Describe the structural adaptations used by several animals to enhance survival in particular environments.
3. Describe the kinds of response behaviours exhibited by various organisms.
4. Describe how we have copied some animal adaptations for our own use.

In the last chapter you learned about the varied ways in which organisms sense environmental changes. Their responses to these changes are also varied. A response may be as simple as a movement. A very complex response may involve learning. In what ways do organisms respond to stimuli (Fig. 7-1)? How are their bodies designed to respond? How do you respond?

Fig. 7-1 This animal enjoys having its ears scratched. What responses does it show to the scratch stimulus? How did the animal stimulate its master into scratching?

7.1 What Is Psychobiology?

Each reaction of an organism to an environmental stimulus is called a **response**. All the responses of that organism make up its **behaviour**. Behaviour may be quite simple or very complex. It may involve the **movement** or **locomotion** of the organism as well as some change in the external environment.

The study of *human* behaviour is known as **psychology**. However, **psychobiology** is the study of the behaviour of all organisms, from the simplest to the most complex.

Behaviour is said to be **adaptive**. That is, it is for the survival benefit of the organism. As a result, we call any *behaviour* or *structure* of an organism that helps it to survive an **adaptation**. Organisms with complex nervous systems exhibit a wider range of behaviours than those with simple nervous systems. Complex organisms have even developed the ability to learn. You will study this adaptive process later in this chapter.

Fig. 7-2 Limewater reacts with carbon dioxide in your breath to produce a cloudy mixture. Can you devise an experiment to prove that your breath has more CO_2 than air? What controls will you use to ensure a fair comparison?

Why Do Organisms Respond?

There are six main reasons why organisms respond to environmental stimuli:

- ***Food*** is needed by all living things. Plants make their own by photosynthesis and they respond to those stimuli (light, water, and carbon dioxide) that will help them produce more food. The paramecium feeds on bacteria. Therefore it responds to the acid environments produced by bacteria. An earthworm also eats bacteria which it finds plentiful in the rich humus soil which it prefers. A grasshopper needs tender grass which it finds using sight and chemical sensors. A perch must catch its prey so it needs sensitive receptors and fast responses. Any organism that fails to respond adequately to its need for food will die.
- ***Waste elimination*** is a response to internal stimuli. For instance, you exchange gases with your environment in response to the concentration of waste carbon dioxide in your blood stream. When the concentration becomes high (a toxic condition), your breathing rate increases. Carbon dioxide is given off as you breathe out. You can verify this by trying the experiment shown in Figure 7-2. Other internal stimuli cause the **voiding** (elimination) of feces and urine.
- ***Escape or defence*** is also essential to survival. Even plants have defence responses. Can you think of some? What happens to any individual or species that fails to respond effectively to a threat (Fig. 7-3)?
- ***Reproduction*** is necessary for a species to be successful. Males and females must locate each other by sensing and responding to the signals each uses.
- ***Orientation*** is an organism's response to its own body position or location. This is necessary for maintaining balance, growing in the right direction, finding shelter, and for migrating.
- ***Communication*** is common among large animals. By sharing information about food, predators, or other environmental factors, individuals help other members of the same species survive. Even plants communicate. Can you guess how?

Fig. 7-3 The call of the loon is a symbol of our northern wilderness. Perhaps someone in your class has tried to approach a loon in a canoe. How does the loon respond? How does this behaviour benefit the loon and the species?

No matter what the response, the reason is survival. A **biologically successful organism** is one that survives and **reproduces**. Without appropriate senses and responses, this will never happen.

Biological Success: The Insects

We humans like to think of ourselves as the world's most successful species. In fact, we are badly outnumbered by a much more successful group: insects. In fact, the insects outnumber all other animal groups combined! Part of the reason for the insect success story is their ability to respond by adapting to new environments, new food, and new stresses such as insecticides. As you study the ways in which organisms respond, pay particular attention to the best responders of all, the insects.

Section Review

1. **a)** What is the behaviour of an organism?
   b) Why do organisms have behaviour?
2. **a)** What is psychobiology?
   b) Distinguish between psychology and psychobiology.
3. Describe six reasons why organisms have responses.
4. What two things must an organism do to be successful?
5. What do we mean when we say a response is adaptive?

Fig. 7-4 This Monarch butterfly hatching from its chrysalis will survive over winter as an adult. Butterflies hatched in late summer do not reproduce until the following spring. However, butterflies hatched in the spring or early summer reproduce shortly thereafter.

As you learned in Chapter 6, all living things respond to changes in their environment. That is, they are **irritable**. However, organisms differ in the way that they respond. Let us look at two common ways.

Chemical Responses

Chemical responses are poorly observed by us because we lack the sensory equipment to detect most of the chemicals. However, these responses are very common. For example, when a tree is infested with caterpillars, its only defence is chemical. It certainly cannot run away or shake off these parasites. Its response to being eaten (a stimulus) is to produce chemicals in its leaves that are disagreeable or even toxic to the pests. Interestingly, the tree also releases hormones into the air which stimulate nearby trees of the same species to produce the same toxins. Clearly, the trees are communicating with each other about a common problem. How do these responses help the trees survive?

Monarch butterflies are thought to respond to the changing **photoperiod** (length of daylight) and changing temperature in a chemical way (Fig. 7-4). If the photoperiod is increasing, as it does in the spring, a newly-emerged adult responds by producing certain chemicals (hormones) that cause its reproductive system to work immediately. However, if the photoperiod and temperature are decreasing, as they do in the fall, a new adult will not produce these hormones until the following spring. Can you explain why this species uses photoperiod and temperature to "shut down" its reproduction at a certain time of the year? How does this improve the Monarch's survival?

As you know, during their brief breeding season, male moths locate females of their own species by scent. Certain spiders attract male moths to their webs by releasing a copy of the female odour. Recent experiments suggest that these spiders respond to a changing photoperiod by switching odours to attract different moth species. This adaptation synchronizes the spider's "attractiveness" with whichever species of prey is abundant at that time in the season. Note that this chemical response is not caused by the appearance of the prey. Instead, it is caused by the season at which the prey should appear.

Growth Responses

Many organisms respond to stimuli by altering their growth pattern. These responses are easily observed in plants. You might find it interesting to try the experiments shown in Figure 7-5. Growth responses that involve a direction are called **tropisms**. The oat seedlings in Figure 7-5 grow *towards* the light stimulus, an example of **phototropism** (*photo* means light). The bean seedling is showing **geotropism** (*geo* means earth) by growing *away* from the gravitational force of the earth. Plants also show **hydrotropisms** (growth towards water) and **thigmotropisms** (growth away from touched objects such as an underground rock).

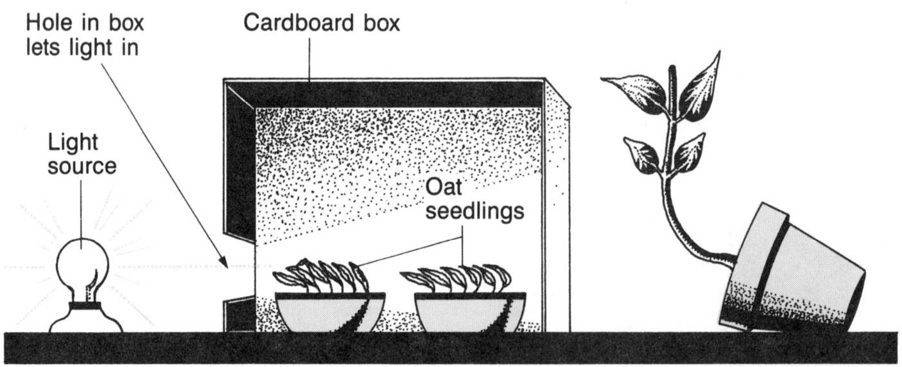

Fig. 7-5 Oat seedlings will grow towards light as seen in Experiment 1. In the second experiment, a young bean seedling has been repositioned on its side. It responds by changing its direction of growth. Can you explain why plants respond to light and gravity? How does your response to these stimuli compare to the plant's response?

Plant seeds as well as the eggs of many animals become active in response to temperature and moisture changes. Interestingly, plants stop their growth in response to other stimuli. For example, the mid-season change in the photoperiod causes plants to cease their growth and to prepare for fall and winter. These growth responses are not tropisms because no direction is involved.

Section Review

1. Describe three examples of chemical responses. Explain how each is adaptive.
2. How does your behaviour to the stimuli of light and gravity differ from that of a plant? Explain why you have a different response to each stimulus.
3. Name and describe four types of tropisms.

Fig. 7-6 Study a *Mimosa* plant (A) or a Venus' flytrap (B) in your classroom. How fast can the leaves close? What kind of stimuli produce this response?

7.3 Responding with Movement

Movement is a universal kind of response—every organism can move. Before you have visions of trees running around, remember that movement and **locomotion** are not the same thing. Locomotion is movement from place to place in the environment. Organisms that can locomote are called **motile**, whereas those that cannot are **sessile**. Even sessile organisms like plants move certain parts of themselves. Can you devise a simple experiment to prove that leaves turn slowly towards a light source? Because plant movement is very slow compared to animal movement, we are fascinated by fast-moving plants such as those shown in Figure 7-6.

Some Types of Movement

Flagellate movement is performed by the use of thread-like structures called **flagella** (singular: **flagellum**). In many protists, a single flagellum projects forward from the cell (Fig. 7-7,A). As it rotates, it pulls the cell behind it. Some protists have more than one flagellum. In animal sperm cells, a vibrating flagellum projects rearward and propels the cell forward (Fig. 7-7,B).

Ciliate movement uses short hair-like projections similar to flagella. Each cell has numerous cilia which beat in a rhythmic coordinated fashion (Fig. 7-8). Some protists use cilia to propel themselves through their aquatic medium. In contrast, sessile protists use cilia to push water past their bodies and extract microscopic bacteria for food.

You have ciliated cells in the lining of your breathing system. Just like sessile protists, these cells "sweep" materials by. However, these cells do not feed on the materials they are sweeping. They are just cleaning out damaging substances. A number of chemicals, including some in cigarette smoke, paralyze the action of cilia. Can you explain why smokers often develop a cough and, eventually, lung disease?

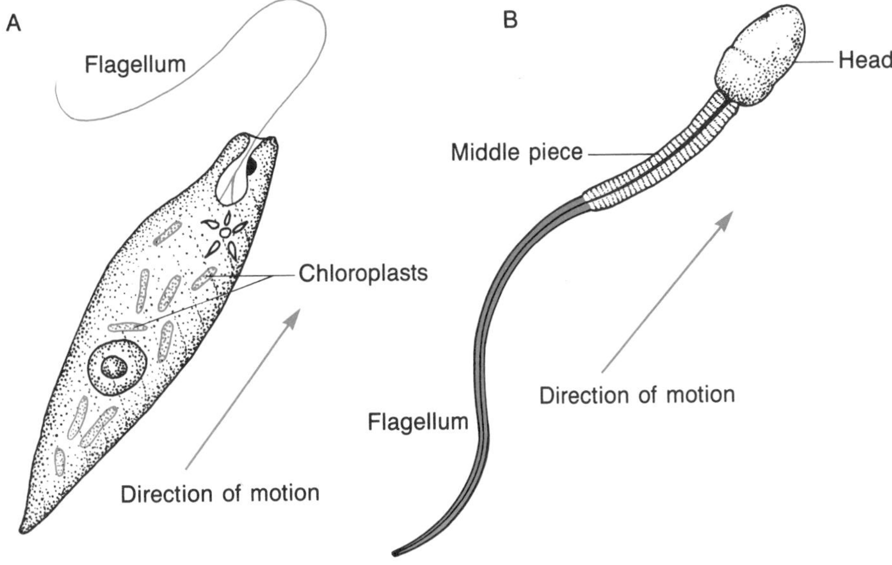

Fig. 7-7 Flagella are efficient locomotive systems for single cells such as *Euglena* (A) and human sperm (B).

Fig. 7-8 Paramecia make excellent subjects for studying ciliate movement.

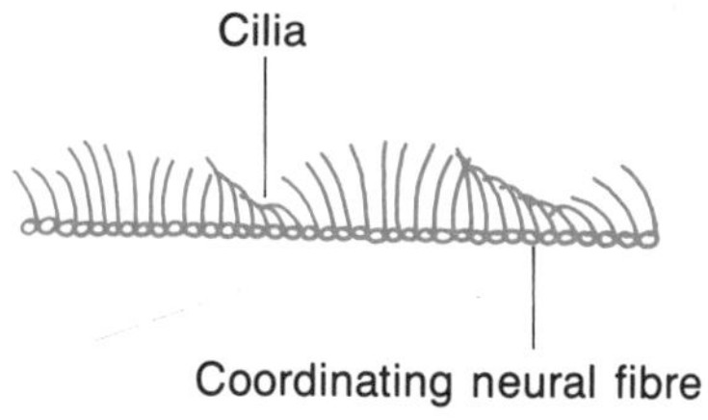

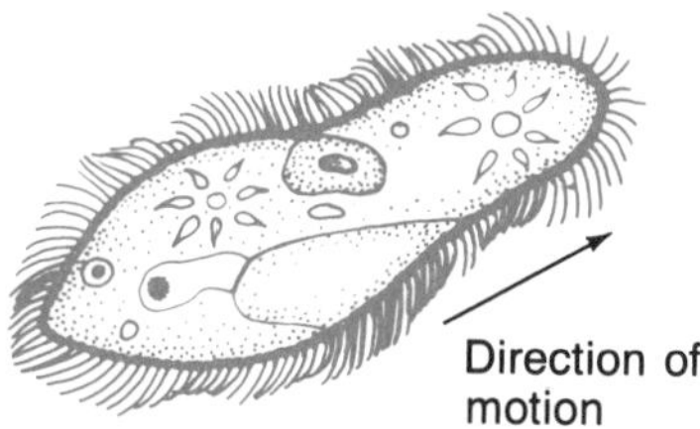

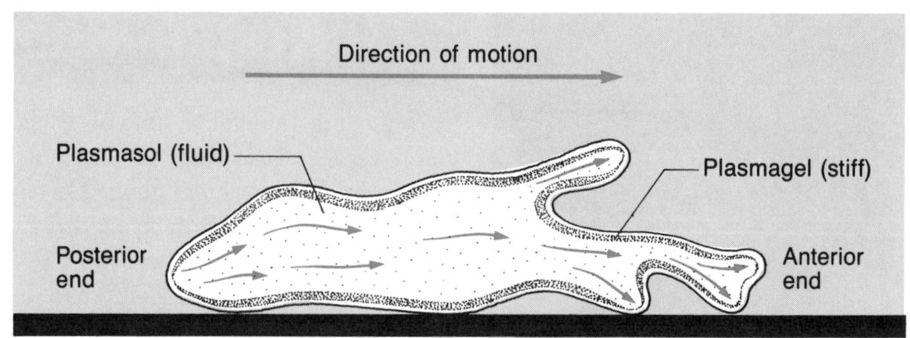

Fig. 7-9 The amoeba moves by causing its liquid plasmasol to flow forward and change to solid plasmagel. The process is reversed at the posterior end. Why does the amoeba move so slowly?

Amoeboid movement is named after a common protist, the amoeba. This organism is unusual in that it has no fixed shape. Instead, it ''flows'' along any solid surface in its underwater environment (Fig. 7-9). This type of movement is even used by certain cells in your body. White blood cells move out of the bloodstream and into your tissues using amoeboid movement.

Amoeboid and ciliate movement may be observed using live protists like amoebas and paramecia.

Turgor movement is commonly used by plants. **Turgor** refers to the water pressure inside plant cells. Most plant cells have a thick cell wall. If the cell is full of water (turgor pressure is high), then the cell contents press firmly against the cell wall. This cell is said to be **turgid**. However, if the cell has a low water content, the cell contents do not press against the cell wall and the entire cell is limp or **flaccid**. If a group of cells on one side of a stem change their turgor pressure by diffusing water in or out, then the entire stem bends. This movement permits a plant's leaves to ''follow'' the sun from morning to evening. How does this response help the plant (Fig. 7-10)?

Muscular movement involves specialized muscle cells designed to alter their shape by shortening. This change in shape causes movement that is much faster than turgor movement because diffusion is not involved. Inside each muscle cell are alternating filaments which slide over each other when the cell is stimulated by nerve impulses. These filaments are attached to opposite ends of the cell. Thus, when the cell is stimulated, it shortens. When stimulation of the cell stops, the cell ''relaxes.'' A stimulated cell exerts considerable force when the fibres contract. However, it exerts no force in the opposite direction when it relaxes. As a result, muscular movement uses pairs of muscles, each counteracting the pull of the other (Fig. 7-11). Muscles that perform opposite movements are called **antagonistic pairs**.

Fig. 7-10 Sunflowers got their name because they follow the sun across the sky during the day. The entire top of the plant, including leaves, obtains maximum exposure to the sun by doing this. Have you ever wondered when sunflowers turn back to the east to get ready for the morning sun?

Rate of Response

Certain responses such as escape movements must be fast. The structure of the nervous system assists animals in speeding up these nervous responses. **Reflexes** are one way in which the body can respond to stimuli quickly. A reflex operates as shown in Figure 7-12. In chordates this response is controlled by the spine. Thus, by the time the brain is aware that a stimulus has occurred, the body is already responding. How would this help an organism survive?

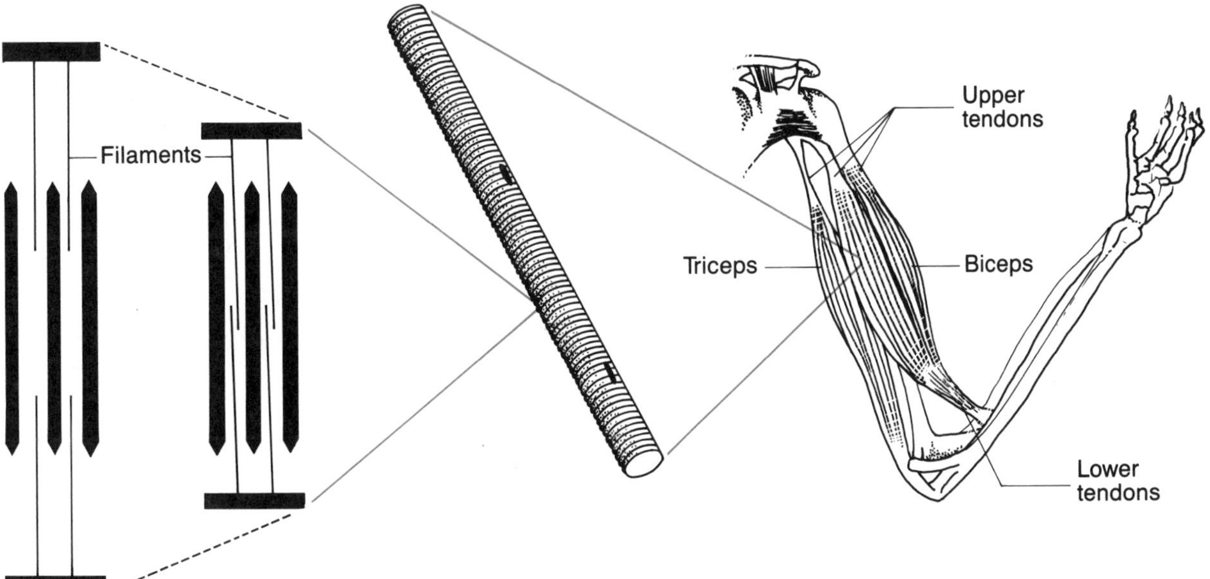

A. Sliding muscle filaments in the relaxed state (left) and the contracted state (right)

B. One muscle cell contains many filaments.

C. Each muscle contains many cells.

Fig. 7-11 Sliding muscle filaments (A) shorten the length of a muscle cell (B) when stimulated by effector neurons. The entire muscle shortens and moves the bones and limb to which the muscles are attached (C). When stimulation stops, the muscle relaxes. An antagonistic muscle (in this case the triceps) moves the limb in the opposite direction.

Insects have some of the fastest reflexes. The common cockroach detects and responds to an object moving above it in a few thousandths of a second. In Activity 7.4 you will measure your own response time. How do you compare to the cockroach?

Section Review

1. **a)** Distinguish between movement and locomotion.
   b) Distinguish between motile and sessile.
2. List the five kinds of movement.
3. How do flagellate and ciliate movement differ? How are they similar?
4. Explain why muscles are grouped in antagonistic pairs.
5. **a)** What is a reflex?
   b) How is a reflex adaptive?

7.4 Activity: Measuring Your Reaction Time

The length of time that passes between sensing a stimulus and beginning the response movement is called reaction time. In this activity, you and your lab partner will measure your reaction time using a ruler test.

Problem

What is your reaction time?

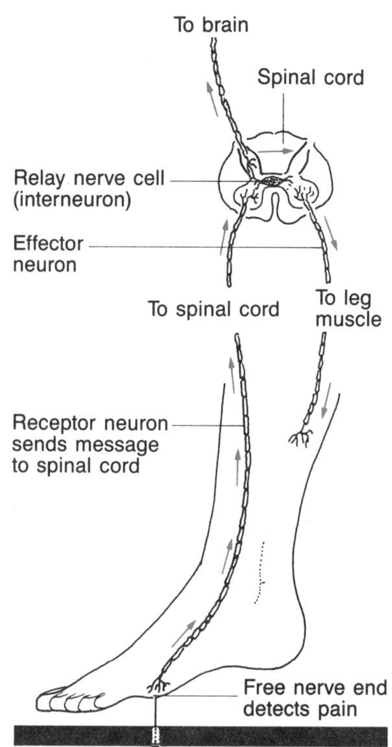

Fig. 7-12 A stimulus received by a sensory receptor is passed onto the spine. Here, a response signal is relayed to the effector muscles even before the brain receives the sensory signal. As a result, the foot is lifted off the nail sooner than it would have been if the brain were involved.

Fig. 7-13 How far does the ruler drop before you react?

Materials

metre stick or 30 cm ruler

Procedure

a. Copy Table 7-1 into your notebook.
b. Rest your left arm on your desk with your hand over the edge. Hold your thumb and first finger about 1 cm apart.
c. Have your partner hold the ruler so that the zero end is between your thumb and finger as shown in Figure 7-13.
d. While you watch the zero end, have your partner drop the ruler without warning.
e. Catch the ruler and record the distance it travelled in your table.
f. Repeat the experiment until you have performed ten trials with each hand.
g. Change positions with your partner and repeat steps (b) to (f).
h. Calculate each reaction time using the following information: The first 10 cm travelled needs 0.15 s. Each additional centimetre requires a further 0.005 s. Thus 10 cm requires 0.15 s, 16 cm requires 0.18 s, 20 cm requires 0.20 s, 30 cm requires 0.25 s, and so on.

Table 7-1 Measuring Reaction Time

Trial	*Left hand (cm)*	*Reaction time (s)*	*Right hand (cm)*	*Reaction time (s)*
1				
2				
3				
⋮				
10				

Discussion

1. Was there a difference in reaction time between hands? If there was, can you account for the difference?
2. Did your reaction time change with practice?
3. How does your reaction time compare to that of your partner? your other classmates? a cockroach? Why are cockroaches difficult to catch?

Extension

Your school's physics department will likely have an electronic timer that can be set up to measure human reaction times. Determine the reaction times students require to ''hit the brakes'' while pretending to drive. How does this leg time compare to the hand reaction time? Can you explain the difference? At 100 km/h how far does a car travel between the time a driver senses and responds to a braking situation?

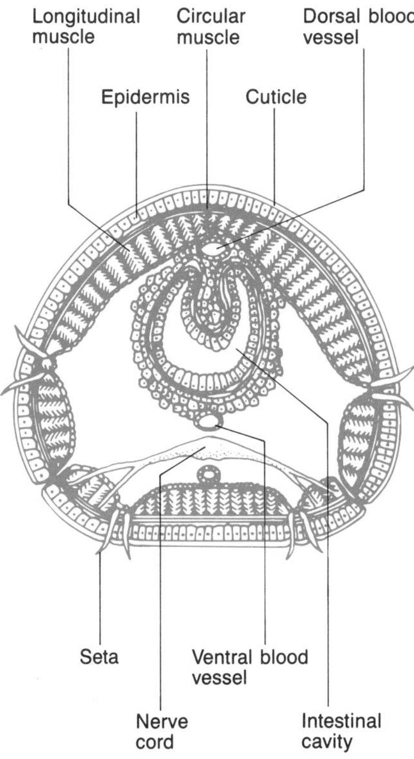
Longitudinal muscle
Circular muscle
Dorsal blood vessel
Epidermis
Cuticle
Seta
Ventral blood vessel
Nerve cord
Intestinal cavity

Fig. 7-14 Cross section of an earthworm. Earthworms have circular muscles wrapped around their body and longitudinal muscles running the length of the body. The worm also has retractable bristle hairs called setae which are used to anchor its body in place.

7.5 Structural Adaptations for Movement

To cope with the challenges of their environments, many organisms have developed specialized body parts for efficient response. We shall look at a few of the ways that organisms are designed for movement responses.

The Earthworm: Locomotion in Soil

Earthworms have no bones to which muscles can be attached. Yet they are still able to travel through soil using muscles. Instead of opposing muscle pairs like those in your arms (see Figure 7-11), earthworms have two sets of muscles arranged as shown in Figure 7-14. When contracted, the circular muscles squeeze the contents of the body, causing the worm to lengthen. This is similar to the response of a balloon or the contents of a tube of toothpaste that is squeezed in the middle. The opposite thing happens when the longitudinal muscles contract. The body shortens but enlarges in girth. Just like your skeletal muscles, a worm's muscles are antagonistic.

By alternating the use of front and rear setae as well as the two sets of muscles, a worm slowly pushes its way through the soil (Fig. 7-15). Notice that a tunnel is left behind by the worm. These tunnels let air and moisture penetrate below the surface. For this reason, soil without earthworms is unsuitable for many kinds of agriculture.

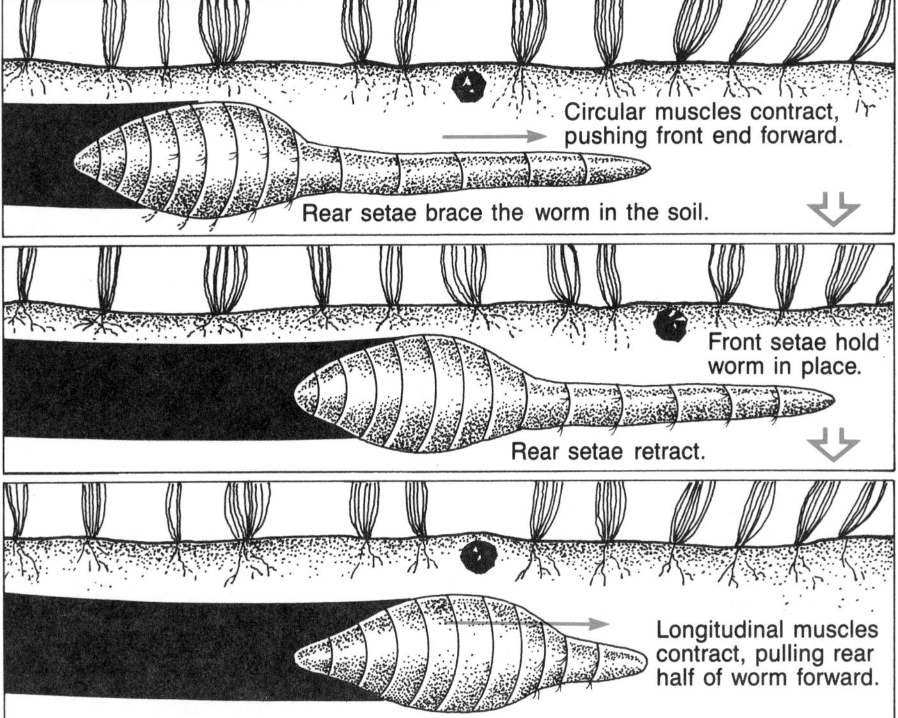
Circular muscles contract, pushing front end forward.
Rear setae brace the worm in the soil.
Front setae hold worm in place.
Rear setae retract.
Longitudinal muscles contract, pulling rear half of worm forward.

Fig. 7-15 Alternating use of a worm's two types of muscles allows the worm to travel along underground.

The Perch: Locomotion in Water

Bony fish like the perch have two highly specialized structures for movement: fins and a swim bladder. The fins are appendages operated by antagonistic sets of muscles. The tail or **caudal** fin provides forward propulsion (Fig. 7-16). The other fins, such as those just behind the gills, steer and provide delicate adjustments to the fish's position. Can you suggest the specific ways that the dorsal fins, anal fin, pelvic fins, and pectoral fins might do this?

Depth changes are important to fish. By changing depth by only a few metres, a perch finds large differences in temperature, light, oxygen supply, and food supply. What kinds of stimuli do you think would cause a perch to rise? to sink?

The Canada Goose: Locomotion in the Air

Feathers are marvelous adaptive structures. They insulate a bird's body with fluffy down and streamline it for flight. Feathers also make flight possible. If you examine the flight feathers from a bird's wing, you will notice that the quill is not in the centre of the vane. This permits the feather to twist as air pushes against it in flight (Fig. 7-17). If a few of these flight feathers are clipped off, the goose cannot fly. Birds are often kept in captivity by doing this.

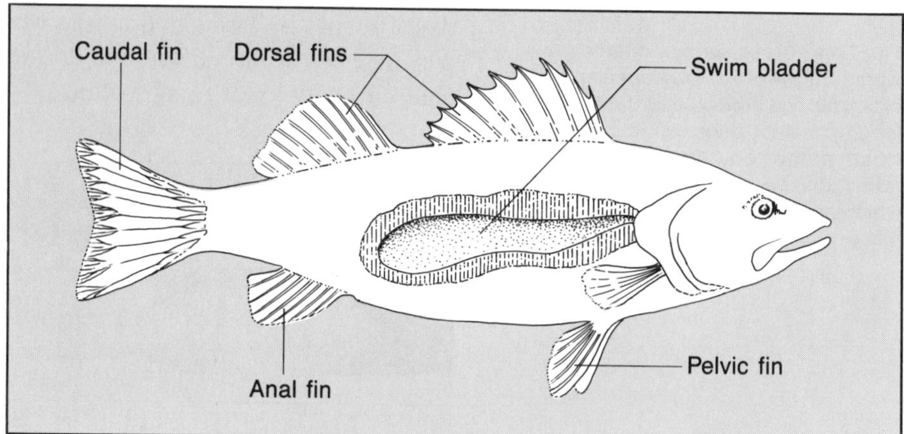

Fig. 7-16 The internal structure of a perch includes a gas-filled swim bladder used to maintain or adjust this animal's depth. The perch can alter its buoyancy by changing the size of the bladder. How do you suppose it does that?

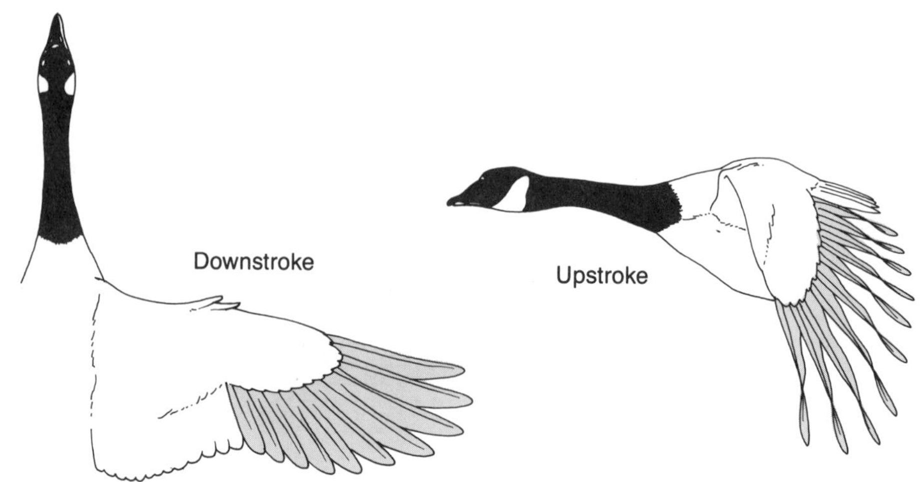

Fig. 7-17 On the goose's downstroke, the flight feathers (coloured) overlap each other, presenting a flat surface to push against the air. However, on the upstroke these feathers twist, letting air slip through the gaps in the wing.

The Octopus: Jet Propulsion

Several animals, including the octopus (Fig. 7-18) and the dragonfly nymph, are able to move rapidly by using the jet principle. Motion is caused by squirting fluid under high pressure out of a nozzle. Both animals use jetting as an escape response. Neither animal can sustain this locomotion for long. Both must stop to rest and refill their water chambers.

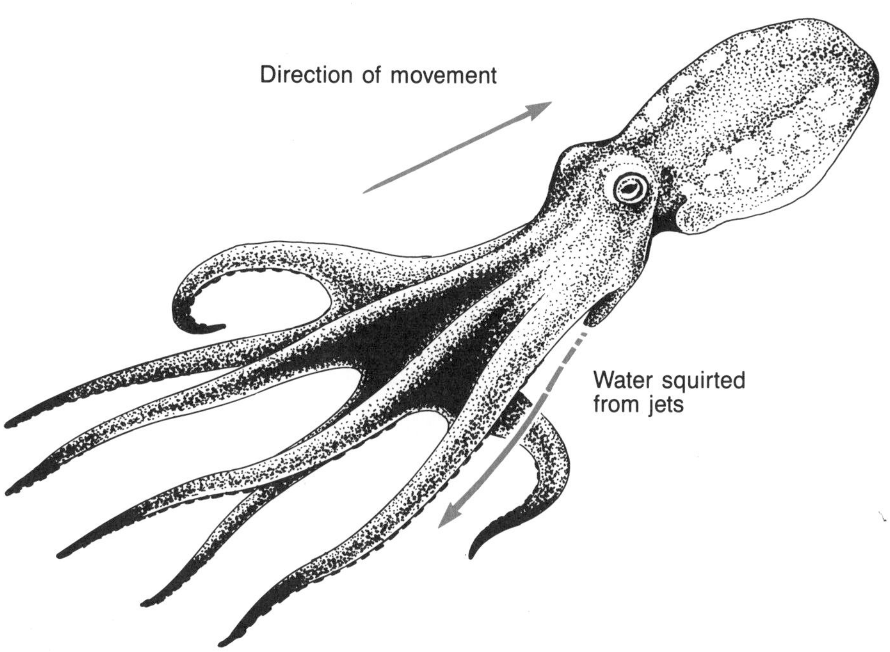

Fig. 7-18 The octopus escapes rapidly by squirting water from two jets at the side of its head.

Application: Jet Air Travel

Humans invented the first flying machines by copying nature's designs. The contour of a bird's wing is copied in the wing of every jet and plane as well as in the propellers of helicopters. The jetting action of animals like the octopus has also been copied in the jet engine. Unlike the animals from which it was copied, the jet engine is capable of continuous output as long as there is fuel aboard.

Section Review

1. Why are antagonistic muscles necessary for locomotory responses?

2. a) How do the functions of caudal and other fins differ?

b) Make a list of the fins on a perch. Opposite each name suggest a specific function of that fin.

3. Describe three ways in which feathers are adaptive.

4. a) What is the jet principle?

b) How have we copied animal structures for high speed air travel?

7.6 Activity: Examining Adaptations for Sensing and Responding

Different organisms use different structures to detect and respond to their environments. In Activity 6.3 you saw how protists (single-celled organisms) responded to a variety of stimuli. In this activity, you will examine the specialized structures used by two different multi-celled animals to sense and respond to their environments.

Problem

How are perch and grasshoppers designed to detect and respond to their different environments?

Materials

fresh or preserved perch
preserved lubber grasshopper
preserved winged grasshopper
dissecting tray
hand lens
tweezers
scissors

CAUTION: Wash all preservative from your hands at the end of this activity.

Procedure

a. Obtain the two grasshoppers, a tray, and a hand lens.
b. Locate and examine the antennas, simple eyes, compound eyes, and palps (around mouth) on each grasshopper using the hand lens.
c. Draw a labelled diagram of the grasshopper's head as seen from the front.
d. Locate and examine the tympanum (''ear drum'') just behind the rear legs.
e. Most grasshoppers have two methods of locomotion: walking (or jumping) and flying. Locate and examine the structures used for these responses (Fig. 7-19).
f. Draw a diagram of a winged grasshopper as seen from the side with its wings unfolded.
g. Return the grasshoppers and obtain a perch.
h. Make a sketch of a side view of the perch. Now locate and sketch the perch's sensory organs (eyes, nostrils, and lateral line) and its locomotory organs (fins).
i. Identify those fins that fold tightly against the body, and those that do not.

Fig. 7-19 How does this animal sense and respond to its environment?

j. Following your teacher's instructions, open the side of the fish to locate the swim bladder. In fresh specimens, the bladder looks like a transparent sausage. However, in preserved specimens, the bladder membrane breaks easily, leaving a cavity where it was located.

Discussion

1. **a)** What differences did you note between the grasshopper's simple and compound eyes?
b) What different functions might be served by the two kinds of eyes?
2. What can you conclude about the lubber grasshopper's locomotion based on its wing structure?
3. Which legs are used to jump? How do you know?
4. Based on body structure, which grasshopper species do you think has more predators? Explain your answer.
5. Unlike your eyes, the perch's eyes are not aimed forward but, rather, to the side. Of what advantage is this for the perch? What disadvantage does it offer?
6. Where are the fish's hearing organs? Explain why this location is an advantage to the fish.
7. Why do all fins except the caudal fin fold tightly against the animal's body?
8. Explain why grasshoppers and fish have such different sensory and locomotory organs. Your answer should discuss how these animals are adapted to their separate environments.

Extensions

1. Examine other organisms for their sensory and locomotory organs. Explain how each animal is adapted to its particular environment.
2. Write a research report discussing the reasons for insect success. Your report should include adaptability, body structure, size, flight, and reproductive rate.

7.7 Responding with Behavioural Adaptations

As you have seen, organisms are *structurally* adapted to their environments. To cope with their changing environments, organisms have developed some fascinating *behavioural* adaptations as well.

Reasons for Behavioural Adaptations

Why do some animals change colour? Why do bees, ants, and apes live in groups? Why do chipmunks become dormant for periods of time during the

Fig. 7-20 You have likely noticed how very active a chipmunk is as it gathers food for its winter store. To conserve this food in the winter, the chipmunk frequently curls up in its den and lowers its metabolism. However, on a sunny day, tracks in the snow show that the chipmunk periodically resumes activity.

winter? All of these animals are responding to an environmental challenge with a behavioural adaptation. For example, a chameleon blends with its background to escape visual detection by a predator. Social organisms like bees have found that group living improves survival. A chipmunk reduces its food requirement during cold weather by slowing down its metabolism from time to time (Fig. 7-20). These behaviours are examples of ways in which a few animals improve their likelihood of success.

Dominance

Dominance is a ranking behaviour found in social chordates such as chickens, horses, wolves, and baboons. Each individual has a social rank in the group. At the top of this "pecking order" are the **dominant** individuals. At the bottom are the **subordinates**. Dominance is often established by fighting or, at least, by the threat of a fight. Dominant individuals usually receive the best of everything—food, shelter, mates, and so on. Subordinates get whatever is left. In a food shortage, subordinates often die because dominant individuals will not share available food. How can this behaviour be adaptive? How does it benefit the species? You will find it interesting to research this behaviour further. If you do, share your findings with your class.

Territorialism

Territorialism is a widespread behaviour among animals. Individuals, mating pairs, or packs claim a certain space for their own use and do not allow others of their own species access to this space. For instance, a wolf pack marks and defends a space of about 25 km^2 per wolf. Other wolves are not allowed in. In the spring, the dominant pair mate but the entire pack is involved in rearing the pups. Thus the behaviour of the wolves limits their own population and keeps it in balance with the available food supply. How is this adaptive?

Learning

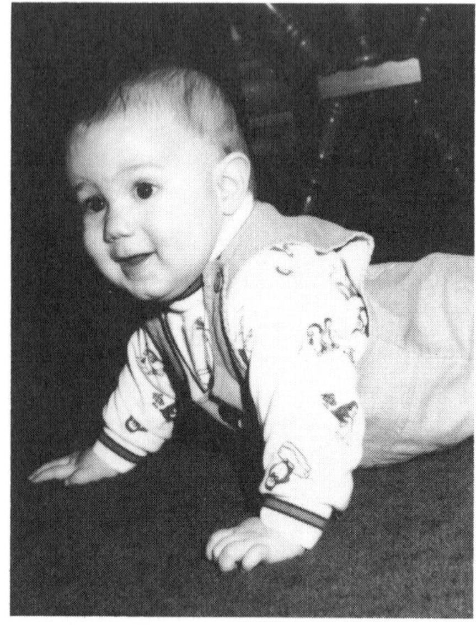

Fig. 7-21 Think of all the things this child must learn before adulthood. Then think of all the things a baby fish needs to learn before it becomes a mature fish.

Learning is a behaviour found in animals from planaria to humans. Each individual adapts to its surroundings with behaviours acquired through experience rather than through instinct. For example, you were born with certain **instinctive** or **innate** behaviours such as breathing, suckling, and voiding wastes. However, you had to learn most other behaviours such as walking, communicating, reading, and playing sports (Fig. 7-21). In fact, we learn an unusually large fraction of behaviours compared to other animals. By contrast, baby fish know how to swim, catch food, and escape predators as soon as they are born. Such organisms are said to be **precocious**. That is, they demonstrate mature behaviour at a very early age.

Of those organisms capable of learning, most learn by the **trial and error** method. For example, people learning to ski for the first time certainly know what the behaviour of skiing looks like. However, these people will make many attempts to imitate the correct technique before they also learn what works and what doesn't (Fig. 7-22). You will have a chance to investigate trial and error learning in the next section.

Fig. 7-22 Humans learn new skills using trial and error behaviour. After a certain number of tries, this skier will not repeat the error he made. How do other animals acquire their life skills? Is their behaviour innate or do they also learn?

A few organisms can learn by **insight** or **reasoning**. That is, they can analyze a situation and respond properly the first time. An organism that lacks the ability to reason will find new situations to be difficult (Fig. 7-23). Can you think of some examples where you have learned by reasoning?

Section Review

1. Describe five examples of behavioural adaptations.
2. How is dominance of benefit to a species?
3. **a)** What survival advantage does the holder of a territory have over an individual that does not have one?
   b) Which individuals are most likely to own territories, dominants or subordinates?
4. **a)** Upon hatching, a baby alligator is able to walk, swim, and catch food. What two terms describe this mature behaviour?
   b) Do these same terms apply to human behaviour at birth? Explain.
   c) What behaviour do we demonstrate a great deal of that alligators show little of?
5. Both innate and learned behaviour have survival advantages for animals. What is the major advantage of innate behaviour? Why is learning a better behaviour to an animal in an unfamiliar environment?

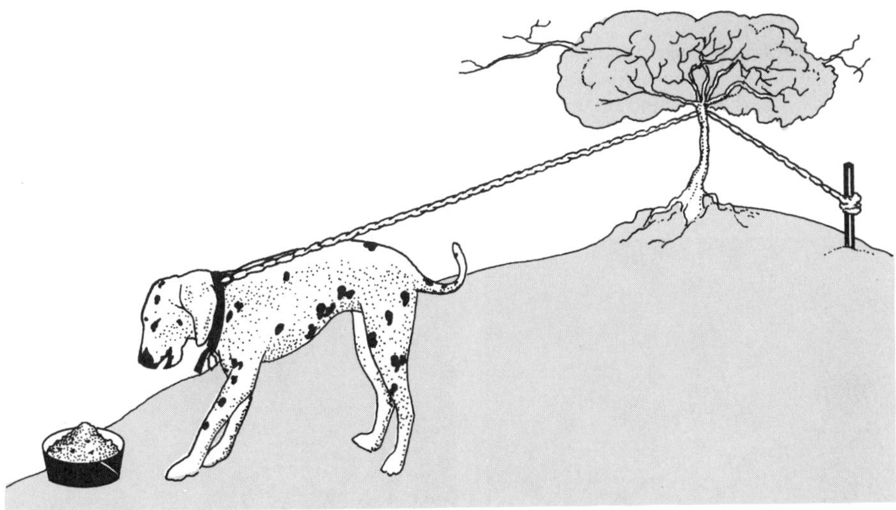

Fig. 7-23 This dog cannot reach its food because it lacks insight. A monkey tied up in the same situation would go around the tree and reach the food. The dog might learn to reach the dish by trial and error.

7.8 Activity: Trial and Error Learning

Many animals acquire knowledge about their surroundings through trial and error. We can observe such knowledge and learning by an animal's ability to run through a maze (Fig. 7-4). When less time is required to complete the

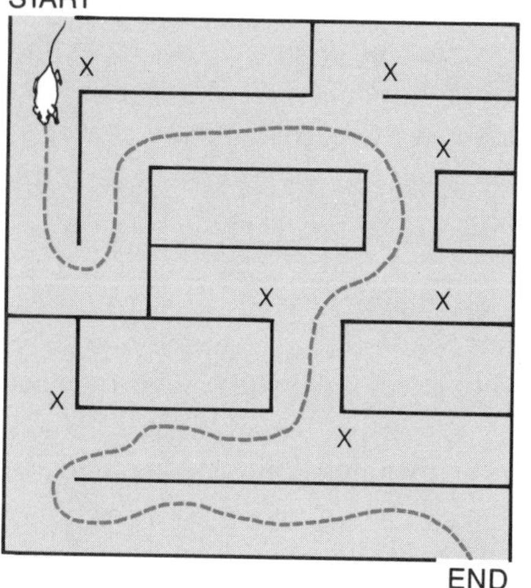

Fig. 7-24 A hungry mouse can learn a simple maze, especially when a food reward is found at the end. Mistakes are simple and shown with an "X".

maze and as fewer mistakes are made, we know that the animal is learning the correct route.

In this activity, you will simulate this trial and error learning behaviour in a maze of your own design. To prevent you from reasoning to determine the best route, each learner will be blindfolded while attempting to learn. You will record your observations on each learner in order to prove that learning has occurred.

Problem

How do we prove that an organism can learn by trial and error?

Materials

cardboard boxes
scissors
pencil
tape or glue
clock or watch

Procedure

a. On paper, design a rectangular maze similar to the one in Figure 7-24. Your maze should have:
- a START and an END
- 10 to 12 simple mistakes
- only one correct route

b. Work in groups of three or four students. Select one of your group's mazes to build.

c. Redraw the maze on a large rectangular piece of cardboard that has been cut from a box. Make all channels the same width (2 to 2.5 cm is fine).

d. Tape or glue cut-out cardboard onto your large piece to form sides along the channels as shown in Figure 7-25.

Fig. 7-25 A finger maze enables you to simulate the learning behaviour of other animals. Care should be taken not to show the maze to the learner because learning will take place by insight rather than by trial and error.

e. When the maze is complete, blindfold one member of your group. The blindfold is not to be removed until the maze has been attempted several times.
f. Trade your maze with another group so that the blindfolded learner is working with an unfamiliar maze.
g. Select one member of the group to record the elapsed time for each attempt by the learner to get from start to finish.
h. Select another person to *silently* count the mistakes. Each wrong turn and each reversal counts as a mistake.
i. Place the blindfolded learner's index finder at "START". The timer should then tell the learner to start.
j. When the learner has completed the maze, record the learner's name, attempt number (1, 2, 3, 4, etc.), the time, and number of mistakes in tabular form.
k. Repeat steps (i) and (j) at least 8 times or until the learner completes the maze quickly with few mistakes on two consecutive attempts.
l. Switch learners and repeat steps (e) to (k). Continue until all members of the group have tried one maze.
m. Prepare two graphs for each member of your group. The first should have "ATTEMPT NUMBER" on the horizontal axis and "TIME" on the vertical. The second should have "ATTEMPT NUMBER" horizontally and "MISTAKES" vertically.

Discussion

1. Over several attempts, what happened to each learner's time and mistakes? How do you know that they have learned the correct route?
2. How would this trial and error learning help a rabbit survive? (*Hint*: Think about what a rabbit eats and what eats it.)
3. How would learning help an animal survive in an unfamiliar environment? Discuss how learning behaviour helps the animal find its basic needs of food and shelter.

Extensions

1. Design and try an experiment to test the learning behaviour of earthworms or sow bugs. For those animals that will not take food as a reinforcement, a mild electric shock can be tried. Do these animals learn? How fast do they learn?
2. Write a research report on the chemistry of learning. How is memory stored in the brain? How can this be demonstrated experimentally?

7.9 Activity: Surviving Canadian Winters

Winter is a severe test of the ability of animals to survive. Food and water become scarce at a time when extra food may be needed to keep warm.

Fig. 7-26 How does this animal survive through the winter? Is this behaviour innate or learned?

Migration and **hibernation** are two behaviours that greatly improve the survival of some species. In this activity, you will use your school's resource centre and other libraries to prepare a report on how a Canadian animal uses one of these behaviours (Fig. 7-26). Your teacher will guide you as to the length and format of the report. Appendix C gives you suggestions for conducting your research.

Problem

How does one Canadian animal improve its winter survival?

Materials

reference materials in your resource centre and local libraries

Procedure

a. With the help of your teacher/librarian, select one species to research for your report. Here are some suggestions:
Migrators: caribou; harpseal; spermwhale; monarch butterfly; Canada goose (or any other waterfowl); snowy owl (or any other raptor); any other migratory bird or mammal.
Hibernators and semi-hibernators: chipmunk; black bear or polar bear; garter snake (or any other reptile); leopard frog (or any other amphibian); honeybee (or any other insect).

b. For migrators, your research should answer the following questions:
- What route does the animal cover on its journey? (A map and a distance calculation should be included in your report.)
- How long does the journey take and at what speed?
- What environmental change triggers this behaviour?
- What changes in diet (if any) occur before, during, or after the trip? Why?
- What special structures assist this behaviour?
- What would happen if the animal did not make the trip? Why?
- When and where does the animal rear its young? Why?
- How have scientists investigated this migratory behaviour?

c. For hibernators or semi-hibernators, your research should answer the following questions:
- How does the animal avoid predators during hibernation?
- What happens to the animal's metabolism (temperature, breathing rate, etc.) during hibernation? Why?
- What stimuli cause hibernation to start and finish? How long does it last?
- What energy sources and insulating materials are used?
- What special body parts and animal-built structures assist this behaviour?
- How have scientists investigated this hibernation behaviour?
- How do humans imitate "hibernation" to improve survival during certain kinds of surgery?

Fig. 7-27 Honeybee colonies have one queen (Q), many sterile female workers (W), and a few male drones (D). How does insect social behaviour help their survival?

7.10 Activity: Surviving with Social Behaviour

Some species have learned to improve their chances of survival through social behaviour. Humans and our closest relatives, monkeys and apes, are not the only ones to use such behaviour. Certain fish, birds, mammals, and molluscs also use social behaviour. However, the most complete social behaviour is found among insects like bees, ants, wasps, and termites. In fact, a honeybee colony has been described as a perfect society by some sociologists (Fig. 7-27). In this activity you will research the social behaviour of one social insect and write a report showing how this behaviour enhances its survival. Your teacher will provide guidance as to the length and format of the report.

Problem

How does insect social behaviour promote survival?

Materials

reference materials from a resource centre

Procedure

a. With the help of your teacher/librarian, select one social insect for your research (e.g. honeybee, termite, carpenter ant, army ant, paper wasp).

b. Your research should answer the following questions:
- What social roles are played by the fertile females and males?
- What social roles are played by the sterile workers?
- How long do the insects live?
- What structural adaptations (if any) are shown by workers for the performance of their role(s)?
- What use is made of the female's hormones in controlling worker behaviour? What do the workers do if these hormones are missing?
- How are new colonies established?
- Why do the males have wings and large eyes?
- How does this division of tasks help this insect species survive better?

Extension

Successful organisms seldom raise another individual's offspring. In genetic terms, this is because each parent is striving to promote its own genes which will be present only in its own offspring. However, social insect workers energetically raise young that are not their own. These workers are even incapable of having their own. Is this a violation of this genetic principle, or are social organisms really promoting their own genes? How can organisms be successful when they raise someone else's young? Write a research report that addresses these questions.

Chapter Highlights

1. Psychobiology is the study of the response of organisms to environmental stimuli.
2. Organisms respond chemically, by growing, and by moving.
3. Each organism has structural adaptations designed to respond appropriately in its own environment. These structures may be inappropriate in a different environment.
4. Animals demonstrate a number of behavioural adaptations.
5. Animals are capable of various amounts of learning in response to environmental change.
6. We have copied animal adaptations for our own use.

Key Terms

adaptation	learning	reasoning
adaptive	locomotion	reflex response
antagonistic pair	migration	sessile
dominance	motile	territorialism
hibernation	precocious	trial and error
insight	psychobiology	tropism

Recognizing the Concepts

Each of the following statements or questions is followed by four responses. Choose the correct response in each case. (Do not write in this book.)

1. If placed in a lighted area, an earthworm moves to seek a darker area. This is most likely
   a) a learned behavioural response **c)** a reflex
   b) a tropism **d)** an innate behaviour
2. Arctic terns successfully migrate a great distance on their first attempt. This indicates that such behaviour is
   a) acquired by trial and error **c)** innate
   b) reasoned **d)** precocious
3. Which of the following is *NOT* a chemical response?
   a) releasing hormones **c)** producing toxins
   b) hydrotropism **d)** a skunk releasing odour
4. Reflexes are used by animals to
   a) speed up the response time to certain stimuli
   b) guarantee a response in case the stimulus is not passed on to the brain
   c) speed up the rate of learning
   d) improve the survival rate of sessile organisms
5. An adaptive behaviour or structure is one that
   a) is found only among organisms living in a particular environment
   b) improves an organism's chances of being successful
   c) can be adapted by humans for our own use
   d) is found in all organisms in the same kingdom

Understanding the Concepts

1. We say that movement is a characteristic of all living things. Explain how this applies even to sessile organisms.
2. Distinguish between psychology and psychobiology.
3. Describe one sensory, one locomotory, and one behavioural adaptation used by an organism for survival in each of the following environments: underwater, on land, in the air.
4. The muscles in your body occur in antagonistic pairs. Why is this so? What would happen if one half of each pair was missing?
5. Why do organisms respond to certain stimuli? What happens if they fail to respond properly?
6. Give one example of how two different animals respond to the same stimulus in two completely different ways.

Applying the Concepts

1. Select three animals (one bird, one fish, and one insect) and discuss the responses each uses to meet its basic needs.
2. The dodo bird, the passenger pigeon, and the wooly mammoth are no longer successful organisms; they are extinct. Discuss the reasons for their lack of success in terms of inappropriate responses to environmental change.
3. The sensitive plant, *Mimosa*, and Venus' flytrap in Figure 7-6 and the sundew in Figure 7-28 show responses to touch. What type of response is this? How is each response adaptive?
4. The cells of your body display four kinds of movement: flagellate, ciliate, amoeboid, and muscular. Name a type of cell that uses each type of movement and explain why that is the best type of movement for that cell's job in your body.
5. Explain how the concept of antagonistic pairs applies in the case of the earthworm.
6. Cartilaginous fish such as sharks and rays do not have swim bladders. Explain why these animals do not "wash up" on a beach when they die the way that bony fishes do.
7. Discuss how territorialism and dominance help keep the population of wolves in control. Why do wolves need such control mechanisms?
8. Explain how feathers help a bird to respond to such stimuli as temperature changes, hunger, and predators.
9. What relationship exists between brain size and ability to learn (see Figure 6-10, page 160). Which part of the brain controls learning?

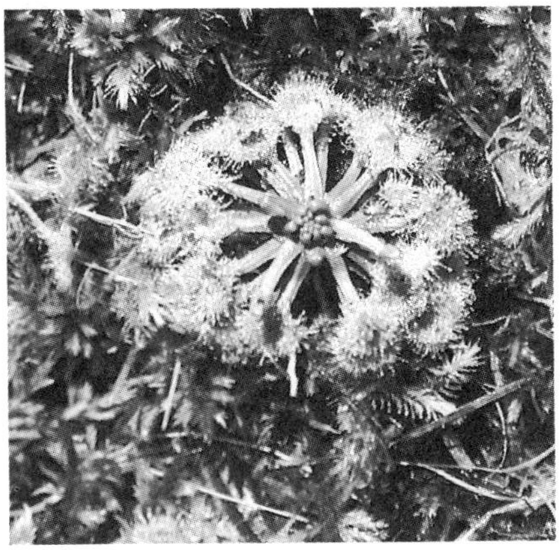

Fig. 7-28 The Sundew folds its sticky leaves over insects that land on them. What type of response is this?

Investigations

1. Set up a classroom aquarium for tropical or local freshwater fish. Observe how these animals use their various fins for certain kinds of movement. Watch also for evidence of territorialism and dominance.
2. Write a research report on the navigational methods that are thought to be

Fig. 7-29 Can you maintain your balance while blindfolded? on one leg? standing on a pillow? all three? What responses do you have to the loss of sensory stimuli?

used by birds on their long distance migrations. Are these learned or innate behaviours?

3. To maintain equilibrium or balance, your body uses a number of sensory receptors besides those in the ears. Try the demonstration in Figure 7-29. Where do you think these extra receptors are located? What responses does your body have to a reduction in equilibrium sensory information? What kinds of responses are these?
4. Within a species, variations exist with respect to sensory ability. Have your entire class attempt to taste the chemical on PTC paper. (Your teacher will have some.) How do you explain the results? If your survival depended on the detection of PTC and an appropriate response, what would you conclude about certain members of your class?
5. Design and do an experiment to show that your biceps and triceps make up an antagonistic pair of muscles.
6. We measure the intelligence of a chordate by the rate at which it learns a new task. Design an experiment to compare the intelligence of dogs and housecats. Which species is more intelligent?
7. Design and conduct an experiment to determine whether or not *Mimosa* can learn (see Figure 7-6, page 183). Does it always respond to a touch stimulus, or does it learn to ignore a touch? Be careful to control variables such as temperature and light.
8. Visit a local zoo to observe social behaviour among apes and monkeys. What behaviours do you see? Explain how these are adaptive.

Biography

Norah and Fred Urquhart: Zoologists

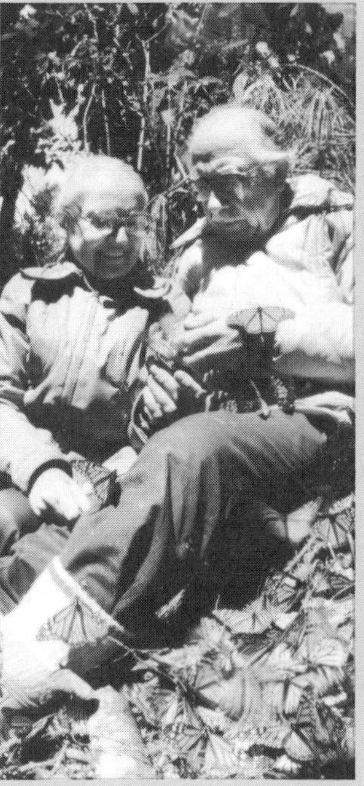

The Urquharts have devoted their research careers to a study of the migration patterns of the Monarch butterfly. As a boy, Fred had been told that Monarchs hibernate—but no evidence of this was found. Observers noticed thousands of butterflies moving south in the fall, but no one knew where they went!

Tags, each with a unique serial number, are the basic tool used to study migrating animals. Metal tags used for birds are unsuitable for butterflies. Through trial and error, Fred developed light-weight, water-resistant tags with return instructions.

Each fall, Fred and Norah captured, tagged, and released thousands of Monarchs. As the tagged butterflies travelled south, some Monarchs were noticed and caught by people because of the unusual white spot on their wings. After returning the tagged butterfly to the University of Toronto, these same people often volunteered their time to help with further tagging efforts. In all, about three thousand volunteers helped tag three hundred thousand butterflies.

Eventually, the migration route was traced to the overwintering site high in the mountains of central Mexico. Here, Norah and Fred are shown among millions of Monarchs congregating until spring. Moments after this photo was taken, they discovered a Monarch tagged and released in Minnesota!

The Urquharts' research work continues to fill in gaps in our knowledge. The recent discovery of magnetite ore in the Monarch's body suggests that navigation may occur by sensing the earth's magnetic field. Of great importance to the Urquharts are the protected areas set aside for the Monarch as a result of their research.

The Urquharts have written two books on the Monarch butterfly which are available through your library system.

VISTA

AIDS, AUTOIMMUNITY, AND OUR IMMUNE RESPONSE

How does your body respond to the stimulus of being attacked by disease microbes? As with any other stimulus, you must first detect invading microbes, then communicate a message to the response organs, and, finally, carry out an appropriate response. If any part of that sense/communication/response process fails, you will develop the symptoms of the disease.

Your body has a chemical defence system called your **immune system**. Whenever this system detects a foreign protein in your body (that is, any protein not made by you), it responds by building "attack" chemicals called **antibodies**. Each antibody molecule is designed to destroy one invading protein and thereby destroy the microbe on which that protein is located. Thus your immune system builds different antibodies for each disease organism it discovers: one for polio, another for mumps, and so on.

A number of things can go wrong with your immune response. First, this response is slow. Your system may take several days to several months to make enough antibodies to destroy the microbes. To combat this, doctors give you a **vaccination** of disease microbe protein to trick your immune system into making appropriate antibodies before you catch the real disease. Once vaccinated you are **immunized** against that disease.

Second, your immune system may mistake some of your proteins for a foreign protein. It builds antibodies which attempt to destroy the cells to which these proteins are attached. If the protein is on the outside of your neurons, you develop **multiple sclerosis** as you gradually destroy your own nervous system. If the protein is on the islet cells of your pancreas, you develop **Type I diabetes** as these cells are completely destroyed. Such diseases are called **autoimmune** diseases because you are immune to some part of yourself. Our ability to deal effectively with the causes of autoimmune diseases is very limited.

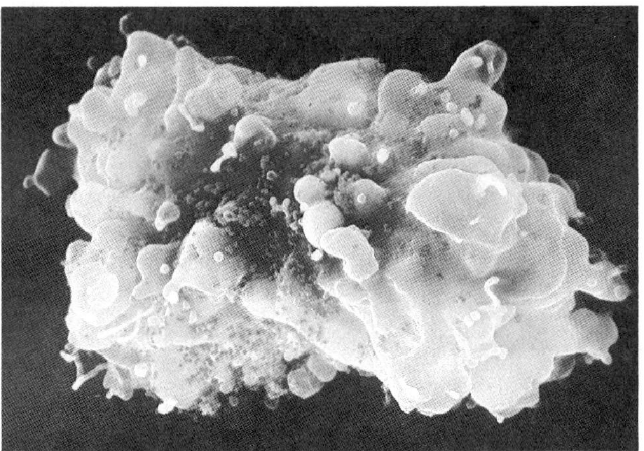

AIDS virus particles, seen here as numerous tiny dark dots on the face of this human T4 lymphocyte cell, are capable of destroying the immune system.

Third, your response may be inappropriate or ineffective. Antibodies do not work against the **AIDS virus**, and the **herpes viruses** (herpes I and II, mononucleosis, and chicken pox). Each of these viruses infects a human victim permanently and can "flare up" at any time. The AIDS virus actually destroys critical cells in the immune system, eventually preventing its operation. AIDS victims die of other diseases, such as pneumonia and Kaposi's sarcoma, to which their damaged immune systems can no longer respond.

Understanding and manipulating our immune system appears to be the best hope in the fight against all of these diseases and cancer. If we can improve the ability of our immune systems to detect and respond effectively, all of these diseases may disappear. But that understanding will require considerable research, money, talent, and time.

UNIT 3 Organisms and Their Internal Environment

CHAPTERS

Organisms vary widely in size and complexity: from tiny one-celled monerans to giant many-celled animals like whales. But, whether they are one-celled or many-celled, all organisms must carry out most of the same life processes if they are to survive. Materials must flow from an organism's external environment into the organism. And waste materials must flow in the opposite direction. Within an organism, materials must flow to where they are needed. Some of these materials must provide the energy needed to support life processes. And some materials must provide atoms for building new cells and new cell parts.

This unit focuses on three processes that provide these needs: feeding and digestion, gas exchange, and internal transport. These processes occur in the **internal environments** of organisms. Though the processes differ in some ways from species to species, they are alike in many ways. This squirrel shares many processes with an amoeba, a hydra, a grasshopper, and you. What are they?

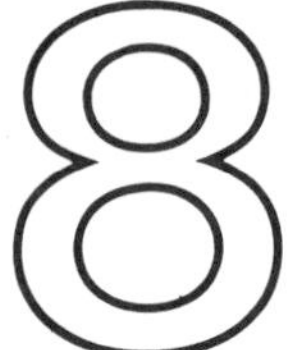

Feeding and Digestion

CHAPTER CONTENTS

CHAPTER OBJECTIVES

After completing this chapter you should be able to:

1. Describe the need for food by all organisms.
2. Compare feeding, digestion, and absorption for selected organisms.
3. Investigate feeding mechanisms and digestive systems for selected organisms.

In order to survive, all organisms need **energy** and **matter**. Energy provides the "power" for life processes. It is needed for movement, elimination of wastes, growth, and all other life processes. Matter provides the atoms needed for growth and for the repair of worn-out parts.

Heterotrophic organisms get their matter and energy from **food**. That is, they eat other organisms or non-living organic matter. Food is the "fuel" that provides the required energy. It is also the source of the required matter. In this chapter you will explore the wide variety of ways organisms obtain and use food. Your exploration will begin with a simple protist, move through some invertebrates, and end with a vertebrate, the fish (Fig. 8-1).

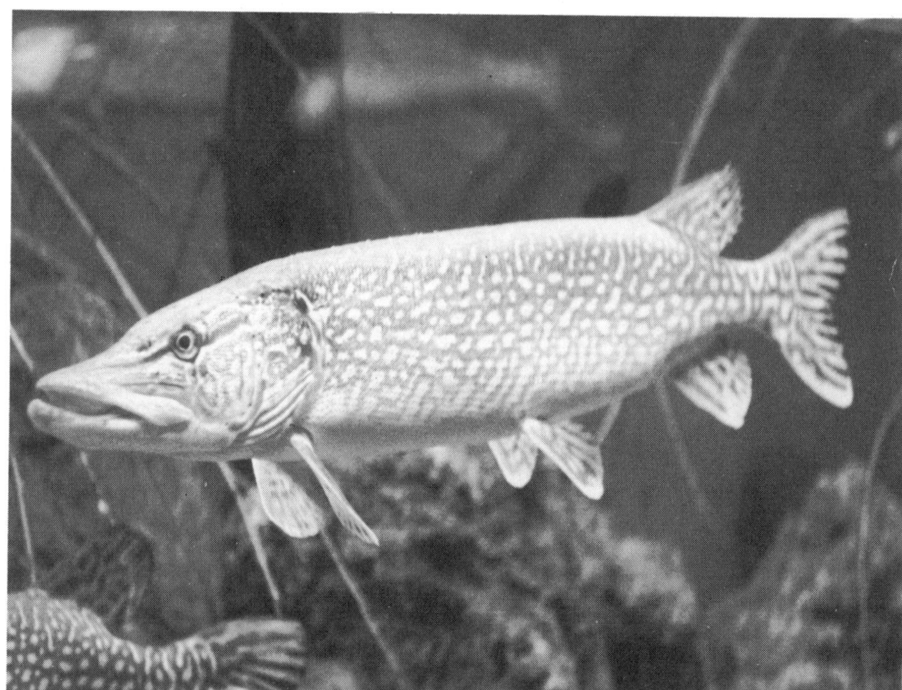

Fig. 8-1 Like all heterotrophs, this fish uses food as a source of energy and matter. How does its feeding and use of food compare to that of protists and invertebrates?

8.1 The Need for Food

The raw materials which provide the essential energy and matter for life are called **nutrients**. These nutrients can be divided into six main categories—carbohydrates, fats, proteins, vitamins, minerals, and water. Let us look briefly at the nature and functions of these nutrients.

Carbohydrates

Carbohydrates are molecules composed of carbon, hydrogen, and oxygen atoms. They are a major energy source for organisms. As well, they act as a storehouse for energy and as vehicles for moving stored energy from place to place in organisms.

The simplest carbohydrates are sugars such as glucose. These can be used by organisms with no digestion (breaking down) required. A somewhat more complex carbohydrate is sucrose, or table sugar. Still more complex are starch and cellulose. Sucrose and starch must be digested into glucose before they can be used by organisms. Many organisms, like humans, cannot digest cellulose at all. However, it does provide essential bulk, or roughage, which aids digestion. Herbivores can digest cellulose, but only with the help of countless mutualistic microbes in their digestive tracts.

Fats, like carbohydrates, also have molecules consisting of carbon, hydrogen, and oxygen atoms. They, too, serve as a source of energy. In fact, a gram of fat may release over twice as much energy as a gram of carbohydrate. Besides being an energy source, fats may be stored near an organism's surface and around internal organs. Such stored fat serves as a storage house for energy. It also insulates and protects organs and other parts of organisms.

Proteins are large complex molecules made of amino acids linked together. All amino acid molecules contain carbon, hydrogen, oxygen, and nitrogen atoms. All living organisms contain proteins. Some of these proteins are enzymes that aid processes such as digestion. Others are important parts of cells such as cell membranes. Proteins also serve as an energy source.

Organisms make their proteins from amino acids. Most heterotrophs cannot make all their own amino acids. Those which they cannot make must be obtained from the food they eat. Such amino acids are called **essential amino acids**. To get these amino acids, a heterotroph must ingest (take in) protein and then break it down by digestion into amino acids. About 20 kinds of amino acids are commonly found in the various proteins of heterotrophs. About eight are essential for almost all heterotrophs.

Vitamins

Vitamins, unlike the three nutrients described so far, are required in only very small amounts. They do not have to be broken down, or digested, before they can be used. The vitamin requirements vary from organism to organism. For example, we must have vitamin C (ascorbic acid) in our diets, but most other mammals can make their own. Vitamins are enzymes needed for a wide variety of reactions in cells.

Minerals

Carbon, hydrogen, oxygen, and nitrogen are the four most common elements in organisms. However, a number of other elements are needed in small amounts to maintain life functions. These elements are called **minerals**. Among them are such elements as calcium, phosphorus, sulfur, iron, and iodine. Over 20 minerals are needed for the complete nutrition of complex heterotrophs like vertebrates. You are likely familiar with the functions of some of these minerals in your diet.

Water

About 70% of your body mass is water. This proportion is about the same for most other heterotrophs. Water aids in the absorption and digestion of food. It helps transport materials within organisms. It aids in the elimination of wastes and, in some organisms, it helps regulate temperature.

Most organisms get much of the water they need by taking in water directly. They also get it indirectly from foods that they eat, since most foods contain water.

Section Review

1. a) What two needs does food provide for organisms?
   b) What are nutrients?
   c) Name the six main categories of nutrients.
2. a) What functions do carbohydrates perform in organisms?
   b) Name four types of carbohydrates and compare them with respect to the need for digestion.
3. What functions do fats perform in organisms?
4. a) What element do proteins contain that is not present in carbohydrates and fats?
   b) What functions do proteins perform in organisms?
   c) What are essential amino acids?
5. Make a brief summary of the need for each of the following by organisms: vitamins, minerals, water.

8.2 Feeding: Taking Food In

Each species of organism has unique ways of feeding. It meets its nutrient requirements by selecting certain foods. Then it uses specialized ways of obtaining these foods from its external environment (Fig. 8-2). In this section

Fig. 8-2 This bird, the Clark's nutcracker, lives in coniferous forests in Alberta and British Columbia, generally well up in the mountains. It feeds mainly on conifer seeds which it must get out of the cones. How is this species adapted for feeding?

you will see how five species feed. As you read about how they feed, think about the relationships between feeding, the complexity of the organisms, and their habitats. The selected organisms are:

- amoeba (a protist)
- hydra (a simple invertebrate)
- earthworm (a more complex invertebrate)
- grasshopper (a still more complex invertebrate)
- perch (a vertebrate)

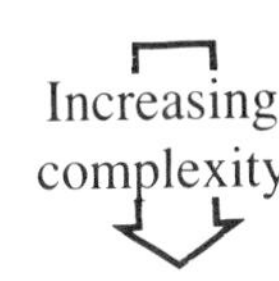

What Is Feeding?

The term **feeding** refers to the process by which organisms obtain their food. It includes the method by which the food is captured and the method by which the food is taken into the organism. The taking in of food is also called **ingestion**. Now, let us look at feeding for the selected organisms. In the next section you will find out what happens to the food after it has been ingested.

Feeding by the Amoeba

The **amoeba** is a single-celled aquatic organism that feeds mainly on smaller protists and, to a lesser extent, bacteria. Its method of feeding is quite simple: It engulfs, then ingests the food. Its protoplasm forms **pseudopods** (false feet) which flow over and around the food (Fig. 8-3). Then the parts of the cell membrane that are around the food join together. As a result, part of the cell membrane now surrounds the food and the water in which the food is suspended. This membrane, the water, and the food make up a **food vacuole**. The food is now in the amoeba, ready for digestion.

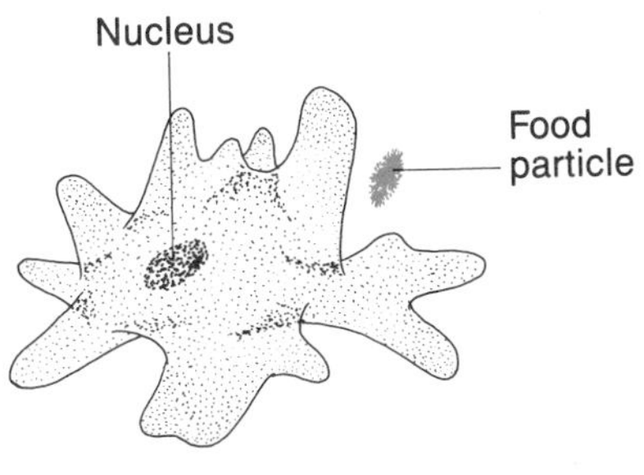

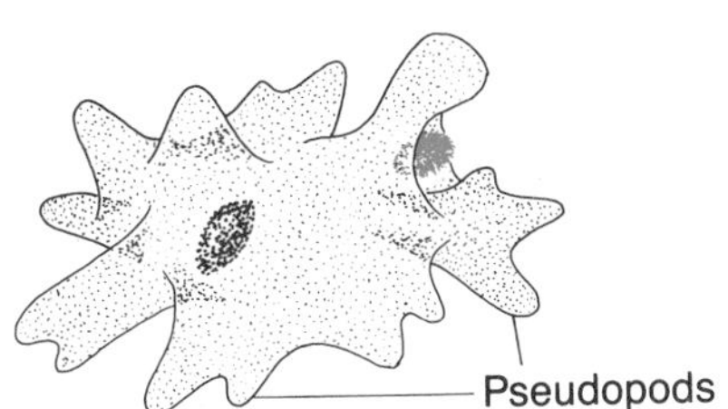

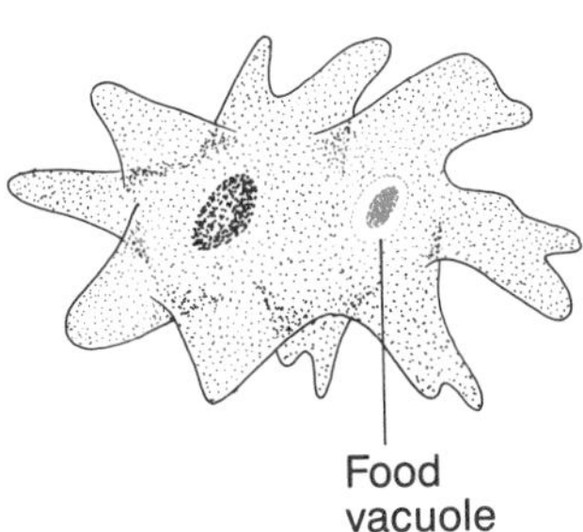

Fig. 8-3 An amoeba engulfs its food with pseudopods and then ingests it.

Fig. 8-4 A longitudinal section of a hydra showing detail of cellular structure. Note the structure of the nematocyst before discharge (A) and after discharge (B).

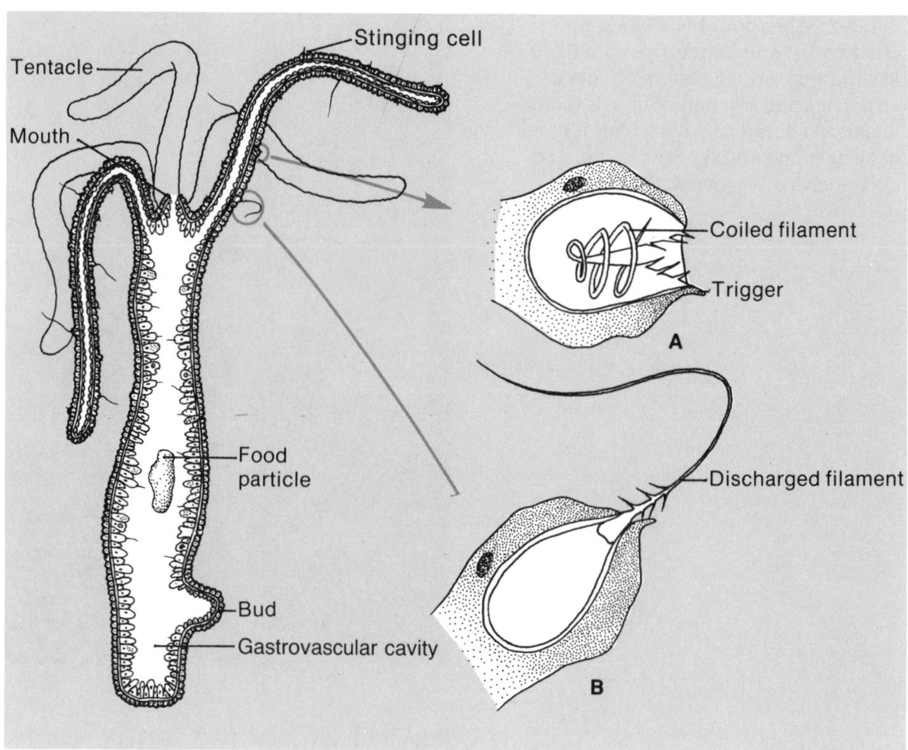

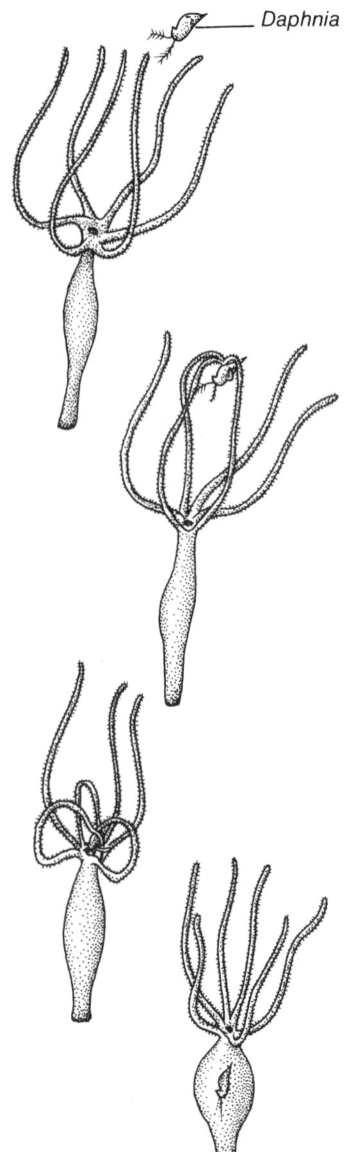

Fig. 8-5 Feeding by a hydra. Here a *Daphnia* is captured by the tentacles and then ingested.

The **hydra** is a many-celled animal that lives in ponds, lakes, and streams. This invertebrate feeds mainly on smaller invertebrates like *Daphnia*. Like all carnivores, it has specialized structures for capturing and ingesting its prey. The hydra uses **nematocysts**, or ''stinging cells'', to paralyze its prey (Fig. 8-4). The nematocysts are located in specialized cells along the outer cell layer of the hydra's tentacles. They are thread-like filaments coiled within a capsule with a hair-like trigger sticking outward. When the prey touches the trigger, the nematocyst ejects the coiled filament. Some nematocysts are barbed and can penetrate the prey's body. Others are whip-like and can wrap around the victim. A paralyzing poison is then injected into the prey through the filament. Tentacles seize the prey and carry it to the hydra's mouth (Fig. 8-5). There it is drawn into the **gastrovascular cavity** by contractions of the body wall. The food is now in the hydra, ready for digestion.

Feeding by the Earthworm

The **earthworm** is a much more complex invertebrate than the hydra. This animal tunnels through organic-laden soil. In fact, it actually eats its way through the soil. The soil is sucked in through the mouth by the muscular **pharynx** (Fig. 8-6). This muscular structure forces the food into the **esophagus**, which transports the food to the **crop** for temporary storage. The organic matter in the food must be ground up before digestion can begin. The earthworm has no teeth for this purpose. Instead, the muscular **gizzard** grinds up the organic matter by mixing it with sand grains in the soil. The ground food passes into the **intestine**, where digestion (breaking down of the food) continues.

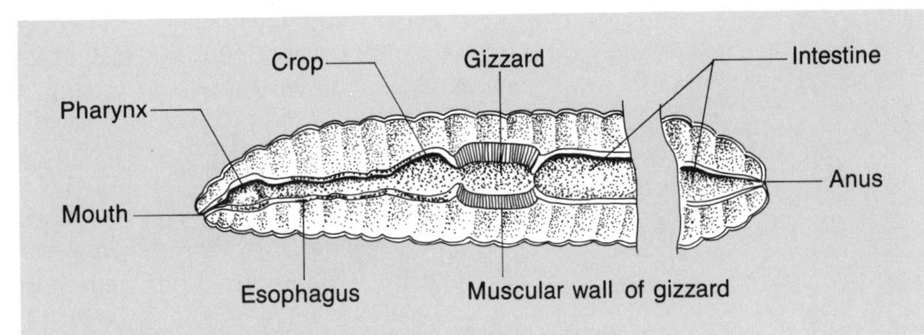

Fig. 8-6 The earthworm's digestive system is adapted to its feeding habits.

Extension

Birds also have a crop and a gizzard. Find out what advantage it is to a bird to have these organs.

Feeding by the Grasshopper

The **grasshopper**, another complex invertebrate, has biting and chewing mouthparts which enable it to feed on plants (Fig. 8-7). This insect has a broad, hinged **upper lip (labrum)** and a **lower lip (labium)**. The labium has a deep notch to help direct food into the mouth. A toothed set of **jaws (mandibles)** grind the food. A pair of **lesser jaws (maxillae)** have curved prongs that act like a fork and spoon. A fleshy **tongue** is located in the mouth behind the mandibles. Finally, there are **palps** on the maxillae and lower lip. These jointed appendages probably help the grasshopper tell one type of food from another.

Fig. 8-7 The mouthparts of a grasshopper are typical of insects with biting and chewing mouthparts.

If you ever get a chance, watch a grasshopper feed. The mouthparts work

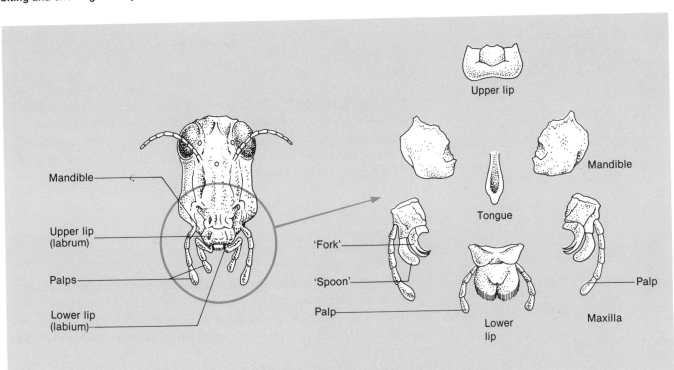

in perfect coordination to select, pulverize, and ingest the food. The palps constantly tap the food as if tasting it. The mandibles grind the food and the maxillae "shovel" it into the mouth, where the digestive system begins.

Extension

Some insects feed on fluids or very soft tissues. Therefore their mouthparts show adaptations to these feeding habits. Find out how the mouthparts of a butterfly and housefly differ from those of the grasshopper.

Feeding by the Perch

The **perch**, a vertebrate animal, is well-adapted to detecting, capturing, and ingesting its prey (Fig. 8-8). When it is less than 2 cm long, the perch feeds on plankton (small, often microscopic organisms). With increasing size, the food changes to aquatic insects, snails, small crayfish, and other invertebrates. Adult perch eat small fish, which clearly are difficult to catch and ingest. How is this accomplished?

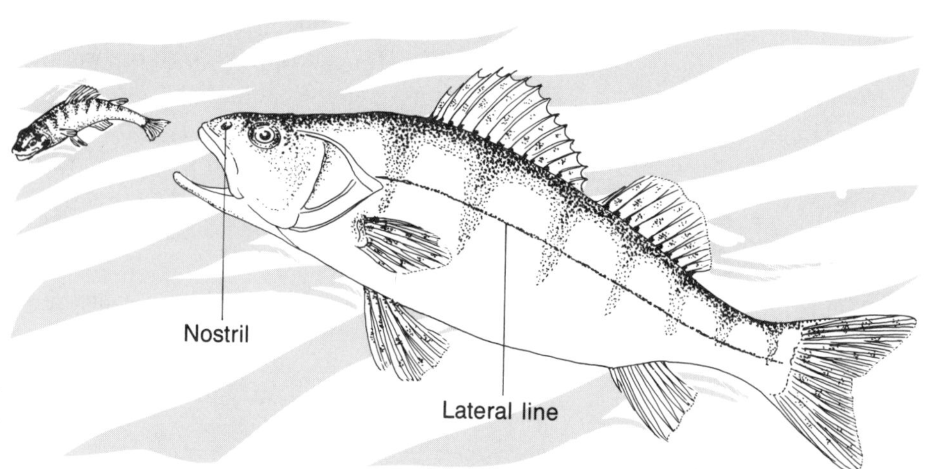

Fig. 8-8 The yellow perch is a carnivore that is well-adapted to seizing and ingesting fast-moving prey.

Using a combination of sensory organs—nostrils, eyes, and lateral lines—the fish detects its prey (see Section 6.5, page 160). Then a coordinated action of the fins direct the open-mouthed fish quickly to its prey. The prey is seized and held in the mouth by rows of inward slanting "teeth" on the jaws. The food has been ingested and digestion can begin.

Section Review

1. **a)** What is feeding?
   b) How does ingestion differ from feeding?
2. Make a summary of feeding for each of the following organisms: amoeba, hydra, earthworm, grasshopper, perch.
3. The five organisms that you read about increase in complexity from amoeba to perch. How is this increase in complexity reflected in their feeding mechanisms?

8.3 Digestion: Breaking Food Down

What Is Digestion?

As you know, all organisms require nutrients as a source of energy and as a source of matter for growth and repair. Heterotrophic organisms get these nutrients by ingesting food from their external environments. However, before these nutrients are of any value to an organism, they must be transported to the cytoplasm and organelles of the cells that make up the organism. It is in the cells that the processes requiring matter and energy occur. For example, you may have eaten toast and jam for breakfast. But the carbohydrates in the jam and toast will not provide you with energy for movement until they reach your muscle cells.

You learned last year that particles must be very small to enter a cell. That's because they have to pass through spaces between the molecules that make up the cell membrane. To do so, the particles must be very small molecules or ions (atoms or groups of atoms with a charge). Heterotrophs, like the five we discussed in Section 8.2, ingest their food as very large particles. These may consist of large carbohydrate molecules, large protein molecules, large fat molecules, and, most likely, mixtures of all of these. Therefore the food ingested by heterotrophs must be broken down into small particles. The process by which large food molecules are broken down into simple nutrient units, small enough to enter cells, is called **digestion**.

Digestion is accomplished with the aid of proteins called **enzymes**. For example, you have an enzyme called amylase in your saliva which breaks down starch into sugars. Your pancreas produces another amylase as well as other enzymes which break down proteins and fats.

Intracellular and Extracellular Digestion

Intracellular digestion is characteristic of single-celled organisms such as the amoeba. *Intra* means "inside". Therefore intracellular digestion is digestion that occurs *inside* the cell. In the case of the amoeba, the ingested food is enclosed in a food vacuole. Then digestive enzymes are secreted from the cytoplasm into the vacuole. These enzymes break the food down into small nutrient molecules. These diffuse out of the vacuole and into the cytoplasm where they are used for life processes. Unused food fragments are released or **egested** from the cell as shown in Figure 8-9.

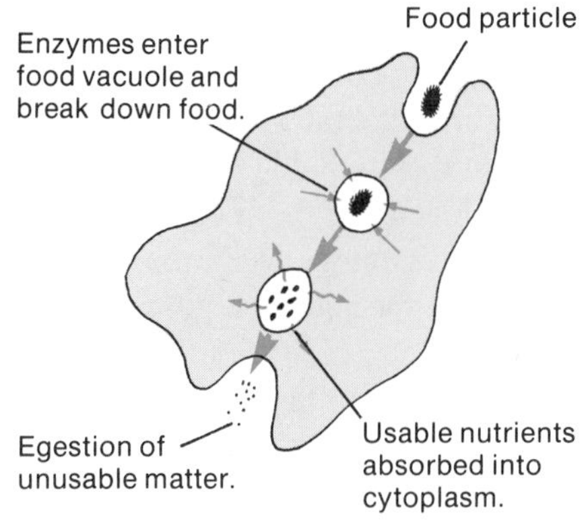
Enzymes enter food vacuole and break down food.
Food particle
Egestion of unusable matter.
Usable nutrients absorbed into cytoplasm.

Fig. 8-9 Intracellular digestion in the amoeba

Intracellular digestion is clearly limited to very small food particles. They must be small enough to be ingested by individual cells. Also, intracellular digestion cannot meet the needs of many-celled organisms. For example, each cell in your body could not possibly ingest and digest its own food. One reason is that most cells in your body simply do not come in contact with food.

Extracellular digestion, as the name implies, is digestion which occurs *outside* the cell. During this process, digestive enzymes are secreted from the

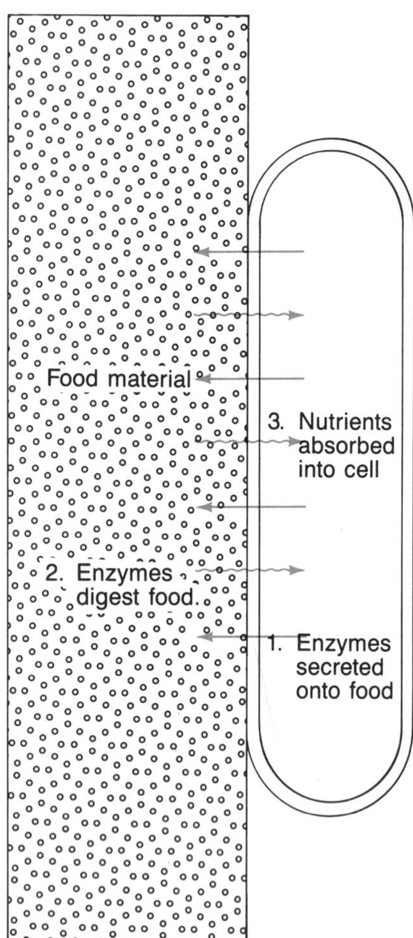

Fig. 8-10 Extracellular digestion by a bacterium

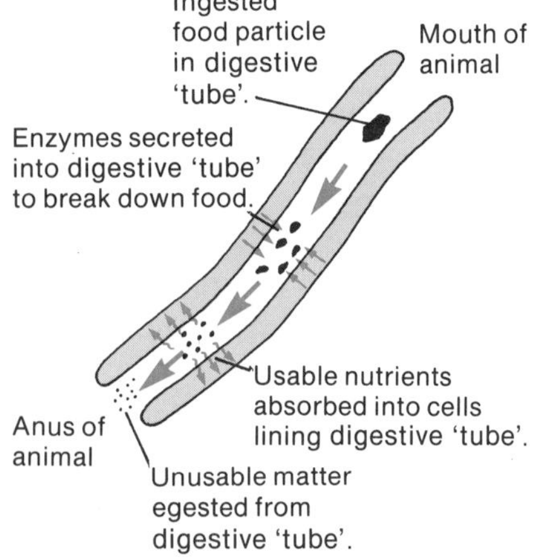

Fig. 8-11 Extracellular digestion in an animal with a one-way digestive tube, or alimentary canal

cell onto food which is in the cell's external environment. These enzymes break the food down into nutrient molecules small enough that they can be absorbed into the cell.

Bacteria use extracellular digestion. The bacteria that decay your favourite food are not doing this just to be mean to you. They are secreting enzymes onto the food to break it down, or digest it, so it can be absorbed into their cells (Fig. 8-10).

Extracellular digestion is characteristic of most many-celled animals. In these animals food is broken down in a digestive cavity of some kind. Then the resulting small nutrient molecules are absorbed and distributed to all cells throughout the animal. Extracellular digestion enables an organism to get food from large food masses.

Digestive Systems with One Opening

The **hydra** (see Figures 8-4 and 8-5) has a very simple digestive system. Unlike yours, it has only one opening to the external environment. Food enters and indigestable wastes leave by the same opening, the mouth.

As you read earlier, a hydra catches its prey with tentacles. Then the tentacles feed this food into the open mouth. The food now is in the **gastrovascular cavity**. (*Gastro* means "stomach" and *vascular* means "conducting".) This cavity serves both as a place for digestion and as a means of getting digested food to all cells in the organism. Once the food is in the gastrovascular cavity, digestive enzymes are released from **gland cells** into the cavity to begin extra-cellular digestion. Flagella on other cells help mix the enzymes with the food. (Look closely at Figure 8-4. Can you see the flagella?) When the particles of food become small enough, they are taken in by the **digestive cells** in the form of food vacuoles. Within these cells, intracellular digestion continues to break the food down. The hydra is a simple animal. Note how most of its cells are in close contact with the gastrovascular cavity. Therefore most cells can absorb the digested nutrients directly from the cavity's contents. Cells not in contact with the cavity get their needed nutrients by cell-to-cell diffusion. Unusable food materials are expelled, or **egested**, from the hydra's mouth.

Digestive Systems with Two Openings

The gastrovascular system of the hydra can meet the needs of such a simple organism. However, a much more advanced and specialized digestive system is needed for more complex invertebrates and for vertebrates. These animals have a *one-way digestive tube* or **alimentary canal** (Fig. 8-11). This tube has two openings to the external environment. One opening, the mouth, ingests the food. At the other end of the tube a second opening, the **anus**, egests undigested remains. An alimentary canal system has specialized regions within it.

Right after the mouth there is usually a region that breaks large food particles into smaller ones. Sometimes this is called **mechanical digestion**. This region is often preceded or followed by a storage region where food can be held undigested temporarily. The next region is the one in which digestion occurs. Here enzymes are secreted onto the food and extracellular digestion occurs.

Sometimes this is called chemical digestion to distinguish it from the simple grinding which occurs earlier. The final region is the one in which absorption of nutrients into the rest of the organism occurs.

Digestive System of the Earthworm The earthworm's digestive system shows the specialization within an alimentary canal system (see Figure 8-6). Soil is sucked in through the mouth by the muscular pharynx. It then moves to the esophagus which forces it into the crop. Here the food is temporarily stored. The food then enters the gizzard, a muscular organ for grinding the food up. Coarse sand particles taken in as part of the soil assist in the grinding. The food then enters the intestine. Cells lining the intestine secrete enzymes onto the food. These enzymes digest the food. Required nutrients can then be absorbed into the earthworm's circulatory (blood) system. Unused material passes out of the digestive system through the anus. Have you ever noticed the coiled ''casts'' at the entrance to an earthworm's burrow? These ''casts'' are made of undigested matter left by the worm.

Digestive System of the Grasshopper Like the earthworm, the grasshopper also has an alimentary canal digestive system with specialized parts (Fig. 8-12). Specialized mouthparts mechanically break down the food into smaller pieces during feeding (see Figure 8-7). Salivary glands secrete saliva which is mixed with the food in the mouth. Saliva aids in the passage of food along the esophagus. It also contains enzymes which begin chemical digestion of the food. Food passes along the esophagus into a temporary storage organ called the crop. The crop enables the grasshopper to eat large quantities of food at one time and then digest it later. The ''brown juice'' that a grasshopper spits when disturbed is really a mixture of partly digested food and saliva forced out of the crop.

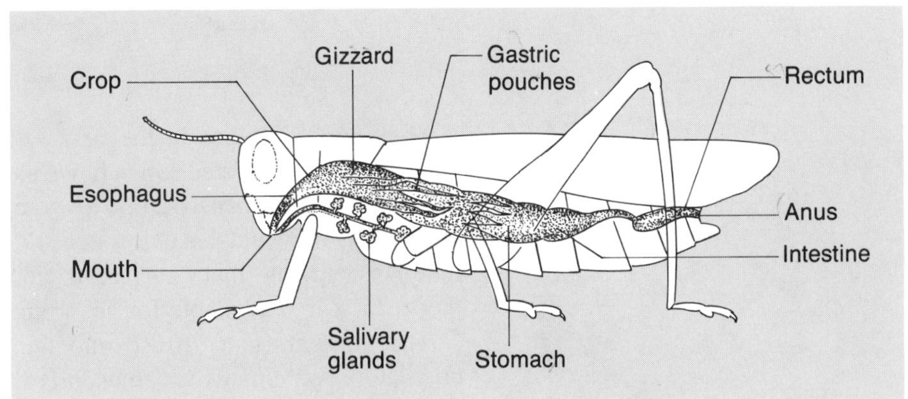

Fig. 8-12 The digestive system of a grasshopper is a one-way tube, or alimentary canal.

In the muscular gizzard, food is further broken down by the shredding and grinding action of teeth-like plates. The food then enters the stomach. Six pairs of gastric pouches, located outside the stomach wall, manufacture a digestive juice containing enzymes. These enzymes are secreted into the stomach. Once mixed with the food, they complete the digestive process. Usable digested nutrients are absorbed into blood vessels surrounding the stomach wall. The remaining food passes into the **intestine**, through the **rectum**, and out the **anus**.

Digestive System of the Perch The **perch** also has an alimentary canal digestive system (Fig. 8-13). It is representative of the systems found in most vertebrates. Food first enters the **mouth**, which is equipped with backward-slanting teeth to prevent the escape of the prey. These teeth are not used for chewing, or mechanical digestion, as they are in many other vertebrates. The food now moves to the **esophagus** which, by muscular contractions, moves the food to the **stomach**. This thick-walled organ secretes digestive enzymes and hydrochloric acid onto the food, mixes them into the food, and extracellular digestion begins. Note that the stomach is almost in a straight line with the esophagus. This allows the fish to swallow very large prey. Sometimes you can see the tail of a fish sticking out of another fish's mouth. Likely the head is being digested at that time!

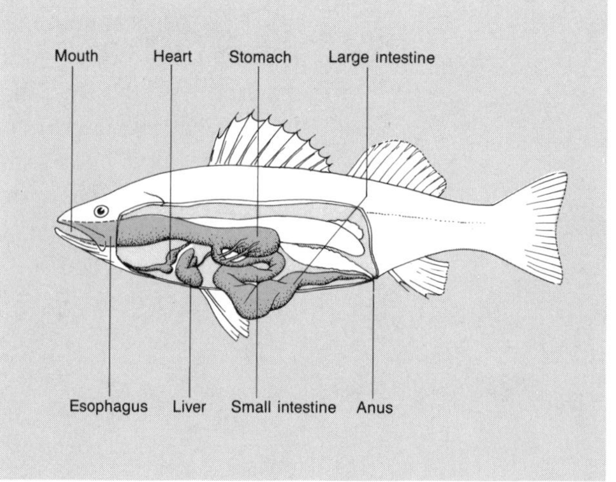

Fig. 8-13 Digestive system of the yellow perch

Digestion continues in the first part of the **small intestine**. Then, as the nutrients and undigested solids move along the remainder of the small intestine, absorption of nutrients occurs. If you looked at a cross section of the small intestine, you would see that it doesn't look just like a water hose or any other tube. Instead, the inner surface is ridged (Fig. 8-14). This greatly increases the surface area available for absorbing nutrients. Can you see why?

The nutrients that diffuse into the cells of the small intestine enter the circulatory system, which transports them throughout the body. Meanwhile, the undigested matter moves into the **large intestine**. Here the waste is made into a concentrated, more solid form, ready for elimination. This is accomplished by two actions. First, the large intestine absorbs some of the water from the waste. And, second, mutualistic bacteria living in the large intestine digest some of the waste. Finally the waste is temporarily stored in the before being eliminated, on occasion, from the **anus**.

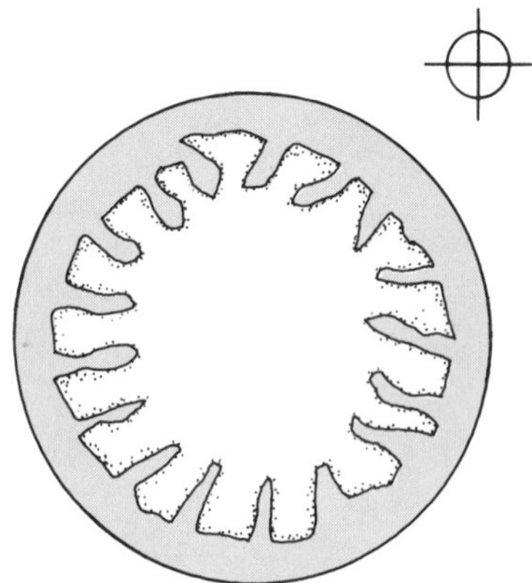

Fig. 8-14 Cross section of the small intestine of a perch

Section Review

1. a) Why is digestion necessary?
   b) What is digestion?
   c) What is the function of digestive enzymes?
2. a) Distinguish between intracellular and extracellular digestion.
   b) Describe intracellular digestion in the amoeba.
   c) Describe extracellular digestion in bacteria.
3. a) What is meant by "a digestive system with one opening"?
   b) Describe the digestive system of the hydra.
4. a) Give a general description of a digestive system with two openings.
   b) Make a table that compares the digestive systems of the earthworm, grasshopper, and perch.

8.4 Activity: Feeding and Digestion in a Protist, the Paramecium

All heterotrophic organisms, single-celled or many-celled, must be able to obtain food from their environment. They must also be able to digest the food so that essential nutrients in the food become available to the organisms. As we have seen, the feeding mechanisms that organisms use to obtain food depend on the form the food is in. Once ingested, the food is digested or broken down into basic units which are small and soluble. They can then be absorbed into the organism and put to their necessary use.

In this activity you will observe the feeding mechanism used by the **paramecium**, a single-celled organism. You will also observe the process of digestion that occurs within the food vacuoles of the paramecium following ingestion of the food. The food will be yeast that is coloured with a dye called Congo red.

Problem

How does a paramecium obtain and digest its food?

Materials

paramecium (living culture)
yeast, in Congo red solution
microscope
microscope slide (depression type)
cover slip
droppers (2)
1.5% methyl cellulose
toothpick

Procedure

a. Using a dropper, place 2 drops of the paramecium culture into a depression slide.

b. Using a second dropper, add a drop of methyl cellulose to the culture. The methyl cellulose will slow down the movement of the paramecia, making them easier to observe.

c. Add a small amount of yeast that has been dyed with Congo red to the culture. Add only the amount you can get on the end of a toothpick. Cover the depression with a cover slip.

d. Place the prepared slide under low power of the microscope. Find a paramecium that is not moving too much. Once you have located a paramecium, switch to medium, then high power.

e. Locate the cilia, oral groove, and gullet (Fig. 8-15).

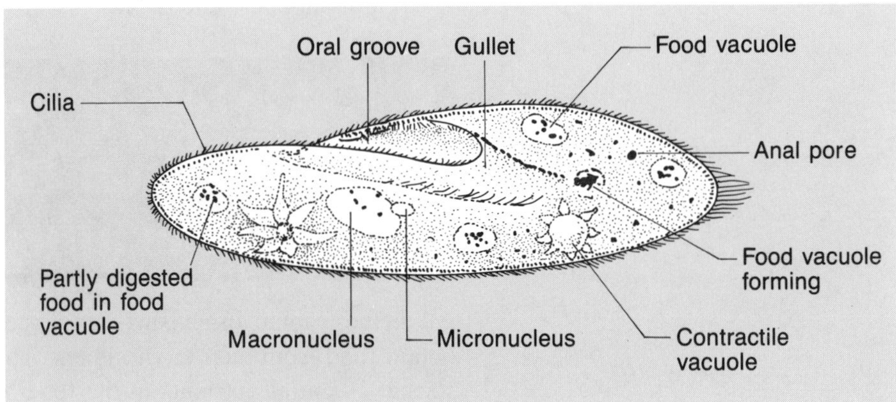

Fig. 8-15 This diagram should help you trace ingestion, digestion, and egestion in a paramecium.

f. Observe the feeding process and the formation of a food vacuole. The dyed yeast cells will be visible within the vacuole. BE PATIENT.

g. Observe a newly formed food vacuole for several minutes. You should observe a colour change in the yeast cells within the food vacuole. How long does the colour change take to occur?

h. The paramecium eliminates, or egests, spent food material through an **anal pore**. You may see this occur if you observe closely.

Discussion

1. How is the food (yeast) moved into the oral groove of the paramecium?
2. a) What is the likely reason for the colour change that occurred in the food vacuole? (*Note*: Congo red turns blue in the presence of an acid.)
   b) Do further colour changes occur?
3. a) What will eventually happen to the ingested yeast?
   b) What will eventually happen to the food vacuoles?
4. You will recall that food vacuoles are bounded by a membrane. How do required nutrients resulting from digestion within the vacuole get into the cytoplasm of the paramecium where they can be used?
5. Is the paramecium's digestive process intracellular or extracellular? Explain.
6. Compare ingestion of food by the paramecium and amoeba (Section 8.2). Why is the paramecium's method more specialized?

Extension

Design and do an experiment to investigate feeding in another protist such as *Amoeba*, *Stentor*, or *Vorticella*. The latter two are ciliates like *Paramecium*. Find out how they differ from *Paramecium* before you choose your experimental organism.

8.5 Activity: Feeding and Digestion in a Simple Invertebrate, the Hydra

The hydra is a simple invertebrate that catches its prey with tentacles and digests them in a gastrovascular cavity that has only one opening to the external environment. In this activity you will try to observe hydra feeding. You will also examine a slide that shows the gastrovascular cavity. You read about feeding in Section 8.2 and digestion in Section 8.3. Read those sections again and use them as guides to make this activity successful.

Problem

How does the hydra catch and digest its prey?

Materials

dissecting (or compound) microscope
droppers (3)
watch glass
solution of 1% acetic acid
hydra culture
Daphnia culture
probe
cavity slide
prepared slide of hydra

Procedure A Feeding

a. Using the dropper, put five drops of water in the middle of a watch glass.
b. Using the dropper, remove a hydra from the culture jar. Put the hydra into the water in the watch glass.
c. Wait a minute or so for the hydra to recover from the change. Look at it with your unaided eye. Can you see it move? How long is it? How many tentacles does it have? Record your observations.
d. Place the watch glass on the stage of the microscope. Focus on the hydra using low power. Observe its appearance now. Record your observations.
e. Gently touch the probe to one of the hydra's tentacles. How does the hydra react to this? Record your observations.
f. Using a second dropper, transfer a *Daphnia* (water flea) to the watch glass containing the hydra. Observe what happens over the next few minutes. Record your observations.

g. Place another hydra into a few drops of water in the cavity of a cavity slide. Observe the hydra under medium power. Record your observations.
h. Using the third dropper, add a drop of 1% acetic acid solution to the cavity. Observe the reaction of the hydra. Record your observations.

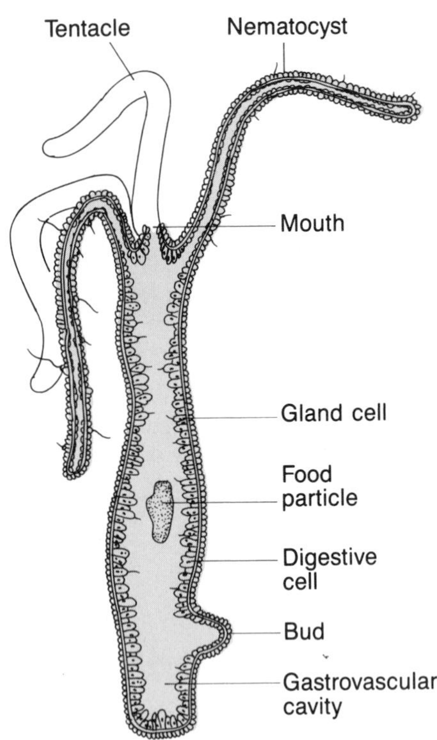

Fig. 8-16 Longitudinal section of a hydra

Procedure B Digestion

a. Examine the prepared slide of hydra under low, then medium power. Try to find each part that is labelled in Figure 8-16. Make a drawing of the whole animal. Draw what you see; do not copy Figure 8-16. Label the parts you can identify.
b. Examine the gastrovascular cavity and the cells that line its wall. Make an enlarged drawing of a portion of the wall of the cavity. Label the unique features you see.

Discussion

1. Describe how a hydra captures and immobilizes its prey.
2. Describe ingestion of the prey.
3. How is the gastrovascular cavity equipped for digestion of food?

Extension

Obtain a living specimen of the flatworm *Dugesia* from your teacher. Obtain, also, a prepared slide of a cross section of *Dugesia*. With the help of library sources, design and do an experiment to investigate feeding and digestion in *Dugesia*.

8.6 Activity: Digestive System of the Grasshopper

Every organism has special adaptations which increase its chances of survival. The grasshopper is no exception. In this activity you will examine the grasshopper's digestive system from mouth to anus. As you do so, pay particular attention to how this system is adapted to facilitate feeding on plant material.

Comment on Dissections

This activity involves the dissection of an organism. Organisms must be dissected if we are to progress in our understanding of biology. However, you should realize that all life is valuable, even that of a grasshopper. Therefore you must not waste your specimen. Learn all you can from it. You will be well prepared for this learning if you read the following material again:

- ''Feeding in the Grasshopper'' in Section 8.2
- ''Digestive System of the Grasshopper'' in Section 8.3

Problem

What parts are used by the grasshopper for feeding and digestion? In what ways are these parts specialized to match the grasshopper's diet?

Materials

preserved grasshopper
dissecting tray
hand lens
forceps
dissecting pins
dissecting scissors
probe
10 cm × 10 cm piece of Bristol board
transparent tape

CAUTION: Wear safety goggles, an apron, and plastic gloves while doing the dissection. Wash your hands with soap and water after handling the specimen. Follow your teacher's instructions for the safe use of dissecting equipment.

Procedure A Examination of Feeding Parts

a. Make a copy of Table 8-1 in your notebook. It should be a page long.

Table 8-1 Feeding Parts

Part	Structure	Function	How structure complements function
Antenna			

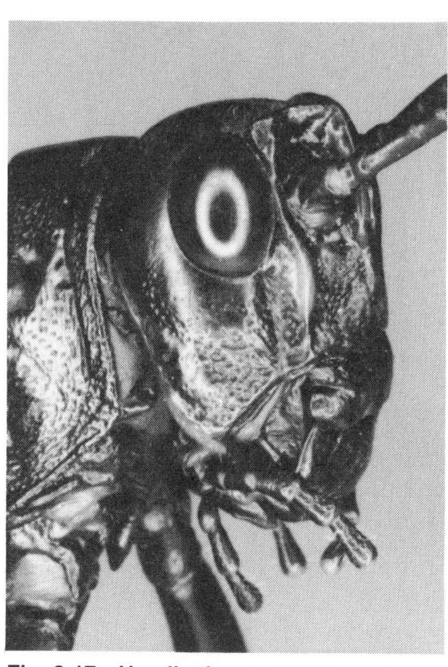

Fig. 8-17 Handle the specimen carefully so that you do not damage it.

b. Rinse your specimen with running water to wash off as much preservative as possible. Now place the specimen in the dissecting tray.

c. The **antennae** are not feeding parts, but they play an important role in feeding by helping the grasshopper find its food. Examine the antennae *closely*. Note their overall structure and the nature of the surface. Record your observations under "Structure" in your table.

d. Using Figure 8-7, page 209, as a guide, examine the mouth region of the insect (Fig. 8-17). Follow these directions *closely* as you examine the mouthparts:

- Probe the **labrum** gently. Note and record its structure and apparent function.
- Lift the labrum with the forceps and examine the **mandibles** underneath. Record your observations. Note particularly how the mandibles are adapted.
- Locate the **maxillae**. Investigate their structure and record your results. Look closely at the **palps**.
- Examine the **labium** by probing it gently. Record your results. Examine its palps closely.

e. Now, remove all the mouthparts from the insect. Do this as follows: Trace each mouthpart to its point of attachment. Then grasp it there with the forceps and gently remove it. Tape the mouthparts on the Bristol board in the arrangement shown in Figure 8-7. Label all the parts and put the animal's name and yours on the Bristol board.

Procedure B Examination of Digestive System

a. Make a full-page table similar to Table 8-1 in your notebook. Title it "Digestive System".

b. To see the parts of the digestive system that follow the mouth, you will have to cut the body open. To do so, follow these instructions *closely*.

- Pin the grasshopper to the dissecting tray.
- Cut along the *ventral* (lower) surface from anus to head. Keep the inserted point of the scissors up against the exoskeleton so you don't damage the internal organs.
- Use the forceps to lift the exoskeleton up so you can see the internal organs (Fig. 8-18). If the exoskeleton will not lift far enough, make a cut from rear to head along the *dorsal* (upper) surface and remove one half of the exoskeleton.

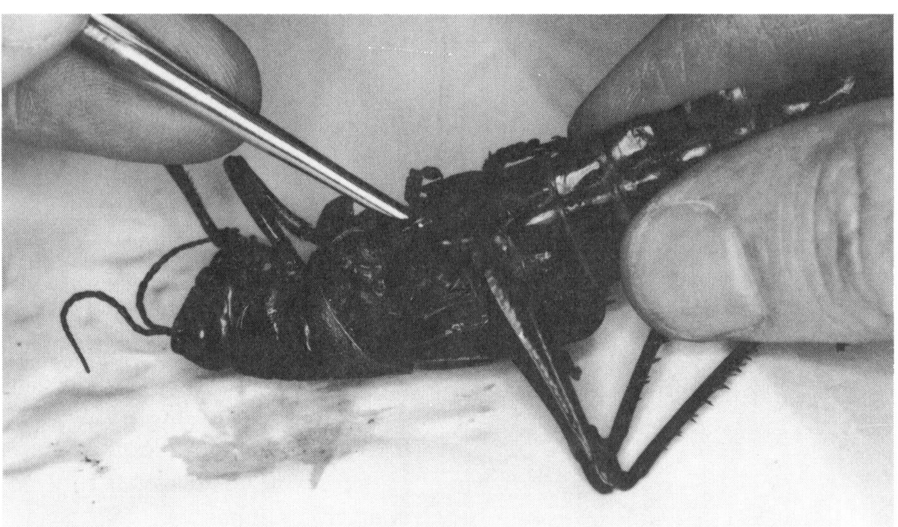

Fig. 8-18 Cut carefully and not too deeply. You simply want to remove the exoskeleton (outer body covering).

c. Using Figure 8-12, page 213, as a guide, examine the following parts of the digestive system. Note the structure of each part and think about how that structure complements the function. Put your results in your table.

- the **mouth**
- the **salivary glands**
- the **esophagus**
- the **crop** (Probe it gently. Is it soft or rigid?)
- the **gizzard** (Probe it gently. Is it soft or rigid?)
- the **stomach**

- the **gastric pouches**
- the **intestine**
- the **rectum**
- the **anus**

d. Draw a full-page diagram of your dissected specimen. Label all the parts listed in step (c).

e. Open the crop, gizzard, and stomach of your specimen. Compare the structure of these organs. Compare, too, the nature of the contents. Can you see evidence of progressive stages in digestion?

f. Place your specimen in the collecting container provided by your teacher. Wash and dry all dissecting equipment.

Discussion

1. Discuss this statement: The mouthparts of a grasshopper are adapted to a diet of vegetation.
2. Explain how the digestive system of a grasshopper illustrates how structure and function complement each other.
3. Why does a grasshopper need a gizzard while you do not?

Extension

Grasshopper plagues often sweep grassland regions. Find out why these occur from time to time but not every year. What control measures are used? How do these control measures make use of our knowledge of the grasshopper's structure and habits?

Looking Ahead

To complete your comparison of the five animals introduced in this chapter, you should now study the digestive systems of the **earthworm** and **perch**. However, these two animals will also be used in Chapters 9 and 10. To save specimens, we will look at all three systems—digestive, gas exchange, and internal transport—at the same time, in Chapter 10.

Chapter Highlights

1. All organisms require nutrients which supply energy and matter.
2. Nutrients can be divided into six main categories—carbohydrates, fats, proteins, vitamins, minerals, and water.
3. Each species of organism has a specialized feeding mechanism.
4. Each part of a digestive system has a structure which complements its function.

5. Digestion is the breaking down of food into particles small enough to be absorbed.
6. Digestive systems increase in complexity as the organisms become generally more complex.

Key Terms

alimentary canal
anus
carbohydrate
chemical digestion
digestion
egestion
enzyme
esophagus
extracellular digestion
fat
food vacuole
gastrovascular cavity
gizzard
ingestion
intestine
intracellular digestion
labium
labrum
mandible
maxilla
mechanical digestion
mineral
nematocyst
nutrient
palp
pharynx
protein
pseudopod
rectum
stomach
vitamin

Recognizing the Concepts

Each of the following statements or questions is followed by four responses. Choose the correct response in each case. (Do not write in this book.)

1. Which one of the following is *not* an energy source for heterotrophs?
   a) carbohydrates **b)** fats **c)** proteins **d)** vitamins
2. Heterotrophs get their essential amino acids by
   a) ingesting, then digesting proteins
   b) making them from carbohydrates
   c) absorbing them from food
   d) making them from fats and minerals
3. After an amoeba engulfs its food, the food is taken into the cytoplasm as a food vacuole. This taking in of food after it has been engulfed is best called
   a) feeding **b)** ingestion **c)** digestion **d)** egestion
4. Intracellular digestion is used by the
   a) amoeba and hydra **c)** amoeba and paramecium
   b) grasshopper and earthworm **d)** hydra and earthworm
5. The decay of food by bacteria is an example of
   a) extracellular digestion **c)** mechanical digestion
   b) intracellular digestion **d)** engulfing of nutrients
6. Which one of the following statements is true for all alimentary canal digestive systems?
   a) The canal is relatively straight.
   b) The canal includes a crop.
   c) The canal has two openings to the external environment.
   d) The canal includes a gizzard.

Understanding the Concepts

1. Why do organisms require a variety of nutrients instead of, for example, just two types like fats and carbohydrates?
2. What was our central purpose in studying feeding and digestion in five organisms in this order—protist, hydra, earthworm, grasshopper, perch?
3. **a)** Earthworms, grasshoppers, birds, and many other animals have crops for storage of food. Of what advantage is this adaptation to the organisms?
   b) How would a grasshopper's feeding habits and "lifestyle" have to change if it were to survive without a crop?
4. Why must most food be digested before it can be used by an organism?
5. What advantages does an alimentary canal digestive system offer over a gastrovascular cavity system?
6. Identify and account for the main differences in the digestive systems of earthworms and grasshoppers.

Applying the Concepts

1. Why is it important that your daily diet includes certain amounts of all six kinds of nutrients?
2. Think about birds that you have observed feeding. Why is a crop important to the survival of birds?
3. Have you ever been so hungry that you felt weak? Why do you have to wait for some time after a meal before your strength returns?
4. Some detergents used for washing clothes have enzymes in them to help remove food stains. How can enzymes do this?
5. Your hair is made of proteins. Many shampoos contain proteins "to strengthen your hair". Discuss this claim, based on your knowledge of absorption of nutrients.
6. A banana that is left in a warm place for several days gradually turns brown and mushy. What has happened?
7. Your esophagus and stomach do not connect in a straight line as they do in a fish.
   a) What limit does this put on your feeding?
   b) Why is this adaptation not important to your survival?
8. Tapeworms are parasites that live in the digestive systems of other animals, including humans. In fact, tapeworms over 15 m long have been found in humans! These animals have no digestive system, not even a mouth. Yet, as you are well aware, its close relative the earthworm does. How do you suppose tapeworms get their needed nutrients? Check your hypothesis using a biology text or animal encyclopedia.

Investigations

1. Research the digestive system of ruminants like cattle to see how this system is adapted for digesting cellulose (Fig. 8-19).

Fig. 8-19 Cattle chew their cud. What does this mean? What function does it serve?

2. Your appendix appears to serve no useful function in your body. However, the appendix of a rabbit is essential to its survival. Find out why this is so.
3. If you eat another animal's intestine, as you may do when you eat sausages, you digest it. Find out why your digestive enzymes do not digest your own stomach and intestines. On occasion, this may happen and an **ulcer** forms. Investigate the formation of ulcers.
4. Find a diagram of the human digestive system. Compare this system to the digestive system of the perch and account for any differences.

Biography

Joanne Anderson: Public Health Nurse

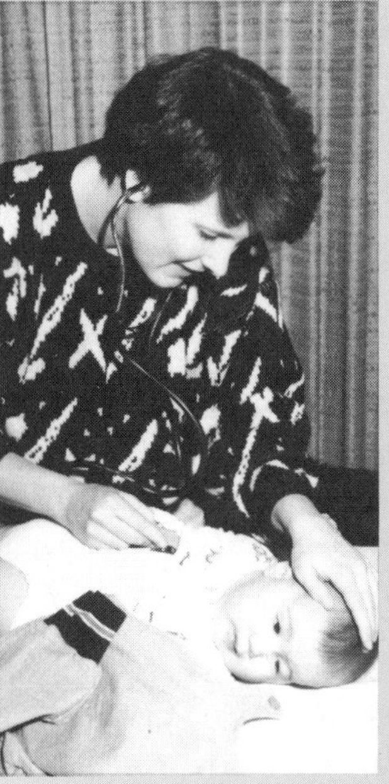

Joanne Anderson is a Public Health Nurse for the Scarborough Health Department. She currently works at Scarborough Grace Hospital. There she acts as a liaison between doctors, nurses, social workers, pastoral care workers, patients, families, and the community nurses who offer follow-up care after patients return home. Anderson also works in the Family Planning Clinic of the Scarborough Health Department one-half day per week.

Prior to holding this position, Joanne Anderson visited secondary schools on behalf of the Scarborough Health Department. As a counsellor and teacher, she taught birth control, parenting skills, communication skills, and other health-related topics. She also held immunization clinics and follow-up sessions for all levels of schools. She conducted vision and hearing screening at elementary schools, a STD clinic at the Health Centre, and a wide variety of other tasks. Home visiting was a major part of this position. She visited patients in their homes when the hospital, doctors, or patients requested a visit. She assessed the physical and mental status of the patients and the safety of their home environments.

Clearly, a public health nurse has a challenging, responsible, and demanding job. However, Joanne says she likes the variety, the people contact, and the independence her job offers.

How did she prepare for this job? Joanne says it all started in secondary school. She loved science and has found it important in her work. She spent four years at the University of Western Ontario getting a B.Sc.N. and she also is an R.N. You can become a registered nurse by studying at a community college, but the B.Sc.N. enables Joanne to be a public health nurse.

VISTA

BROCCOLI: THE ANTI-CANCERVEGETABLE

A recent study at the University of Melbourne in Australia showed that three factors significantly help reduce the incidence of cancer of the colon in humans:

- eating lots of vegetables, particularly those in the family Cruciferae (cabbage, cauliflower, broccoli, brussels sprouts)
- maintaining a high-fibre diet
- maintaining a diet rich in Vitamin C

Of all the things you can eat, broccoli fits this description best. It is a vegetable in the family Cruciferae. It contains more fibre than any other food except bran cereals, apples, and beans. And a normal serving of broccoli contains 70 mg of vitamin C, about as much as an orange. The only other vegetable that has more vitamin C is the green pepper.

You have likely seen the warning on a package of cigarettes that says "*Smoking may be hazardous to your health.*" Perhaps there should be one on broccoli which says "*Not eating broccoli may be hazardous to your health.*"

9 Gas Exchange

CHAPTER CONTENTS

CHAPTER OBJECTIVES

After completing this chapter you should be able to:

1. Explain why gas exchange is necessary.
2. Demonstrate how surface area and volume affect gas exchange.
3. Describe gas exchange for several aquatic and terrestrial organisms.
4. Describe the human gas exchange system.
5. Evaluate the effects of air and water pollution on gas exchange.

In order to live, organisms need oxygen. They must, somehow, get this oxygen from their external environment. As a by-product of respiration, organisms produce carbon dioxide. They must get rid of this gas as fast as it is produced or they will die. The exchange of these two gases, oxygen and carbon dioxide, between organisms and their external environment is the topic of this chapter. How does such gas exchange occur? Does the size and complexity of an organism make a difference? What special adaptations do aquatic and terrestrial organisms have to ensure maximum gas exchange (Fig. 9-1)?

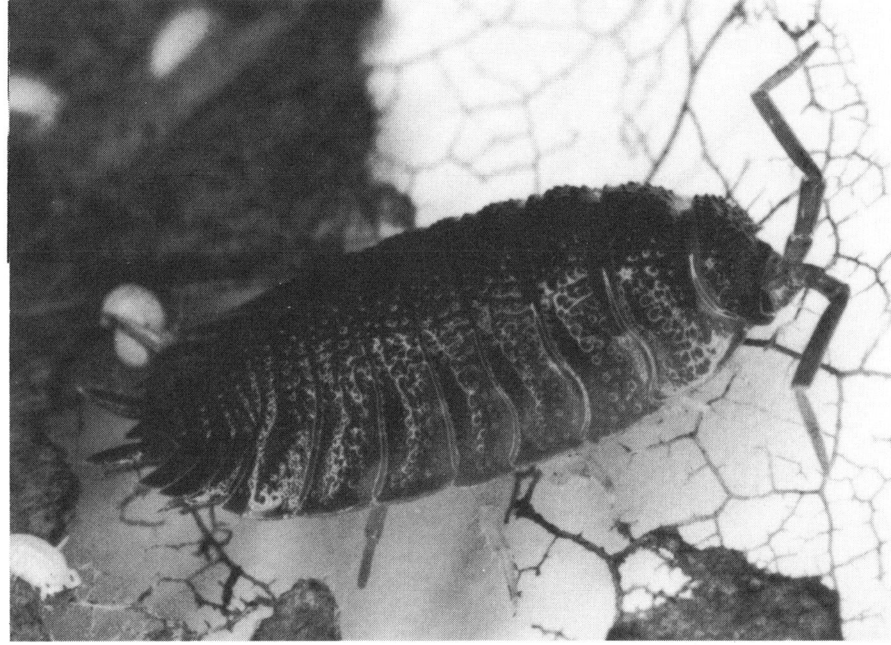

Fig. 9-1 This familiar animal, the sow bug, will die if it is removed from its common habitat—moist areas under rocks, logs, and vegetation. The moisture is needed to keep gas exchange going. Why do you suppose this is so?

9.1 The Need for Gas Exchange

Why is gas exchange needed? Simply stated, the answer is to keep organisms alive. Gas exchange brings oxygen into organs for the vital process of respiration. It also rids organisms of excess carbon dioxide. What is respiration and why does it necessitate gas exchange?

Fig. 9-2 How are the burning of wood and respiration in your cells alike? How are they different?

What Is Respiration?

Respiration is the process by which molecules such as glucose are broken down to release the chemical potential energy that is stored in the bonds of the molecules. The released energy is needed for life processes. Much of this energy is heat energy.

Don't confuse respiration and breathing. Respiration is a series of chemical reactions that occur in the cytoplasm and mitochondria of cells. In fact, respiration is often called **cellular respiration** to emphasize this fact. **Breathing** is simply the exchange of gases between an organism and its environment. It is not a chemical reaction.

In some respects, respiration is similar to the burning of fuels such as coal, wood, and oil. When a fuel is burned, chemical potential energy in the molecules of the fuel is released as heat and light energy. In like manner, when glucose is "burned" in cells, chemical potential energy in the glucose molecules is released partly as heat energy. However, there is one important difference between the burning of fuel and the "burning" of glucose in cells (Fig. 9-2). The burning of fuel produces very high temperatures. Clearly such high temperatures cannot occur in cells. The cells would be destroyed. Thus, during respiration, the rate of "burning" must be controlled. As a result, it occurs in several small steps. Each step is assisted by an **enzyme**. The enzyme permits that step to take place at the normal temperature of the organism. Some steps of respiration take place in the cytoplasm. Others occur in the mitochondria.

The Summation Equation for Respiration

Cellular respiration requires oxygen. The oxygen combines with atoms in the glucose molecules, thereby breaking down the molecules. The energy that is released supports life processes. Water and carbon dioxide are produced as by-products. The process of respiration is summed up in the following word and chemical equations:

$$\text{Glucose} + \text{Oxygen} \rightarrow \text{Carbon dioxide} + \text{Water} + \text{Energy}$$
$$C_6H_{12}O_6 + 6\,O_2 \rightarrow 6\,CO_2 + 6\,H_2O + \text{Energy}$$

This summation equation only "sums up" *what* happens during respiration. It tells us *what* respiration starts with and *what* it ends with. However, it does not tell us *how* this process occurs.

You learned last year that the glucose was formed, in the first place, by photosynthesis. During that process, chemical potential energy was stored in the bonds of the glucose molecules. During respiration, this glucose is broken down with the help of enzymes. Oxygen is involved in the process. Much of the energy stored in the bond of the glucose is released.

The function of gas exchange in organisms is to bring oxygen to the cells for respiration and to rid cells of the carbon dioxide that is formed.

Section Review

1. What is the basic function of gas exchange?
2. a) What is respiration?
   b) Why is respiration often called cellular respiration?
3. a) How are respiration and the burning of a fuel alike?
   b) How are they different?
   c) How is the temperature controlled during respiration?
4. a) Write the summation equation, both word and chemical, for respiration.
   b) Why is this called a *summation* equation?

9.2 Activity: Do You Produce Carbon Dioxide?

Since you are a living organism, you must respire. As a result of this process, you produce carbon dioxide. Can you prove that you produce carbon dioxide? Proving experimentally that you produce carbon dioxide is more complicated than you may think. Therefore, before you begin this activity, read the procedure carefully and think about what happens during each step.

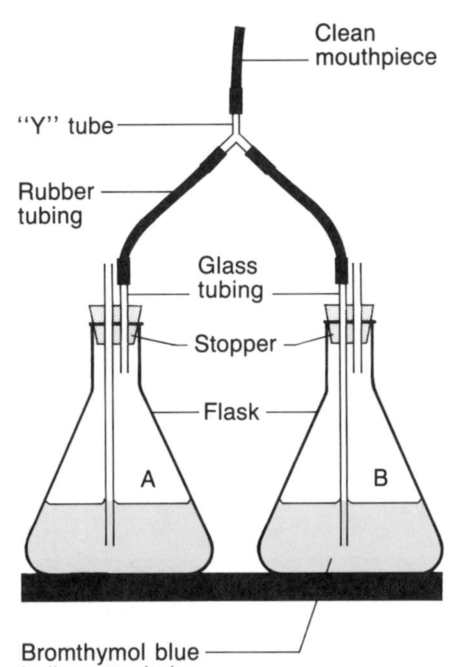

Fig. 9-3 How will air flow through this apparatus when you breathe in and out through it?

Problem

Can you prove that you produce carbon dioxide?

Materials

bromthymol blue indicator solution
drinking straw
50 mL beaker
apparatus shown in Figure 9-3
sterilized mouthpiece

CAUTION: Do not share the mouthpiece. Obtain a sterilized one from your teacher.

Procedure

a. The **test for carbon dioxide** that you will employ in this activity uses bromthymol blue indicator. If carbon dioxide is present, this indicator changes colour from blue (or green) to yellow. Rehearse this test as follows: Place about 20 mL of the bromthymol blue indicator solution in the beaker.

Fig. 9-4 Blow gently or you will expel some of the solution from the beaker.

Blow gently through the straw into the solution (Fig. 9-4). Continue blowing until a colour change occurs.

b. Obtain the apparatus shown in Figure 9-3 from your teacher.

c. Exhale gently into the mouthpiece. Note the flask in which bubbling occurs. Record your observation in a table similar to Table 9-1.

d. Now inhale through the same mouthpiece. Note the flask in which bubbling occurs. Record your observation.

e. Continue to exhale and inhale through the apparatus until there is a difference in colour between the 2 flasks. Record your results in your table.

Table 9-1 Do You Produce Carbon Dioxide?

	Flask A	*Flask B*
Effect of exhaling		
Effect of inhaling		
Appearance at end		

Discussion

1. a) Describe the bromthymol blue test for carbon dioxide.
   b) Why does carbon dioxide affect bromthymol blue in this way? (Consult Chapter 19 for an answer.)
   c) Why does step (a) not prove that you produce carbon dioxide? Where else could the carbon dioxide have come from?
2. a) Which flask bubbles when you exhale? Explain why this happens.
   b) Which flask bubbles when you inhale? Explain why this happens.
3. a) In which flask is the indicator solution not affected by the bubbling?
   b) Why is this observation so important?

Extensions

1. What else besides carbon dioxide is added to exhaled air by your body? Design and do an experiment to prove this.
2. Design an experiment to show that another animal produces carbon dioxide during respiration. Fish, frogs, insects, gerbils, and hamsters are good subjects. *Do not do this experiment until your teacher assures you that your procedure will not harm the animals.*

9.3 The Basic Requirements for Gas Exchange

Respiration requires oxygen and produces a harmful by-product, carbon dioxide. Therefore organisms must have a way of obtaining oxygen and a way of getting rid of carbon dioxide. In other words, **gas exchange** must occur between organisms and their environments.

Gas exchange is usually a simple process in single-celled and small many-celled organisms. All the cells in such organisms are in direct contact with or close to the external environment. Therefore each cell can exchange gases directly with the environment by **diffusion**.

Gas exchange is a more complex process in larger animals. Such animals may have many cells deep within their body, far from the external environment. Diffusion alone is too slow at moving gases across a large number of cells. Therefore larger animals must have some other mechanism for carrying the gases to and from every cell. Usually special regions for gas exchange are present in larger animals. These regions are called **gas exchange surfaces**.

In order for gases to pass into or out of cells, they must first be dissolved in a liquid (usually water). They can then diffuse across cell membranes. Moisture, therefore, is required for gas exchange to occur. Obviously this is not a problem for aquatic animals. For terrestrial (land) animals, however, this presents a serious problem. Air is a relatively dry environment. But gas exchange surfaces must be kept moist. Therefore, terrestrial animals must have ways to solve this problem. Can you think of some ways?

The gas exchange surface of an animal must be large enough to exchange gases for all the cells of the animal. In some animals the gas exchange surface may involve the entire body surface. In others it may consist of infoldings or outfoldings of the body surface.

Summary of Basic Requirements

- The gas exchange surface must be of adequate size to service all cells in the organism.
- The gas exchange surface must be thin and kept moist to allow diffusion to occur.
- There must be some means of transporting the gases between the gas exchange surface and every cell in the organism.

As you study gas exchange in various organisms, see if you can determine how these three requirements are met in each case. Also, compare carefully the gas exchange surfaces of the organisms.

Section Review

1. Why is gas exchange a simple process in single-celled and small many-celled organisms?
2. Why is gas exchange more complex in larger animals?
3. **a)** What is a gas exchange surface?
   b) Why must this surface be moist?
4. Summarize the three basic requirements for gas exchange.

9.4 Activity: Gas Exchange: The Size Factor

One factor that determines how much oxygen an animal needs is its size. In general, the larger an animal is, the more oxygen it requires. The animal's gas exchange surface must permit oxygen intake at a rate adequate to meet its needs. Also, the surface must permit an adequate rate of carbon dioxide release. In this activity you will study the effect of an increase in size upon the ratio of surface area to volume. Then, you will try to determine the implications this has for gas exchange in large many-celled animals.

Problem

How does size affect the surface area to volume ratio?

Materials

sheet of graph paper

Procedure

a. Look at Figure 9-5. Calculate the surface area and the volume of a cube in which l = 2.0 cm. Then calculate the surface area to volume ratio for this cube. Record all your results in a table similar to Table 9-2. To serve as an example, the table has been completed for l = 1.0 cm.

b. Repeat step (a) for l = 3.0 cm, 4.0 cm, 5.0 cm, 6.0 cm, 7.0 cm, and 8.0 cm.

c. Plot a graph with the length of the side on the horizontal axis and both surface area and volume on the vertical axis.

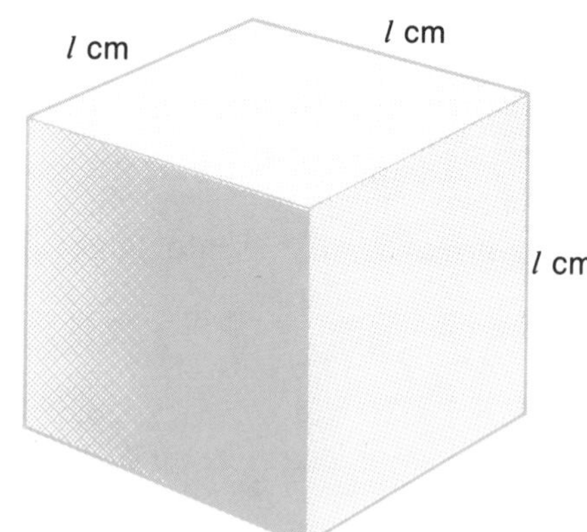

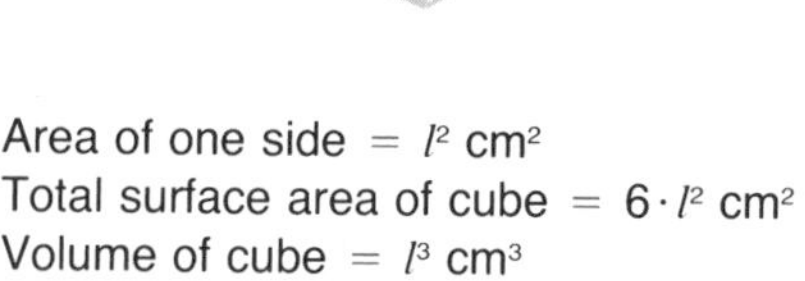

Area of one side = l^2 cm^2
Total surface area of cube = $6 \cdot l^2$ cm^2
Volume of cube = l^3 cm^3
$\frac{\text{Surface area}}{\text{Volume}} = \frac{6 \cdot l^2 \text{ cm}^2}{l^3 \text{ cm}^3}$

Fig. 9-5 The surface area of the cube represents the area of an organism's gas exchange surface. The volume of the cube represents the volume of the organism. How does the surface area to volume ratio change as the value of *l* is increased? Or, how does the ratio of the area of the gas exchange surface to the volume of the organism change as *l* is increased? What problem does this cause for large organisms?

Table 9-2 Surface Area to Volume Ratio

Length of side (cm)	*Surface area (cm^2)*	*Volume (cm^3)*	*Surface area to volume ratio (cm^{-1})*
1.0	6.0	1.0	$\frac{6.0}{1.0} = 6.0$
2.0			
3.0			
4.0			
5.0			
6.0			
7.0			
8.0			

Discussion

1. a) Use your calculations and your graph to describe what happens to the ratio of surface area to volume as the cube gets larger.

b) What do you think will happen to the ratio of the area of the gas exchange surface to the volume of an organism as the organism gets larger?

2. a) The results of this activity suggest that a serious problem could arise as an animal increases in size. What is this problem?

b) How might an animal grow larger, yet avoid this problem?

9.5 Gas Exchange in an Aquatic Environment

Gas exchange can occur only across a moist membrane. Aquatic organisms are completely surrounded by water. Therefore, their gas exchange surfaces are constantly kept moist. As a result, diffusion of gases can easily occur across these surfaces. In small simple organisms gas exchange is accomplished by **direct diffusion** between the water and the cells. However, larger animals need special surfaces that increase the surface area available for gas exchange. These surfaces are called **gills**. Let us examine a few representative organisms to see how they meet their need for gas exchange.

Use of Direct Diffusion

The Amoeba Single-celled aquatic organisms such as the **amoeba** do not require any special gas exchange system (Fig. 9-6). Dissolved oxygen in the surrounding water diffuses across the cell membrane into the organism's body. Carbon dioxide in the cell diffuses outward into the surrounding water. The oxygen requirements of such organisms are so low that direct diffusion can provide all the gas exchange needed.

The Hydra In like manner, many simple aquatic animals do not have special gas exchange surfaces. Also, they usually do not have any special systems for transporting oxygen and carbon dioxide to and from every body cell. In the **hydra**, for example, all body cells are in direct contact with water (Fig. 9-7). They either contact the surrounding water or the water in the gastrovascular cavity (see Figure 8-4, page 208). Therefore direct diffusion is adequate for gas exchange.

The Planarian The **planarian**, or flatworm, is more complex than the hydra, but still a relatively simple animal. Its flattened shape means that no cell is very far from the body surface (Fig. 9-8). Therefore, oxygen and carbon dioxide

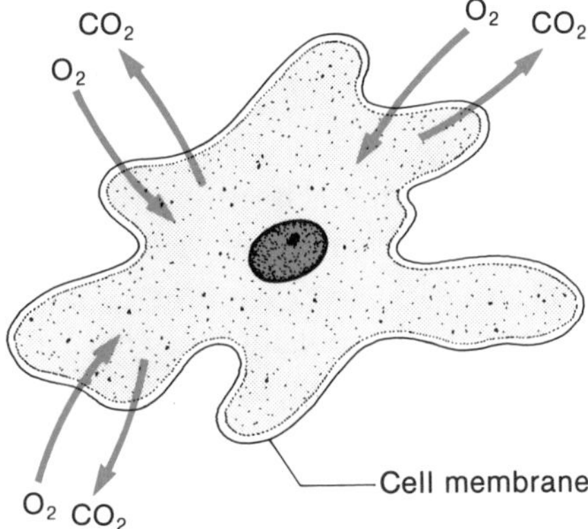

Fig. 9-6 Gas exchange in an amoeba. The entire surface of this single-celled organism is in contact with water. Therefore oxygen and carbon dioxide can easily be exchanged across any part of the cell membrane.

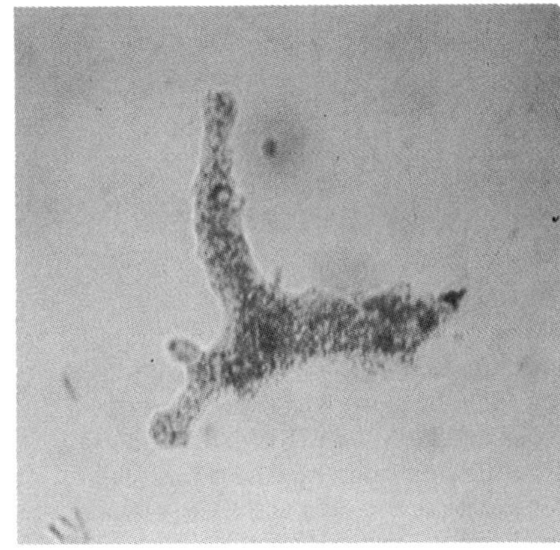

Fig. 9-7 Direct diffusion is sufficient for small animals like this hydra. Would it be sufficient for the much larger octopus and squid which look like the hydra?

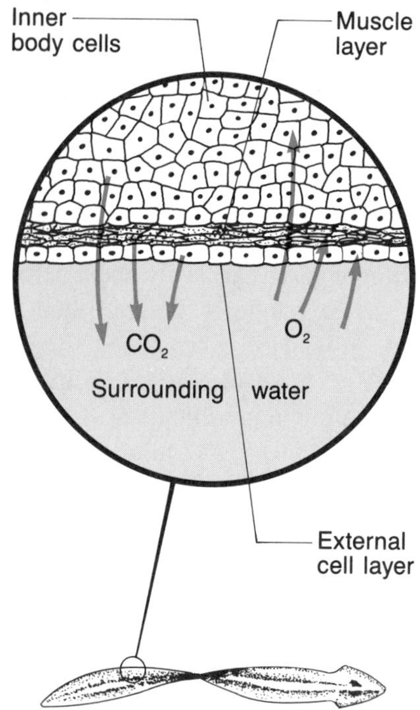

Fig. 9-8 Gas exchange in a planarian (flatworm). All cells in this flattened animal are very close to the surrounding water. This lets all cells exchange gases without a special transport system.

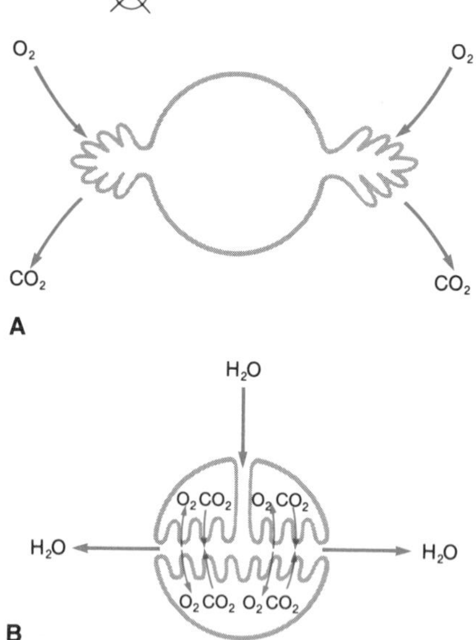

Fig. 9-9 Gills are a means of increasing the surface area for gas exchange. The gills of many invertebrates are external (A). In fish (B), water enters through one opening (the mouth), moves over the gills where gases are exchanged, and out through different openings.

can be exchanged with the surrounding water by direct diffusion or by diffusion from cell to cell. There is no need for a special transport system to move gases from the interior to the body surface.

Use of Gills

In most large aquatic animals, gas exchange cannot occur directly between all body cells and the surrounding water. Most cells in these animals are far from the body surface. Diffusion from cell to cell occurs too slowly to keep the cells alive. As a result, these animals have special gas exchange surfaces called **gills**. They also have special **internal transport systems**, or **circulatory systems**, to transport gases between the gas exchange surface and all body cells.

Gills are thin-walled and finely divided structures. They provide a very large surface area for gas exchange. Also, they have a rich supply of blood vessels. Dissolved oxygen and carbon dioxide can easily be exchanged across the thin membrane that separates the blood vessels from the surrounding water. The blood vessels contain **blood**, which transports the dissolved gases to and from all body cells.

Gills may differ somewhat from animal to animal (Fig. 9-9). However, all gills usually have the same characteristics: They provide a large surface area for gas exchange. Also, they contain blood vessels (part of the circulatory system) to transport the gases.

The Crayfish The **crayfish** is an example of an invertebrate that uses gills for gas exchange. The feather-like gills occur in rows in a chamber on both sides of the crayfish. They are just beneath part of its exoskeleton called the **carapace** (Fig. 9-10). The chamber is open at both ends and along the lower edge. Water enters the gill chamber near the walking legs and passes upwards and forwards over the gills, and leaves the chamber near the mouth.

When the crayfish is not moving, water is circulated over the gills in currents created by **gill bailers**. The gill bailers are fan-like structures attached to the maxillae at the forward end of the gill chamber. Waving **swimmerets** assist by pushing water forward toward the gills. As water passes over the **gill filaments**, oxygen diffuses from the water into the blood vessels and carbon dioxide diffuses out of the blood and into the surrounding water. Oxygen-rich blood is transported to all parts of the crayfish's body through its circulatory system.

The Fish Most **fish** have four pairs of gills which are located on the sides of the pharynx (Fig. 9-11). **Gill slits** separate each gill and permit water to flow past them. Each gill consists of a support made of cartilage called the **gill arch**. A double row of feathery **gill filaments** is attached to each arch. Blood vessels called **capillaries** are found within the thin-walled filaments. The inner surface of the gill arch has numerous projections, the **gill rakers**, which act as straining devices. They prevent large particles from passing over the delicate gill filaments. Water enters through the mouth into the pharynx. The mouth is then closed and the floor of the pharynx and mouth is raised. This action forces the water out through the gill slits and past the gill filaments. Gas exchange takes place across the thin membranes of the gill filaments.

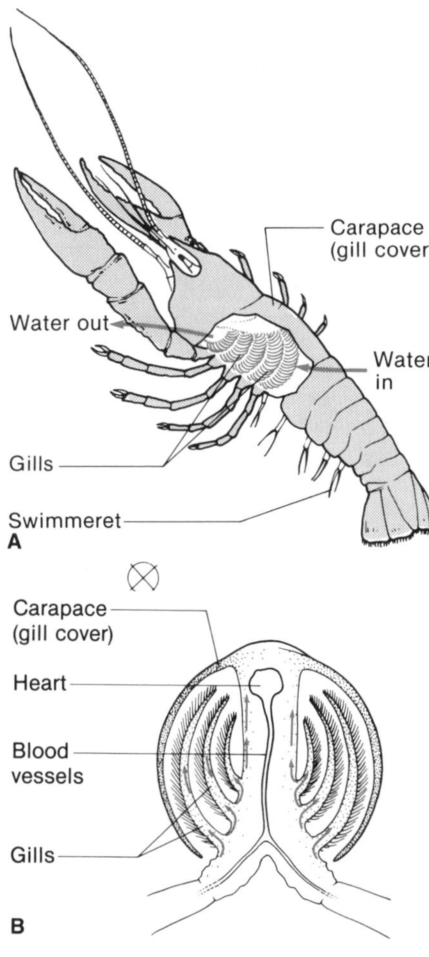

Fig. 9-10 A crayfish with part of the carapace removed to show the feather-like gills (A). Note the direction in which the water moves. The cross section view (B) shows the arrangement of the gills.

Fig. 9-11 Gills of a fish: a gill cover protects the gills (A); gill cover cut away to show a gill (B); path of water through gills (C); cross section through a gill filament (D).

Gas exchange in aquatic animals is complicated by the fact that very little oxygen is dissolved in water (around 0.005%). This amount decreases as the temperature of the water increases. Furthermore, the rate of diffusion of oxygen into water is very slow. Therefore, organisms that require large amounts of oxygen must have some means of constantly moving water over the gills. Swimming and the action of the pharynx does this for a fish. How is it accomplished for a crayfish?

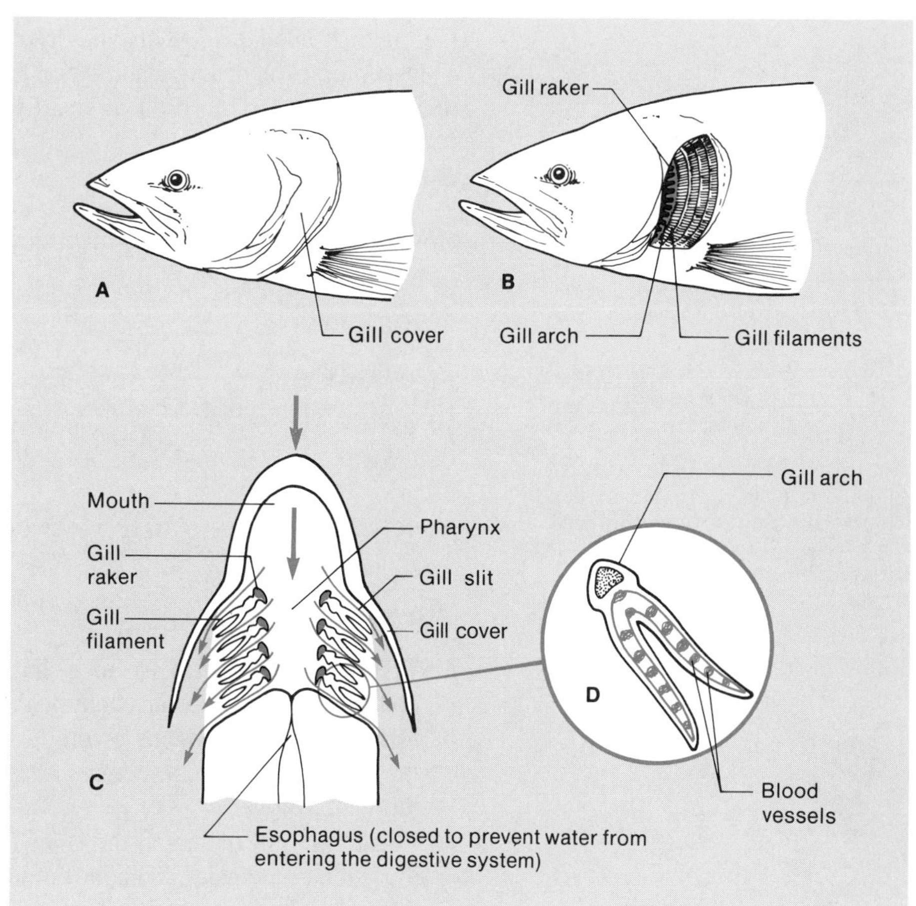

Section Review

1. What advantage do aquatic organisms have over terrestrial organisms insofar as gas exchange is concerned?
2. **a)** What is meant by "direct diffusion"?
   b) Describe gas exchange in the amoeba.
3. **a)** Explain why the hydra can function with just direct diffusion as a means of gas exchange.
   b) How is the planarian adapted to maximize gas exchange by diffusion?
4. **a)** Why are gills essential in most large aquatic animals?
   b) What role does the circulatory system play in gas exchange?
   c) Describe gas exchange in the crayfish.
   d) Describe gas exchange in a fish.

9.6 Activity: Breathing Movements of a Crayfish

You read in Section 9.5 that organisms which need large amounts of oxygen must have some means of constantly moving water over the gills. Each species of organism has special adaptations for doing this. You read briefly about how the crayfish is adapted. This activity explores this topic more thoroughly.

Depending on the availability of crayfish, your teacher may demonstrate this activity or let you do it in small groups.

Problem

How is a crayfish adapted to maximize the flow of water over its gills?

Materials

live crayfish
shallow container of fresh water
dropper
dark food colouring

CAUTION: Handle the crayfish carefully so that you do not harm it or let it harm you.

Note: Consult Figure 9-10 as you work through the following procedure.

Procedure

a. Transfer the live crayfish to a shallow container of fresh water. Hold the container so that you can examine the ventral (lower) surface of the crayfish.
b. Describe the movements of the tiny appendages (swimmerets) attached to the abdomen. These structures assist in moving water. In what direction is the water moved?
c. Locate the gill bailers at the sides of the mouth. Describe any movements the gill bailers make. What does the name of these structures tell you about their function?
d. Carefully place a couple of drops of food colouring into the water at the posterior (rear) end of the gill cover. Try not to disturb the crayfish. Observe the movement of the food colouring.
e. Remove the crayfish from the container and place it back in its original tank.

Discussion

1. How is the crayfish adapted, both structurally and behaviourally, to maximize the flow of water over the gills?
2. a) In a stream, a crayfish need not use its gill bailers. Why?
b) Would you expect to find a crayfish in a stream facing upstream or downstream? Why?

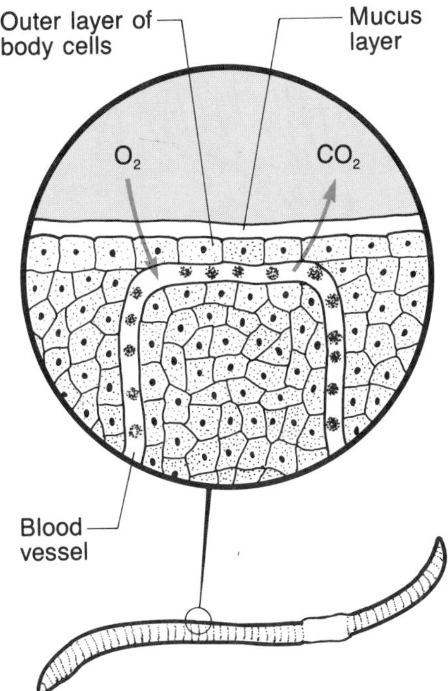

Fig. 9-12 The gas exchange system of an earthworm is simply its moist skin. The skin acts as a gas exchange surface between the air and the animal's circulatory system.

Fig. 9-13 This earthworm was forced from its burrow by overwatering of a lawn. It will likely survive because it is not far from its burrow.

9.7 Gas Exchange in a Terrestrial Environment

You might think that gas exchange would not be a problem for animals which live on land. After all, compared to water, the terrestrial (land) environment is quite rich in oxygen. (Air is about 21% oxygen by volume.) Remember, though, that a gas exchange surface must be kept moist. Air is a very dry environment. Land animals, therefore, must have some means of keeping their breathing surfaces from drying out. Let us examine a few land animals to see how they solve this problem.

The Earthworm: A Simple Gas Exchange System

The **earthworm** does not have an organized gas exchange system. However, it is well-adapted for gas exchange in its terrestrial environment. The earthworm exchanges gases through its skin. Its skin consists of a very thin membrane that is kept moist by the secretion of **mucus**. As a further aid in keeping the skin moist, the earthworm lives in moist soil.

The skin of the earthworm also has a rich supply of blood vessels. Oxygen can easily dissolve in the film of moisture covering the skin and diffuse into the blood vessels. Carbon dioxide diffuses outward from the blood into the soil (Fig. 9-12). This process occurs all over the body. Therefore, the gas exchange surface of the earthworm is large enough to meet the gas exchange needs of this animal.

Have you ever noticed dead earthworms on the ground or sidewalk after a rain (Fig. 9-13)? As water filled their burrows, they came to the surface to avoid drowning. These worms, unable to get back into the soil, probably died from lack of oxygen once their moist skins dried out.

Insects: A Tracheal Gas Exchange System

A **tracheal gas exchange system** is characteristic of terrestrial arthropods such as **insects**. Let us look at the tracheal system of a grasshopper to see how such a system works.

The grasshopper has a series of small openings called **spiracles** along the sides of its body (Fig. 9-14). These openings lead into a system of branched tubes called **tracheae** (singular: **trachea**). The tracheae subdivide into smaller and smaller tubes called **tracheoles** which reach all the cells in the insect's body (Fig. 9-15). The inner ends of the smallest tubes contain a fluid. This fluid provides the moist surface needed for gas exchange by diffusion. In addition, a double row of **air sacs**, for air storage, is located opposite the spiracle openings.

As the lower part of the grasshopper's abdomen pulses up and down, air enters and leaves the spiracles. It then travels directly to the body cells by the system of tracheal tubes. Oxygen and carbon dioxide are easily exchanged across the moist membranes of the cells.

Air sacs

Spiracles Tracheae

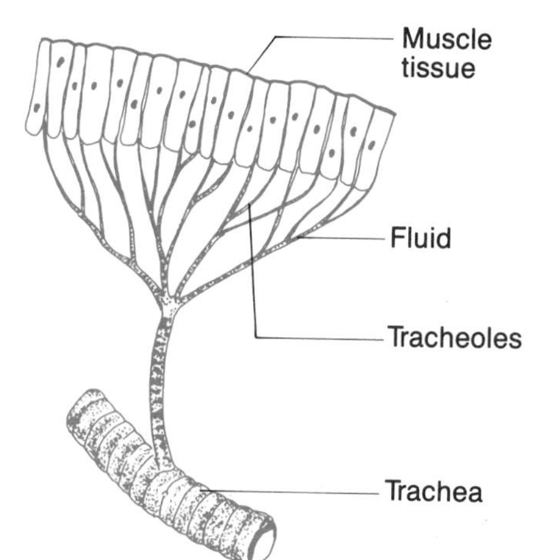

Fig. 9-14 The grasshopper's tracheal system for gas exchange. A network of air-filled tubes, or tracheae, carry gases to and from all parts of the body. Air enters and leaves the tracheal system through openings called spiracles.

Fig. 9-15 The tracheal system carries oxygen to and carbon dioxide from each cell (here, muscle tissue). Why do muscle cells require such an extensive tracheal system?

Amphibians: A Lung Gas Exchange System

The gas exchange system of an adult **frog** is quite different from that of the earthworm and insects. The frog can actually exchange gases in three ways. In the winter, a frog hibernates in the mud at the bottom of a pond. During this time, oxygen and carbon dioxide are exchanged through the frog's thin moist **skin**. Blood vessels beneath the skin transport these gases to and from all body cells. In fact, at all times of the year, the skin is the major breathing surface when the frog is under water.

Gas exchange can also occur across the lining of the frog's mouth. This thin membrane is covered with a moist mucus coating. Also, it has a large supply of blood vessels beneath its surface. This is usually referred to as **mouth breathing**.

The frog also has a pair of special gas exchange structures called **lungs** that resemble thin-walled sacs (Fig. 9-16). A network of small blood vessels sur-

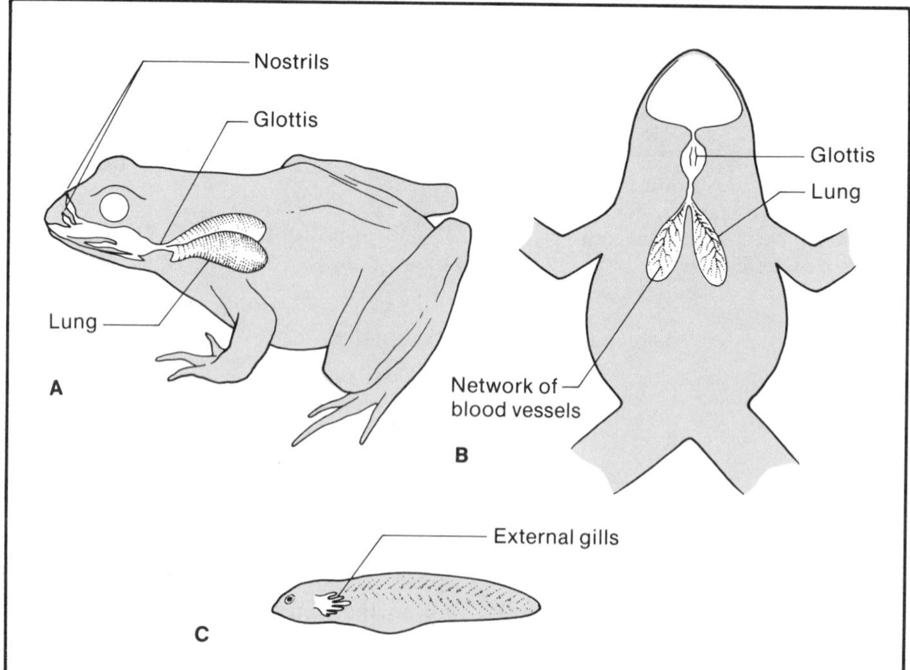

Fig. 9-16 The gas exchange system of a frog. An adult frog has lungs, seen from the side (A) and the top (B). In the early tadpole stage (C) the gas exchange surfaces are external gills.

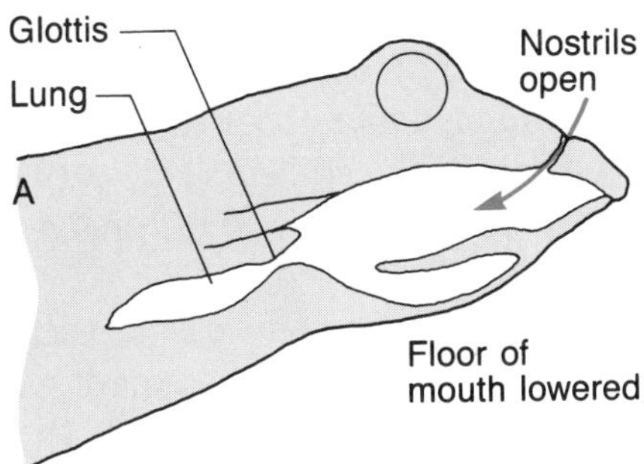

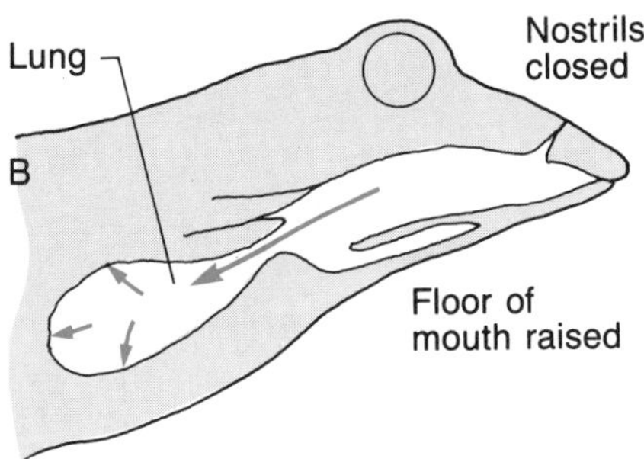

Fig. 9-17 Air enters the mouth cavity as the nostrils are opened and the floor of the mouth is lowered (A). Air is forced into the lungs as the nostrils are closed and the floor of the mouth is raised. The elastic lungs expand (B).

rounds each lung. As the floor of the mouth is lowered air enters the frog's mouth cavity (Fig. 9-17). The nostrils are then closed and the mouth floor raised. This forces air into the lungs. Oxygen is absorbed into the blood vessels and carbon dioxide is released into the lungs. Air is forced out of the lungs by contraction of muscles in the body wall.

A few fish, most amphibians, and all reptiles, birds, and mammals have lung gas exchange systems. Although they may vary slightly in structure, they are all designed to solve the problem of gas exchange for land animals.

The Human Gas Exchange System

Like all mammals, you have a lung gas exchange system. Your lungs differ in structure from those of a frog since you need more oxygen per unit mass than a frog does. How are your lungs adapted to provide this additional oxygen (Fig. 9-18)?

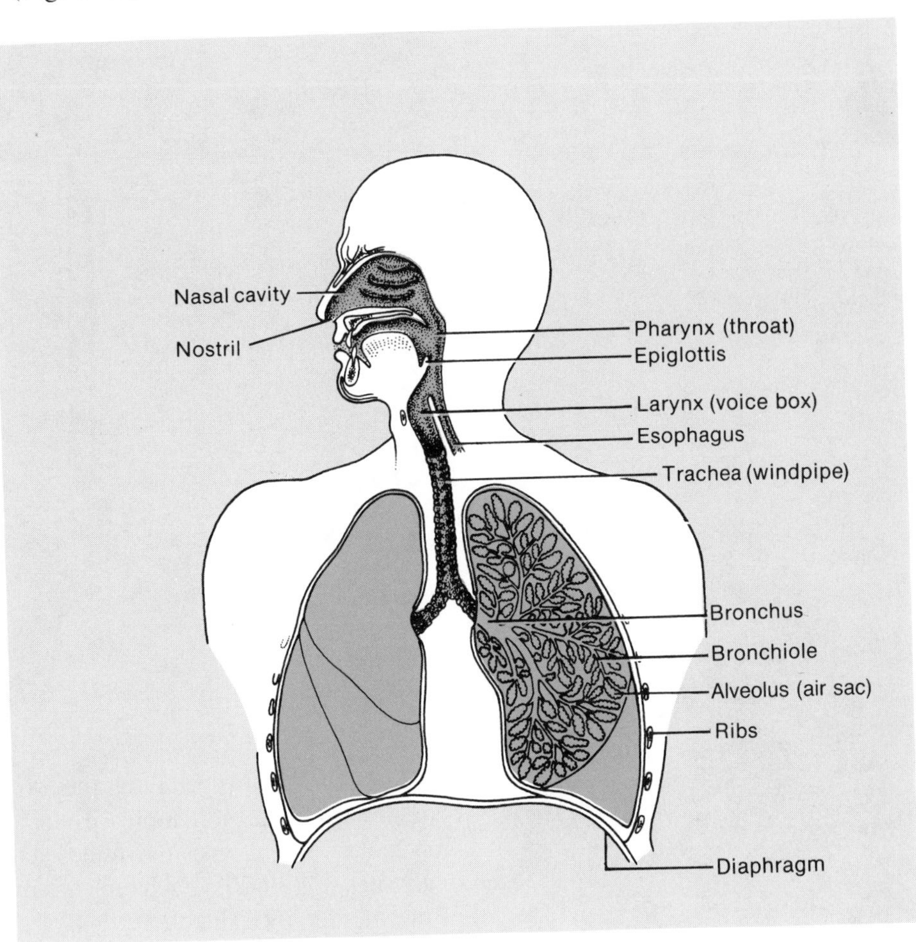

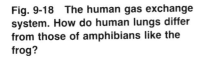

Fig. 9-18 The human gas exchange system. How do human lungs differ from those of amphibians like the frog?

The Air Passage Air usually enters your breathing system through the **nostrils**. Hairs in the nostrils filter dust particles from the air. The air then moves to the **nasal cavity**. Here the moist lining traps small particles that got past the hairs in the nostrils. This lining also moistens and warms the air.

The air now enters the **pharynx**, or **throat**. Here the air may join with air inhaled by the mouth. You can breathe faster through your mouth, but the air is not warmed as much. Nor is it as well filtered and moistened.

Next, the air goes down the **trachea** or **windpipe**, a tube about 10 cm long. It is prevented from collapsing by U-shaped pieces of cartilage (Fig. 9-19). The trachea is lined with hair-like **cilia** that sweep particles up to the pharynx so you can swallow them or cough them out.

The top of the trachea is the **larynx** or **voice box**. It contains the **vocal cords** that vibrate to make sounds when you speak or sing. The bottom of the trachea branches into two **bronchi**, and each **bronchus** leads to a **lung**.

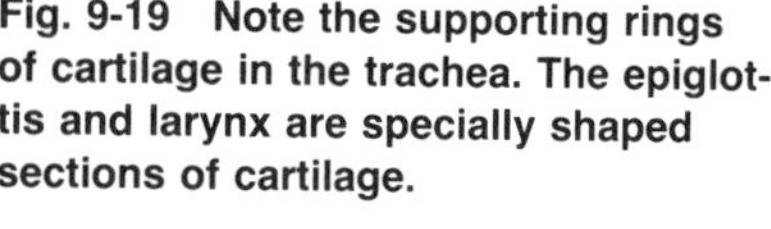
Fig. 9-19 Note the supporting rings of cartilage in the trachea. The epiglottis and larynx are specially shaped sections of cartilage.

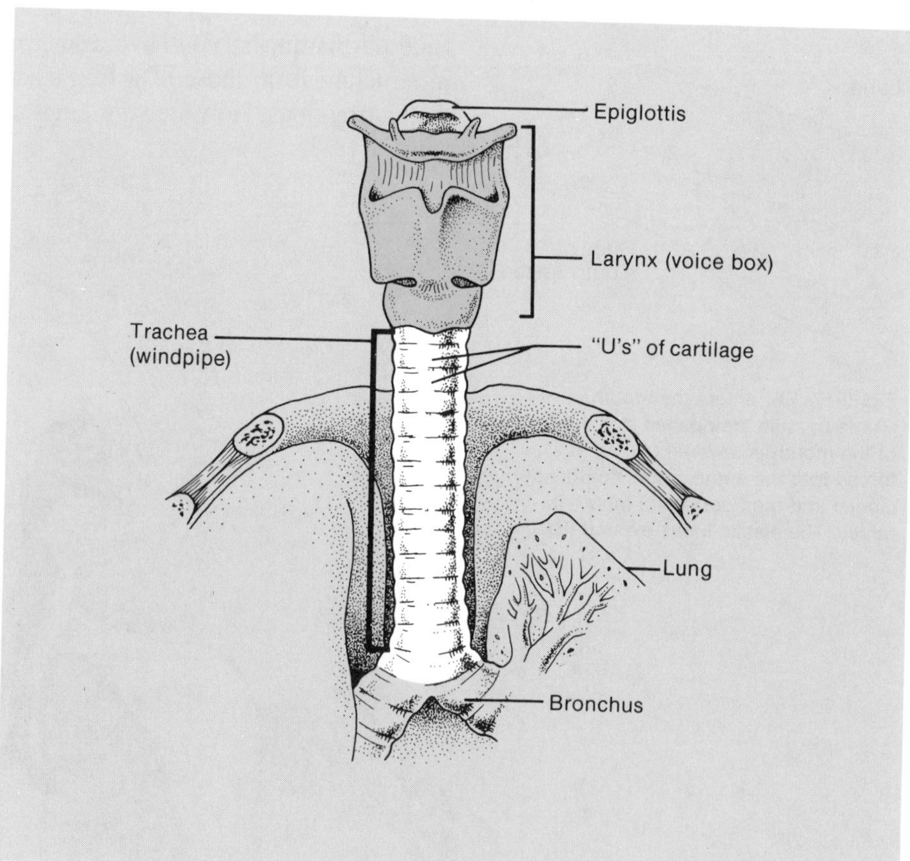

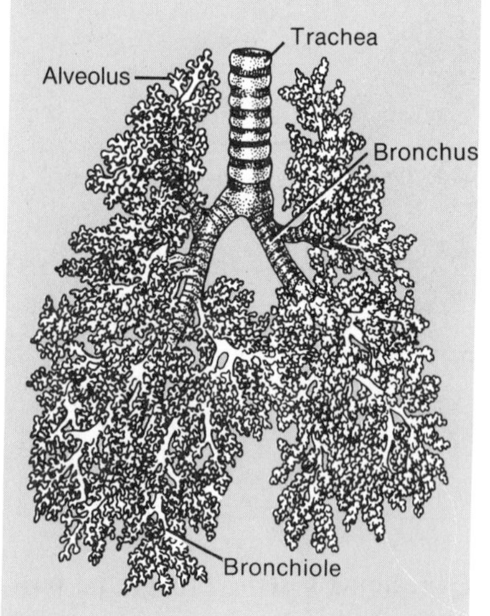

Fig. 9-20 A model of the air passages of the lungs

The Lungs Within each lung, the bronchus branches into smaller tubes called **bronchioles**. The bronchioles divide again and again into millions of tiny bronchioles. The air goes down these bronchioles to **alveoli** (singular: **alveolus**), or **air sacs** (Fig. 9-20). Each lung has over three hundred million (300 000 000) of these grape-like alveoli.

The alveoli have very thin walls which are moist and full of tiny blood vessels called **capillaries**. Blood flows through the capillaries as shown in Figure 9-21. Oxygen diffuses from the alveoli into the blood, and carbon dioxide diffuses from the blood into the alveoli. Now, can you answer the question we asked before? How are your lungs adapted to provide more oxygen per unit mass than a frog's lungs can?

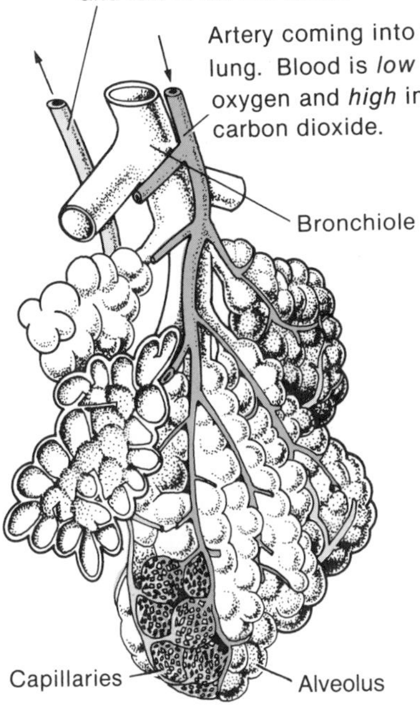
Vein leaving the lung. Blood is *high* in oxygen and *low* in carbon dioxide.
Artery coming into the lung. Blood is *low* in oxygen and *high* in carbon dioxide.
Bronchiole
Capillaries
Alveolus

Fig. 9-21 The grape-like clusters of alveoli occur at the ends of the bronchioles.

Section Review

1. Though air is rich in oxygen, gas exchange can be a problem for terrestrial animals. Why?
2. Describe gas exchange in the earthworm.
3. Describe the tracheal gas exchange system of a grasshopper.
4. Describe three methods by which a frog can exchange gases with its environment.
5. **a)** Describe the human gas exchange system.
   b) How does a human lung differ from a frog's lung?
   c) Why is this difference necessary?

9.8 Activity: What Is Your Usable Lung Capacity?

Breathe as deeply as you can, then exhale all the air you can. The volume of air you exhaled is your **usable lung capacity**. What is the difference between your usable lung capacity and your actual lung capacity?

Many factors determine your usable lung capacity (Fig. 9-22). In this activity you will determine your usable lung capacity. Then, by comparing the results with those of your classmates, you will try to discover some of the factors that determine a person's usable lung capacity.

Fig. 9-22 Why might one person have a greater usable lung capacity than another?

Problem

What is your usable lung capacity? What factors determine your usable lung capacity?

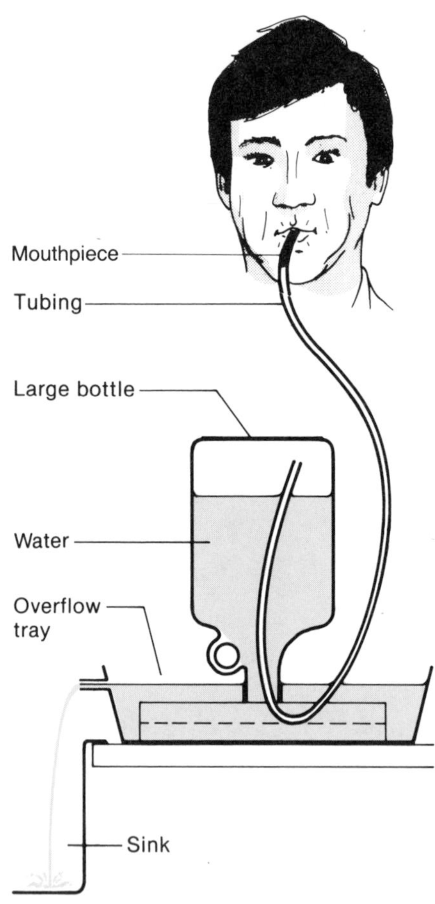

Fig. 9-23 Measuring your usable lung capacity

Materials

large bottle (at least 5 L)
100 mL graduated cylinder
overflow tray and sink
tubing
glass plate
glass mouthpiece

CAUTION: Do not share the mouthpiece. Obtain a sterilized one from your teacher.

Procedure

a. Fill the large bottle with water.
b. Invert it in the overflow tray as shown in Figure 9-23. Use the glass plate so that you do not lose any water from the jar.
c. Shove the tubing well up into the bottle.
d. Inhale as deeply as you can. Then exhale as much of your breath as you can through the tubing.
e. Remove the tubing, then cover the mouth of the bottle with the glass plate.
f. Remove the bottle from the tray and set it upright on the desk.
g. Add water with the graduated cylinder until the jar is full. Keep track of how much you add. This is the volume of air that was in the bottle.
h. Repeat steps (a) to (g) two times.
i. Average your three results.
j. Make a list of the factors you think might determine a person's usable lung capacity.

Discussion

1. a) What is your usable lung capacity?
b) Do you expect that it will increase or decrease as you get older? Why?
2. a) Compare your usable lung capacity to that of your classmates.
b) What factors do you feel are responsible for the differences?
c) Some of these factors are inherited and others are due to environmental influences. What is the difference between these two groups of factors? Illustrate your answer with examples.

Extension

Design a method of measuring your usable lung capacity using a plastic bag. List two advantages this method has over the method you used in this activity. What disadvantage does it have?

9.9 How Pollution Affects Gas Exchange

In Unit 1, Interactions, you learned that each species is adapted to its environment. As a result, if the environment changes, all species will be affected (Fig. 9-24). If the environmental change occurs slowly over hundreds of years, some species can adapt and survive. If, however, the change occurs over just

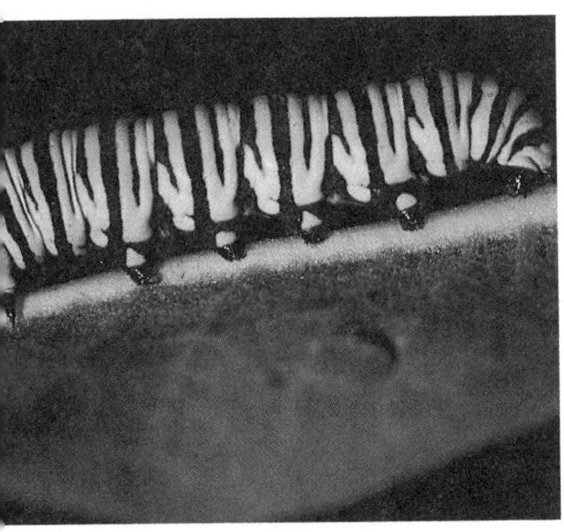

Fig. 9-24 This caterpillar is the larva of the Monarch butterfly. It feeds on milkweed, a common weed in Ontario. This weed competes with food crops like soybeans. Therefore, in parts of Ontario milkweed has been reduced in numbers by the use of herbicides. In those parts of Ontario, Monarch butterflies are now seen less frequently than they were a few decades ago.

a few years, most species must either emigrate or die. For example, trout are adapted to highly oxygenated water. Therefore, if the oxygen concentration of a stream is lowered, the trout will suffer. If the watershed that feeds a stream is gradually deforested over many years, the oxygen concentration of the stream will usually decrease slowly. Therefore the trout may have time to emigrate to a more suitable stream. However, if the decrease occurs suddenly due to a chemical spill or excess sewage, the trout will die.

Both water and air pollution can harm organisms in two ways:

- They may interfere with gas exchange.
- They may enter the organisms' bodies by way of their gas exchange surfaces.

Let us look at some specific examples to see how the harm is done.

Air Pollution

Two components of air pollution—particulates and certain gases—can affect organisms through their gas exchange surfaces.

Particulates The term **particulate** refers to tiny particles suspended in the air. These particles may be either solid or liquid. You cannot see the individual particles with your unaided eye. Collectively, however, they often make the air hazy. Combustion of fuels in homes, cars, and industries are a major source of particulates. Some of these particles are unburned or partially burned fuel. Others may be additives, such as lead, in the fuel. Some of these particles harm organisms by coating their gas exchange surfaces and thereby reducing the efficiency of gas exchange. Others, such as lead, enter the organism by absorption through the gas exchange surface and then poison the organism. Many industrial processes also emit particulates into the air (Fig. 9-25).

Fig. 9-25 Particulates from this pulp and paper plant darken the sky under certain weather conditions. They also coat the gas exchange surfaces of organisms in the area.

Toxic Gases Many gaseous forms of air pollution harm organisms. For example, if cars are improperly tuned, they produce large quantities of **carbon monoxide**. This gas is particularly harmful to terrestrial animals that have hemoglobin in their blood. Carbon monoxide enters the blood through the gas exchange surface. It then combines with the hemoglobin and reduces its ability to transport oxygen.

A second gas, **nitrogen dioxide**, is also produced mainly by cars. This gas combines with water on a gas exchange surface to produce nitric acid. In time this acid damages the gas exchange surface. Further, nitrogen dioxide is a carcinogen—it causes cancer. Catalytic converters, if properly maintained, greatly reduce the amount of nitrogen dioxide entering the air.

A third gas, **sulfur dioxide**, is produced mainly by smelters, power plants, and industrial and residential heating devices (see Section 4.9, page 110). This gas reacts with water on gas exchange surfaces to produce sulfuric acid. Like nitric acid, this corrosive acid damages gas exchange surfaces.

A wide range of other gaseous pollutants either damage gas exchange surfaces or enter organisms through their gas exchange surfaces. We are fortunate in Ontario that great strides are being made in the reduction of such pollutants. However, the air is still not as clean as it could and should be.

Tobacco Smoke Humans are the only animals which deliberately damage their gas exchange surfaces. About 35 000 Canadians will die this year as a direct result of smoking. A heavy smoker can inhale 2 L of tar per year! This tar and other particulates coat the lungs and reduce gas exchange. Further, they carry many carcinogens deep into the lungs. In fact, over 80% of **lung cancers** are caused by smoking.

Chemicals in the smoke also cause **emphysema**, a disease in which the alveoli (air sacs) of the lungs lose their elasticity. In advanced cases, the smoker experiences great difficulty in breathing and must carry a cylinder of oxygen gas at all times in order to stay alive.

Like emphysema, **chronic bronchitis** tends to be a disease of smokers. Chemicals in the smoke, such as sulfur dioxide, cause the bronchi and bronchioles to swell up and become laden with mucus. As a result, the transport of gases becomes difficult.

Smoking is still our most serious health problem. However, as you undoubtedly know, public awareness of the dangers of smoke, even second-hand smoke, is greatly reducing this health hazard.

Water Pollution

A number of forms of water pollution can affect organisms through their gas exchange surfaces.

Organic Pollution Organic matter often enters lakes and rivers as sewage, farm run-off, or effluent from pulp and paper plants. Much of this organic matter is **biodegradable**. That is, it can be broken down by decomposers in the water. However, as the decomposers feed on this organic matter, they use large quantities of oxygen. As a result, gill breathers in the water are adversely affected.

Acid Deposition Acid deposition can make lakes and streams acidic, particularly in northern Ontario (see Section 4.9, page 110). Acidic water dissolves aluminum from rocks. This aluminum forms a gelatinous coating on the gills of fish and other gill breathers. Suffocation eventually results. Acidic water also dissolves poisonous metals like mercury from rocks. These metals enter organisms through their gas exchange surfaces. Eventually they can accumulate to toxic concentrations.

Suspended Solids You have likely seen a river that is brown as a result of soil erosion. The tiny particles of suspended silt and clay coat the gas exchange surfaces of gill breathers, making gas exchange difficult. Death often results.

It is no doubt discouraging for you to read about such negative things as those discussed in this section. Remember, though, that Ontario has a Ministry of the Environment that is actively working on a reduction in all these forms of pollution.

Section Review

1. Why do sudden changes in the environment adversely affect organisms?
2. In what two general ways can air and water pollution harm organisms?

3. a) What are particulates?
   b) Describe how particulates can affect organisms through their gas exchange surfaces.
4. a) Describe how each of the following gases affects organisms: carbon monoxide, nitrogen dioxide, sulfur dioxide.
   b) Make a summary of the effects of tobacco smoke on humans.
5. Describe how each of the following affects gill breathers: biodegradable organic matter, acid deposition, suspended solids.

Chapter Highlights

1. The exchange of oxygen and carbon dioxide between organisms and their environments is essential to the survival of the organisms.
2. Gas exchange requires a thin moist surface that is large enough to meet an organism's requirements.
3. Small aquatic organisms can exchange gases by direct diffusion; larger ones require special gas exchange surfaces like gills.
4. The gas exchange systems of terrestrial animals range in complexity from the skin, through tracheal systems, to lung systems.
5. Each species, aquatic or terrestrial, is adapted to maximize gas exchange in its environment.
6. Many environmental factors can affect the efficiency of gas exchange surfaces.

Key Terms

acid deposition
alveolus
breathing
bronchus
bronchioles
cellular respiration
gas exchange
gas exchange surface
gills
organic pollution
particulates
respiration
suspended solids
toxic gases
trachea
tracheal system
usable lung capacity

Recognizing the Concepts

Each of the following statements or questions is followed by four responses. Choose the correct response in each case. (Do not write in this book.)

1. During cellular respiration
   a) oxygen is produced
   b) energy is consumed
   c) gases are exchanged between an organism and its environment
   d) glucose molecules are broken down, releasing energy
2. To maximize gas exchange, many breathing systems have
   a) a high surface area to volume ratio
   b) a low surface area to volume ratio
   c) a clean dry gas exchange surface
   d) a thick membrane on the gas exchange surface

3. Which one of the following pairs of organisms use direct diffusion as a means of gas exchange?
   a) crayfish and fish
   b) crayfish and planarian
   c) amoeba and hydra
   d) amoeba and crayfish
4. The tracheal system of an insect
   a) connects with the insect's circulatory system
   b) leads directly to the insect's body cells
   c) ends in large sacs comparable to lungs
   d) begins with a large tube called a bronchus
5. Carbon monoxide harms organisms by
   a) forming an acid on gas exchange surfaces
   b) coating gas exchange surfaces
   c) acting as a carcinogen
   d) reducing oxygen transport by the blood

Understanding the Concepts

1. a) Distinguish between breathing and respiration.
   b) Compare the burning of a fuel like wood with cellular respiration.
2. Why does an increase in the size of an animal make gas exchange more complicated?
3. Why must a gas exchange surface be thin and moist?
4. Explain why neither the hydra nor planarian requires a transport system to take gases to and from cells.
5. a) Give a general description of the structure of a gill.
   b) Explain why this structure is an advantage to aquatic organisms.
6. One requirement for gas exchange is that the gas exchange surface be moist. Why, then, does an earthworm suffocate if it is placed in water?
7. A frog can perform gas exchange in three ways.
   a) List those three ways.
   b) Which method do you think can perform gas exchange most efficiently? Why?
   c) A frog that is hibernating during the winter requires only diffusion through the skin to keep it alive. Why?
8. Reptilian lungs have a greater number of infoldings than amphibian lungs. Explain why this is an advantage.
9. Make a list of things you could do that might increase your usable lung capacity.
10. In what ways can air and water pollution interfere with gas exchange?

Applying the Concepts

1. Why is the term ''artificial breathing'' more correct biologically than the commonly used term ''artificial respiration''?
2. a) What is the likely cause of death if a fish is caught and then allowed to die on the bank of a stream?
   b) What would be a more humane way to kill fish?
3. If an oil tanker spills oil into the ocean, many fish usually die. Why is this so?

4. a) Design an earthworm with a more efficient gas exchange surface than earthworms have.
   b) Why is this design not likely to occur in nature?
5. a) The cilia in the trachea of a smoker often become so coated with tar that they cannot move. Why is this condition potentially harmful?
   b) Heavy smokers often get a tickle in their throats and begin to cough if they are deprived of cigarettes for many hours. The tickling stops after the smoker resumes smoking. Account for these observations.
6. Both sulfur dioxide and nitrogen dioxide contribute to the development of emphysema in smokers. What property of these gases is responsible for promoting this disease?
7. State and defend your opinion on recent laws that confine smoking in public places to certain restricted areas.

Investigations

1. Find out how terrestrial snails and slugs perform gas exchange. How is this method related to their selection of habitat?
2. Find out how thermal (heat) pollution from electric generating stations affects gas exchange in gill breathers.
3. Use the resource centre to prepare a report on the gas exchange system of a bird (Fig. 9-26). How does this system make long distance flying easier for birds?

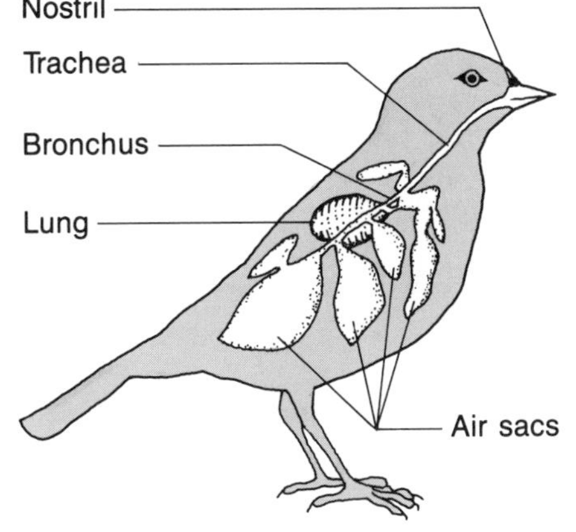

Fig. 9-26 The air sacs play an important role in increasing the efficiency of a bird's gas exchange system. What is that role?

4. Research the structure and operation of the gas exchange system in whales or another marine mammal.
5. Find out what a catalytic converter on a car is. What is its structure? What are its specific functions?
6. Design and conduct an experiment to show that biodegradable organic matter decreases the oxygen concentration of water.
7. Design and do an experiment to show that suspended solids could coat the gas exchange surfaces of gill breathers. Do not use living organisms in your experiment.

Career: *MEDICAL ARTIST*

HELP WANTED: MEDICAL ARTIST
Commercial art firm requires artist to prepare creative but accurate diagrams for zoology and medical textbooks. B.Sc. degree in biology an asset.

As you know from reading this text, good artwork makes the written material easier to understand. This is particularly true when the book deals with the complex material that occurs in zoology, medical, and dental textbooks.

The artists who draw such artwork are called medical artists. They are often employed by a commercial art firm and frequently work in teams on a project. Medical artists are also employed by universities, hospitals, veterinary hospitals, medical centres, dental clinics, and research institutes to prepare artwork for books, journals, and lectures. A medical artist may be asked to dissect and draw a specimen or part of it. Also, a medical artist may be asked to draw specimens observed with a microscope. Therefore a strong background in both biology and art is required. A typical preparation for this career is a B.Sc. degree in biology followed by a diploma in art.

Biography

Donna Murphy: Dental Hygienist

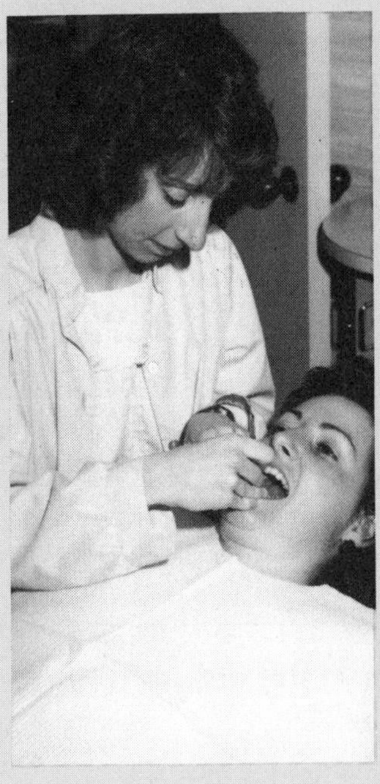

Donna Murphy is a Certified Dental Assistant (C.D.A.) and a Registered Dental Hygienist (R.D.H.). In order to obtain these qualifications, Murphy attended George Brown College in Toronto. She spent one year getting the C.D.A. qualification and then, as required, worked as a Dental Assistant for a minimum of one year before returning to George Brown College to obtain the R.D.H. qualification. Though only an Ontario Secondary School Diploma is required for admission to these courses, Donna Murphy completed Grade 13 (now 6 OAC credits) and, further, obtained a three-year B.Sc. degree from the University of Toronto. She says that her secondary school science and university science prepared her well for courses such as microbiology which she studied at George Brown College.

Donna works 2.5 d a week in a general dentistry practice, cleaning teeth and assisting people with their general dental health. For 2 d a week she works in a surgical practice which deals with the treatment of gum diseases. Donna enjoys the interaction with people and obtains satisfaction from helping them with their general dental health. Her job offers independence—she has her own patients and makes some decisions. People with her qualifications can also work for public health departments and as hygienists in hospitals. An R.D.H. with a B.Sc. can often obtain employment with a dental company, either in the laboratory or in sales.

Internal Transport

CHAPTER CONTENTS

CHAPTER OBJECTIVES

After completing this chapter you should be able to:

1. Justify the need for internal transport systems.
2. Describe internal transport in the amoeba and hydra.
3. List the general characteristics of blood circulatory systems.
4. Describe the circulatory systems of selected invertebrates and vertebrates.
5. Explain homeostasis in organisms.
6. Perform dissections of an earthworm and perch.
7. Identify the parts of a mammalian heart and list their functions.
8. Determine your HPS.

In Chapter 8 you investigated the means by which organisms obtain and digest food. But how are the resulting nutrients transported to all cells within the organism? And how are harmful by-products taken away from those cells?

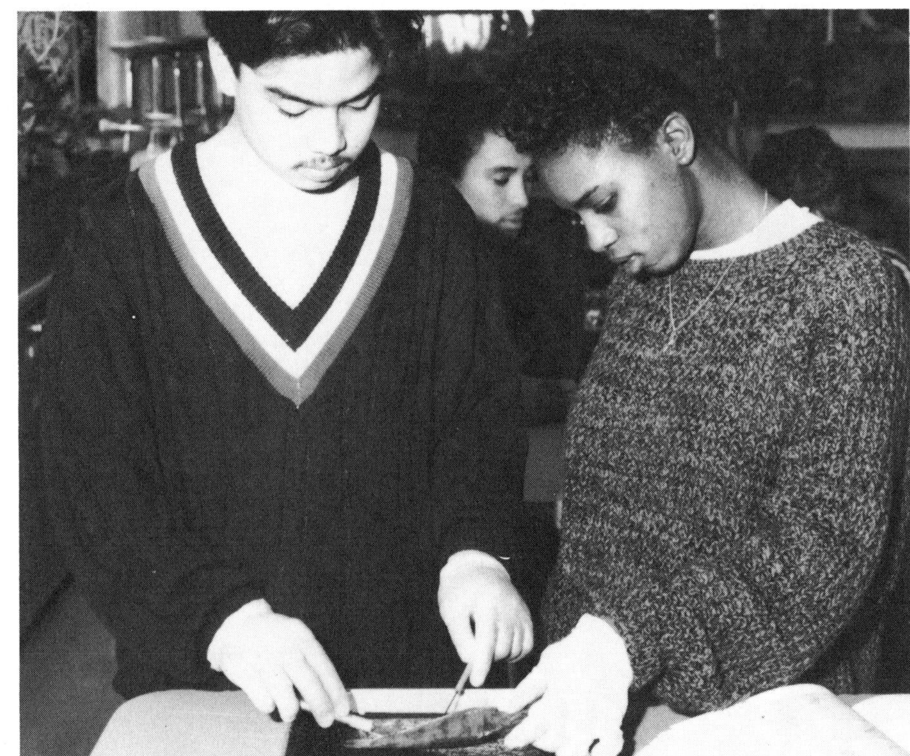

Fig. 10-1 A careful dissection of a perch can reveal how fish transport nutrients, wastes, and gases between every body cell and the external environment.

In Chapter 9 you studied the ways in which organisms exchange gases with their external environment. But how are the gases, oxygen and carbon dioxide, moved to and from every cell within an organism?

This chapter answers these questions about the internal transport of nutrients, wastes, and gases. We will look at the special means that single-celled organisms and small invertebrates have for internal transport. Then we will examine the unique systems that larger invertebrates and vertebrates have for transporting materials to and from all body cells. You will perform some dissections as you investigate these systems (Fig. 10-1).

10.1 The Need for Internal Transport Systems

Your body has about 60 000 000 000 000 (sixty million million) cells, and each one needs nutrients and oxygen. Also, each one must get rid of wastes such as carbon dioxide. How are these needs met?

Transport Systems Carry Nutrients, Oxygen, and Wastes

You are not unique in your need for the internal transport of materials. In order to remain alive, *every cell* of *every organism* must receive materials from its external environment and release materials to its external environment.

For single-celled organisms living in water, there is no problem in this respect. They are completely surrounded by water. They can get needed materials from it and can dispose of their wastes in it. Even in some simple many-celled aquatic animals, every cell is either surrounded by, or very close to, a water medium.

Some larger and more complex animals, however, do have a problem in this respect. Many cells may be far removed from an external medium. In such animals a **division of labour** occurs. This means that certain groups of cells specialize to perform certain life functions. For example, gas exchange may take place in lungs and digestion may occur in a special digestive system. Materials must be carried between these special structures and all cells of the animal. An **internal transport system** is required to do this.

Regardless of the size or complexity of the organisms, their internal transport systems share the following tasks:

They transport to the cells

- nutrients obtained from digested food
- water, a nutrient required for many life processes
- oxygen which is required for cellular respiration

They transport from the cells

- metabolic wastes such as urea and carbon dioxide
- excess water

Transport Systems Carry Special Chemicals and Cells

In some animals, specialized cells produce important substances that must be delivered to every cell. **Hormones** are examples of such substances. They are

Fig. 10-2 When a skier encounters a challenging slope, extra adrenalin will be released. How does it get to the sites in the body where it performs its functions?

chemical messengers which help control and coordinate cell activities. A hormone may be produced by specialized cells in one part of an organism, yet it may control the actions of some cells in another part of an organism. Obviously, there is a need in such an organism for an internal system to transport these hormones. For example, a hormone called **adrenalin** is produced in glands on your kidneys. It is released into your circulatory system when you become angry, frightened, or excited (Fig. 10-2). It makes your heart beat faster and raises your blood pressure. It causes your liver to put more sugar into your blood, giving you strength for fighting (or running away). As you can see, although this hormone is produced on the kidneys, it acts far from the kidneys. Your circulatory system is responsible for delivering the adrenalin to the action sites.

The transport systems of many animals, including humans, contain and distribute antitoxins. These are substances which counteract toxins (poisons) that bacteria release into organisms. Your transport system also contains special cells which engulf bacteria that get into your body. Hormones, antitoxins, and special cells are just three examples of the many things that transport systems carry and distribute.

Section Review

1. State in one sentence the basic reason that organisms need transport systems.
2. a) Why do single-celled and simple many-celled organisms not require transport systems?
   b) Why do larger, more complex animals require transport systems?
3. What are the main things transport systems move to and from cells?
4. a) What is a hormone?
   b) Why is an internal transport system often needed in organisms that produce hormones?
   c) List two other things that transport systems often contain and distribute.

10.2 Transport in Simple Organisms

Transport in Protists

As you have read in earlier chapters, **diffusion** plays a key role in the transport of materials in single-celled organisms and in some small many-celled animals (Fig. 10-3). Diffusion carries materials from where they enter or are formed in these organisms to where they are used or disposed of by the organisms. However, diffusion is a very slow means of transport. Often it cannot, by itself, transport materials fast enough to meet an organism's needs. Therefore, in most organisms, the cytoplasm within the cells moves. Materials in the cytoplasm get carried along with it. Such movement can be seen in an amoeba when it is observed under high power on a compound microscope. This movement of the cytoplasm is called **cytoplasmic streaming** Materials can be transported by this means much faster than by diffusion.

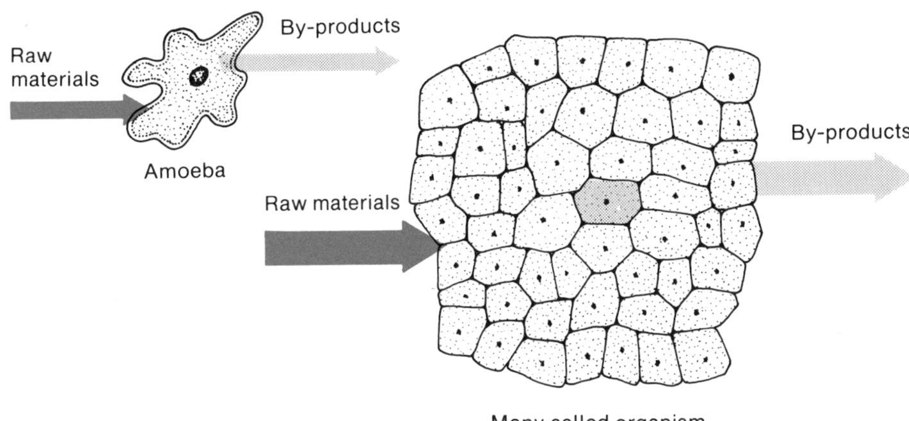

Fig. 10-3 Diffusion moves materials into and out of protists like the amoeba. Cytoplasmic streaming helps move materials through the organisms. Would this be sufficient for the coloured cell? Could you change the shape of the "many-celled organism" to make it sufficient?

Transport in Hydra

The hydra has a body shape that brings all cells close to its external environment (see Fig. 8-4, page 208). The inner layer of cells is in direct contact with water because of the presence of a body cavity (the gastrovascular cavity). Special cells with flagella provide a sweeping action that creates a current in the water. In addition, special muscle cells enable the hydra's body wall to contract. These contractions and currents cause circulation of water in the cavity. This ensures that a constant supply of water, rich in raw materials, enters the cavity. Furthermore, waste-laden water can be forced out of the cavity at the mouth opening.

Each cell of the hydra exchanges oxygen and carbon dioxide directly with its water environment. Not all cells take in food. However, since no cell is very far from the special ones that do, this food is easily transported to all cells by diffusion.

Section Review

1. a) Why is diffusion sometimes sufficient to meet the internal transport needs of a protist?
   b) How does cytoplasmic streaming assist diffusion in meeting those needs?
2. Explain why the hydra has no need for an internal transport system.

10.3 Blood Circulatory Systems

What Is a Blood Circulatory System?

Most many-celled animals have special internal transport systems that move materials from place to place in their bodies. In these animals, a body fluid, usually called **blood**, circulates through the body by a system of tubes. Such a system is called a **blood circulatory system**. Blood circulatory systems generally contain:

- A fluid transport medium, the blood;

- A pumping device called a heart to make the blood circulate;
- Valves to control the direction of blood flow;
- Tubes or vessels through which blood travels to all parts of the body and then back to the heart;
- A means by which all body cells can get required raw materials from the blood and release their waste by-products to the blood.

Blood circulatory systems have the ability to regulate the flow of blood to tissues depending on their varying requirements. There is not enough blood in any one animal to completely fill every blood vessel at the same time. As a tissue or organ becomes active, vessels supplying blood to it will increase in diameter or **dilate** to increase the blood flow to meet the demand. At the same time, vessels leading to other parts of the body will decrease in diameter or **constrict**, thereby decreasing the flow of blood to those parts. An example of this is evident after you eat a full meal. Your digestive organs are very active and require a great deal of blood. Therefore, blood is directed to them. Drowsiness is then experienced because the flow of blood to your brain is somewhat restricted.

All blood circulatory systems perform the same basic function. They ensure that the materials which they transport can be freely exchanged with any cell in the body.

Open and Closed Circulatory Systems

In some animals, blood is pumped through vessels into large open spaces known as **sinuses**. As a result, tissues and organs within these sinuses are bathed in blood, and materials are exchanged by diffusion directly through the cell membranes. The blood eventually gets transported out of the sinuses by means of another set of vessels, thereby completing its circuit. This type of system is called an **open circulatory system**. It is characteristic of invertebrates such as arthropods (including insects) and most molluscs.

In other animals, blood flows within vessels throughout the *entire* circuit. This type of system is called a **closed circulatory system**. The cells of tissues are bathed in tissue fluid. Substances in the blood capillaries pass out into the tissue fluid and then into the cells of the tissues. The reverse process also takes place. The tissue fluid forms a vital link in the closed circulatory system. Annelids, some molluscs (squid and octopus), and all vertebrates have this type of closed system. With a closed system, materials can be transported to a given location much more rapidly than with an open system because the blood flows more rapidly. Therefore, very active organisms have their needs met more efficiently by a closed system.

Section Review

1. List the main parts of a blood circulatory system.
2. Why are the dilation and constriction of blood vessels important to organisms?
3. Compare open and closed transport systems.
4. a) What type of circulatory system do you have?
   b) Why is it an advantage to you to have such a system?

10.4 Invertebrate Circulatory Systems

The grasshopper and crayfish, like all arthropods, have an open circulatory system. In contrast, the earthworm, like you, has a closed circulatory system. This section compares the circulatory systems of these three animals so you can better understand how open and closed systems differ.

The Grasshopper

The grasshopper has an open circulatory system (Fig. 10-4). A single **dorsal (upper) blood vessel**, running through the insect's abdomen and thorax, carries a colourless blood. The posterior (rear) portion of this vessel functions as a **heart**. The anterior (front) end is called an **aorta**. Blood is pumped forward from the aorta and out the open anterior end into the body sinus. There it bathes the internal organs. As the blood moves through the body sinus from the anterior to the posterior end, it distributes nutrients to all tissues and picks up waste products from them. The blood finally reaches the heart and enters it through a one-way series of valves called **ostia** (singular: **ostium**). As you know, the circulatory system of a grasshopper does not transport oxygen and carbon dioxide. This role is carried out by a tracheal system.

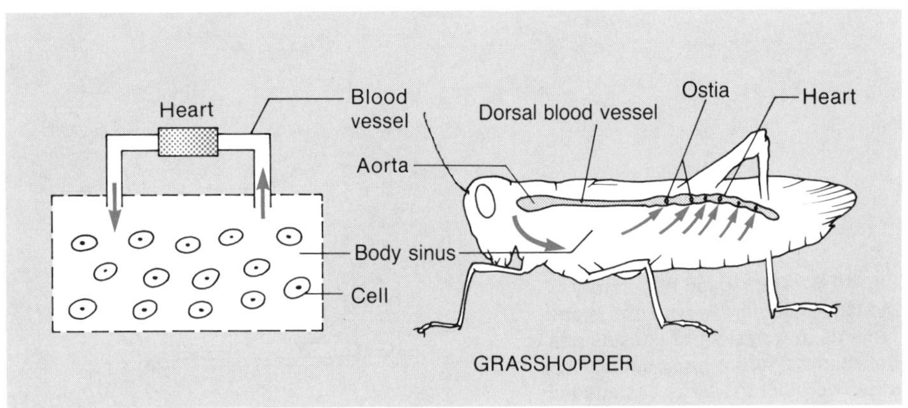

Fig. 10-4 The open circulatory system of a grasshopper. The blood is dumped into a body sinus where it bathes tissues and organs.

The Crayfish

The crayfish also has an open circulatory system and, generally speaking, it functions much like that of the grasshopper. Blood flows between a series of vessels and the open body sinus (Fig. 10-5). In the body sinus, blood bathes the tissues and organs. This allows materials to be exchanged between cells and blood. However, unlike the grasshopper, the blood of the crayfish does carry oxygen and carbon dioxide. Tiny capillaries extend into the **gills** of a crayfish. Here oxygen and carbon dioxide are exchanged with the water.

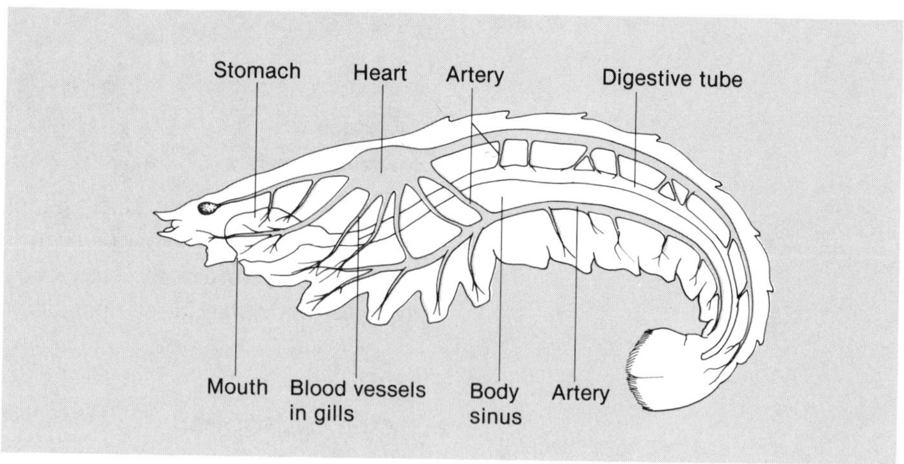

Fig. 10-5 The open circulatory system of a crayfish. How does it differ from that of a grasshopper?

The Earthworm

The earthworm has a closed circulatory system (Fig. 10-6). A **dorsal blood vessel** carries the red blood forward to the anterior end of the earthworm. The blood returns to the posterior end through a **ventral (lower) blood vessel**. Small, thin-walled vessels called **capillaries** connect the dorsal and ventral vessels throughout the earthworm. Exchange of materials between the blood and body cells takes place through the capillary walls.

In the anterior end of the earthworm, five pairs of muscular tubes called **aortic arches** function as hearts. They pump the blood from the dorsal to the ventral vessel. Nutrients, gases, and waste products are all transported within this system.

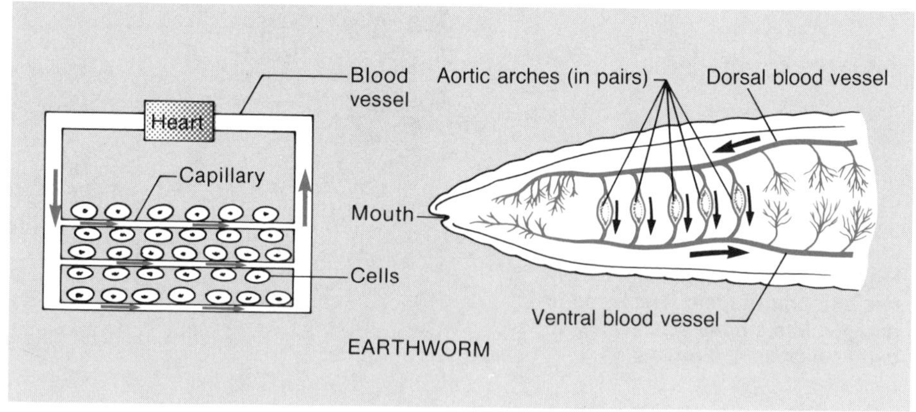

Fig. 10-6 The closed circulatory system of an earthworm. The blood remains in a system of vessels and is not dumped into a body sinus. Capillaries connect the large vessels but, because of their small size, they are not shown in the earthworm above.

Section Review

1. a) Describe the circulatory system of a grasshopper.
   b) Why is it called an open system?
   c) Why is it unnecessary for the grasshopper's blood to carry oxygen?
2. Compare the circulatory system of the crayfish to that of the grasshopper.
3. a) Describe the circulatory system of an earthworm.
   b) Why is it called a closed system?
   c) Where and how would food and oxygen enter the earthworm's circulatory system? (If necessary, look back to Chapters 8 and 9.)

10.5 Vertebrate Circulatory Systems

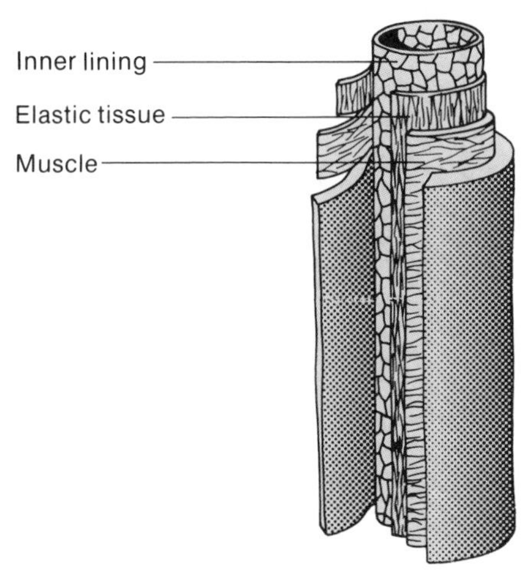

Fig. 10-7 An artery. Note the thick wall with elastic tissue and muscle fibres.

Transportation occurs much more rapidly in a closed circulatory system than in an open system. Therefore, very active and complex animals usually have a closed system. All vertebrates, for example, have a closed system. In this section you will compare the circulatory systems of three classes of vertebrates—fish, amphibians, and mammals. Fish are, generally speaking, simpler organisms than amphibians, and amphibians are simpler organisms than mammals. Watch for evidence of this as you compare the circulatory systems of these animals.

A General Description of Vertebrate Circulatory Systems

The closed circulatory system of a vertebrate consists of a pumping device called a **heart** and blood vessels of three basic kinds: arteries, veins, and capillaries. **Arteries** carry blood *away from* the heart. Since arteries carry blood under high pressure, they must have strong walls. As Figure 10-7 shows, they are thick-walled tubes wrapped with elastic tissue and muscle fibres. Small arteries are generally called **arterioles**.

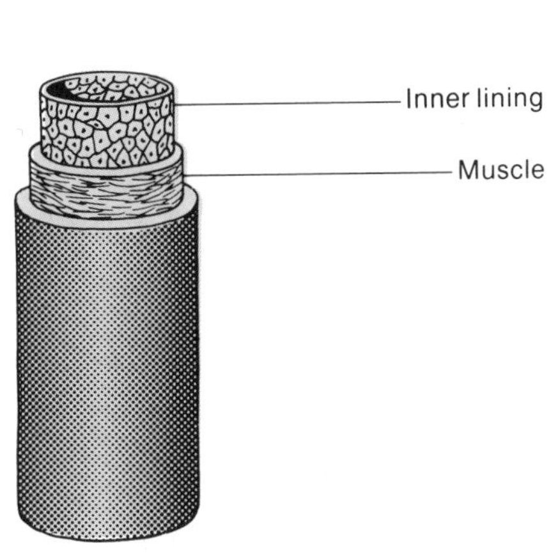

Fig. 10-8 Why do veins not need walls as thick and elastic as those of arteries?

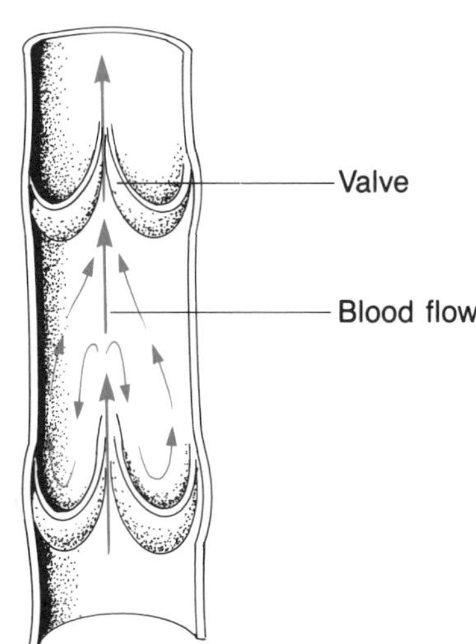

Fig. 10-9 Valves in veins ensure that blood returning to the heart does not flow the other direction.

Veins carry blood *toward* the heart. The blood in veins is under lower pressure than the blood in arteries. Therefore the walls of veins do not need to be as thick or elastic as those of arteries (Fig. 10-8). Some veins in vertebrates have one-way **valves** which ensure that the blood flows only toward the heart (Fig. 10-9). Without these valves, the low pressure would let the blood flow the other way. Leaky valves cause a condition called **varicose veins** Blood builds up in the veins and stretches them. If varicose veins occur near the skin surface in humans, you can easily see them bulging out. Small veins are called **venules**.

Capillaries are a finely divided network of tiny tubes which connect arterioles and venules within all tissues (Fig. 10-10). The walls of capillaries are just one cell thick. Therefore nutrients and oxygen can diffuse through the walls from the blood to the tissues and wastes can diffuse from the tissues into the blood.

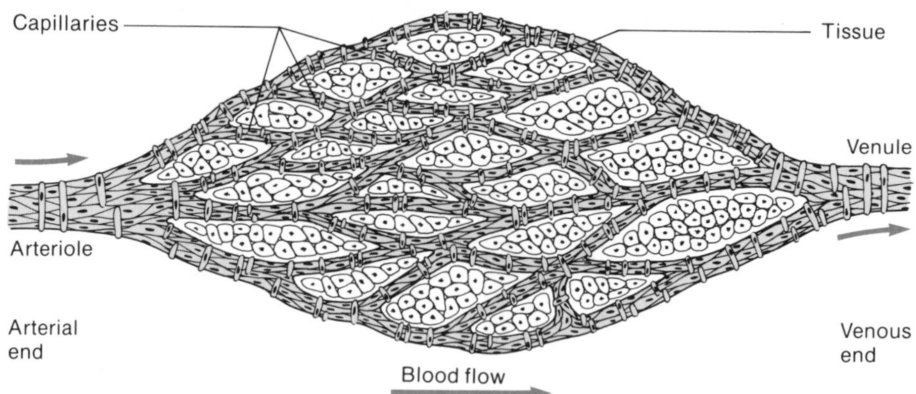

Fig. 10-10 Capillaries are thin-walled tubes that run through all tissues in an organism.

Together, all these vessels and the heart form a closed circuit. The heart pumps blood into the arteries which carry the blood to all parts of the organism. The arteries branch again and again into arterioles and, finally, capillaries. Exchange of materials occurs in the capillaries and the blood moves through venules and into veins. The veins complete the circuit by carrying the blood back to the heart (Fig. 10-11).

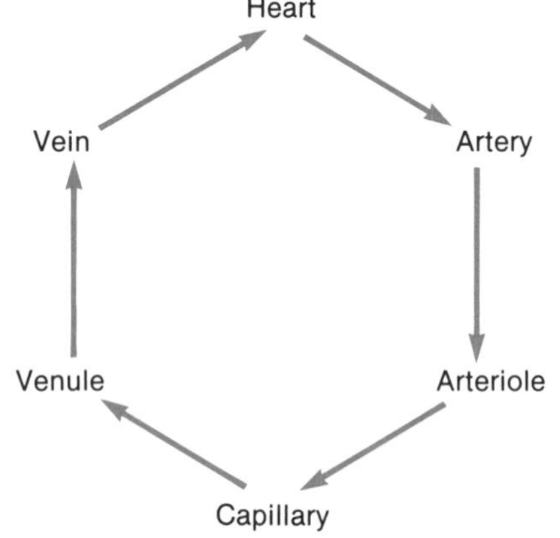

Fig. 10-11 The path followed by blood in a closed circulatory system

Keep in mind these common features of vertebrate circulatory systems as you read the following comparison of the circulatory systems of fish, amphibians, and mammals.

A Comparison of Vertebrate Circulatory Systems

Follow Figure 10-12 as you read the following descriptions.

Fish The heart of a fish is *two-chambered*. It consists of one thin-walled **atrium** which takes oxygen-poor blood from the veins and delivers it to the thicker-walled **ventricle**. This muscular ventricle pumps the blood into the arteries toward the gills. There the blood picks up oxygen and releases carbon dioxide. The oxygen-rich blood now moves to the body tissues. By the time the blood reaches the capillaries in the tissues, its pressure is low, since it has already been forced through capillaries in the gills. This is a major disadvantage of a circulatory system with a two-chambered heart.

Amphibians The heart of an amphibian like a frog is *three-chambered*, two atria leading into one ventricle. The left atrium (LA) receives oxygen-rich blood from the lungs; the right atrium (RA) receives oxygen-poor blood from the body tissues. The two atria pump in unison. Therefore oxygen-rich and oxygen-poor blood are forced into the ventricle where they mix somewhat. This mixture is then pumped to all body tissues. This mixing is a major disadvantage of a circulatory system with a three-chambered heart. Why?

Mammals The heart of a mammal like you is *four-chambered*, two atria and two ventricles. Oxygen-rich blood, found only in the left atrium and ventricle, is completely separated from oxygen-poor blood in the right atrium and ventricle. There are, in effect, two hearts—one that pumps oxygen-rich blood

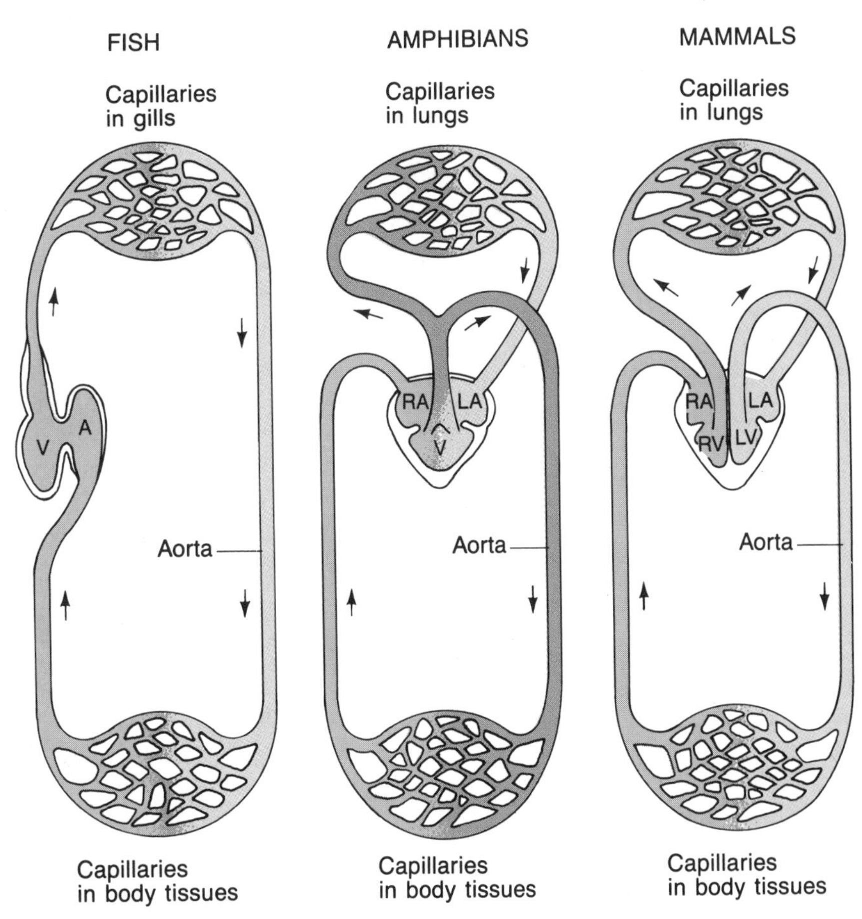

Fig. 10-12 Diagrammatic representations of the circulatory systems of three classes of vertebrates. How are they alike? How are they different?

through the body tissues and one that pumps oxygen-poor blood through the lungs.

Here's how this heart works: The right atrium receives oxygen-poor blood from the body tissues. This blood is forced into the right ventricle which, in turn, pumps the blood through the lungs. From the lungs, the oxygen-rich blood returns to the left atrium. It is forced into the left ventricle from which it is pumped to the body tissues. This "*double heart*" structure allows fully oxygenated blood to be pumped under high pressure to the body tissues. This is a major advantage of a four-chambered heart and correlates with the constant body temperature of mammals, their high degree of activity, and their high metabolic rate.

Section Review

1. Why do complex, active animals usually have a closed circulatory system?

2. a) For each of the following parts of a closed circulatory system, describe the structure and function: arteries, veins, capillaries.

b) Identify each of the following: arterioles, venules, varicose veins, valves.

3. a) Compare the circulatory systems of fish, amphibians, and mammals.

b) Give the major disadvantage of a two-chambered heart and a three-chambered heart.

c) Why is a four-chambered heart often called a double heart?

d) Why is a four-chambered heart an advantage to mammals?

10.6 Circulatory System of a Fish—The Yellow Perch

In Section 10.5 you read a general description of the circulatory system of a fish. This section examines that system in more detail so you will be prepared for the dissection in Section 10.10.

This description of the flow of blood through a fish begins with blood *returning to* the heart. The **anterior cardinal vein** brings blood back to the heart from the head region (Fig. 10-13). The **posterior cardinal vein** brings it back from the rest of the body. This oxygen-poor blood enters the **atrium** of the heart, from which it is passed on to the muscular **ventricle**. The ventricle forces the blood under high pressure into the **ventral aorta**. This artery branches into two arteries which carry blood to the gills on each side of the head. Then, at the gills, each of these two arteries branches into four arteries, each of which carries blood into a gill.

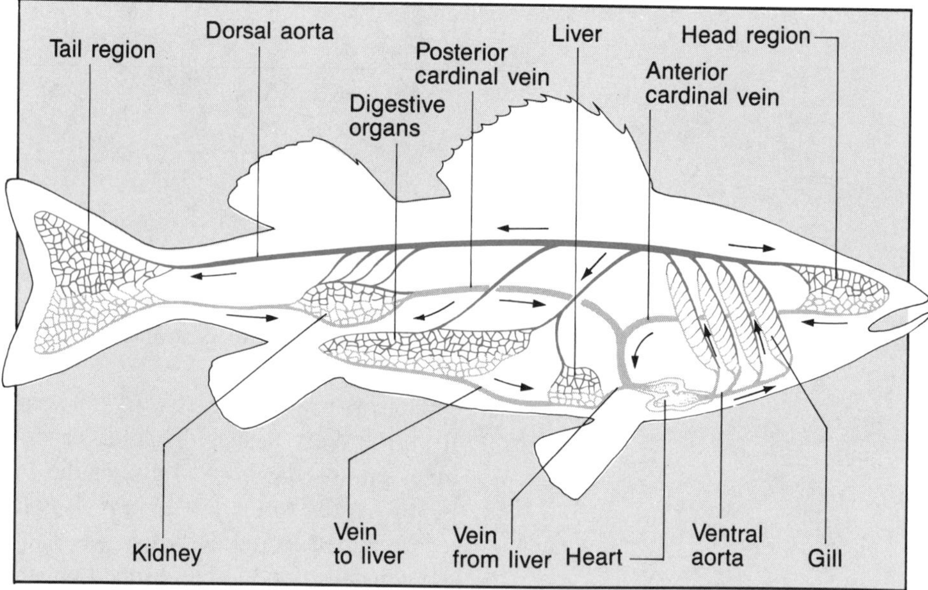

Fig. 10-13 The circulatory system of yellow perch. Remember that this is a simplified drawing. The system does not look exactly like this. Blood vessels permeate *all* tissues.

An artery carries the oxygen-poor blood into each **gill filament** (Fig. 10-14,B). Each gill filament consists of **lamellae** (singular: **lamella**) which have **capillaries** imbedded in them (Fig. 10-14,C). The oxygen-poor blood flows through the lamellae in one direction and water flows over the lamellae in the opposite direction. This maximizes gaseous exchange. Oxygen-rich blood leaves the lamellae, gill filaments, and gills by a system of arteries comparable to the set that brought blood in. The blood now enters the **dorsal aorta**. Branches of the dorsal aorta send blood to all organs and tissues in the fish. After the blood passes through capillaries in the tissues, it returns through a venous system to the **cardinal veins**. The circuit is now complete.

Section Review

1. Trace the path of blood through a yellow perch, beginning with oxygen-poor blood in the cardinal veins.

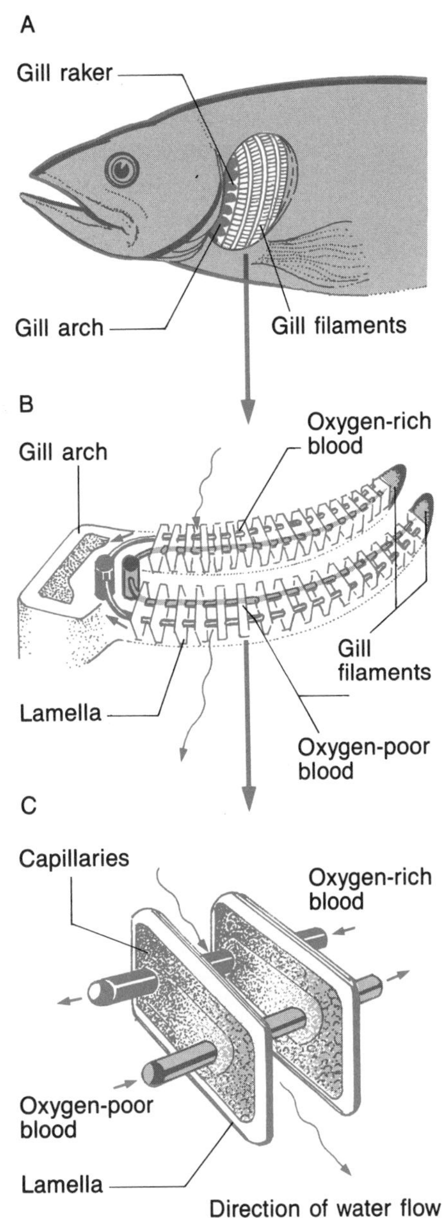

Fig. 10-14 The flow of blood through the gills. The gill cover has been removed to show the gills (A). A pair of gill filaments is enlarged to show lamella and the direction of blood flow(B). Two lamella are enlarged to show their capillary network (C).

2. Explain how the gills are designed to maximize gaseous exchange.

10.7 Homeostasis: Internal Balance in Organisms

The environment of any organism is always changing. Some of the factors that can change are the temperature, the food supply, and the availability of water and oxygen. If an organism is to survive, it must adjust to the changing conditions. It must maintain a balance in its internal life processes even though changes occur in the external environment. This internal balance is called **homeostasis**.

You can probably better understand the meaning of homeostasis by first considering this analogy. In the winter your home is kept at a fairly constant temperature by **feedback control**. The thermostat feeds signals back to the furnace controlling whether it comes on or goes off. When the temperature drops, the thermostat turns the furnace on. When the temperature gets up to a certain point, the thermostat turns the furnace off. This system is self-regulated. It maintains constant or nearly constant conditions in the home without any outside help. You do not have to keep turning the furnace off and on.

A similar type of feedback control regulates homeostasis in your body. For example, your body temperature must remain close to 37.5°C for you to stay healthy. If your body gets too warm, circulation of blood to the skin increases. Your face flushes. This allows some of the excess heat to radiate from your body. Also, you begin to sweat more. The evaporation of sweat uses up heat. If your body gets too cold, blood withdraws from the skin to conserve heat. You begin to shiver. Shivering produces heat that warms the body. All these processes are self-regulating. You do not have to say to yourself, "I am cold; I should start shivering," or "I am hot; I should start sweating." A **homeostatic feedback mechanism** in your body regulates these processes (Fig. 10-15).

In this unit you have investigated digestion, gas exchange, and internal transport for several organisms. You have seen that these processes do not function separately. Instead, they work together to help maintain an internal balance, or homeostatic condition, in the organisms. For example, the gas exchange system of a fish absorbs oxygen from water. The circulatory system takes this gas to the cells. It also takes nutrients from the digestive system to

Fig. 10-15 The maintenance of a relatively constant body temperature is an example of homeostasis. Homeostatic feedback is often illustrated with a "figure eight" diagram like this.

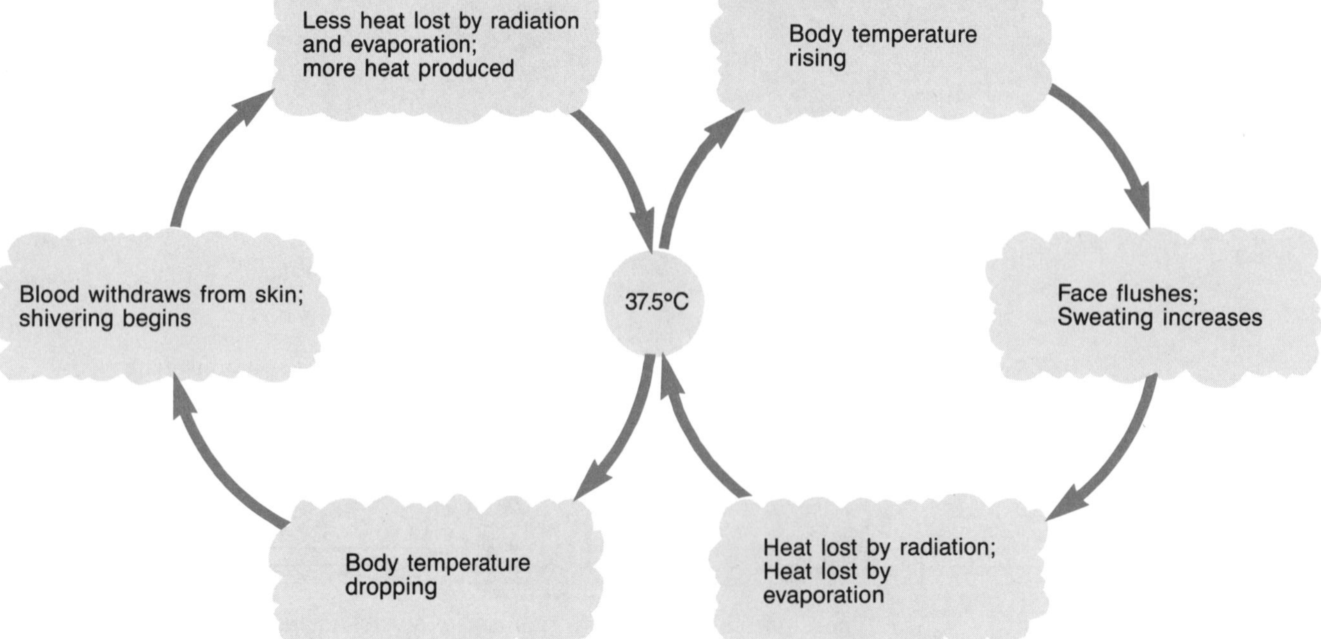

the cells. The fish simply could not live if these systems did not function together in an orderly way to maintain homeostasis.

Extension

Organisms have more than the three systems described in this unit. You will investigate them if you elect to study senior biology. All of these systems must function together to maintain a homeostatic condition. One system, the **excretory system**, is particulary important in this respect. Find answers to these questions:

1. What is excretion?
2. Why is excretion so important to homeostasis?
3. How do protists like the amoeba and paramecium excrete wastes?
4. How do the excretory systems of the earthworm, grasshopper, and fish compare?

Section Review

1. **a)** What is homeostasis?
   b) Why is it necessary?
2. **a)** What is feedback control?
   b) How does feedback control keep a home at a fairly constant temperature in the winter?
3. Describe how feedback control keeps your body temperature near 37.5°C.
4. **a)** Illustrate how digestion, gas exchange, and internal transport are interdependent in an organism.
   b) Why must all of these processes contribute to homeostasis?

10.8 Activity: Internal Structure and Behaviour of an Amoeba

In this unit you have read about the amoeba under the following headings:

- Feeding by the Amoeba, Section 8.2, page 207
- Intracellular Digestion, Section 8.3, page 211
- Gas Exchange in an Aquatic Environment, Section 9.5, page 233
- Transport in Protists, Section 10.2, page 252

Read these sections again. Then you will be ready to do this activity which will help you pull together your knowledge about the structure and behaviour of the amoeba.

Can you observe the structure and behaviour of the amoeba?

Materials

microscope
microscope slide
cover slip
paper towel
lens paper
dropper
amoeba culture (live)
prepared slide of amoeba

Procedure

a. Examine the prepared slide of amoeba under low power. Now switch to medium, then high power. Make a sketch of an amoeba, including the general shape and internal structure. Label the nucleus, cytoplasm, cell membrane, food vacuoles, contractile vacuole, and pseudopods. (You have not yet read about the contractile vacuole. It is a globular inclusion in the cytoplasm that collects liquid wastes and expels them from the amoeba.)
b. Suck up a drop or two of the amoeba culture with the dropper. The cloudy sludge at the bottom of the culture jar is usually best.
c. Prepare a wet mount of the sample. Lower the cover slip slowly. Then you won't squash the amoebas.
d. Scan the sample slowly under low power. Be patient! It may take a few minutes to find an amoeba. Start at one corner of the cover slip and move back and forth in parallel lines.
e. Once you have found one, study its locomotion closely. Make sketches of its shape every 30 s for 2 or 3 min. Put arrows on the sketches to show the direction in which the cytoplasm is moving.
f. Switch to medium, then high power. Look for the nucleus, cytoplasm, food vacuoles, contractile vacuole, and pseudopods.
g. Make a diagram of the amoeba you saw. Label as many parts as possible.
h. If time permits, watch a contractile vacuole until it bursts. Continue to observe the amoeba for a few more minutes. You should see a new vacuole form.
i. You may be lucky enough to see an amoeba feed. If you do, share your microscope with your classmates. Describe carefully how the amoeba feeds. If possible, observe a food vacuole for several minutes.

Discussion

Your sketches and laboratory notes are your write-up for this activity. Make sure they are complete.

10.9 Activity: Dissection of an Earthworm

In this unit you have read about the earthworm under the following headings:

- Feeding by the Earthworm, Section 8.2, page 208
- Digestive System of the Earthworm, Section 8.3, page 213
- The Earthworm: A Simple Gas Exchange System, Section 9.7, page 237
- Invertebrate Circulatory Systems: The Earthworm, Section 10.4, page 256

In this activity you will dissect an earthworm so you can observe the digestive and circulatory systems. You will, of course, see other systems and structures during the dissection.

Preparing for the Dissection

Dissection is the scientific technique that allows you to separate one tissue from another. Dissection of an organism is not simply a matter of cutting and slicing. The immediate aim of a complete dissection is to separate the structures of one body system from the structures of the other systems. In this way you can see for yourself the marvellous way an organism is put together. You should see that each organism is a unique collection of intricate structures. Of course, you will *not* see this unless you dissect with care and dexterity.

A dissection is complicated by several factors. First, most animal tissues are very soft. A misplaced cut with scissors or scalpel can easily damage an important structure. Second, sometimes the structures of one system seem jumbled with the structures of another. And, finally, unless the animal is freshly killed, the preserving process can misshape and discolour some key tissues.

How do you best prepare for a dissection? Like a surgeon preparing for an operation, you should first study related diagrams, descriptions, and instructions. Therefore, *read again the four sections on the earthworm listed at the start of this activity*. Mark the pages so you can easily locate the diagrams and descriptions as you dissect your specimen. If you study this material before you make your first incision, you will know what structures to expect and how they are interconnected. Remember that the diagrams are simplified. No organism looks exactly like them.

We wish to remind you of a comment made in Section 8.6: All life is valuable, even that of this earthworm you are about to dissect. It was killed so you could learn more about its systems and their functioning. Do not waste your specimen with careless cuts.

Problem

Can you dissect an earthworm to reveal its digestive, circulatory, and other systems?

Materials

preserved earthworm
dissecting tray
scalpels
dissecting scissors
forceps
dissecting pins
hand lens

CAUTION: Wear safety goggles, an apron, and plastic gloves while doing the dissection. Wash your hands with soap and water after handling the specimen. Follow your teacher's instructions for the safe use of dissecting equipment.

Procedure

Making Your Dissection Notes

The following dissection instructions include, from time to time, an *italicized sentence* with a small *superscript numeral*. When you come to such a sentence, write the numeral in your notebook and, after it, respond to the statement or question in italics. If you do this, you will end up with a detailed set of dissection notes, arranged in a logical fashion.

Some External Features

Pick up the earthworm. *How do you know it is an invertebrate?*[1] Examine the dorsal, ventral, anterior, and posterior surfaces (Fig. 10-16). *How can you distinguish these by coloration?*[2] Locate the **clitellum**. It is about 31 segments from the anterior end. It produces the mucus that makes a living worm so slippery. *Describe the colour and shape of the clitellum.*[3] Compare the anterior and posterior ends. *How can you tell them apart?*[4] Look closely at the anterior end. The **mouth** is situated beneath an overhanging lip called the **prostomium**. Use a hand lens to see the parts, then sketch a head-on view of the worm. Label the first segment, the mouth, and the prostomium. *Does the mouth run vertically or horizontally (laterally)?*[5] Examine the anal (last) segment of the worm. *Does the* **anal slit** *run vertically or horizontally?*[6] *Compare the shape of the posterior 15 segments with that of the anterior 15 segments.*[7] *Suggest a reason for the difference.*[8] Rub your finger along the lateral (side) and ventral surfaces to locate the rows of bristles or **setae**. *How many setae are on each segment?*[9] *What might their function be?*[10]

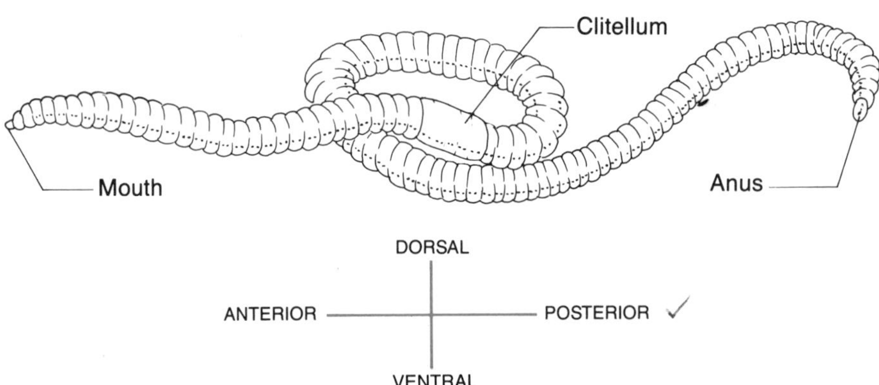

Fig. 10-16 Make sure you know the meanings of the terms on this diagram.

The Dissection

Place the worm in the dissecting tray, dorsal side up. Pinch up a fold of skin just in front of the clitellum. Snip with the scissors to make a *small shallow* cut through the dorsal body wall. Now lay the worm across your hand, dorsal side up (Fig. 10-17). Insert the scissor point under the dorsal wall. Cut slowly and carefully toward the anterior end, keeping the hidden scissor point from digging into the body cavity. Be especially careful when you reach segment 1.

Now lay the worm straight out, incision side up, on the dissecting tray. Pin the anal and first segments to the wax surface. Use the scalpel and forceps to separate the body wall from the internal organs. You will have to cut through the **septa**, which are tissues that hold the body wall in place and separate one segment from another (Fig. 10-18). Pin down the body wall at regular intervals to keep the internal organs exposed. Your finished dissection should resemble Figure 10-19.

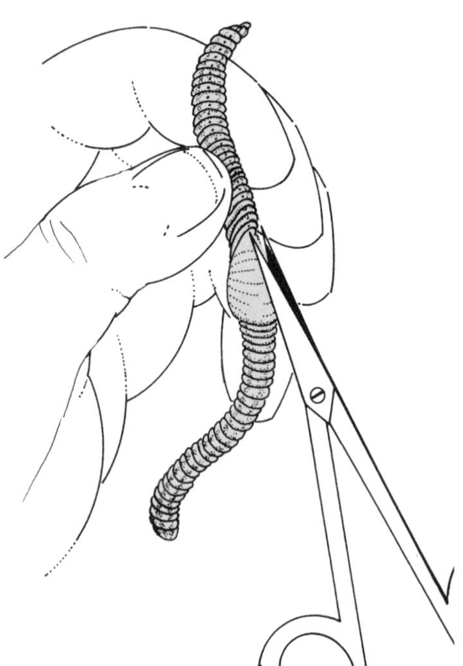

Fig. 10-17 Keep the scissor blade up against the body wall so it won't damage any internal organs.

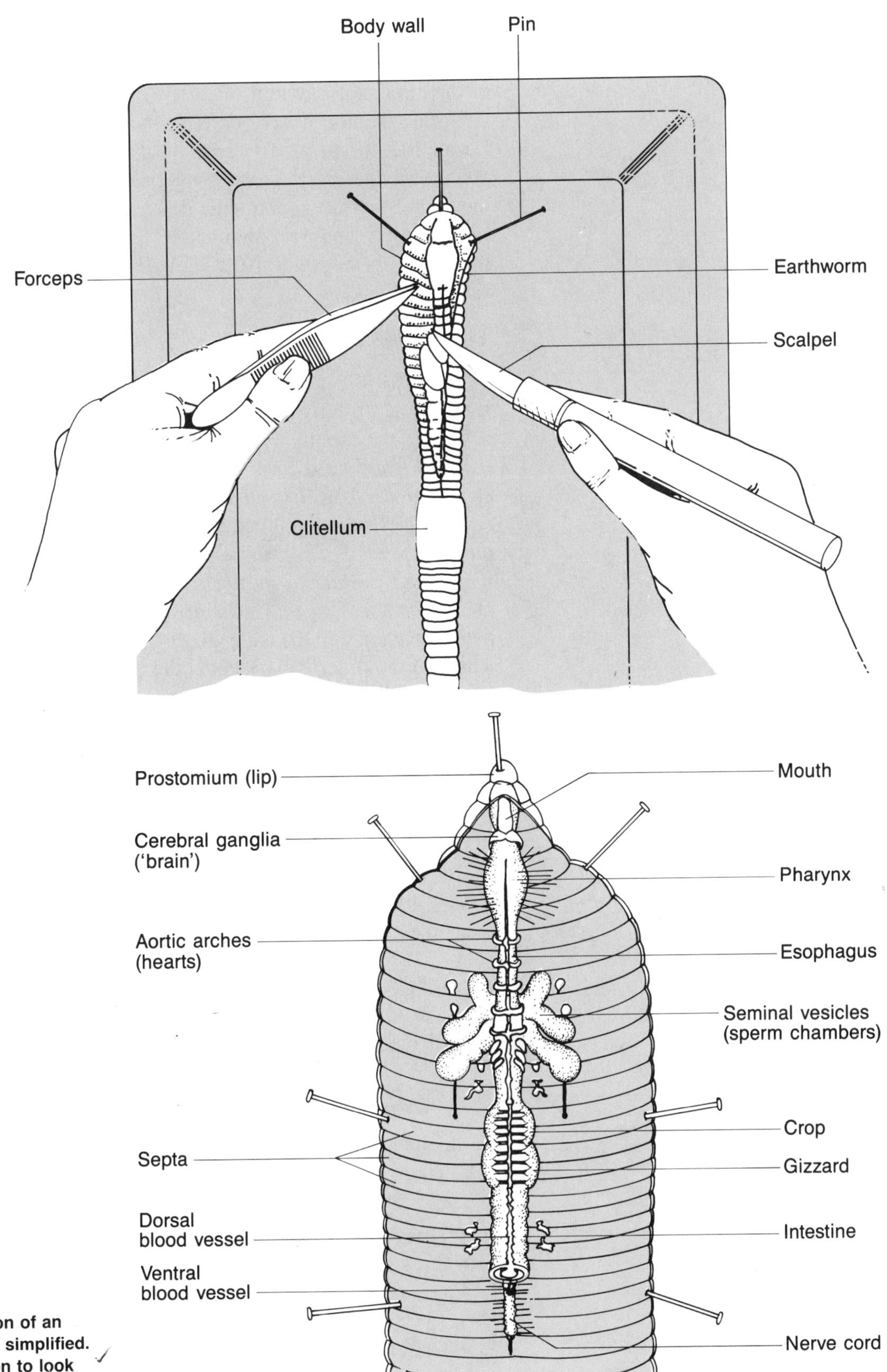

Fig. 10-18 Cut carefully!

Fig. 10-19 Dorsal dissection of an earthworm. This diagram is simplified. Don't expect your dissection to look exactly like this.

The Circulatory System

Use Figures 10-6 and 10-19 to help you with identification of the major parts of the circulatory system.

Locate the **aortic arches**. *How many are there?*[11] *What is their function?*[12] Locate the **dorsal blood vessel** on the intestine. *In which direction did blood flow in this vessel?*[13] Tease away part of the intestine from the body wall on the ventral surface. You should see the white nerve cord on the body wall. Look closely and you should see the **ventral blood vessel** attached to the intestine (on the ventral surface). *In which direction did blood flow in this vessel?*[14]

The Digestive System

Use Figures 8-6 and 10-19 to help you with the identification of the major parts of the digestive system.

Locate the mouth. Follow the digestive system to the **pharynx**. *Describe its colour and structure.*[15] *How is its structure related to its function?*[16] The **esophagus** is hard to see since the creamy-yellow seminal vesicles and the aortic arches surround it completely. Carefully remove these structures. *Describe the esophagus.*[17] *Describe the colour and structure of the crop.*[18] *How does its structure relate to its function?*[19] Open the crop. *Describe its contents.*[20] *Describe the colour and structure of the gizzard.*[21] *How is its structure related to its function?*[22] Open the gizzard. *Describe its contents.*[23] The remaining length of the digestive system is the intestine. *What colour is it?*[24] As you can see, the intestine is well-supplied with blood vessels. *Why is this so?*[25]

Discussion

Your completed dissection notes are your write-up for this activity.

Extension

If you finish early, investigate closely the system or tissues responsible for another life process such as gas exhange, reproduction, or excretion. Your teacher will give you reference materials.

10.10 Activity: Dissection of a Yellow Perch

In this unit you have read about fish, in particular the yellow perch under the following headings:

- Feeding by the Perch, Section 8.2, page 210
- Digestive System of the Perch, Section 8.3, page 214
- Gas Exchange in an Aquatic Environment: The Fish, Section 9.5, page 234
- Circulatory System of a Fish: The Yellow Perch, Section 10.6, page 260

In this activity you will dissect a yellow perch so you can observe the digestive, circulatory, and gas exchange systems. Before you begin, read again the section titled "Preparing for the Dissection" in Section 10.9. Also, read the four sections on the yellow perch listed on the preceding page and mark them for ready reference during the dissection. Finally, read the section "Making Your Dissection Notes" in Section 10.9.

Problem

Can you dissect a yellow perch to reveal its digestive, circulatory, and gas exchange systems?

Materials

preserved yellow perch	dissecting scissors	dissecting pins
dissecting tray	forceps	hand lens
scalpels	probe	

CAUTION: Wear safety goggles, an apron, and plastic gloves while doing the dissection. Wash your hands with soap and water after handling the specimen. Follow your teacher's instructions for the safe use of dissecting equipment.

Procedure

Some External Features

Place the fish on its side in the dissecting tray. Locate all the external features shown in Figure 10-20. *Describe the structure of each fin and hypothesize how that structure is related to the function of that fin.*[1] (Examination of a living fish in an aquarium will help confirm your hypotheses.) Open the mouth of the fish. *Describe the appearance, location, and abundance of teeth.*[2] *What do you suppose their function is?*[3] Use the forceps and probe to locate the tongue. *Describe it.*[4]

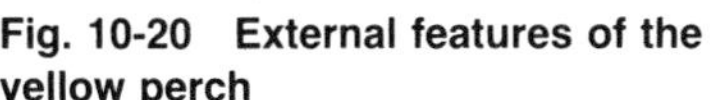

Fig. 10-20 External features of the yellow perch

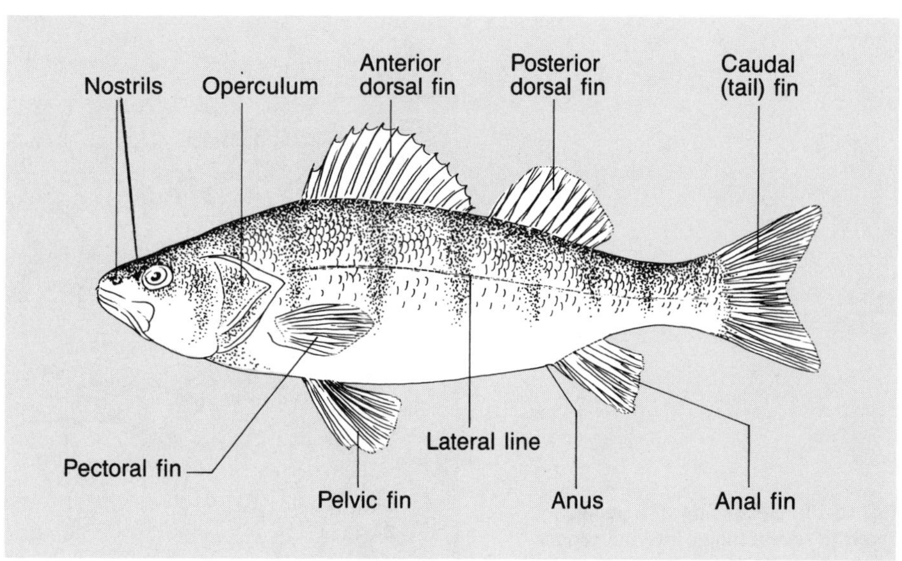

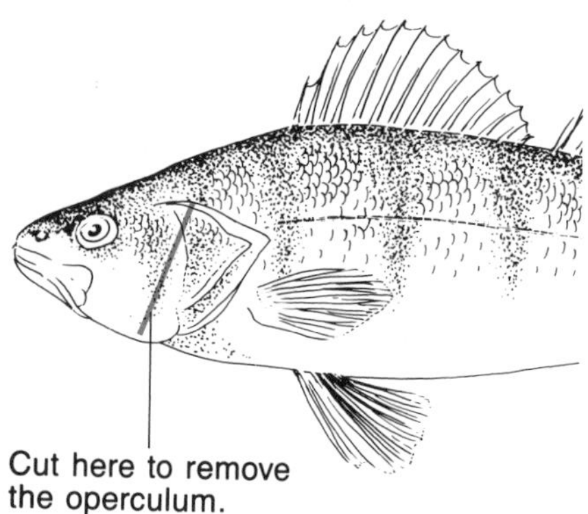

Fig. 10-21 Carefully remove the operculum (gill cover) from one side to reveal the gills.

Use Figures 9-11 and 10-14 to help you with the identification of the major parts of the gas exchange system.

Remove the **operculum** (gill cover) from one side of the head by cutting along the coloured line shown in Figure 10-21. *CAUTION: The operculum can be hard to cut. Be careful that you do not cut yourself. Always cut away from your body.* Examine the **gills**. *How many are there?*[5] *Describe their overall appearance and texture.*[6] Carefully remove one gill. *Note the structure and function of the* **gill rakers**, **gill arch**, *and* **gill filaments**.[7]

Exposing the Internal Organs

Hold the fish upside down, with its dorsal surface on the dissecting tray. Make a cut, using scalpel and scissors, along the ventral surface from the anus to below the opercula (gill covers). This is line 1 in Figure 10-22. You are cutting the body wall so you can eventually remove it. Do not cut deeply enough to damage the internal organs. *CAUTION: Be careful that you do not cut yourself as you cut through this tough tissue.* Now make the other three cuts shown in Figure 10-22, always being careful not to damage internal organs. Remove the section of body wall to expose the internal organs. Your finished dissection should resemble Figure 10-23.

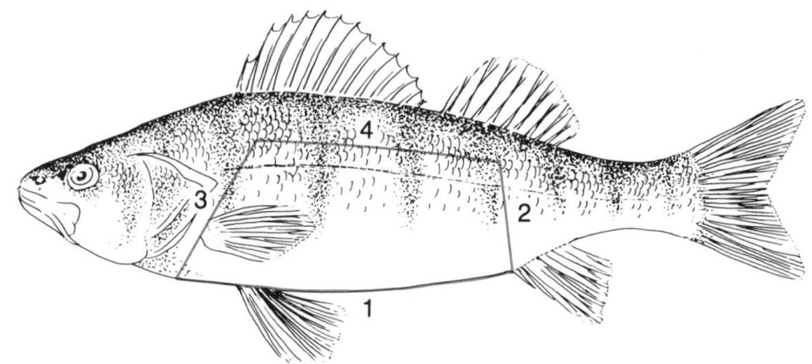

Fig. 10-22 Remove the body wall from one side by making incisions as shown here. Do not cut too deeply or you will damage the internal organs.

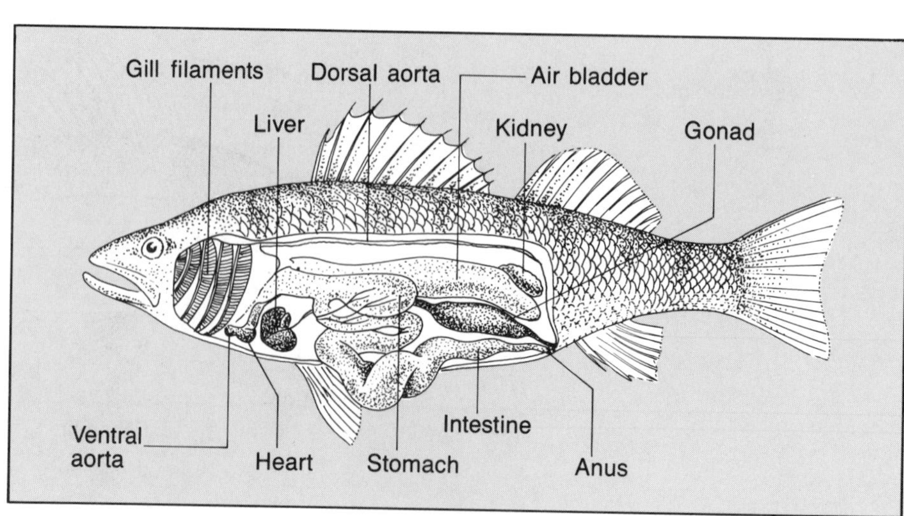

Fig. 10-23 Dissection of a yellow perch to reveal major internal organs and structures

The Circulatory System

Locate the **heart** of your specimen. You may have to remove the **liver** to see the heart. *Describe the shape and structure of the heart.*[8] Locate the **ventral aorta**. *In which direction did blood flow in this vessel?*[9] Locate the **dorsal aorta**. *In which direction did blood flow in this vessel?*[10]

The Digestive System

Carefully remove the digestive system, intact, from the fish. Lay it out in linear fashion in the dissecting tray. *Describe the* **esophagus**.[11] *How does its structure relate to its function?*[12] *Describe the* **stomach**.[13] *How does its structure relate to its function?*[14] Open the stomach and examine the contents. *Describe the contents.*[15] The remaining length of the digestive system is the **intestine**. *Describe the intestine.*[16] *How does its structure relate to its function?*[17] *Is it, like that of the earthworm, well-supplied with blood vessels?*[18]

Other Structures

You have, no doubt, noticed the **air bladder**. *From its structure and location, what do you think its function is?*[19] Note the large elongated **kidney**. *What is its function?*[20] *Is your specimen a male or female?*[21] If it is a male, the gonads will be a pair of **testes**, elongated whitish structures. If it is a female, the single gonad will be a large, yellow **ovary**.

Discussion

Your completed dissection notes are your write-up for this activity.

Extension

If you finish early, investigate closely another system such as the nervous, reproductive, or excretory system.

10.11 Activity: Dissection of a Mammalian Heart

Depending on the availability of specimens, your teacher may demonstrate this dissection or allow you to do it in groups. Once again, we remind you to study the diagram, descriptions, and instructions carefully before you begin the dissection.

Problem

How is a mammalian heart adapted to simultaneously pump blood through a pulmonary (lung) circuit and a body circuit?

Materials

fresh untrimmed mammalian heart (cattle, pig, or sheep)

dissecting tray	dissecting scissors	probe
scalpels	forceps	hand lens

CAUTION: Wear safety goggles, an apron, and plastic gloves while doing the dissection. Wash your hands with soap and water after handling the specimen. Follow your teacher's instructions for the safe use of dissecting equipment.

Procedure

Follow Figures 10-24 and 10-25 as you read the following preparatory information.

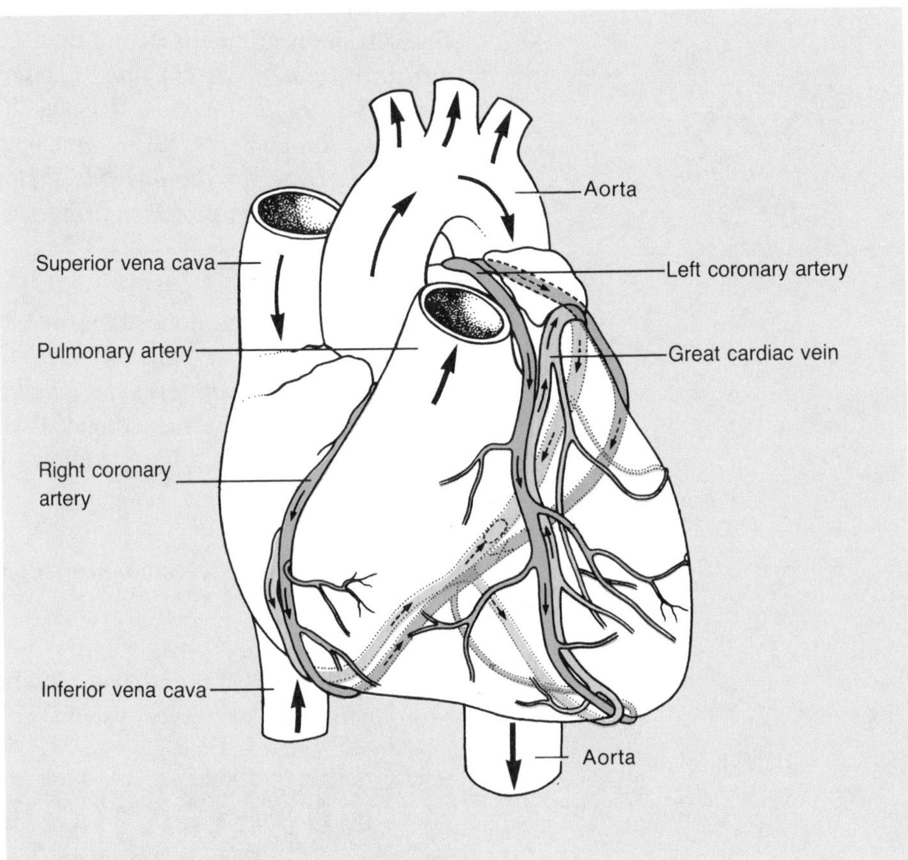

Fig. 10-24 Exterior view of a mammalian heart

How the Heart Functions

You read earlier that the mammalian heart is, in effect, two hearts in one. The left side of the heart pumps blood through the body circuit and the right side pumps blood through the pulmonary (lung) circuit. Let us trace the path of the blood through the two circuits, beginning with oxygen-poor blood entering the heart. Be sure to trace this path on Figures 10-24 and 10-25 so that you can later identify the parts and their functions.

- Oxygen-poor blood returns from the body to the **right atrium** of the heart. The **superior vena cava** vein brings it from the head and arms and the **inferior vena cava** vein brings it from the lower body and legs.
- The right atrium contracts and forces this blood into the **right ventricle**. An **atrio-ventricular valve** prevents backflow.
- The right ventricle contracts and pumps the blood into the **pulmonary artery** which branches to each lung. A **pulmonary valve** prevents backflow.

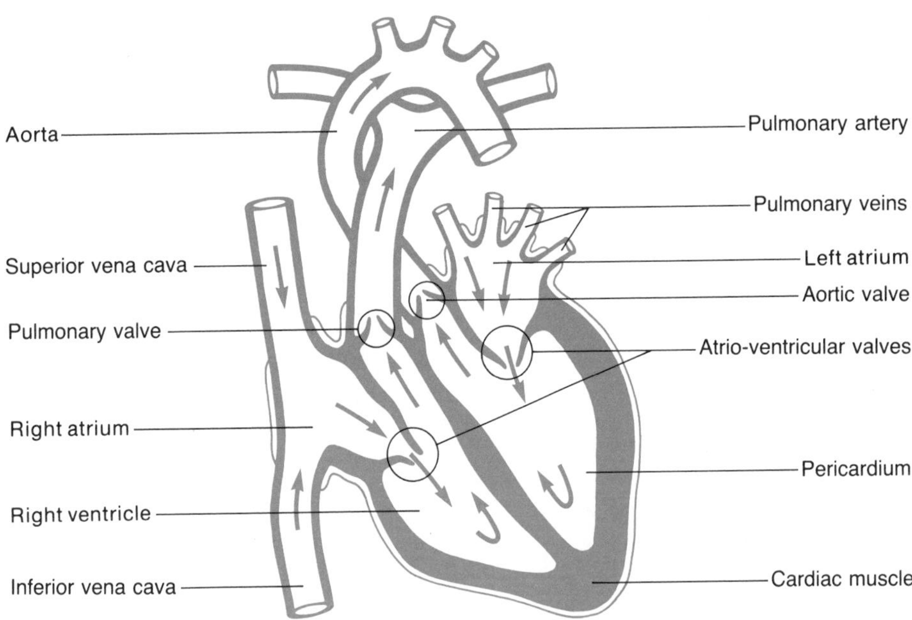

Fig. 10-25 Interior view of a mammalian heart

- Gaseous exchange occurs in the capillary beds in the alveoli of the lungs.
- The resulting oxygen-rich blood returns to the **left atrium** of the heart via the **pulmonary veins**.
- The left atrium contracts and forces this blood into the very muscular **left ventricle**. An **atrio-ventricular valve** prevents backflow.
- The left ventricle contracts and forces the oxygen-rich blood into the **aorta**. An **aortic valve** prevents backflow. The aorta branches to all parts of the body.
- The blood passes through capillaries in the tissues and returns, oxygen-poor, via veins to the superior or inferior vena cava.

Note: The left and right coronary arteries and the great cardiac vein (Fig. 10-24) service the heart muscles.

The Heartbeat

"Lub-dub . . . lub-dub . . . lub-dub . . . " Have you ever wondered what causes that familiar sound?

The "lub" sound is caused by the closing of the atrio-ventricular valves. They close when blood is being forced from the ventricles into the arteries. The "dub" sound is caused by the closing of the pulmonary and aortic valves. They close when blood is being forced from the atria into the ventricles. These valves prevent the blood that was just forced out of the ventricles from flowing back to where it came from.

Pre-dissection Investigations

Place the heart in the dissecting tray, oriented as shown in Figures 10-24 and 10-25. *Are you looking at the dorsal or ventral side of the heart? How do you know?*[1] Carefully trim away the layer of fatty tissue on the heart. Now look for the **left coronary artery**, **right coronary artery**, and **great cardiac vein**. *Describe and account for the number of branches from these vessels.*[2]

Now, let's follow the path described earlier, examining the various parts. Locate the superior vena cava and the inferior vena cava. *To what part of the heart do they connect?*[3] Insert the blunt end of the probe into this part of the heart via one of the vena cava veins. *Can you feel the* **atrio-ventricular valve?**[4] Locate the pulmonary artery. *Describe and account for its structure.*[5] If possible, probe carefully down the pulmonary artery to see if you can locate the pulmonary valve. *What did you discover?*[6]

Turn the heart over and locate the pulmonary veins. *Describe and account for their structure.*[7] If you are using a large heart, you may be able to locate the atrio-ventricular valve with a probe. Return the heart to its original position on the tray and locate the aorta. *Describe and account for its structure.*[8] Insert the blunt end of the probe into the aorta and see if you can feel the aortic valve.

The Dissection

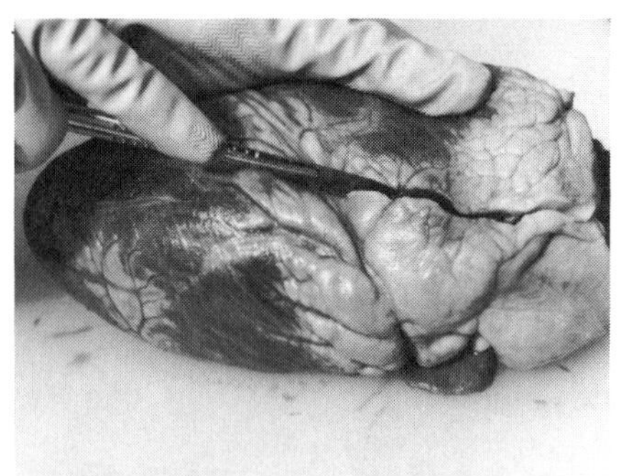

Fig. 10-26 Make a cut around the perimeter and parallel to the surface of the dissecting tray.

Make sure the heart is in the dissection tray oriented as shown in Figures 10-24 and 10-25. The purpose of this dissection is to cut the heart in half so you can see the view illustrated in Figure 10-25. However, you cannot simply slice the heart in half. This would damage internal parts that you want to examine. To avoid damaging valves and other interior parts, cut around the perimeter of the heart just deeply enough to cut through the walls of the heart (Fig. 10-26). You could compare this cut to cutting through the skin of an orange prior to peeling it off. Now carefully remove the top half. You will have to do some trimming to get it off. Examine your dissected specimen and answer these questions: Compare the two atrio-ventricular valves. *One is called a* bicuspid valve *and the other a* tricuspid valve. *Why?*[9] *Compare and account for the thicknesses of the walls of the left and right ventricles.*[10] *Describe the pulmonary and aortic valves.*[11]

Discussion

Your completed dissection notes are your write-up for this activity.

Extension

Open a coronary artery and look for evidence of fatty deposits. What problem can such deposits cause?

10.12 Activity: How Efficient Are Your Gas Exchange and Circulatory Systems?

When you exercise, your muscle cells require additional energy. This means that they need additional nutrients like glucose and additional oxygen. As a result, your gas exchange and circulatory systems must work harder to meet the demand. That is why your heartbeat rate, or pulse rate, increases when you exercise.

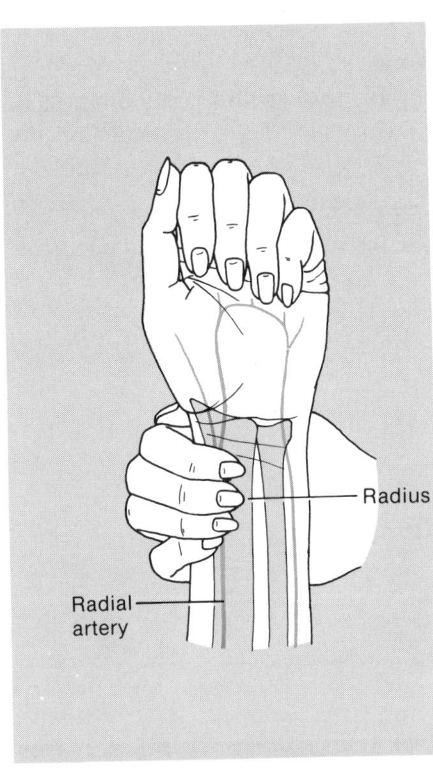

Fig. 10-27 Finding your pulse. This pulse is called your radial pulse since it occurs in the radial artery that runs along the radius, a bone in your arm.

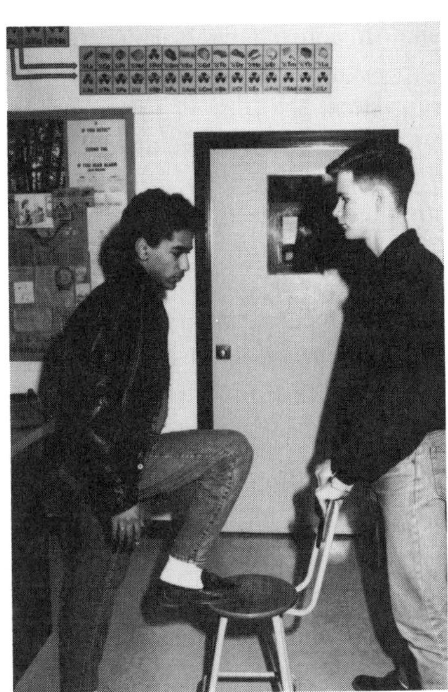

Fig. 10-28 Hold the chair securely. Step up as described in step (f).

The amount that your pulse rate increases depends on how fit you are. That is, it depends on the strength of your heart, the elasticity of your arteries, and the efficiency of your lungs. In this activity you will determine what is called your **Heart Performance Score (HPS)**. This is a good general measure of your overall fitness.

Problem

What is your heart performance score? What is your general fitness level?

Materials

watch or timer that reads in seconds
chair

CAUTION: If you have any respiratory or circulatory disorders, do not do this activity. Inform your teacher.

Procedure

a. Practise finding your pulse rate until you can do it quickly and accurately. It is best to take your radial pulse for 20 s, then multiply by 3 (Fig. 10-27). This gives your pulse rate in beats per minute.

b. Copy Table 10-1 into your notebook without the numerals. Record all measurements in this table. Sample measurements have been placed in our table.

Table 10-1 Finding Your HPS

Pulse rate while lying down	70
Pulse rate while standing	85
Difference between the above	15
Pulse rate after exercising	130
Pulse rate after resting	105
Your HPS (add the 5 numerals)	405

c. Lie down for 2–3 min. Find your pulse rate while lying down.

d. Stand up, wait for 10 s, then find your pulse rate.

e. Calculate the difference between the two pulse rates you have measured.

f. Exercise as follows: Obtain a chair about 0.5 m high. Have your partner hold it securely. Then, raise your left leg and step up on the chair (Fig. 10-28). Stand right up on it with both feet. Then get off the chair using your right leg. Switch legs after every 5 complete steps. (A complete step is an up and down motion.) Continue this exercise for 60 s. You must do about 15 complete steps in the 60 s.

g. Immediately find your pulse rate.

h. Rest for 60 s. Then find your pulse rate again.

i. Calculate your HPS by adding the 5 numerals you have put in your table.

Discussion

1. Find your general fitness level from Table 10-2.

2. What is the average HPS for your class?
3. What is the average HPS for males? females?
4. Compare your HPS to the class average. Try to account for any difference.
5. Compare your HPS to the average for your sex. Try to account for any differences.
6. Why does the heartbeat rate increase during exercise?

Table 10-2 HPS and Fitness Level

HPS	*General fitness level*
200–250	Endurance athlete
250–300	Athletic
300–325	Very good
325–350	Good
350–375	Fairly good
375–400	Fair
400–450	Poor
450–500	Very poor

Chapter Highlights

1. Transport systems move nutrients, oxygen, wastes, and other materials through organisms.
2. Protists and some simple animals rely on diffusion and cytoplasmic streaming for internal transport.
3. All arthropods have an open circulatory system.
4. Most active complex animals, including all vertebrates, have a closed circulatory system.
5. Vertebrate circulatory systems have a structure that meets the requirements of the organism.
6. The mammalian heart functions as a double heart.
7. Homeostasis is the maintenance of an internal balance in an organism.
8. A careful dissection can reveal a great deal about the internal structure of organisms.
9. Your heart performance score depends on the efficiency of your gas exchange and circulatory systems.

Key Terms

aorta
arteriole
artery
atrium
blood circulatory system
capillary
closed circulatory system
cytoplasmic streaming
dissection
feedback control
heart performance score
homeostasis

inferior vena cava
internal transport system
open circulatory system
pulmonary artery
pulmonary vein
superior vena cava
varicose veins
vein
ventricle
venule

Recognizing the Concepts

Each of the following statements or questions is followed by four responses. Choose the correct response in each case. (Do not write in this book.)

1. Which one of these organisms does not have an internal transport system?
   a) hydra **b)** earthworm **c)** grasshopper **d)** perch
2. The smallest blood vessels in a closed circulatory system are the
   a) arteries **b)** arterioles **c)** capillaries **d)** veins
3. An open circulatory system means that
   a) the blood is open to the air or water surrounding the animal
   b) arteries and veins are separated by open body spaces
   c) the circulatory system can be easily seen
   d) oxygen-poor and oxygen-rich blood mix in the heart
4. Which one of the following statements is false?
   a) Arteries always carry oxygen-rich blood.
   b) Arteries carry blood away from the heart.
   c) Veins carry blood to the heart.
   d) Arterioles are small arteries.
5. In a four-chambered heart, blood is pumped to the body tissues by the
   a) right atrium **c)** left atrium
   b) right ventricle **d)** left ventricle
6. Homeostasis is best described as
   a) the use of feedback control to maintain a constant body temperature
   b) the adaptation of an organism to its environment
   c) the interaction of the gas exchange and circulatory systems within an organism
   d) the maintenance of an internal balance in an organism
7. An organ from an animal is found to have thick muscular walls and to contain grains of sand. This organ is most likely a
   a) gizzard **b)** crop **c)** stomach **d)** intestine

Understanding the Concepts

1. **a)** Why does a protist not require an internal transport system?
   b) Why does "division of labour" in an organism necessitate an internal transport system?
2. Why is it not necessary for the grasshopper's circulatory system to carry oxygen?
3. Why does a grasshopper not have the same need for a closed circulatory system as you do?
4. Compare, in tabular form, the circulatory systems of fish, amphibians, and mammals under the following headings: number of chambers, blood pressure in body tissues, oxygen concentration in the blood when it reaches

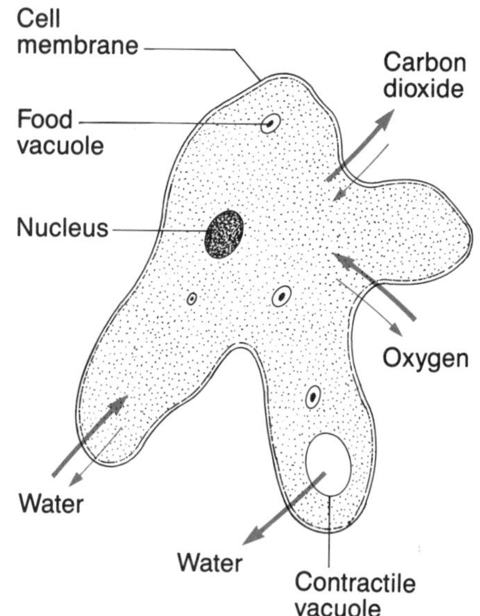

Fig. 10-29 Homeostasis is essential to the survival of even a single-celled organism like the amoeba.

body tissues, number of times the blood passes through the heart during one trip through the body.

5. Why is a two-chambered heart sufficient for a fish?
6. What function do valves perform in a circulatory system?
7. Why does your pulse rate increase when you exercise?
8. Why is the wall of the left ventricle of a mammalian heart thicker than the wall of the right ventricle?

Applying the Concepts

1. Describe the problems you would have if you had a two-chambered heart like a fish.
2. Like mammals, birds have a four-chambered heart. Why is this structure essential for birds?
3. Examine Figure 10-29 carefully, then refer to it as you explain the caption for this figure.
4. How does your blood help keep your body temperature constant?
5. What symptoms might a person exhibit who had poorly functioning atrioventricular valves?
6. A person had a resting pulse rate of 75 beats/min. After this person exercised vigorously for six months, this rate became 55 beats/min. How many fewer beats does the heart make in a day? What is responsible for this decrease in pulse rate?

Fig. 10-30 Would you expect the crayfish to be more like a grasshopper or an earthworm? Why?

Investigations

1. Examine a living earthworm with a hand lens to determine its heartbeat rate.
2. Perform a dissection of a crayfish to investigate its gas exchange, circulatory, and digestive systems (Fig. 10-30).
3. Find out how the air bladder of a fish functions. What does it do and how does it accomplish this? What variations in structure and function are there among different species of fish?
4. The heart of a reptile is slightly more advanced than that of an amphibian. Find out what this advance is.
5. Hypothermia sets in when a person becomes so cold that feedback cannot restore homeostasis in body temperature. Find out what hypothermia is, what causes it, how it can be prevented, and how it can be treated.
6. Design and do an experiment to determine the effects of caffeine in coffee on the pulse rate.
7. Find out what a coronary bypass operation is. Why is it necessary? How is it done? What does it accomplish?
8. An important lifesaving method is called cardio-pulmonary resuscitation (CPR). Find out what this is and how it is carried out.

Biography

Grace Kwan: Veterinarian

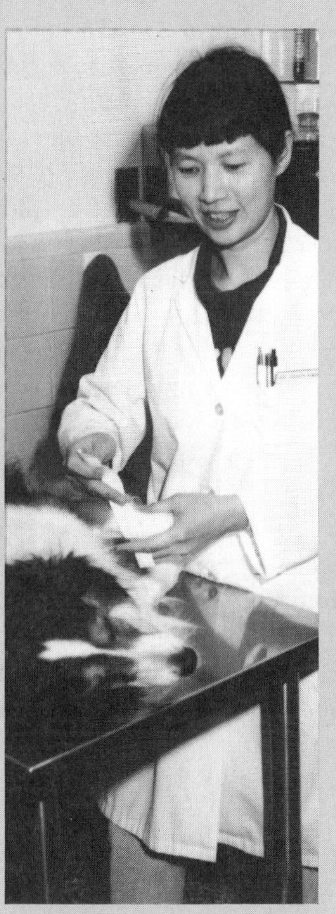

Grace Kwan is a Doctor of Veterinary Medicine (D.V.M.) employed by Brown's Animal Hospital in North York, Ontario. At this hospital, Kwan is involved mainly in preventive medicine such as general checkups, vaccinations, neutering/spaying for population control, and the treatment of minor ailments like ear infections and abscesses. Grace Kwan says that her greatest satisfaction comes from making a sick animal well. In fact, about 20% of her time is spent saving the lives of animals that would otherwise have died or been put to sleep. Her saddest moments come when she has to put an animal to sleep because it can't be helped, because it is homeless, or because the owners cannot afford to have the animal treated.

Grace came to Canada from Hong Kong with the equivalent of six OAC credits. She says that, to be a veterinarian, you must have very good marks in OAC Chemistry, Biology, Physics, and Mathematics. You must also have at least one year of general science at university with a minimum average of 75% before applying to veterinary college. Then you attend the Ontario Veterinary College at the University of Guelph for five years, the first of which is a pre-vet course.

Grace points out that competition for entry into the Ontario Veterinary College is intense. Therefore it is important you be well qualified when you apply. At this time, about 25-30% of applicants hold a graduate degree in science. It is also necessary that you gain experience working with animals, both large and small, before you apply. For example, you could work on a horse farm for a summer and work part-time for two years in a small animal clinic.

VISTA

THE RETURN OF THE MEDICINAL LEECH

In 1985 a young boy in Massachusetts had his ear bitten off by a dog. The ear was reattached. However, in a few days, the ear began to swell and discolour. Blood was accumulating because the veins had not yet healed. Dr. Upton, the attending surgeon, wanted some way to *slowly* draw off blood until the veins healed. He decided to try the **medicinal leech** (*Hirudo medicinalis*). This animal is an annelid, a close relative of the earthworm that you have been studying in this unit. Dr. Upton had to go to Britain to get the leeches. One by one, eight leeches were attached to the ear to do their job. A few days later, the boy went home with a successfully attached ear.

Written history records the use of leeches for medicinal purposes as early as the second century B.C. But experts think they were used in India long before that. Leeching, as it is called, reached its peak in the period from 1820–1850. Nosebleeds, high blood pressure, obesity, and a wide range of diseases were treated with leeches. The common belief was that all these ailments were caused by bad blood. Therefore you could make the sick person well by removing that blood. The main proponent of leeching was a French doctor, François Broussais. He treated his own indigestion by applying over 50 leeches each day for 15 days. Due to his leadership, leeches removed about 360 000 L of French blood per year! Demand was high enough to drive the medicinal leech to the brink of extinction. Leech gatherers simply walked barelegged through ponds, collecting hundreds of leeches a day. Today they are cultured in special laboratories, so don't expect to get a summer job collecting leeches!

Leeches may never return to that level of popularity. However, they are being studied closely today for another reason. Biologists have discovered that a leech needs up to half a year to digest its blood meal. Yet, during that time, the blood does not clot or decompose. Therefore scientists are analyzing the internal secretions of the leech to find out what chemicals keep the blood this way. Perhaps they will find chemicals to treat human circulatory problems such as the clot formation that causes strokes and heart attacks.

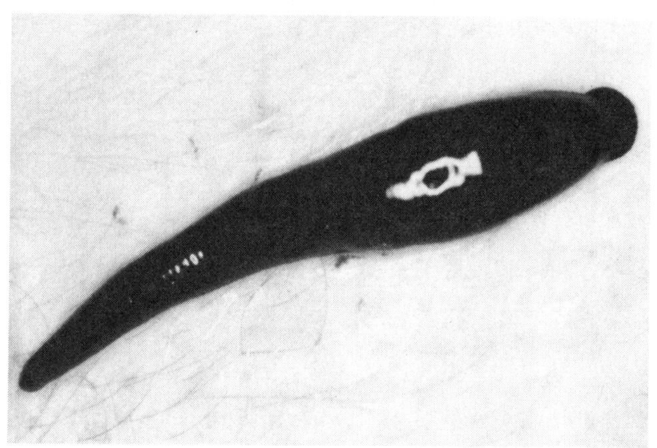

UNIT 4 Heat

CHAPTERS

Lightning flashes across the sky, tracing a jagged path from the clouds to the earth. One of its prongs strikes the tinder-dry forest, causing it to burst into flame. Soon many square kilometres of forest are destroyed. This is an example of energy out of control. Can you think of an example of energy under control?

In this unit you will be introduced to the kinds and forms of energy. You will review how thermal energy is transferred from one place to another and how heat affects matter. You will learn how to measure temperature and heat. Hopefully, this will enable you to control heat and use it wisely.

11 Heat Transfer and Thermal Expansion

CHAPTER CONTENTS

CHAPTER OBJECTIVES

After completing this chapter you should be able to:

1. Distinguish between conduction and convection.
2. Describe applications of conduction and convection.
3. Describe the travel, absorption, and emission of radiant energy.
4. Describe applications of conduction, convection, and radiation.
5. Describe thermal expansion and how it applies to thermometers.
6. Give examples of applications of thermal expansion.
7. List and apply the postulates of the Kinetic Molecular Theory of heat.

Why is the surface of a lake warmer than the bottom in summer? Why are a flat-plate solar collector and a car radiator the colour they are (Fig. 11-1)? How do the expansion of solids, liquids, and gases compare and how is this used to measure temperature? How is a theory tested? You will find answers to these and other questions in this chapter.

Fig. 11-1 A solar-heated home. The roof contains solar collectors to trap heat energy from the sun's rays. Why do you suppose the collectors are black on the inside?

11.1 How Heat Travels in Solids, Liquids, and Gases

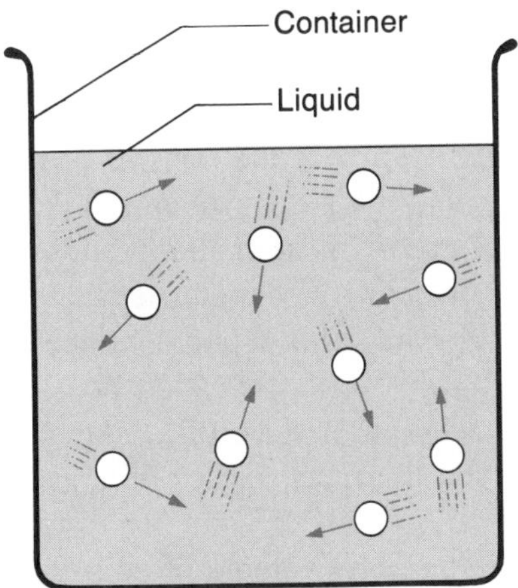

Fig. 11-2 Thermal energy is the energy an object has due to the random motion of its molecules.

What Is Thermal Energy?

Thermal energy is the energy an object has as a result of the random motion of its molecules. The molecules in a hot object move faster than the molecules in a cold object. Also, the molecules in a substance all move in different directions. Because no two molecules move in exactly the same way, we say the motion is random. Figure 11-2 shows the random motion of molecules of a liquid. The random motion of colliding molecules is different than the organized motion of a baseball. Try to imagine the random motion in the molecules of superheated steam which turn steam turbines.

What Is Heat?

Heat is thermal energy being transferred from one object to another. We know that heat is energy because it can do work by exerting a force and making things move. A good example of this is the vigorous motion of water when it is heated to the boiling point (Fig. 11-3).

All forms of energy can be converted to heat energy. In fact, the end form of all forms of energy is waste heat energy. For example, chemical energy is stored in fuel oil and natural gas. Fuel oil and natural gas are burned in furnaces to heat homes. All the heat energy produced by this burning eventually ends up in the environment. However, it is spread out so widely that it cannot be collected and used economically. That is why there is so much concern about wasting fossil fuels. Once the energy has been changed to heat energy, it becomes too costly to retrieve and is effectively lost forever.

Fig. 11-3 What evidence do these people have that heat is energy?

Conduction

Heat moves through solids by a process called conduction. **Conduction** is the movement of heat from one place to another in a material without the material moving along with it. Figure 11-4 shows an upright metal cross being heated at the centre with a burner. If drops of wax are placed on the ends of the arms, the wax melts on both the vertical and horizontal arms. This demonstrates that heat moves in all directions. During conduction, heat moves equally well up, down, and sideways. Heat also moves from the hot part of an object to the cooler parts. A material which permits heat to move is called a **conductor**. Different materials have different abilities to conduct heat. Copper and silver are two of the best conductors of heat. That is why the bottoms of some cooking pans are made of copper. Aluminum is also a good conductor of heat.

Materials which restrict the flow of heat are called **insulators**. Cork, glass. and some plastics are insulators. It may surprise you that water is also a poor conductor. To verify this, hold a test tube containing water in your hand by

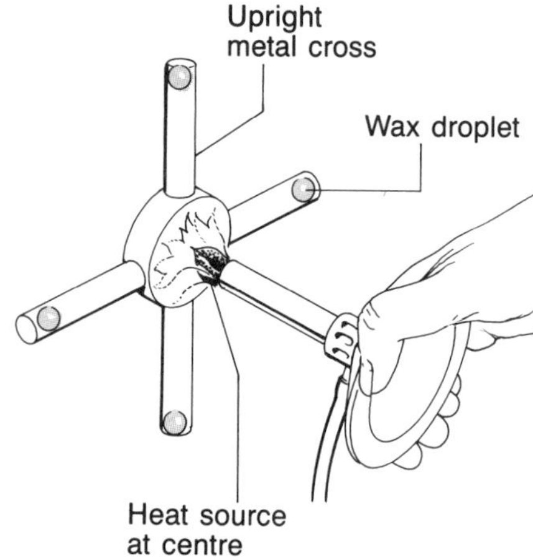

Fig. 11-4 Heat travels by conduction through solids.

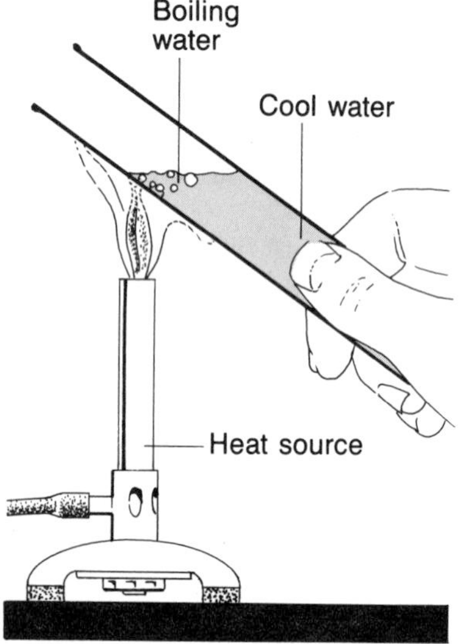

Fig. 11-5 What evidence is there that water is a poor conductor of heat?

the base. Incline it at an angle of 45° and heat the water near the upper surface as shown in Figure 11-5. If water is a poor conductor, what do you expect to observe?

Convection

Water heated near the surface of an inclined test tube boils at the surface, yet the water at the bottom remains cool. However, if the test tube is heated at the bottom, all the water eventually becomes hot. This is because heat travels in a liquid or gas by a process called convection. Liquids and gases are fluids. A **fluid** is anything that flows. **Convection** is defined as the transfer of heat by the movement of a fluid. Both hot liquids and hot gases rise and in doing so transfer heat upward. Convection does not transfer heat in all directions as does conduction. When a layer of hot water is below cold water it rises. As the cold water sinks, it pushes the hot water upward. This action continues as long as the water at the bottom is warmer. However, convection does not occur if the bottom layer is colder. That is why the surface of a lake stays warmer than the bottom in the summer. Do you think the surface of a lake is warmer or cooler than the bottom in the winter?

A hot fluid rises because it is lighter than the same volume of cold fluid. In order for this to happen it must expand when heated. This makes it less dense than the surrounding fluid. The less dense fluid rises for the same reason that a hot air balloon rises. Thus hot water rises and cold water sinks; hot air rises and cold air sinks. Now can you explain why a hot water tank in a home needs one heater at the top and another at the bottom?

Section Review

1. **a)** How do we know that heat is a form of energy?
   b) Name five sources of heat energy.
   c) What is the end form of all forms of energy?
2. **a)** Define conduction.
   b) Describe and give three examples of a good conductor.
   c) Define and give an example of an insulator.
3. Define the term fluid and give two examples.
4. **a)** What are two differences between conduction and convection?
   b) What conditions are needed before convection can take place?

11.2 Applications of Conduction and Convection

There are many applications of conduction and convection. In this section we look at some of these applications in detail.

Conduction

Home Decorating You may have noticed that if you stand with one bare foot on a ceramic tile floor and the other on a wool carpet, one feels colder

Fig. 11-6 How do you know that the ceramic tile and the wool carpet are at the same temperature?

than the other (Fig. 11-6). Why? The ceramic tile conducts heat better than the wool carpet. Hence the ceramic feels colder to the touch than the wool. Conduction is an important consideration in home decorating. Can you identify other examples?

Mine Safety Conduction has also played a key role in improving mine safety. Prior to 1815, underground miners used open flames for visibility. The flames were open to the air to enable oxygen to support combustion. But dangerous gases collect underground and coal miners around the world were being killed by explosions of these gases. Heat from the open flames caused the gases to reach their kindling temperature. Sir Humphry Davy (1778–1829) designed a way to overcome this problem. He hypothesized that if the temperature of the open flame was kept lower than the kindling temperature of the gas, the explosions would not occur. He looked for a way to improve conduction near the flame. This would dissipate the heat and lower the temperature of the flame. Scientists of the time knew that metals are better conductors than gases. Davy surrounded the flame with a cylindrical metal gauze. This dissipated the heat but still enabled oxygen to reach the flame. This arrangment was named the Davy lamp (Fig. 11-7). Electric lamps powered by batteries have since replaced the Davy lamp.

Home Insulation There are many situations where we want to minimize heat transfer. A tremendous amount of energy is wasted by heat escaping through the surfaces of buildings (Fig. 11-8). Insulating materials are stuffed in floors, walls, and attics to minimize heat loss. There are many kinds of insulation, so how do we choose the most suitable one? One factor to consider is thermal resistance. The **thermal resistance value**, commonly called the **RSI value**, is a measurement of the resistance of the material to heat transfer. The higher the resistance value, the less heat escapes. One centimetre of styrofoam has an RSI value of about 1.5 times that of one centimetre of loose fibreglass. Table 11-1 shows the resistance values for one centimetre of several common insulation materials. The resistance value is generally listed on the outside of cartons of insulation and is specified for a given thickness (Fig. 11-9).

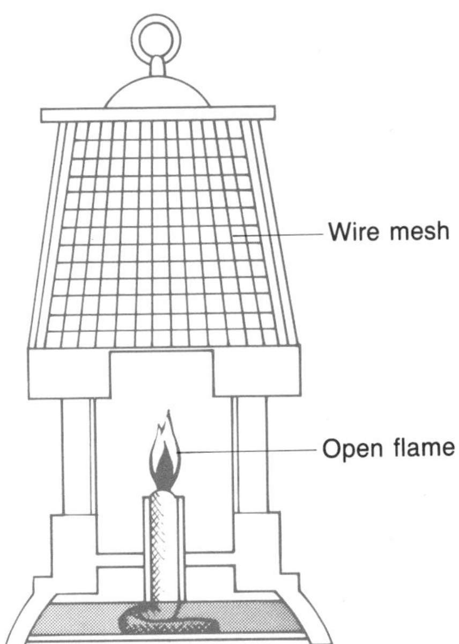

Fig. 11-7 A Davy lamp

Table 11-1 RSI Values for One Centimetre of Some Insulation Materials

Material	*RSI value of 1 cm (RSI/cm)*	*Material*	*RSI value of 1 cm (RSI/cm)*
Wood shavings	0.16	Cellulose fibre	0.26
Vermiculite	0.16	Expanded polystyrene	0.26
Loose rock wool	0.19	Styrofoam	0.32
Loose fibreglass	0.21	Polyurethane slabs	0.39
Batt fibreglass	0.23		

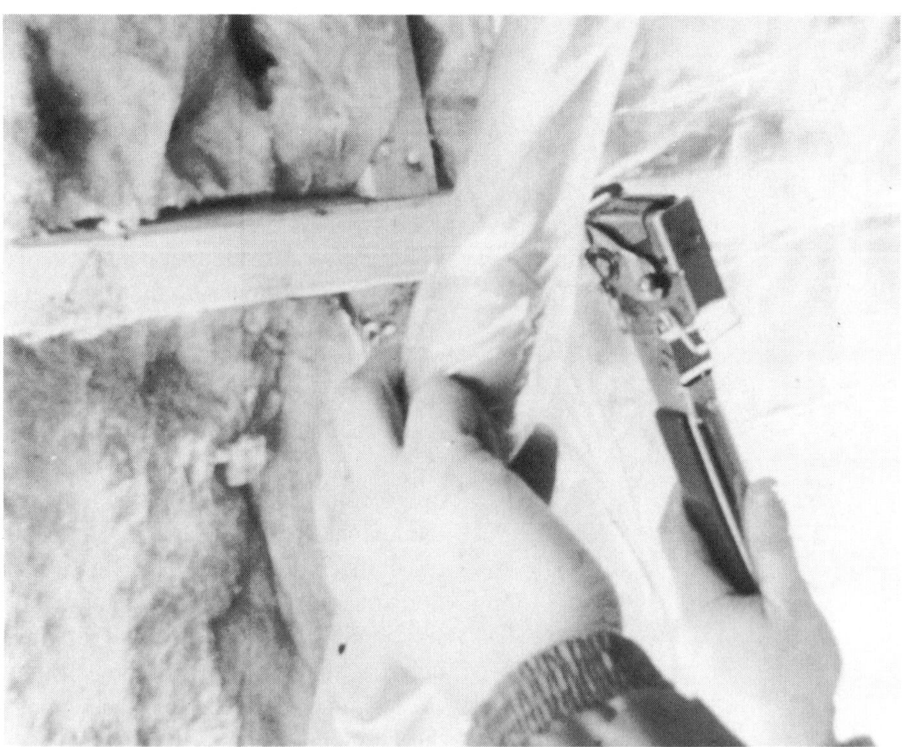

Fig. 11-8 Fibreglass decreases heat loss from buildings.

When deciding which insulation material to purchase, look up the resistance value of the material. However, also consider other factors such as the space you have for the insulation, its cost, the ease of installation, and the resistance of the material to fire and pests.

Fig. 11-9 The RSI value is marked on the outside of bags of insulation.

Space Flights Conduction plays an important role in space flights. When an object moves through air at very high speeds, air friction generates a dangerous amount of heat. You may have seen the path of shooting stars as they burn up in the atmosphere. To guard space shuttles from the same fate, scientists have developed a way to minimize the effects of air friction during re-entry. They created a super insulator with a high melting point. The insulator prevents the extreme heat generated by the friction of re-entry from being conducted to the main shuttle. Tiles made of this material are glued to the surface. The surface of the tile, bombarded by the air, turns white hot; however, the inner surface of the super insulator remains cool.

Home Heating Most heating systems are designed to transfer heat by convection. In electric baseboard heating (Fig. 11-10), the source is the electric heater. Air which collides with the hot heater is warmed and rises. Cool air from near the floor flows in to take its place. As the hot air cools, it falls and returns to the heater. This process creates convection currents which carry heat to all parts of the room.

In hot water heating, steam from the furnace is piped to every radiator in the house by convection (Fig. 11-11). Heat is conducted from the steam to

Fig. 11-10 Convection current in a room heated with a baseboard electric heater

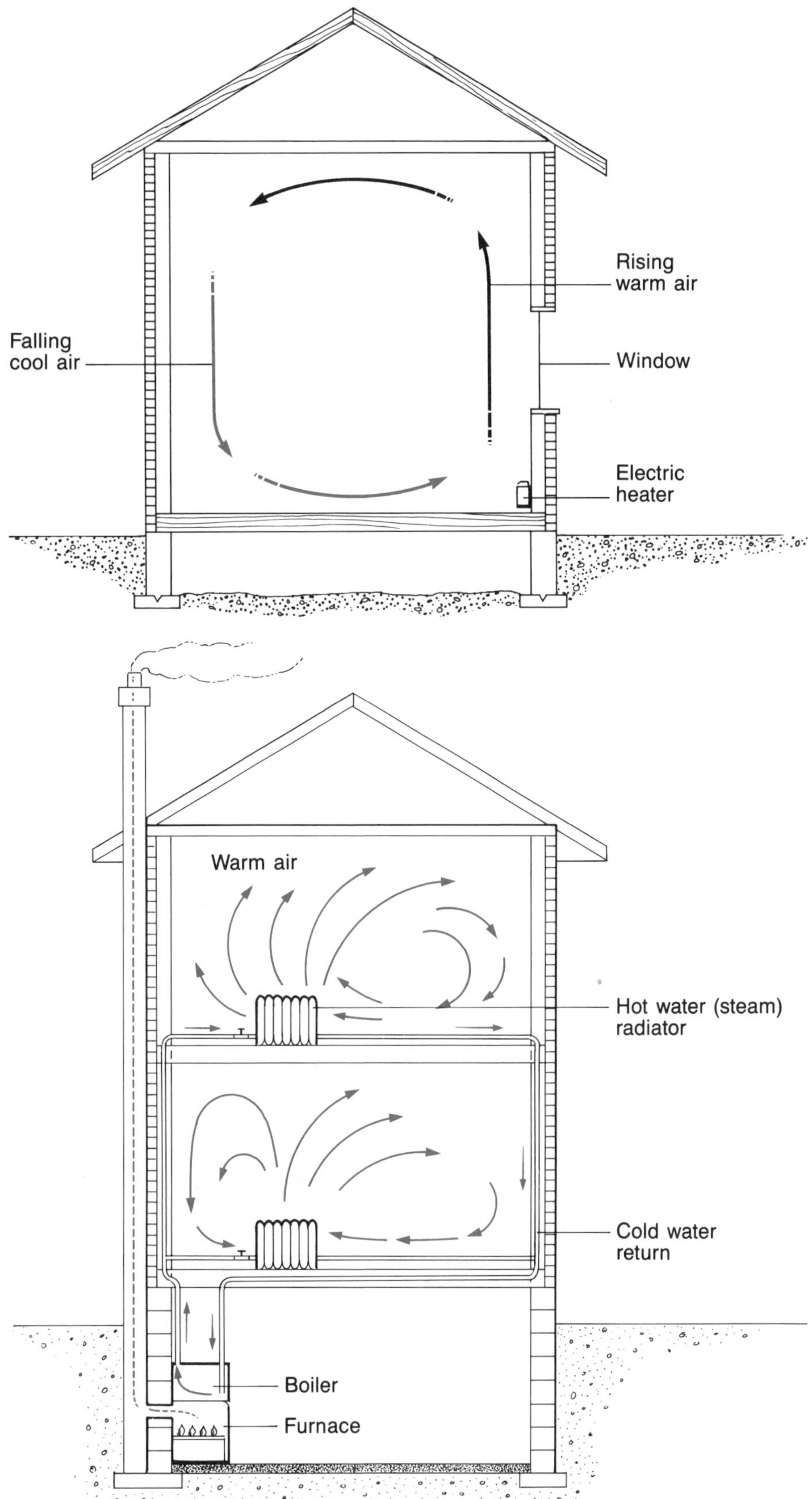

Fig. 11-11 Hot water heating system

Fig. 11-12 Hot air heating system

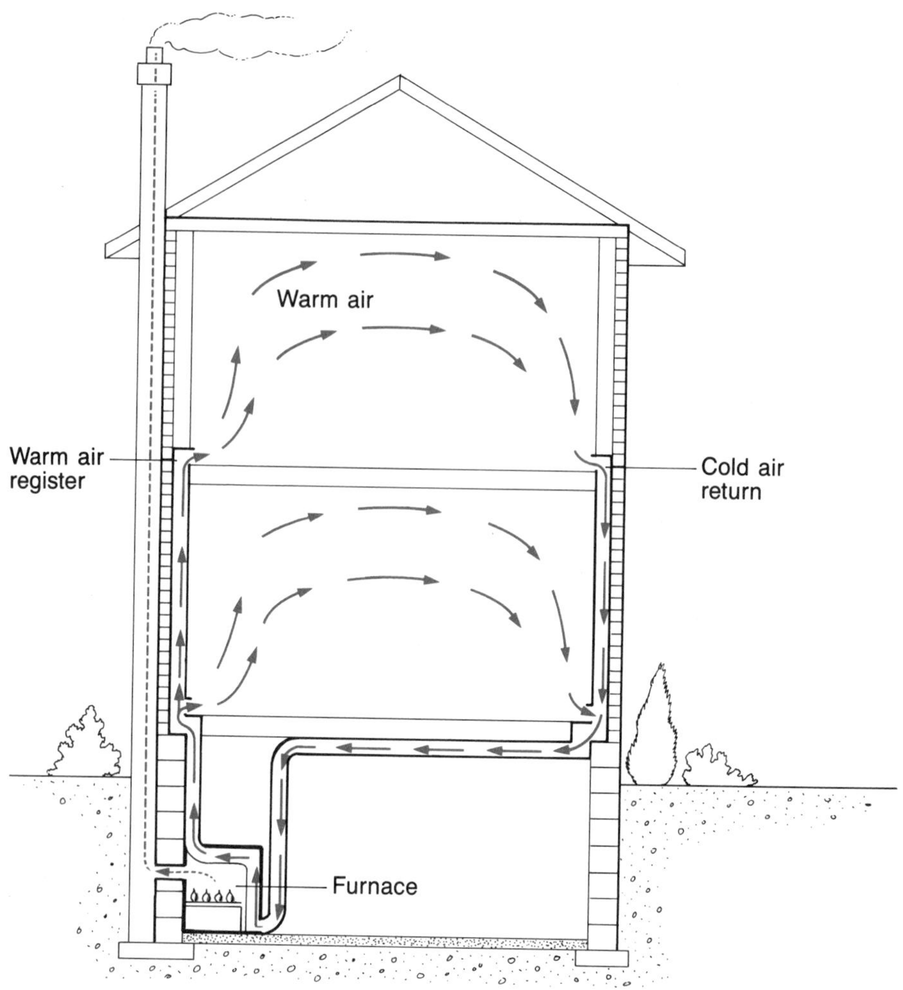

the radiator, and from the radiator to the air. There is also some radiation. (Radiation will be discussed later.) The air heats up and rises, setting up convection currents as with the electric heater. A similar process occurs with a hot air heating system (Fig. 11-12).

Hot Air Balloons A hot air balloon depends on the convection of hot gases for its operation. A fuel is burned to heat the air inside the balloon. Hot air is less dense than cold air. As a result, the balloon and its load rise. The balloon is returned to the earth by letting some of the hot air escape. Where should the openings in the balloon be to let the hot air escape?

Section Review

1. Based on conduction, should the floor of a bathroom be made of ceramic or vinyl tile? Explain.
2. Explain the function of the metal gauze in the Davy lamp.
3. Which is a better conductor of heat, loose rock wool or polyurethane slabs?
4. Explain the importance of the super insulation on the outside of the space shuttle having a high melting point.
5. Why do forced air heating systems require both hot air and cold air vents?

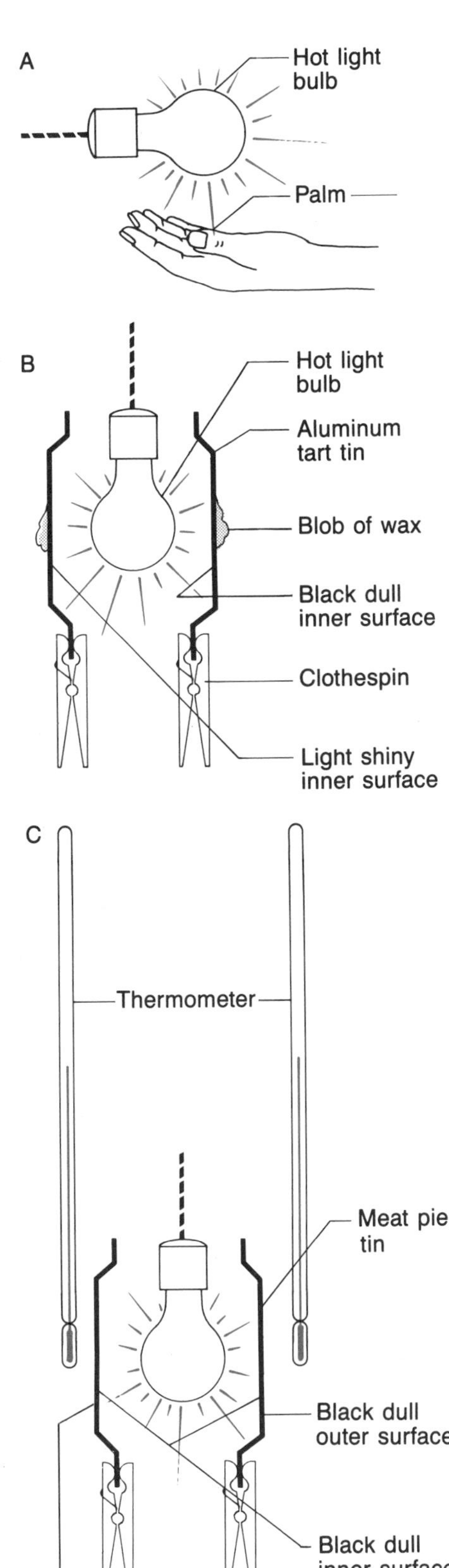

Fig. 11-13 Investigating the transfer of radiant energy

11.3 Activity: The Transfer of Radiant Energy

The third method of heat transfer is called radiation. **Radiation** is the process by which radiant energy travels. Light is one form of radiant energy; radio waves is another. Radiation is the only way energy can travel through empty space. However, radiant energy can also travel through air.

Problem

To study the travel, absorption, and emission of radiant energy.

Materials

timer
matches
candle
thermometers (2)
2 clothespins
incandescent light bulb (100 W)
small tart tin with both surfaces shiny
small tart tin with inside surface dull black and outside surface shiny
small meat pie tin with inside surface dull black and outside surface shiny
small meat pie tin with both surfaces dull black

Procedure A Travel

a. Set up the light bulb so that it points sideways as shown in Figure 11-13,A. Turn on the light bulb.

b. Face the palm of your hand toward the bulb and place it about 2 cm from the bulb. Hold your hand below, beside, and above the bulb. Determine if heat reaches your hand in each location.

Procedure B Absorption

a. Set up the light bulb so that it points down.

b. Use the candle to place a blob of wax on the centre of the outside surface of each tart tin.

c. Grasp each tart tin with a clothespin. Then bring the inner surface of each tin the same distance from the light bulb (Fig. 11-13,B).

d. Record the time it takes before the wax starts to melt on each tin.

Procedure C Emission

a. Grasp each meat pie tin with a clothespin. Bring the inner surface of each tin about 1 cm from the light bulb.

b. Have your partner hold the bulbs of the two thermometers vertically about 5 mm from the outside surface of each tin (Fig. 11-13,C).

c. Measure the temperature change of each thermometer during the same 2 min time interval.

Discussion

1. a) Describe the direction of heat travel by radiation.
   b) How does this compare to conduction? convection?
2. a) How are the two tart tins the same? different?
   b) On which tart tin did the wax melt first?
   c) What kind of surface has the greater ability to absorb radiant energy?
3. a) How are the meat pie tins the same? different?
   b) Which thermometer changed temperature the most?
   c) What kind of surface emits radiant energy better?

Extension

Predict the effect of the surface area of the emitter on the emission of radiant energy. Design and do an experiment using a tart tin and a meat pie tin to test your prediction.

11.4 Applications of Conduction, Convection, and Radiation

Fireplaces

A modern fireplace applies all three methods of heat transfer. Heat is transferred directly from the burning logs to the room by radiation. The fire is fed by convection currents originating in the room. Heat travels through the grate and the firebrick by conduction. Unfortunately, much of the warm room air is convected up the chimney with the combustion gases. This can be controlled by installing glass doors. Glass prevents convection, but transmits radiant energy to the room. Adjustable vents are included in the doors to control the air feeding the fire. The heating efficiency is further improved if a hollow chamber, called a **heatilator**, is installed around the firebox (Fig. 11-14). The walls next to the fire become very hot as a result of radiation. The steel conducts heat to the hollow chamber. Cool air enters near the bottom of the heatilator. It picks up heat from the metal walls, and exits at the top. The air cools as it circulates throughout the room. Eventually cool air returns to the heatilator to repeat the convection cycle. Unfortunately, a heatilator can only be installed at the time the fireplace is built. However, fireplace inserts have been designed to fit directly into the fireplace (Fig. 11-15). They operate on the same principle as the heatilator.

Thermos Bottles

A thermos bottle is designed to minimize heat transfer by all three methods (Fig. 11-16). The cap, the double-walled glass bottle, and the bottom support are poor conductors. So also is the air which surrounds the bottle. The inner and outer surfaces of the bottle are silvered. This minimizes transfer by radiation. A vacuum exists between the two walls of the bottle to stop convection.

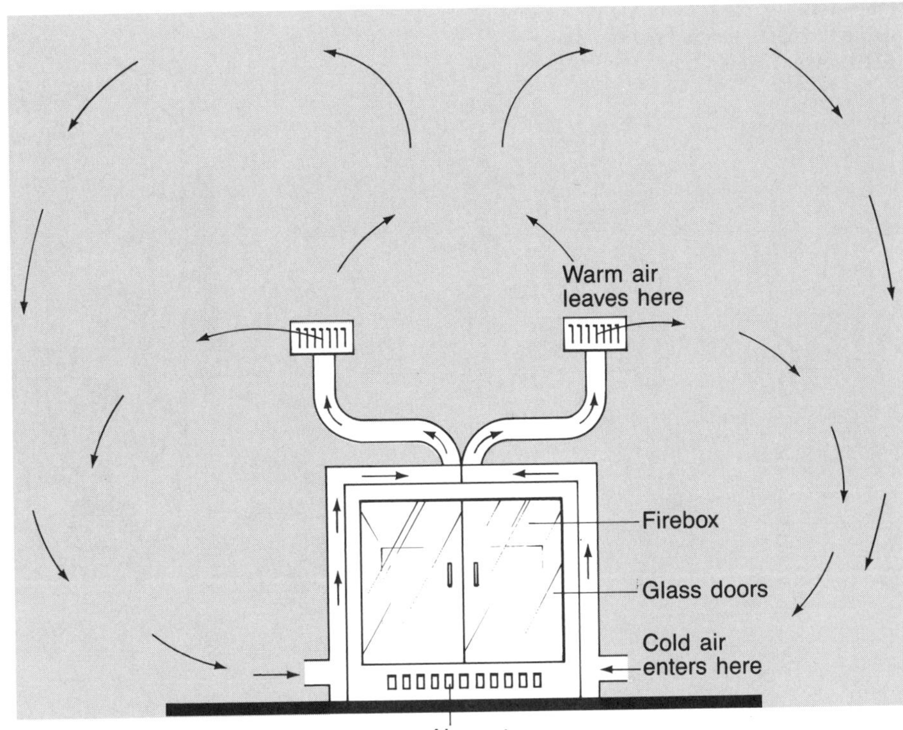

Fig. 11-14 **A fireplace with a heatilator heats the room by convection and radiation. Where does radiation take place?**

Fig. 11-15 **A fireplace insert**

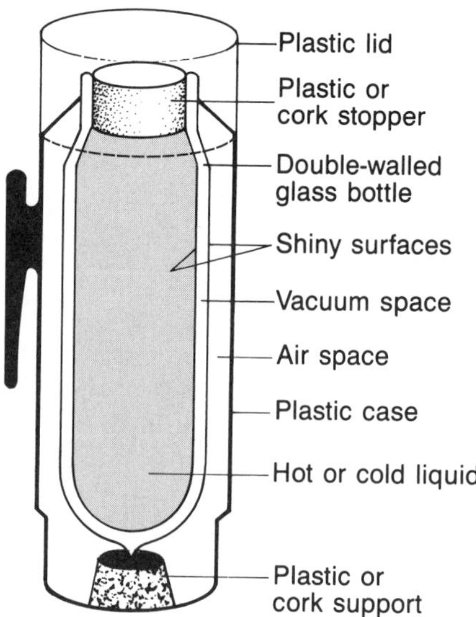

Fig. 11-16 A thermos bottle is designed to minimize heat transfer both ways. Explain how.

Have you ever wondered why the radiator of a car is painted black (Fig. 11-17)? A black surface is a much better radiator than a white surface. Hence, a black radiator loses its heat to the environment much more efficiently. To improve conduction between the liquid and the metal and the metal and the air, the car radiator has many small tubes through which the cooling liquid passes. This increases the surface area for conduction. Convection also plays a key role in dissipating the heat. For best convection the liquid from the engine enters the radiator at the top and exits from the bottom. Can you explain why?

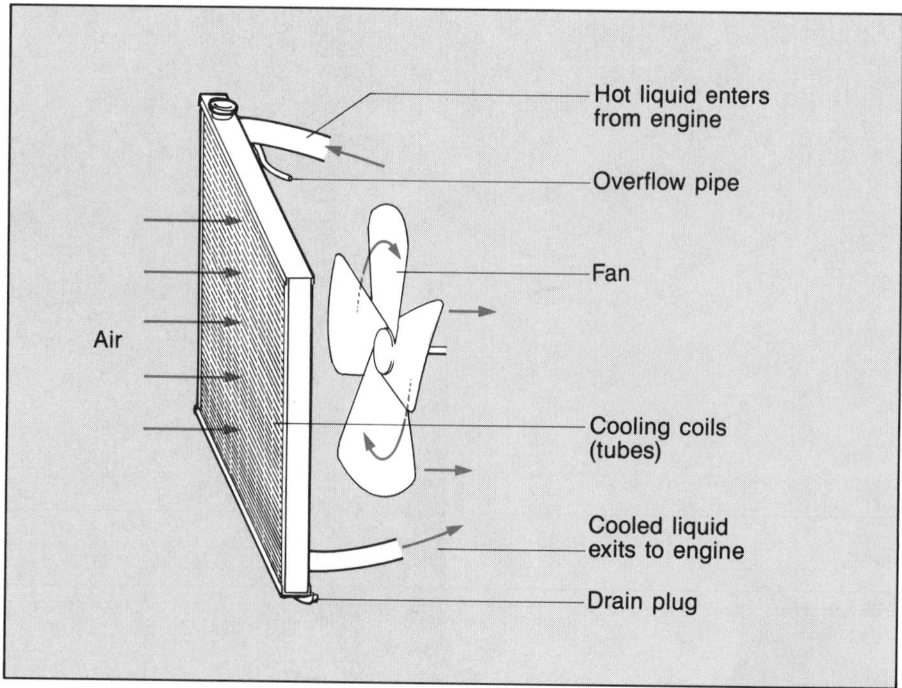

Fig. 11-17 A car radiator is painted black. Why?

Solar Collectors

A solar collector is designed to maximize the absorption of radiant energy. Then conduction and convection operate to transfer and store the thermal energy. A flat plate collector with air circulation and rock storage is shown in Figure 11-18. First, solar radiation is absorbed by the black metal plate. Then this heat is conducted to the adjacent air. Pumps and convection force the air through the rocks. Finally the rocks absorb heat by conduction. This cycle is continued as long as the sun shines.

The air is forced to take a different path at night. It travels from the warm rocks through the house and back again. In this way thermal energy stored in the rocks during the day is used to heat the home at night. Solar collectors and storage areas are more sophisticated than this. However, the same basic principles apply.

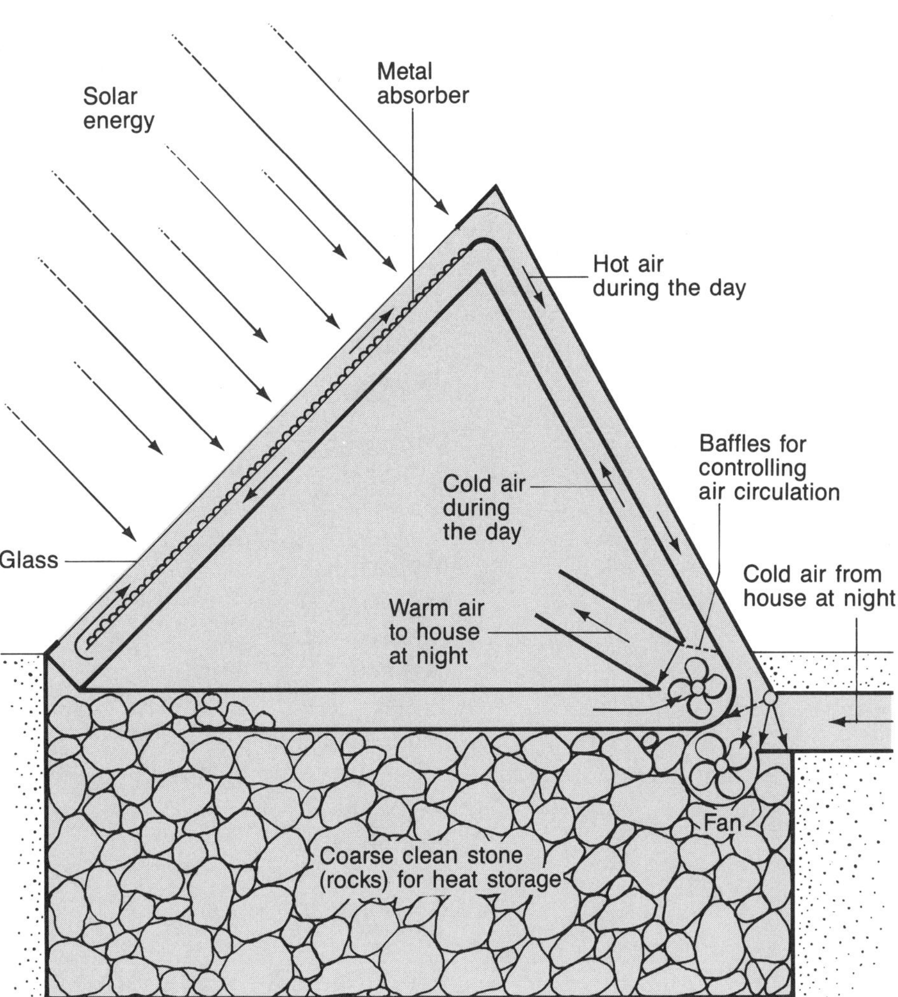

Fig. 11-18 A solar heating system. Where do each of radiation, convection, and conduction occur?

Thermography

Heat transfer also plays a key role in diagnosing areas of the body infected by diseases such as arthritis and cancer. Diseased areas are usually warmer than the surrounding tissue. Hence, more energy is conducted to the surface of the skin from these areas. A warmer surface radiates more heat than a cooler surface. Pictures taken of the body, using film sensitive to heat, pinpoint the hot spots. This process is called **thermography**. Thermographs are also taken of homes to pinpoint areas needing more insulation. Can you identify the role of convection in cooling the human body?

Section Review

1. What role do each of the following play in a heatilator or a fireplace insert:
   a) conduction? **b)** convection? **c)** radiation?
2. How is radiation minimized in a thermos bottle?
3. Why are the coils on the back of a refrigerator painted black?
4. Are fans really needed in flat plate collector systems like that shown in Figure 11-18? Discuss.
5. What is a thermograph and how is it used?

11.5 Activity: Thermal Expansion and Contraction

Solids, liquids, and gases expand when heated and contract when cooled. How do the expansions of two different liquids compare? Do all solids expand at the same rate? Make predictions. Then do the activity to test your predictions.

Problem

To compare the expansion of two different solids and two different liquids.

Materials

test tubes (2)
coloured water
coloured alcohol (ethyl)
masking tape
tongue depressor
coffee urn
ring stand
400 mL beaker
1 brass welding rod and 1 steel welding rod of the same length and diameter
1-hole rubber stoppers with 15 cm lengths of glass tubing inserted (2)
Bunsen burner
wooden block and scale
adjustable clamp
drinking straws

CAUTION: Do not bring the alcohol near the Bunsen burner flame.

Procedure A Expansion of Liquids

a. Fill one test tube with coloured water and the other with coloured ethyl alcohol.
b. Insert a one-hole rubber stopper and glass tube into each test tube. Wipe off the excess liquid.
c. Push down gently on the rubber stoppers and adjust the level of the liquids in the two glass tubes to the same level.

d. Use masking tape to mark the height of the liquid in each glass tube.

e. Half fill a 400 mL beaker with hot water from the coffee urn.

f. Partially immerse the two test tubes in the hot water as shown in Figure 11-19.

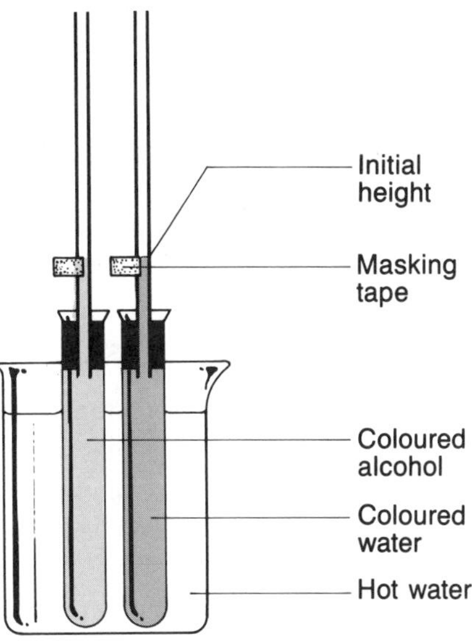

Fig. 11-19 Investigating the expansion of liquids

g. Mark the maximum height reached by each liquid after 2 min.

a. Wrap two turns of masking tape around one end of each welding rod to create a groove the same width as a tongue depressor (Fig. 11-20).

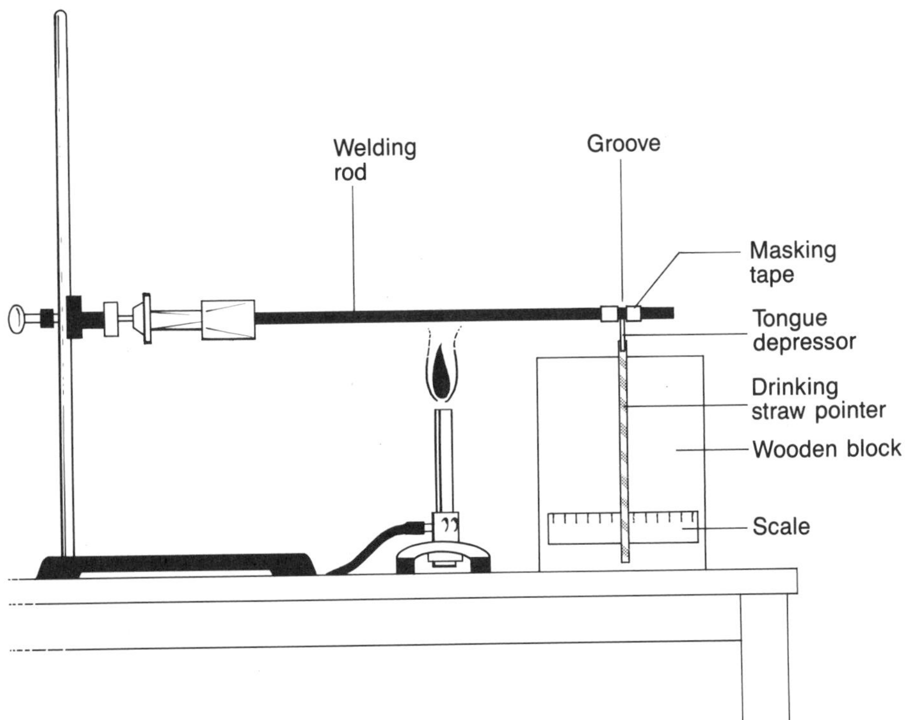

Fig. 11-20 Investigating the expansion of solids

b. Use masking tape to attach a drinking straw perpendicular to one end of the tongue depressor. This will act as a pointer.
c. Clamp the steel welding rod between the jaws of the adjustable clamp and rest the free end on the wooden block.
d. Place the tongue depressor between the wooden block and the groove on the welding rod as shown in Figure 11-20. Adjust the apparatus until the pointer is in the middle of the scale attached to the wooden block.
e. Adjust the Bunsen burner to give a low flame and heat the middle of the welding rod for about 1 min.
f. Record the number of scale divisions moved by the pointer.
g. Without adjusting the flame, repeat steps (c) to (f) for the brass welding rod.

Discussion

1. **a)** Compare the expansion of alcohol and water.
   b) What variables were controlled in this part of the experiment?
2. **a)** Compare the expansion of steel and brass.
   b) What variables were controlled in this part of the experiment?
   c) What variable was not controlled?
3. What generalization can you make about the expansion of different solids and different liquids?

Extension

Sketch the shape of the graph you expect to get if the level of a liquid in a glass tube is recorded at various temperatures. Design and perform an experiment using water to test your prediction.

11.6 Thermal Expansion and Measuring Temperature

Thermal Expansion

Most solids and liquids and all gases expand when heated and contract when cooled. Different solids expand different amounts for the same temperature change. For example, pyrex expands less than ordinary glass. Therefore, it is used to make test tubes because it doesn't break when heated quickly (Fig. 11-21). Different liquids also expand different amounts. Water above 20°C expands about three times as much as mercury does. Ethyl alcohol expands about six times as much as mercury.

Based on the behaviour of solids and liquids, one might predict that different gases expand different amounts. But in fact, most gases expand just about the same amount. This example points out the importance of gathering evidence to test predictions. Never jump to conclusions. In science, experiments are done to collect data and the data are carefully analyzed before conclusions are reached.

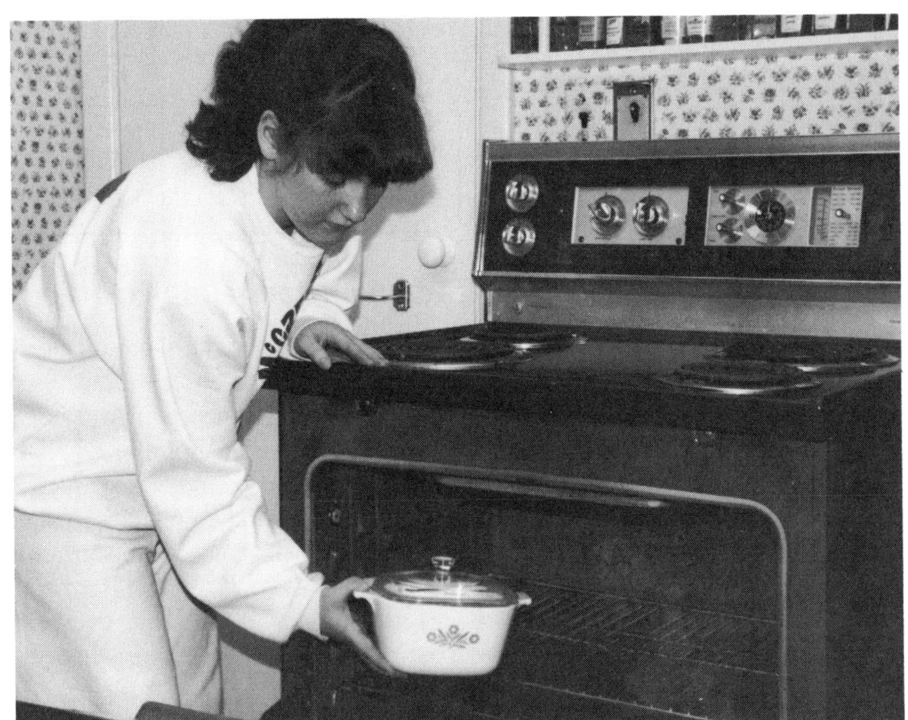

Fig. 11-21 Household dishes that can be put directly from the freezer into the oven are also made of pyrex or a material with similar properties. Why is this so?

A

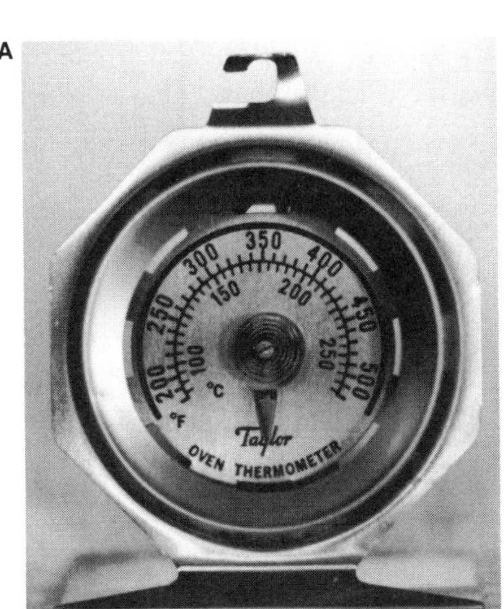

B

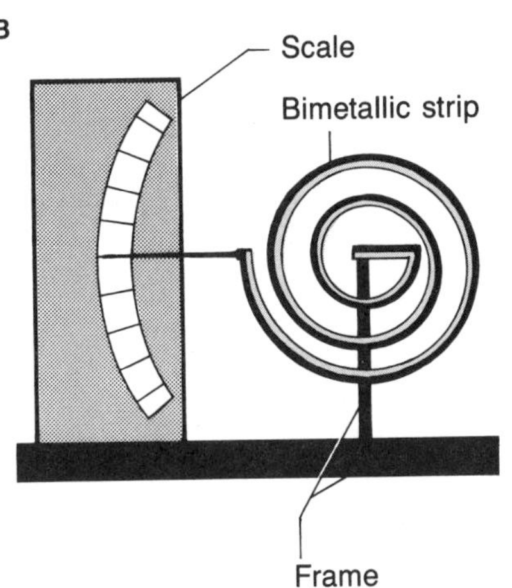

Fig. 11-22 If you look inside a dial thermometer (A), you can see the bimetallic strip (B). Why does this strip move the pointer when the temperature changes?

Thermal Expansion and Temperature

A **thermometer** is an instrument used to detect and measure temperature accurately. The change in the volume of gases, liquids, and solids with temperature is used in the design of most common thermometers. Fortunately, the volume changes of solids, liquids, and gases are linear over small ranges in temperature. That is, the volume of liquids like alcohol or mercury changes the same amount for the 10°C interval between say 10°C and 20°C as it does between 30°C and 40°C. This enables thermometers to be constructed that have scales divided into equal-sized increments.

The first thermometer invented by Galileo in 1592 depended on the expansion of a gas for its operation. Gas thermometers are very sensitive. Can you explain why?

A **dial thermometer** is based on the unequal expansion of different metals. It consists of two different metals with their sides attached to form a bimetallic strip (Fig. 11-22). The strip is wound in the form of a coil. One end is firmly attached to a frame. The other end is free to move and takes a specific position for each temperature. Metal thermometers can withstand high temperatures. As a result, some oven thermometers are of this type.

A **liquid thermometer** also depends on expansion. It has a thin glass bulb which is filled with a liquid (Fig. 11-23). The liquid expands up the bore in the glass tube. Most liquid thermometers contain alcohol or mercury. To see why, examine Table 11-2. Water freezes at 0°C and changes to a gas at 100°C. Mercury stays a liquid at high temperatures and alcohol stays a liquid at low temperatures. Which thermometer would you use in the Arctic? Why?

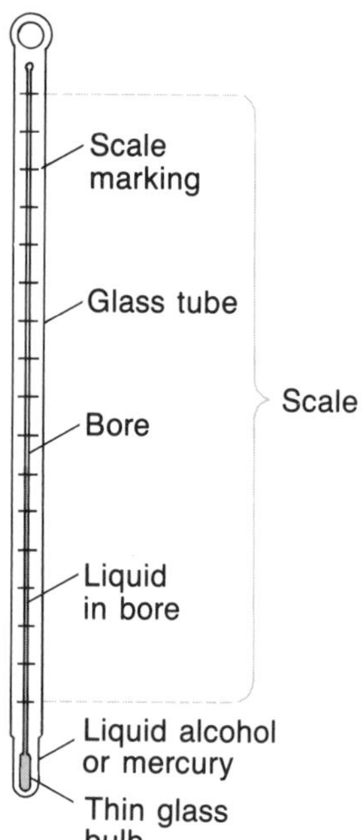

Fig. 11-23 The parts of a liquid thermometer

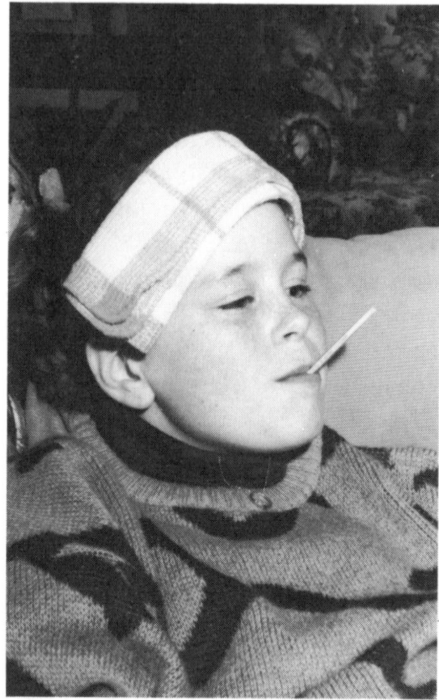

Fig. 11-24 You might find it interesting to take your temperature at regular intervals during the day for several days. Is there a relationship between your temperature and what you are doing? Does the time of day make a difference?

Table 11-2 Freezing and Boiling Points of Three Common Liquids

Liquid	*Freezing point (0°C)*	*Boiling point (0°C)*
Water	0	100
Alcohol (ethyl)	−118	78
Mercury	−39	320

Thermometers and Fixed Points

Until the mid-1600s, all thermometers had one major fault: they did not have a common scale. In order to have a common scale, thermometers must have the same two reference points. These reference points, or standard temperatures, are called **fixed points**. Once fixed points were identified, the interval between the fixed points was marked off into equal-sized divisions.

Common temperature reference points were difficult to find. Scientists looked for behaviours that always occurred at the same temperature. The freezing point of water is constant; therefore scientists chose it as one of the fixed points. Early thermometers used the temperature of the human body as the second fixed point. However, this proved to be unsuitable because body temperature varies slightly from person to person. In fact, a person's body temperature changes slightly during the day and when the person becomes ill (Fig. 11-24). Scientists finally chose the boiling point of water at normal atmospheric pressure as the second fixed point. Why do you think the pressure of the liquid is important?

The Celsius Temperature Scale

The temperature scale in common use today is the Celsius scale. The **scale** was determined by setting the freezing point of water at 0°C and the boiling point at 100°C. The interval between these two fixed points was then divided into 100 equal intervals known as **degrees Celsius**. The Celsius scale extends below 0°C using negative numbers; the coldest theoretical temperature is −273.15°C. It extends above 100°C without known limit. For example, deuterium nuclei reach a temperature of about 100 000 000°C before fusion takes place in the sun. The symbol °C is used to denote temperature intervals as well as specific temperatures. Thus normal body temperature is quoted as 37°C; a temperature rise of thirty-seven degrees Celsius is also written as 37°C.

Section Review

1. a) Describe temperature.

b) Two objects A and B are placed in contact. Object A has a higher temperature than object B.

(i) In which direction will heat flow?

(ii) How will their temperature change with time?

2. a) What characteristics do fixed points on temperature scales have in common?

b) For what temperature range can each of mercury and alcohol be used in modern thermometers?

c) Why is the temperature of the human body unsatisfactory as a fixed point on temperature scales?

11.7 Other Applications of Thermal Expansion

Have you ever noticed the spaces between the cement slabs on a sidewalk or on a concrete highway? These **expansion seams** allow for the expansion and contraction of the concrete as the temperature changes. Most substances expand when heated and contract when cooled. There are numerous applications of thermal expansion.

Applications of Linear Expansion

Engineers must allow for linear expansion and contraction when building steel structures such as bridges. One end of each span is fixed. The other end rests on rollers or skids which permit the bridge to expand and contract easily (Fig. 11-25). **Expansion grills** are included at the free end of each span to compensate for expansion and contraction (Fig. 11-26). The Burlington Skyway bridge has six expansion grills in a distance of 2.5 km. Expansion gaps are also needed in railway tracks.

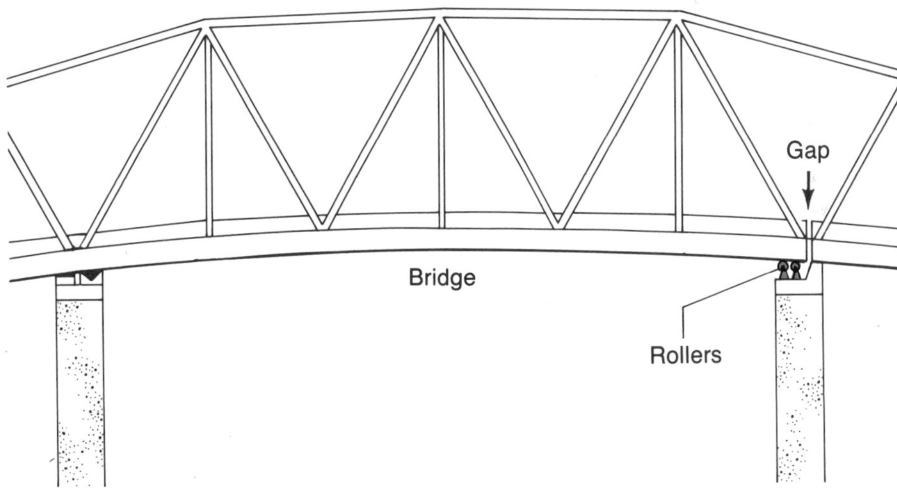

Fig. 11-25 Why is one end of the span fixed and the other end free on rollers?

Fig. 11-26 An expansion joint on a bridge roadway compensates for the expansion and contraction of the roadway as the temperature changes. During which season was this photograph taken?

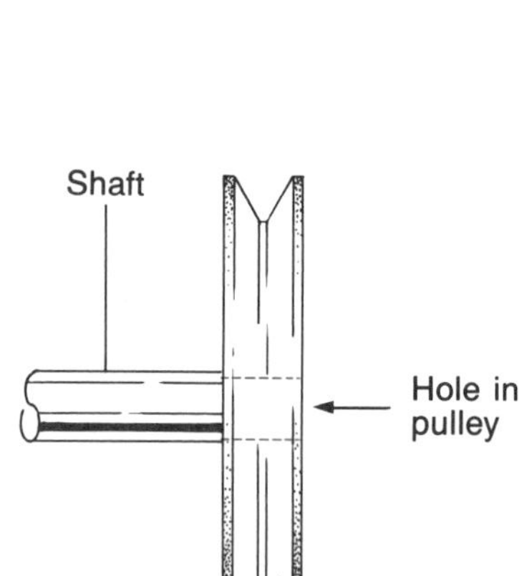

Fig. 11-27 Why is the hole in the pulley only slightly smaller than the shaft?

Machinists fit steel tires on the rims of train wheels using thermal expansion and contraction. The tire is machined slightly smaller than the rim at room temperature. The tire is then expanded and fitted onto the rim by heating it above room temperature. When the tire cools it shrinks and fits securely on the rim. The same procedure is sometimes used to fit collars and pulleys onto shafts (Fig. 11-27).

Another application of linear thermal expansion is the thermostat. A **thermostat** consists of a bimetallic strip—two metal strips such as brass and iron with different abilities to expand. These strips are welded or bolted together and bent into a spiral as shown in Figure 11-28. One end of the bimetallic strip is attached to the control ring and the other is free to move. When the temperature changes, the unequal expansion of the two metals causes the strip to bend. This changes the slope of the glass envelope and the mercury flows to make or break the electrical circuit. This arrangement is called a **mercury switch**. Metallic oven thermometers, balance wheels for some watches, and circuit breakers also make use of differential expansion.

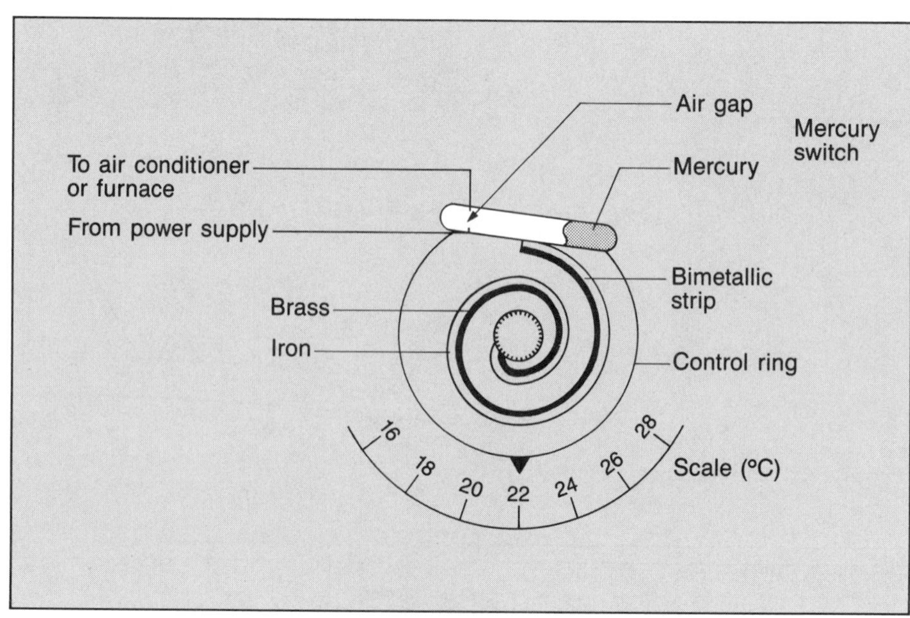

Fig. 11-28 A thermostat and a mercury switch

Applications of Volume Expansion

When an object changes temperature, every dimension expands or contracts. Thus the length of the sides, the surface area, and the volume changes. In liquids and gases we are concerned only with volume expansion, since they take the shape of their container.

Drivers of gasoline-powered motor vehicles must consider volume expansion for two reasons. As the temperature of the tires increases, so also does the volume of the air in the tire and hence the tire pressure. Knowledgeable drivers monitor tire pressure on long trips. Also, because solids expand at a slower rate than liquids, a gasoline tank which is overfilled may overflow as the temperature increases.

Section Review

1. What is the difference between linear and volume expansion?
2. A mechanic finds an aluminum nut locked tightly on a steel bolt. Aluminum expands more than steel for the same temperature change. Should the mechanic cool or heat the combination to loosen the nut?
3. Long steam pipes often contain a U-shaped section. Why?
4. Electrical transmission lines sag more in the summer than the winter. Why?
5. Explain why a gasoline tank filled too full will overflow if left in the sun.

11.8 The Kinetic Molecular Theory of Heat

What Is a Theory?

Scientists make up theories to explain observations. A **scientific theory** consists of a set of assumptions or postulates which are used to explain observations and make predictions. If the theory explains all the observations it is considered a good theory. However, if it cannot explain the observations, it must be changed or discarded. A theory is tested by predicting the results of new experiments. (*Note*: If this summary has not refreshed in your mind the meaning of theory, you should read the Introduction again.) The modern theory of heat is based on the **Particle Theory** of matter.

Postulates of the Particle Theory

Some key postulates of the Particle Theory are:

- All matter is made up of particles called molecules.
- The distance between molecules is large compared to the size of the molecules.
- The molecules are held together by electric forces.
- The molecules attract one another at certain distances.
- If they are closer than this distance they repel one another.

Figure 11-29 shows an array of molecules making up a solid. The electric forces between molecules are drawn as elastic springs. Such springs do not

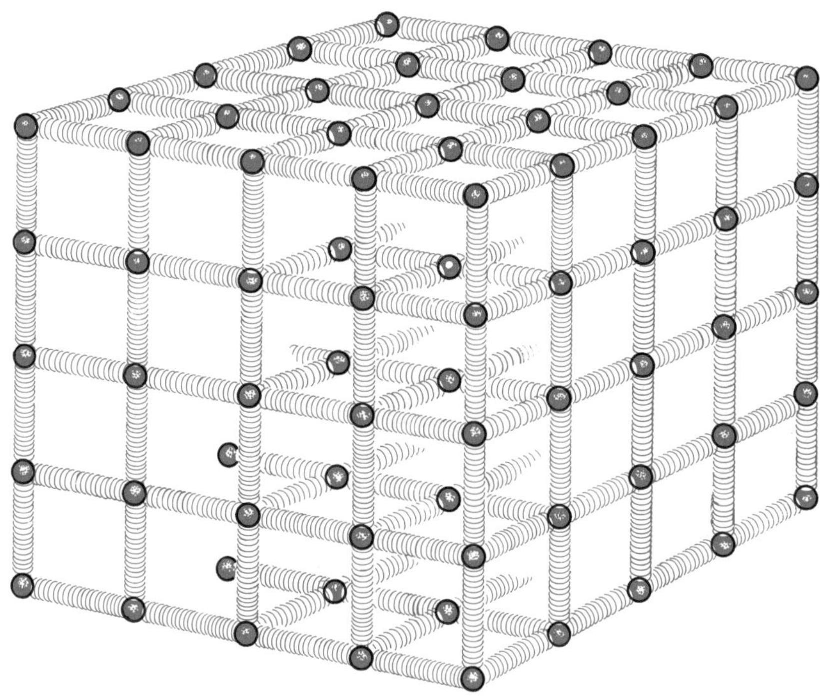

Fig. 11-29 A model of a cubic array of molecules making up a solid. The springs represent electric forces.

exist, but they provide a simple and useful model. The coils attract when stretched and repel when pushed together. Molecules behave in a similar way.

Postulates of the Kinetic Molecular Theory

The presently accepted theory of heat is called the **Kinetic Molecular Theory**. The postulates of the Kinetic Molecular Theory are:

- Heat is a form of energy.
- This energy is carried by molecules.
- Molecules have two kinds of energy: elastic potential energy and kinetic energy.
- Elastic potential energy results from the electric force between molecules.
- Kinetic energy results from the motion of the molecules.
- Energy is continually being converted between these two forms.
- The molecules of matter are always moving.

Fig. 11-30 If you pound a nail into hard wood, you can feel the nail get warmer. Where did the heat come from? Does the hammer get warmer too?

Explanations Using the Kinetic Molecular Theory

The Kinetic Molecular Theory can explain the source of heat. When two substances are rubbed together, this causes the molecules to move faster and is sensed as heat. If you pound a nail with a hammer, the molecules move faster and the nail gets warmer (Fig. 11-30). Suppose a Bunsen burner heats an iron rod. The molecules leaving the heat source move very fast. They collide with the molecules of iron, causing the molecules of iron to move faster and the rod to heat up.

The Kinetic Molecular Theory explains expansion and contraction. When matter is heated the molecules move faster. They jostle one another and move

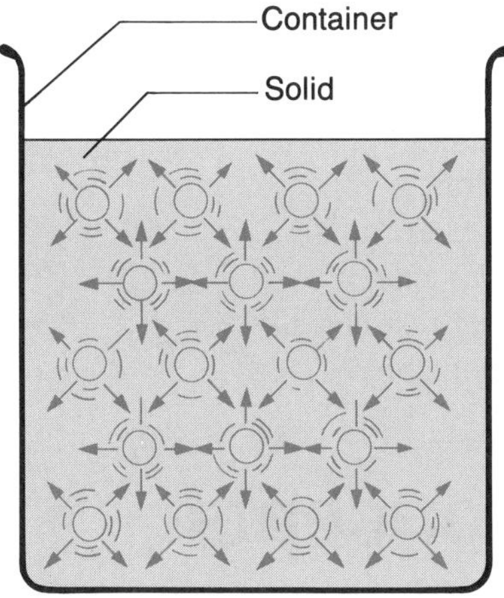

Fig. 11-31 In solids the molecules do not move from place to place. They vibrate back and forth.

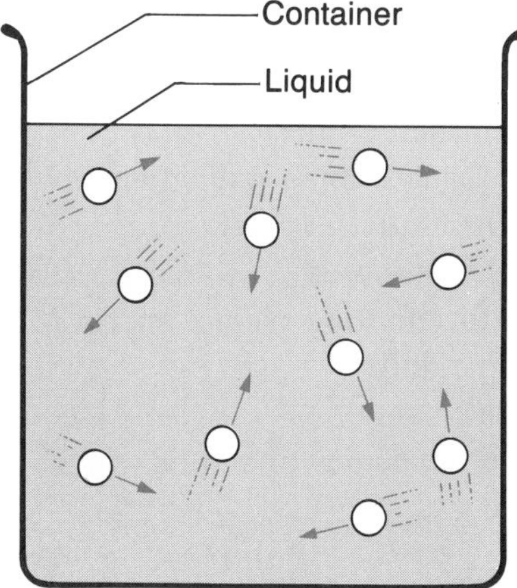

Fig. 11-32 In liquids the molecules are further apart and move from place to place.

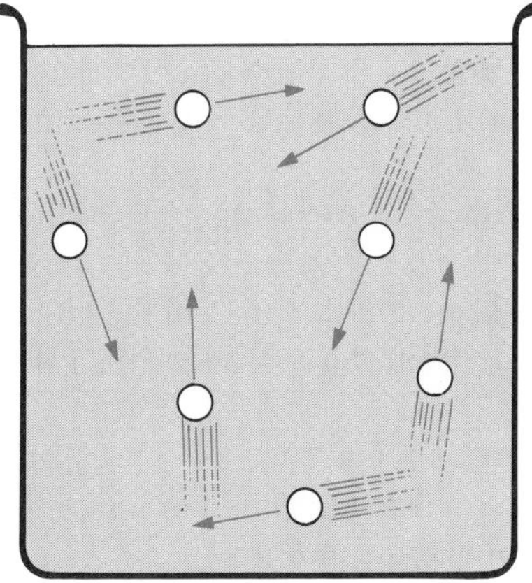

Fig. 11-33 In gases the molecules are very far apart and move very quickly. They also move apart until they fill the entire container.

further apart, causing the matter to expand. During cooling the molecules move more slowly. The slower molecules are attracted closer together and the matter contracts.

The theory explains conduction and convection. In solids the molecules are in fixed positions (Fig. 11-31). They cannot move from place to place; therefore convection does not occur. But they can vibrate back and forth. Hot molecules vibrate faster than cold ones, and they cause adjacent molecules to vibrate faster. This is how heat is transferred from molecule to molecule in a solid. This is how conduction takes place.

In liquids the vibrating molecules are further apart. As a result, little conduction occurs in liquids. However, the molecules in liquids are not in fixed positions. They can move from place to place (Fig. 11-32). The molecules of a hot liquid are further apart than those of a cold liquid. As a result, the hot liquid is less dense and it rises. This is how convection takes place.

In gases the molecules are very far apart (Fig. 11-33). As a result, conduction does not occur. The molecules are moving very fast, so convection takes place quickly. However, if the path for the travel of the molecules is limited, convection decreases. This explains why materials such as styrofoam, which contain small air pockets, are good insulators.

The Kinetic Molecular Theory also explains the constant temperature that accompanies a change in state. **Temperature** is a measure of the average kinetic energy of the molecules in a substance. When heat is added to ice at 0°C it forms water at 0°C. During melting, the average vibrational kinetic energy of the molecules stays the same. Therefore, the temperature stays constant during melting. However, the heat increases the elastic energy of the molecules. This elastic energy permits the molecules to break out of their fixed positions. The ice at 0°C has melted to become water at 0°C.

Section Review

1. List the postulates of the Particle Theory of Matter.
2. List the postulates of the Kinetic Molecular Theory of heat.
3. Use the Kinetic Molecular Theory to explain each of the following:
   a) expansion in liquids
   b) why conduction occurs in solids but not in gases
   c) why convection occurs in liquids but not in solids
   d) the constant temperature during the freezing of water

Chapter Highlights

1. Thermal energy being transferred is called heat.
2. Heat travels in solids by conduction.
3. Heat travels in fluids (liquids and gases) by convection.
4. Heat travels in all directions in space by radiation.
5. Black dull surfaces are the best absorbers and emitters of radiant energy.
6. There are many applications of heat transfer.
7. Expansion and contraction of solids and liquids have many applications.
8. The Kinetic Molecular Theory says that heat is caused by the motion of the particles that make up matter.

Key Terms

conduction
convection
energy
heat
insulators
Kinetic Molecular Theory
Particle Theory
radiation
temperature
thermostat
thermal energy
thermal resistance value
thermography

Recognizing the Concepts

Each of the following statements or questions is followed by four responses. Choose the correct response in each case. (Do not write in this book.)

1. Heat is distributed through a liquid mainly by
a) conduction **b)** convection **c)** expansion **d)** radiation

2. Where should ice be placed in a picnic cooler for the best cooling effect throughout the cooler?
a) at the top
b) at the bottom
c) at the sides
d) it doesn't matter

3. Which of the following is the best surface for absorbing radiant energy?
a) black, dull
b) black, shiny
c) light, dull
d) light, shiny

4. Which of the following is the best surface for emitting radiant energy?
a) black, dull
b) black, shiny
c) light, dull
d) light, shiny

5. The Kinetic Molecular Theory says that the molecules of a solid
a) move about more slowly than those of a gas
b) cannot move
c) move about more slowly than those of a liquid
d) vibrate back and forth about one spot

Understanding the Concepts

1. a) What is the difference between thermal energy and heat energy?
b) Use an example to show that the end form of elastic energy is thermal energy.

2. a) Why is the hot water return to the radiator of a car at the top and not at the bottom?
b) Why is a hot air furnace placed in the basement rather than in the attic?
c) Why does air in a hot air balloon escape from the top rather than the bottom?

3. Why is an air tight stove more efficient than a fireplace?

4. Which expands more for the same temperature change, a solid or a liquid?

5. Why is mercury used in some thermometers and alcohol in others?

6. The metal lid of a glass jar can be loosened by placing the jar in hot water. Why does this help?

7. Use the Kinetic Molecular Theory to explain the expansion of a liquid and conduction in a solid.

Applying the Concepts

1. Exposed hot water pipes are sometimes wrapped with fibreglass insulation. But fibreglass is a better conductor than air. Why wrap the pipes?
2. Why does a metal rod inserted into a roast make it cook faster?
3. a) Explain the role convection plays in the operation of a glider plane.
   b) Should the glider pilot fly in the morning or the afternoon, or does it matter? Explain.
4. A thick glass is more likely to crack than a thin one when both are filled with hot water. Why?
5. Explain why the pressure inside tires increases during driving.
6. Sally notices that a train ride is more bumpy in the winter than in the summer. She asks you why. What is your explanation?
7. Use the Kinetic Molecular Theory to explain
   a) why different liquids expand different amounts for the same temperature change
   b) the expansion of a metallic bridge in summer
   c) the constant temperature that accompanies the change in state from water to steam

Investigations

Fig. 11-34 Watch your teacher's technique closely as he or she shows you how to make a thermometer.

1. Design and do an experiment to show that conduction occurs in all directions while convection occurs only in the vertical direction.
2. Design and perform an experiment to compare the insulating ability of styrofoam, fibreglass, cellulose fibre, and air. Make sure you control all variables.
3. What effect might compacting fibreglass have on its insulating ability? Why? Design and do an experiment to test your prediction. Make sure you control the variables.
4. Kitchen aluminum foil has one side shiny and the other side dull. Which side should be on the outside when you wrap potatoes for baking? Make an hypothesis about the cooking time and the way the potatoes are wrapped. Design and do an experiment to test your prediction.
5. Design an experiment to test the hypothesis ''A rubber band expands when heated and contracts when cooled.'' Check the experimental design with your teacher.
6. Ask your teacher to demonstrate how to make an alcohol thermometer from soft glass tubing (Fig. 11-34). Then, under your teacher's supervision, make a thermometer. Use water baths at temperatures of 0°C and 50°C to calibrate your thermometer. *Caution: Hot glass and alcohol are dangerous! Follow your teacher's instructions closely.*

Career: *CERAMICS ENGINEER*

HELP WANTED:
CERAMICS ENGINEER
A large automobile manufacturer requires a ceramics engineer to work on the design of an improved turbine engine for use in cars and trucks.

A ceramics engineer is concerned with the design, development, and analysis of all materials used in engineering works. Included are ceramics, glasses, metals and their alloys, polymers, and composites. Engineers test strength, hardness, durability, corrosion, wear resistance, and temperature effects.

A ceramics engineer studies the problems of producing desirable products out of ceramics. For example, ceramics engineers are trying to improve the efficiency of engines by making turbine engines out of ceramics. They analyze samples of ceramics at various stages of production and investigate improved production and fabrication techniques. They advise operations personnel on process changes and prepare a cost budget. The engineer also supervises technologists and technicians as they implement the procedures.

People interested in this career must be able to communicate clearly and must enjoy working with large and small groups of people. Above average ability in mathematics and the physical sciences is necessary. In addition, they must enjoy applying scientific principles to solve technological problems. A Bachelor of Engineering degree is required. McMaster University offers the only ceramics engineering program in Canada. Students are required to work in the ceramics industry during the summer between the third and fourth year. To practise as a professional engineer in Ontario, the graduate must pass a closed book examination set by the Professional Engineers of Ontario, and join the Association.

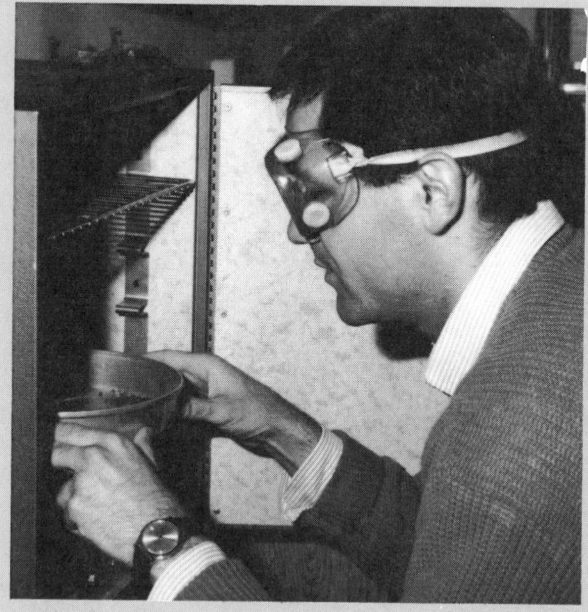

VISTA

LOW-EMISSIVITY WINDOWS

About 15% of the energy used in Canada goes into heating homes. A third of this can be saved by minimizing heat transfer. Such simple measures as installing double-glazed or triple-glazed windows, insulating walls and roofs, and plugging holes help tremendously. But this approach is like wrapping the building in a heavy overcoat. New discoveries are making it possible to turn the skin of the building into a semi-permeable membrane; preventing heat from entering or leaving, but transmitting light both ways.

Most of the heat wasted from buildings escapes through windows. However, new windows are being designed that trap heat inside in the winter and reflect it outside in the summer. These windows are referred to as **low-emissivity** or "**low-e**" windows. Standard insulated windows consist of two panes of glass separated by a 1 cm air gap. In low-e windows the outer surface of the inner pane is coated with a thin film of metal or metal oxide. This fragile coating is only a few hundred atoms thick. But it reflects the heat energy radiated by all the warm indoor objects (Fig. A). Thus the low-e window traps heat indoors, providing the same insulating value as would a third pane of glass. This is achieved at a lower cost with a much lighter window.

Low-e glass is designed to trap heat inside. However, it also prevents heat from sources other than sunlight from entering the building. And it does this while transmitting valuable sunlight. The metallic or metallic oxide layer reflects back outside the long-wavelength infrared radiation from hot buildings, asphalt, pavement, and motor vehicles.

Some manufacturers are placing the low-e coating on a polyester membrane halfway between the two layers of glass. This has the advantage of adding a second air space and decreasing heat transfer by convection (Fig. B). It also helps protect the delicate reflective coating against the damaging effects of touch and atmospheric exposure.

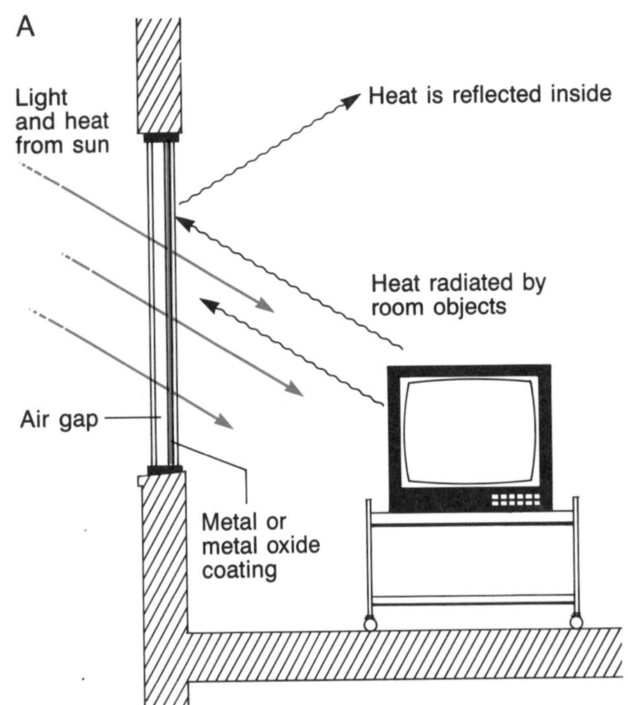

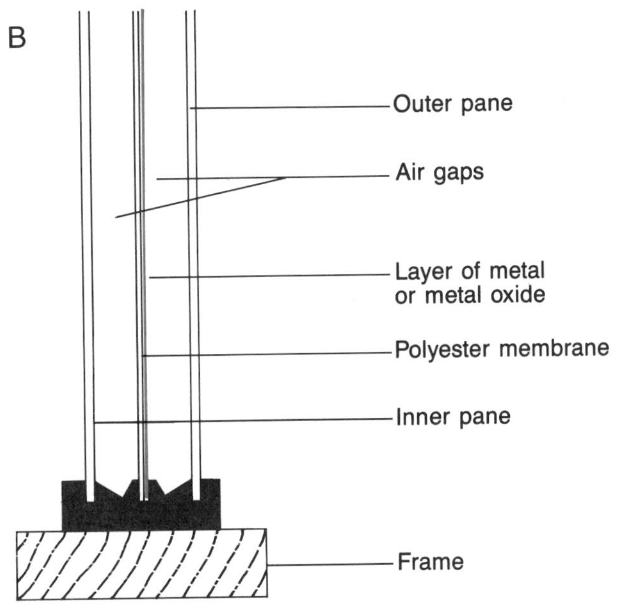

A new transparent material called **aerogel** is also under development. It is one of the few known porous materials that traps air, but is transparent to ordinary light. A 1 cm slab of aerogel sandwiched for support between two panes of glass bottles heat eight times as efficiently as a conventional double-glazed window. This performance arises from the material's structure. Particles of pure silica are hooked together to form pockets of air only a billionth of a metre in diameter (Fig. C). Millions of air molecules are isolated from one another by the silica. This minimizes the transfer of heat by convection. Who knows, we may soon be living in homes with windows having the same thermal resistance as walls!

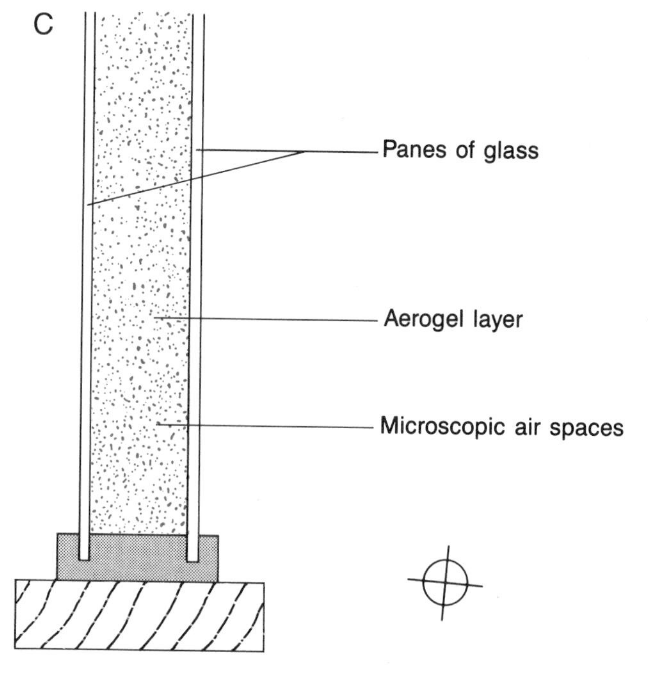

12 Quantity of Heat

CHAPTER CONTENTS

CHAPTER OBJECTIVES

After completing this chapter you should be able to:

1. Distinguish between thermal energy, heat, and temperature.
2. Sketch and describe the heating and cooling curves for a pure substance.
3. Describe the three factors that affect the quantity of heat.
4. Distinguish between heat capacity and specific heat capacity.
5. Solve problems involving heat capacity and specific heat capacity.
6. Apply the Principle of Heat Exchange to experiments and problems.
7. Determine the specific heat capacity of a substance.

You learned last year that heat can change the temperature and the state of a substance (Fig. 12-1). How can we tell how much the temperature will change? Does the mass of the substance make any difference? Does the kind of material affect the temperature change? If two liquids or a liquid and solid are mixed, how is the heat transferred? What principle describes the heat exchange? You will find answers to these and other questions in this chapter.

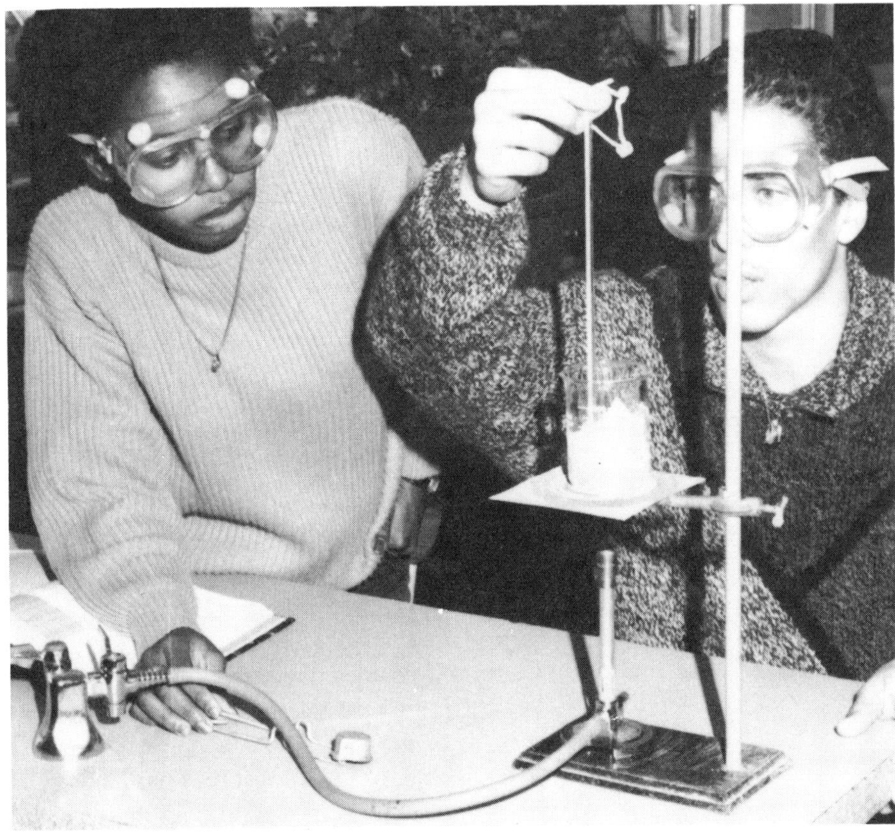

Fig. 12-1 What happens to the temperature when ice is slowly melted? What happens to the temperature after the ice is melted?

12.1 Temperature, Thermal Energy, and Heat

Marija claims that temperature and heat are two words which refer to the same thing. Jackie claims that they have entirely different meanings. Who is correct? Read on and find out.

Temperature

Temperature is a measure of the average kinetic energy of the molecules making up an object. Temperature determines the direction of heat flow. Heat flows from an object at a higher temperature to an object at a lower temperature. This occurs because the molecules of the hotter object move faster than the molecules of the cooler object. When the faster and slower molecules collide, the slower molecules speed up and the faster molecules slow down (Fig. 12-2). Heat ceases to flow when the two objects reach the same temperature because at the same temperature the molecules have the same average kinetic energy. A thermometer measures only the average kinetic energy of the molecules striking the bulb.

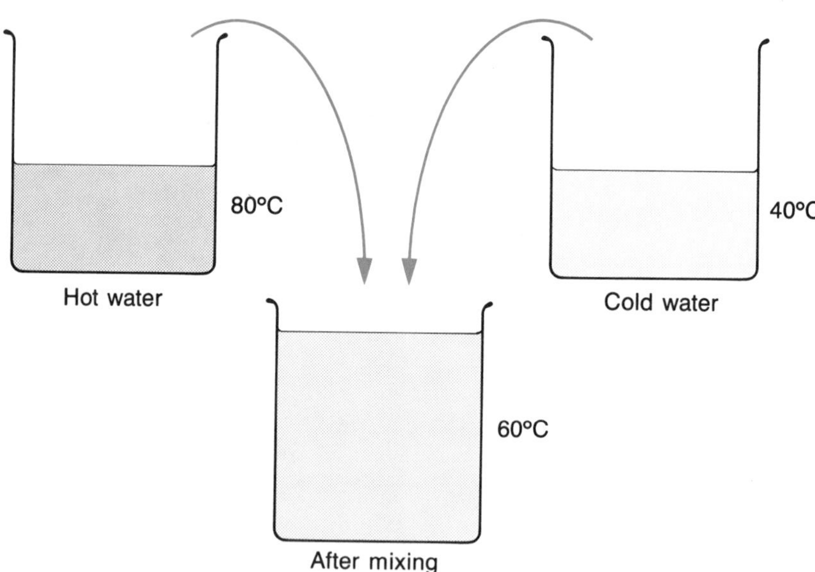

Fig. 12-2 The molecules in a hot liquid move faster than those in a cold liquid. When mixed, the molecules move at about the same average speed.

Thermal Energy and Temperature

Molecules have two kinds of energy. One is elastic energy due to the electric force between the particles. Another is kinetic energy due to the random motion of the particles. **Thermal energy** is the total elastic and kinetic energy an object has as a result of the random motion of its particles. Figure 12-3 shows two cubes of a solid with the same mass. One cube is at a higher temperature

t = 200°C
m = 1 unit

t = 400°C
m = 1 unit

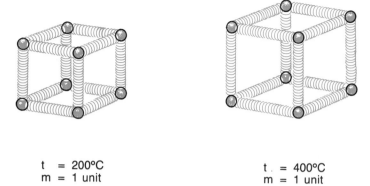

Fig. 12-3 Thermal energy and temperature when the mass is the same. There is more thermal energy in a cube at a temperature of 400°C than in a cube at 200°C when both have the same mass.

than the other. As a result its molecules are vibrating faster and have a greater than average kinetic energy. Note that the hotter cube also occupies more space. Its molecules are further apart and have more elastic energy than the cooler cube. The mass of the two cubes is the same, but the cube at a higher temperature has more thermal energy.

Thermal Energy and the Number of Molecules

Temperature is a measure of the *level* of thermal energy. But temperature does not measure the *quantity* of thermal energy. For example, a cup and a kettle of boiling water have the same temperature. Thus the water molecules in both have the same average kinetic energy. But there is more thermal energy in the kettle than in the cup (Fig. 12-4). This is because there are more molecules in the kettle.

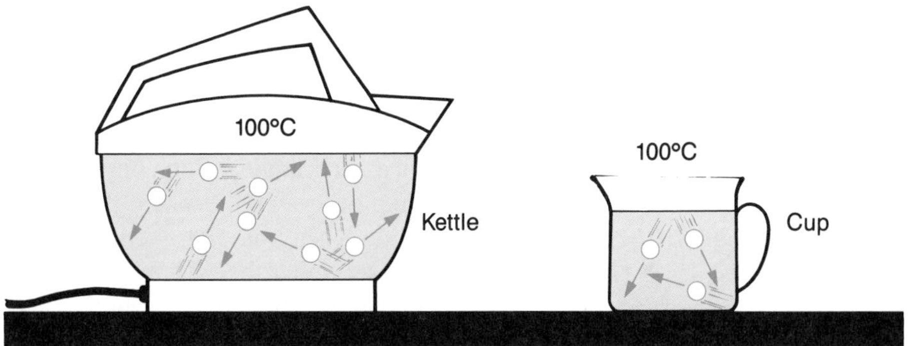

Fig. 12-4 There is more thermal energy in a kettle of hot water than in a cup when both are at the same temperature.

Thermal Energy and Heat

Suppose we add thermal energy to a cube using a hot flame. The molecules in the gas in the hot flame are moving at high speeds. They possess a great deal of thermal energy. As they strike the cube, some of their kinetic energy is transferred to the molecules making up the cube. On average, the molecules in the cube now vibrate faster and are further apart. As a result, the thermal energy of the cube increases. Thermal energy transferred from one substance to another is called **heat**. Heat may be added to or removed from a given material. However, heat travels naturally from a substance at a higher temperature into a substance at a lower temperature.

Heat is not always transferred from a substance with more thermal energy into a substance with less thermal energy. For example, there is twice as much thermal energy in 100 g of boiling water as in 50 g of boiling water. But, since both are at the same temperature, no heat is transferred when they are mixed.

Heat can be transferred from a substance with less thermal energy to a substance with more thermal energy. A hot piece of charcoal has much less thermal energy than a swimming pool. However, if the charcoal is submerged in the swimming pool, heat flows from the hotter charcoal to the cooler water.

Section Review

1. a) Define thermal energy.
b) What two kinds of energy make up thermal energy?
2. a) What is temperature?
b) Distinguish between thermal energy and temperature. Use an example.
3. a) Define heat.
b) Distinguish between thermal energy and heat. Use an example.
4. Compare the amount of thermal energy in each of the following:
a) a hammer and a nail, both at 30°C
b) a kettle of boiling water and a cup of boiling water
c) a cup of coffee at 80°C and a cup of coffee at 60°C
d) 20 kg of hydrogen at −260°C and 10 kg of hydrogen at 100°C

12.2 Activity: Heat and the Temperature of Water

Provided the flame remains unchanged, a Bunsen burner is a constant source of heat. In this activity you add heat at a constant rate to melting ice. After the ice is all melted, you continue heating the resulting water and, finally, the boiling water. You measure the temperature at equal time intervals during the heating. Then you plot a temperature-time graph of the data.

Before doing the activity, sketch the temperature-time graph you expect to get with time plotted on the horizontal axis. Then do the activity to check your prediction.

Problem

What is the shape of a temperature-time graph as ice melts, water warms to the boiling point, and water boils?

Materials

ring stand, iron ring, adjustable clamp, wire gauze
finely crushed ice (or snow) — Bunsen burner
250 mL beaker — string

stirring rod
watch or clock
thermometer

CAUTION: Wear safety goggles during this activity. Be careful when you work with hot water.

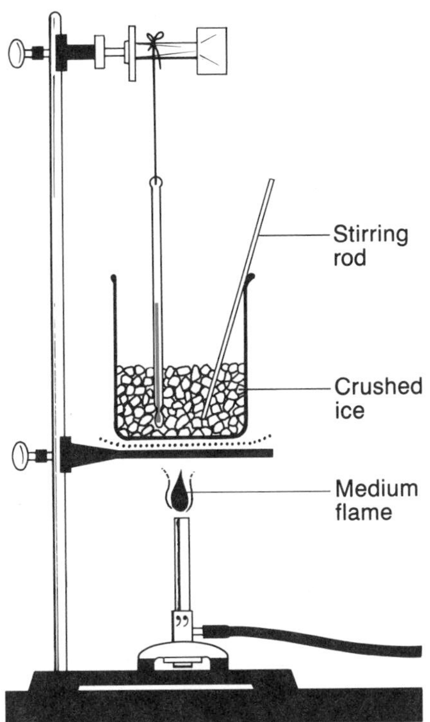

Fig. 12-5 Finding the effect of heat on the temperature of melting ice

Procedure

a. Prepare a data table with the column headings Time, Temperature, and Observations.
b. Half fill the 250 mL beaker with crushed ice.
c. Set up the apparatus as shown in Figure 12-5. Set the Bunsen burner to give a medium flame.
d. Keep the thermometer toward the centre of the contents of the beaker. Do not let it touch the bottom.
e. Stir the contents of the beaker continuously with the stirring rod. *CAUTION: Do not stir with the thermometer—it may break* (Fig. 12-6).

Fig. 12-6 Keep the thermometer in the centre. Stir carefully around it with the stirring rod.

f. Record the temperature every 30 s. Write down key observations, especially the time when all the ice has melted and also when boiling begins.
g. Continue to record the temperature for about 5 min after the water begins to boil. However, do not let the beaker boil dry.
h. Plot a temperature-time graph, with time on the horizontal axis.

Discussion

1. Describe the temperature change during melting, warming, and boiling.
2. Describe the direction of heat transfer during melting, warming, and boiling.

3. Account for the shape of the heating curve for water during melting, warming, and boiling.

Extension

Sketch the temperature-time graph you expect to get if half the ice used in this experiment is heated to the boiling point. If time permits, perform an experiment to test your predictions.

12.3 The Effects of Heat on Matter

A Heating Curve

Heat can change the state of a substance and it can change the temperature of the substance. Imagine that heat is added at a constant rate to 100 g of melting ice and the temperature is measured at equal time intervals. Assume that no heat escapes to the surroundings. In other words, all the heat is added to the ice. A temperature-time graph of the results is called a **heating curve**. As indicated, the temperature remains constant while the ice changes state. But as soon as all the ice has melted, the temperature of the water begins to increase. In equal intervals of time, the temperature changes equal amounts. In Figure 12-7,A, it changes 30°C every 2 min. When the temperature reaches the boiling point of water, it remains constant at 100°C while the water changes to steam.

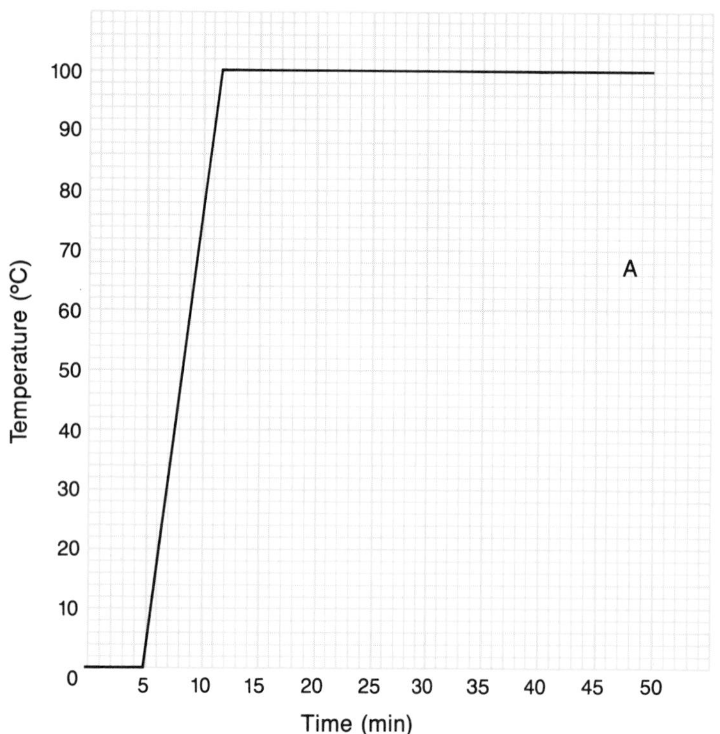

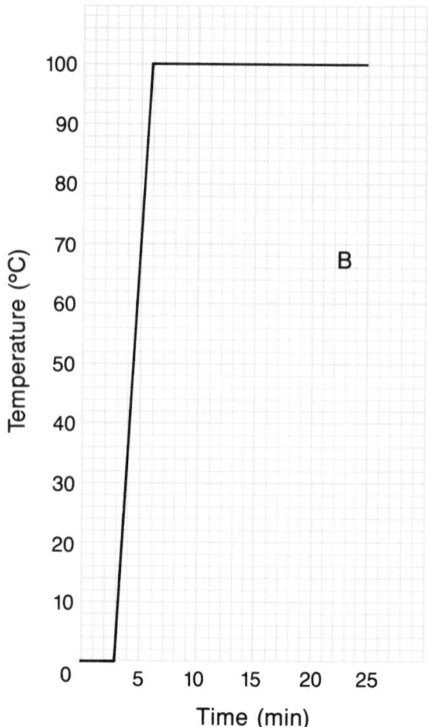

Fig. 12-7 Heating curves for two masses of ice

A Cooling Curve

Suppose the 100 g sample of ice is heated with a source that produces heat at twice the rate. What changes will be observed in the heating curve? First, it will take half as long to melt the ice (Fig. 12-7,B). Therefore the lower plateau will be half as long. This will also be true for the upper plateau. Second, it will take half the time to change the temperature of the water from 0°C to 100°C. Thus, in every 2 min time interval, the water will increase in temperature by 60°C rather than 30°C.

Suppose twice the mass of ice is heated with the stronger heat source. What will the heating curve look like? Can you explain why the heating curve will be the same as in Figure 12-7,A?

A **cooling curve** is the reverse of a heating curve (Fig. 12-8). The temperature of the water stays constant while steam at 100°C changes to water at 100°C. Then the water cools until it reaches the freezing point. Water at 0°C stays at constant temperature until it becomes ice at 0°C. Then the ice cools to the temperature of the surroundings.

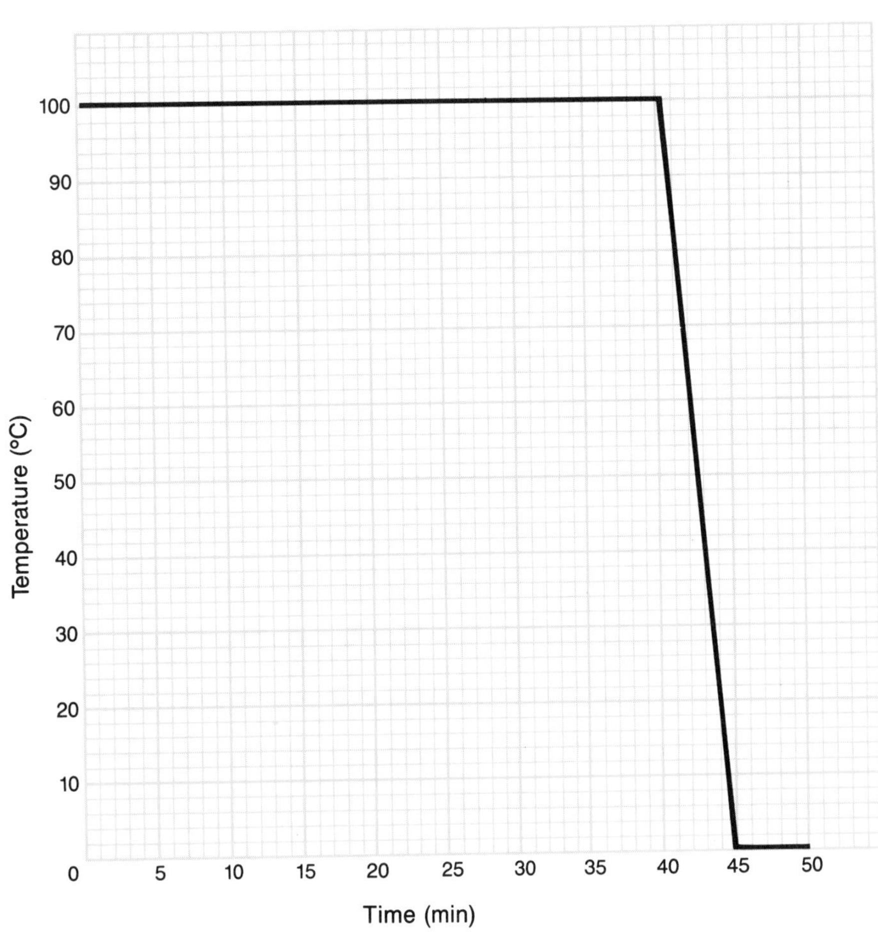

Fig. 12-8 A cooling curve for water

Explaining Heat and Changes of State

When heat is added to ice at 0°C, the temperature remains constant during melting. The faster heat is added, the faster the ice melts. During a change in state, the heat is used to increase the elastic energy of the molecules. The molecules have the same average kinetic energy because they move at the same average speed. But they vibrate further apart. Eventually they start to move throughout the material rather than only vibrating back and forth. When this happens, the solid ice has changed to liquid water.

Explaining Heat and Temperature Changes

Except during a change in state, the heat that is added is used to increase both the elastic and kinetic energy of the molecules. The molecules in a solid vibrate about a fixed point. The hotter the solid, the faster and further apart the molecules vibrate. The molecules in a liquid move slowly from one place to another throughout the liquid. The hotter the liquid, the faster the molecules move from place to place. The molecules are, on average, further apart. The molecules in a gas are very far apart and move rapidly throughout the entire volume of the container. Molecules of steam at a temperature of 200°C move faster than molecules at 150°C.

Section Review

1. How does mass affect the heating curve for a pure substance? Give an example.
2. How does the power of the heat source affect the heating curve for a pure substance? Give an example.
3. **a)** Where does the heat go that is added during a change in state?
   b) Where does the heat go that is added when there is no change in state?
4. Sketch the cooling curve for steam initially at a temperature of 100°C until it cools to ice at −10°C.

Extension

Sketch the shape of the cooling curve you expect to get when water vapour at 100°C is cooled until the water eventually freezes. Assuming you have unlimited equipment, design an experiment to test your prediction. Do *not* do the experiment.

12.4 Activity: Heat and Different Substances

In this activity you will heat equal masses of different substances and produce the same temperature change in both. Before you begin, predict whether the heat required to produce the same temperature change will be the same or different.

Problem

How does the heat compare to raise the temperature of the same mass of water and ethylene glycol the same amount?

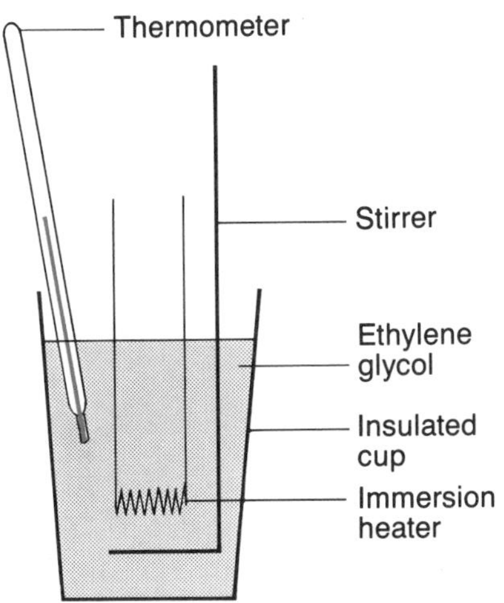

Fig. 12-9 Apparatus for studying the effect of heat on different substances

Materials

insulated cups (2)
immersion heater
thermometer
stirring rod
100 mL graduated cylinder
timer
water
ethylene glycol

Note: An electric immersion heater is used to add a known quantity of heat. The heater has a known power—say 30 W. A heater with this power produces 30 J of heat every second. In 2 s it produces 60 J. The quantity of heat added (J) = power (W) × time (s).

Procedure

a. Copy Table 12-1 into your notebook.
b. Enter the power of your heater in the table.
c. Add 91 mL of cold ethylene glycol to an insulated cup. 91 mL of ethylene glycol have a mass of 0.1 kg.
d. Place the heater in the ethylene glycol (Fig. 12-9). Be sure the heating element is covered with ethylene glycol.
e. Record the starting temperature of the liquid.
f. Turn on the heater. Start the timer. Record the time it takes in seconds to produce a temperature change of 40°C.
g. Add 100 mL of cold water to the other insulated cup. 100 mL of water have a mass of 0.1 kg.
h. Repeat steps (d), (e), and (f) for water.
i. Calculate the heat energy added to each liquid.

Table 12-1 Heat and Different Substances

Substance	*Mass (kg)*	*Temperature change (0°C)*	*Heater power (W)*	*Time (s)*	*Heat energy (J)*
Ethylene glycol	0.1	40			
Water	0.1	40			

Discussion

1. Compare the heat added to warm the same mass of water and ethylene glycol through the same temperature change.
2. Calculate the heat in joules needed to warm 1 kg of each substance 1°C. Your teacher will help you. This is called the **specific heat capacity**.
3. Obtain a class value for the specific heat capacity of each substance. Your teacher will help you.
4. The accepted value for the specific heat capacity of water is 4200 J/(kg·°C). It is 2200 J/(kg·°C) for ethylene glycol. Compare the class values with the accepted values. Account for any differences.
5. How could the experiment be changed to get better results? (*Hint*: Consider the initial temperature of the liquids compared to room temperature.)

Extension

Ethylene glycol is antifreeze. It is mixed with water in the cooling systems of cars to prevent freezing in the winter. However, car makers recommend that the same mixture be used in the cooling systems in the summer. You just discovered that water has a higher specific heat capacity than ethylene glycol. Therefore it would appear wise to use only water in the summer. Find out why the car manufacturers recommend an ethylene glycol–water mixture.

12.5 Measuring Quantities of Heat

There is no instrument for measuring the quantity of heat directly. Instead, we measure the factors which affect the quantity of heat that is transferred. Three factors affect the quantity of heat transferred during a temperature change: the mass of the substance, the temperature change produced, and the type of material. Let us see how these factors operate.

Mass

We can compare quantities of heat by warming different masses through the same temperature change. Suppose we heat 1 kg of water until its temperature rises 1°C. Then we heat 2 kg of water until the temperature rises 1°C (Fig. 12-10). The heat needed to produce the same temperature change with twice the mass is twice as large.

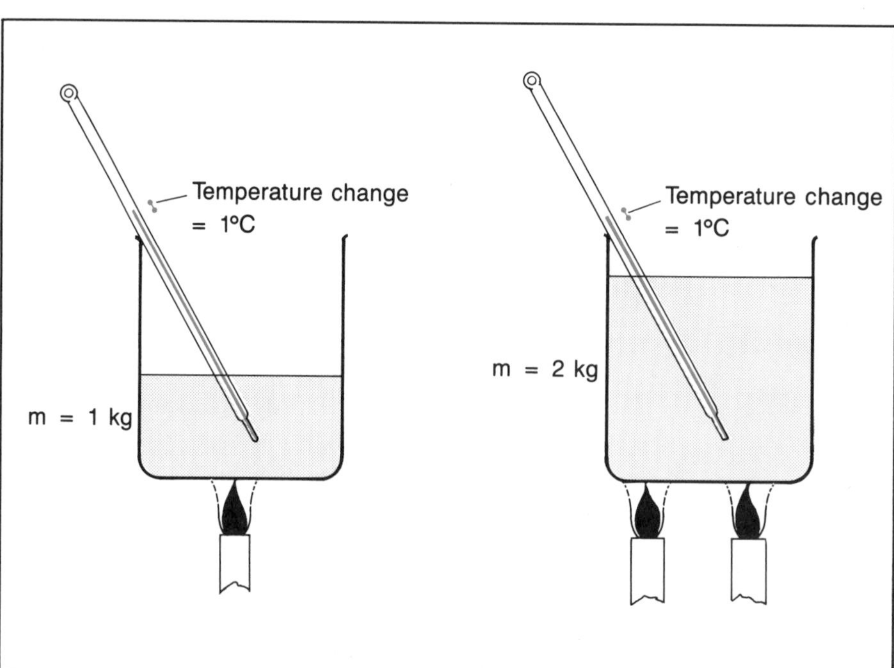

Fig. 12-10 It takes twice as much heat to warm double the mass through the same temperature change.

Temperature Change

We can also compare quantities of heat by the temperature changes they cause. Suppose we heat 1 kg of water until it rises 1°C. Then we heat the same mass

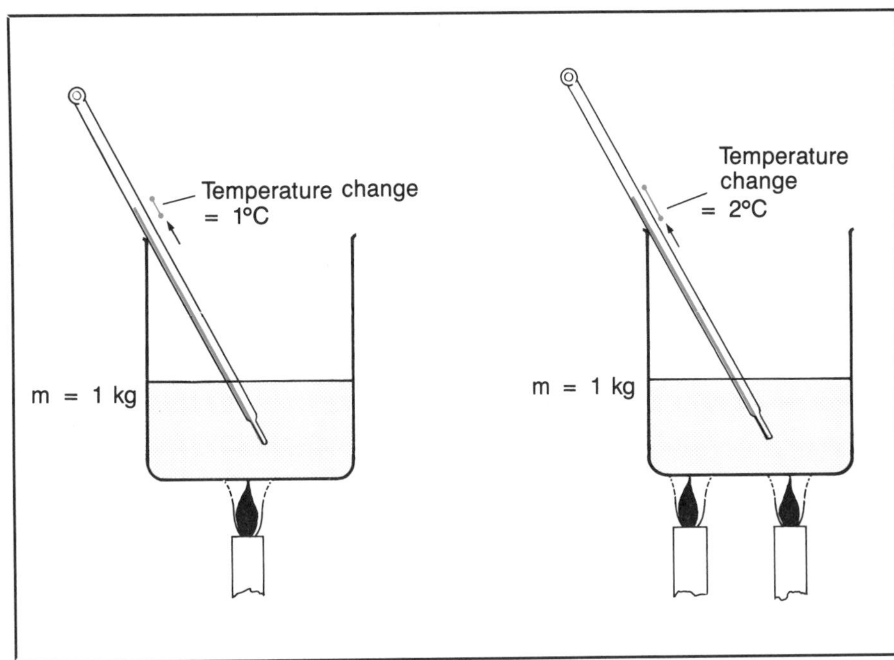

Fig. 12-11 It takes twice as much heat to produce twice as large a temperature change with the same mass.

of water until its temperature rises 2°C (Fig. 12-11). The quantity of heat needed to produce twice the temperature change is twice as large.

The Heat Capacity of an Object

A lake stores more heat than a swimming pool. A car radiator filled with water stores more heat than the same radiator filled with ethylene glycol. We say that objects with a different ability to store heat have a different heat capacity. Objects with a small heat capacity warm rapidly because they absorb less heat energy for a given temperature change. They also cool more rapidly because they have less heat to give up.

Heat capacity is the quantity of heat in joules needed to raise the temperature of an object by 1°C.

$$\textbf{Heat capacity} = \frac{\textbf{quantity of heat}}{\textbf{temperature change}}$$

Heat capacity is given the capital symbol $\boldsymbol{C}$, quantity of heat the symbol $\boldsymbol{Q}$, and temperature change the symbol $\boldsymbol{\Delta t}$. Thus $\boldsymbol{C} = \dfrac{\boldsymbol{Q}}{\boldsymbol{\Delta t}}$. The unit for heat capacity is the joule per degree Celsius (J/°C). Heat capacity is affected by two factors: the mass of the object and the type of material. The greater the mass, the greater the heat capacity. A litre of water has a greater heat capacity than a litre of ethylene glycol. Why do you think that this is so?

Sample Problem

It takes 5400 J to increase the temperature of a block of steel 4°C. Calculate the heat capacity of the block.

Given
$Q = 5400$ J
$\Delta t = 4°C$

Required
C

Analysis
Use $C = \frac{Q}{\Delta t}$

Solution
$$C = \frac{Q}{\Delta t}$$
$$= \frac{5400 \text{ J}}{4°\text{C}} = 1350 \text{ J/°C}$$

Statement
The heat capacity of the steel block is 1350 J/°C.

Specific Heat Capacity

The heat capacity of a large body such as a lake is difficult to measure directly. A more useful description of the heat capacities of different substances results if equal masses are compared. Such a quantity is called **specific heat capacity.** Specific heat capacity is the quantity of heat needed to raise the temperature of 1 kg of a substance through a change in temperature of 1°C.

$$\textbf{Specific heat capacity} = \frac{\textbf{quantity of heat}}{\textbf{mass} \times \textbf{temperature change}}$$

Specific heat capacity is given the symbol small c, quantity of heat the symbol Q, mass the symbol m, and temperature change the symbol Δt. Thus, $c = \frac{Q}{m\Delta t}$.

The derived unit for specific heat capacity is the joule per kilogram degree Celsius [J/(kg·°C)]. The specific heat capacity is different for various materials.

Specific Heat Capacity and Substances

Experiments show that it takes 4200 J of heat to raise the temperature of 1 kg of water 1°C. This is true for all samples of pure water. However, it takes only 2200 J to raise the temperature of 1 kg of ethylene glycol by 1°C. Thus water has about twice the specific heat capacity of ethylene glycol. The specific heat capacities of some common substances are listed in Table 12-2. These, together with densities and melting points, are used to identify unknown substances, because all are characteristic physical properties.

Table 12-2 Specific Heat Capacities

Substance	Specific heat capacity [J/(kg·°C)]	Substance	Specific heat capacity [J/(kg·°C)]
Aluminum	900	Methanol	2500
Copper	390	Oxygen	920
Ethylene glycol	2200	Paraffin oil	2100
Gold	130	Sand	800
Ice	2100	Silver	240
Iron	450	Water	4200
Lead	130	Water vapour	2000
Magnesium	980	Zinc	390

Calculating the Quantity of Heat

Once we know the mass, temperature change, and the specific heat capacity of a substance, we can calculate the quantity of heat added or removed using the formula $\boldsymbol{Q = m \cdot \Delta t \cdot c}$.

Sample Problem

Find the quantity of heat needed to raise the temperature of 500 g of methanol from 20°C to 60°C.

Given

$m = 500\ \text{g} = 0.5\ \text{kg}$

$t_{initial} = 20°\text{C}$

$t_{final} = 60°\text{C}$

$c = 2500\ \text{J/(kg·°C)}$ (from Table 12-2)

Required

Q

Analysis

Find Δt

Substitute into the equation $Q = m \cdot \Delta t \cdot c$

Solution

$$\begin{aligned}\Delta t &= t_{final} - t_{initial} \\ &= 60°\text{C} - 20°\text{C} = 40°\text{C} \\ Q &= m \cdot \Delta t \cdot c \\ &= 0.5\ \text{kg} \times 40°\text{C} \times 2500\ \text{J/(kg·°C)} \\ &= 0.5 \times 40 \times 2500\ \text{J} \\ &= 50\ 000\ \text{J} \\ &= 50\ \text{kJ}\end{aligned}$$

Statement

The quantity of heat added to the methanol is 50 kJ.

Application: Effects of Different Heat Capacities

Look closely at Table 12-2. Water has the largest specific heat capacity listed. It is over five times that of sand. Thus it takes more energy to heat up water than sand. As a result, sand on a beach gets much hotter than water on a hot sunny day. The air above the sand heats up and rises as a result of convection. Then cold air moves in from over the water to take its place. That is why the breeze often travels toward the beach from the water on a hot day. Can you explain why the breezes reverse direction in the evening?

Water has to lose more energy than sand when it cools on a cold winter night. As a result, a large body of water has a moderating effect on climate. That is, the temperature changes more slowly near water than inland. This is why people like a beach on a hot summer day. It is also why some people prefer Vancouver temperatures over Calgary temperatures in winter and in summer.

Section Review

1. **a)** Name three factors that affect the quantity of heat.
  b) How does each factor affect the quantity of heat?

2. **a)** Define heat capacity.
  b) What is the unit of heat capacity?
  c) Explain why the climate near a large body of water is more moderate than the climate near a small body of water.

3. Calculate the heat capacity in each of the following cases:
  a) 25 200 J of heat increases the temperature of water 3°C.
  b) 48 000 J of heat raises the temperature of sand from 20°C to 28°C.

4. a) Define specific heat capacity.
   b) What is the unit for specific heat capacity?
   c) How is the specific heat capacity of a substance determined?
   d) Explain why the climate near a large body of water is more moderate than the climate inland.
5. Calculate the amount of heat transferred in each of the following cases:
   a) 200 g of water warms from 15°C to 35°C.
   b) 0.40 kg of water warms from 30°C to 71°C.
   c) 75 g of water cools from 90°C to 52°C.
   d) 4.8 kg of ethylene glycol cools from 35°C to 20°C.
6. Determine the temperature change in each of the following cases:
   a) 200 g of water gains 8400 J of heat.
   b) 15 kg of water loses 252 kJ of heat.
7. Determine the specific heat capacity in each of the following cases:
   a) 720 J of heat warms 40 g of aluminum from 20°C to 40°C.
   b) 3500 J of heat removed from iron cools it from 100°C to 50°C.
8. Determine the mass of the substance in each of the following cases:
   a) 126 kJ of heat produce a temperature change of 30°C in water.
   b) 7.8 kJ of heat change the temperature of copper from 20°C to 25°C.

12.6 Activity: Heat Exchange in Mixtures

Chilled cream cools hot coffee. The cream warms up and the coffee cools down slightly. The cream gains heat in warming and the coffee loses heat in cooling. This example shows that heat is transferred when substances at different temperatures are mixed.

Problem

Suppose hot and cold water are mixed. How does the heat lost by the hot water compare to the heat gained by the cold water?

Materials

Teacher
large electric kettle or coffee urn
100 mL graduated cylinder
class set of styrofoam cups
balance

Student Groups
thermometers (2)
100 mL graduated cylinder
large styrofoam cup
stirrer

CAUTION: Wear safety goggles during this activity. Also, be careful with the hot water.

Procedure

a. Your teacher will heat water using a kettle or a coffee urn.
b. Copy Table 12-3 into your notebook.

c. Carefully measure the mass of a styrofoam cup. Then add about 150 mL of cold water to the cup.
d. Measure the mass of the cold water plus the cup.
e. Obtain about 100 mL of hot water in a small styrofoam cup from your teacher. *CAUTION: Be careful with this hot water!*
f. Take the initial temperatures of the hot water and the cold water as shown in Figure 12-12. Record this in the table.

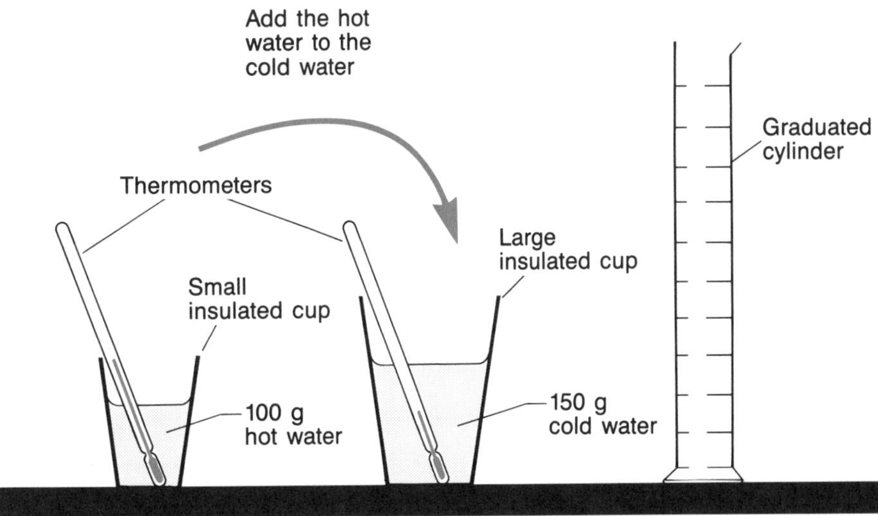

Fig. 12-12 Apparatus for studying heat exchange in mixtures

g. Immediately add the hot water to the cold water. Then stir the mixture.
h. Record the highest temperature reached by the mixture.
i. Measure the total mass of the cup and its contents.
j. Subtract to find the mass of the cold water and the mass of the hot water. Enter these in the table.
k. Calculate the heat lost by the hot water. Use the formula $Q = m \cdot \Delta t \cdot c$.
l. Calculate the heat gained by the cold water in the same way.

Table 12-3 Heat Exchange in Mixtures

Mixture	*Water*	*Mass (kg)*	*Temperature (0°C)*			*Specific heat capacity J/(kg·°C)*	*Heat exchanged (J)*
			Initial	*Final*	*Change*		
Large cup	Hot					4200	
	Cold					4200	

Discussion

1. Compare the heat lost by the hot water with the heat gained by the cold water.

2. If the heat lost is not equal to the heat gained, which should be greater? Why?
3. How could you modify the activity to get better results?
4. Complete the following statement: In any mixture the heat gained by a ▒▒▒▒▒ substance in warming ▒▒▒▒▒ the heat lost by a ▒▒▒▒▒ substance in cooling. This is the **Principle of Heat Exchange** for mixtures.

Extension

Design an experiment which uses the method of mixtures to compare the specific heat capacity of table cream with that of skim milk. Perform the experiment if you have time.

12.7 Energy Conservation and Mixtures

Energy Conversions

The pendulum in Figure 12-13 shows energy being converted from one form to another. Energy is converted from gravitational energy to bulk kinetic energy. Then it is converted back to gravitational energy. When the mass of the pendulum is pulled from its rest position to one side (point A) it rises. A force raises the mass through a height *h*. This force does work. The work done is stored in the mass as gravitational energy.

When the mass is released from point A, some of this gravitational energy changes to bulk kinetic energy. The further the mass falls, the more bulk kinetic energy it gains and the more gravitational energy it loses. At the bottom of the swing (point B), all the gravitational energy stored in the raised mass is gone. The mass now has its greatest speed and greatest bulk kinetic energy.

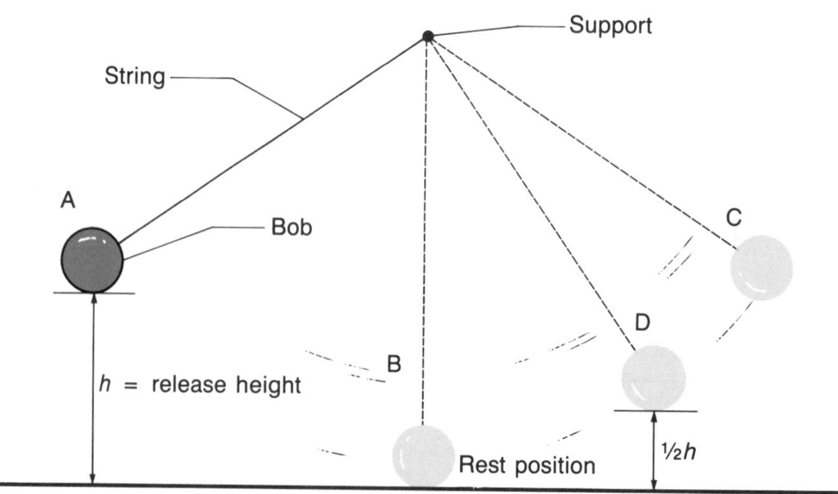

Fig. 12-13 Energy conversions in a pendulum

During the rest of the swing, the bulk kinetic energy changes back into gravitational energy. At the far side of its swing (point C) all the bulk kinetic energy has changed back into gravitational energy. This conversion between gravitational and bulk kinetic energy repeats itself many times. Eventually, the pendulum stops swinging, and its bulk kinetic energy becomes zero. Also, the mass is back at the height where it started. Thus it has no gravitational energy with reference to the starting point. Where has the energy gone? Some of the stored energy has been given to the air molecules hit by the pendulum. They move faster than before. The molecules in the support have gained the rest. They, too, move faster. The bulk kinetic energy and gravitational energy have become thermal energy.

The Law of Conservation of Energy

Scientists have studied energy conversions in simple machines like levers and in complex machines like cars. The results show that we cannot get more useful energy out of a system than has been put into it. In fact, we cannot break even. This is because friction limits the efficiency of energy conversions to less than 100% (Fig. 12-14).

Fig. 12-14 The efficiency of an automobile can be increased by lowering the friction in the form of air resistance. How has this been done on this car?

Even when friction is present, the energy which disappears is not destroyed. It becomes thermal energy in the nearby molecules of matter. The thermal energy gained by these molecules has been found to be exactly equal to the amount of bulk kinetic and gravitational energy which disappears.

The study of the various forms of energy and energy conversions has given us one of the great laws of science. This law is called the **Law of Conservation of Energy**. It states: Energy cannot be created or destroyed. It can be changed from one form to another; but the total amount of energy in the universe stays constant. Three scientists laid the foundations for this great law. They were Julius Robert Mayer, a German doctor and physicist; James Prescott Joule, an English physicist; and Hermann von Helmholtz, a German physiologist and physicist.

The Principle of Heat Exchange

A particular case of the Law of Conservation of Energy is called the **Principle of Heat Exchange**. It states: Whenever two substances at different temperatures are mixed, the amount of heat lost by the hotter substance is equal to the amount of heat gained by the colder substance. Thus thermal energy is conserved when two different temperature substances are mixed. The measurement of the heat exchanged when substances are mixed is called the **method of mixtures**.

Imagine that you get up one morning and decide to take a bath. You run the water and find its temperature to be 70°C. Your body temperature is 37°C. The temperature of the bath water is much too hot to stand. How much cold water must be added to the hot water to cool it to body temperature? We can use the Principle of Heat Exchange and the method of mixtures to find the answer.

Sample Problem

A bathtub contains 50 kg of water at a temperature of 71°C. The temperature of the cold water from the tap is 20°C. What mass of cold water is needed to adjust the temperature of the hot water to 37°C?

Given

$t_{hot} = 71°C$
$m_{hot} = 50$ kg
$t_{cold} = 20°C$
$t_{mixture}$ = body temperature
$= 37°C$

Required

m_{cold}

Analysis

Find the changes in temperature of the hot and cold water. Use the heat transfer equation and the Principle of Heat Exchange. Solve for m.

Solution

$\Delta t_{hot} = 71°C - 37°C = 34°C$
$\Delta t_{cold} = 37°C - 20°C = 17°C$
$Q_{lost} = m \cdot \Delta t_{hot} \cdot c$
$= 50 \text{ kg} \times 34°C \times 4200 \text{ J/(kg·°C)}$
$= 7.14 \times 10^6 \text{ J}$
$Q_{gained} = m \cdot \Delta t_{cold} \cdot c$
$= m \times 17°C \times 4200 \text{ J/(kg·°C)}$
$= m \times 7.14 \times 10^4 \text{ J}$
$Q_{lost} = Q_{gained}$ (Principle of Heat Exchange)

$7.14 \times 10^6 \text{ J} = m \times 7.14 \times 10^4 \text{ J}$
$m = (7.14 \times 10^6)/(7.14 \times 10^4) \text{ kg}$
$= 100 \text{ kg}$

Statement

100 kg of cold water must be added to produce a final temperature of 37°C.

Section Review

1. Figure 12-13 shows a pendulum at various points in its swing.
  a) Where does the mass have its greatest height? its greatest gravitational energy?
  b) Where does the mass have its greatest speed? its greatest bulk kinetic energy?
  c) Describe the energy conversion taking place as the mass moves from A to B; from B to C.
  d) Compare the gravitational energy and the bulk kinetic energy at point D.

e) Write a word equation for the total energy the mass has at any point in its swing.

2. a) State the Law of Conservation of Energy.
   b) State the Principle of Heat Exchange and explain how it is a special case of the Law of Conservation of Energy.
   c) Describe the method of mixtures.
3. How much ethylene glycol at a temperature of 20°C must be added to 5 kg of water at a temperature of 60°C to create a mixture at a temperature of 30°C?
4. When 1.0 kg of an unknown liquid at a temperature of 25°C is added to 2.0 kg of water at a temperature of 45°C, the final temperature of the mixture is 40°C. What is the specific heat capacity of the unknown liquid?

12.8 Activity: Measuring the Specific Heat Capacity of a Metal

Every substance has a definite specific heat capacity. In this activity you will find the specific heat capacity of some metals. To do this you will use the Principle of Heat Exchange and the method of mixtures.

Problem

How can the specific heat capacity of metals be determined?

Materials

samples of several metals (aluminum, copper, iron, lead, zinc)

ring stand	ring clamp	wire gauze
Bunsen burner	100 mL graduated cylinder	thermometer
200 mL beaker	insulated cup	balance

Procedure

a. Copy Table 12-4 into your notebook.
b. Choose one metal. Find the mass of the sample. Enter this in the table.
c. Attach a thread to the metal. Suspend it in water in a beaker (Fig. 12-15). Do not let it touch the bottom.
d. Heat the water to the boiling point. Allow it to boil for about 5 min to let the metal reach the temperature of the water.
e. Take the temperature of the hot water. Record this as the temperature of the metal.
f. Add 100 g of cold water to a cup. Measure and record its temperature.
g. Quickly transfer the metal sample from the hot water to the cold water.
h. Stir the mixture and record the highest temperature reached by the mixture.
i. Use the Principle of Heat Exchange to calculate the specific heat capacity of the metal. Use the equation $Q = m \cdot \Delta t \cdot c$. Equate the heat lost by the metal to the heat gained by the water. Then solve for c.

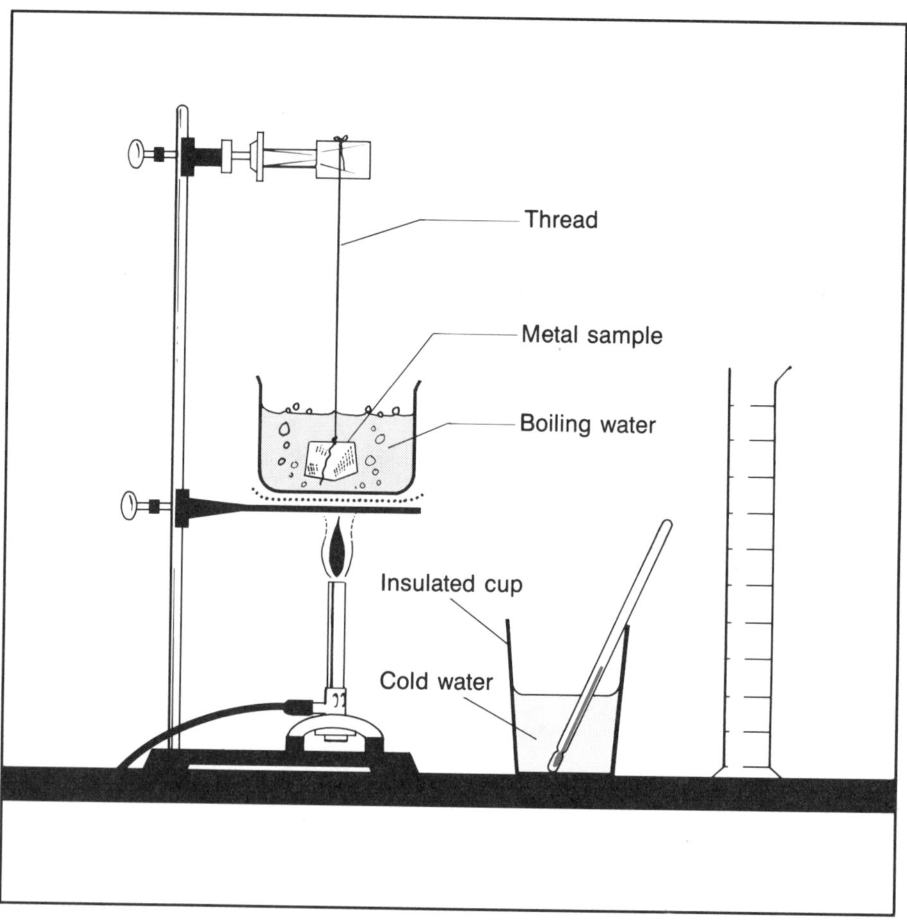

Fig. 12-15 Apparatus for studying specific heat capacity of a metal

Table 12-4 Determining the Specific Heat Capacity of a Metal

Component of mixture	*Mass (kg)*	*Temperature (°C)*			*Specific heat capacity J/(kg·°C)*	*Heat exchanged (J)*
		Initial	*Final*	*Change*		
Metal					*c*	
Water	0.10				4200	

Discussion

1. Compare the value you obtained for the specific heat capacity with other values obtained by your class for the same metal. Your teacher will help you.
2. Compare the class value with the accepted value. (See Table 12-2.)
3. List possible sources of error in the experiment. Indicate for each error whether it raises or lowers the value of specific heat capacity. Suggest changes to overcome the errors.

Extension

If time permits, do the experiment differently. Place the metal sample used in Activity 12.8 in the freezer compartment of a refrigerator. Transfer the cold metal to water above room temperature. Compare the value you obtain for specific heat capacity using the two methods.

12.9 Applications of Specific Heat Capacity

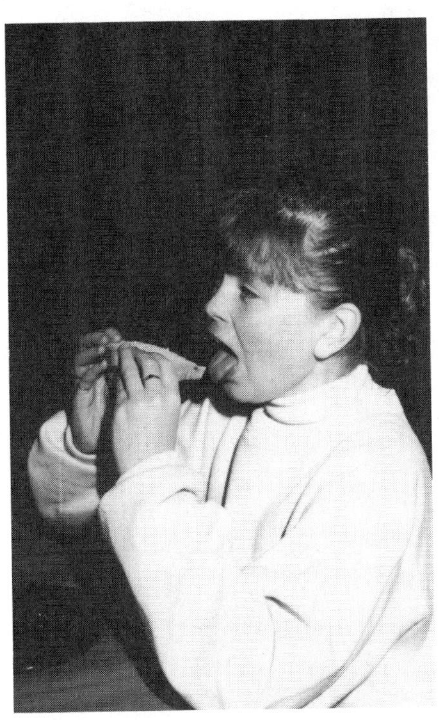

Fig. 12-16 Why does the crust of a pizza cool off faster than the topping?

Specific Heat and Hot Foods

Have you ever wondered why some foods remain hot longer than others? Perhaps you have touched the crust of a pizza and found it to be pleasantly warm. But when you sank your teeth into the cheese and tomato topping, your lips, mouth, and tongue became badly burned (Fig. 12-16). Why does the crust cool off faster than the covering? The answer lies in specific heat capacity.

Water has a specific heat capacity of 4200 J/(kg·°C). The crust of the pizza contains flour but very little water. Hence it has a specific heat capacity less than half that of water, about 1700 J/(kg·°C). Tomatoes and cheese toppings, on the other hand, have a specific heat capacity about double that of the crust, between 3400 and 3900 J/(kg·°C). So, before you bite into a hot pizza think about specific heat capacity!

Have you noticed that it takes less time to warm up some foods than others? Consider a freshly made pizza and a cherry pie of the same size, both uncooked. Suppose you place both at the same time into an oven at a temperature of 220°C. The pizza becomes hot much faster than the cherry pie. Can you explain why?

Specific Heat and Solar Heating

Fig. 12-17 Why is the flat plate collector painted black?

Many people have installed flat plate collectors to heat the water for their home or swimming pool (Fig. 12-17). The flat plate collectors are oriented toward the sun to collect and convert solar energy directly into heat. Pipes in the solar collector carry water, that absorbs the heat, to the swimming pool or hot water tank. The temperature of a swimming pool can be raised several degrees even on a cool sunny day by this method, which is called **active solar heating**. Why is water, not air, used as the medium? Water has a larger specific heat capacity than air. It can absorb and transport a lot of heat for a very small temperature change.

For home heating, air is sometimes the medium used to carry heat from the flat plate collector to the storage area. Air has a specific heat capacity of only 1.0 J/(kg·°C). But air does not freeze on a cold day. Also, air causes less rust damage to pipes than water. The hot air is circulated through rocks or coarse stones in the basement of the home. The specific heat capacity of rock averages about 0.8 J/(kg·°C). During the day these rocks absorb heat from the air and heat up. During the night the rocks cool down as they transfer their heat to the home. Suppose a basement contains 5 t of rock. Can you calculate how much heat can be stored in the rock for a temperature change of 12°C?

The simplest and least expensive way to capture heat from the sun is through **passive solar heating**. When a building has most of its windows facing south,

Fig. 12-18 Why are stones used for this wall rather than plywood?

this allows solar energy to enter the building in winter when the sun is low in the sky. Inside, heavy stone or brick walls and floors store heat during the day and radiate it back at night (Fig. 12-18). The huge mass of these building materials can store a significant amount of heat. But walls containing water would work much better. Can you explain why?

Specific Heat and Sleeping

Pioneers used to fill bottles with hot water and place them in their beds prior to bedtime. The heat stored in these hot water bottles was transferred to the bed, making it comfortable for sleeping. Today many people have water beds with electrical heaters. The heaters warm up the water inside the mattress to the desired comfort temperature. Even if the electricity goes off during the night there is plenty of heat in the water to keep the sleeper warm. Can you explain how a water bed might be modified to cool the sleeper during the summer?

Specific Heat and Climate

The average January temperature in Vancouver, British Columbia is 4°C. It is −4°C in Halifax, Nova Scotia, and −18°C in Winnipeg, Manitoba. What causes the differences? Two key factors affect the temperature of a region: proximity to a large body of water, and wind direction.

The winds in the latitudes of Canada are westerly. As a result, on the west coast the winds blow off the Pacific Ocean onto the land. Because of its high specific heat capacity, the temperature of the ocean stays fairly constant—winter to summer. During winter, some of the moving air mass picks up heat from the ocean and carries it inland.

On the east coast of Canada the winds are moving offshore to the Atlantic Ocean. Soil and rock, because of their lower specific heat capacities, change temperature faster. Since the wind reaches Halifax from over the land, this city is cooler than Vancouver in the winter. Fortunately, the nearby Atlantic Ocean has some moderating effect. But Winnipeg is too far inland to benefit from the high specific heat capacity of water. That is why Winnipeg gets much hotter in the summer and much colder in the winter than coastal cities.

Section Review

1. Explain why a piece of pizza cools down faster than a piece of apple pie, even when both are cooked at the same temperature.
2. The aluminum foil covering frozen foods can be removed by hand almost immediately after cooking. Why does the foil cool faster than the food?
3. Distinguish between active and passive solar collectors.
4. Which is better in the summer, to sleep on a mattress filled with water or on one filled with air? Explain.
5. Explain why Québec has a lower average January temperature than Toronto.

Chapter Highlights

1. Temperature is a measure of the average kinetic energy of the particles of a substance.
2. Thermal energy is the sum of the elastic and kinetic energy an object has as a result of the random motion of its particles.
3. Heat energy is thermal energy being transferred from one substance to another.
4. The temperature-time graph of a substance heated from the solid state to the vapour state is called its heating curve.
5. Heat transferred depends on mass, temperature change, and specific heat capacity.
6. The heat capacity of a substance depends on its mass and type.
7. Specific heat capacity is constant for a given substance, but is different for different substances.
8. Water has one of the largest specific heat capacities—4200 J/(kg·°C).
9. Quantity of heat is calculated using $Q = m \cdot \Delta t \cdot c$.
10. The Principle of Heat Exchange is based on the Law of Conservation of Energy.

Key Terms

cooling curve
heat
heat capacity
heating curve
Law of Conservation of Energy
method of mixtures
Principle of Heat Exchange
specific heat capacity
temperature
thermal energy

Recognizing the Concepts

Each of the following statements or questions is followed by four responses. Choose the correct response in each case. (Do not write in this book.)

1. Heat is exchanged between two objects when they have a different
   a) specific heat capacity
   b) mass
   c) temperature
   d) ability to conduct heat
2. The same mass of liquids x and y are heated using identical immersion heaters. Liquid x increased in temperature by 20°C in 4 min. Liquid y increased in temperature by 10°C in 2 min. The specific heat capacity of liquid y
   a) is larger than that of liquid x
   b) is the same as that of liquid x
   c) is smaller than that of liquid x
   d) cannot be compared to that of liquid x
3. The amount of heat needed to raise the temperature of a substance by 1°C is called the
   a) heat capacity
   b) joule
   c) specific heat capacity
   d) watt
4. Specific heat capacity depends on the
   a) mass
   b) temperature change
   c) heat energy
   d) substance
5. According to the Principle of Heat Exchange the quantity conserved is
   a) temperature
   b) heat capacity
   c) thermal energy
   d) specific heat capacity
6. It takes 256 kJ of heat energy to raise the temperature of a 0.80 kg potato from 20°C to 100°C. What is the specific heat capacity of potato?
   a) 2.6 kJ/(kg·°C)
   b) 3.2 kJ/(kg·°C)
   c) 4.0 kJ/(kg·°C)
   d) 16 kJ/(kg·°C)

Understanding the Concepts

1. Describe a way to increase the thermal energy of a substance without transferring heat to it.
2. Explain how rubbing two rough surfaces together increases the thermal energy of the materials.
3. Compare the amount of thermal energy in each of the following:
   a) a cup of coffee and a pot of coffee, both at 75°C
   b) a block of ice and an ice cube
   c) a cup of tea at 80°C and a glass of iced tea at 10°C
   d) 20 kg of steel at 400°C and 10 kg of steel at 100°C

4. Sketch a heating curve for ice at 0°C until it boils away. On the same axis sketch the heating curve for half the mass of ice.
5. Explain the constant temperature that accompanies a change in state.
6. Why does the wind near a lake reverse direction in the evening?
7. An object at a temperature of 40°C has a heat capacity of 3000 J/°C. What temperature change results if 7500 J of heat are removed from it?
8. What is the temperature change when 200 g of water gains 8400 J of heat?
9. What is the specific heat capacity if 20 kJ changes the temperature of 10 kg of a substance by 4°C?

Fig. 12-19 A demonstration of energy conservation. Does the person need to move back when the mass returns?

Applying the Concepts

1. When people say "It's cold outside" are they referring to heat, temperature, or thermal energy? Explain.
2. The heat energy collected in a solar energy system is sometimes stored in liquids in underground tanks.
   a) Which liquid will hold more heat, ethylene glycol or water? Why?
   b) What advantage does a mixture of ethylene glycol and water have over pure water? (Hint: Ethylene glycol is antifreeze.)
3. Figure 12-19 shows a person demonstrating energy conservation. She is releasing a heavy pendulum mass. The mass has been pulled so it touches the nose. When the mass returns, does the person need to move back to be safe? Explain your answer.
4. The electric energy needed for some bicycle headlights is made by a generator touching the tire. A bicycle salesperson claims that such a bicycle is harder to pedal when the light is on than if it is burned out. Do you agree or disagree? Explain.
5. Use the Kinetic Molecular Theory of heat to explain the temperature change which occurs when a hot liquid is added to a cold liquid.
6. A mixture is made by adding 75 g of an unknown liquid at a temperature of 25°C to 60 g of water at a temperature of 90°C. The final temperature of the mixture is 65°C. Calculate the specific heat capacity of the liquid. What is the liquid? Can you be sure your identification is correct? Discuss.
7. The Principle of Heat Exchange is a special case of the Law of Conservation of Energy. Explain.
8. Why must both the heat transfer equation and the method of mixtures be used in the experiment to determine the specific heat capacity of a metal?
9. Explain why oatmeal cookies cool faster than cherry tarts when removed at the same time from the same oven.
10. How much heat is lost by 40 g of ice in cooling from -5.0°C to -15°C?
11. What temperature will the steam become if 40 kJ of heat are added to 1 kg of steam at 100°C?

Investigations

1. Design and carry out an experiment to compare the specific heat capacity of dry and wet sand. Would crops in dry or wet soils be hurt more by frost? Why?

2. Design and do an experiment to compare the specific heat capacity of water with that of a mixture of water and ethylene glycol.
3. Get a coil spring and a 500 g mass (Fig. 12-20). Design and do an experiment to determine the forms of energy present and the energy conversions taking place as the spring vibrates. Study how well it shows the Law of Conservation of Energy.

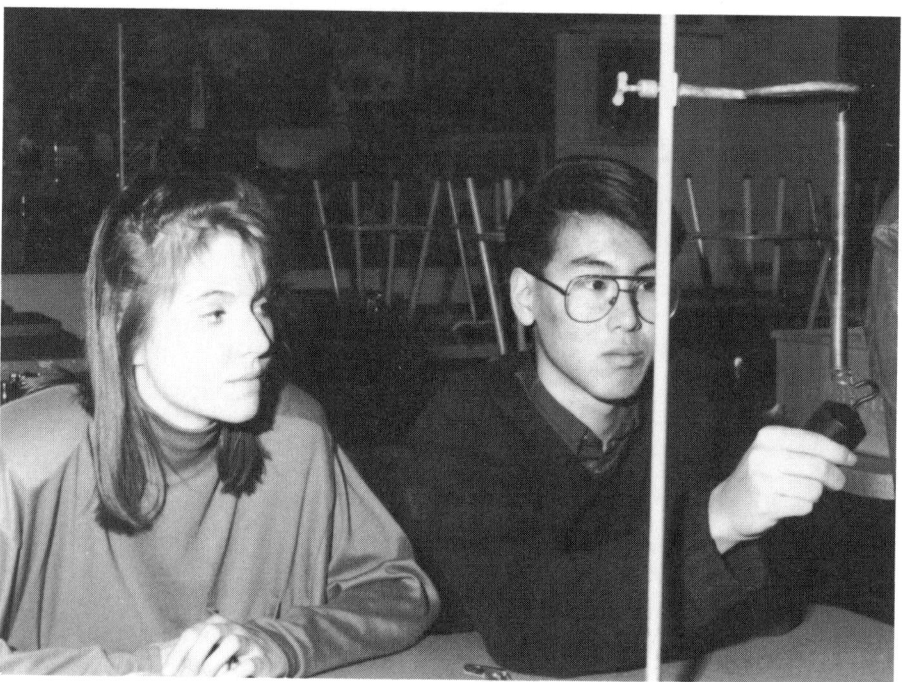

Fig. 12-20 Can you proceed from here?

4. A person's coffee is too hot to drink. Suppose the person wants it to be as cool as possible at the end of 5 min. Is it better to add cold cream immediately, or wait five minutes before adding the cream, or does it matter? Design and do an experiment to answer the question. Be careful to control all the variables.
5. Do a library search to determine the contribution made by one of Hermann von Helmholtz, James Prescott Joule, or Julius Robert Mayer to the development of the Law of Conservation of Energy.

VISTA

AUTOMATIC DISHWASHER OR DISHPAN?

Have you been told that it takes more energy to wash dishes by hand than with an automatic dishwasher? Did you agree or disagree? Dishwasher manufacturers often make this claim. It will become important to know the answer if we encounter another energy crisis. Let us apply the heat transfer equation to investigate this important question.

The argument is based on the claim that it takes more water to wash dishes by hand three times a day than by using a machine once a day. Since most of the energy goes into heating the water, the more water used, the more energy consumed.

Washing dishes by hand usually requires the equivalent of two sinks of water. One is used for washing and the other for rinsing. This amounts to about 26 kg of water. The temperature of the wash water is slightly above body temperature, about 40°C. We will assume that the water was at room temperature (20°C) before being heated. Thus the energy required to heat the water for the sinks was

$Q = m{\cdot}\Delta t{\cdot}c = 26\ \text{kg} \times (40°\text{C} - 20°\text{C}) \times 4.2\ \text{kJ/(kg}{\cdot}°\text{C}) = 2184\ \text{kJ}$. Washing the dishes after every meal would require three times as much heat, or $3 \times 2184\ \text{kJ} = 6552\ \text{kJ}$.

Automatic dishwashers require very hot water to remove the dirt from the dishes. The recommended temperature is 60°C. They use about 40 kg of water for a complete cycle. If the initial temperature of the water is 20°C, then the energy required to heat the water for the dishwasher is

$Q = m{\cdot}\Delta t{\cdot}c = 40\ \text{kg} \times (60°\text{C} - 20°\text{C}) \times 4.2\ \text{kJ/(kg}{\cdot}°\text{C}) = 6720\ \text{kJ}$.

If the dishes are washed by hand once a day the savings are substantial. Even if the dishes are washed three times a day there is a slight saving. And we haven't even taken into consideration the energy required by the dry cycle. Clearly, it normally requires less energy to wash dishes by hand than by machine!

Does it take more water to wash dishes by hand or with the automatic dishwasher?

13 Heat and Changes of State

CHAPTER CONTENTS

CHAPTER OBJECTIVES

After completing this chapter you should be able to:

1. Define specific latent heat.
2. Compare the specific latent heats of fusion and vapourization of water.
3. Measure the specific latent heats of fusion and vapourization of water.
4. Describe the operation of a heat pump.
5. Determine the specific heat of combustion of a food.
6. Explain the need for a balance of food and exercise.
7. Explain why we need to conserve concentrated forms of energy.

Heat melts ice. Yet, in spite of summer heat, glaciers stay around all summer (Fig. 13-1). Why is this so? And why do farmers spray water on fruit crops when sub-freezing temperatures threaten their crops?

Boiling also requires heat. Could boiling, therefore, be used to cool something? Why is water an excellent coolant to use in a car radiator? Why is a burn from steam more severe than one from boiling water?

These are just a few of the interesting problems you will explore in this chapter.

Fig. 13-1 The Athabasca Glacier in the Columbia Icefield. Like most glaciers in Canada, this one is slowly receding. Yet, even on a hot summer day, you have trouble seeing any water on the ice. Why?

13.1 Heat Transfer During Changes of State

You learned last year that heat can either raise the temperature of matter or cause it to change state. This section looks more deeply into the role heat plays during changes of state.

Latent Heat

A definite amount of heat is required to raise the temperature of 1 kg of a substance by 1°C. This quantity is called the **specific heat capacity** of the substance. The specific heat capacity of a substance is different in each of the three states. For example, the specific heat capacity of ice is 2100 J/(kg·°C), whereas that of liquid water is 4200 J/(kg·°C) and that of water vapour is 2000 J/(kg·°C). This difference is due to the arrangement of the water molecules in each of the three states.

A definite amount of heat is also required to change the state of a substance. You know from your study of melting and boiling points that no temperature change takes place during a change of state. Heat which causes a change in state is called **latent heat**. The word *latent* means *hidden*. We say the heat is hidden because no change in temperature occurs.

Specific Latent Heat of Fusion

Do you remember a spring in which a long warm spell came while the ground was still deeply covered in snow? At such a time, temperatures well above freezing can occur for several days. The air temperature may be above 20°C every day, but at the end of this hot spell there is still snow on the ground.

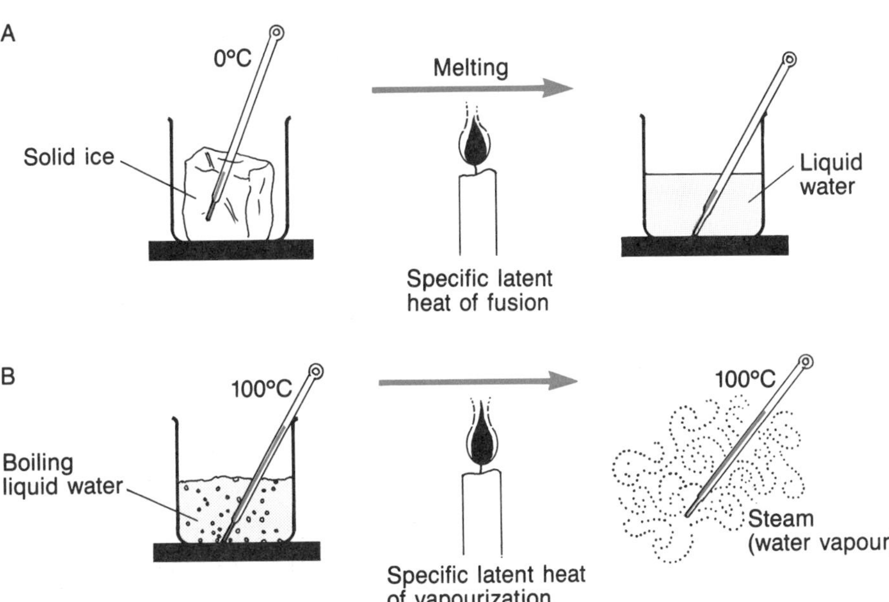

Fig. 13-2 Latent heat causes a change in state, not a change in temperature.

Apparently it takes much more heat to melt the snow than to warm the air.

The quantity of heat required to change 1 kg of a substance from the solid state to the liquid state without changing its temperature is called the **specific latent heat of fusion** (l_f) (Fig. 13-2,A). Since the temperature does not change, the average kinetic energy of the molecules does not change. The heat added to the solid is used to break up the orderly arrangement of the molecules and move them further apart. As a result, the elastic energy of the molecules increases. In other words, the heat of fusion is used to increase the elastic energy of the molecules. Water molecules in the liquid state have about 80 times the elastic energy of water molecules in ice.

Specific Latent Heat of Vapourization

Have you ever been burned by the steam from a boiling kettle? A burn is much more severe from steam than from boiling water, even though the temperature of the water and the steam are the same. Why? There must be more heat energy in the steam than in the boiling water.

A definite amount of heat is required to change a substance from a liquid to a vapour. The quantity of heat required to change 1 kg of a substance from the liquid state to the gaseous state without a change in temperature is called the **specific latent heat of vapourization** (l_v) (Fig. 13-2,B). During this change of state, there is a large increase in the distance between molecules. One millilitre of water expands to occupy about 1700 mL when it becomes water vapour. The specific latent heat of vapourization is used to increase the elastic energy of the molecules. Molecules in the gaseous state have a much greater elastic energy than those in the liquid state. Molecules of water in steam have about 540 times the elastic energy of water molecules in the liquid state.

Units of Specific Latent Heat

Specific latent heat has units of energy per unit mass. If heat energy is represented by Q, mass by m, and latent heat by l, the equation of latent heat is $l = \frac{Q}{m}$. Rearranging this becomes $Q = m \cdot l$. The SI derived unit for specific latent heat is the joule per kilogram (J/kg). However, since small masses are used in laboratories, another acceptable unit is the joule per gram (J/g).

Discussion

1. Compare specific heat capacity and specific latent heat.
2. **a)** Define specific latent heat of fusion (l_f).
   b) Define specific latent heat of vapourization (l_v).
3. Why is the temperature constant during a change of state?
4. What kind of energy changes take place in a substance when it changes state?
5. What is the unit for specific latent heat?
6. What is the relationship between joules per kilogram and joules per gram?

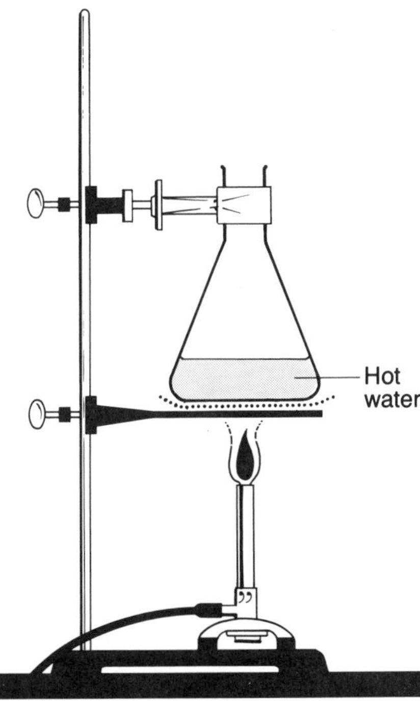

Fig. 13-3 Heating apparatus for finding the specific latent heat of fusion of ice

13.2 Activity: Specific Latent Heat of Fusion of Ice

It requires more heat to melt 1 kg of ice than to change its temperature by 1°C. Just how much heat is required? In this activity you will use the method of mixtures and the Principle of Heat Exchange to determine the specific latent heat of fusion of ice (l_f).

Problem

What is the specific latent heat of fusion of ice?

Materials

Bunsen burner
ring stand, ring clamp, wire gauze
adjustable clamp
Erlenmeyer flask
100 mL graduated cylinder
insulated cups (2)
thermometer
balance
ice cubes
paper towel

CAUTION: Wear safety goggles during this activity. Be careful around the hot water.

Procedure

a. Copy Table 13-1 into your notebook.
b. Set up the heating apparatus as shown in Figure 13-3.
c. Add 100 mL of water to the Erlenmeyer flask. Heat the water to a temperature of about 80°C.
d. Find the mass of an insulated cup.
e. Dry an ice cube and add it to the cup (Fig. 13-4). Measure the mass of the cup plus the ice cube.
f. Subtract (d) from (e) to obtain the mass of the ice cube.
g. Pour the hot water into a second cup. Find and record the temperature of this water.
h. Add the hot water to the ice cube. Stir the mixture. Measure the final temperature of the water as soon as all the ice is melted.
i. Measure the mass of the cup plus its contents. Subtract (e) from (i) to obtain the mass of the hot water.
j. Calculate the quantity of heat needed to melt 1 g of ice as follows:
1) Calculate the heat gained by the ice in melting. Use the formula $Q = m \cdot l_f$. The specific latent heat of fusion l_f is the unknown in the equation.
2) Calculate the heat gained by the melted ice water in warming. Use the formula $Q = m \cdot \Delta t \cdot c$. Remember that this water has an initial temperature of 0°C.
3) Calculate the heat lost by the hot water in cooling. Use the formula $Q = m \cdot \Delta t \cdot c$.

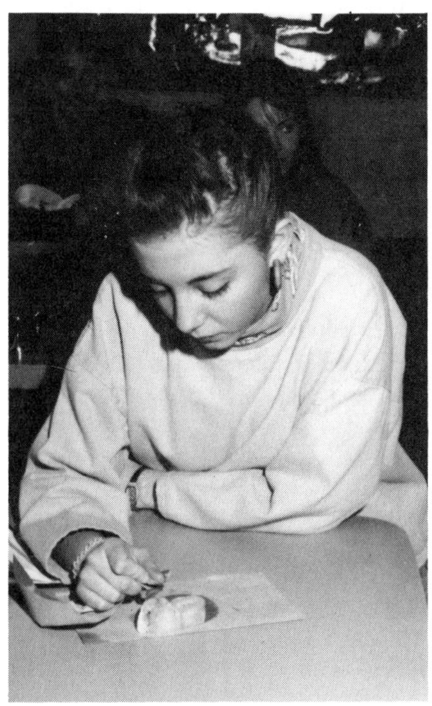

Fig. 13-4 Why is it important that the ice cube be dry in this experiment?

4) Set up the following relationship:

Heat gained by ice in melting + Heat gained by melted ice in warming = Heat lost by hot water in cooling

5) Solve for the specific latent heat of fusion of ice (l_f).

Table 13-1 Determining the Specific Latent Heat of Fusion of Ice

Components of mixture	Mass (kg)	Temperature (°C)			Specific heat J/(kg·°C)	Heat exchanged (J)
		Initial	Final	Change		
Hot water						
Melted ice		0				
Ice		0	0	0	Specific latent heat of fusion ℓ_f (J/kg)	

Discussion

1. a) What is your value for the specific latent heat of fusion of ice?
   b) How much heat would be required to melt 5 kg of ice?
2. Compare your value with other values in the class. Your teacher will help you get a class value.
3. The accepted value for the specific latent heat of fusion of ice is 336 kJ/kg. Compare the class value with the accepted value.
4. What was the temperature of the ice cube when the hot water was added?
5. List sources of error in the experiment. Suggest changes to make these errors smaller.
6. Why does the temperature of an ice-water mixture remain constant during melting and freezing?

Extension

What effect will crushing the ice with an ice crusher prior to placing it in the hot water have on the value you obtain for specific latent heat of fusion of ice? If you have time, perform the activity to test your prediction.

13.3 Demonstration: Specific Latent Heat of Vapourization of Water

It takes more heat to vapourize 1 kg of water than to warm 1 kg of water from 0°C to 100°C. But, even with all this heat, no change in temperature occurs during vapourization. In this demonstration you will find out how much heat

Fig. 13-5 Apparatus for finding the specific latent heat of vapourization of water

is needed to vapourize 1 kg of water—the specific latent heat of vapourization of water.

Problem

What is the specific latent heat of vapourization of water?

Materials

electric kettle (without an automatic shut-off)
top loading balance (2 kg)
timer

CAUTION: Your teacher will demonstrate this experiment.

Procedure

a. Copy Table 13-2 into your notebook.
b. Record the power of the kettle in watts in the table.
c. Fill the kettle about half full of water and place it on the balance as shown in Figure 13-5.
d. Plug in the kettle and bring the water to a boil.
e. Measure and record the combined mass of the kettle and water in kilograms.
f. At the same time as you measure the mass, start the timer.
g. Boil the kettle for about 5 min. *CAUTION: Make sure water always covers the heating coil.*
h. Unplug the kettle and stop the timer.
i. Record the time the water boiled in seconds.
j. Measure and record the mass of the kettle and hot water.
k. Calculate the mass of water that has vapourized.
l. Calculate the heat energy used to vapourize the water.
m. Use the data to calculate the heat needed to vapourize 1 kg of water.

Table 13-2 Finding the Specific Latent Heat of Vapourization of Water

Kettle power = ______ W	Mass of kettle and cold water = ______ g = ______ kg
Boiling time = ______ s	Mass of kettle and hot water = ______ g = ______ kg
Heat added = ______ J	Mass of water vapourized = ______ g = ______ kg

Discussion

1. a) What is your value for the specific latent heat of vapourization of water?
b) Compare your value with other values in the class. Your teacher will help you get a class value.
2. a) The accepted value for the specific latent heat of vapourization of water is 2268 kJ/kg. Compare the class value with the accepted value.
b) Why does the class value differ from the accepted value?
3. List sources of error in the experiment. Suggest ways to reduce the errors.
4. How much heat would be required to vapourize 5 kg of water at 100°C?

Extension

Assuming that you have unlimited equipment, design a procedure you could use to determine a more accurate value for the specific latent heat of vapourization of water. Do *not* perform the experiment.

13.4 Applications of Latent Heat

Latent Heat of Fusion of Ice

Water has one of the largest specific latent heats of fusion of all substances. The specific latent heat of fusion of ice is 336 kJ/kg. In other words, 336 kJ of heat are used up every time 1 kg of ice melts. This is about 80 times as much heat as that needed to change the temperature of water by 1°C. Can you show that this is true? For this reason ice is an excellent refrigerant to use in picnic coolers. When the ice melts it *takes heat from* its surroundings, in this case, the contents of the cooler.

Conversely, when water freezes it *gives heat to* its surroundings. In fact, when 1 kg of water freezes, it releases 336 kJ of heat into its surroundings. Farmers often use this fact to protect crops from frost damage. When they expect a frost they turn on the irrigation (sprinkler) system. The water from the irrigation system falls on the plants and freezes, releasing heat to the plants. This heat helps prevent damage to the cells of the plants (Fig. 13-6).

Fig. 13-6 A water sprinkler system can prevent frost damage. In this photograph a strawberry patch is being irrigated because the air temperature fell to -2°C. This temperature could destroy the blossoms on the strawberry plants.

Sample Problem

How much heat is given off when 200 g of water at 0°C freezes into ice at 0°C?

Given

$m_{water} = 200 \text{ g} = 0.200 \text{ kg}$

$l_{f(ice)} = 336 \text{ kJ/kg}$

Solution

$$Q = m \cdot l_f$$
$$= 0.200 \text{ kg} \times 336 \text{ kJ/kg}$$
$$= 67.2 \text{ kJ}$$

Fig. 13-7 The water is warm and the breeze blowing across the pool is warm. Yet this swimmer feels quite cool. Why?

Required
Q

Analysis
$Q = m \cdot l_f$

Statement
The heat given off when the water freezes is 67.2 kJ.

Latent Heat of Vapourization of Water

When water vapourizes it *takes heat from* its surroundings. The specific latent heat of vapourization of water is 2268 kJ/kg. In other words, 2268 kJ of heat are used up to vapourize 1 kg of water. This is about 540 times as much heat as that needed to raise the temperature of water by 1°C. Can you show that this is true?

Swimmers usually feel cool when they step out of the water, particularly when it is windy (Fig. 13-7). This is because water evaporates from the skin. If only 10 mL of water evaporates from the skin, 22 680 J of heat are required. Much of this heat comes from the swimmer's body. As a result, the skin cools down.

When steam condenses it *gives heat to* its surroundings. This explains why a burn from steam is much worse than a burn from boiling water. When the steam condenses on a person's skin, it gives off heat. If only 1 mL of water condenses, 2268 J of energy are transferred to the skin. That alone is enough to cause a severe burn. The condensed steam also cools from 100°C to body temperature of 37°C. This transfers another 265 J to the skin. So don't pass your arm across the spout of a boiling kettle!

Sample Problem

What mass of water at 100°C can be changed into steam at 100°C by the addition of 3.40×10^6 J of heat?

Given
$Q = 3.40 \times 10^6$ J
$l_v = 2.268 \times 10^6$ J/kg

Required
m

Analysis
$$m = \frac{Q}{l_v}$$

Solution
$$m = \frac{Q}{l_v}$$
$$= \frac{3.40 \times 10^6 \text{ J}}{2.268 \times 10^6 \text{ J/kg}}$$
$$= 1.50 \text{ kg}$$

Statement
The heat can vapourize 1.5 kg of water.

Section Review

1. a) What is the direction of heat transfer when ice melts? when water freezes?
   b) Why is ice an excellent refrigerant?
   c) Why is a sprinkler system often used on fruit crops when there is a frost warning?
2. a) How much heat is given off when 2.4 kg of water at the freezing point freezes?
   b) What mass of ice at the freezing point requires 2500 J of heat to melt?

3. a) What is the direction of heat transfer when steam condenses? when water vapourizes?
   b) Why do swimmers feel cool when they come out of a pool or lake?
   c) Why is a steam burn so severe?
4. A kettle is rated at 1200 W (1200 J/s). What is the least time the kettle must operate to completely vapourize 0.150 kg of water at the boiling point?

13.5 Latent Heat and the Heat Pump

Heat pumps are used in many homes to increase the efficiency of electrical heating. A **heat pump** is a machine that efficiently transfers heat between indoors and outdoors. In the summer it air conditions the house by transferring heat outdoors. In the winter this process is reversed. A heat pump can transfer 2–4 times more energy in heat than it uses in electricity.

The refrigeration unit of a heat pump contains a substance called the refrigerant. It has a high specific latent heat of vapourization and can be easily liquefied or vapourized. The state is changed by adding or removing heat and by changing the pressure on the refrigerant.

During cooling, the heat pump forces liquid refrigerant through the indoor coils (Fig. 13-8). This cools the coils. Warm indoor air is passed over the coils by the furnace blower. This cools the air and also removes moisture from it. The cool dry air is then circulated through the building by the blower. In the coils, the refrigerant changes from a liquid to a gas as it absorbs heat. An amount of heat equal to the specific latent heat of vapourization of the refrigerant is removed from the air in the house for every kilogram of refrigerant that changes state. Refrigerant in the vapour state is circulated to the outdoor unit. There electrical energy is used to run a compressor and fan to change the refrigerant to a liquid again. When this change in state occurs, the latent heat of vapourization is transferred to the outside air. This cycle is repeated again and again during the cooling cycle.

During heating, a reversing valve changes the direction of refrigerant flow. Now the refrigerant absorbs heat outdoors from air forced over it by the fan

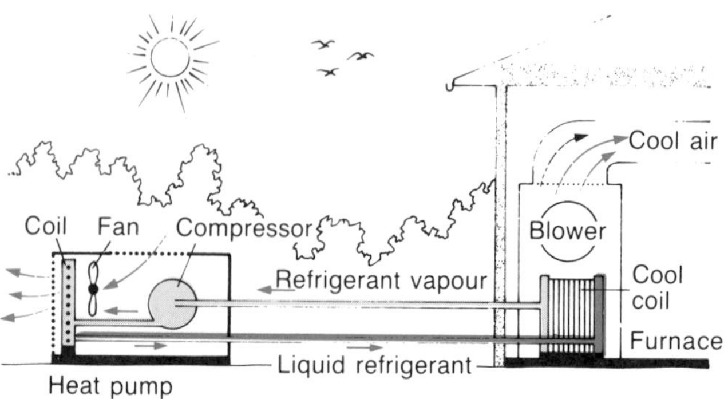

Fig. 13-8 A heat pump in operation during a cooling cycle

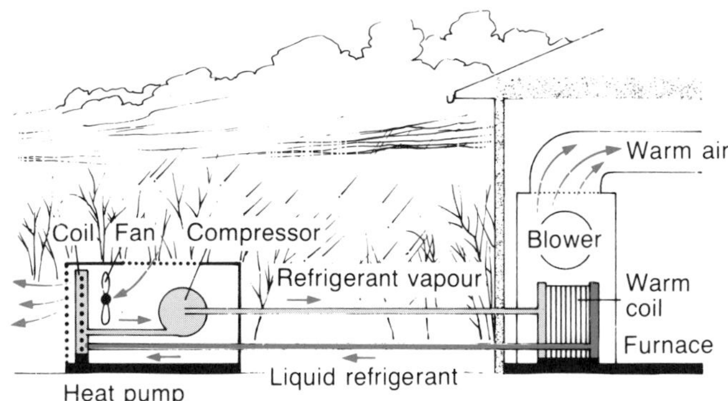

Fig. 13-9 A heat pump during a warming cycle

(Fig. 13-9). This outside air contains heat even on the coldest day. The refrigerant absorbs the specific latent heat as it vapourizes. This heat is carried in the resulting warm vapour and is pumped through the indoor coil. This warms the coil. The blower forces indoor air over the warm coil, thereby warming this air. As the warm vapour in the coil cools, it condenses, giving up its latent heat of vapourization. The resulting liquid refrigerant returns to the outdoor coils to repeat the cycle.

Unfortunately, the colder the outside air becomes the more electrical energy it takes to extract the heat. In many heat pumps a balance point is reached at

Fig. 13-10 An earth-coupled heat pump showing the coils buried in the ground

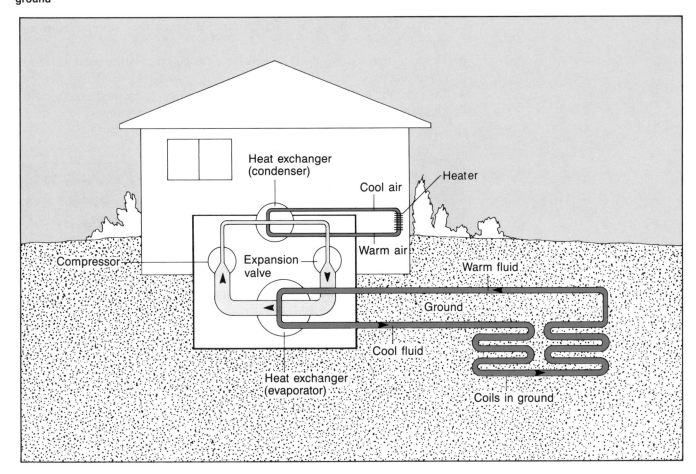

an outside air temperature of about −2°C. Below this temperature it takes more electrical energy to extract and transport the heat than the heat made available. When the air reaches this temperature, the heat pump is disengaged. A thermostat automatically engages an oil or gas furnace or an electrical resistance heater to provide the heat.

To overcome the need for auxiliary heating, heat pumps are being designed to extract heat from water in wells, lakes, rivers, or from the ground. They maintain their efficiency deep into winter because the water and the ground below the frost level stay within a fairly narrow temperature range year-round. However, these systems are about twice as expensive to install as air systems. An earth-coupled heat pump puts the outside heat pipe in a horizontal trench beneath the frost level (Fig. 13-10). Typically, a water or water-antifreeze mixture is pumped through the pipes, bringing heat from the earth to the heat pump. Earth-coupled systems can be made about 25% more efficient than they are now by pumping the refrigerant directly into the earth-coupled piping rather than through a heat exchanger. The key to installing the earth-coupled system on small city lots is to install the pipes vertically to a depth of about 25 m. In the future, better refrigerants and better exchange systems should make heat pumps even more efficient.

Section Review

1. What is a heat pump?
2. Compare a heat pump to a refrigerator. How are they similar? How are they different?
3. Describe the cooling cycle, when the heat pump is being used as an air conditioner.
4. Describe the heating cycle, when the heat pump is being used as a furnace.
5. Describe efforts to increase the efficiency of the heat pump.

13.6 Activity: The Energy Content of Foods

Foods contain chemical energy, a form of potential energy. Your body "burns" food to do work. Some of the food's potential energy is stored in your muscles. Some becomes bulk kinetic energy as your arms, legs, and blood move. Much of the energy is changed to heat energy. This energy is used to replace the heat lost from the body. Without it your body temperature would not stay at 37°C.

In this activity you will burn some foods. You will capture the heat that is produced by letting it warm up some water. This will give you the information you need to solve the problem that follows.

Problem

How many joules of chemical energy are in 1 kg of some foods?

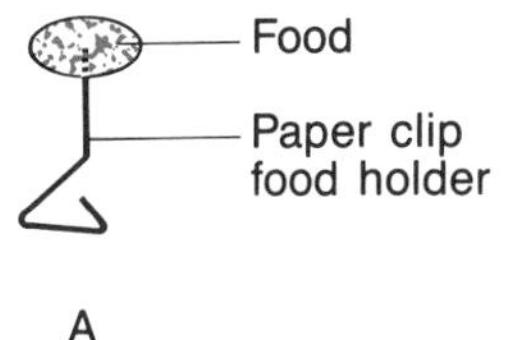

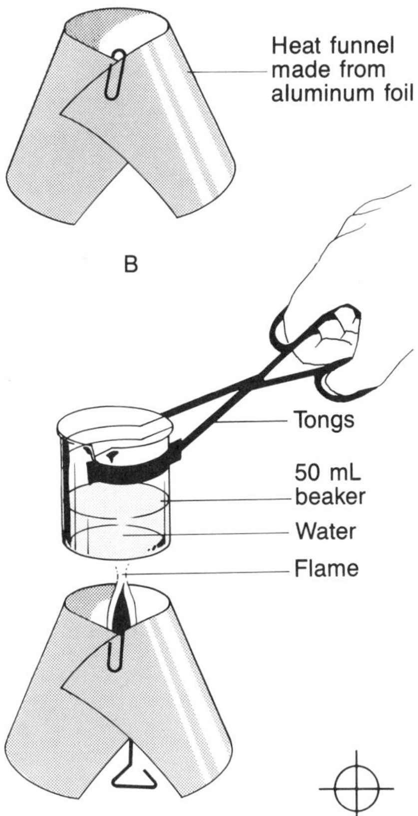

Fig. 13-11 Apparatus for studying the energy content of foods

Materials

50 mL beaker
paper clips (2)
beaker tongs
balance
peanuts, walnuts, spoon-sized shredded wheat
10 mL graduated cylinder
sheet of aluminum foil 10 cm × 15 cm

CAUTION: Wear safety goggles during this activity.

Procedure

a. Copy Table 13-3 into your notebook.
b. Make a food holder out of a paper clip by bending it as shown in Figure 13-11,A.
c. Make a heat funnel by folding the sheet of aluminum foil to form a cone with an opening at both ends. Fasten the ends together with a paper clip as shown in Figure 13-11,B.
d. Find the mass of a piece of walnut in grams. Insert the end of the paper clip holder into the sample. Do not lose any of the food! *CAUTION: Be careful not to puncture your hand.*
e. Place 30 mL of cold water in the 50 mL beaker. Record the temperature of the water.
f. Ignite the food with a match. Place the heat funnel over the food as shown in Figure 13-11,C. Hold the bottom of the beaker in the tip of the flame until the food is burned to an ash. Support the beaker using the tongs.
g. Record the highest temperature reached by the water.
h. Repeat steps (c) to (f) for a peanut and for one spoon-sized shredded wheat.
i. Calculate the energy content in joules per kilogram of each food. Determine the class value. Your teacher will help you do this.

Table 13-3 Energy Content of Some Foods

Food burned		*Water heated*					
			Temperature (°C)				
Food	*Mass (kg)*	*Mass (kg)*	*Initial*	*Final*	*Change*	*Specific heat capacity (J/kg·°C)*	*Heat from food (J)*
Walnut						4200	
Peanut						4200	
Shredded wheat						4200	

Discussion

1. What is the class value for the energy content of walnuts, peanuts, and shredded wheat in joules per kilogram (J/kg)?
2. The accepted values are: walnuts 27 300 kJ/kg; peanuts 24 600 kJ/kg; shredded wheat 14 900 kJ/kg. Compare the class values with the accepted values. Account for any differences.

3. If you were going on a long hike, what food might make an excellent addition to your pack? Why?

Extension

If time permits, repeat this experiment with another food provided by your teacher. For example, you may want to try another cereal or a marshmallow, so you can compare its energy content with that of shredded wheat.

13.7 Heat Energy, Food, and Exercise

In Activity 13.6 you discovered that some foods release large quantities of heat when they are burned. Of what importance is this to you? What relationship is there between the foods you eat and the kinds of exercise you do? Read on to find out.

Specific Heat of Combustion

The molecules of foods are made mainly of carbon and hydrogen atoms. These molecules store the sun's energy as chemical potential energy in the bonds between the atoms. When completely burned in oxygen, foods produce carbon dioxide, water, and heat energy. The heat energy released when 1 kg of a substance is burned is called the **specific heat of combustion**. The specific heat of combustion of substances is measured in kilojoules per kilogram. The

Table 13-4 Specific Heats of Combustion of Some Foods

Food	*Specific Heat of Combustion (kJ/kg)*
Bacon, raw	27 900
Beef, t-bone steak	16 700
Bread, white	11 300
Bread, whole wheat	10 200
Carrot, raw	1 800
Cereal, oatmeal	16 400
Cereal, shredded wheat	14 900
Eggs, fried	9 100
Eggs, hard boiled	6 800
Peanuts	24 600
Potatoes, boiled	3 200
Potato chips	23 900

Fig. 13-12 Running is one of the best ways to use up surplus food energy. However, even running cannot make up for careless eating habits. How long, for example, would you have to run to use up the energy in one kilogram of potato chips (see Tables 13-4 and 13-5)?

complete combustion of 1 kg of shredded wheat produces 14 900 kJ of heat. Therefore the specific heat of combustion of shredded wheat is 14 900 kJ/kg.

The specific heat of combustion of walnuts is 27 300 kJ/kg. Walnuts have about twice as much chemical potential energy as the same mass of shredded wheat. Now you know why people on diets should not eat nuts. Some heats of combustion for foods are given in Table 13-4.

Food and Exercise

A 50 kg boy from the age of 13 to 15 needs about 13 000 kJ of energy daily for good nutrition. At the same age, a 50 kg girl needs about 11 000 kJ. This energy is used for growth and activity. Different exercises make your body burn joules at different rates. By exercising you get somewhat the same result as cutting down your food intake. For example, you could burn as many joules as are found in a piece of bread by walking for 15 min. About 10 min of bicycling, 7 min of swimming, or 4 min of running do the same thing (Fig. 13-12). The rates of energy use for different forms of activity are shown in Table 13-5.

Table 13-5 Activity and Energy Use

Activity (70 kg person)	*Rate of energy use (kJ/min)*
Reclining	6
Walking fast	22
Bicycling	35
Swimming	47
Running	82

The Calorie

Before scientists knew that heat was just another form of energy, they defined a unit of heat called the calorie (cal). No doubt you have heard of it. A **calorie** is equal to 4.2 J.

Table 13-6 Joule Content of a Dinner

Food	*Energy content (kJ)*
85 g sirloin roast	1071
1 medium-sized baked potato	777
115 mL cooked carrots	84
115 mL cooked broccoli	84
57 mL white sauce	441
1 large white flour roll	483
9 cm wedge of double-crusted apple pie	1995
1 glass of whole milk	693
Total	5628

Now that we know heat is just another form of energy, there is little sense in using two different units to measure the same thing. The calorie is an outdated unit. The SI unit of heat, the joule, has replaced the calorie. Although the energy content of foods may still be quoted in some cookbooks in **Calories** (one Calorie = one thousand calories), joules should be used. Table 13-6 shows the joule content of a typical dinner. Does it meet the energy needs of the average boy or girl? How would you adjust this meal if you were overweight? if you under-exercised?

Section Review

1. Define specific heat of combustion.
2. What are the units of specific heat of combustion?
3. Suppose that a person reclines for 15 min. Then this person bicycles for 15 min to a swimming pool. The swim lasts 30 min. How much energy is used in the hour?
4. Look at the heat of combustion of foods in Table 13-4. Why should a person on a diet stay away from potato chips, fried foods, and nuts?
5. **a)** Define the calorie and the Calorie.
   b) Why is the calorie an outdated unit of energy?
   c) What is the relationship between the calorie and the joule?

13.8 The Fate of All Forms of Energy

Some people claim that we have an energy shortage. Others argue that there is plenty of thermal energy, claiming that this energy is just difficult to extract. What do you think?

Energy Conversions

All forms of energy eventually become thermal energy as they are used. You converted electric energy and chemical energy into heat energy in earlier activities. The heat energy became thermal energy in the environment. Joule and other scientists converted gravitational energy and bulk kinetic energy into thermal energy. It is easy to convert various forms of energy into thermal energy, but it is difficult to convert thermal energy into other useful forms.

The Fate of Concentrated Forms of Energy

Suppose, for example, that a litre of gasoline is placed in the gas tank of a car. Where does the chemical energy in the gasoline go? It is first burned in the engine to produce heat. Some of the heat is carried to the environment by the car's cooling and exhaust systems. Some is converted into bulk kinetic energy in the engine and other moving parts of the car. This kinetic energy gradually becomes heat energy in the engine, tires, brakes, and air molecules. Eventually all of the chemical energy in the fuel becomes thermal energy. This thermal energy is so widely spread in the environment that it is impossible to get it back. Imagine the task of collecting all of the thermal energy produced during a trip of 200 km!

All forms of energy, through use, eventually become thermal energy. The chemical energy in foods and fuels becomes thermal energy. The bulk kinetic energy of the moon is gradually becoming thermal energy. The nuclear energy in uranium is becoming thermal energy. But, all of this thermal energy is so widely spaced that it is difficult to harness. This is one more reason for conserving the chemical energy the sun has given us. It makes sense to harness the energy in the tides, the sun, and the wind (Fig. 13-13). We might as well use these forms of energy and save the concentrated chemical energy stored in fossil fuels for other uses. Besides, the energy from tides, the sun, and the wind is non-polluting.

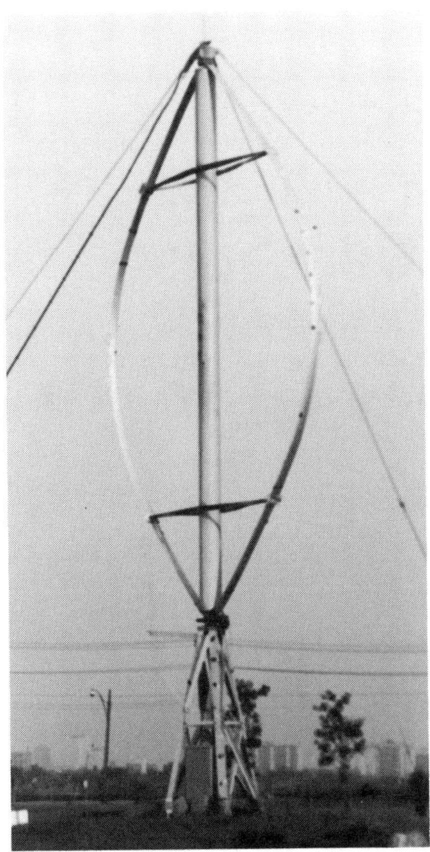

Fig. 13-13 This Canadian-designed windwill can reduce our dependence on fossil fuels as an energy source. Though this windmill, the Darrieus rotor, was invented many years ago, few are yet to be found in Canada. Why do you suppose this is so?

Section Review

1. What eventually happens to all forms of energy as they are used?
2. The more the human body exercises, the more energy it uses. For example, a person shovelling snow for an hour uses about 2710 kJ of energy. The same person using a snowblower uses about 1115 kJ of energy. But, in addition, the snowblower uses 0.2 kg of gasoline.
   a) How much energy is consumed by the human and the machine when the snowblower is used? Assume that 1 kg of gasoline is equivalent to about 50 000 kJ of energy.
   b) Trace the energy conversions that take place in both cases until the initial energy becomes thermal energy.
   c) Should a snowblower be used to remove snow from small sidewalks and driveways? Discuss.

Chapter Highlights

1. Latent heat causes a change in state rather than a change in temperature.
2. The amount of heat needed to change the state of 1 kg of a substance is called the specific latent heat.
3. It takes about 80 times as much heat to melt 1 kg of ice as it does to warm 1 kg of water 1°C.
4. Farmers use the high specific latent heat of fusion of ice to protect crops from frost damage.
5. It takes about 540 times as much heat to vapourize 1 kg of water as it does to warm 1 kg of water 1°C.
6. A steam burn is much more severe than a hot water burn because of the high specific latent heat of vapourization of water.
7. Heat pumps are machines that use electrical energy to transfer heat between the inside and outside of a building.
8. The specific heat of combustion of a substance is the amount of heat released when 1 kg of the substance completely burns.
9. Food must be balanced with exercise to prevent overweight.
10. The end form of all forms of energy is thermal energy.

Key Terms

heat pump
latent
specific heat of combustion
specific latent heat of fusion
specific latent heat of vapourization

Recognizing the Concepts

Each of the following statements or questions is followed by four responses. Choose the correct response in each case. (Do not write in this book.)

1. The term latent heat means that which of the following will not change?
   a) state **b)** temperature **c)** mass **d)** potential energy
2. How much heat does 1 kg of ice give up when it freezes?
   a) 2268 kJ **b)** 336 kJ **c)** 4.2 kJ **d)** 2.1 kJ
3. What effect does evaporation have on the temperature of a substance?
   a) increases the temperature
   b) decreases the temperature
   c) does not affect the temperature
   d) the effect depends on the substance
4. How much heat does 4.0 kg of water at 100°C absorb as it changes to steam at 100°C?
   a) 5.7×10^2 kJ **c)** 9.1×10^3 kJ
   b) 2.3×10^3 kJ **d)** 9.1×10^5 kJ
5. During the heating cycle, the refrigerant in the outside coils of a heat pump
   a) changes from a liquid to a gas and releases heat
   b) changes from a gas to a liquid and releases heat
   c) changes from a liquid to a gas and absorbs heat
   d) changes from a gas to a liquid and absorbs heat
6. During a heavy snowfall it becomes warmer outside because of
   a) evaporation **b)** condensation **c)** freezing **d)** melting
7. Which of the following activities makes your body burn joules the fastest?
   a) bicycling **b)** running **c)** swimming **d)** walking fast
8. The end form of all forms of energy is
   a) bulk kinetic **b)** elastic **c)** thermal **d)** chemical

Fig. 13-14 A refrigerator operates on the same principle as an air conditioner. Does this mean that you could cool your home simply by leaving the refrigerator door open?

Understanding the Concepts

1. Approximately how much larger is the specific latent heat of fusion of ice than the specific heat capacity of ice?
2. Approximately how much larger is the specific latent heat of vapourization of water than the specific heat capacity of water?
3. Why is a heat pump less efficient at extracting heat from the outside when the outside air temperature is lower?
4. A football player would be wise to eat a package of nuts before a game rather than a large apple. Why?
5. Explain why shaking water in an insulated bottle raises its temperature.
6. Is it possible to cool the kitchen by leaving the refrigerator running with the door open (Fig. 13-14)? Discuss.

7. Explain why both exercising and dieting are essential components of a program for losing excess mass.
8. Why do glaciers stay around in summer when it's warm enough for grass to grow nearby?

Applying the Concepts

1. Some hot water radiators have a single pipe connected to them. The steam comes to the radiator and the water leaves in the same pipe. The steam and the water are both at a temperature of 100°C. Where does the heat come from to warm the room?
2. A 100 W immersion heater is placed in an insulated container holding 250 g of water at 10°C.
   a) What is the minimum length of time needed for the water to reach a temperature of 30°C?
   b) What assumption did you make to do the problem? Is this valid?
3. The high specific latent heat of vapourization of water contributes to its usefulness as a cooling agent in the radiators of cars. Explain why.
4. An engineer claims that we do not have a shortage of energy. There is just as much energy in the universe as there was in 1492. Do you agree or disagree? Explain.
5. What mass of ice at 0°C can be changed to a liquid at 0°C by 0.8 kg of water at 100°C?
6. Calculate the quantity of heat required to melt 100 g of ice at an initial temperature of −20°C.
7. Calculate the quantity of heat needed to convert 50 g of ice, initially at −10°C, into water at 80°C.
8. How much heat is needed to change 60 g of water at 100°C into steam at 100°C?
9. Calculate the minimum amount of heat needed to vapourize 4 kg of water at 80°C.
10. How much heat is released when 150 g of steam at 130°C is condensed and cooled to 30°C?
11. Calculate the quantity of heat needed to convert 80 g of ice at −40°C into steam at 160°C.
12. One kilogram of fat stores 30 000 kJ of energy. Suppose you take in 500 kJ more energy each day than you burn off through physical activity. (This is the energy in a small bag of potato chips.)
    a) How many kilograms will you gain in 36 d?
    b) Assume that you are carrying 5 kg of excess fat. How many days of running 20 min per day will it take you to get rid of the excess fat?

Investigations

1. Design an experiment using an immersion heater to find the specific latent heat of fusion of ice (Fig. 13-15). If your teacher approves of your design, try your experiment and compare your results to those you got in Activity 13.2.

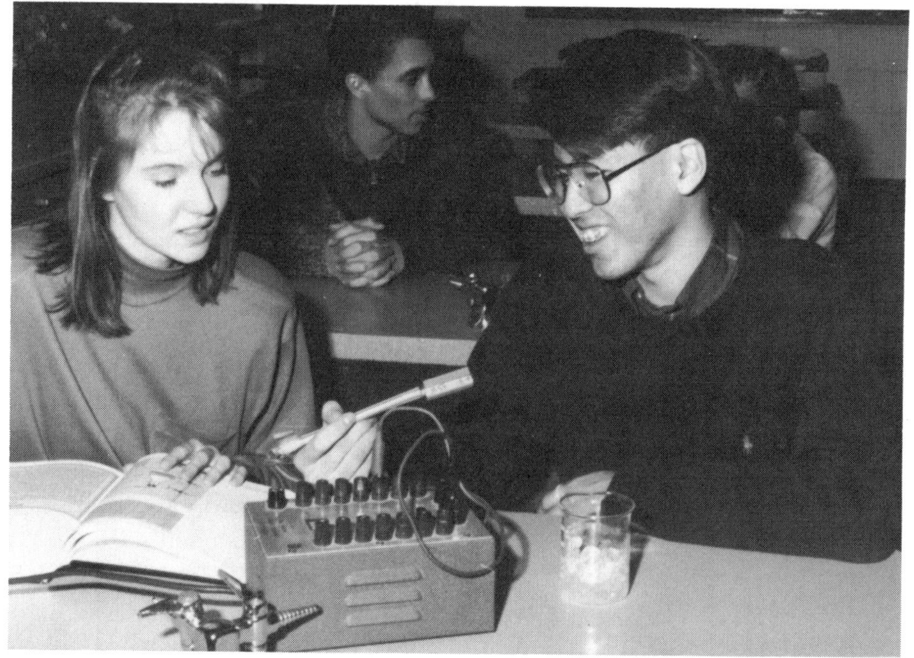

Fig. 13-15 You found the specific latent heat of fusion of ice in Activity 13.2 by using the method of mixtures. But you can also find it by using an immersion heater. Can you design an experiment to do this? (Hint: Think about the way you found the specific latent heat of vapourization in Section 13.3.)

2. Design an experiment using a steam generator, a water trap, a container of cold water, a thermometer, and a balance to find the specific latent heat of vapourization of water. *CAUTION: Steam burns.*
3. Keep track of the food you eat during a typical day. Also record your activity for the day. Consult a cookbook to find the energy content of the food. Calculate how long it will take you to burn off each meal.
4. Design an experiment to compare the energy content of different kinds of cereals. For example, you could compare corn flakes, rice krispies, and bran flakes.
5. Research what a bomb calorimeter is and how it is used to determine the specific heat of combustion of foods and fuels.

Career: *METEOROLOGICAL TECHNICIAN*

HELP WANTED:
METEOROLOGICAL TECHNICIAN

A small airport requires a meteorological technician to carry out technical duties to provide information for weather reports and forecasts; must be prepared to work shifts.

A meteorological technician observes, records, and transmits in a special code, information about the existing state of the atmosphere. Surface weather observers use a variety of instruments to measure pressure, temperature, humidity, wind speed, precipitation, and cloud cover from the earth's surface. Aerological technicians record data to a height of 30 km using gas-filled balloons, radio receivers, and computers. The data are recorded and transmitted hourly to weather offices across North America and around the world. Many weather stations are located in isolated areas. In fact, some technicians observe ice conditions in Canada's navigable waters from aircraft or from icebreakers. Information provided by technicians is used by pilots, sailors, farmers, forecasters, and industrial personnel, among others.

Meteorological technicians must enjoy working with people, and be able to express themselves clearly. They must also have the skill to work with precision instruments. An aptitude for mathematics, physical sciences, and geography is essential. All training required of technicians is provided by the Atmospheric Environment Service Training Branch, Environment Canada, Downsview, Ontario. Technicians can take correspondence courses to improve their qualifications on the job.

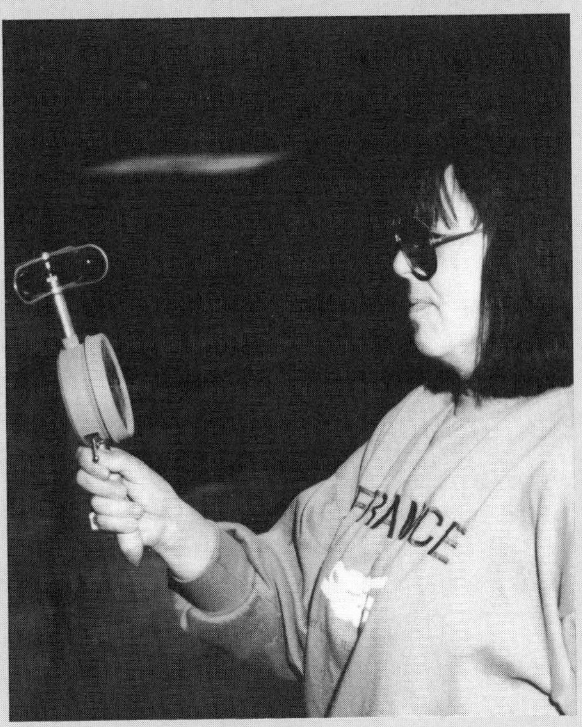

Biography

David J. Young: Electrical Engineer

David Young heads a small group of engineers and technologists working on heat pumps and related thermal systems in the Electrical Research Department of Ontario Hydro. Heat pumps "gather" heat from their surroundings and "deliver" more energy to their owners than they consume in electricity input. Therefore they are important tools for energy conservation and energy substitution in the electric industry.

Young graduated from the University of Toronto in 1972 with a Bachelor's degree in Engineering Science. He joined Ontario Hydro's Utilization Section, which researches technical questions on the wide variety of ways that electricity is put to use by the customers of this large utility. Energy use studies, instrumentation design, and wiring safety testing were among the jobs he tackled first. However, by 1977, almost all of David Young's time was spent in the design and testing of new types of heat pumps more suited to Canada's cold climate than the ones that had been on the market previously. Although his background is mainly in electrical engineering, David claims that the solid grounding in thermodynamics from his university physics courses has never let him down in the analysis of heat pumps, which combine a variety of electrical and mechanical aspects. As the author of several international papers on heat pump design, David Young is consulted by manufacturers in Canada and abroad in their work to make better products for consumers in cold climates. Today, about two-thirds of David's time is spent in planning and reviewing the laboratory and field work of his unit on heat pump performance, design, and analysis.

VISTA

STORING HEAT THROUGH PHASE CHANGES

Have you ever wished that you could turn on a switch in January and bathe in the warmth of July? Scientists are researching ways to do exactly that. Heat from the sun is already being absorbed and stored in massive brick or stone walls during the daytime and radiated back into rooms at night. The amount stored depends on the mass of the wall, its temperature change, and the specific heat capacity of the rock. But is there a way to store more heat and for longer periods of time?

Scientists and engineers are experimenting with phase changes as a way to store large quantities of heat. A material which undergoes a phase change at a desirable temperature is placed in walls, floors, ceilings, and 2000 L tanks (Fig. A). The amount of thermal energy stored depends on the mass of the material and on its specific latent heat. A material with a high specific latent heat of fusion and a melting point between 20°C and 25°C is ideal. During sunny days the material absorbs heat from the sun and melts (Fig. B). When the surroundings become cooler than its freezing point, this heat is released as the material refreezes (Fig. C). As long as there is enough of the substance that it never completely melts or freezes, the building remains close to the freezing temperature of the substance. (For comparison, as long as there is some ice in a glass of liquid it stays close to 0°C.)

Glauber's salt (hydrated crystals of sodium sulfate) is the most common material used. It has water of hydration attached to molecules of sodium sulfate. Glauber's salt has several merits. First, it costs very little. Second, it has an excellent ability to store heat; the latent heat of fusion of Glauber's salt is very large. Third, it has a melting point close to the human body comfort temperature. However, it has drawbacks. It tends to supercool below its melting temperature before freezing. Thus the stored heat is released below the most comfortable temperature. Also, repeated freezing and thawing breaks down the hydrate. The water of hydration is released from the sodium sulfate. This decreases the ability of the substance to store heat. Glauber's salt is also sensitive to humidity; it performs poorly if the air is too dry or too damp. And Glauber's

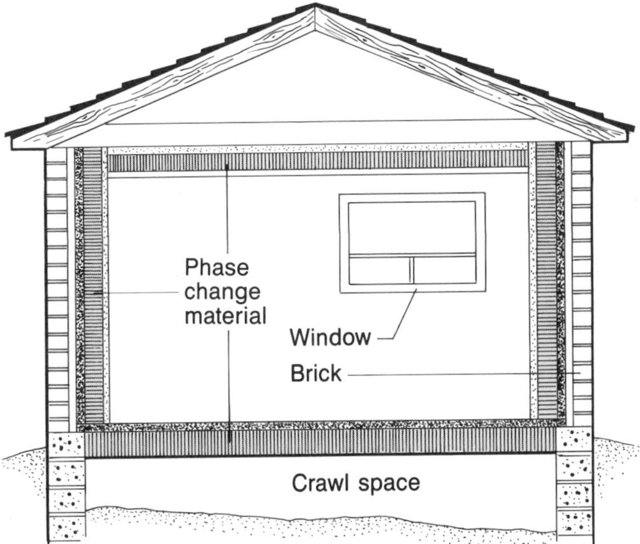

A cross section of a house showing a material with a high specific latent heat of fusion in the walls, floor, and ceiling.

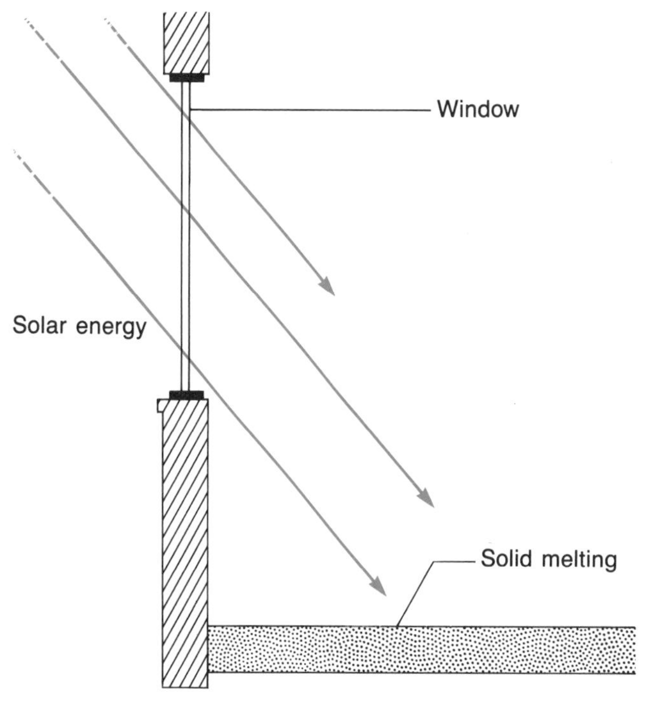

During the day, the solid absorbs heat and melts.

salt is a poor conductor; heat absorbed at the surface takes a long time to permeate inward. All of these problems can be overcome but at considerable cost.

Scientists are now experimenting with paraffin, a byproduct of the oil refining industry. Different kinds of paraffin have melting points between 16°C and 38°C. They can be blended to produce melting points between these two extremes. A mixture of paraffins with a desirable melting point could be encapsulated into building materials to act as heat reservoirs. One drawback is that paraffin wax is flammable. However, it burns slowly like a candle rather than explosively like gasoline. Also, it can be impregnated with a fire retardant material.

Materials which store heat as a result of a phase-change have other uses as well. They can be stitched into clothing to improve their insulating ability. They can be included in the walls of thermos jugs and mugs to keep liquids hot longer. And they can be mixed with the asphalt and concrete used on overpasses to prevent the buildup of dangerous ice. It is impossible to predict all the future uses of materials that store heat by a phase change. But they will certainly be used for seasonal and daily storage, saving up heat at one time for use at another.

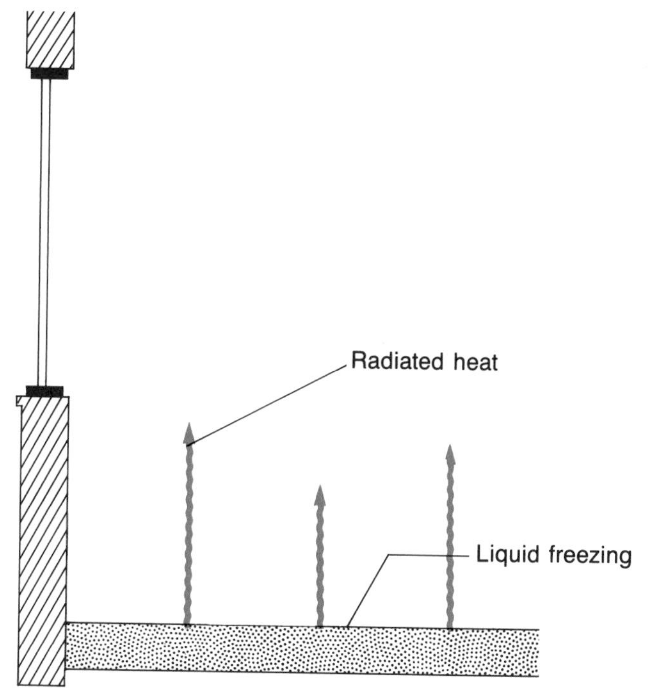

At night the liquid gives up heat to the room and freezes.

UNIT 5 Magnetism and Electricity

CHAPTERS
14. Magnetism
15. Static Electricity
16. Cells and Batteries
17. Electric Circuits
18. Electromagnetism

Magnetism and electricity are important in our lives. Magnetism is used for such diverse things as fastening cupboard doors, finding one's way in the outdoors, and separating iron from copper and aluminum. Electricity heats homes, lights neon signs and streets, starts cars, and runs microcomputers.

Electricity also has magnetic effects. You may have seen a large crane suspend a disc above a heap of scrap metal. Suddenly the metal leaps to the disc. Pieces appear to defy the force of gravity. Why? The disc is an electromagnet. The crane operator has directed electricity to the disc. The disc becomes magnetic and attracts the metal. Turn off the electricity and the electromagnet ceases to operate.

In this unit you will first study magnetic attraction and repulsion and the Domain Theory of Magnetism. Then you will study electric charge at rest and in motion, and the properties of series and parallel circuits. Finally you will study the magnetic effects of an electric current. Learn as much as you can about magnetism and electricity because they have a profound effect on how we live.

14 Magnetism

CHAPTER CONTENTS

CHAPTER OBJECTIVES

After completing this chapter you should be able to:

1. Distinguish between: magnetic and non-magnetic materials; natural and artificial magnets; cylindrical and horseshoe magnets; induced and permanent magnets.
2. Describe magnetic, north-seeking, and south-seeking poles.
3. Describe an action-at-a-distance force and measure the force exerted by a magnet.
4. State and apply the Law of Magnetic Attraction and Repulsion.
5. Define and describe a magnetic field and a magnetic line of force.
6. Outline the postulates of the Domain Theory of Magnetism.
7. Apply the Domain Theory of Magnetism to explain common phenomena.
8. Describe applications of permanent and induced magnets.

In this chapter you will study magnetism (Fig. 14-1). You will investigate the properties of magnets and discover the nature of the forces around and between magnets. You will also trace the direction and location of these forces. You will make induced and permanent magnets. You will study the theory scientists use to explain the properties of magnets. Finally, you will study several applications of magnets.

Fig. 14-1 Which of these substances are magnetic? Which are magnets?

14.1 Magnets and Magnetic Substances

Magnetic Substances

Substances that are not attracted to a magnet are called **non-magnetic** substances. Paper, leather, copper, glass, aluminum, plastic, and wood are examples. Substances which are attracted to a magnet are called **magnetic** substances. Materials which contain iron, nickel, and cobalt are strongly attracted to a magnet. As a result, they are magnetic substances. Canadian five cent pieces have been made of pure nickel since 1922, so they are strongly attracted. A United States five cent piece shows little attraction to a magnet since it is only 25% nickel. The rest is copper. Steel is mostly iron so steel is a magnetic substance. A lodestone contains iron so it, too, is a magnetic substance.

Types of Magnets

An object that attracts magnetic substances is called a **magnet**. A **lodestone** is a **natural magnet**. A substance that acquires the properties of lodestone is said to be **magnetized**. **Artificial magnets** are made from magnetic substances. Most artificial magnets are made from steel, which is mainly a mixture of iron and carbon. Some magnets also contain cobalt and nickel. Sometimes aluminum is added to these materials to make a very strong, light magnet called an Alnico magnet. An Alnico magnet contains steel, aluminum, nickel, and cobalt.

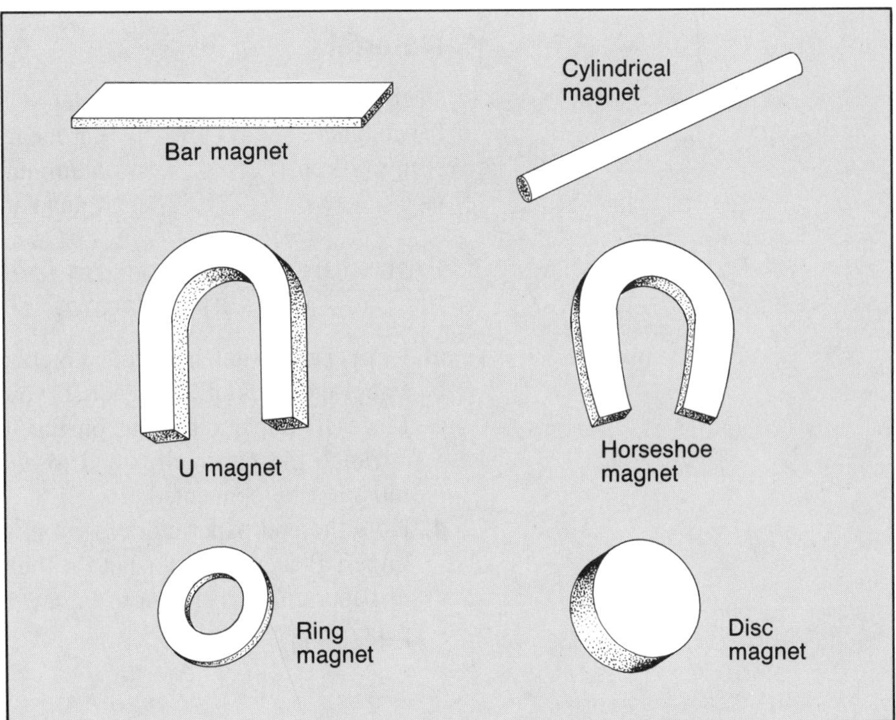

Fig. 14-2 Magnets are made in different shapes.

Magnets are classified into groups based on shape. Common examples are bar magnets, cylinder magnets, and U-shaped magnets. One in the shape of a horseshoe is called a horseshoe magnet. There are also ring magnets and disc magnets. Different shaped magnets are shown in Figure 14-2.

Section Review

1. **a)** What is a magnet?
   b) Distinguish between a magnet and a magnetic substance.
   c) Name three magnetic substances.
2. What substances are used to make artificial magnets?
3. Name and sketch five different shapes of magnet.

14.2 Activity: The Magnetic Force

In this activity you will compare the forces at the ends of a magnet. You will also study the ability of a magnet to exert a force on a magnetic substance without touching it. Finally, you will see if a magnetic force can pass through substances.

Problems

How do the strengths of the poles of a magnet compare? Does the magnetic force pass through substances?

Materials

steel paper clips (10)	ruler	wax paper
bar magnet	cardboard	glass
string (20 cm)	aluminum foil	plastic lid
tape	Canadian penny (1¢)	iron lid of a can

Procedure A Comparing the Magnetic Force at the Poles of a Magnet

a. Copy Table 14-1 into your notebook.
b. Label the ends of a magnet so you can tell them apart.
c. Place 10 paper clips flat on the table. The table must not be magnetic. Arrange the paper clips end to end in a line. The ends should touch but must not be connected.
d. Hold the end paper clip closest to the magnet in a fixed position with your finger. Place a magnet flat on the table. Slide the magnet toward the line of paper clips as shown in Figure 14-3. Stop when the magnet touches the paper clip.

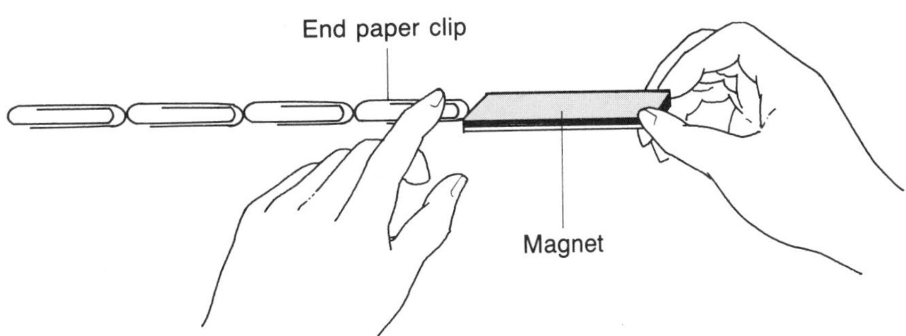

Fig. 14-3 Comparing the magnetic force at the poles of a magnet

e. Lift your finger from the paper clip. See how many paper clips the magnet will drag along the table. Do the activity several times. Use the same end of the magnet each time. Record the results in your table.

f. Repeat steps (c), (d), and (e) using the other end of the magnet.

g. Compare the number of paper clips pulled by each pole. Compare your results with those of your classmates.

Table 14-1 The Forces at the Poles of a Magnet

Trial number	*Number of paper clips pulled*	
	First pole	*Second pole*
1		
2		
3		
4		
Average		

Procedure B Travel of the Magnetic Force Through Substances

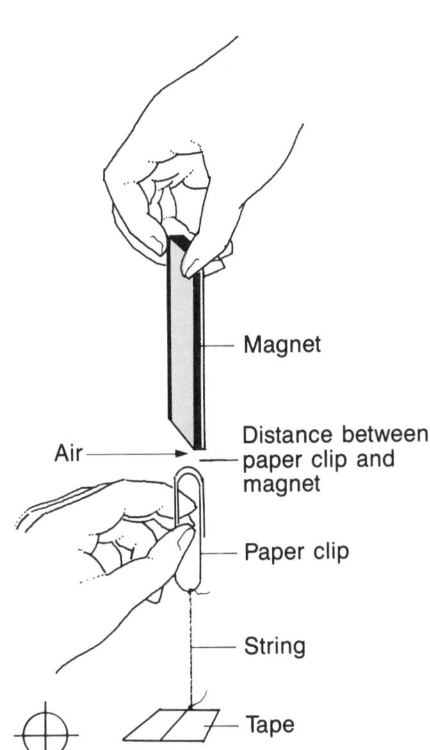

Fig. 14-4 Travel of the magnetic force through substances

a. Tie a 20 cm length of string to one end of a paper clip. Tape the other end of the string to the table.

b. Hold the paper clip in the air with the string tight as shown in Figure 14-4. Hold the magnet about 5 mm above the paper clip. Do not let the magnet touch the paper clip. Now release the paper clip.

c. Move the magnet slowly upward until the paper clip drops. Estimate the distance in millimetres between the magnet and the paper clip when it drops.

d. Repeat steps (b) and (c), placing different substances between the magnet and the paper clip each time. Try cardboard, aluminum foil, copper (1¢), wax paper, glass, a plastic lid, and the lid of a can which contains iron.

e. Repeat step (b). Then insert the lid of the can slowly between the paper clip and the magnet. Observe what happens.

Discussion

1. a) Compare the number of paper clips dragged by each end of your magnet.
   b) Based on the class results, compare the forces at each end of a magnet.
2. a) Describe the results when the lid containing iron is placed between the magnet and suspended paper clip.
   b) Compare the ability of the magnetic force to pass through magnetic and non-magnetic substances.
3. a) Describe the ability of a magnet to exert a force on a magnetic substance without touching it.
   b) Do all magnets in the class exert a force through air for the same distance?
   c) What do the class results indicate about the strength of different magnets?

14.3 Some Properties of a Magnet

Every magnet has several properties in common. Let's examine some of these properties.

Magnetic Poles

Every artificial magnet has two magnetic poles. A **magnetic pole** is the place on a magnet which attracts magnetic substances the most. The poles of a bar magnet are located at its ends. As a result, a magnet is strongest at its ends and weakest in the middle.

A magnet free to turn always lines up pointing in the same direction. One pole, called the **north-seeking pole**, always points north. This pole is labelled N. By definition it is a north magnetic pole. The pole that points south is called the **south-seeking pole** or the south magnetic pole and is labelled S. Thus every artificial magnet has a north-seeking and a south-seeking magnetic pole.

Magnetic Forces

The force exerted by a magnet is called the **magnetic force**. The magnetic forces at both poles of a magnet are the same size.

A magnetic force passes through non-magnetic substances. For example, it passes through cardboard, plastic, aluminum, copper, and glass. A magnetic force also passes through air. Indeed, it even passes through a vacuum. As a result, a magnet can attract a magnetic substance without touching it. A force from one object that affects another object without the objects touching is called an **action-at-a-distance force** (Fig. 14-5).

A magnetic force does not pass through magnetic substances. A paper clip attached to a string can be held in mid-air by a magnet as shown in Figure 14-5. The magnet and the paper clip need not touch. But the paper clip falls when the lid of a can which contains iron is placed between the two. The iron in the lid shields the paper clip from the magnetic force (Fig. 14-6). Do you think a Canadian nickel will have the same effect? Magnetic substances are used to shield delicate instruments from magnetic forces. For example, watches are protected against magnetism with special cases that contain iron and nickel.

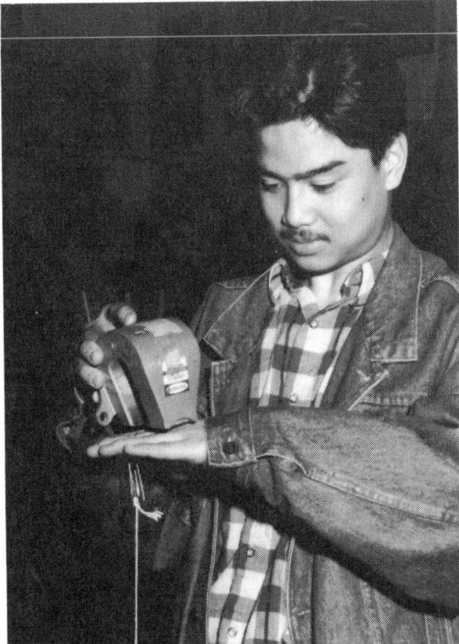

Fig. 14-5 A magnetic force is an action-at-a-distance force.

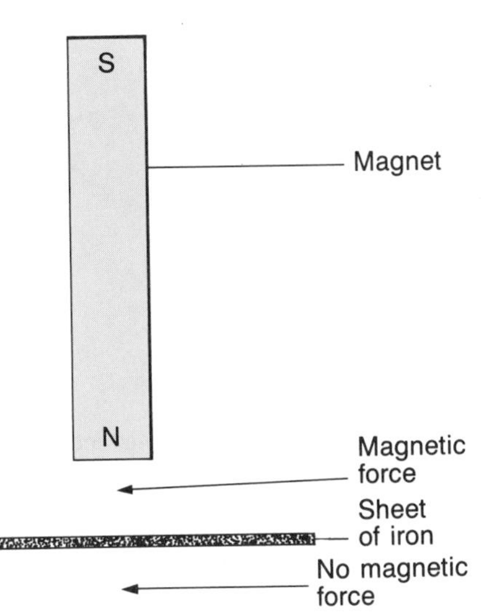

Fig. 14-6 Magnetic materials shield against the magnetic force.

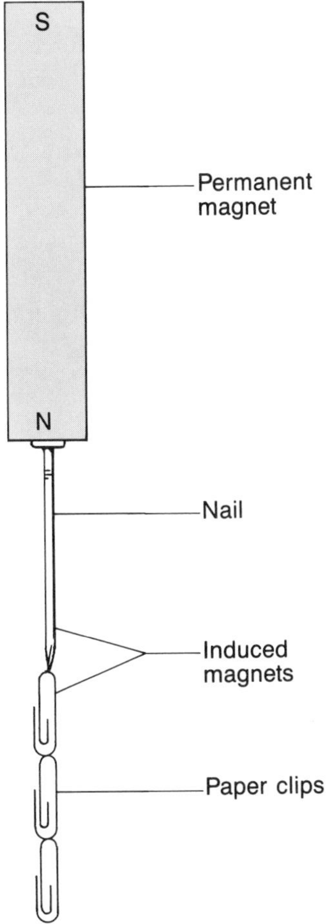

Fig. 14-7 Permanent and induced magnets

Making a Magnet

Magnets are used to make other magnets. For example, a soft iron nail becomes a magnet when it is near a permanent magnet. A magnet that gets its magnetism from a nearby magnet is called an **induced magnet** (Fig. 14-7). Soft iron is easy to magnetize in this way. However, it loses its magnetism quickly when the source of magnetism is removed. Hardened steel is more difficult to magnetize, but once it is magnetized it keeps its magnetism better. A magnet that keeps its magnetism when the source is removed is called a **permanent magnet**. Alnico magnets are strong permanent magnets. One way to make a permanent magnet is to stroke a substance containing steel with a magnet. The strokes must be in the same direction and with the same pole of the magnet.

Special precautions are needed to prevent a permanent magnet from being destroyed. Jarring or hammering often destroys a magnet. A high temperature may also destroy a magnet. Storing magnets together weakens them unless they are stored with opposite poles next to one another. Special soft iron keepers are placed across the poles to protect the magnets (Fig. 14-8).

Extension

Try to make a large iron nail into a permanent magnet (Fig. 14-9). Ask your teacher for the materials you need.

Section Review

1. a) What is a magnetic pole?
b) How would you find the poles of a bar magnet?
c) Where are the poles of a bar magnet located?
d) Where is a bar magnet the weakest?

2. a) What names are given to the poles of a bar magnet?
b) How do you know that the poles of a bar magnet are different from one another?

Fig. 14-8 Magnet keepers help protect the magnets.

N
S
S
N
Soft iron keepers

A. Keepers on bar magnets

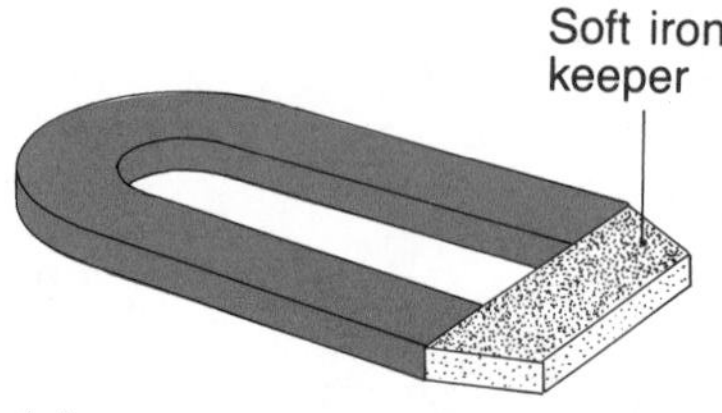

B. A keeper on a horseshoe magnet

Fig. 14-9 Can you make a nail into a permanent magnet? Design a procedure for doing this and for testing your magnet. Then your teacher will let you try this.

3. a) Define magnetic force.
   b) Compare the size of the magnetic force at the poles of a bar magnet.
4. a) What substance does a magnetic force pass through?
   b) What substances shield a magnetic force?
   c) Explain why a magnetic force is called an action-at-a-distance force.
   d) In order to be an action-at-a-distance force, a force must pass through air or a vacuum. Discuss this statement.
5. a) Distinguish between an induced and a permanent magnet.
   b) What substance is used to make induced magnets? Why?

14.4 Activity: Interactions Between Magnetic Poles

Two objects are said to interact when they affect each other. In this activity you will study the interaction between two magnets. Write in your notebook a prediction of what you think will happen if two S poles are brought near one another. Do the same for two N poles and also for a N and a S pole. Then do this activity to test your predictions.

Problem

How do magnetic poles affect each other?

Materials

bar magnets with poles labelled N and S (2)
rollers made of 5 cm of plastic soda straw (4)
ruler

CAUTION: Make sure the poles of the bar magnets are marked correctly. Your teacher will help you if you do not know how.

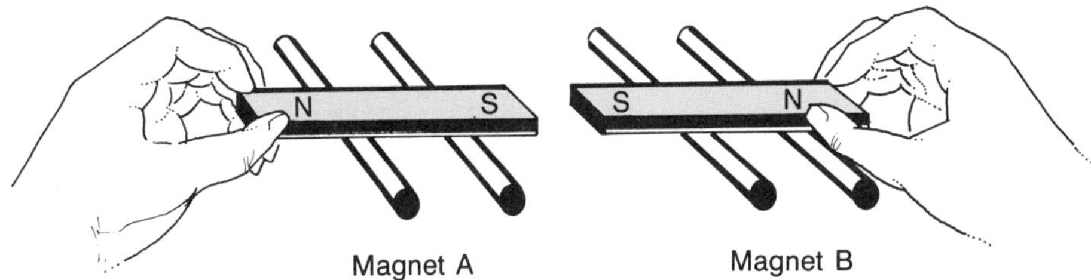

Fig. 14-10 Interactions between magnetic poles

Procedure

a. Copy Table 14-2 into your notebook.
b. Set up the apparatus as shown in Figure 14-10. Place the magnets on rollers. Hold the two S poles about 5 mm apart.
c. Release both magnets at the same time. Record in the table what happens.
d. Repeat steps (b) and (c) with the two N poles facing each other.
e. Repeat steps (b) and (c) with the N and S poles facing each other.

Table 14-2 Interactions of Magnetic Poles

Poles of magnets facing		*Interaction between poles*
Magnet A	*Magnet B*	
S pole	S pole	
N pole	N pole	
N pole	S pole	
S pole	N pole	

Discussion

1. a) What happens when like poles are brought close together and released?
b) What happens when unlike poles are brought close together and released?
c) Write a statement that summarizes the interaction between like and unlike poles. This is the **Law of Magnetism**.

14.5 The Law of Magnetism

Our universe is predictable. For example, a dropped stone always falls; it does not rise one day and fall the next. Scientists formulate laws to describe the way the universe and its parts behave. However, before a description is accepted as a law, it is verified by many other scientists. Scientists throughout the world check one another's results to make sure the descriptions are accurate. They test one another's results under the same conditions many times.

A scientific law is useful in a number of ways. A law summarizes into one concise statement the results of many observations. A law also predicts the results of further investigations. Therefore scientific laws both summarize and direct our study of the universe.

Scientists have stated a law to describe the interaction between the poles of a magnet. They observed that like poles always repel. That is, south-seeking magnetic poles repel one another and north-seeking magnetic poles repel one another. In contrast, unlike poles always attract. That is, south-seeking magnetic poles always attract north-seeking magnetic poles.

The law which describes the attraction and repulsion of magnetic poles is called the **Law of Magnetism**. It states that like magnetic poles repel and unlike magnetic poles attract. This law is useful because it summarizes the results of many investigations with magnets. It also predicts interactions between two or more magnetic poles. For example, two bar magnets on rollers with like poles facing roll apart. However, when unlike poles are near one another, the magnets attract. Similarly, the N pole of a floating magnet is repelled by another N pole. However, it is attracted by a S pole. Figure 14-11 shows a wire magnet floating with its axis placed vertically above a bar magnet. What do you think will happen when the floating magnet is released?

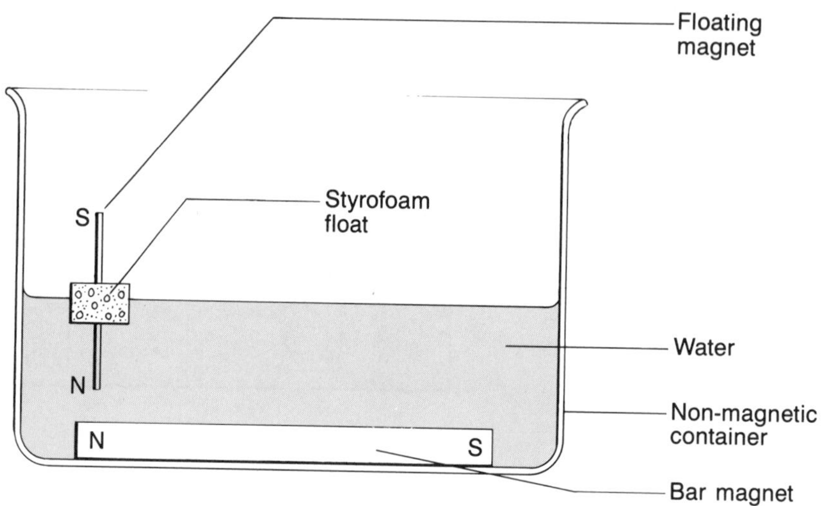

Fig. 14-11 The Law of Magnetism predicts the movement of one magnet floating above another. What will happen here?

Extension

Make a floating wire magnet. Then test the prediction that you made by answering the question accompanying Figure 14-11.

Section Review

1. a) Define a scientific law.
   b) What must be true before a description of nature becomes a law?
   c) What functions are served by a scientific law?
2. a) State the Law of Magnetism.
   b) Use the Law of Magnetism to predict why the N pole of a bar magnet turns toward the north.
   c) Compare a north-seeking pole of a bar magnet with the south magnetic pole of the earth.

3. Two cylindrical magnets are placed parallel and side by side. Like poles are next to each other. Use the Law of Magnetism to predict the interaction between the magnets.
4. Two bars of steel labelled A and B look alike. The two bars are placed to make a T. When bar A forms the base and bar B the cap, no interaction is observed. When the bars are interchanged, attraction is observed. Why is this so?
5. Suppose you are given two pieces of iron that look alike, except one is a magnet. How would you find out which one is the magnet? You may not use any other materials.

14.6 Activity: The Magnetic Force Around a Magnet

We have seen that a magnet exerts a force on magnetic substances and on other magnets. A magnetic force is present whether the objects are touching or not. Therefore a magnetic force must be present in the space around a magnet.

In this activity you will study the magnetic force around a single magnet. You will then study the magnetic force around two magnets close together.

Problem

What is the appearance of the magnetic force around a single bar magnet and around two bar magnets?

Materials

iron filings
sheet of plain paper
bar magnets (2)
acetate sheet
pencil

CAUTION: Do not let the iron filings come in contact with the magnet. It is very difficult to remove the filings from the magnet.

Fig. 14-12 Preparing for an investigation of the magnetic force around a bar magnet

Procedure A The Pattern of the Magnetic Force Around a Bar Magnet

a. Place a sheet of white paper on the table.
b. Place a bar magnet flat on top of the paper.
c. Lay an acetate sheet over the magnet (Fig. 14-12).
d. Sprinkle iron filings over the acetate as shown in Figure 14-13,A.
e. Tap the acetate lightly with a pencil until a pattern becomes clear.
f. Draw the outline of a bar magnet in your notes. On your diagram sketch the pattern made by the iron filings.
g. When you are ready to return the filings to the container, lift the acetate sheet and iron filings away from the magnet. Do not draw the magnet from beneath the acetate. Why not?

Fig. 14-13 Investigating the pattern of magnetic force around magnets

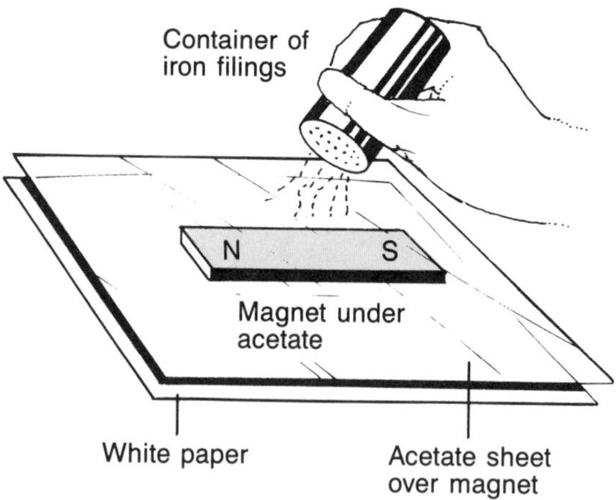

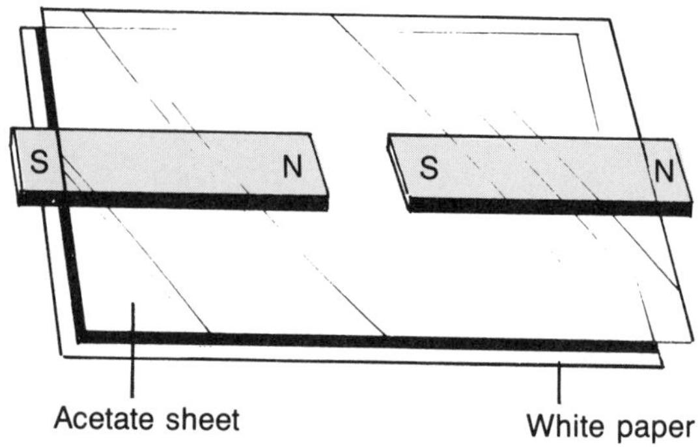

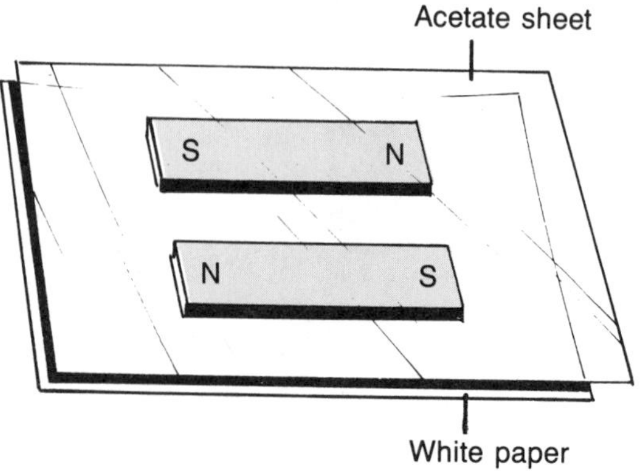

Procedure B The Pattern of the Magnetic Force Around Two Bar Magnets

a. Place two bar magnets with two *unlike* poles about 2 cm apart as shown in Figure 14-13,B. Now repeat Procedure A.
b. Place two bar magnets with two *like* poles about 2 cm apart. Now repeat Procedure A.
c. Place two bar magnets side by side with the pairs of *unlike* poles about 2 cm apart as shown in Figure 14-13,C. Repeat Procedure A.
d. Place two bar magnets side by side with the pairs of *like* poles about 2 cm apart. Repeat Procedure A.

Discussion

1. As you discovered, the iron filings arrange themselves into a pattern of lines around a bar magnet. Study the pattern closely and answer these questions:
a) Where do the lines seem to come from?
b) Where are the lines closest together?
c) Where are the lines furthest apart?
d) Do the lines ever cross?
2. Study and describe the pattern of lines between two bar magnets in the following positions. For each position, answer the questions given in item 1 of this Discussion.
a) unlike poles facing
b) like poles facing
c) unlike poles side by side
d) like poles side by side

Extension

Sketch the pattern of the magnetic force you expect to see around a single horseshoe magnet. Ask your teacher for a horseshoe magnet, iron filings, and an acetate sheet, and test your prediction.

14.7 Magnetic Field and Magnetic Lines of Force

There is a region around every magnet which experiences a magnetic force. This region is called the **magnetic field**. The magnetic field of a magnet can be mapped with iron filings. If you place an acetate sheet on top of a magnet and sprinkle the iron filings over the acetate, each filing in the magnetic field becomes a small induced magnet. A gentle tap of the acetate helps the filing turn to take up a definite position. Each filing lines up parallel to the magnetic field as shown in Figure 14-14. A compass can also be used to map a magnetic field. Can you explain how?

Scientists have invented the concept of **lines of force** to help us picture the magnetic field. By definition, lines of force emerge from the N pole and enter the S pole of a magnet. They pass in air from the N pole to the S pole and

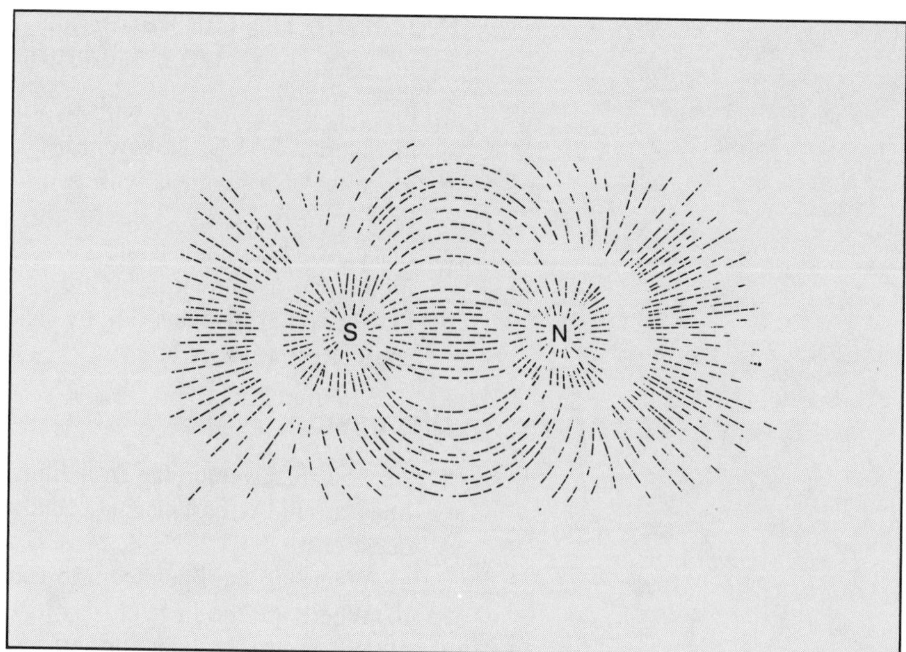

Fig. 14-14 Iron filings can be used to show the magnetic field around a magnet.

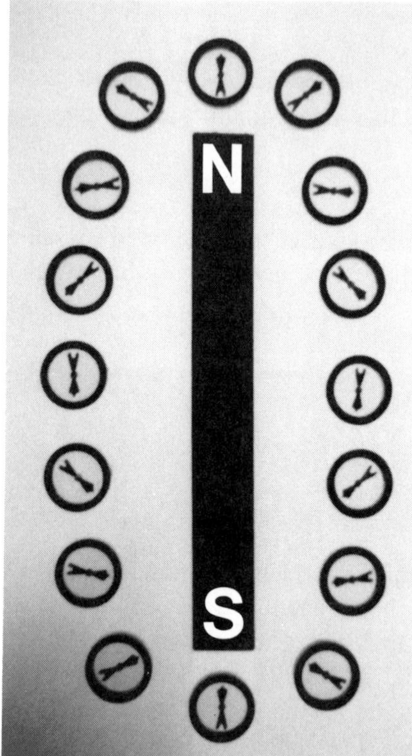

Fig. 14-15 A compass can be used to show the direction of the magnetic field.

inside the magnet from the S pole to the N pole. Arrowheads are used to show the directions of the lines of force. Lines of force are always parallel to the magnetic field. Therefore they show the direction of the magnetic field. Iron filings line up parallel with the field. A magnetic compass works even better. When placed in a magnetic field, the compass lines up parallel to the field with the N pole pointing in the direction of the field, as shown in Figure 14-15.

Figure 14-16,A shows the pattern of lines of force around a bar magnet. The pattern shows the properties of the lines of force. Lines of force never cross. Lines of force which have the same direction repel one another. Thus they are closest at the poles and spread apart (diverge) as they go away from the poles. The magnetic field is strongest where the lines of force are closest together. Therefore the magnetic field is strongest at the poles. It becomes weaker further away from the poles.

Figure 14-16,B shows the lines of force between unlike poles. Notice that the lines of force connect unlike poles. These lines of force contract. In contrast, the lines of force from like poles repel (Fig. 14-16,C). The lines of force help explain the Law of Magnetism. When like poles are next to one another, the lines of force repel. This pushes the magnets apart. When unlike poles are near, the lines of force joining the unlike poles contract like elastic bands. This pulls the magnets together.

Section Review

1. a) Define magnetic field.
   b) Describe how iron filings can be used to map a magnetic field.
   c) What is the reason for tapping the acetate covered with iron filings?
2. a) Are magnetic lines of force real or imagined?
   b) What function is served by magnetic lines of force?

A. Lines of force around a bar magnet

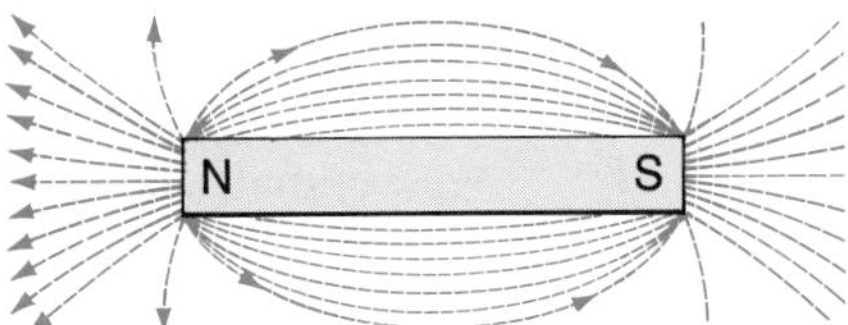

B. Lines of force from unlike poles contract

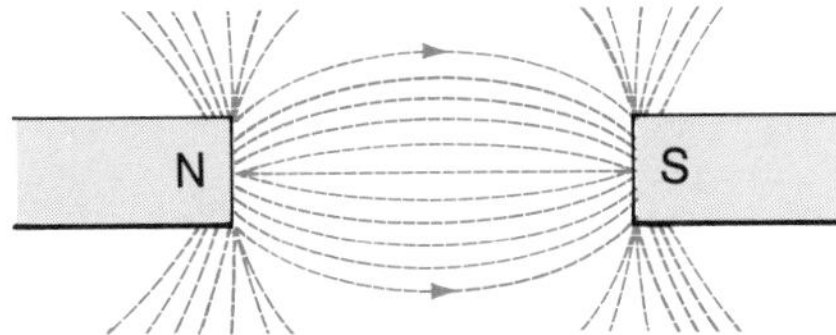

C. Lines of force from like poles repel

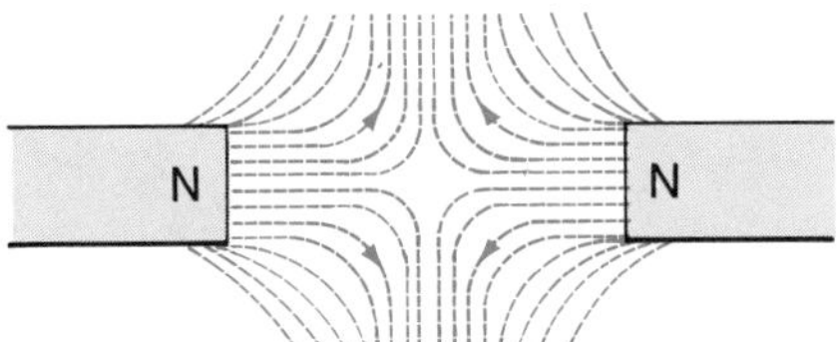

Fig. 14-16 The magnetic field and lines of force around bar magnets

   c) Compare the direction of a line of force and the direction of the magnetic field.
   d) Sketch a bar magnet. Draw a line of force. Show where it emerges from the magnet and where it enters the magnet. Use an arrowhead to show the direction in air and inside the magnet.

3. **a)** List three properties of magnetic lines of force.
   b) Use the three properties of magnetic lines of force to explain the behaviour of two cylindrical magnets placed side by side. Explain the results when like poles are near. Also explain the results when unlike poles are near.

4. Use lines of force to explain why magnets attract when unlike poles are near.

5. Draw a side view of the earth. Show the magnetic force lines around the earth.

14.8 The Domain Theory of Magnetism

Scientific theories are created by scientists to explain observations and laws. Let us look at the **Domain Theory of Magnetism**. It explains many of the observations with magnets.

When a magnet is cut into two smaller pieces, each is found to be a smaller magnet. Each piece has its own N pole and S pole (Fig. 14-17). If each smaller piece is cut, four smaller magnets are produced. If this division could be continued until no smaller pieces could be made, an atom of iron would eventually be isolated. Scientists believe that each atom of a magnetic material has its own N and S pole. As a result, atoms of all magnetic substances act as tiny magnets. The postulates of the **Domain Theory of Magnetism** are listed below.

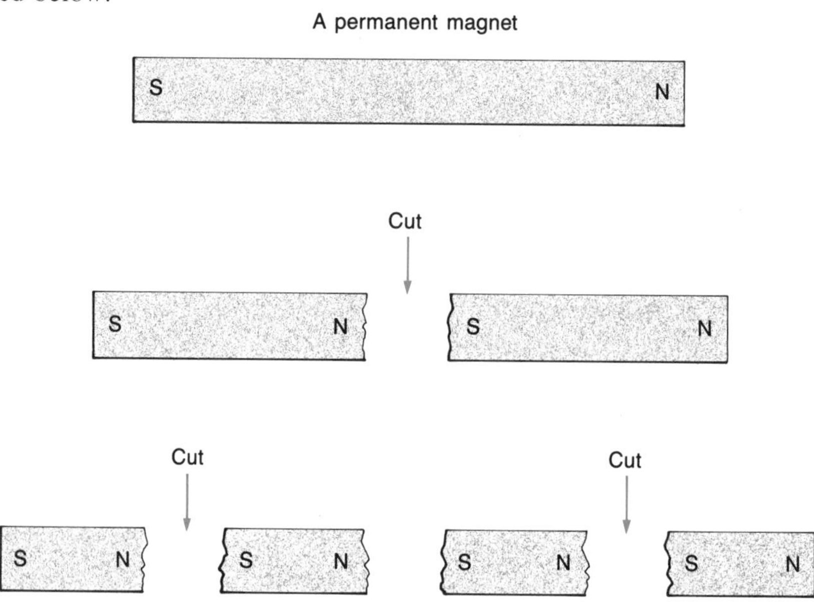

Fig. 14-17 Cutting a bar magnet into pieces

Postulates of the Domain Theory of Magnetism

1. Each atom of a magnetic material has a N and a S pole.
2. A group of magnetic atoms is called a domain.
3. In an unmagnetized object, the atoms are oriented randomly.
4. In a fully magnetized object, like poles face in the same direction.
5. A magnetic field can be used to align like poles in a domain.
6. The strength of a magnet depends on the fraction of the atoms aligned.

Applications of the Domain Theory of Magnetism

A theory is only as good as its ability to account for observations. Therefore, let's test the Domain Theory of Magnetism. The unmagnetized nature of a magnetic substance can be explained by assuming a random arrangement of the tiny magnets. The forces arising from the randomly arranged N and S poles cancel one another as shown in Figure 14-18,A. As a result, no external magnetic force is evident. When the unmagnetized substance is stroked with one pole of a bar magnet in a constant direction, the tiny magnets line up in one direction. That is, all the N poles point in one direction and all the S poles point in the opposite direction. This is shown in Figure 14-18,B. The forces arising from the poles along the length of the magnet cancel out. This is because a N pole always faces a S pole. Therefore no magnetic force exists in the

Fig. 14-18 The Domain Theory of Magnetism

A. Unmagnetized substance

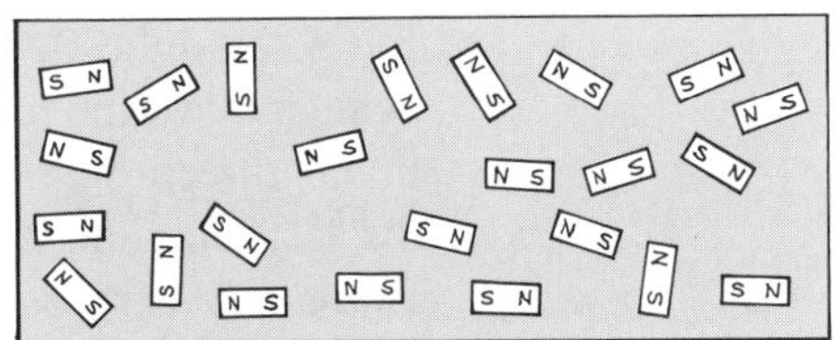

B. Magnetized substance

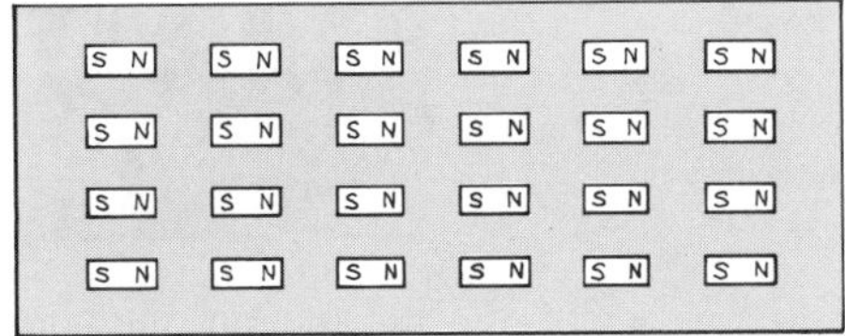

C. A magnet cut in half

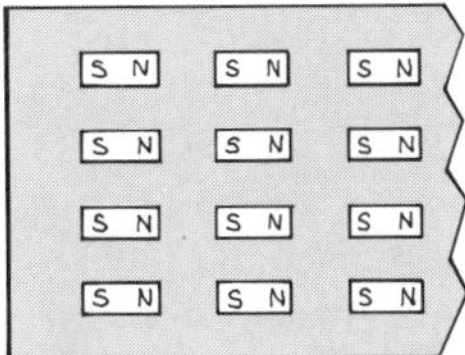

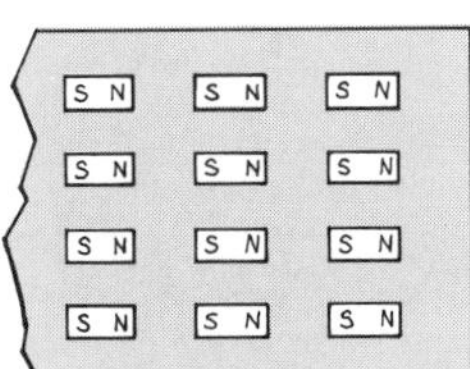

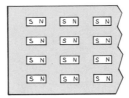

middle. However, there is a surplus of N poles at one end and a surplus of S poles at the other end. This explains the strong magnetic forces at the ends of a magnet. It also explains the opposite polarities of the ends.

The production of two smaller weaker magnets when a magnet is cut is also explained by this theory. When the magnet is cut, a set of tiny N poles is exposed in one magnet and a set of tiny S poles is exposed in the other. These are not cancelled out. Therefore each smaller magnet has its own N and S pole. This is shown in Figure 14-18,C. Since fewer atoms are present in the smaller magnets, fewer N poles and S poles exist. Therefore the smaller magnets are weaker than the original magnet.

Section Review

1. A postulate is a statement that is assumed to be true and that is used to support a claim. What are the postulates of the Domain Theory of Magnetism?

2. Use the Domain Theory of Magnetism to explain the following:

a) When a magnet is cut into sections, the sections are magnets.

b) When a magnet is cut into sections, the smaller magnets are weaker.

c) The magnetic force is concentrated at the ends of a magnet.

d) There is no magnetic force at the centre of a magnet.

e) The magnetism in a bar magnet is destroyed by heating the magnet to a high temperature and by hitting the magnet with a hammer.

f) Some substances produce magnets which exert a greater magnetic force than others.

Extension

Fill a test tube 3/4 full with iron filings. Close the open end with a rubber stopper. Test the test tube and its contents for magnetism. Stroke the test tube in one direction several times with a magnet. Again test for magnetism. Shake the test tube and repeat the test for magnetism. Explain the results using the Domain Theory of Magnetism.

14.9 Applications of Permanent Magnets

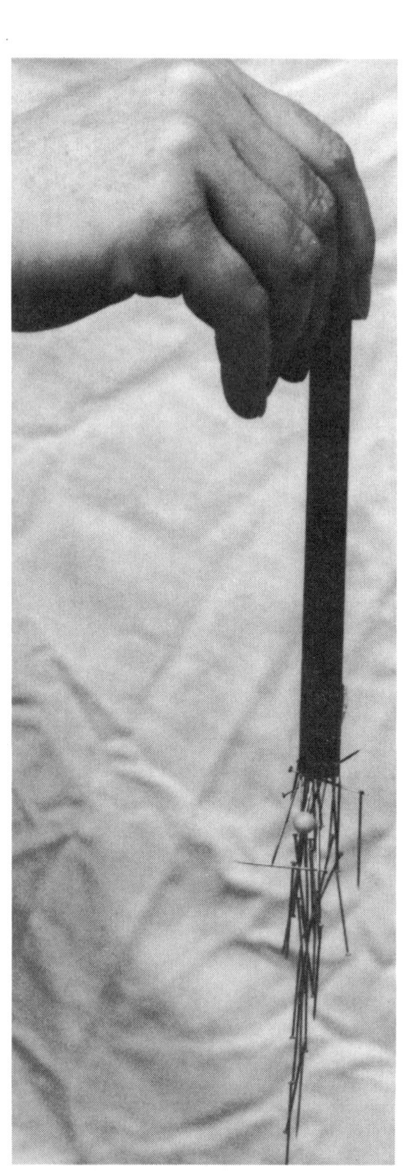

Fig. 14-19 A magnet being used to pick up pins. What limits are there to what can be picked up?

Permanent magnets are used in the home, in industry, and in business in many ways. You may have used a magnet on the end of a long string to lift a fallen screw out of an inaccessible place or to pick up small magnetic objects such as steel pins or iron nails (Fig. 14-19).

Magnetic Fasteners

Magnetic fasteners are found on cupboard doors, refrigerator and freezer doors, and even on shower stall doors. Why? Because they are convenient, effective, and relatively inexpensive.

Magnetic Sealants

Scientists have recently discovered how to make magnetic liquids. These magnetic liquids can be sprayed into small cracks in magnetic materials to act as seals against fine dust particles. They are also being used in loud speakers to dissipate the heat, permitting the power output to be increased. Magnetic liquids are also used in motors and on the heads of the disk drives of computers.

Magnetic Homing Devices

Scientists may have found the mechanism homing pigeons and bees use to navigate. Small samples of magnetite have been found in the bodies of migrating birds, bees, tuna fish, and even bacteria. Magnetotactic bacteria contain chains of magnetite crystals. These tend to align the bacteria along the earth's magnetic field. Can you explain how bees might make use of the magnetite to find their way back to the hive?

Magnetic Switches

Switches called magnetic reeds have also been developed. Two strips of magnetic material called reeds are enclosed in a sealed glass container (Fig. 14-20). The glass is non-magnetic. Thus it permits a magnetic field to influence the magnetic reeds. When a magnetic field exists, the reeds become induced magnets. Opposite poles are attracted to each other and the reeds make contact. This closes the switch. When the magnetic field is absent, the reeds spring apart, opening the switch.

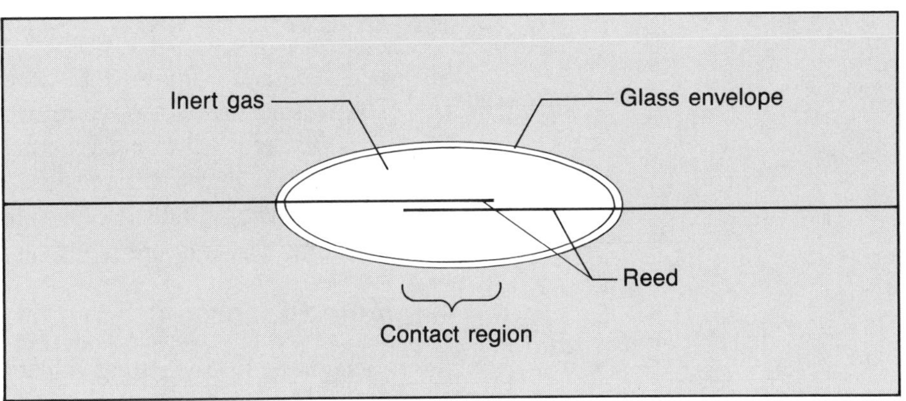

Fig. 14-20 A magnetic reed switch

Magnetic Bearings

Industry is in need of super bearings to decrease the friction between moving parts. Engineers have developed magnetic bearings. Turning shafts are supported by magnetic fields. As a result there is almost no contact of the shaft with the bearings. Give the shaft a slight turn and it continues moving with very little energy loss.

Magnetometers

Geologists are continually searching for new mineral deposits. Deposits beneath the surface of the earth are difficult to locate. However, a magnetometer can be used to locate minerals containing iron. Iron deposits cause variations in the magnetic field of the earth. These are sensed by the magnetometer (Fig. 14-21).

Fig. 14-21 A magnetometer

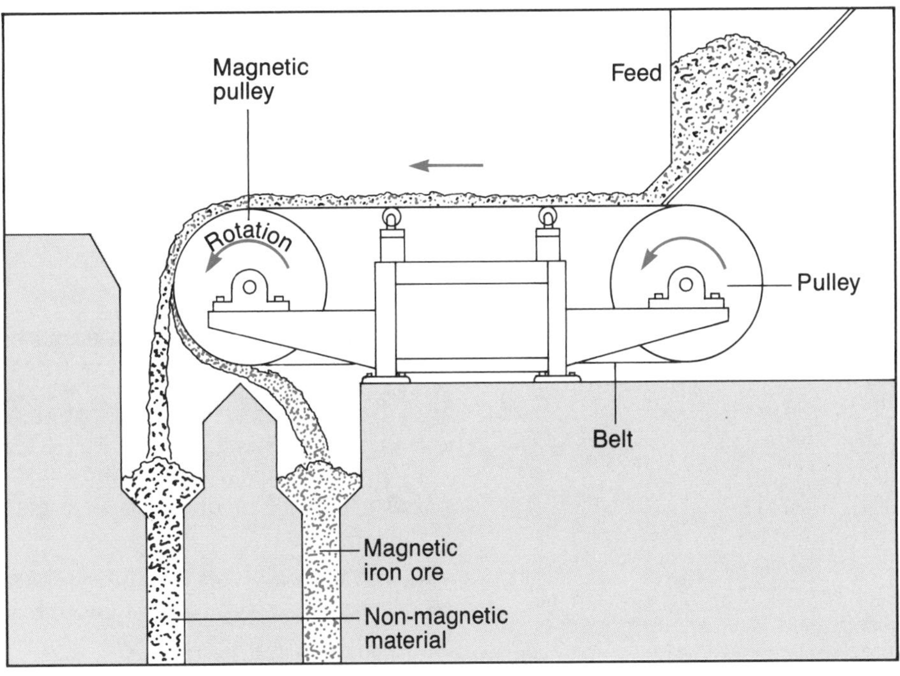

Fig. 14-22 Magnetic separation method

Magnetic Separators

Magnetic separators are used to concentrate iron ores as shown in Figure 14-22. Raw iron ore is a mixture of magnetic and non-magnetic materials. The ore is first crushed to make particles no larger than about 6 mm. Then it is placed on a conveyor belt and passed over a rotating magnetic pulley. The non-magnetic material falls into one bin. The concentrated iron ore is collected in another bin. The iron ore is further processed by other means.

Magnetic Biosorbent

A new technique for separating valuable wastes combines magnets and microorganisms. Tiny magnetized plastic beads are impregnated with microorganisms. The combination is called a **magnetic biosorbent**. The magnetic biosorbent is mixed with waste-containing liquids. The microorgansims selectively grab onto some elements and not others. External magnets are used to remove the magnetic biosorbent and the element. The element is then separated from the magnetic biosorbent. Some applications are: removing low level radioactive waste, separating tracers of heavy metals from mining and industrial wastes, and cleaning up accidental spills of hazardous substances.

Section Review

1. Suppose you are attaching two strips of metal together using brass screws. One screw falls into a crack in the workbench. Can you lift the screw out of the crack using a small magnet and a string? Explain.
2. Does it make any difference what kind of material is used for the plate in a magnetic door fastener? Discuss.
3. What uses are made of magnetic liquids?
4. Explain the operation of a magnetic reed switch.
5. Explain how a magnetic biosorbent works.

Extension

Examine a magnetic door fastener. Locate the magnet and the metal frame. Predict where the poles are located on the magnet. Design and do an experiment to test your prediction.

Chapter Highlights

1. A magnet attracts magnetic substances such as iron, cobalt, and nickel.
2. An induced magnet acts as a magnet only when a permanent magnet is nearby.
3. Every magnet has a N pole and a S pole located at the ends of the magnet.
4. A magnetic force passes through non-magnetic substances but not through magnetic substances.

5. Iron, cobalt, and nickel are used to shield objects against a magnetic force.
6. The region around a magnet which experiences a magnetic force is called a magnetic field.
7. The properties of magnetic lines of force are: they never cross; those in the same direction repel; they contract like rubber bands to attract unlike poles.
8. The Law of Magnetism states that unlike poles attract and like poles repel.
9. The Domain Theory of Magnetism states that each atom of a magnetic substance acts like a tiny magnet. When these tiny magnets are aligned, a magnet results.
10. Magnets have many practical uses.

Key Terms

action-at-a-distance
artificial magnet
Domain Theory of Magnetism
induced magnet
Law of Magnetism
lines of force
lodestone
magnet
magnetic
magnetic biosorbent
magnetic field
magnetic force
magnetic pole
magnetized
natural magnet
non-magnetic
north-seeking pole
permanent magnet
south-seeking pole

Recognizing the Concepts

Each of the following statements is followed by four responses. Choose the correct response in each case. (Do not write in this book.)

1. Which substance is a natural magnet?
   a) aluminum **b)** copper **c)** lodestone **d)** Alnico
2. A bar magnet is used to stroke a steel paper clip in one direction. When the bar magnet is removed, the paper clip will attract an iron nail. The paper clip is said to be
   a) a permanent magnet
   b) a temporary magnet
   c) an induced magnet
   d) a natural magnet
3. The Law of Magnetism states that
   a) S poles repel and N poles attract
   b) N poles repel and S poles attract
   c) like poles attract and unlike poles repel
   d) like poles repel and unlike poles attract
4. Which diagram in Figure 14-23 correctly shows the magnetic field lines when unlike poles are opposite one another?
5. Which diagram in Figure 14-24 correctly shows the magnetic field lines when like poles are opposite one another?

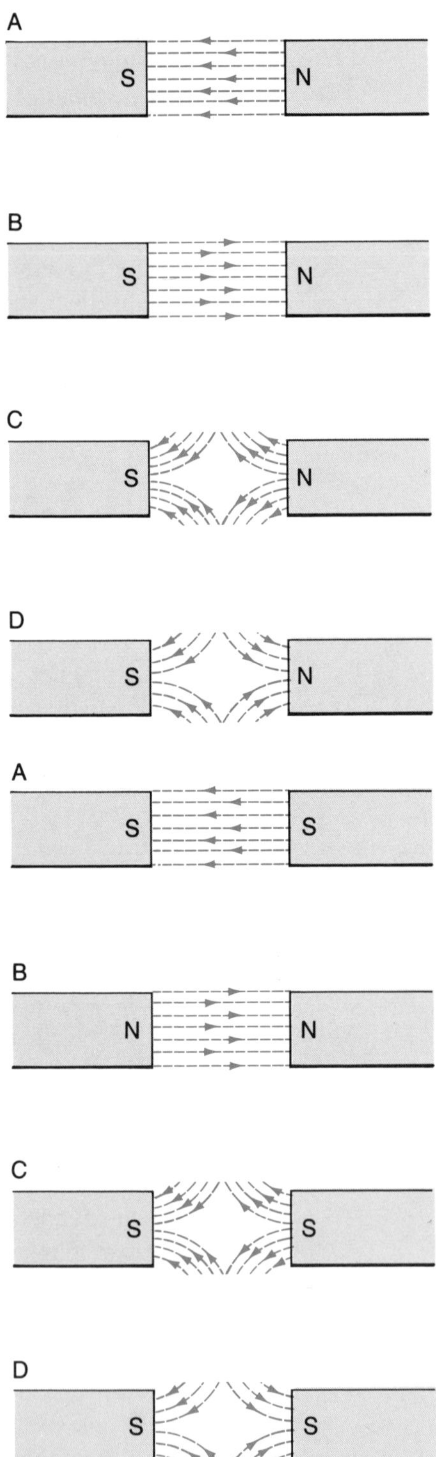

Fig. 14-23 Which diagram is correct?

Fig. 14-24 Which diagram is correct?

Understanding the Concepts

1. Suppose that a company makes a machine which uses a magnet to pick up substances. A salesperson tells you that this machine picks up all kinds of nails and screws. What would you say to this claim?

2. Imagine that a magnet is cut in half. Use the Domain Theory and Law of Magnetism to predict the interaction between the cut faces.
3. Explain why some screwdrivers are made with magnetic tips.
4. Explain how to tell the difference between magnetic and non-magnetic materials.
5. Explain how to tell the difference between a permanent and an induced magnet.
6. Draw a sketch to show the proper method for storing two cylindrical magnets.
7. Figure 14-25 shows part of the pattern of iron filings around two bar magnets. The polarity of one of the poles is labelled. What are the polarities of the other poles?

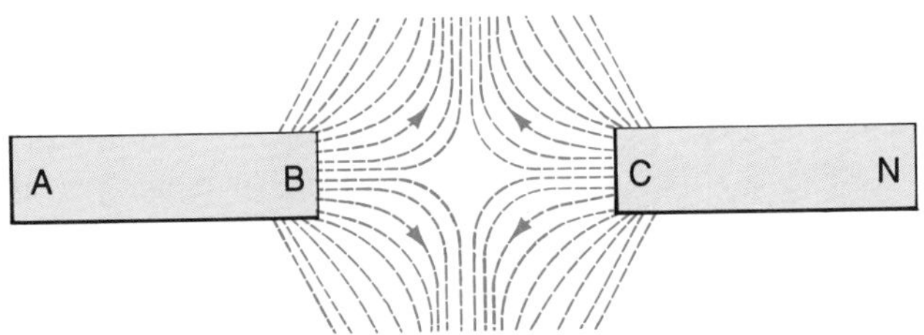

Fig. 14-25 What is the polarity of the other poles?

Applying the Concepts

1. a) Sketch a diagram showing three bar magnets arranged so that the poles of the magnets form the vertices of a triangle. Label the poles so that repulsion occurs at two vertices and attraction at the third.
   b) Repeat part (a). Label the poles so that repulsion occurs at one vertex and attraction at two vertices.
   c) Can a triangle of bar magnets have repulsion (or attraction) at all three vertices? Explain.
   d) Can a triangle made from two bar magnets and a bar of soft iron have attraction at all three vertices? Explain.
2. A magnetic bar used as a knife rack contains two bar magnets. Sketch the rack and explain why it includes two magnets.
3. A bar of nickel is placed next to a bar magnet as shown in Figure 14-26. Explain how a compass needle can be used to map the magnetic field around the bar of nickel. Include a diagram in your answer.

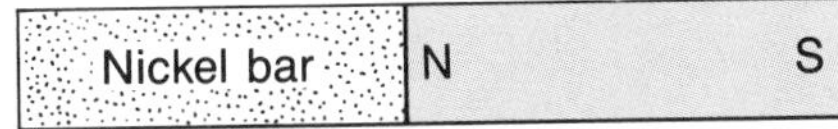

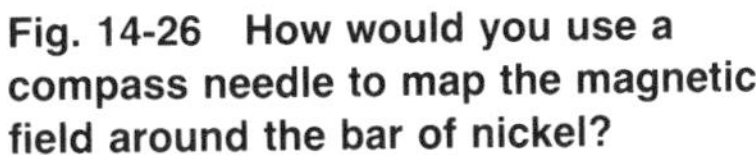

Fig. 14-26 How would you use a compass needle to map the magnetic field around the bar of nickel?

4. Draw a bar magnet in your notebook. Label the N pole and the S pole. Draw circles at four locations around the magnet to represent a compass case. Draw an arrow in each circle. The head of the arrow is the N pole of the compass needle.
5. Use the Domain Theory of Magnetism to explain the following:
   a) magnetic induction in an iron nail
   b) the difference between a strong magnet and a weak magnet

c) the strength of the magnetic field in the centre of a bar magnet
d) the destruction of a U-shaped magnet by heating

Investigations

1. Aluminum is not a magnetic substance. Do a library search to determine why aluminum is used in some magnets.
2. Design a procedure using a Newton spring scale to compare the strength of the poles of a bar magnet (Fig. 14-27).
3. How do you think the polarity of the pole of the magnet used to make a magnet by stroking compares to the polarity of the magnet produced? Perform an experiment to test your prediction.
4. Design and implement a procedure using a small compass to trace out a magnetic field line on each side of a bar magnet.
5. Research the composition of the magnetic strips used to seal freezer doors.
6. Do a library search to find out what a magnetometer is. Describe what it is used for.

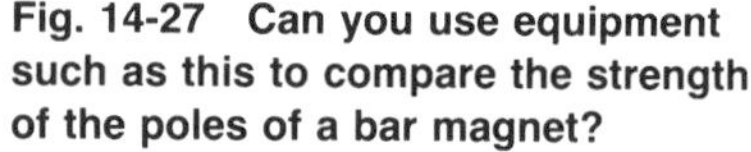
Fig. 14-27 Can you use equipment such as this to compare the strength of the poles of a bar magnet?

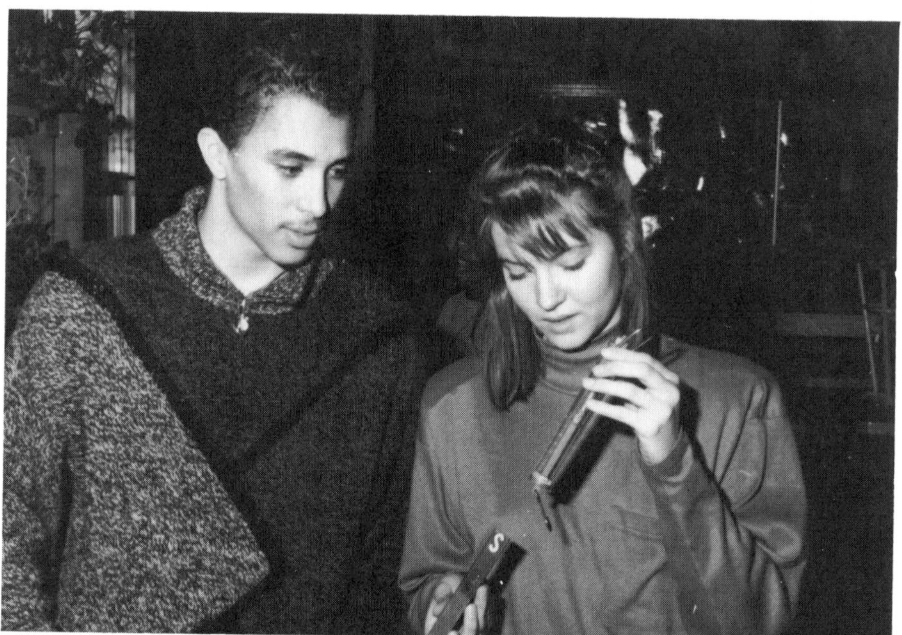

15 Static Electricity

CHAPTER CONTENTS

CHAPTER OBJECTIVES

After completing this chapter you should be able to:

1. Describe static electricity.
2. State and apply the Law of Electric Charges.
3. State and apply the Electron Theory of Charge.
4. Explain charging an electroscope by contact and by induction.
5. Explain several applications of electrostatics.

Ominous clouds began to appear on the horizon. Soon the sky was illuminated by fireworks far more spectacular than any devised artificially (Fig. 15-1).

What causes lightning? How do lightning rods protect tall buildings? Why does a comb attract hair sometimes but not other times? How can we tell the kind of static charge on an object? What is the theory to explain charging? What are some applications of electrostatics? You will find answers to these and other questions in this chapter.

Fig. 15-1 A lightning flash can either go from the ground to a cloud, or from a cloud to the ground. How does this happen?

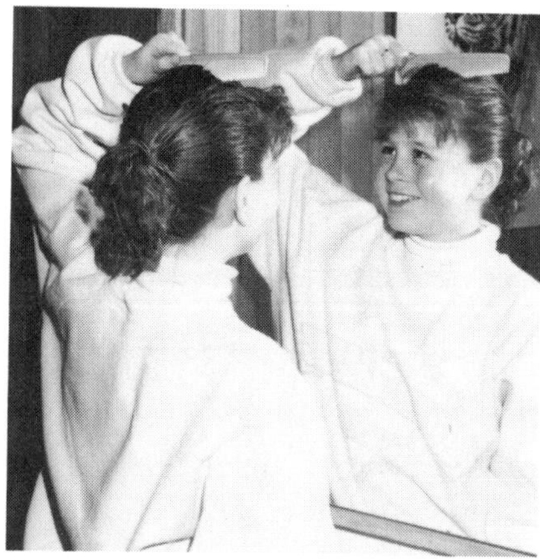

Fig. 15-2 Static electricity causes the attraction between your hair and a comb. What is static electricity?

Electricity is a general term that refers to electric charge. Electric charge at rest is called **static electricity**. The attraction between a comb and combed hair results from static electricity (Fig. 15-2). Clothes cling together in a clothes dryer because of static electricity. The study of electric charge at rest is called **electrostatics**.

How Static Electricity Is Produced

Static electricity is produced by rubbing different substances together. The first person to study static electricity was the Greek philosopher, Thales, who lived about 600 B.C. He noticed that when a brownish solid called amber was rubbed with fur it behaved strangely. Rubbed amber attracted small pieces of paper, straw, and wood shavings. Without rubbing, there was no attraction.

When two different materials are rubbed together, both become charged. Both an ebonite rod and the fur used to rub it become charged. Also, a glass rod and a silk cloth both become charged when rubbed together.

Fig. 15-3 A charged object attracts a neutral object. Both the ebonite rod and fur are charged, and both will attract paper.

How a Charged Object Affects a Neutral Object

An object without a charge is said to be **neutral**. Small pieces of paper and sawdust are neutral. However, a comb drawn through hair becomes **charged**. A charged comb attracts neutral paper. An ebonite rod rubbed with fur attracts neutral paper (Fig. 15-3). The paper is also attracted to the fur. In fact, any charged object attracts any neutral object. However, two neutral objects do not have an electrical attraction for one another.

Section Review

1. Define static electricity and electrostatics.
2. How is static electricity produced?
3. How does a neutral object affect another neutral object?
4. How does a charged object affect a neutral object?

15.2 The Law of Electric Charges

The Law of Charges

Scientists have discovered that a charged object attracts a neutral object and that charged objects affect each other. Two charged ebonite rods repel one another and two charged glass rods repel one another. But not all charged objects repel. Ebonite and the fur used to rub it attract each other. Both are charged, so there must be a different charge on the ebonite than on the fur. The same is true of glass rubbed with silk. Indeed, any two materials rubbed together get different kinds of charge.

Scientists have stated a law to summarize the interaction between charged objects. The **Law of Electric Charges** states that like charges repel and unlike charges attract.

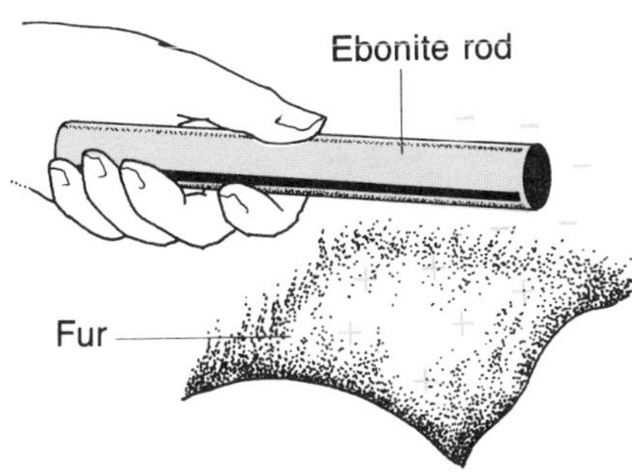

A. An ebonite rod charged with fur is negative. The fur is positive.

B. A glass rod charged with silk is positive. The silk is negative.

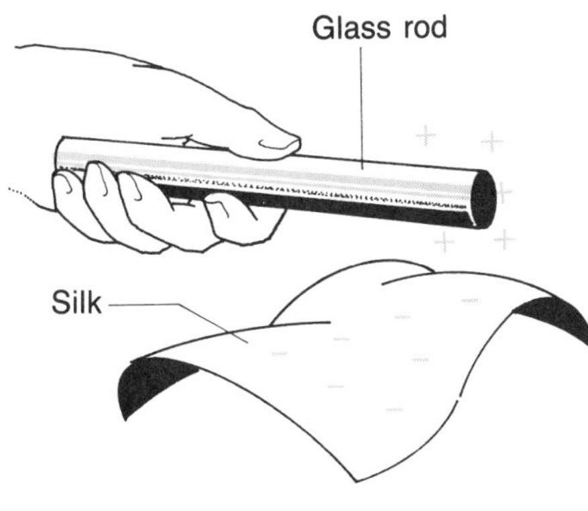

Fig. 15-4 The two kinds of charges

Kinds of Charges

There are only two kinds of charges, positive and negative. The charge on an ebonite rod rubbed with fur is **negative** (Fig. 15-4,A). The charge on a glass rod rubbed with silk is **positive** (Fig. 15-4,B).

Testing for Charge

You can find out the charge on a object by seeing how it affects an object with a known charge. If the two repel, the charges are alike. If they attract, the charges are opposite. If you think the object is neutral, test it with another neutral object. A neutral object does not electrically attract another neutral object. But a neutral object is electrically attracted by an object with either a positive or negative charge.

The Electron Theory of Charge

Scientists usually make up theories to explain their observations. In this case they have proposed the Electron Theory of Charge to explain the behaviour of charged objects, the charging of objects, and the two kinds of charge. Let us examine the postulates of the Electron Theory.

Postulates of the Electron Theory

The **Electron Theory** says that matter consists of atoms. Each atom is made up of many smaller particles. Three of these are the **proton**, the **neutron**, and the **electron**. Protons are heavier than electrons. Each proton has one unit of positive charge and is found in the nucleus of the atom. The neutron is also found in the nucleus but it is neutral. An electron is much lighter than the proton and has one unit of negative charge. Electrons move at high speeds and form a cloud-like region around the nucleus.

All atoms are neutral. That is, each atom has the same number of protons and electrons. A simple model of a carbon atom is shown in Figure 15-5. A carbon atom has six protons and six neutrons in the nucleus. It has six electrons moving around the nucleus.

Fig. 15-5 A simple model of a carbon atom

How the Electron Theory Explains Charging by Rubbing

Scientists use the postulates of a theory to explain observations. Let us see how the Electron Theory explains charging by rubbing.

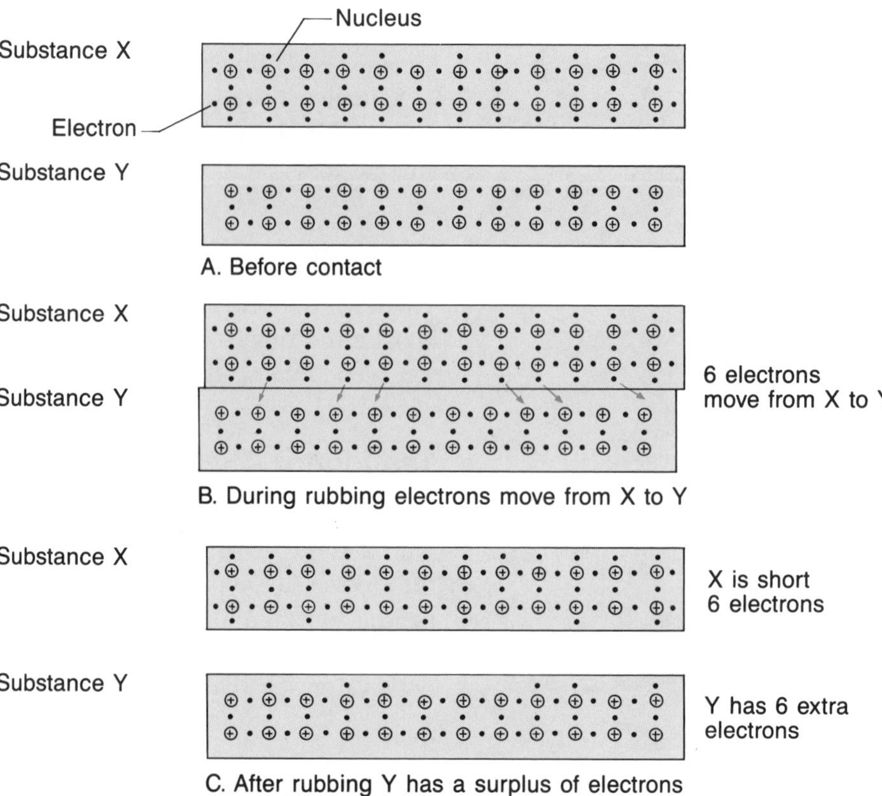

Fig. 15-6 Charging by rubbing. The rubbing transfers electrons from one substance to another.

The action of rubbing removes loosely held electrons from atoms. But protons cannot be removed by rubbing. When two different materials are rubbed together, electrons move from one material to the other. As a result, one material gains electrons and the other loses electrons. The material which gains electrons gets a negative charge. (Remember, electrons have a negative charge.) The material which loses electrons gets a positive charge. In other words, a material that has a *deficiency of electrons* has a *positive charge*. A material that has a *surplus of electrons* has a *negative charge*. The charging process is shown in Figure 15-6.

The Electron Theory explains why rubbed materials get opposite charges. Some materials hold their electrons more strongly than others. When rubbed together, one material loses electrons and the other gains electrons. Thus one becomes positive and the other negative. Through experiments, scientists have developed a list of materials in order of their tendency to lose electrons. This list is called an **electrostatic series**. An electrostatic series for some common materials is shown in Table 15-1. A material higher in the list will get a negative charge when rubbed with one lower down.

Table 15-1 Electrostatic Series for Some Common Materials

Material	*Tendency to lose electrons*	*Relative charge*
ebonite	least	negative
rubber	↓	↓
polyethylene		
orlon		
dacron		
cotton		
silk		
nylon		
wool		
glass		
cellulose acetate		
cat's fur	most	positive

The Electron Theory predicts that rubbed materials get the same *quantity* of charge. Scientists have found that an ebonite rod rubbed with fur gets the same number of electrons as the fur loses.

Section Review

1. State the Law of Electric Charges.
2. Name the two kinds of electric charges.
3. Give an example of each kind of charge.
4. How can you find the kind of charge on an object?
5. Suppose pieces of straw are attracted to both a negative and a positive rod. What charge is on the straw? How do you know?
6. **a)** What particles in the atom are responsible for electric charge?
b) Which particle moves? Which particle stays relatively fixed?
7. Describe the number and kind of charged particles in each of the following:
a) a neutral object **c)** a negative object
b) a positive object
8. **a)** What is an electrostatic series?
b) What kind of charge will each of the following get when they are rubbed together: polyethylene and glass; rubber and ebonite?

15.3 Activity: Charging a Metal Leaf Electroscope by Contact

An **electroscope** is an instrument used to detect and identify charge. The parts of a metal leaf electroscope are shown in Figure 15-7. The electroscope consists of an insulating case, a metal rod and sphere (**knob**), and one or two small

Fig. 15-7 Metal leaf electroscopes

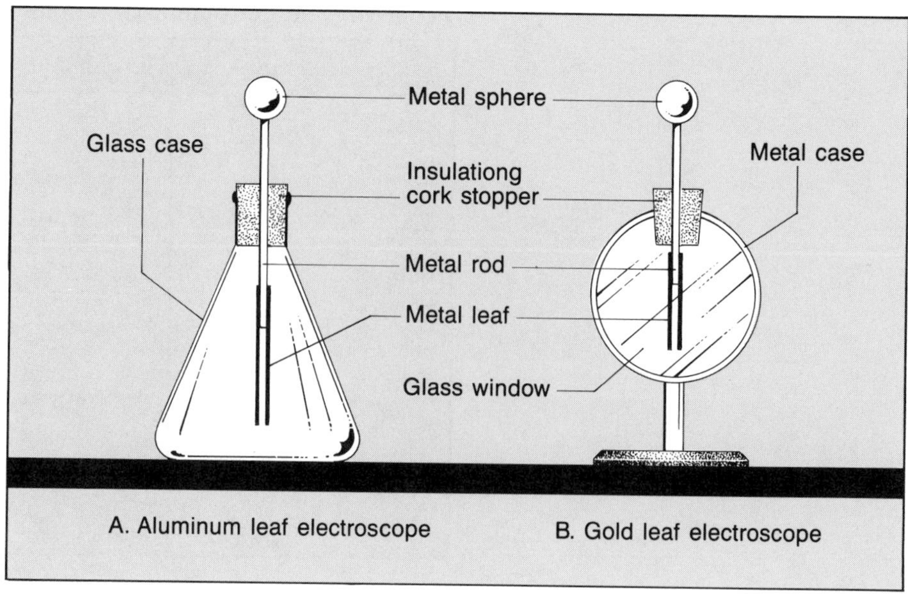

metal **leaves**. These leaves are attached at their upper ends to the metal rod and enclosed in a case. The case prevents moving air from damaging the leaves. In this activity you will study the parts of the electroscope. Then you will give the electroscope a known charge by contact. Finally, you will use the electroscope to detect and identify charge.

Problem

How can an electroscope be charged by contact?

Materials

metal leaf electroscope	ebonite rod	comb
glass rod	fur	wool
silk		

Procedure

a. Examine the metal leaf electroscope. Find the parts shown in Figure 15-7.
b. Touch the metal sphere with your fingers. This will neutralize the electroscope if it has a charge on it.
c. Rub an ebonite rod with fur to make the rod negative. Approach but do not touch the sphere of the electroscope with the negative rod. Watch the metal leaves. Remove the rod. Record your observations.
d. Touch the sphere with the negative rod. Watch the metal leaves. Remove the rod. Record your observations.
e. Approach but do not touch the charged electroscope with a negative rod. Record your observations.
f. Repeat step (e) with a positive rod.
g. Charge a comb by rubbing it with wool.
h. Use the charged electroscope to identify the charge on the comb and on the wool (Fig. 15-8).

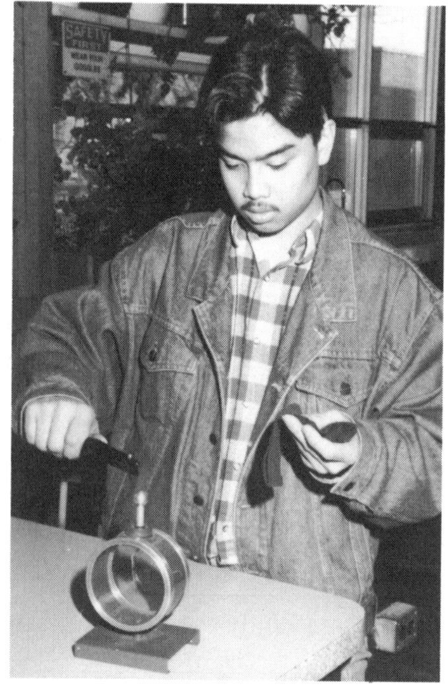

Fig. 15-8 How can you find out the kind of charge on the comb and on the wool?

Discussion

1. a) State what was observed during each step of charging the metal leaf electroscope by contact.
   b) Use diagrams to illustrate your answer. Your teacher will help you.
2. Compare the kind of charge on the electroscope with that on the charging rod when the electroscope is charged by contact.
3. a) What kind of charge was on the comb? How do you know?
   b) What kind of charge was on the wool? How do you know?
   c) Use the Electron Theory to account for the kind of charge on the comb and wool.

Extension

Design a procedure using an ebonite rod, cat's fur, and an electroscope to determine whether a substance is a conductor or an insulator. Ask your teacher for conductors and insulators to test.

15.4 Charging a Conductor by Contact

Charging by Friction

One object can be charged by rubbing it with another. This method is called **charging by friction**. One object loses electrons and becomes positive. The other object gains electrons and becomes negative. The rubbed objects end up with equal amounts of the opposite kinds of charge. Can you use the Electron Theory to explain why?

Transferring Charge

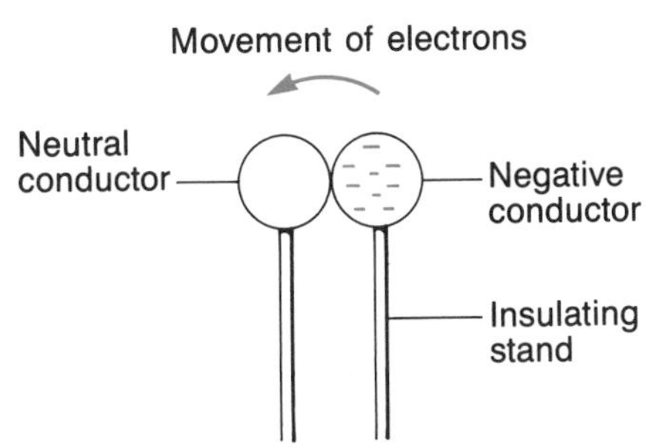

Fig. 15-9 Charging a conductor negative by contact

A charged object can be used to charge a neutral object. The neutral object must be a conductor. A **conductor** is a material in which the electrons can travel easily from one place to another. Copper, silver, and aluminum are excellent conductors. The conductor must be supported on an insulator. An **insulator** is a material in which the electrons do not travel easily. Wood, glass, and plastics are insulators. When the neutral object touches the charged object, charge is transferred. As a result, the conductor gets the same kind of charge as the charged object. For example, if the charged object is negative, some electrons move to the neutral body as shown in Figure 15-9. The neutral body gets a negative charge. If the charged object is positive, it has a deficiency of electrons. Some electrons move from the neutral object to the charged object. This gives the neutral object a positive charge.

Sharing Charge

Charge can be shared between objects. Suppose you have two identical conductors. One has a negative charge and the other is neutral. How can half of

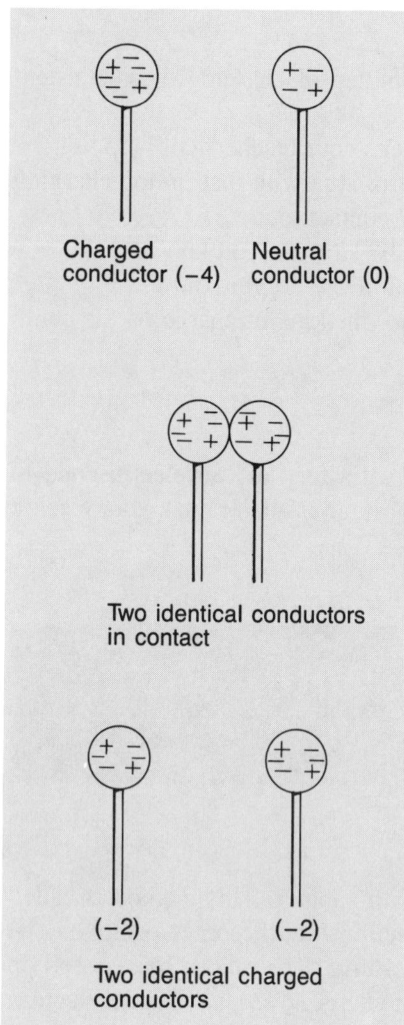

Fig. 15-10 Sharing charge between two identical conductors

the negative charge be placed on the neutral conductor? The process is called **sharing**. First, the two conductors are placed in contact. Provided the conductors are identical, half the charge moves to the neutral conductor as shown in Figure 15-10. Then the conductors are separated. Now each conductor shares half the original charge.

The Location of Charge on a Conductor

Where do you think charge resides on a conductor? Scientists performed experiments similar to the following to answer that question. A hollow conductor was supported on an insulated stand (Fig. 15-11). Charge was placed on the outside of the conductor. Then a proof plane was used to sample the inside and the outside of the conductor for charge. A **proof plane** is a small conductor about the size of a quarter. It is attached to an insulating handle so that it can be used to transfer charge. Scientists found no charge on the inside of the hollow conductor. All of the charge was on the outside.

In a second experiment all the charge was placed on the inside of the conductor. When the conductor was tested for charge, scientists again found all of the charge on the outside surface. Thus charge always resides on the outside of a conductor. Can you use the Law of Electric Charges to explain the movement of charge to the outside?

Figure 15-12 shows a pear-shaped conductor on an insulated stand. When charge is placed on such a conductor, it is found that more charge resides on the pointed end than on the rounded end. Thus charge has a tendency to move to the more pointed end of a conductor. Does this make sense to you?

The Escape of Charge from a Conductor

Suppose two objects with the same surface area are given the same amount of charge. One is a sphere, and the other has a needle-like end. Which object will lose charge to the air more readily? A conductor with a pointed surface loses charge much faster than one with a more rounded surface. If this is true, what will happen to the conductor shown in Figure 15-13?

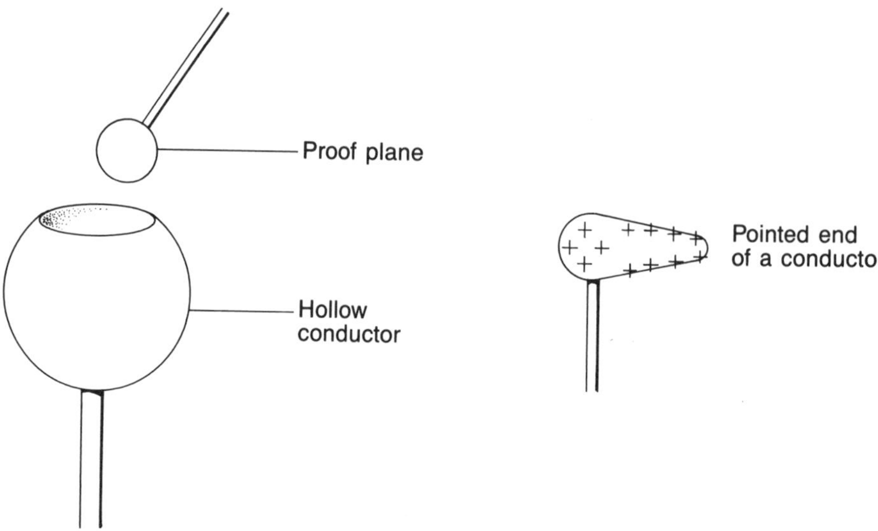

Fig. 15-11 Is charge located on the outside or inside of a hollow conductor?

Fig. 15-12 The charge density is greatest on the pointed end of a conductor.

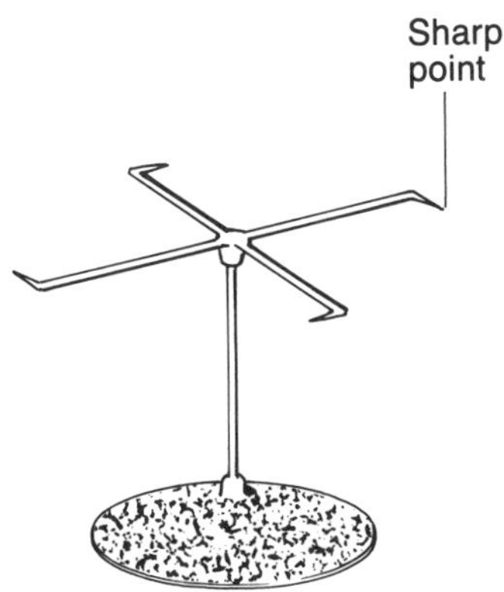

Fig. 15-13 If negative charge is continually fed to the sharp points, which way will the cross rotate?

There will be a greater concentration of electrons at the pointed end. Air has numerous positive and negative ions, especially when the humidity is high. More positive ions are attracted to the pointed end than to the rounded surface. At the pointed end, each positive ion removes one electron and becomes a neutral atom. As a result, one electron is removed for each positive ion that reaches the surface. The process is reversed if the conductor has a positive charge.

Section Review

1. Compare the charge on two neutral objects that have been rubbed together.
2. a) Distinguish between a conductor and an insulator. Give an example of each.
   b) When charging one object by contact with another, why should both objects be conductors?
3. Suppose you have two identical conductors. One is charged. Describe a procedure to give both conductors one-quarter the original charge.
4. Describe the distribution of charge on a pear-shaped conductor.
5. Describe how a positive conductor with a pointed end loses its charge in air.

15.5 Activity: Charging a Metal Leaf Electroscope by Induction

We can give the leaves and sphere of a neutral electroscope opposite charges without touching them (Fig. 15-14,A). If you bring a negative rod close to, but not touching, the sphere, the leaves spread apart. Why does this happen? Electrons are repelled from the sphere to the leaves (Fig. 15-14,B). Therefore

Fig. 15-14 Giving an electroscope a temporary charge by induction

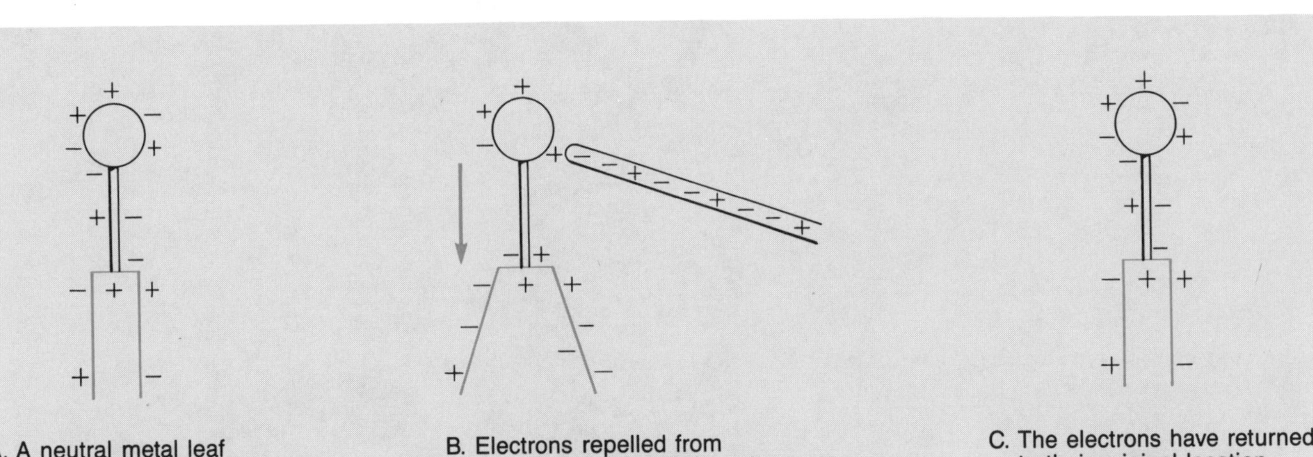

A. A neutral metal leaf electroscope showing some electrons and protons

B. Electrons repelled from sphere to leaves. Sphere has an induced charge of positive two. Leaf has an induced charge of negative two.

C. The electrons have returned to their original location. All parts of the electroscope are neutral.

the sphere becomes positive while the leaves become negative. The process of producing a charge on an object using a nearby charged object is called **induction**. The charge produced is called an **induced charge**. The induced charge in this example is temporary. When the charged rod is removed, the shifted electrons return to the sphere and the leaves collapse (Fig. 15-14,C).

How can you produce a permanent charge on the electroscope by induction?

metal leaf electroscope
ebonite rod
fur
glass rod
silk

a. Touch the sphere of the electroscope with your fingers. This will neutralize the electroscope if it has a charge on it.
b. Approach but do not touch the sphere of the electroscope with a negative rod. Watch the metal leaves.
c. Without removing the rod, touch the sphere with your finger as shown in Figure 15-15. Watch the metal leaves.
d. With the rod still near, remove your finger from the sphere. Then remove the negative rod. Record your observations.

Fig. 15-15 Charging an electroscope permanently by induction

e. Approach but do not touch the sphere with a positive rod (glass). Remove it. Record your observations.
f. Repeat step (e) using a negative rod.

Discussion

1. Define induction.
2. Define induced charge.
3. State what was observed during each step of charging the metal leaf electroscope by induction. Use diagrams to illustrate your answer. Your teacher will help you.
4. Compare the charge on the electroscope with the charge on the rod when an electroscope is being given a permanent charge by induction.
5. Describe how to give the electroscope a negative charge using a glass rod and silk.
6. You touched the sphere with your finger in steps (a) and (c). What did this do?

Extension

Anti-static sprays and rinses are used to remove charge from clothing and records. Design and perform an experiment to test the effectiveness of different kinds of anti-static spray. For example, see how effective each is at discharging an electroscope.

15.6 Charging Objects Permanently by Induction

Grounding a Conductor

A conductor can be given a permanent charge without touching it. This process is called **charging by induction**. All that is needed is a nearby charged object and a method of grounding the conductor. **Grounding** is the process of providing a path for charge to move between a conductor and the earth. Grounding uses two properties of the earth. One is that the earth, because of its size, is a source for an infinite amount of charge. It can either give up or receive billions of electrons without a significant change in its own charge. The other is that the earth is a relatively good conductor. Induction limits the amount of charge transferred to the conductor. In the case of the electroscope, charging by induction prevents damage to the leaves.

Charging an Electroscope by Induction and Grounding

A neutral electroscope contains the same number of protons and electrons—billions of each. For simplicity, the electroscope in Figure 15-16 shows only 7 electrons and 7 protons. The first step in giving the electroscope a permanent charge by induction is to bring the charged object near, but not touching, the knob of the electroscope. Figure 15-16,B shows a negative rod near the knob

Fig. 15-16 Charging an electroscope permanently by induction

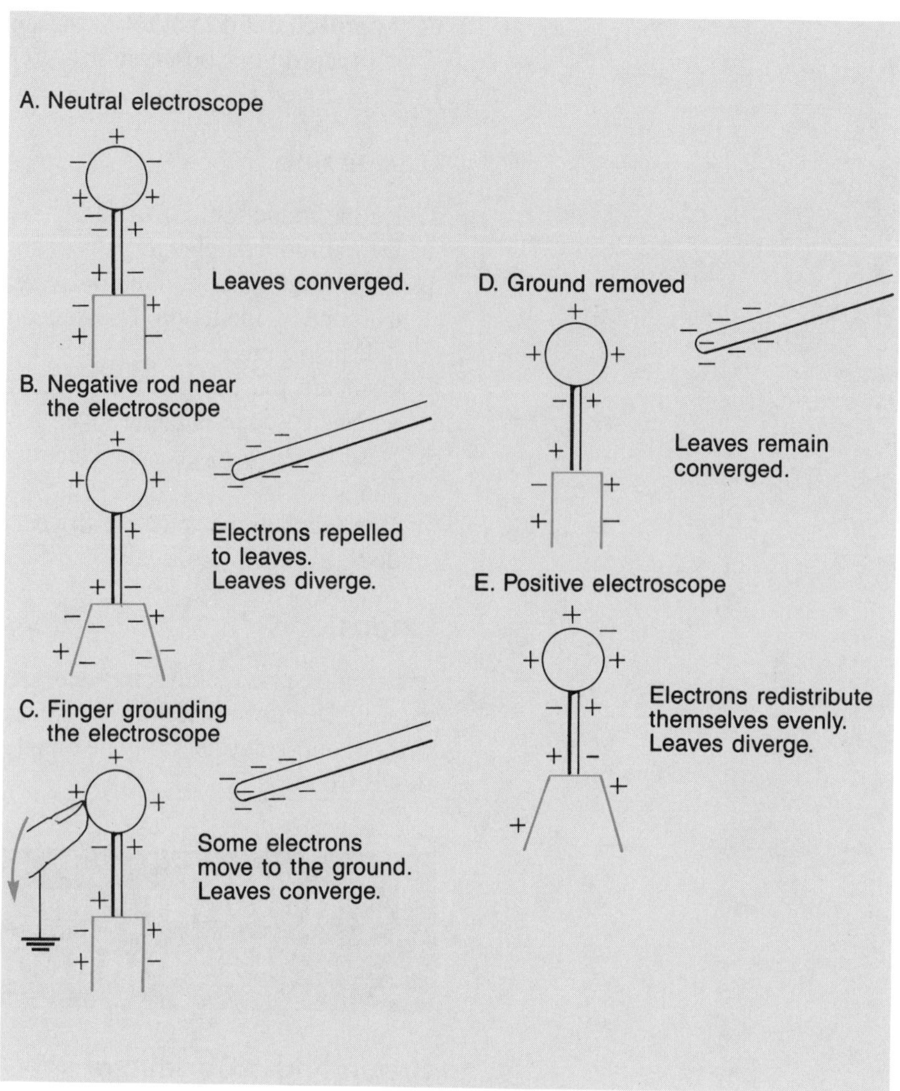
A. Neutral electroscope
Leaves converged.
B. Negative rod near the electroscope
Electrons repelled to leaves.
Leaves diverge.
C. Finger grounding the electroscope
Some electrons move to the ground.
Leaves converge.
D. Ground removed
Leaves remain converged.
E. Positive electroscope
Electrons redistribute themselves evenly.
Leaves diverge.

of the electroscope. The leaves have diverged since some electrons have been repelled from the knob to the leaves. This results in an excess of electrons on the leaves and a deficiency on the knob. How should the excess of electrons compare to the deficiency? Can you explain why?

The second step is to ground the knob of the electroscope with your finger without removing the charged rod (Fig. 15-16,C). The finger and body provide a path for some of the electrons to be repelled from the electroscope to the earth.

The third step is to remove the ground from the knob with the charged rod still in place (Fig. 15-16,D). This prevents charge from the earth returning to the electroscope when the charged object is taken away.

Finally, remove the charged rod. The leaves of the electroscope diverge as shown in Figure 15-16,E. This indicates that the electroscope is permanently charged. Note that the charge on the electroscope is positive. This is opposite to the charge on the charging rod. An object charged permanently by induction always ends up with a charge opposite to that on the charging agent.

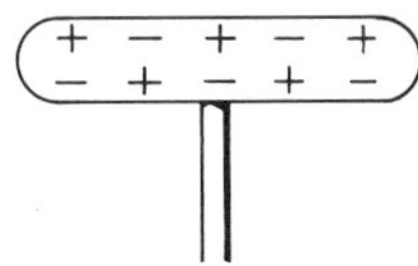

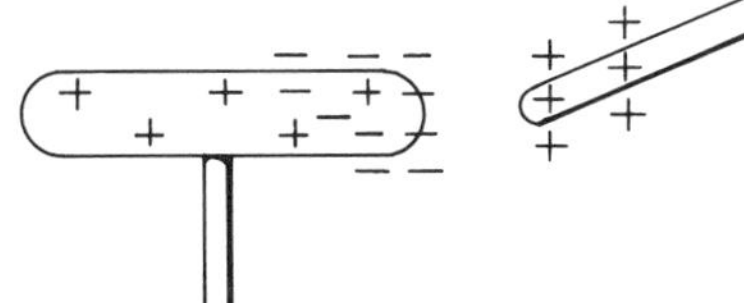

Electrons

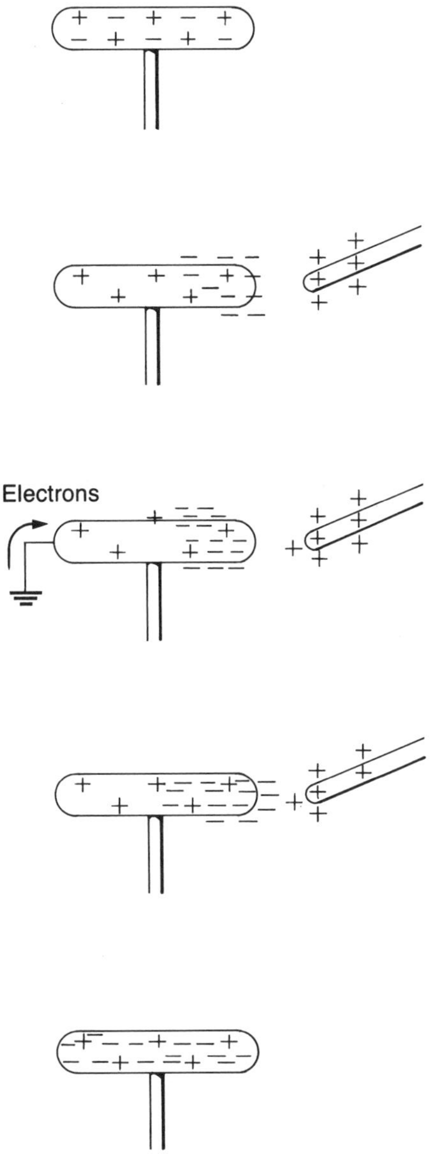

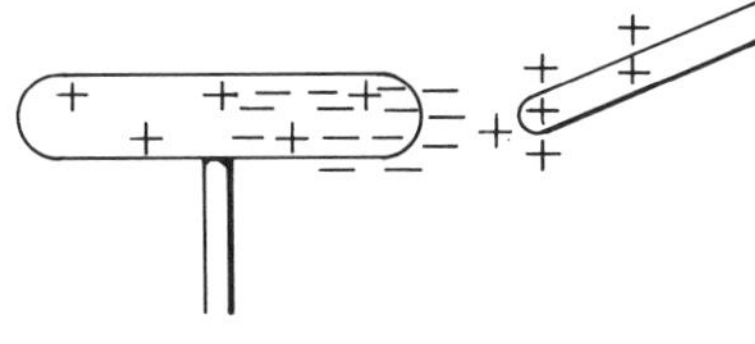

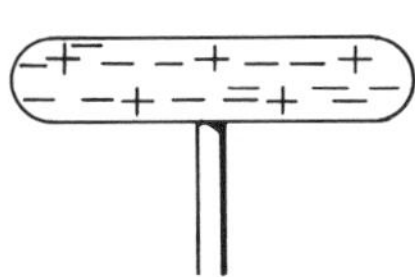

Fig. 15-17 Charging an oblong conductor by induction and grounding

Charging an Oblong Conductor by Induction and Grounding

The same steps can be used to charge any conductor. The only difference is that there is no visible evidence of the charging process. Figure 15-17 shows an oblong conductor being given a negative charge with a positive rod. To simplify the diagrams, only 5 protons and 5 electrons are shown on the neutral conductor.

Charging Spheres by Induction and Separation

Suppose you have two neutral spherical conductors. Both are on insulated stands. How could induction be used to give one sphere a positive charge and the other a negative charge? Neither sphere can be grounded and both charges must be the same size.

A. Two identical neutral conductors in contact

Charges are distributed uniformly.

B. Positive rod is brought near one conductor

Electrons are attracted to the conductor next to the positive rod.

C. The conductors are separated

The electrons cannot return to the far conductor.

D. The positive rod is removed

The two conductors have equal but opposite charges.

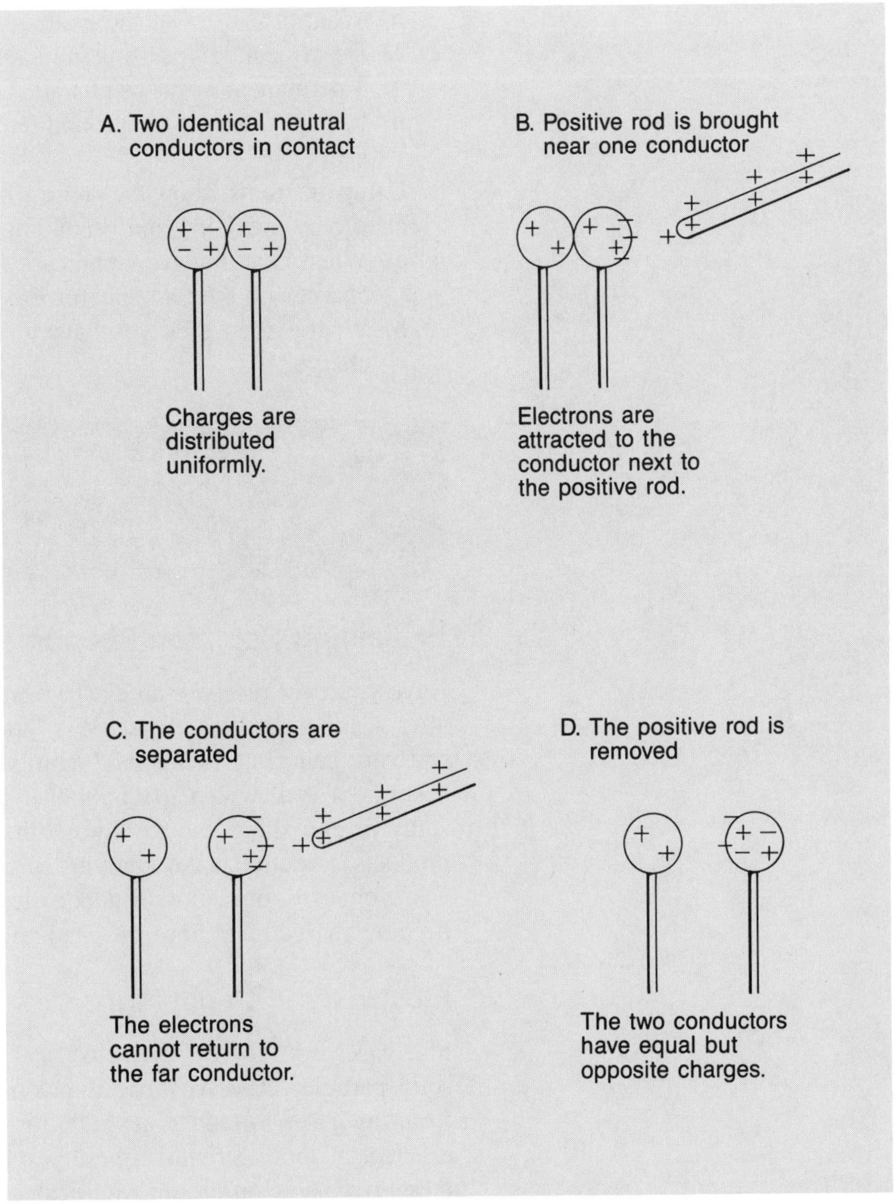

Fig. 15-18 Giving two conductors equal but opposite charges by induction and separation

The process of giving two objects equal amounts of the opposite kind of charge is called charging by **separation**. The charging rod can be either positive or negative. The example shown in Figure 15-18 uses a positive rod. First, the two neutral conductors are placed in contact. Then, a positive rod is brought near one of the conductors. This attracts electrons to the side of the conductor next to the positive rod. Next, the conductors are separated without removing the charged rod. The presence of the positive rod prevents electrons from returning to the far conductor. Finally the positive rod is removed. The near conductor now has a negative charge and the far one a positive charge. What charge would the near conductor obtain if the charging rod was negative? How must the size of the charges compare?

Section Review

1. **a)** What is meant by the term grounding?
   b) What properties of the earth are used in grounding?
2. **a)** Describe the steps using induction and grounding to give an electroscope a permanent negative charge. Use diagrams to clarify the steps.
   b) In step 3, why is the ground removed before the charging agent is taken away?
3. Using diagrams, show the process of giving a spherical conductor a positive charge by induction and grounding.
4. **a)** When charging two spheres by induction and separation, why are the charges on the two spheres the same size and of opposite charge?
   b) What evidence do you have to support the principle of conservation of charge?

15.7 Applications of Electrostatics

Explaining Common Phenomena

Have you ever received an electric shock when you touch a metal door knob after walking across a carpet? Why do you think this happens? Have you ever had your hair cling to a comb? You have probably used the same principle to decorate a wall with party balloons. But have you tried using an anti-static spray or anti-static gun to remove the balloons? People frequently use such products to neutralize the annoying static electricity which builds up in clothing. Can you use your knowledge of electrostatics to explain why these items become charged and how anti-static devices work?

Electrostatic Deposition

Flue gases from fossil-fueled electrical generating stations and smelters contain solid particles. **Electrostatic deposition** is a way to remove solid particles from the gases to reduce air pollution. Prior to the early 1900s there was no efficient method to remove these particles. However, by 1912 a method proposed by F.G. Cottrell, an American physical chemist, was in operation. This

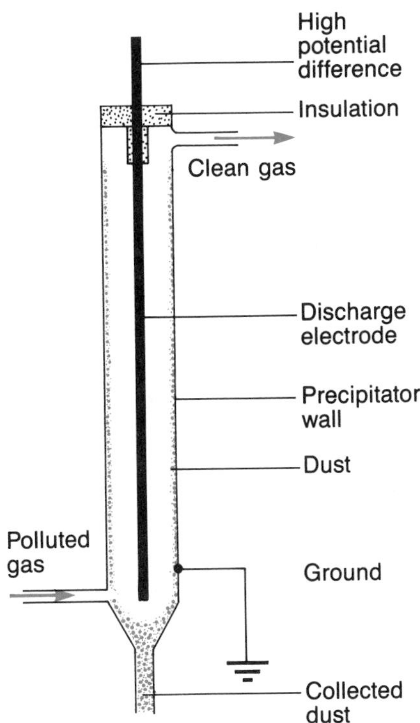

Fig. 15-19 An electrostatic precipitator

method is based on the electrical attraction between a charged particle and a charged collecting surface. The apparatus is called an electrostatic precipitator.

Figure 15-19 shows a simplified schematic diagram of an **electrostatic precipitator**. The precipitator wall is kept at the same electrical potential as the ground. A discharge electrode runs down the centre of the column. It is given a large positive or negative charge by connecting it to a source of high electrical potential difference. The electrical potential difference used is between 10 and 100 kV. Gases and solid particles enter at the bottom. The gases become charged and cause an electrical discharge similar to lightning to occur between the discharge electrode and the precipitator wall. During the discharge, the solid particles become highly charged. They are then attracted to the wall of the precipitator. Here the charge is neutralized. The solid particles clump together. Some clumps break away from the wall naturally and fall to the bottom. Others must be dislodged by vibrating or scraping. These solids collect at the bottom and are removed. At the present time the electrostatic precipitator will remove between 90% and 99.99% of the solid particles from gases.

Electrostatic Air Filters

A similar process is used in the electrostatic air filters which remove pollen and dust particles from air in a home (Fig. 15-20). Here the charged wire is positive. A positive wire produces less ozone during the electrical discharge.

Electrostatic Spray Painting

It is desirable to paint a surface with a coat that is as even and thin as possible. This saves paint, speeds drying, and gives a smooth surface. One method used

Fig. 15-20 An electrostatic air cleaner used in the home

Fig. 15-21 Electrostatic spray painting. Why is there less air pollution with this method?

in industry, called **electrostatic spray painting**, involves static electricity. The object to be painted is grounded. Thus it is neutral. The paint, as it leaves the nozzle of the sprayer, is given a charge (Fig. 15-21). The paint is attracted to the neutral surface. Why do you think the car is grounded rather than being given the opposite charge?

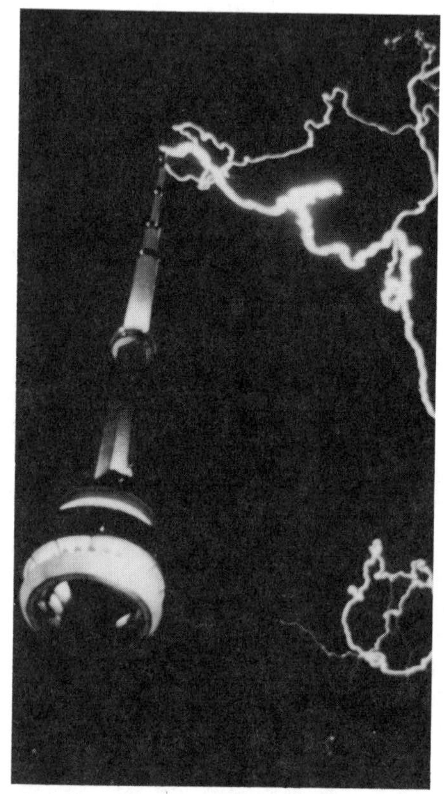

Fig. 15-22 A lightning discharge moves very fast—between 6000 km/h and 500 000 km/h.

Lightning

During a thunderstorm, molecules and atoms in a cloud are forced to move rapidly about. Frequent collisions occur which dislodge electrons from atoms. This produces positive ions and free electrons. The positive ions tend to collect at the top of the cloud. The electrons tend to collect at the bottom. The huge negative charge near the earth induces a large positive charge on objects beneath it. When the induced charge becomes very large, the air becomes a conductor. Then an **electrical discharge** occurs between the cloud and the earth. **Lightning** is an electrical discharge in which we see sparks and brilliant flashes of light (Fig. 15-22).

Lightning can occur between the earth and a cloud or between two clouds. It is the lightning near the earth that causes the most damage. Over 100 bolts of lightning strike the earth every second. This energy can create temperatures in excess of 30 000°C. It can trigger forest and building fires. Little wonder that lightning kills!

Lightning Rods

Lightning rods have been designed to minimize the destruction of lightning. **Lightning rods** are conductors with pointed ends. These conductors are placed on the highest points of a building with the pointed end up (Fig. 15-23). They are connected to the ground by a thick conducting wire. In fact, the end of the conductor is buried deep in the moist ground. Lightning rods protect buildings in two ways. First, when a charged cloud is overhead, an opposite charge is induced on the pointed end of the lightning rod. Charge escapes from

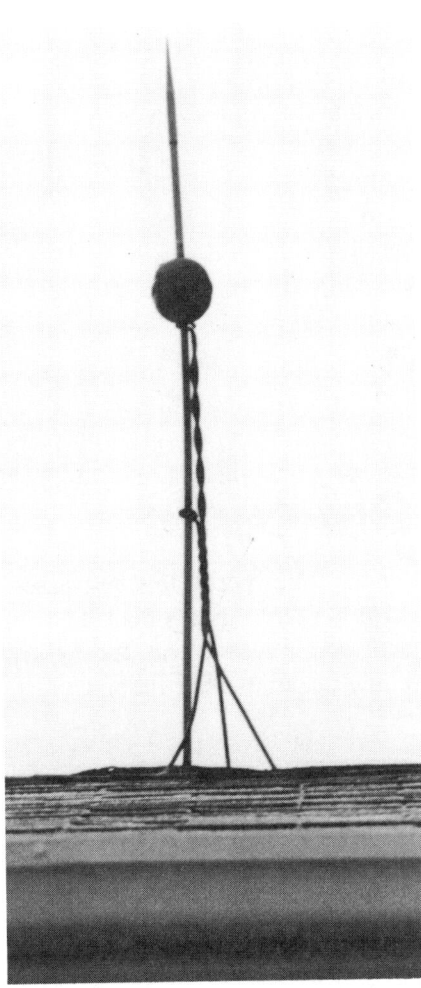

Fig. 15-23 Why must the lightning rod be higher than any other part of the building?

the point and neutralizes some of the charge on the cloud. This gradual process can limit the buildup of charge on the cloud and prevent an electrical discharge. If an electrical discharge does occur, the second safety feature comes into play. The huge electrical current from the discharge travels through the conductor to the earth rather than through the building. This prevents the building from reaching its kindling temperature and bursting into flame.

It is important to stay away from lightning rods during thunderstorms. Imagine the consequences if you became a conductor for the discharge. That is why you should not stand on high points or under trees during storms. Wearing golf shoes with cleats on the bottom accentuates the danger. So does travelling in an aluminum boat on the lake in a storm.

If you are outside during a thunderstorm, squat or lie in a low area away from any trees or boulders. Better still, seek shelter in a closed car. Charge builds up on the outside of the car, not inside. And any electrical discharge is conducted to the ground through the car body and its tires.

Section Review

1. a) What is electrostatic deposition?
   b) What causes the solid particles to be attracted to the precipitator wall?
   c) Why will many of the solid particles eventually fall to the collector region?
2. Why must electrostatic air filters be cleaned frequently?
3. A body shop uses an electrostatic sprayer to paint cars. If the car is given a charge, where would you expect more paint to accumulate, on the flat surface or at a sharp corner? Explain.
4. a) What causes lightning?
   b) Explain two ways in which lightning rods protect buildings.
   c) Draw up a list of things to do and not to do during a thunderstorm.

Chapter Highlights

1. Electrostatics is the study of electric charge at rest.
2. There are two kinds of electric charge: positive and negative.
3. The Law of Electric Charges states that like charges repel and unlike charges attract.
4. An electroscope is used to test for the kind of charge on an object.
5. The Electron Theory of Charge explains all aspects of electrostatics.
6. The electrostatic series is a list of materials in order of their tendency to lose electrons.
7. An electroscope can be charged by contact or by induction.
8. Charge resides on the outside of a conductor and is more concentrated where the conductor is more pointed.
9. The earth is a good conductor and acts as an infinitely large reservoir for charge.
10. There are numerous machines and processes that make use of electrostatic principles.

Key Terms

charged
conductor
electrical discharge
electron
electroscope
electrostatics
electrostatic deposition
electrostatic precipitator
grounding
induced charge
induction
insulator
lightning
negative
neutral
neutron
positive
proton
static electricity

Recognizing the Concepts

Each of the following statements or questions is followed by four responses. Choose the correct response in each case. (Do not write in this book.)

1. A glass rod is rubbed with silk. An ebonite rod is rubbed with fur. Which of the following describes the charge on the materials after rubbing?

	Ebonite	Fur	Glass	Silk
a)	−	−	+	+
b)	+	+	−	−
c)	+	−	+	−
d)	−	+	+	−

2. A metal leaf electroscope is being charged positive by contact. Which particles move? In what direction do they move?
a) Electrons move from the sphere to the metal leaves.
b) Electrons move from the sphere to the charged rod.
c) Protons move from the sphere to the metal leaves.
d) Protons move from the charged rod to the sphere.

3. Which one of the following materials is classified as a conductor?
a) air **b)** aluminum **c)** plastic **d)** glass

4. To charge an electroscope positively by induction, the sphere is touched with a finger when the charging agent is nearby. The finger
a) neutralizes the electroscope
b) repels electrons to the leaf
c) conducts electrons to the ground
d) conducts protons from the ground

5. In an electrostatic precipitator, what kind of charge is on the discharge electrode and on the precipitator wall?

	Discharge electrode	Precipitator wall
a)	negative	positive
b)	positive	negative
c)	negative	neutral
d)	neutral	negative

Understanding the Concepts

1. Imagine that a rubber balloon is rubbed with wool. This balloon repels an ebonite rod rubbed with fur. What charge is on the balloon? the wool?
2. Compare the kind of charge on the charging agent and on the conductor when the conductor is charged by
   a) contact **b)** induction
3. A strip of lucite is rubbed with cat's fur. Explain how a negative ebonite rod and a positive glass rod can be used to determine the charge on the lucite.
4. A cork sphere and an aluminum sphere are suspended by insulating threads. A positive rod attracts the cork sphere and repels the metal sphere. What can we say about the charges on the spheres?
5. **a)** When plastic food wrap is pulled out of the box it becomes charged. Why?
   b) Why does plastic food wrap stick to the top and sides of a dish?
6. What causes the sparks when a nylon sleeping bag is dragged across an air mattress made of rubber?
7. The CN Tower in Toronto does not have lightning rods. It is frequently struck by lightning but it has never been damaged. Why?
8. The anaesthetics used in hospitals are explosive gases. Why must the shoes worn by hospital personnel in operating rooms be good electrical conductors?
9. You can get a shock after walking across a nylon carpet and touching a metal door knob but not a wooden one. Why?
10. Why does a tabletop seem to attract dust more just after it is wiped clean?

Applying the Concepts

1. Lycopodium powder consists of the spores of a club moss. These spores are neutral and are very small. If a negative ebonite rod is placed in the powder, spores cling to the rod. However, a short time later they fly off in all directions. Explain why this happens.
2. Three ping pong balls are suspended from the corners of a triangle using insulating threads. They attract each other. What charges are on the ping pong balls?
3. Four small styrofoam spheres A, B, C, and D are hung from the corners of a square. They are suspended by insulating threads. Spheres D and C repel. Spheres A, B, and C attract each other. If A is positive, what is the electric charge on B, C, and D?
4. A student makes the claim that charge is conserved during electrostatic interactions. Cite evidence to support this claim.
5. Suppose your teacher gives you three unknown materials, A, B, and C, and a negatively charged electroscope. A, B, and C can be rubbed together in any combination. Explain how you could establish an electrostatic series for A, B, and C.
6. An electrical conductor with a sharp point discharges readily whether it is charged negatively or positively. Explain why.

Fig. 15-24 This is a capacitor. What is it and how does it store charge?

7. Car bodies are grounded rather than charged when they are being spray painted at the factory. The paint is charged when it leaves the sprayer. Why is the car not given the opposite charge to the paint? Consider the shape of the car.

Investigations

1. Do a library search to find out what is meant by shielding. Describe where it is used and why it works.
2. Scientists have made an **electrostatic series** to show the electric charge different pairs of materials receive when rubbed together. Do a library search to find an electrostatic series. Perform an experiment to test the accuracy of the series.
3. The Electron Theory of Charge predicts that two objects rubbed together get the same amount of charge. However, the charges are opposite in kind. Design and do an experiment using a metal leaf electroscope, an ebonite rod, cat's fur, and a metal pail to test this prediction.
4. The electrostatic photocopier was invented in the United States in the 1930s by Chester F. Carlson (1906–1968). Research the topic in the library and submit a report on your findings.
5. Contact a large carpet manufacturer. Find out where and how the principles of electrostatics are used in the carpet industry.
6. Find out what a capacitor is and how it makes use of electrostatic principles to store charge (Fig. 15-24).

VISTA

THE ELECTROSTATIC PHOTOCOPIER

Many photocopiers depend on electrostatics for their operation. The key component of the copier is a material which conducts electricity when exposed to light, but acts as an insulator in the dark. A thin layer of this semi-conducting material is placed on top of a sloping conducting plate. The surface is given a uniform positive charge in the dark (A).

Suppose we want to photocopy a page containing the letter F. This page is placed face down on the copier. Light is used to project a real inverted image of the F onto the semi-conductor. Areas exposed to light become conducting and the positive charge is removed. Unexposed areas remain non-conducting and retain their positive charge. These areas correspond to the image of the letter F shown in B.

The next step involves a principle of electrostatics. When two materials far apart in the electrostatic series tumble over one another, both become charged. The toner used in photocopiers is a powdery mixture of carbon black and plastic. The plastic has a low melting point. The toner is mixed with tiny beads of glass, metal, or quartz. These beads have a magnetic core. This mixture is allowed to roll down the slope and over the image as shown in C. As the toner and beads tumble over one another, the beads become positive and the toner becomes negative. Negative particles of toner adhere to the positive image. The positive beads and remaining toner eventually roll off the slope. Any remaining beads are skimmed off with a magnet.

A piece of paper is then positioned over the image and toner. A hot cylinder rolls over the paper and melts the toner onto the paper (D). The permanent image is shown in E. The process is repeated for each new photocopy.

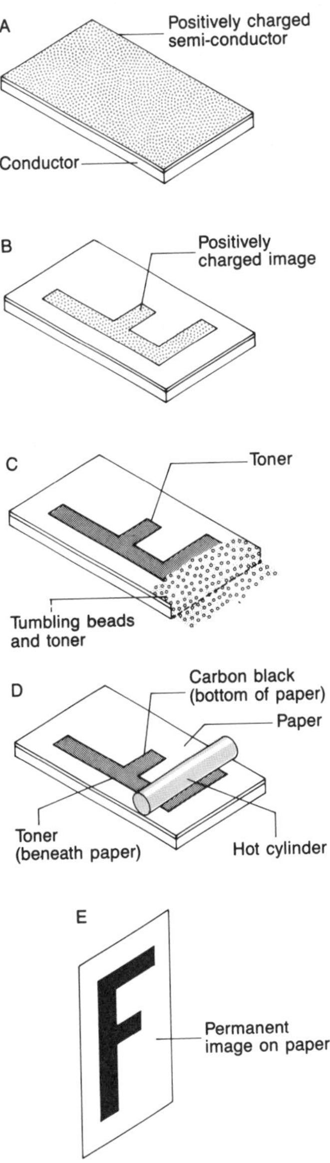

16 Cells and Batteries

CHAPTER CONTENTS

CHAPTER OBJECTIVES

After completing this chapter you should be able to:

1. Distinguish between static and current electricity.
2. Compare Volta's and Galvani's experiments.
3. Describe energy conversion in a thermocouple, a solar cell, a piezoelectric crystal, and a generator.
4. Distinguish between electric potential and electric current.
5. Correctly connect a voltmeter and ammeter in an electrical circuit and read both.
6. Describe a voltaic cell and factors affecting its operation.
7. Compare the voltaic cell and the carbon-zinc dry cell.
8. Distinguish between primary and secondary cells; between a cell and a battery.
9. Describe the operation of the nickel-cadmium storage cell and the lead storage battery.
10. Compare sources of current electricity.

Portable sources of electricity are essential to our modern economy. Thermocouples control electrical devices. Piezoelectric crystals convert sound energy into electrical signals in microphones. Cells and batteries power smoke detectors, radios, pacemakers, and safety lights. In the future, cars driven by batteries may even be practical.

In this chapter you will learn how wet cells, dry cells, and batteries produce an electric current (Fig. 16-1). You will use voltmeters and ammeters to measure electricity. You will also be introduced to some criteria to use when buying cells and batteries.

Fig. 16-1 This lead storage battery delivers electricity to start a car. Then the battery is recharged as the car runs. How does all this happen?

16.1 An Introduction to Current Electricity

The Discovery of Current Electricity

Static electricity deals with electric charges at rest. It has many uses. However, can you imagine having to rub two different materials together to get a source of electricity every time you want to take a flash picture?

The first continuous source of electricity was discovered in 1771 by an Italian doctor, Luigi Galvani (1737–1798). He noticed that the muscle of a dead frog's leg twitched whenever an electrical discharge passed through it. Galvani wondered if this would happen during a thunderstorm. He fastened a frog's leg to a brass hook outside so that it rested against an iron lattice work. When lightning flashed, the muscle twitched. However, the muscle also twitched in the absence of an electrical discharge. It moved whenever it was touched by two different metals at the same time, such as a brass dissection pin and a steel scalpel (Fig. 16-2). After repeated experiments, Galvani concluded that the muscle of the frog was a source of electricity. He hypothesized the existence of animal electricity.

An Italian physicist, Alessandro Giuseppe Volta (1745–1827), had a different explanation for the muscle twitch. He hypothesized that electricity was produced by two different metals used to hold the frog's leg, not the muscle. The twitch was the muscle's reaction to the charge passing through it. Volta tested his hypothesis in 1794 by placing two different metals in a conducting solution. Sure enough, an electrical current was produced. No muscle tissue was needed. Further experiments led to the development of the **voltaic cell**—the first source of current electricity. **Current electricity** is the study of electric charges moving along predetermined paths. The moving charges can be electrons, positive ions, or negative ions. Electrons transfer charge in solid conductors. Electrons, and positive and negative ions, move in liquids and gases.

Devices that Produce Current Electricity

Today there are many sources of electricity. Did you know that current electricity can even be produced by sticking two different metals into a lemon or

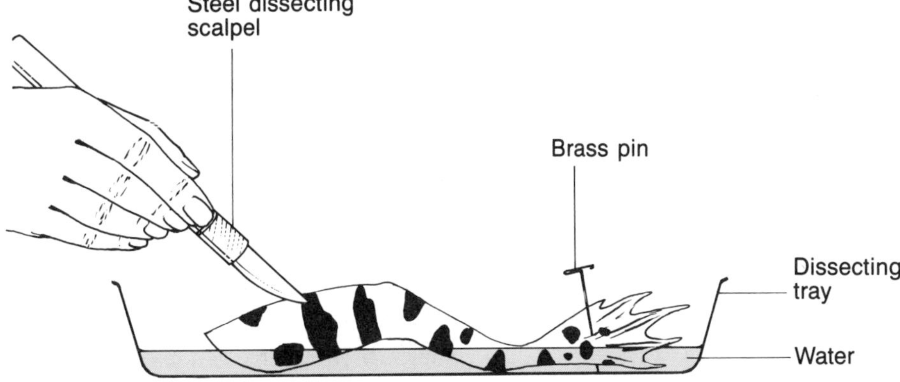

Fig. 16-2 Leg of a dead frog being touched by a scalpel

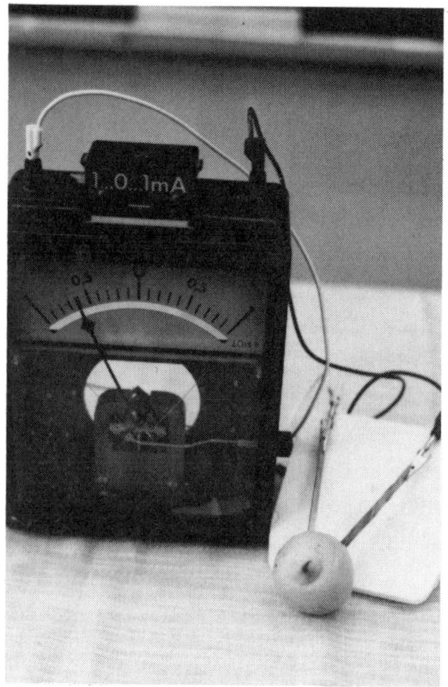

Fig. 16-3 A source of electricity made from a lemon and electrodes made of two different metals

potato (Fig. 16-3)? This is an example of chemical energy being converted to electric energy. We will overview other sources of current electricity before we focus on chemical energy.

Thermocouple

Heat energy can be converted directly into electric energy by a device called a thermocouple (Fig. 16-4). A **thermocouple** consists of two different metals joined together at one end to form a junction. The junction is heated. Thus both metals at the junction are at the same temperature. The unconnected ends are kept at a different temperature. Thus the junction and the unconnected ends are at a different temperature. When a temperature difference exists, the thermocouple acts as a source of electricity. The greater the difference in temperature, the more electricity is produced from heat energy. Thermocouples are used in thermometers to measure high temperatures. They are also used to activate temperature sensitive switches.

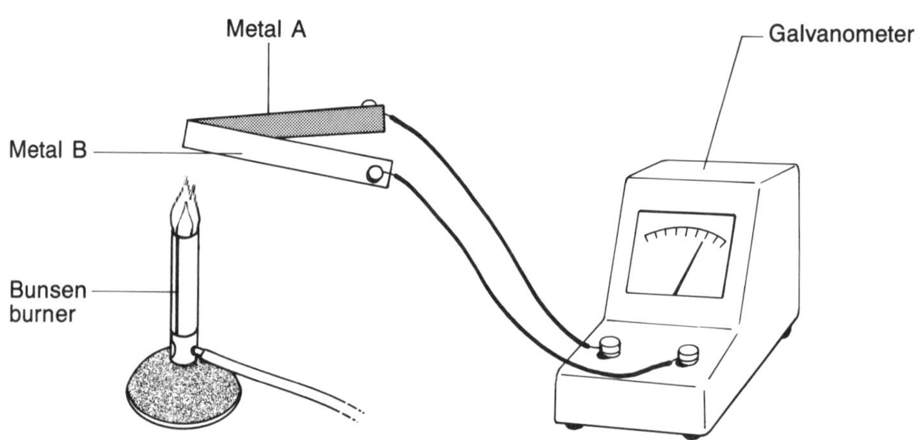

Fig. 16-4 A thermocouple

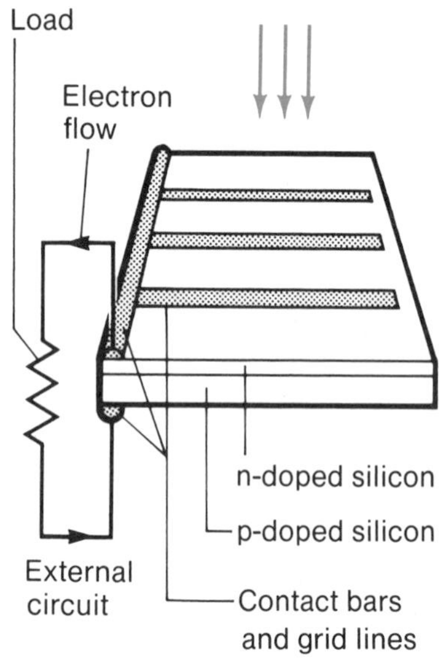

Fig. 16-5 Silicon solar cell

Solar Cell

Solar energy can be changed directly into electric energy using **solar cells**. One kind of solar cell is made of silicon (Fig. 16-5). Light shines on the silicon cell, forcing some electrons from a type of silicon called n-doped to a type called p-doped. The brighter the light, the more electrons are forced across. These electrons can only return to the n-doped silicon through the external circuit. Electrons moving in a circuit have electric energy. Thus, the brighter the light, the more electric energy is produced.

Piezoelectric Crystal

Certain kinds of crystals can convert changes in pressure directly into electric energy. This process is called **piezoelectricity**. If the crystal is compressed, one side becomes negative and the other positive. When a conducting path is connected between the two sides, a current of electrons is produced. If the crystal is stretched, the sides reverse charge. The greater the crystal is compressed or stretched, the more electric energy is produced. Crystals made of quartz or Rochelle salt have this property. These crystals are used in some microphones to convert sound energy to electric energy. They are also found in the tone arm cartridges of less expensive record players. Have you ever used a barbecue lighter that emits sparks when you squeeze it? This kind of lighter never wears out. All it takes to operate it is a little squeeze!

Electromagnetic Generator

The large **generators** present in hydroelectric power plants depend on magnets for their operation. They convert the kinetic energy in moving water into electricity (Fig. 16-6). Generators in fossil-fueled and nuclear-fueled power plants harness the kinetic energy in moving steam in the same way. You will find out how magnets convert kinetic energy into electric energy in Chapter 18.

Fig. 16-6 Kinetic energy in moving water being converted to electricity in a hydroelectric power plant

Section Review

1. **a)** Define current electricity.
   b) Contrast static electricity and current electricity.
2. What role did static electricity play in the discovery of current electricity?
3. What caused Galvani to believe that the frog muscle was a source of electricity?
4. How did Volta prove that the frog's muscle was not the source of the electricity?

5. Explain the operation of a thermocouple.
6. What energy conversion takes place in a solar cell?
7. a) Explain how a piezoelectric crystal produces an electric current.
   b) What are two uses of piezoelectric crystals?

16.2 Electric Potential and Electric Current

Static electricity is produced by rubbing two materials together. The person doing the rubbing does work. This work separates electrons from atoms. One material gains electrons and becomes negative and the other material loses electrons and becomes positive. The work is stored as electric potential energy in the charged materials.

Fig. 16-7 This cell has an electric potential of about 9V (DC). Each electrical device is designed to run at a certain electric potential. The wrong electric potential can damage the device.

Electric Potential

Chemical energy can also be used to do work to separate electrons from atoms. Some of the work done to separate the charge is stored in the separated surplus electrons as potential energy. The energy stored in a group of electrons is called **electric potential**. The electric potential of the surplus electrons on a negative material is similar to the potential energy stored in raised water. If the water is released, it flows from a high to a low level. If the surplus electrons are free to move in a conductor, a current flows from an area with an excess of electrons to an area deficient in electrons. The greater the electric potential of the surplus electrons, the larger the electric current. Electric potential is measured in **volts (V)**. A flashlight D dry cell has an electric potential of about 1.5 V (DC). The cell that you use in your portable stereo has an electric potential of about 9 V (DC) (Fig. 16-7). A car battery has an electric potential of about 12 V (DC).

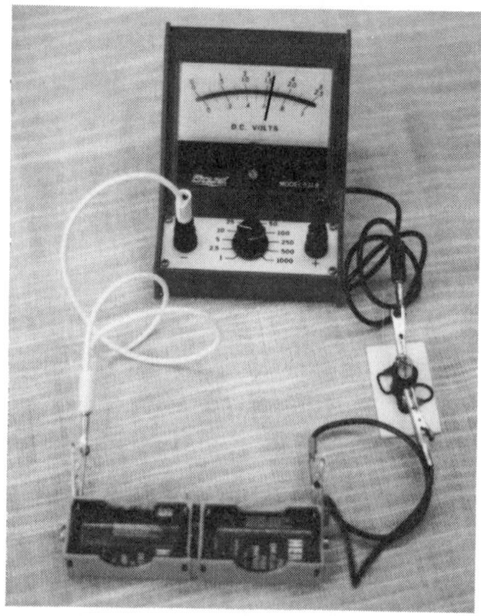

Fig. 16-8 A voltmeter measures electric potential. What is the electric potential in the circuit shown here?

Measuring Electric Potential

We use a **voltmeter** to measure electric potential (Fig. 16-8). When a voltmeter is connected between the terminals of a source of electricity, the needle on the dial moves and points to the number of volts. Also, one type of voltmeter may have a different scale than another type. However, a voltmeter must be connected correctly to prevent damage. The negative terminal of the voltmeter is connected to the negative terminal of the source. Electrons leave the source and enter the voltmeter at the negative terminal. They exit the voltmeter at the positive terminal and return to the positive side of the source. Your teacher will show you how to connect and read a voltmeter.

Electric Current

A water current in a river consists of moving water molecules. In like manner, an electric current in a wire consists of moving electrons. The rate of flow of electrons through a wire is measured in **amperes (A)**. A current of about one ampere (1 A) flows through a 100 W bulb when the bulb is in a normal household circuit. One ampere is a flow of about 6 000 000 000 000 000 000 electrons past a point each second. That's a lot of electrons in a short time!

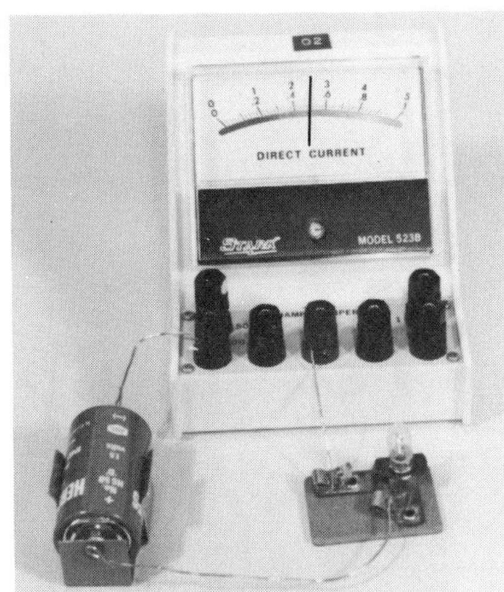

Fig. 16-9 An ammeter measures electric current. What is the electric current in the circuit shown here?

Measuring Electric Current

We use an **ammeter** to measure electric current. When an electric current flows through an ammeter, the needle points to the number of amperes. A typical ammeter is shown in Figure 16-9. An ammeter must also be connected correctly to prevent damage. The positive terminal of the ammeter is again connected to the positive terminal of the source. The negative terminals are also connected. However, there must be a load, such as a light bulb, in the circuit. Electrons leaving the negative terminal of the source must pass through both the load and the ammeter before returning to the positive terminal of the source. Your teacher will show you how to connect and read an ammeter.

Reading Electric Meters

The same steps are followed for reading both ammeters and voltmeters.

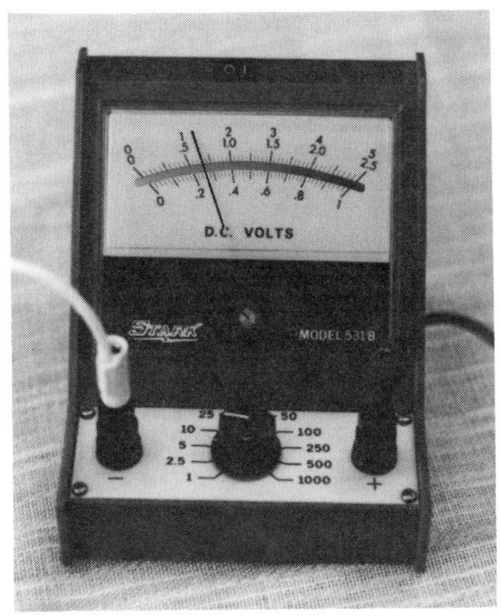

Fig. 16-10 Which terminals of this voltmeter are connected?

Step 1
Connect the terminal for the most appropriate scale of the meter. Figure 16-10 shows a closeup view of the terminals of a voltmeter. Notice that there are several positive terminals. Each one is labelled differently. The label corresponds to full scale deflection on the scale of the meter. For example, if the terminal has a value of 5 V, then one of the scales on the meter will read a full scale deflection of 5 V. When connecting any meter, always connect the terminal with the largest value first. This prevents damage to the meter. If the needle barely moves, reconnect to the terminal with the next largest value. Continue this process until the appropriate terminal and scale are found. For example, if the voltmeter is connected to a 1.5 V source, use the 5 V terminal and read the 5 V scale.

Step 2
Position your eye directly in front of the needle and the scale behind it. This decreases the error when reading the scale. Figure 16-11 shows a voltmeter with three scales. The smallest scale can read up to 5 V. The largest scale can read 100 V for a full scale deflection.

Step 3
Determine the correct scale to read. This depends on the terminal connected to the source. For example, if the 5 V terminal is connected, then read the 5 V scale. In our example we must read the 5 V scale. Can you see why from Figure 16-11?

Step 4
Record the reading warranted by the scale. Figure 16-11 shows the needle halfway between two small scale divisions. Each large scale division on the 5 V scale represents 1 V. There are five small scale divisions between each large scale division. Thus, each small scale division represents 0.2 V. A reading halfway between two small scale divisions represents an additional 0.1 V. The reading in our example is 1.5 volts. Can you explain why?

Fig. 16-11 A voltmeter with three scales

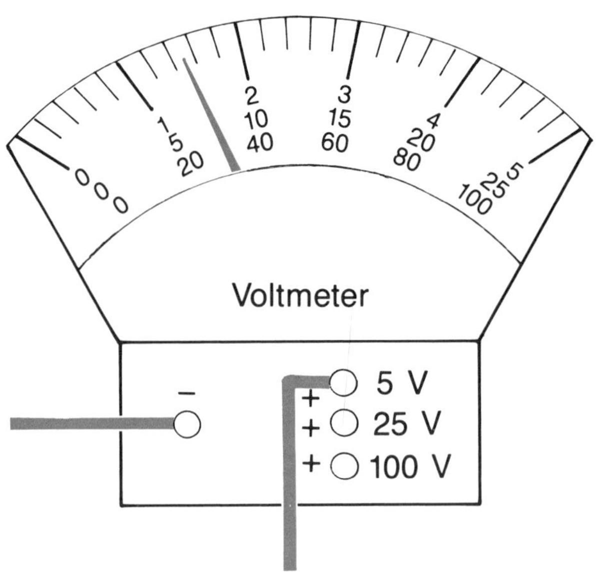

Section Review

1. a) What is electric potential?
   b) What is the unit and symbol for electric potential?
   c) Name the instrument used to measure electric potential.
   d) Explain how this instrument must be connected.
2. a) What is electric current?
   b) What is the unit and symbol for electric current?
   c) What instrument is used to measure electric current?
3. a) List the four steps for reading an electric meter.
   b) Suppose the needle in Figure 16-11 is at the same place but a different terminal is connected. What is the reading if the 25 V terminal is connected? What is the reading if the 100 V terminal is connected?

16.3 Activity: Factors Affecting Current from a Voltaic Cell

A voltaic cell is a source of electricity. It makes an electric current from a chemical reaction. In this activity you will make and study a voltaic cell. You will find out the factors needed to produce an electric current. And you will use an ammeter and a voltmeter to measure electricity.

Problem

What factors affect the electric current from a voltaic cell?

Materials

voltaic cell
tap water
ammeter (0–1 A)
voltmeter (0–1.5 V)
steel wool
copper strips (2)
zinc strip
conducting wires (2)
potassium dichromate
dilute sulfuric acid

CAUTION: Sulfuric acid is corrosive. Wear safety goggles during this activity. Flush skin or clothing immediately with water if you get any acid on them, and call your teacher.

Procedure

a. Copy Table 16-1 into your notebook.
b. Polish the metal strips using steel wool.
c. Half fill the voltaic cell with dilute sulfuric acid solution (Fig. 16-12).

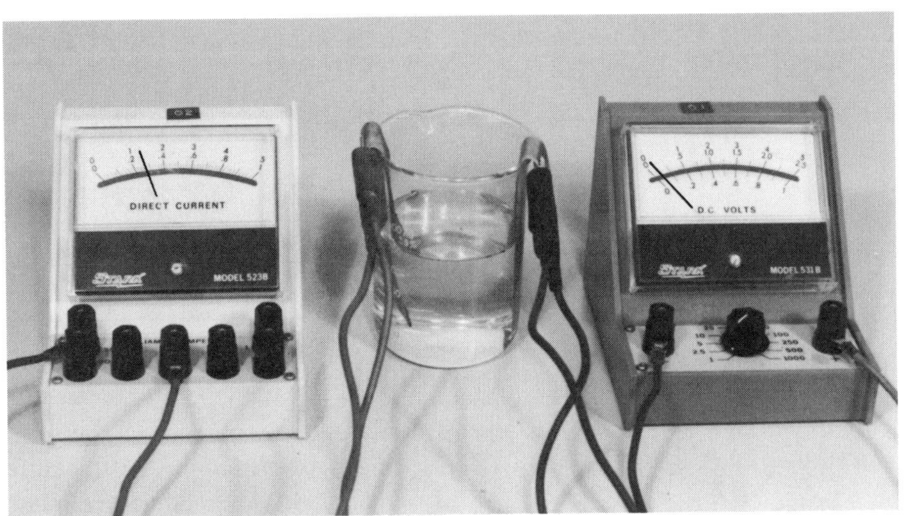

Fig. 16-12 Electrons flow from the zinc electrode through the ammeter to the copper electrode in a voltaic cell.

d. Place a zinc strip and a copper strip in the solution.
e. Connect the zinc strip to the black terminal of the ammeter. Connect the copper strip to the red terminal. Also connect the voltmeter as shown.
f. Record the reading for electric current on the ammeter. Also record the reading for electric potential on the voltmeter. Your teacher will help you read the meters.
g. Watch the surface of the metal strips for bubbles. Record any action.
h. Allow the cell to operate for about 5 min. Read the meters again. Also, note whether bubbles are present.
i. Wipe away any bubbles from the metal strips. Repeat steps (f) and (g).
j. Again let the cell operate for another 5 min. Then add a spoonful of potassium dichromate to the acid solution. Repeat steps (f) and (g).
k. Replace the zinc strip with another copper strip. Place the two copper strips in the solution used in (j). Repeat steps (f) and (g).
l. Rinse the metal strips with tap water. Replace the solution in the voltaic cell with tap water. Then repeat steps (f) and (g) using a zinc and copper strip.

Table 16-1 Current from a Voltaic Cell

Factor changed	*Metal strips*	*Solution*	*Electric current (A)*	*Electric potential (V)*	*Action at strips*
—	Copper and zinc	Sulfuric acid			
Leave 5 min	Copper and zinc	Sulfuric acid			
Wipe bubbles off	Copper and zinc	Sulfuric acid			
Add potassium dichromate	Copper and zinc	Sulfuric acid + potassium dichromate			
Use identical strips	Copper and copper	Sulfuric acid + potassium dichromate			
Change solution	Copper and zinc	Tap water			

Discussion

1. What did you observe on the surface of the copper strip?
2. What happened to the electric current and electric potential as time passed?
3. What effect does adding potassium dichromate have on the cell?
4. Which combination of factors produced the best voltaic cell?

16.4 Chemical Sources of Current Electricity

There are several sources of current electricity. The first continuous source was discovered by an Italian physicist Alessandro Volta. This source of current electricity was named the voltaic cell in honour of Volta.

The Voltaic Cell

A **voltaic cell** consists of two different metal plates in a solution. The plates are called **electrodes** and the solution is called an **electrolyte**. The solution may be an acid, a base, or a salt dissolved in water. Since the electrolyte is always a liquid solution, a voltaic cell is called a **wet cell**.

One kind of voltaic cell has copper and zinc electrodes immersed in sulfuric acid. A chemical reaction takes place between the electrodes and the sulfuric acid. Chemical energy separates the positive and negative charges. The copper gets a positive charge and the zinc gets a negative charge. If the electrodes are connected outside by a conductor as shown in Figure 16-13, electrons move from the negative zinc electrode to the positive copper electrode. The electric current continues as long as the chemical action continues.

The voltaic cell has a number of faults which limit its use. First, the zinc electrode is used up. This is because zinc reacts with the acid and goes into solution. Also, bubbles of hydrogen gas form around the copper electrode. This allows less of the copper to be in contact with the acid and the action of the cell slows down. As a result, less electric current flows. This can be overcome by removing the hydrogen. One way is to wipe the hydrogen off the electrode; another is to use a chemical, such as potassium dichromate, which reacts with the hydrogen to produce water. The main fault of the voltaic cell is the danger of spilling the acid solution. Sulfuric acid is very corrosive and can eat through clothes and burn skin. This fault led to the invention of the dry cell.

Fig. 16-13 A simple voltaic cell connected to an ammeter and a voltmeter

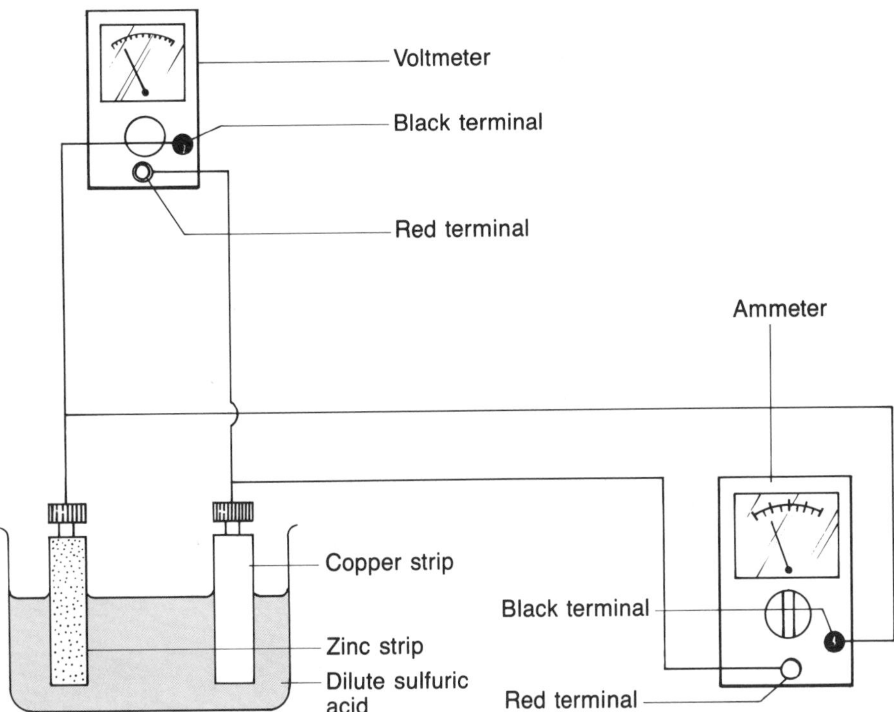

The Dry Cell

The structure of the **dry cell** is shown in Figure 16-14. The cell has a carbon electrode and a zinc electrode. The zinc electrode is the cylindrical container around the outside, while the carbon electrode is the central rod. Between the carbon and zinc electrodes is the electrolyte, a moist paste of ammonium chloride. Since the solution is a paste rather than a liquid, the cell is called a dry cell. Carbon powder is mixed with the electrolyte to improve conduction. The chemical action within the cell removes electrons from the carbon and

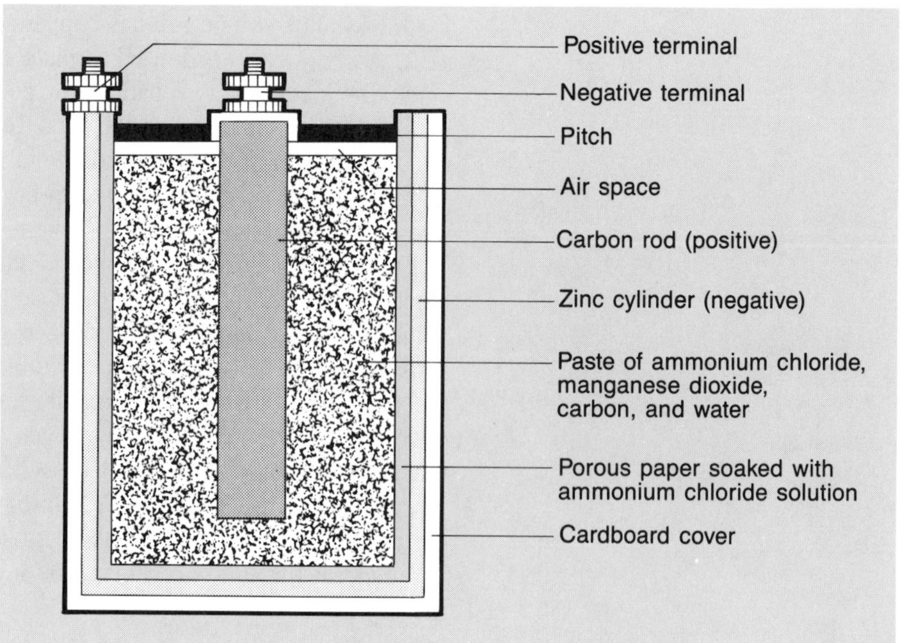

Fig. 16-14 Cross section of a dry cell

gives them to the zinc. Zinc becomes the negative electrode and the carbon becomes the positive electrode. A chemical called manganese dioxide prevents the collection of hydrogen gas on the surface of the carbon electrode. Like the potassium dichromate in a voltaic cell, it reacts with the hydrogen to form water. A metal cap in contact with the carbon electrode is the positive terminal. The negative terminal is another metal cap connected to the zinc container.

Section Review

1. Make a labelled diagram of a simple voltaic cell. Mark the direction of electron flow in the conducting wire and in the solution.
2. What causes the decrease in the current from a voltaic cell? How is this overcome?
3. Make a labelled diagram of a dry cell. Summarize in tabular form the function of each part.
4. What is the main advantage of a dry cell over a voltaic cell?

16.5 Storage Cells and Batteries

The Difference Between a Cell and a Battery

Fig. 16-15 The difference between a cell and a battery

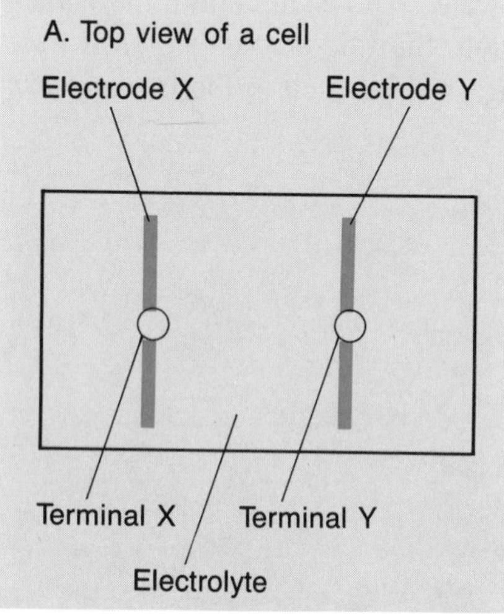

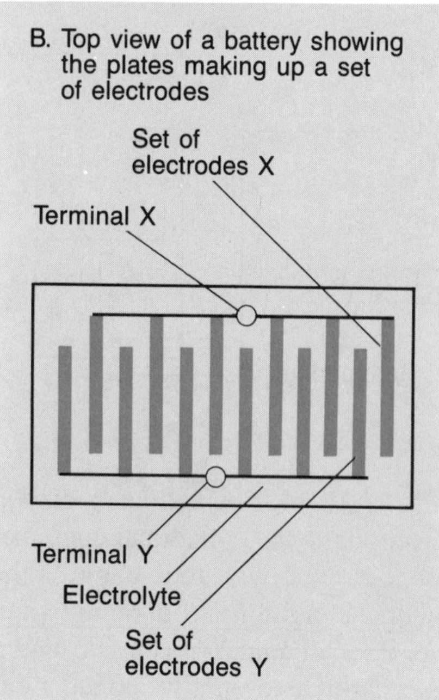

A **cell** has two electrodes made of different materials. For example, the electrodes may be made of zinc and copper. The electrodes do not touch and are covered with an electrolyte. Each electrode is connected to the outside by a terminal. One terminal is positive and the other negative (Fig. 16-15,A).

A **battery** is a number of cells connected together with two sets of electrodes. Each set consists of several parallel plates connected together like the leaves

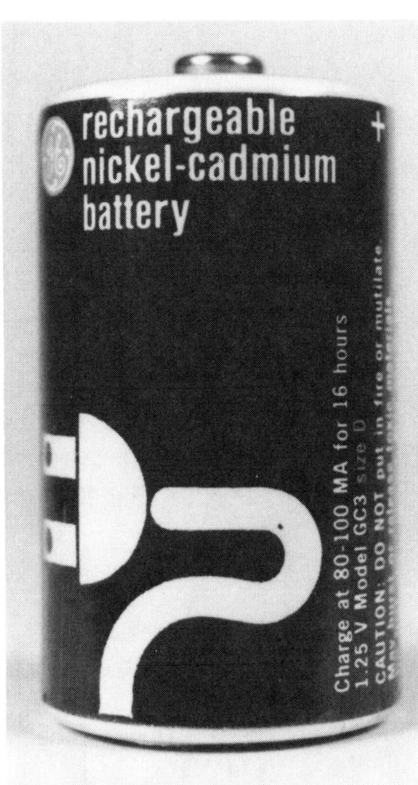

Fig. 16-16 A nickel-cadmium cell is commonly called a nicad.

of a book (Fig. 16-15,B). The electrodes in each set are made of the same material. But the electrodes in different sets consist of different materials. One set is connected to the positive terminal of the battery. The other set is connected to the negative terminal. The two sets of electrodes do not touch but they are covered by the same electrolyte. Since a battery consists of a number of cells connected together, a battery is stronger than a cell.

The Nicad Storage Cell

Many cordless appliances, such as radios and hedge trimmers, are powered by **nicad storage cells** (Fig. 16-16). Pop a charged nicad cell into the radio and it runs for several hours. Leave the nicad in the charger for a few hours and it's ready to power the radio again. The positive electrode of this rechargeable cell is made of nickel hydroxide with graphite. The negative electrode is a mixture of cadmium oxide and iron oxide. The name nicad comes from the two key elements, nickel and cadmium. The two electrodes are separated by an **alkaline** electrolyte. The electrolyte is potassium hydroxide, a highly caustic base. The nicad cell develops a relatively constant electrical potential difference of about 1.2 V. However, it gradually loses its charge when not in use.

The Lead Storage Battery

A rechargeable lead storage battery is used in cars, motorbikes, snowmobiles, and other vehicles. When charged, one set of electrodes is made of black lead dioxide. This set is connected to the positive terminal. The other set of electrodes is made of grey spongy lead. It is connected to the negative terminal. The two sets of electrodes are covered with dilute sulfuric acid. A cutaway view of a battery is shown in Figure 16-17. When the terminals are connected to a load like the headlights of a car, a current flows. The battery acts like a voltaic cell. Both sets of plates undergo a chemical change and become coated with lead sulfate. At the same time, some of the sulfuric acid is converted into water. When both sets of plates change completely to lead sulfate, the current

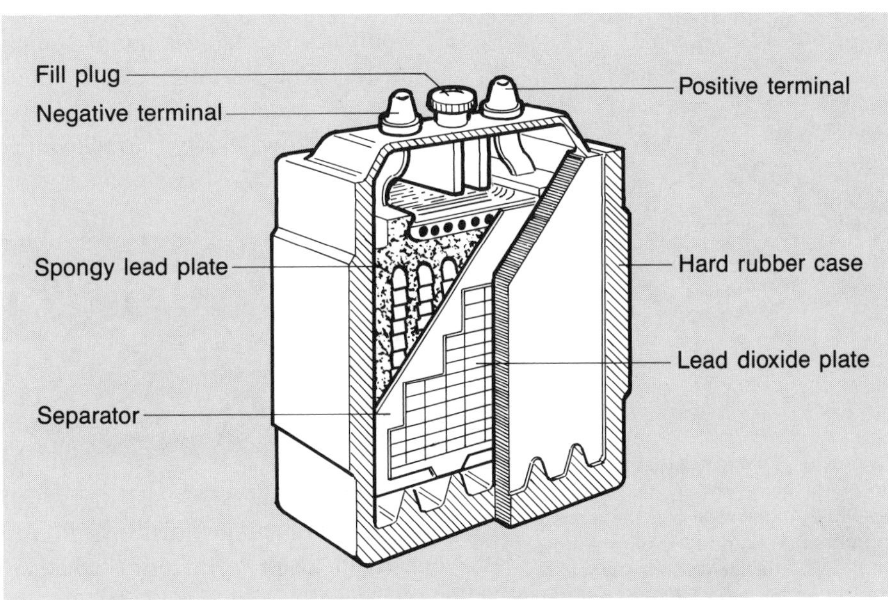

Fig. 16-17 A cutaway view of a lead storage battery. The electrolyte is dilute sulfuric acid.

Fig. 16-18 A battery hydrometer is used to check the charge of a lead acid storage battery.

Fig. 16-19 This lead storage battery stores the same energy as 150 mL of gasoline. An average car has a gasoline tank that holds 70 L of fuel. How many lead storage batteries would you need to do the job of 70 L of gasoline?

stops. An electrical current passed backward through the battery reverses the process. The sulfuric acid is replenished. One electrode becomes black lead dioxide and the other grey spongy lead.

Checking the Charge of a Battery

The charge of a battery is determined by measuring the density of the electrolyte. The electrolyte consists of a solution of sulfuric acid and water. Water has a density of 1000 g/L while pure sulfuric acid has a density of 1800 g/L. When charged, the electrolyte has a density of about 1300 g/L. When discharged, it has a density of about 1190 g/L. As the battery discharges, more water is produced and the density becomes closer to that of water. During charging, more sulfuric acid is produced, and the density approaches that of pure sulfuric acid. As a result, the density of the electrolyte is a measure of the charge of the battery. The density of the electrolyte is measured using an instrument called a **battery hydrometer** (Fig. 16-18).

The Need for New Storage Batteries

The lead storage battery has two problems. Lead is one of the densest metals. Even a small amount of lead is very heavy. And it is also costly for the amount of energy it can store. A car battery contains about 9 kg of lead and stores about the same energy as 150 mL of gasoline (Fig. 16-19). This is enough energy to move a car about 1.5 km. It would take about 500 kg of storage batteries to move the lightest car 80 km. Therefore battery-run cars are not very practical. But engineers and scientists are searching for lighter and more efficient storage batteries. One of these is the mercury battery. Another is the lithium-sulfur battery. A third is the sodium-sulfur battery. Better storage batteries may make the electric car economical in the 1990s. New batteries must have increased deliverable energy, better performance over a wide range of temperatures, and dramatically reduced charging time.

Section Review

1. What is the main difference between a cell and a battery?
2. Compare in a table a simple voltaic cell and a lead storage battery. Use the following headings: electrolyte; kind of electrodes; number of electrodes; size of current; ability to be recharged.
3. Describe how density is used to measure the charge of a lead storage battery.
4. Why is the lead storage battery not suitable for powering electric cars?

16.6 Rechargeable vs. Non-Rechargeable Batteries

Ours is the generation of the battery. Calculators, electronic flashes, flashlights, games, portable radios, and toys all use cells or batteries. Have you ever found yourself in a store wondering whether to buy a non-rechargeable battery, or one that can be recharged (Fig. 16-20)? Before you buy a **non-rechargeable**

Fig. 16-20 Which battery is a better buy?

battery, such as one with zinc-carbon electrodes, or a **rechargeable battery**, such as the nickel-cadmium "nicad" battery, several factors should be considered.

All dry cells or batteries operate by converting chemical potential energy into electrical energy. The chemicals react with one another to produce a surplus of electrons at one terminal and a deficiency at the other. When a load is connected, the battery discharges as the electrons flow through the load. The difference between a rechargeable battery and a non-rechargeable battery is that the rechargeable battery will accept a reverse flow of electrons. Electrons from an external source, the **charger**, can be used to reverse the chemical reaction. This charges the battery (Fig. 16-21). Some batteries can be recharged up to 1000 times.

Fig. 16-21 How much does a charger add to the cost of rechargeable batteries?

What are some of the disadvantages of rechargeables? Nickel-cadmium batteries cost more initially because they can be recharged. Also, there is the added expense of a charger, and a second set of batteries is needed if you want power during recharging. It takes time to recharge batteries: the recommended charging time in many cases is between 10 and 16 h. That's longer than overnight! It is much more convenient to slip in a set of new non-rechargeables (Fig. 16-22).

All batteries discharge themselves when not in use. This process is called **self-discharge**. Rechargeables are more prone to self-discharge. Some discharge in a few weeks. Compare this to alkaline disposables which have a shelf life in excess of two years. Rechargeables have another fault. They run out of charge abruptly while non-rechargeables fade away. Therefore non-rechargeables give you an advance warning that new batteries are needed. Rechargeables also have a **memory** of how they are being used. Suppose you use only half of the nickel-cadmium battery's energy and then recharge it. If you continue to do so over several discharge-charge cycles it will eventually deliver only half of its rated energy before going flat. It is important, then, to completely discharge a nickel-cadmium battery before recharging it. Operating temperature is another consideration. Nicad batteries have an operating temperature of about $-20°C$ to $45°C$. They do not recharge well at temperatures

Fig. 16-22 It is convenient to use replacement batteries, but have you considered the cost to the environment?

Fig. 16-23 A walkman radio needs rechargeable batteries.

below 0°C. So don't try to recharge your nicad in an unheated igloo!

Rechargeable batteries have several key advantages. If you are a heavy user of battery-powered equipment, such as portable radios, it will pay to use rechargeables (Fig. 16-23). A recharged nicad battery stores the same energy as a non-rechargeable battery and it can be recharged many times. Imagine saving the cost of up to 1000 non-rechargeable batteries! Also consider the environment. By using one rechargeable battery 1000 times you will be sending far less metal and electrolyte to the dump.

The key considerations are frequency of use and accessibility to electricity. If you use a battery frequently and are close to a source of electricity, use rechargeables. But if you are an infrequent user of battery-powered equipment and use it in cold, remote locations, non-rechargeable batteries are your better buy.

Section Review

1. What is one key difference between a zinc-carbon dry cell and a nicad? Explain.
2. List the advantages of a rechargeable cell or battery.
3. List the advantages of a non-rechargeable cell or battery.
4. Name the two key factors to consider when buying a non-rechargeable or a rechargeable cell or battery.

Chapter Highlights

1. Current electricity is the study of charge moving along a path.
2. Galvani discovered current electricity, but Volta identified a source of electric current.
3. Thermocouples, solar cells, piezoelectric crystals, and generators convert other forms of energy into electric energy.
4. Electric potential is the energy stored in a group of charges. Electric current is the rate of flow of electric charges.
5. A voltmeter measures electric potential. An ammeter measures electric current.
6. A simple voltaic cell consists of two electrodes and an electrolyte.
7. A dry cell is similar to the voltaic cell, except the electrolyte is a paste.
8. Primary cells, such as the dry cell and voltaic cell, cannot be recharged.
9. Secondary cells, such as the lead storage cell and the nickel cadmium cell, can be recharged.
10. A battery consists of a number of cells connected together.
11. The key considerations in buying a rechargeable vs. a non-rechargeable battery are frequency of use and accessibility to electricity.

Key Terms

alkaline
ammeter
ampere
battery
cell
charger

density
dry cell
electric potential
electrodes
electrolyte
hydrometer
memory
nicad
non-rechargeable battery
primary cells
rechargeable battery
secondary cell
self-discharge
voltaic cell
volts
voltmeter
wet cell

Recognizing the Concepts

Each of the following statements or questions is followed by four responses. Choose the correct response in each case. (Do not write in this book.)

1. Who correctly identified the first source of current electricity?
   a) Ampere **b)** Galvani **c)** Nicad **d)** Volta
2. When an object is squeezed an electric current is produced. The object is a
   a) dry cell
   b) magnet
   c) piezoelectric crystal
   d) thermocouple
3. Figure 16-24 shows the connections to the terminals of an ammeter. What is the reading on the meter?
   a) 0.70 A **b)** 1.70 A **c)** 1.75 A **d)** 3.50 A

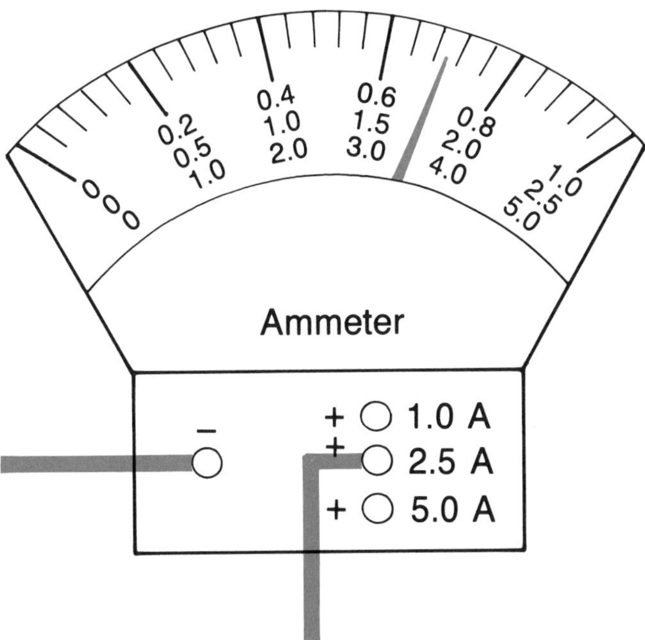

Fig. 16-24 An ammeter

4. What parts are needed to keep a voltaic cell producing current?
   a) two copper electrodes and dilute sulfuric acid
   b) a zinc electrode, a copper electrode, and tap water
   c) a zinc electrode, a copper electrode, and dilute sulfuric acid
   d) a zinc electrode, a copper electrode, dilute sulfuric acid, and potassium dichromate

5. Several factors to consider when deciding whether to purchase a rechargeable or a non-rechargeable battery are listed below:

I initial cost	III frequency of use
II self-discharge time	IV accessibility to electricity

Which two are the most important?

a) I and II **b)** I and III **c)** I and IV **d)** III and IV

Understanding the Concepts

1. Compare the particles that transfer charge in lightning and in conducting wires.
2. What variable did Volta change in his experiment that Galvani did not change?
3. Contrast electric potential and electric current.
4. Describe the proper way to connect a voltmeter in a circuit.
5. Contrast a current of water and an electric current.
6. What is the purpose of the potassium dichromate in the voltaic cell?
7. Contrast a voltaic cell and a dry cell.
8. A nicad source of current electricity has an electric potential of 3.6 V. Is it a cell or a battery? Explain.

Applying the Concepts

1. What is the reason for the sharp pain if a piece of aluminum foil is held between teeth in which there are fillings?
2. A voltmeter is to be connected to a source that has an electrical potential between 25 and 100 V. The voltmeter has a 5 V scale, a 25 V scale, and a 100 V scale. What is the proper procedure for connecting the voltmeter?
3. What do you think will happen if an ammeter is connected to a dry cell without a load in the circuit?
4. Which of the four steps for connecting and reading an electric meter is the most important one in order to get the correct reading?
5. As time passed why did the electric potential and the electric current from the voltaic cell decrease?
6. What factors might cause a decrease in the electric potential of a dry cell with use?
7. A garage mechanic measured the density of a lead storage battery and found it to be 1200 g/L. What is the state of charge of the battery? How do you know?
8. A forest ranger plans to take a flashlight as part of a winter survival kit. What kind of batteries should be used in the flashlight and why?
9. In alkaline batteries, the state of charge cannot be determined by a hydrometer reading since the density of the electrolyte varies only slightly with use. How would you test the state of charge?

Investigations

1. Make a voltaic cell in your mouth. Clean a penny and a nickel with soap and water. Put one on top of your tongue and the other under it. Connect them outside with a conducting wire. What do you feel?
2. Use a potato to detect the electric current from a good dry cell. Slice a potato in half. Attach conducting wires to the dry cell. Push the bare ends closer together into the potato. Do not let them touch. Describe what you see.
3. Do a library search and contact a battery manufacturer to determine the research being done to produce better storage batteries.
4. Automotive and aircraft batteries generally use thin positive and negative plates with thin separation. Standby batteries, such as those used in emergency lights in stores, use thick plates and thin separations. Why the difference? Check your hypothesis in the library.
5. Obtain a used zinc-carbon dry cell. With a hacksaw blade cut the cell from top to bottom down the middle. *CAUTION: Do not touch the inside. The materials can cause burns. Also, do not mutilate an alkaline cell.* Study the parts of the cell. Soak the cell in a solution of ammonium chloride for about half an hour. See if it will light a bulb.
6. Make a voltaic cell using a lemon or a potato. Ask your teacher for the parts you need to make and demonstrate this cell (Fig. 16-25).
7. Find out how lead storage batteries are rated and what the ratings mean.

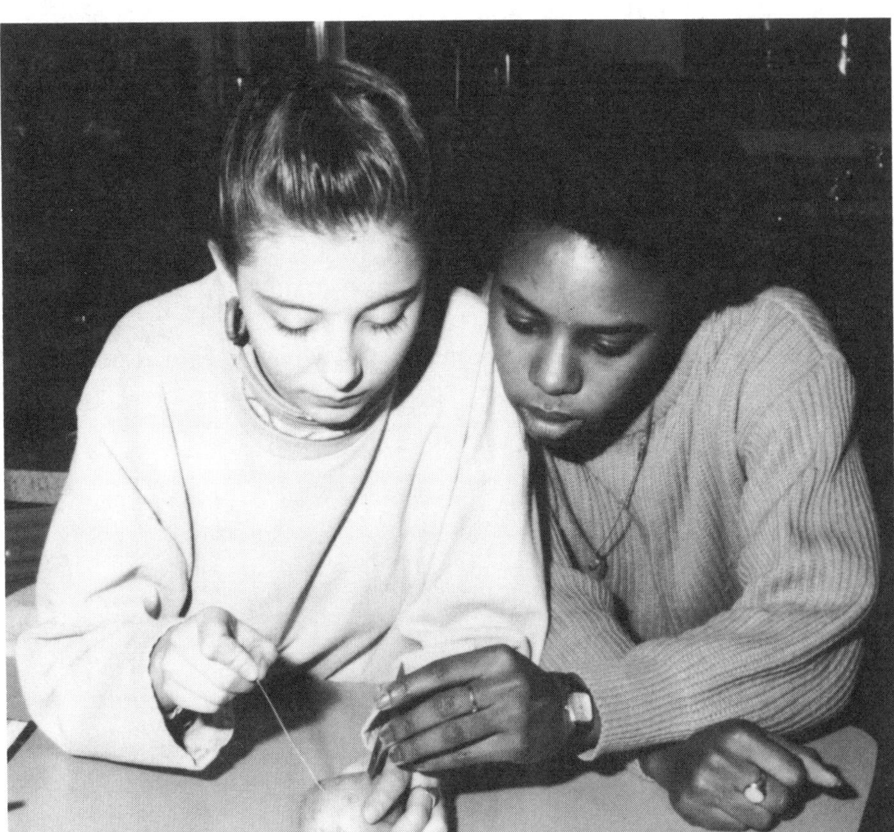

Fig. 16-25 What do you suppose the wires are made of that these people are pushing into the potato?

Career: *ELECTRICAL AND ELECTRONICS TECHNICIAN*

HELP WANTED: ELECTRICAL AND ELECTRONICS TECHNICIAN

Large aircraft manufacturer requires electrical and electronics technician to install, test, adjust, and service radar equipment in aircraft; a willingness to travel extensively is required.

An electrical and electronics technician is concerned with the development, manufacturing, operation, and servicing of electrical and electronics equipment. The electrical and electronics field is broad and varied. Business, industry, and the home are all dependent on electric and electronics devices. Picture a modern home without a telephone or a radio. Imagine a large business without microcomputers and photocopiers. Envisage a jet without radar.

Because the field is so broad and varied, electrical and electronics technicians usually specialize in one or more fields. Since the equipment is used everywhere, technicians work in a variety of places and conditions. Some work entirely in laboratories under the careful scrutiny of scientists and engineers. Others function alone, and in remote places, wherever the equipment needs to be serviced. Imagine spending part of your time in a submarine servicing sonar equipment or on an airplane testing its radar.

Job opportunities in the electricity and electronics field are expected to grow significantly in the years ahead. If you wish to become an electrical or electronics technician, you should take senior chemistry, mathematics, and physics at secondary school. Following graduation, you must attend a post-secondary technical program at a College of Applied Arts and Technology. Go to your guidance department for more information.

17 Electric Circuits

CHAPTER CONTENTS

CHAPTER OBJECTIVES

After completing this chapter you should be able to:

1. Sketch and describe a simple electric circuit.
2. Describe a short circuit and explain the function of a fuse.
3. Describe the effect on light intensity and electric current of connecting light bulbs in series or in parallel.
4. Describe the effect on electric potential difference of connecting cells in series or in parallel.
5. Distinguish between direct current and alternating current.
6. Describe a circuit breaker panel.
7. Describe the connection of circuits in a home.

An electric circuit consists of a source of electric current, conducting wires, a switch, and a load (Fig. 17-1). What is the function of the load? What are the different ways of connecting the parts of a circuit together and how does this affect the circuit? What factors determine the electric energy used in a circuit and how is this energy measured? That is what this chapter is about.

Fig. 17-1 Can you set up an electric circuit?

17.1 Activity: Properties of a Simple Circuit

An **electric circuit** is the path that an electric current follows. In this activity you will connect a simple circuit. You will learn where to place a switch and practise connecting an ammeter. You will also compare the current at various places. Finally, you will compare the current when different light bulbs are used.

Problem

What are the properties of a simple electric circuit?

Materials

D dry cell
D dry cell holder
switch
hand lens
bulb holder
small bulb (V = 2.5 V)
small bulb (V = 2.0 V)
conducting wires (4)
steel wool
ammeter

Procedure

a. Copy Table 17-1 into your notebook.
b. Connect the circuit shown in Figure 17-2,A. Use a 2.5 V bulb.
c. Close the switch. Record the brightness of the bulb and the current.
d. Connect the circuit shown in Figure 17-2,B. Repeat step (c).
e. With the ammeter reading a current, unscrew the 2.5 V bulb. Repeat step (c).
f. Replace the 2.5 V bulb with the 2.0 V bulb. Repeat step (c).

Table 17-1 Properties of a Simple Circuit

Location of switch and ammeter	*Bulb type*	*Bulb brightness*	*Electric current (A)*
Between positive terminal and bulb	2.5 V		
Between negative terminal and bulb	2.5 V		
Between negative terminal and bulb	2.0 V		

Discussion

1. Where can a switch be placed in a simple circuit?
2. Compare the current at various places in the circuit.

Fig. 17-2 Properties of a simple electric circuit

A. The switch and ammeter between the positive terminal and the bulb

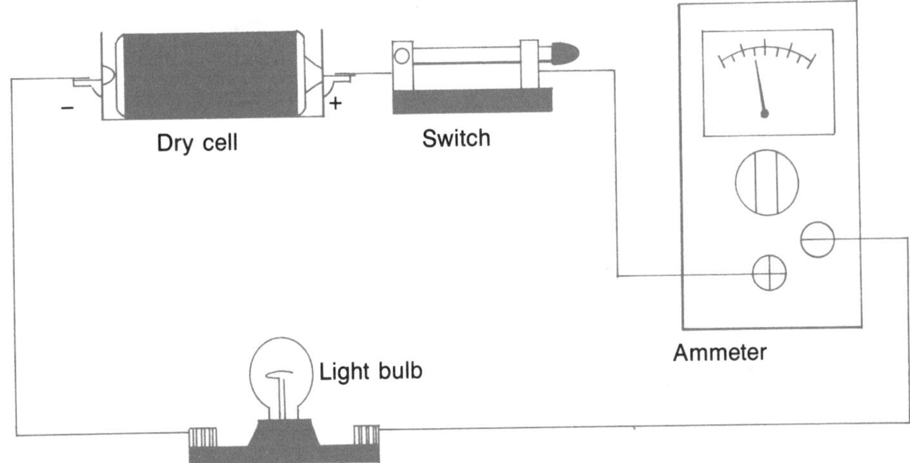

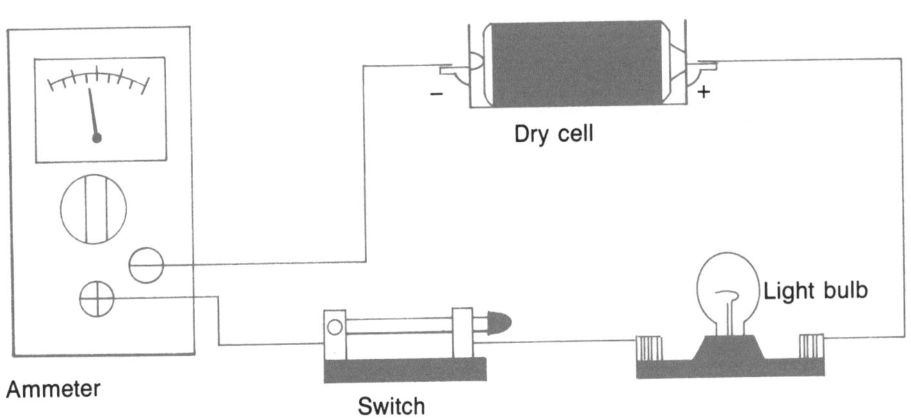

B. The switch and ammeter between the negative terminal and the bulb

3. Account for the reading on the ammeter when the bulb was unscrewed.
4. Which light bulb decreases the current the most?
5. Which light bulb is the largest load?

17.2 A Simple Electric Circuit

A simple electric circuit consists of a switch, a load, a source of electric current, and conducting wires. Let's look more closely at the parts of a circuit.

The Switch

A **switch** controls the movement of electrons in a circuit. With the switch closed, the circuit is complete and the electrons have a path to follow. With the switch open, the circuit is incomplete; electrons cannot flow through an air gap. In a simple circuit it doesn't matter where the switch is placed. It can be placed close to the source or between several loads.

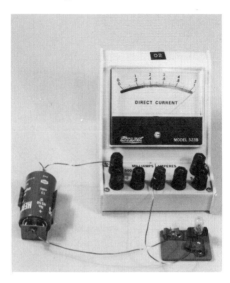

A. Photograph showing a short circuit

B. Symbols showing a short circuit. Bare wires are touching. The current becomes very large because it bypasses the lamp.

Fig. 17-3 A photograph and symbol diagram showing a short circuit

The Load

The **load** changes electric energy to other forms of energy. Motors and light bulbs are example loads. A light bulb changes electricity to light and heat. And a motor changes electricity to kinetic energy and heat. The load limits the size of the electric current. The larger the load, the smaller the current. Without a load, the current is very large, causing overheating of the conducting wires.

The Conducting Wires

The **conducting wires** carry the electric current from the source to the load and back to the source. Conductors are materials that carry electrons with very little loss in energy. Most conducting wires are made of copper or aluminum.

The Short Circuit

Sometimes the insulation on conducting wires breaks down. The bare wires touch, completing the circuit. Current flows but it does not pass through the load. Such an arrangement is called a **short circuit**. Figure 17-3 shows a short circuit. Without a load, the current becomes very large, causing the wires to become very hot. They may either melt or cause a fire in nearby materials. The dangers caused by a short circuit are prevented by a fuse or a circuit breaker.

Fuses and Circuit Breakers

A **fuse** is a safety device that acts as a switch. Fuses are connected into the circuit close to the source. As a result all the current flowing in the circuit passes through the fuse. When too much current flows, the fuse heats up sufficiently to burn out. This creates an air gap and no more current flows. The construction of a plug fuse is shown in Figure 17-4. Other kinds of fuses are cartridge fuses and knife blade fuses. The essential part is the fuse wire or a blade with a low melting point.

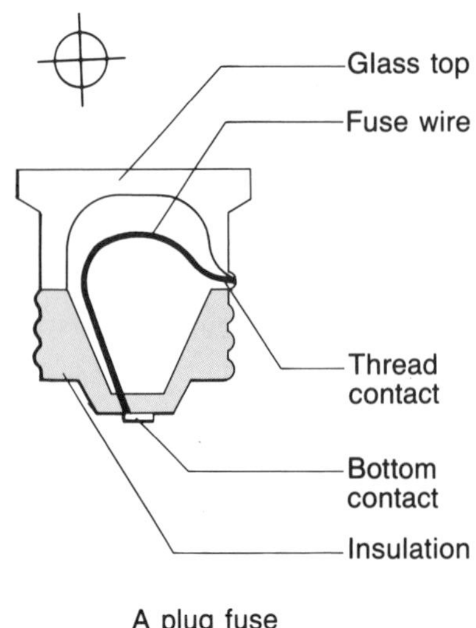

A plug fuse

Fig. 17-4 A fuse. The current flows through the fuse wire connected between the bottom contact and the thread contact. If too much current flows, the fuse wire melts.

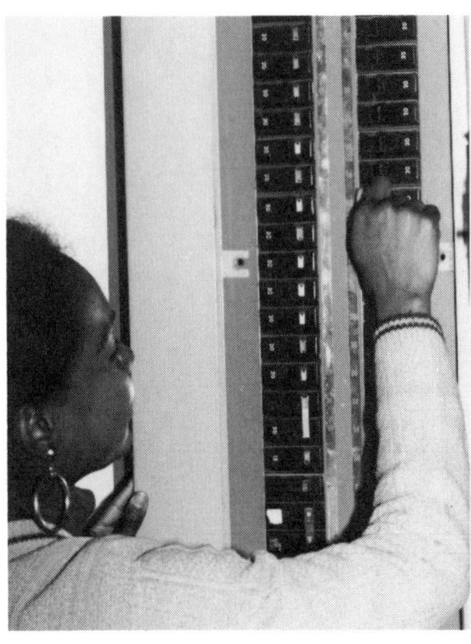

Fig. 17-5 Look closely at the electrical panel of your home. *CAUTION: Do not put your finger into the fuse panel!* **Does it use circuit breakers or fuses?**

Most homes built in recent years use **circuit breakers** instead of fuses in their electrical panels (Fig. 17-5). A circuit breaker is connected in the same place as a fuse would be, and it performs the same function. Unlike a fuse, however, it does not burn out. When too much current flows, the circuit breaker simply opens like a switch. Then, when the problem that caused the excess current has been corrected, you can close the breaker again. What do you suppose causes a circuit breaker to open?

CAUTION: A fuse should never be replaced or a circuit breaker reset until the problem has been corrected. Why? Also, a fuse should never be replaced with one of a higher current rating just to prevent it from burning out. Why?

Symbols

Symbols are used to represent the parts and wiring details of an electric circuit. It is simpler to show them using symbols than to draw diagrams. Some of the most common symbols are shown in Figure 17-6. Refer to these symbols when drawing the electric circuits in the following activities.

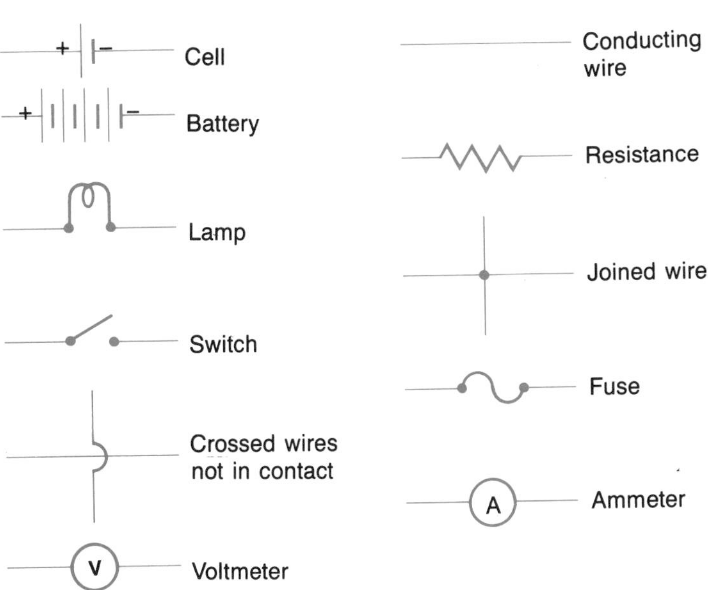

Fig. 17-6 Some electrical symbols

Section Review

1. Draw a diagram using symbols for a simple circuit. Show a source, a switch, a lamp, a fuse, an ammeter, and conducting wires.
2. Describe, in tabular form, the function of each part of the electric circuit you drew.
3. **a)** What causes a short circuit?
   b) What danger results from a short circuit?
4. **a)** What is a fuse?
   b) How does a fuse protect a circuit?
5. **a)** What is a circuit breaker?
   b) How does a circuit breaker protect a circuit?

Extension

From your teacher, obtain a circuit breaker that has been partially dismantled. After studying it carefully, draw a diagram to show its parts. Then write a note which explains how the circuit breaker works. You may have to research circuit breakers in the library.

17.3 Activity: Light Bulbs in Series

A **series circuit** has only one path through which current can flow. A series circuit can be compared to a race track. On the track all cars must follow the same path. In like manner, all electrons in a series circuit must follow the same path. In this activity you will study light bulbs in series.

Problem

How do light bulbs in a series circuit behave?

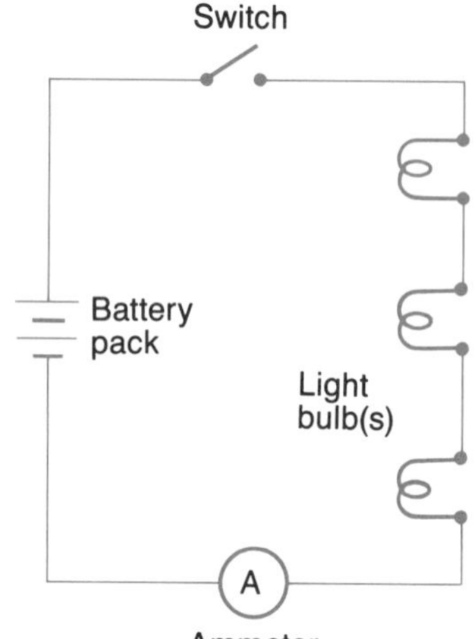

Fig. 17-7 Light bulbs in series

Materials

battery pack
ammeter
switch
identical bulbs (3)
bulb holders (3)
connecting leads (6)

CAUTION: Check with your teacher that the ammeter is connected correctly before closing the switch.

Procedure

a. Copy Table 17-2 into your notebook.
b. Draw the circuit shown in Figure 17-7 in your notebook.
c. Connect the circuit. Use only one bulb. Close the switch.
d. Note the brightness of the bulb. Record the current.
e. Connect a second bulb in series. Repeat step (c).
f. Connect a third bulb in series. Repeat step (c).
g. Unscrew one bulb. Record the effect on the current and the bulb.

Table 17-2 Light Bulbs Connected in Series

Bulbs connected	*Bulb brightness*	*Electric current (A)*
1		
2		
3		
3 (1 unscrewed)		

Discussion

1. As more bulbs are connected in series, what happens to
a) the brightness of each bulb

b) the size of the current
c) the number of paths for the current
d) the size of the load

2. In a series circuit, if one light bulb burns out, what happens to
   a) the current b) the brightness of the remaining bulbs
3. Are the light bulbs in your home connected in series? How do you know?

Extension

Ask your teacher for a hand lens. Examine the filaments of all three light bulbs. How are they the same? How are they different? If one light bulb has a greater load than another, how do you think the filaments will differ? Ask your teacher for a 2.0 V bulb and a 2.5 V bulb and check your predictions.

17.4 Activity: Light Bulbs in Parallel

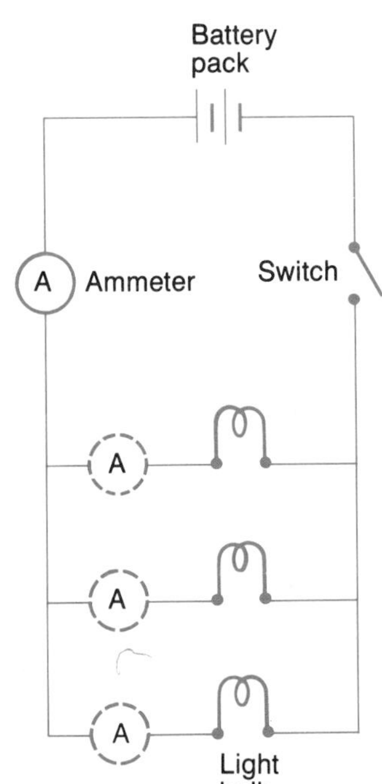

Fig. 17-8 Light bulbs in parallel

A **parallel circuit** has two or more paths called **branches** through which electrons can flow. A parallel circuit is like streets around several city blocks. Cars leaving a house can take different paths before returning home. In like manner, electrons leaving the source can take different paths before returning to the source. Look at Figure 17-8. Here, three light bulbs are connected in parallel. Do you think the current from the dry cell will increase, decrease, or remain the same as more bulbs are connected? What will happen to the brightness of the bulbs? Write predictions in your notebook. Then do this activity to test your predictions.

Problem

How do light bulbs in parallel behave?

Materials

battery pack	ammeter	bulb holders (3)
switch	identical bulbs (3)	connecting leads (8)

CAUTION: Check with your teacher that the ammeter is connected correctly before closing the switch.

Procedure

a. Copy Table 17-3 into your notebook.
b. Draw the circuit shown in Figure 17-8 in your notebook.
c. Connect the circuit. Use only one bulb. Close the switch.
d. Note the brightness of the bulb. Record the reading in the main circuit using the ammeter.
e. Connect a second bulb in parallel. Compare and record the brightness.
f. Record the current in the main circuit. Then record the current in each branch circuit as shown.
g. Connect a third bulb in parallel.

h. Record the effect on the current in the main circuit and in each branch circuit.
i. Unscrew one bulb. Record the effect on the current in the main circuit.

Table 17-3 Light Bulbs Connected in Parallel

Bulbs connected	*Bulb brightness*	*Reading on ammeter (A)*	
		Main circuit	*Branch circuits*
1			
2			
3			
3 (1 unscrewed)			

Discussion

1. As more bulbs are connected in parallel, what happens to
   a) the brightness of each bulb
   b) the current in the main circuit
   c) the current in the branches
   d) the number of paths for the current
   e) the size of the total load
2. In a parallel circuit, if one light bulb burns out, what happens to
   a) the current in the main circuit
   b) the brightness of the remaining bulbs
3. Are the light bulbs in your home connected in parallel? How do you know?

Extension

Suppose that a 2.0 V bulb and two 2.6 V bulbs are connected in parallel. Predict which light bulb(s) will glow more brightly and which bulb(s) will pass more current. Perform an experiment to test your predictions.

17.5 Connecting Loads

Loads can be connected in series or in parallel. Let's look more closely at these two methods of connecting loads.

Series Connection

A **series circuit** has only *one path* for the current. As a result, the current in every part of the circuit is the same. A series connection of three light bulbs is shown in Figure 17-9,A. Three bulbs connected in series are three times the load of one. As the load increases, the current decreases. As a result, as more bulbs are connected, each bulb glows less brightly. If one bulb burns out, all the bulbs go out because the broken bulb creates an incomplete circuit. A burned out bulb is shown in Figure 17-9,B. Some older versions of Christmas tree lights were connected in series to save money. What problems would this cause for the user?

A. Three light bulbs in series

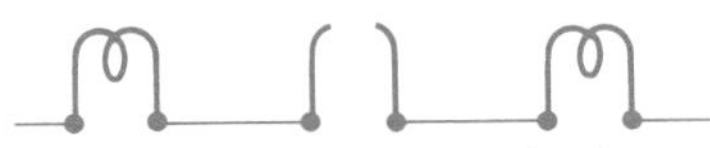

B. One light bulb burned out in a series circuit stops the current

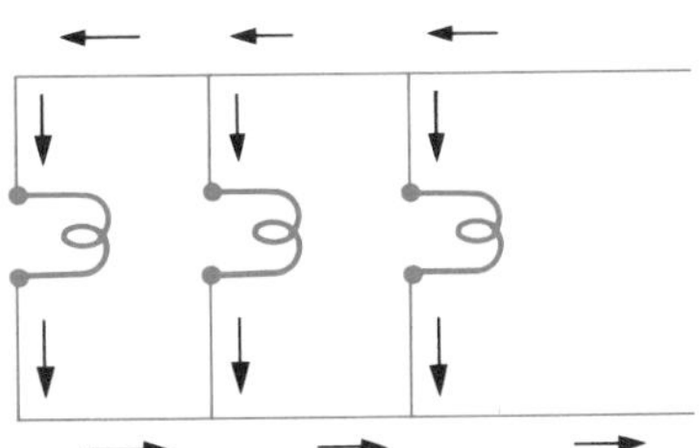

C. Three light bulbs in parallel

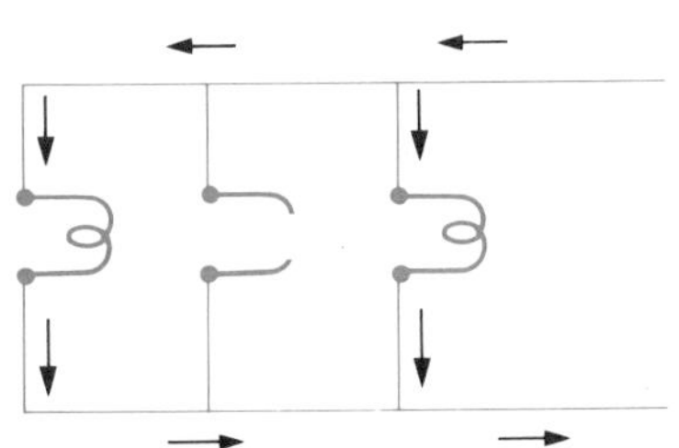

D. One light bulb burned out in a parallel circuit decreases the current

Fig. 17-9 Connections of light bulbs

Parallel Connection

A **parallel circuit** has *two or more branches* for the current. Consider two light bulbs connected in parallel. The current leaving the source splits into parts. Part of the current goes through each bulb, making it easier for the current to flow. It is just like a single lane highway dividing into two lanes. It is easier for cars to travel in two lanes than in one. As a result, more cars can travel on a double lane highway than on a single lane highway. The current from the source increases when two light bulbs are connected in parallel.

Three bulbs connected in parallel are shown in Figure 17-9,C. The current flowing through one bulb is not affected by the other bulbs. Therefore the addition of more bulbs in parallel does not affect bulb brightness. Also, if one bulb goes out, there is still a complete circuit for the current and the remaining bulbs stay lit. A burned out bulb is shown in Figure 17-9,D. Most lights today, including household lights, are connected in parallel. Imagine the difficulty if light bulbs and other loads were connected in series in your home!

Section Review

1. a) Define a series circuit.
   b) Define a parallel circuit.

2. How do you know that house lights are connected in parallel?

3. a) Draw a diagram showing two bulbs connected in series to a battery.
   b) Draw a diagram to show two bulbs connected in parallel to a battery.
   c) Write a paragraph that describes how the circuits drawn in (a) and (b) are different.
   d) Which connection would produce more light? Why?

17.6 Activity: Light Bulbs in a Series-Parallel Circuit

In this activity you will set up a series-parallel circuit containing three identical light bulbs. How do you think the current will compare in the series part of the circuit with the current in the parallel branches? How will the brightness of the bulbs compare? Write predictions in your notebook. Then do this activity to test your predictions.

Problem

How do light bulbs in a series-parallel combination behave?

Materials

battery pack	ammeter	bulb holders (3)
switch	identical bulbs (3)	connecting leads (8)

CAUTION: Check with your teacher that the ammeter is connected correctly before closing the switch.

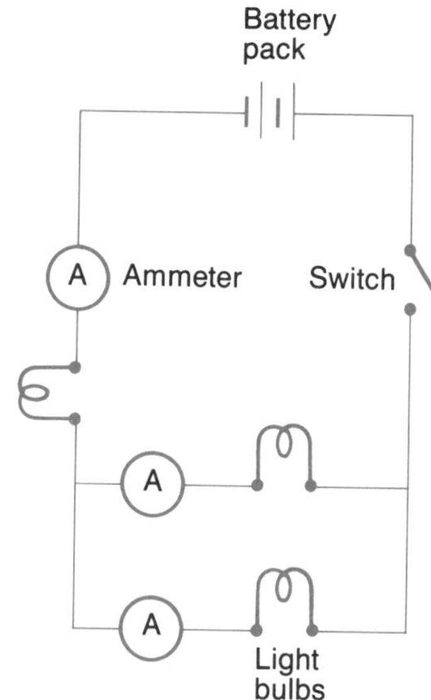

Fig. 17-10 Light bulbs in a series-parallel circuit

Procedure

a. Copy Table 17-4 into your notebook.
b. Draw the circuit shown in Figure 17-10 in your notebook.
c. Set up the circuit shown in Figure 17-10. Close the switch.
d. Compare and record the brightness of all three bulbs.
e. Record the current in the main circuit. Then record the current in each branch circuit as shown.
f. Unscrew the bulb connected in the main circuit and record the effect on the current.
g. Unscrew one of the bulbs in the parallel circuit and record the effect on the current in the main circuit.

Table 17-4 Light Bulbs in a Series-Parallel Connection

Bulb connection	*Bulb brightness*		*Reading of ammeter (A)*	
	Main circuit	*Branch circuits*	*Main circuit*	*Branch circuits*
All three connected				
Bulb in main circuit unscrewed				
Bulb in one branch circuit unscrewed				

Discussion

1. Compare the brightness of the bulb in the main circuit with that of the bulbs in the branches.
2. What relationship exists between the current in the main circuit and the current in the branches?
3. If the bulb in the main circuit burns out, what happens to the current in the branches?
4. If the bulb in one branch burns out, what happens to the current in
   a) the other branch **b)** the main circuit

Extension

Suppose that a 2.0 V bulb and two 2.5 V bulbs are connected in a series-parallel circuit. Predict which bulb(s) will glow more brightly. Also predict the relationship between the current in the branches and the current in the main circuit. Perform an experiment to test your predictions.

17.7 Connecting Sources

Sources such as dry cells can be connected either in series or in parallel. Let's find out the difference.

A. Three dry cells in series. The electric potentials add.

B. Two dry cells connected backwards in series. The electric potentials cancel.

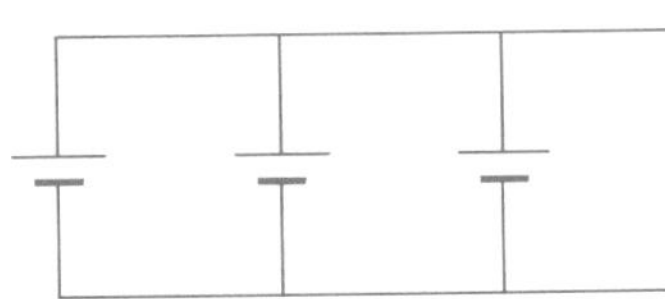

C. Three dry cells in parallel. The electric potential is the same as with one.

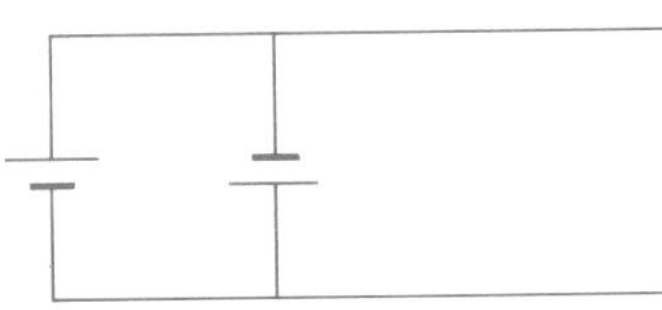

D. Two dry cells connected backwards in parallel. The electric potentials cancel.

Fig. 17-11 Connections of dry cells

Series Connection

Three dry cells connected correctly in series are shown in Figure 17-11,A. Each positive terminal is connected to a negative terminal. Connecting dry cells in series increases the electric potential of the source. That is, the volts add. The increased voltage causes more current to flow through the load. If the load is a light bulb, it gets brighter. Suppose one dry cell is connected backwards to another as shown in Figure 17-11,B. The potential decreases to zero and the current that flows also decreases to zero. Any time a dry cell is connected backwards in a series circuit both the electric potential and the electric current decrease.

Parallel Connection

Three dry cells connected correctly in parallel are shown in Figure 17-11,C. All the positive terminals are connected together. So are all the negative terminals. Connecting dry cells in parallel does not change the electric potential. Nor does it change the size of the current. A light bulb glows with the same brightness. But each dry cell gives only part of the current. With three dry cells, each dry cell gives one-third of the total current. As a result, each dry cell lasts three times longer. If one dry cell is connected backwards to another, as shown in Figure 17-11,D, the electric potential decreases to zero. The current that flows also decreases to zero. Two good dry cells in parallel, except with opposite terminals connected, produce no electric potential and no current. If a dry cell is connected backwards in a parallel circuit, the electric potential and current decrease.

Section Review

1. Describe how dry cells are connected in series. Use a diagram to illustrate your answer.
2. Describe how dry cells are connected in parallel. Use a diagram to illustrate your answer.
3. Suppose that three 1.5 V DC dry cells power a light bulb. Compare the results if the dry cells are connected in series and in parallel. Explain.
4. How are the dry cells connected in a flashlight? How do you know?

17.8 Electric Circuits Around the Home

Kinds of Electric Current

There are two different kinds of electric current: direct current and alternating current. **Direct current (DC)** is electric current that flows in one direction only. It is produced by chemical cells and batteries, solar cells, and thermocouples. Portable devices such as radios, flashlights, and toys are powered by direct current. So is the electrical system in a car. Direct current consists of a flow of electrons from the negative terminal of the battery through the load to the positive terminal.

Alternating current (AC) is electric current that reverses flow at regular time intervals. It is produced by generators in electric power stations. There is some loss of energy when electricity is transmitted long distances. This is less with alternating current than with direct current. That is why electrical current from power stations is sent to the home using alternating current. Non-portable appliances such as lights, air conditioners, refrigerators, stoves, and power tools are powered by alternating current. In an alternating current, electrons vibrate back and forth past a point in a conductor. This occurs many times each second. As a result, the electrons do not travel from the source to the load and back again.

Electricity Entering the Home

Electricity from power stations is transmitted to homes through high voltage power lines. Electric potentials as high as 220 000 V AC are used. The electrical potential is decreased to 240 V AC before it enters the home. A cable containing three colour-coded wires enters the home. One wire is red, one is black, and one is white. The red and black wires are called the **hot wires**, or **live wires**. There is an electrical potential difference of 240 V AC between a red and a black wire. This electrical potential is the energy source for major appliances such as stoves and clothes dryers. The white wire is the **neutral wire**. The electrical potential difference between a red or a black wire and the white wire is 120 V AC. This is the energy source for lights and appliances plugged into wall outlets.

The Circuit Breaker Panel

At the home, the electricity first passes through an electric meter. The **electric meter** records the amount of electric energy used in the home. Then the electricity enters a **circuit breaker panel**. (In some older homes it may enter a fuse panel.) In this panel there is a master circuit breaker. The master circuit breaker can be operated manually to cut off the electricity to the entire home. It opens automatically if the current exceeds the rated value. In homes that have a 100 A service, the master circuit breaker will allow up to 100 A to pass before it pops open.

There are three strips of conducting metal called **bus bars** in the breaker panel. The red wire is connected to one, the black wire to another, and the white wire to the third. As a result, two of the bus bars are live and one is neutral.

Electric Circuits in the Home

All the **electric circuits** within the home originate from the bus bars. Figure 17-12 shows a 240 V AC cable going to a stove. Notice that the cable is connected to all three bus bars. This cable has two circuit breakers, one for the black wire and one for the red wire. Each major appliance has its own 240 V AC circuit.

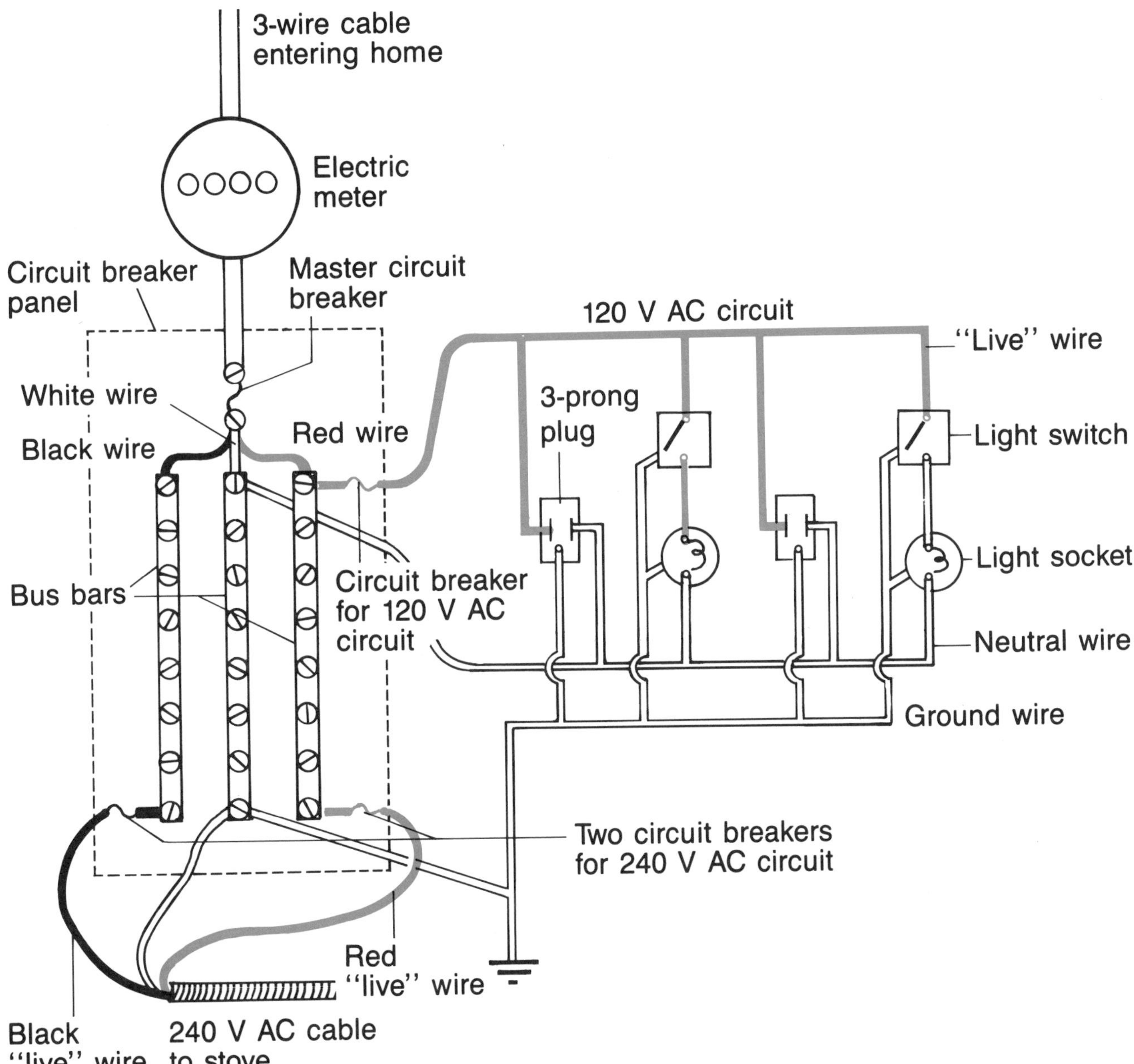

Fig. 17-12 Circuit breaker panel

A 120 V AC circuit is also shown. Notice that only two of the bus bars are used, the neutral bus bar and either of the live bus bars. This circuit also has its own circuit breaker. The 120 V AC circuit consists of the circuit breaker, two three-prong plugs, and two light fixtures and two switches. A ground wire connects all switch and outlet boxes to ground and to the neutral bus bar. This prevents injury if the boxes become live.

Loads in the same circuit, such as wall outlets and lights, are always connected in parallel. If one load burns out the others still operate. Also, as more and more loads are turned on, the electrical potential remains the same. However, the electric current increases. But one load does not affect another unless the circuit becomes overloaded.

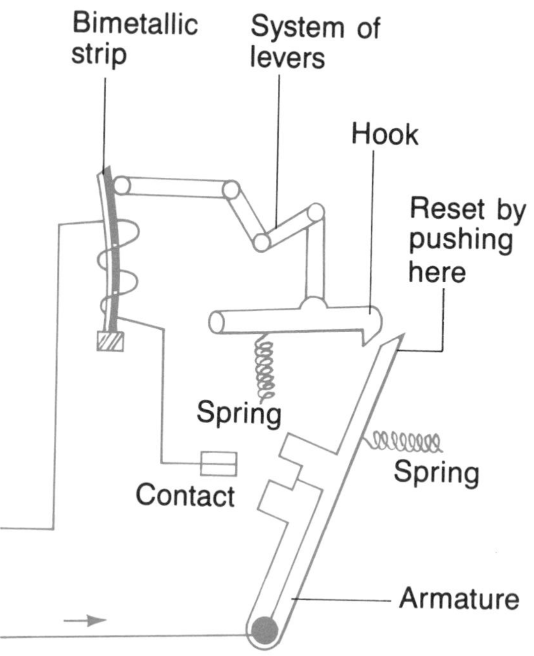

Fig. 17-13 A circuit breaker of the thermal type

The Function of a Circuit Breaker

A **circuit breaker** protects a circuit from becoming overloaded. Figure 17-13 shows a circuit breaker of the thermal type. What has caused this circuit breaker to open?

Notice the wire wrapped around the bimetallic strip. This wire is part of the circuit. The current in this wire generates heat. This heat causes the bimetallic strip to bend. As the strip bends, it activates a system of levers which raises a hook. This hook locks the armature against the contact. When the current reaches a certain value, the hook releases the armature. The spring attached to the armature separates it from the contact. The current in the circuit immediately stops. When there is no current in the wire, the bimetallic strip begins to cool. As it cools it straightens. A **reset button** is used to reconnect the armature to the contact. There is again current in the circuit. A circuit breaker is designed to open when there is more than a specific current in the circuit.

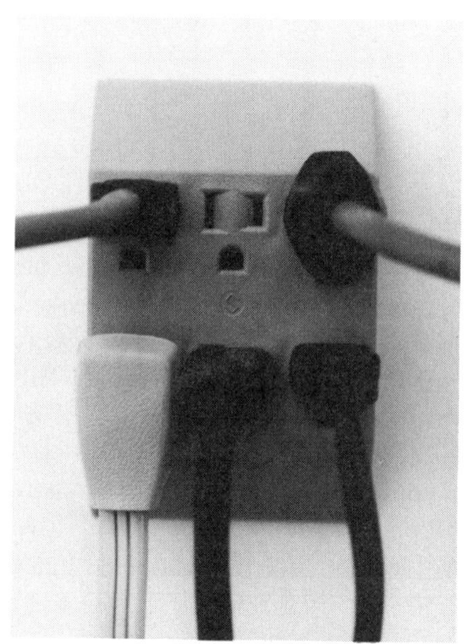

Fig. 17-14 An overloaded plug outlet

Causes of Overloaded Circuits

There are two main causes of overloaded circuits. First, an appliance or a conducting wire can develop a short circuit. Now the current is no longer limited by the load. In this case, current passes from the live wire to the neutral wire or from the live wire to the ground wire without passing through the load. The current becomes very large very fast. This heats up the circuit.

Second, too many appliances can be plugged into the same circuit (Fig. 17-14). Each appliance draws a certain current. The combination can draw too much current and the circuit again heats up.

A circuit breaker is designed to prevent overloading. It trips and opens the circuit as soon as the circuit becomes too hot.

Section Review

1. a) Distinguish between direct current and alternating current.
   b) Why is electricity transmitted from electric generators as alternating current?
2. a) In an electrical cable, what is the difference between the red and black wires and the white wire?
   b) What wires must be used to get an electrical potential of
   (i) 120 V AC (ii) 240 V AC
3. a) What are bus bars?
   b) Distinguish between the three bus bars in a circuit breaker panel.
4. Why are loads in a circuit connected in parallel rather than series?
5. a) What are two causes of overloading in an electric circuit?
   b) Sketch a circuit breaker of the thermal type.
   c) Explain how it operates to prevent overloading.

Chapter Highlights

1. A circuit consists of a source, conducting wires, a switch, and a load.
2. A load converts electric energy to other forms of energy.
3. A fuse or circuit breaker prevents overheating caused by a short circuit or an overload.
4. Light bulbs connected in series increase the load and decrease the current.
5. Light bulbs connected in parallel decrease the load and increase the current.
6. The electric potentials add if dry cells are connected in series.
7. Dry cells connected in series increase the current through the load.
8. The electric potential stays the same if dry cells are connected in parallel.
9. There are two kinds of electric current, direct and alternating.
10. A circuit breaker panel contains the circuit breakers for a home.
11. A circuit breaker panel has three bus bars.
12. All the circuits in a home are connected in parallel to the bus bar.
13. All the loads in a home circuit are connected in parallel.

Key Terms

alternating current
bus bar
circuit
circuit breaker
circuit breaker panel
direct current
electric circuit
electric energy
fuse
hot wire
live wire switch
neutral wire
parallel circuit
power
series circuit
short circuit

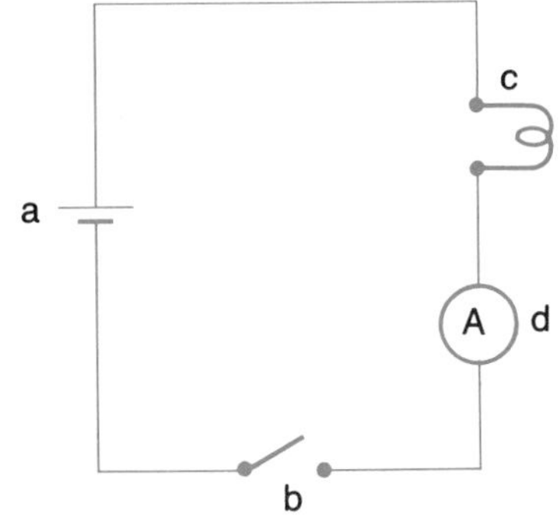

Fig. 17-15 Which one of a, b, c, or d is the load?

Recognizing the Concepts

Each of the following statements or questions is followed by four responses. Choose the correct response in each case. (Do not write in this book.)

1. A symbolic diagram of a simple electric circuit is shown in Figure 17-15. Which symbol represents the load?

2. Where must the switch be placed in a simple circuit?
   a) next to the positive terminal
   b) next to the negative terminal
   c) next to the load
   d) anywhere in the circuit
3. Which of the following statements describes the current in a series circuit? The current is
   a) the same at every point
   b) largest through the load
   c) largest next to the positive terminal
   d) largest next to the negative terminal
4. Two bulbs x and y are connected in series to a dry cell. The switch is closed. If bulb x is then unscrewed, the brightness of bulb y will
   a) double
   b) halve
   c) remain the same
   d) become zero
5. Two bulbs x and y are connected in parallel to a dry cell. The switch is closed. If bulb x is then unscrewed, the brightness of bulb y will
   a) increase
   b) decrease
   c) remain the same
   d) become zero
6. Three dry cells x, y, and z are connected in series to one light bulb. The switch is closed. If one dry cell is then reversed, the current will
   a) increase
   b) decrease
   c) remain the same
   d) become zero
7. A circuit contains a 20 A circuit breaker. How much current will this circuit breaker pass before it opens?
   a) 0
   b) less than 20 A
   c) exactly 20 A
   d) greater than 20 A

Understanding the Concepts

1. If a burned-out plug type fuse is replaced with a copper penny, the current will flow again. Why is this a dangerous thing to do? *CAUTION: DO NOT TRY IT*.
2. Distinguish between a series and a parallel circuit.
3. Figure 17-16 shows a circuit containing a dry cell, conducting wires, a switch, a fuse, and two light bulbs. If the switch is closed will the bulbs light? Explain.

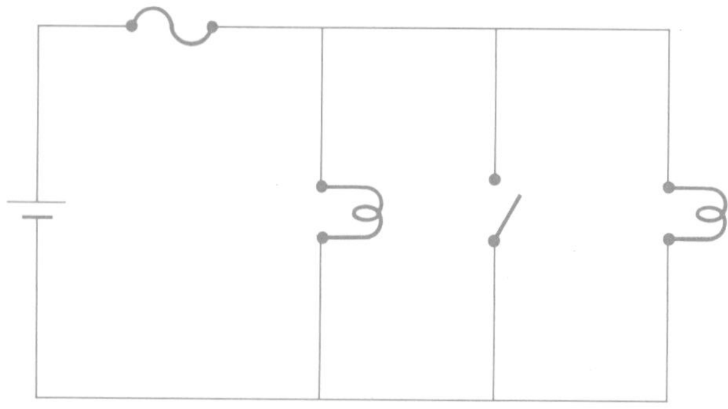

4. Explain how to connect two light bulbs in a circuit so that one bulb will not affect the other.
5. Compare the time a bulb will stay lit connected to two dry cells in series with the time a bulb will stay lit connected to four dry cells in series.
6. Name several devices found in the home that use
   a) direct current **b)** alternating current
7. Name several appliances found in the home that use
   a) 120 V AC **b)** 240 V AC
8. **a)** What is the function of a circuit breaker?
   b) What are two advantages of a circuit breaker over a fuse?

Applying the Concepts

1. Draw a circuit diagram showing a series connection of a dry cell, a switch, and a bulb. Show a voltmeter connected to measure the electrical potential of the source and an ammeter connected to measure the electric current in the circuit. Label the positive and negative terminals of the cell, the voltmeter, and the ammeter.
2. Draw a circuit diagram with a source, a switch, a motor, and a lamp. You want the lamp to tell you if the motor stops working.
3. Draw a circuit diagram showing a dry cell, a switch, a motor, and a lamp. The motor must continue working if the lamp burns out.
4. Draw a circuit with two dry cells, a switch, and three light bulbs. If a cell or a bulb becomes defective the circuit must still work.
5. Use symbols to draw the following: two dry cells are connected in parallel to a parallel connection of two light bulbs. Show three switches in the circuit so that the lights can be turned off independently or all at once.
6. Use symbols to draw a circuit with the following components: a parallel connection of two dry cells and two light bulbs. Show a switch that will turn off both bulbs and another that will disconnect one of the cells.

Fig. 17-17 Can you read the electric meter in your home?

Investigations

1. Do a library search to find out what a circuit breaker is and how it operates. *CAUTION: DO NOT TOUCH ELECTRICAL CIRCUITS IN YOUR HOME.*
2. Get some fuse wire from your teacher. Design a series circuit using dry cells, a switch, conducting wires, fuse wire, and a light bulb to show the action of a fuse.
3. Design and do an experiment to test the ability of different materials to conduct electricity. Use dry cells, an ammeter, a light bulb, and a switch to test the materials.
4. The total electric energy used in a home is measured by using an electric meter. Find out how to read an electric meter (Fig. 17-17). Measure the electric energy consumed in a home in a month. Research ways of minimizing this use.
5. Research the effects electric current has on the human body. Find out what currents are annoying and what currents are fatal. Generate a list of safety measures to take to prevent an electric shock.

18 Electromagnetism

CHAPTER CONTENTS

CHAPTER OBJECTIVES

After completing this chapter you should be able to:

1. Describe the magnetic field of a straight conductor and a helix.
2. Use the Left Hand Rule for a Conductor and a Helix.
3. Describe the properties and uses of an electromagnet.
4. Describe the conditions for electromagnetic induction.

It was not until 1821 that an electric current was seen to act like a magnet. It took scientists and engineers a further ten years to discover how to use magnetism to produce an electric current. Their discovery provided us with the abundance of electricity we have today. Imagine what it would be like if we had to obtain all our electricity from voltaic cells!

In this chapter you will find out how to produce a magnetic effect using an electric current (Fig. 18-1). Finally, you will learn how to produce electricity using magnetism.

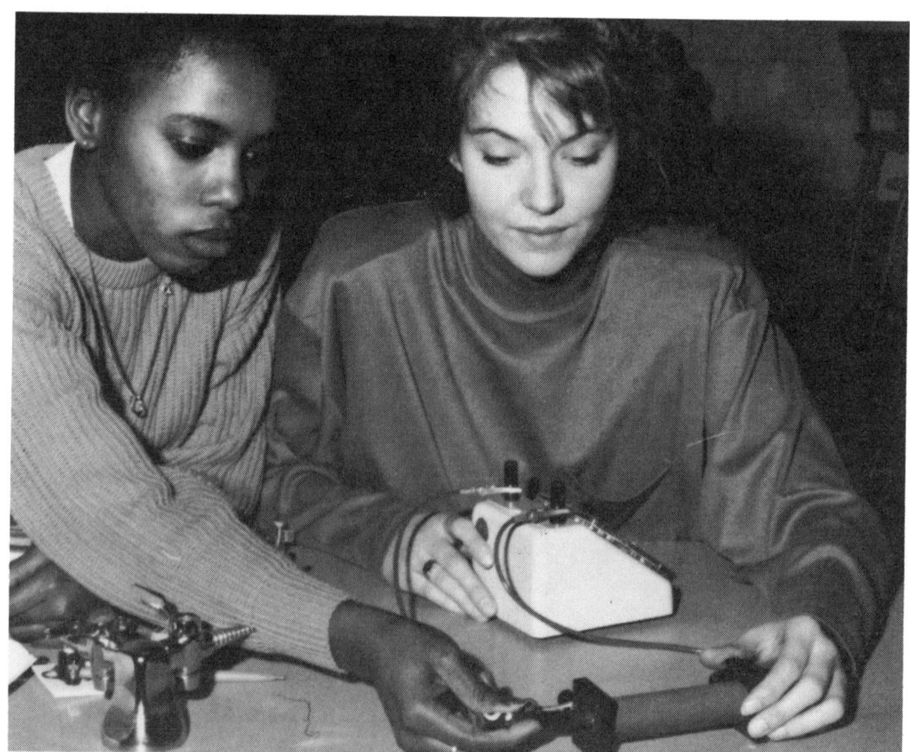

Fig. 18-1 An electric current can be produced using magnetism. You will try this experiment in this chapter.

18.1 Demonstration: Producing Magnetism Using Electricity

As you know, a magnetic force is produced by a magnet. However, a magnetic force is also produced by electrons moving in a conductor. In this activity you will study the magnetic field produced by moving electrons. You will also compare the directions of the field and the electron flow.

Problem

What kind of magnetic field is produced by moving electrons?

Materials

battery pack (4 dry cells in series)
thick bare copper wire (12 gauge)
stiff white cardboard (15 cm × 15 cm)
several small compasses
connecting wires
iron filings

Procedure

a. Support the cardboard horizontally above the desk (Fig. 18-2).
b. Push the thick copper wire through the centre of the cardboard.

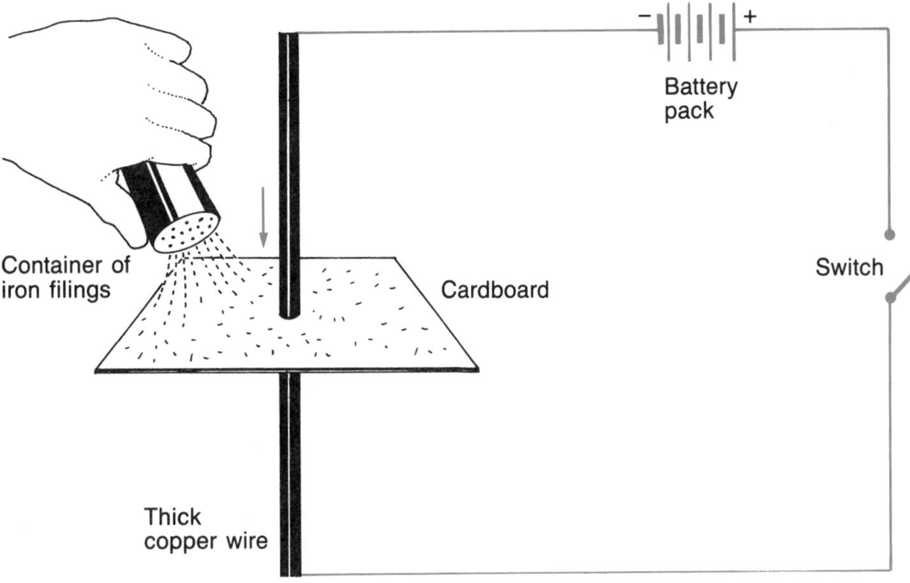

Fig. 18-2 Producing magnetism using electricity

c. Use connecting wires to connect the battery, switch, and thick copper wire as shown in Figure 18-2.
d. Sprinkle a light film of iron filings on the cardboard.
e. Close the switch briefly. Tap the cardboard gently. Open the switch.
f. Draw the wire. Draw the pattern the iron filings make.
g. Place small compasses around the copper wire. Briefly close the switch.
h. Draw the wire. Show the directions the N poles point around the wire. Record on the diagram whether the electrons are moving up or down the wire.
i. Reverse the connections to the copper wire. The current will flow in the opposite direction. Briefly close the switch.
j. Repeat step (h).

Discussion

1. Describe the magnetic field mapped by the iron filings.
2. What happens to the direction the compass points when the electron flow reverses?
3. What happens to the direction of the magnetic field when the electron flow reverses?

18.2 The Magnetic Field of a Straight Conductor

Oersted's Experiment

The magnetic force exerted by moving electrons was first seen by the Danish physicist Hans Christian Oersted (1777–1851) when he was demonstrating the electric current produced in a wire by a battery. The wire was pointing north and south and a compass needle was sitting beneath the wire and parallel to it as shown in Figure 18-3,A. When the wire was connected to a battery, the compass needle turned away from north. The N pole of the compass pointed west when the electrons in the wire flowed south (Fig. 18-3,B). When the direction of the electron flow was reversed, the N pole of the compass pointed east (Fig. 18-3,C).

Because electrons moving in a straight conductor produce a magnetic force, they also produce a magnetic field. This magnetic field can be mapped using iron filings. The iron filings line up with the field, forming concentric circles around the conductors. As the distance from the conductor increases, the size of the circles increases in a non-uniform way (Fig. 18-4). This shows that the magnetic field is weaker further from the conductor.

The direction of the magnetic field can be plotted with magnetic compasses. The compasses line up with the circles (Fig. 18-5). As a result, there is no start or finish to the field. Therefore the magnetic field around a conductor carrying an electric current has no poles.

Fig. 18-3 Diagram of Oersted's experiment. The compass needle is affected by moving electrons. The direction of electron flow affects the results.

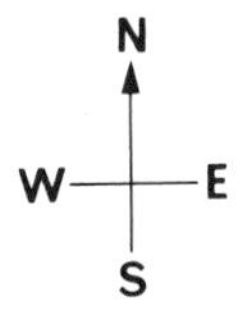

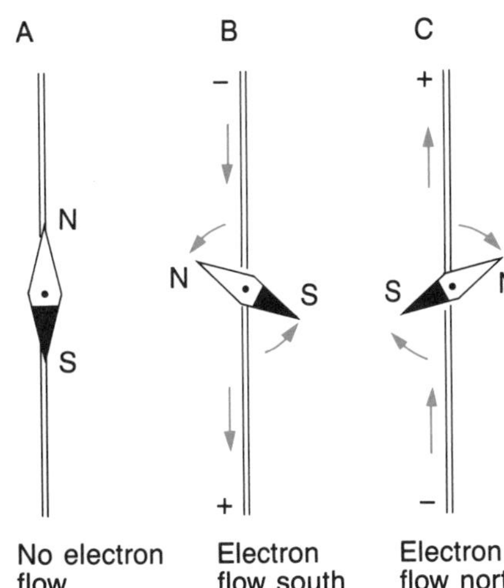

Fig. 18-4 The magnetic field around a straight conductor is in the form of concentric circles.

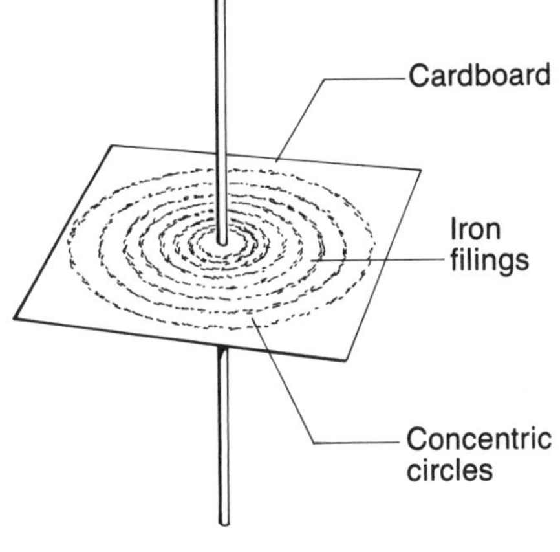

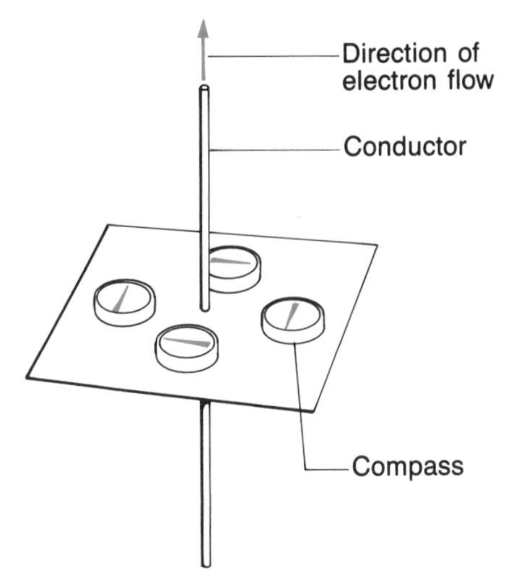

Fig. 18-5 When the electron flow is up the compass needles point clockwise.

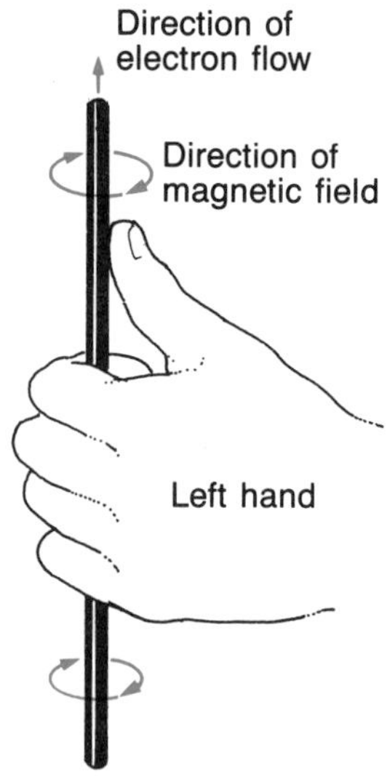

Fig. 18-6 Using the Left Hand Rule to find the direction of the magnetic field in a straight conductor

The Left Hand Rule for a Straight Conductor

The direction of the field is the direction the N pole of a compass points. Suppose the electrons travel up the conducting wire. The magnetic field points clockwise around the conductor as shown by the compasses in Figure 18-5. When the electrons flow down, the field points counterclockwise. A simple rule, called the **Left Hand Rule**, will help you find these directions. This rule says: *Grasp the conductor in the left hand. Point the left thumb in the direction of the electron flow. The curled fingers point in the direction of the magnetic field* (Fig. 18-6). If either of the two directions is known, the other can be found using this rule.

Section Review

1. Write the Left Hand Rule.
2. Two conductors and their magnetic fields are shown in Figure 18-7. Copy the diagrams into your notebook. Use the Left Hand Rule to find the direction of electron flow in each conductor.
3. The direction of electron flow is shown in two conductors in Figure 18-8. Copy the diagrams into your notebook. Draw a magnetic field line around each conductor. Be sure to show the direction of the field.

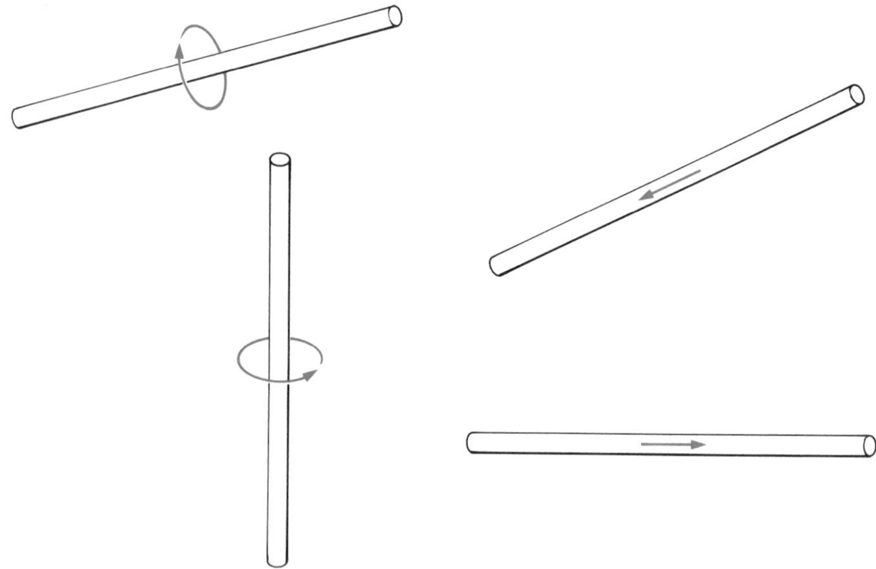

Fig. 18-7 In which direction will electrons flow in each conductor?

Fig. 18-8 What will the magnetic field line look like for each of these conductors?

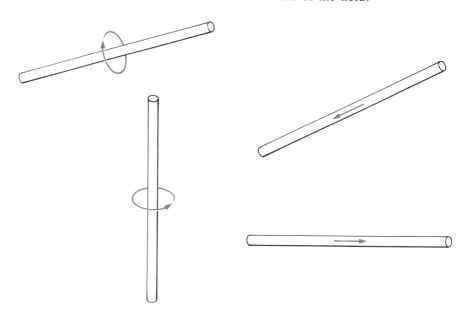

18.3 Activity: The Magnetic Field of a Helix

A stronger magnetic field is produced if a straight conductor is bent into a loop. The magnetic field is even stronger if a number of loops are made close together. A number of loops wound in a spiral is called a **helix**.

In this activity you will map the magnetic field of a helix that is carrying a current. You will find the direction of the magnetic field lines using compasses.

Problem

What are the characteristics of the magnetic field of a helix?

Materials

battery pack
connecting wires
cardboard
iron filings
switch
several small compasses
prepared helix and support

Procedure

a. Connect one end of the helix to one terminal of the battery pack.
b. Connect the other end of the helix to an open switch.
c. Connect the switch to the end terminal of the battery pack as shown in Figure 18-9.
d. Lightly sprinkle iron filings on the cardboard both inside and outside the helix.

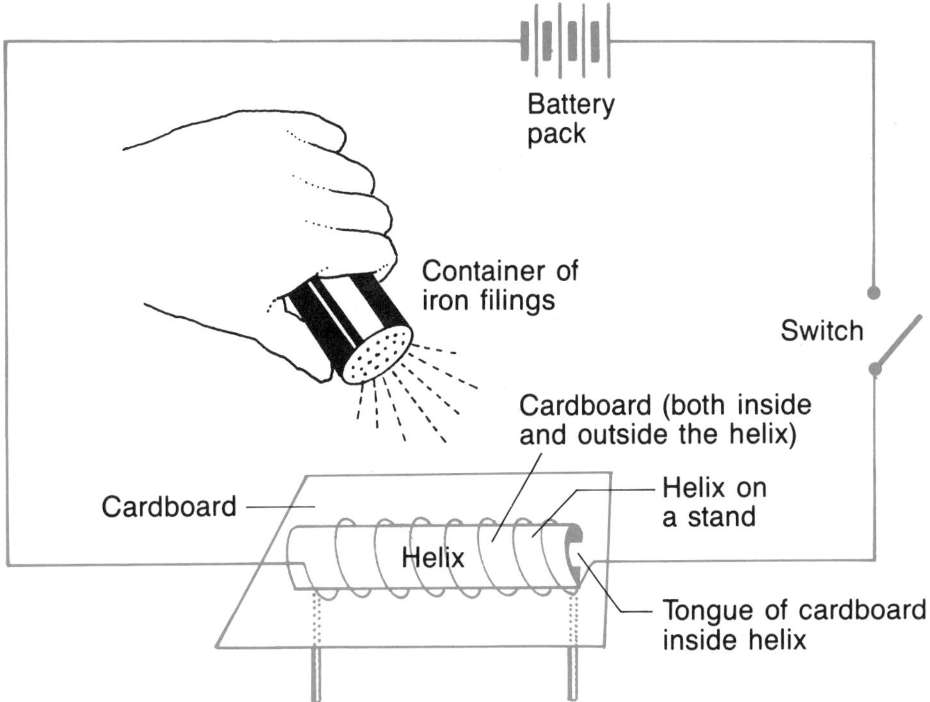

Fig. 18-9 Finding the magnetic field of a helix

e. Close the switch briefly. Tap the cardboard gently. Open the switch.
f. Draw the helix. Show the pattern of iron filings. Return the iron filings to the container.
g. Place a small compass at each end of the support.
h. Close the switch briefly. Find the N pole and S pole of the helix.
i. Note the direction of electron flow through the helix.
j. Draw the helix. Show the N and S poles and the direction of electron flow in the helix.
k. Reverse the connection to the battery pack. Repeat steps (h), (i), and (j).

Discussion

1. What is a helix?
2. Describe the magnetic field lines inside the helix.
3. Compare the spacing of the field lines inside and outside the helix.
4. Describe the magnetic field lines at the ends of the helix.
5. What happens to the poles of the helix when the electron flow reverses?
6. Try to find a relationship between the direction of the electron flow and the N pole of the helix.

18.4 The Magnetic Field of a Loop and a Helix

A Loop

A **loop** is a straight conductor bent into a circle. Think of a loop as made up of many straight parts. The electron flow in each straight part produces a magnetic field around it in the form of circles. The direction of the lines of force inside the loop is found using the Left Hand Rule as shown in Figure 18-10,A. The magnetic lines of force in the centre of the loop are all in the same direction (Fig. 18-10,B). This increases the magnetic force inside, which results in the field inside a loop being stronger than that around a straight conductor.

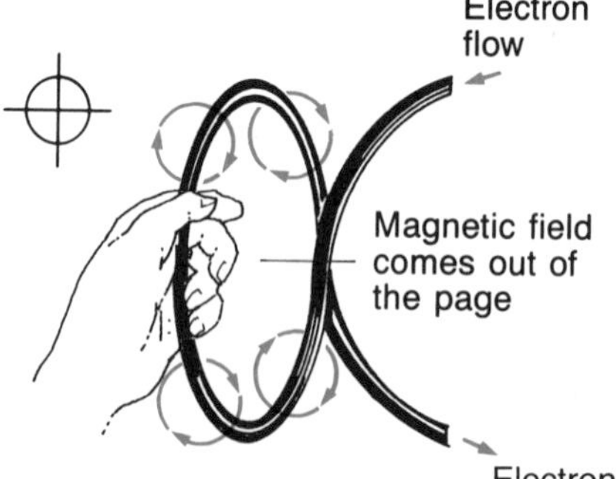

A. When a straight wire is bent into a loop, the field can be found by the use of the Left Hand Rule for a straight conductor.

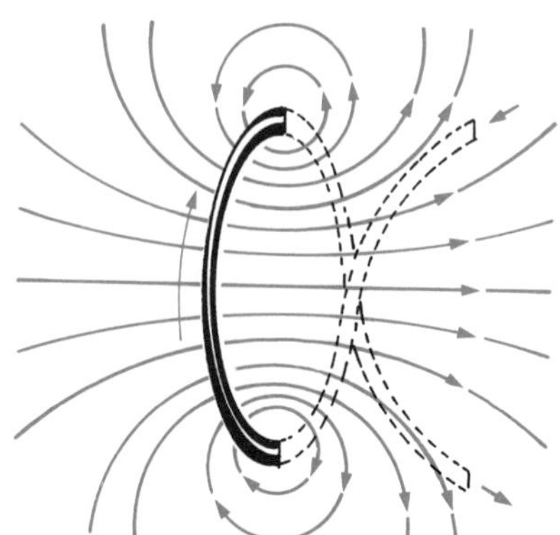

B. The magnetic field lines inside all point in the same direction.

Fig. 18-10 The magnetic field of a loop

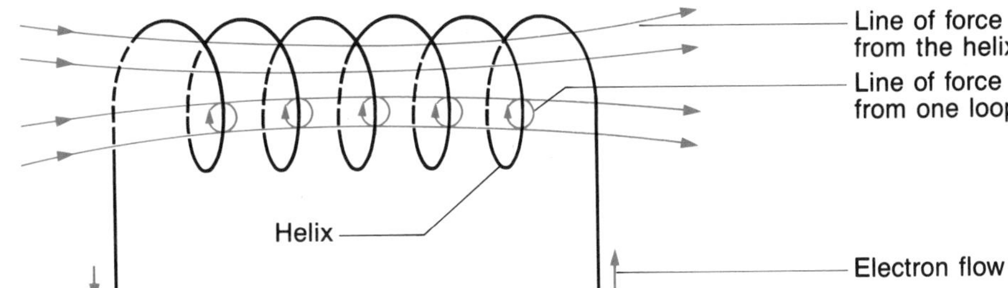

Fig. 18-11 The lines of force from each loop inside a helix are all in the same direction.

A Helix

A **helix** is a conductor made of several loops, with each loop producing a magnetic field. The lines of force inside the loops are all in the same direction as shown in Figure 18-11. This strengthens the magnetic field.

The Left Hand Rule for a Helix

A helix acts like a bar magnet when electrons flow through it. One end of the helix becomes a N pole. This end repels the N pole of a compass. The other

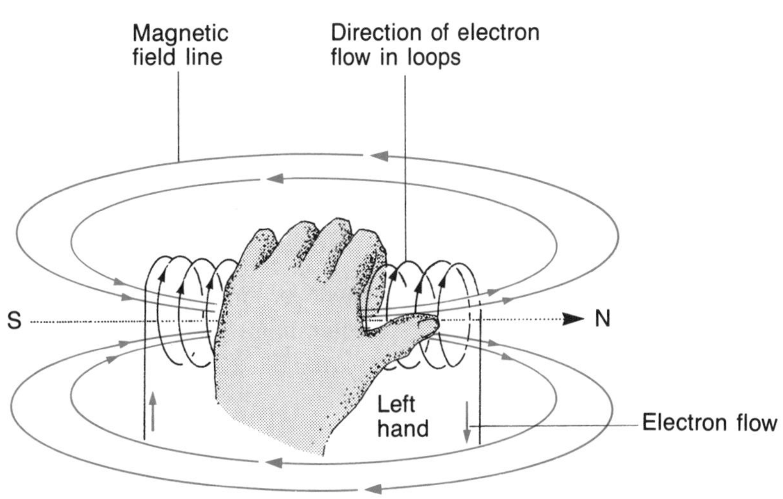

Fig. 18-12 The Left Hand Rule for a helix

end of the helix becomes a S pole. This end attracts the N pole of a compass. If the electron flow in the helix is reversed, the poles of the helix reverse.

There is a simple rule for finding either the N pole or the direction of electron flow. It is called the **Left Hand Rule for a Helix**. *Grasp the helix in the left hand. Curl the fingers in the direction of the electron flow in the loops. The thumb points toward the N pole of the helix* (Fig. 18-12).

Section Review

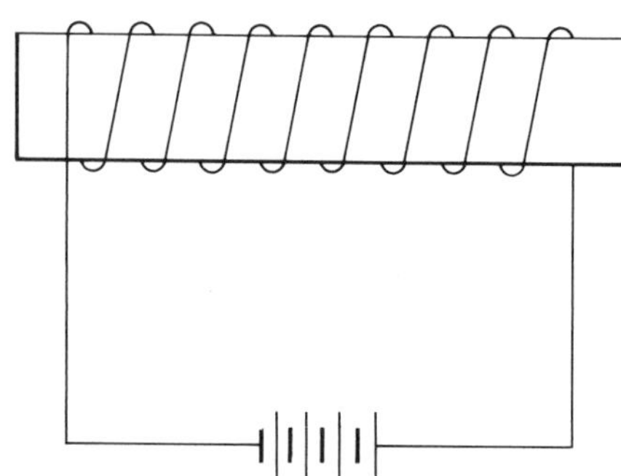

Fig. 18-13 Helix connected to a battery

1. Describe the magnetic field inside a loop.
2. Describe the magnetic field inside a helix.
3. How is a helix like a bar magnet?
4. State the Left Hand Rule for a Helix.
5. Figure 18-13 shows a helix connected to a battery. Copy the diagram into your notes. Add the following to the diagram:
   a) arrows to show the direction of electron flow in the helix
   b) several magnetic field lines around the helix with the directions shown
   c) a compass needle at each end of the helix with the direction of the N pole shown

18.5 Activity: The Strength of an Electromagnet

An **electromagnet** consists of a helix wound on a cylinder called the **core**. An electromagnet is more useful than a permanent magnet because it can be turned on and off and the strength can be changed.

In this activity you will make an electromagnet. You will find how to change its strength. What factors will increase the strength of an electromagnet? Make predictions. Then do the activity to test your predictions.

Problem

What factors affect the strength of an electromagnet?

Materials

wooden dowel	insulated copper wire	tape
aluminum nail	dry cells (3)	paper clips
iron nails (2)	dry cell holders (3)	

Procedure

a. Copy Table 18-1 into your notebook.
b. Make four different electromagnets (Fig. 18-14). Wind 20 turns of wire on the wooden dowel, the aluminum nail, and one iron nail (Fig. 18-15). Wind 40 turns on the other iron nail.
c. Connect each electromagnet in turn to one dry cell. Record how many paper clips each picks up (Fig. 18-16).

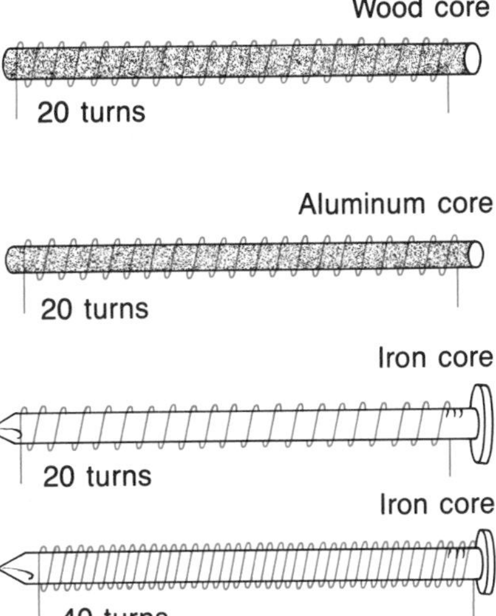

Fig. 18-14 Factors affecting an electromagnet

Fig. 18-15 Wind the wire as tightly as possible and space the loops as evenly as possible.

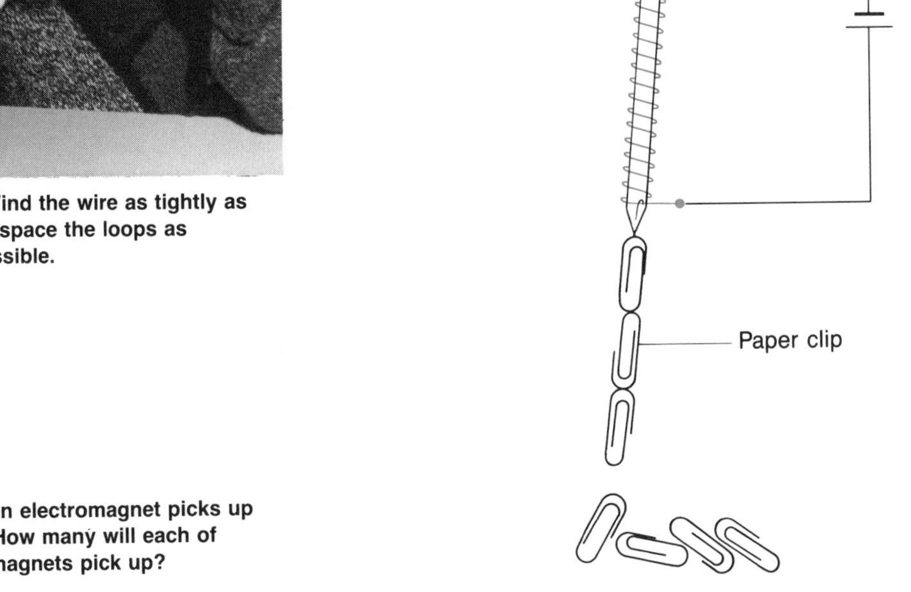

Fig. 18-16 An electromagnet picks up paper clips. How many will each of your electromagnets pick up?

d. Connect the 40 turn electromagnet to two and then three dry cells in series. Record how many paper clips are picked up each time.

Table 18-1 The Strength of an Electromagnet

Electromagnet		*Electric potential (V)*	*Load lifted*
Core	*No. of turns*		
Wood	20	1.5	
Aluminum	20	1.5	
Iron	20	1.5	
Iron	40	1.5	
Iron	40	3.0	
Iron	40	4.5	

Discussion

1. Which core produced the strongest electromagnet?
2. How does the number of turns affect the strength?
3. How does the electric potential (or current) affect the strength?

18.6 Electromagnets and Their Uses

Electromagnets have two major advantages over permanent magnets: they can be turned on and off and their strengths can be adjusted. These properties have made electromagnets quite useful. This section investigates some of these uses.

The Strength of an Electromagnet

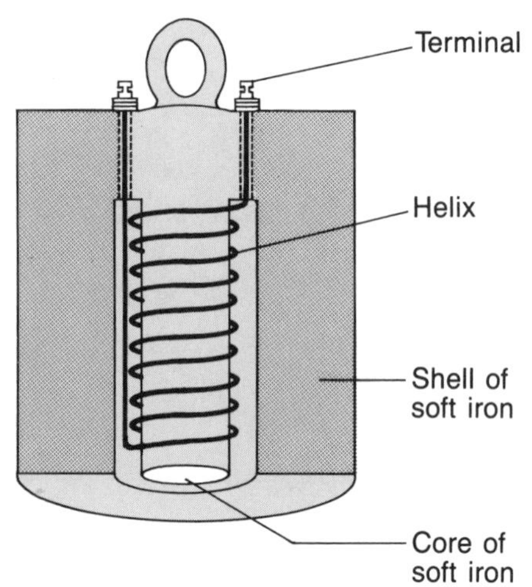

Fig. 18-17 A longitudinal section of a lifting magnet

A helix carrying electrons behaves like a magnet. An electromagnet is a helix wound on a core made of magnetic material, usually soft iron. The strength of an electromagnet is increased in four ways. A larger current in the helix increases the strength. A soft iron core makes a magnet several thousand times stronger than aluminum. Increasing the number of loops in the helix increases the strength. Also, winding the loops on a smaller diameter core increases the strength of the electromagnet.

Electromagnets have many uses. Scrap metal cranes, relays, electric bells, sound speakers, and electric motors use electromagnets.

Lifting Magnets

Electromagnets are used to lift and carry scrap iron and steel beams. A diagram of a lifting electromagnet is shown in Figure 18-17. The helix is wound on a core of soft iron. Around the helix is a shell of soft iron. The shell protects the helix from damage and increases the strength of the magnet. If you look back to the opening page of Unit 5 (page 359), you can see a lifting magnet in action.

Relays

A **relay** is a switch that is closed by an electromagnet. A diagram of a simple relay is shown in Figure 18-18. A relay contains two circuits. The electric circuit in the first circuit is used to close a switch in a second circuit. The first circuit contains a **helix** wound on a U-shaped iron core. The second circuit contains an **armature**. An armature is a lever made of soft iron fixed at one end and free to move at the other end. When the armature moves, it touches a contact. This completes the second circuit. Ordinarily the armature is held away from the contact by a spring.

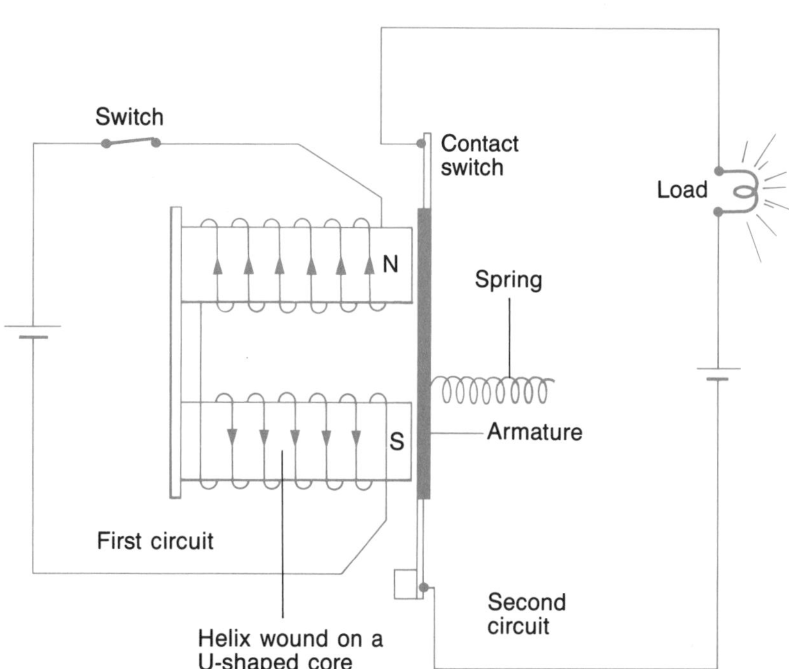

Fig. 18-18 An electromagnetic relay is a switch that is closed by an electromagnet.

When a current flows through the helix in the first circuit, the core becomes a magnet. It now attracts the armature, closing the switch in the second circuit. Now the current flows in the second circuit. Then a load such as a lamp is turned on. Suppose the current stops flowing through the helix. The core loses its magnetism. The spring attached to the armature pulls it away from the contact. This opens the switch. The current stops in the second circuit, and the load is turned off.

Section Review

1. What is an electromagnet?
2. Describe the factors that affect the strength of an electromagnet.

3. Draw a diagram of a lifting magnet. Explain how it operates.
4. Draw a diagram of a relay. Show a lamp in the second circuit. Describe how the relay works to turn on the lamp.

18.7 Activity: Producing Electricity Using Magnetism

You learned in preceding sections that an electric current can produce magnetism. In this activity you will investigate the reverse process: how to produce electricity in a coil using magnetism. The presence of an electric current will be detected using a sensitive meter called a **galvanometer**.

Problem

What conditions are needed to produce electricity from magnetism?

Materials

galvanometer
large diameter coil
bar magnet
soft iron core

Procedure

a. Connect the coil to the galvanometer as shown in Figure 18-19. Observe the movement of the needle of the galvanometer during each step of the procedure that follows.
b. Hold the coil stationary and thrust the bar magnet *quickly* into the centre of the coil. Keep the magnet stationary inside the coil for several seconds. Then withdraw the magnet *quickly* from the centre of the coil.
c. Hold the magnet stationary and thrust the coil *quickly* around the magnet. Keep the coil stationary around the magnet for several seconds. Then withdraw the coil *quickly* from around the magnet.
d. Insert the soft iron core inside the coil. Bring one pole of the magnet in contact with one end of the core. Hold it in contact for several seconds. Then withdraw the magnet *quickly*.

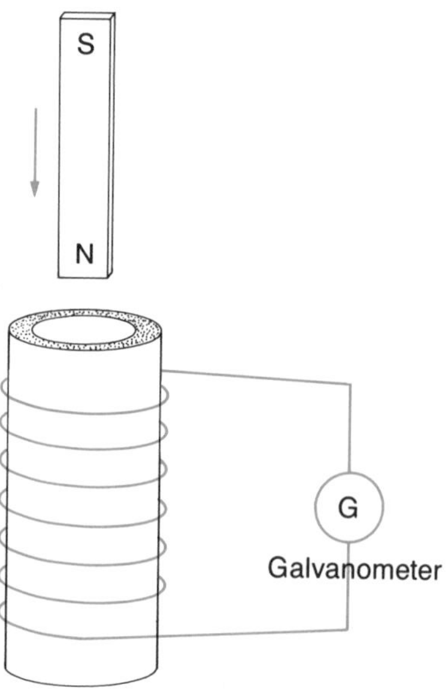

Fig. 18-19 Producing electricity using magnetism

Discussion

1. Is an electric current produced when the coil and bar magnet are at rest with reference to each other?
2. What happens when the magnet is moved and the coil is kept at rest?
3. What happens when the magnet is kept at rest and the coil is moved?
4. What happens when the strength of the magnetic field inside the coil is changing?
5. What conditions are needed to produce electricity using magnetism?

18.8 Electromagnetic Induction

The process of producing electricity using magnetism is one of the most useful discoveries humans have ever made. Do you know where it is used?

The Discovery of Electromagnetic Induction

If electricity can produce magnetism, then magnetism should be able to produce electricity. Following Oersted's discovery of electromagnetism in 1821, scientists performed experiments to try to produce an electric current using magnets. They placed conducting wires next to magnets, but no current was detected. Stronger magnets, better conductors, and more sensitive current-detecting devices failed to produce an electric current. Finally, in 1831, an English scientist, Michael Faraday, solved the problem. He discovered that, when the conductor or the magnet are in motion with reference to each other, an electric current is produced. When they are moving relative to each other the magnetic field around the conductor changes. An electric current produced by a changing magnetic field is called an **induced current**. The production of electricity using magnetism is called **electromagnetic induction**.

Faraday's Law of Electromagnetic Induction

There are three ways to change the magnetic field about a conductor. First, the conductor can be moved through the magnetic field. For example, moving a conductor back and forth between the jaws of a horseshoe magnet as shown

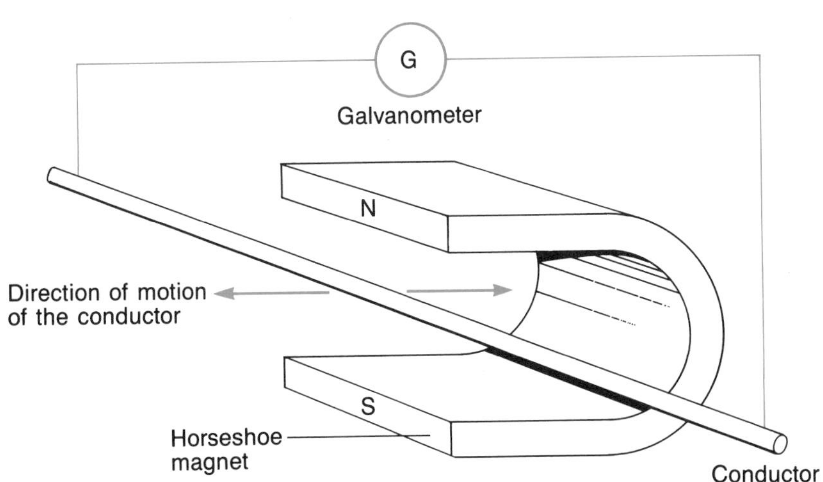

Fig. 18-20 Moving a conductor in a magnetic field produces a current in the conductor.

in Figure 18-20 produces a changing magnetic field and, hence, an induced current in the conductor. Second, the magnetic field can be moved near the conductor. For example, inserting a bar magnet inside a coil creates an induced current in the coil (Fig. 18-21). Withdrawing it has the same result. However, leaving it at rest produces no current. Third, the strength of the magnetic field near the conductor can be changed. Figure 18-22 shows a soft iron core inside a coil. If a magnet is brought in contact with the end of the core, the core becomes a magnet. The strength of the magnetic field inside the coil increases from zero. The changing strength of the magnetic field induces a current in the coil. However, once the soft iron core reaches its maximum magnetic strength, the magnetic field remains constant. As a result, the induced current falls to zero. However, when the permanent magnet is removed from contact with the core, an induced current is produced in the coil as the strength of the magnetic field decreases to zero.

The conditions needed to produce an induced current are summarized in **Faraday's Law of Electromagnetic Induction**. It states: *Whenever the magnetic field surrounding a conductor is moving or changing in magnitude, an electric current is induced to flow in the conductor.*

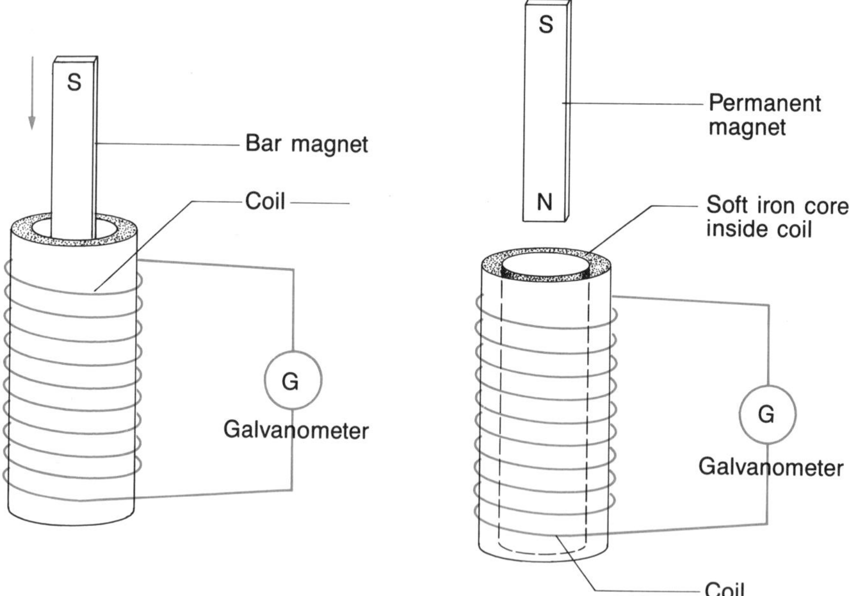

Fig. 18-21 Moving a magnet near a conductor produces a current in the conductor.

Fig. 18-22 Changing the strength of the magnetic field around a conductor produces a current in the conductor.

Generating Electricity

Faraday's discovery paved the way for the methods used today to produce the huge quantities of electricity demanded by modern society. Steam or hydraulic powered turbines turn electric generators giving them bulk kinetic energy. The turbines are connected to electric generators and cause them to rotate. **Electric**

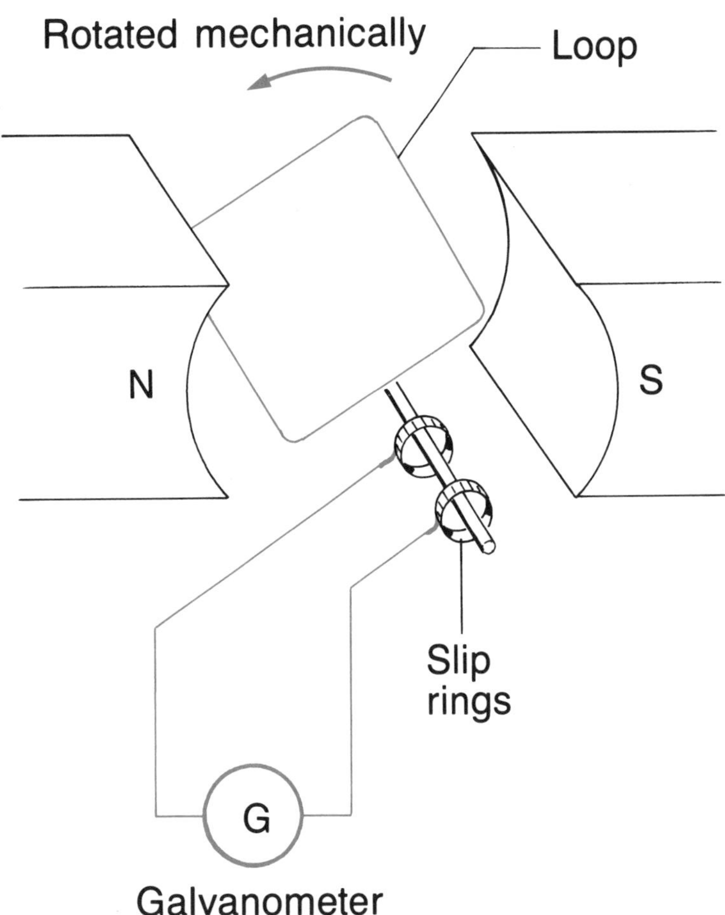

Fig. 18-23 Conducting coils rotated in magnetic fields in an electric generator produce an electric current.

generators contain conducting coils located between magnets (Fig. 18-23). When these coils are rotated in the magnetic field, induced electric currents are produced.

Section Review

1. Distinguish between electromagnetism and electromagnetic induction.
2. Define induced current.
3. Describe the conditions needed to produce electricity using magnetism.
4. Where does electromagnetic induction take place in a hydraulic power plant?

Chapter Highlights

1. Moving electrons produce a magnetic field.
2. The magnetic field around a straight conductor consists of circles of different diameters.
3. The Left Hand Rule for a Conductor describes the direction of electron flow and the magnetic field.
4. The magnetic field around a helix is similar to that around a bar magnet.

5. The Left Hand Rule for a Helix describes the direction of electron flow and the location of the N pole.
6. An electromagnet is a helix wound on a core, usually made of soft iron.
7. Electromagnets are used in lifting cranes, relays, bells, telephones, and speakers.
8. A magnetic field must be changing to induce an electric current in a conductor.

Key Terms

armature
core
electric generator
electromagnet
electromagnetic induction
helix
induced current
Left Hand Rule for a Conductor
Left Hand Rule for a Helix
loop
magnetic compass
magnetic field
relay

Recognizing the Concepts

Each of the following statements or questions is followed by four responses. Choose the correct response in each case. (Do not write in this book.)

1. The region of magnetic force around a magnet is called a
   a) line of force **b)** field **c)** N pole **d)** S pole
2. When using the Left Hand Rule for a Straight Conductor, the fingers curl around the conductor in the direction of the
   a) electron flow **b)** magnetic flow **c)** N pole **d)** S pole
3. When using the Left Hand Rule for a Helix, the thumb points in the direction of the
   a) electron flow **b)** magnetic field **c)** N pole **d)** S pole
4. In air, the magnetic field lines at a S pole
   a) do not exist
   b) point toward the pole
   c) are further apart than at the N pole
   d) are closer together than at the N pole
5. Which of the following *decreases* the strength of an electromagnet? *Increasing* the
   a) current in the helix **c)** voltage of the source
   b) number of loops in the helix **d)** diameter of the core

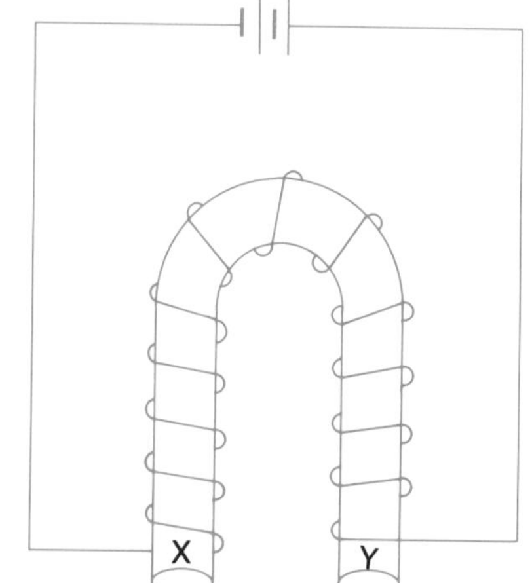

Fig. 18-24

6. The simple electromagnet shown in Figure 18-24 consists of a helix wound around a U-shaped metal core. The U-shaped metal core is made of
   a) hard steel and X is the N pole
   b) hard steel and Y is the N pole
   c) soft iron and X is the N pole
   d) soft iron and Y is the N pole
7. Which of the following devices does *not* make use of an electromagnet?
   a) relay **c)** sound speaker
   b) electric bell **d)** thermocouple

Understanding the Concepts

1. Suppose a straight conductor is pointing directly toward you. Describe the magnetic field lines around the conductor when the electrons are
   a) moving toward you **b)** moving away from you
2. **a)** What is the difference between a loop and a helix?
   b) Which is stronger, the magnetic field around a loop or the magnetic field around a helix? Explain.
3. Compare the Left Hand Rule for a Conductor and the Left Hand Rule for a Helix.
4. List three factors that affect the strength of an electromagnet and describe how each factor affects its strength.
5. What two changes in a magnetic field surrounding a conductor induce a flow of electrons in the conductor?

Applying the Concepts

1. Draw a helix wrapped around an iron nail. Show the direction of electron flow in the helix if the head of the nail is to become a N pole.
2. Figure 18-25 shows a helix wound on a soft iron core with space left for the diagram of a battery. The circles around the helix represent compasses. The polarity of the helix is indicated. Copy the diagram into your notes. Then
   a) add arrows to the helix to show the direction of electron flow.
   b) draw a schematic diagram of a battery showing the correct polarity.
   c) draw several magnetic field lines around the helix and add arrows to show their directions.
   d) add a correctly oriented compass needle to each compass.
3. Suppose the magnetism in a permanent bar is destroyed by dropping it. Explain how an electromagnet could be used to repair the magnet.

Fig. 18-25

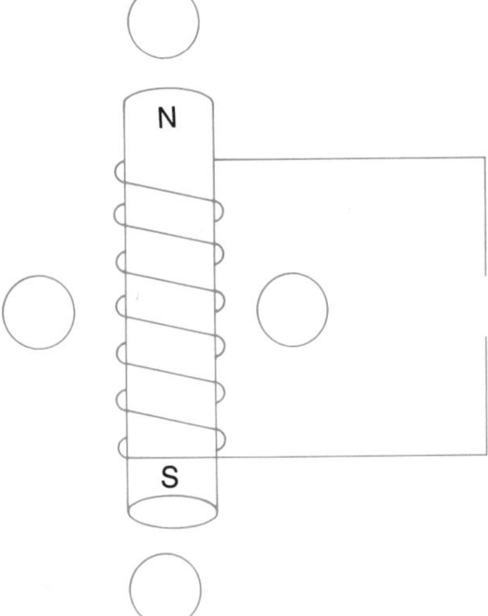

Fig. 18-26

4. Electromagnets are sometimes shaped in a U as shown in Figure 18-26.
   a) Describe how you could find the polarity of each arm of the U.
   b) Label the magnetic polarity of each pole of the magnet.

Investigations

1. Do a library search to find how a telegraph works. Build a model telegraph.
2. Obtain an electric bell from your teacher. Design and do an experiment to find out how it works (Fig. 18-27).
3. The theory of magnetism cannot be used to explain that earth is a large magnet. The high temperatures inside earth would destroy the alignment of the small magnets. Find out how scientists explain that earth is a magnet.
4. Visit an electric generating station. Find out how the station produces electricity.
5. Examine a sound speaker (Fig. 18-28). Then do a library search to find out how it works.
6. Research the use of electromagnets in computer disk drives. Submit a report of your findings.

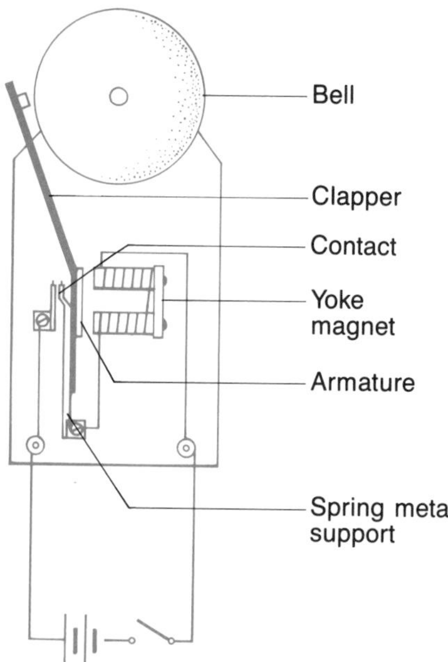

Fig. 18-27 A simplified diagram of an electric bell. Why will the armature move back and forth?

Fig. 18-28 How does a stereo speaker produce sound?

Career: *ELECTRICAL ENGINEER*

HELP WANTED:
ELECTRICAL ENGINEER

Large power generating company requires electrical engineer to supervise the construction of a new electrical generating facility.

Electrical engineering is the largest branch of engineering. Electrial engineers design, develop, test, and supervise the manufacturing of a variety of electrical and electronics equipment. Examples are electric power generating stations, communication systems including telephones and modems, and electronic controls such as thermostats and relays. Electrical engineers are at the cutting edge of technology as they attempt to design efficient electric cars, television sets that hang from the wall like a picture, and computers that think. Even the accurate diagnosis of internal medical problems depends on medical electronic devices designed by electrical engineers. For example, the nuclear magnetic resonance (NMR) scanner enables doctors to detect swollen brain tissue without surgery.

Some electrical engineers work in research laboratories. Others work in industrial plants, or at construction sites. Imagine the challenge of designing and supervising the James Bay Hydro Electrical Project.

Students interested in becoming electrical engineers must take mathematics, physics, and chemistry at the secondary school level. A bachelor's degree in engineering is required. To practise as a professional engineer in Ontario, the graduate must pass a closed book examination set by the Professional Engineers of Ontario, and join the Association. Because of the rapid advances in technology, electrical engineers must be willing to continue their education throughout life.

THE EARTH'S CHANGING MAGNETIC FIELD

The Theory of Magnetism cannot be used to explain that the earth is a large magnet. The high temperatures inside the earth would destroy the alignment of the small magnets. What then is the explanation?

Figure A shows the approximate structure of the earth. The outermost layer is called the **mantle**. The orientation of the domains in the magnetic rocks in this mantle provide a record of geological time. The **inner core** is at a very high temperature. From the reflection and refraction of the waves caused by earthquakes, scientists believe that it is solid. Between the mantle and the inner core lies a layer of liquid called the **outer core**. Density and other indirect measurements indicate that much of this liquid is molten iron and that it is moving. The movement of the liquid creates a magnetic field similar to that caused by moving electrons.

The movement of the liquid in the outer core is due to two factors: the rotation of the earth on its axis and convection currents in the hot liquid itself. Because the earth is so large, the speed of the liquid would only need to be about one millimetre per second to account for the strength of the magnetic field. At that speed it would take a tortoise about twelve days to move one kilometre!

You may already know that the direction of the magnetic field of the earth is changing. But do you know that the strength of the field has decreased by over 5% in the last hundred years? Do you realize that it was close to zero several times in the past? Scientists have evidence that the polarity of the poles reverses on average once in every half-million years. Data showing the reversal of the magnetic field come from the magnetic properties of the rocks at different depths in the earth's mantle (Fig. B). Iron atoms in a molten state align themselves with the magnetic field of the earth. When the liquid iron changes to a solid, the domains are frozen in this direction. The orientation of the domains can be measured with sensitive instruments. An examination of the rocks from different depths in the earth's mantle indicates that there have been over 14 reversals in the last 4.5 million years.

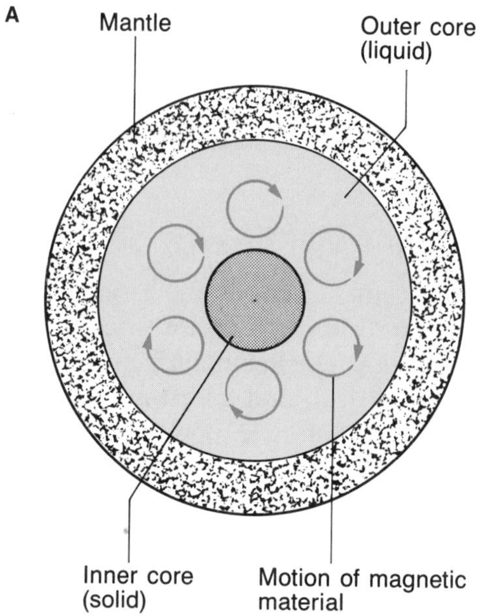

Structure of the earth showing the molten core

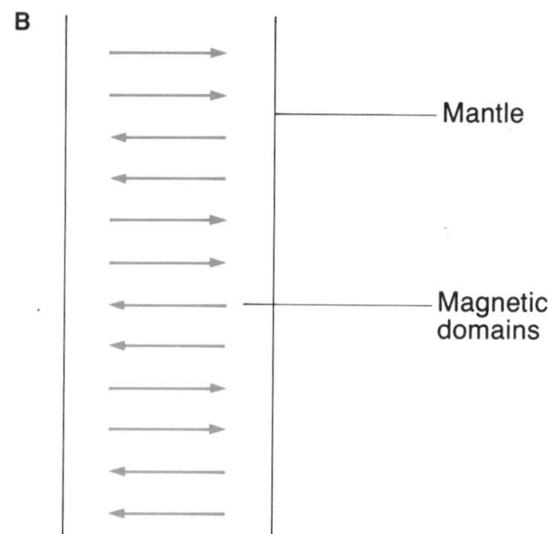

Magnetic domains indicate the reversal of the magnetic field

The last reversal took place over 700 000 years ago and the next one is predicted for about 2000 years from now. But who knows, the precocious earth may change its mind before then.

UNIT 6 Applied Chemistry

CHAPTERS

Chemicals and the results of chemical processes play a large part in your daily life. The food you eat is made of chemicals. So is the air you breathe. The water you drink has been subjected to chemical treatment to make it safe for drinking. Cosmetics, dyes, plastics, drugs, detergents, fertilizers, and much of your clothing are examples of products obtained by chemical processes.

In this unit, you will make some of these products. Also, you will find out about the role of chemistry in your home. And you will investigate the properties of acids and bases and a few of their many uses in your daily life.

19 Acids and Bases in Everyday Life

CHAPTER CONTENTS

CHAPTER OBJECTIVES

After completing this chapter you should be able to:

1. Describe safety procedures in the laboratory.
2. State the characteristic properties of acids and bases.
3. Explain the behaviour and strength of acids and bases.
4. Estimate the pH of common substances using universal indicator paper and classify them as acidic, basic, or neutral.
5. List some common household substances and foods that are acidic and some that are basic.
6. Explain and test the action of antacid tablets.
7. Give examples of acids and bases that are used around the home.

Acids and bases are two important classes of chemical compounds. You may think, as many people do, that all acids and bases are very corrosive. But do you know that your stomach contains hydrochloric acid which is necessary for digestion? And do you know that remedies for "acid stomach", such as Tums, contain bases, which, when swallowed, can provide relief from the symptoms of "acid stomach"? Many of the foods you eat and liquids you drink also contain acids and bases.

In this chapter, you will study the properties of acids and bases and some of their many uses around your home. You will also find out which common household substances are acidic and which are basic (Fig. 19-1).

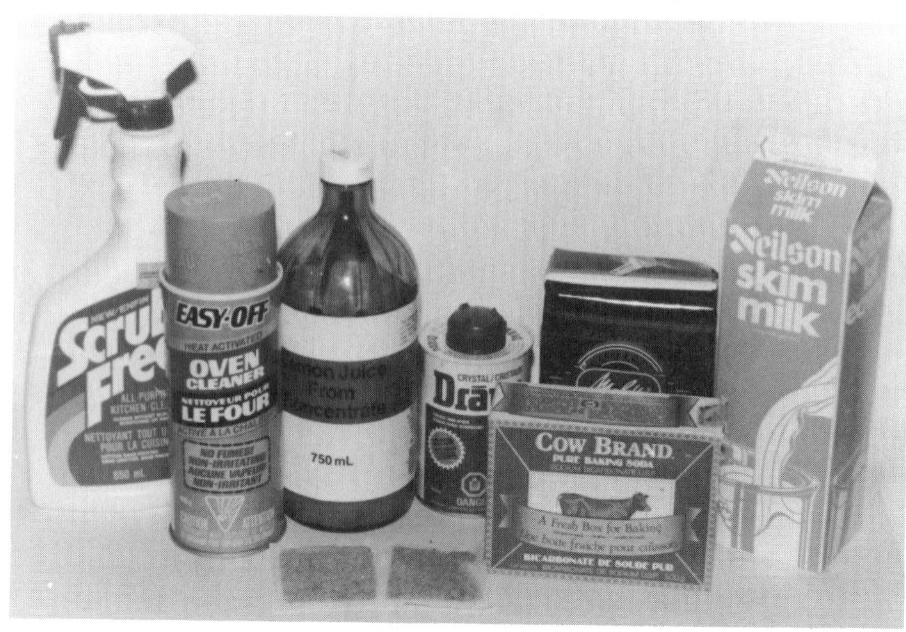

Fig. 19-1 Which of these common household substances do you think are basic and which are acidic?

Throughout this unit, you will have fun conducting a number of experiments using chemicals. Handled properly, these chemicals are very safe. However, *handled improperly, some of these chemicals can cause harm*. For this reason, safety precautions are indicated with each activity. *You must follow the precautions stated, as well as any others indicated by your teacher*. If you are unsure about any procedure, do not perform that procedure until you know how to do it safely.

Direct Effects of Lab Chemicals on You

Fig. 19-2 Do not be deceived by the appearance of some chemicals. Sodium hydroxide pellets react vigorously with moisture. Concentrated sulfuric acid reacts with water and with skin. Make sure that you are aware of the potential dangers of any chemical before you use it.

None of the activities in this unit uses chemicals which are strong toxins (poisons). However, this does not mean that the chemicals are safe to eat! Therefore, wash your hands thoroughly with soap and water after each activity to remove residues which would otherwise be ingested at your next meal.

Some chemicals can get into your body through your lungs or skin. Fume hoods and gloves should be used if you use toxic or irritating materials that can be absorbed in this way. Your teacher will demonstrate the use of fume-removal equipment.

Some chemicals can react with your skin and moist surfaces such as your eyes. For instance, sodium hydroxide comes in pellet form (Fig. 19-2). These pellets *look* like they could be touched and handled as if they were beads. Be careful! Use gloves or tweezers and safety goggles. Flush with water if the pellets contact moist surfaces.

Some chemicals, particularly sulfuric acid, react with certain fabrics as well as with skin. A plastic apron is recommended. Flush with water if contact occurs.

Expect the Unexpected

The activities in this unit are designed to minimize the possibility of accidents. However, you should prepare *now* to handle unexpected problems.

One lab hazard is fire. The natural gas in your lab is combustible. So are some chemicals that you will use, such as methanol. Consequently, you must keep *all* combustible materials (and their vapours!) away from open flames. This includes clothing and hair.

Occasionally, explosions occur in labs. While this should not happen in your lab, you should get in the habit of minimizing the potential damage from an explosion by:

- keeping reactive materials away from heat
- keeping quantities of reacting materials small
- wearing safety equipment

The most common accident in secondary school labs occurs during heating. Materials that are heated too strongly in a test tube may suddenly boil, causing some of the contents to "jump" out of the test tube. To avoid problems, heat cautiously and keep the test tube pointed away from people or open flames.

Before You Begin

Have your teacher instruct you in these safety procedures:

- Where are the safety goggles, gloves, aprons, and fire blankets?
- Where is the fire extinguisher and a back-up?
- How do you use the fire extinguisher?
- How do you shut off the gas jet at your lab station?
- How do you shut off the main gas valve in the lab?
- How and where are acids, bases, and other reactive chemicals dispensed in the lab?
- Where is the eyewash station? How is it used? For how long?
- How do you treat an acid spill on skin, clothes, or the floor?
- What is the lab evacuation procedure?
- Where is the fire alarm?

Discuss as a class:

- Use of fire extinguishers and smothering equipment
- Use of gloves, goggles, and aprons
- Use of open flames versus hot plates when combustibles are involved
- Do you pull the fire alarm for any fire or just one that cannot be extinguished quickly?
- Disposal procedures

Have Fun!

Chemistry is an exciting science because of unexpected and unpredictable results. With proper safety procedures, all of your unexpected results will be pleasant ones.

Section Review

1. Why must certain chemicals not be touched?
2. Why are you advised to wash your hands at the completion of an activity?
3. Why should long hair and loose clothing be tied back before doing a chemistry activity?
4. Why should test tubes not be pointed at people while the tubes are being heated?
5. How do you treat an acid spill on skin, clothes, or on the floor?

19.2 General Characteristics of Acids and Bases

Let us begin our investigation of acids and bases by seeing how they differ from the other substances on this earth.

Classification of Substances by Their Behaviour

In order to remember the properties of matter, it is helpful to group substances with common properties together. The process of grouping substances according to common properties is called **classification**. In previous science courses,

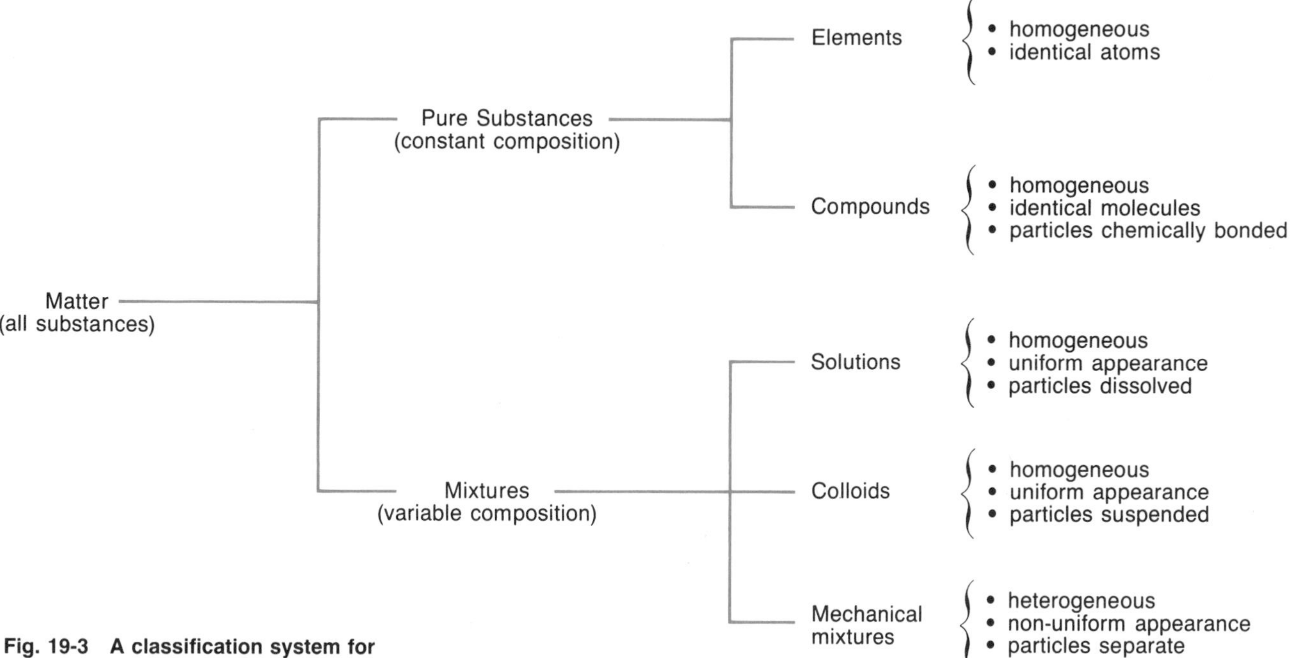

Fig. 19-3 A classification system for matter. This system uses composition to organize the different types of matter.

you classified matter into three groups—solids, liquids, and gases. This classification system was useful for studying matter and many of its physical properties. You also learned that matter can be classified by **composition** (Fig. 19-3). Matter can also be classified by **chemical behaviour**. Observing the chemical behaviour of compounds provides a way for organizing this large group of substances into several smaller groups. Acids and bases make up two classes of compounds that have been classified by their chemical behaviour.

Fig. 19-4 Lemons have a sour taste due to the presence of an acid called citric acid.

Properties and Definition of Acids

If you have tasted a lemon you are aware of its sour taste. Lemon juice contains an acid. Spoiled milk, orange juice, and grapefruit juice also taste sour due to the presence of acids (Fig. 19-4). Sour taste is a property common to compounds classified as acids.

Another property of acids is how they behave when they contact an active metal. (**Active** means ''reactive''. Some metals such as magnesium and zinc are active. Others like silver and gold are not active. Inactive metals are called **precious** metals. Why?) When a common laboratory acid, such as hydrochloric acid, and zinc metal are mixed together, bubbles are produced and the zinc metal dissolves. When tested, the bubbles are found to be hydrogen gas. A similar reaction occurs when other acids are reacted with zinc metal or other active metals such as magnesium. This general behaviour of acids can be summarized by this equation:

Acid + Metal → Salt + Hydrogen

In the case of hydrochloric acid and the zinc, the equation for the reaction is:

$$\text{Hydrochloric acid} + \text{Zinc} \rightarrow \text{Zinc chloride} + \text{Hydrogen}$$

$$2HCl_{(aq)} + Zn_{(s)} \rightarrow ZnCl_{2(aq)} + H_{2(g)}$$

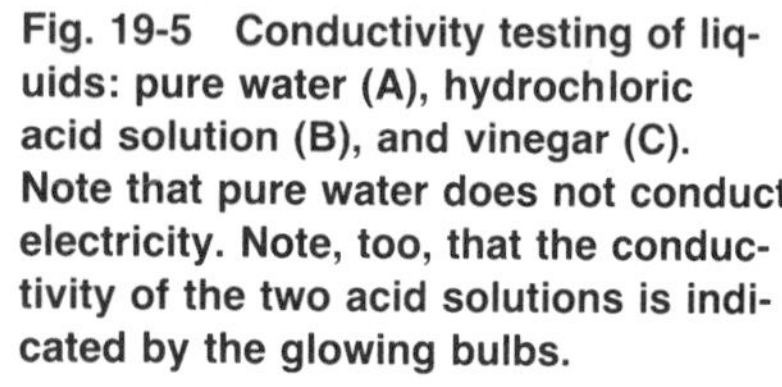
Fig. 19-5 Conductivity testing of liquids: pure water (A), hydrochloric acid solution (B), and vinegar (C). Note that pure water does not conduct electricity. Note, too, that the conductivity of the two acid solutions is indicated by the glowing bulbs.

Acid solutions also conduct electricity. The apparatus shown in Figure 19-5 is used to test electrical conductivity. If the liquid in the beaker is a conductor, the bulb glows. An electric current is not conducted through pure water or sugar solutions, but is conducted through acid solutions.

Another common behaviour of all acids is their effect on the colour of certain substances called **indicators**. An example of an indicator is litmus. Blue litmus paper turns red in the presence of an acid. You will learn more about indicators in Section 19.4. Finally, acids react with carbonates to give off carbon dioxide gas. Marble and limestone are two types of rock made up of carbonate. Acids react with these rocks and corrode them. You will verify these properties of acids in your next activity.

These experimentally observed properties of acids and their solutions provide a definition for this class of compounds. An **acid** is a compound that dissolves in water to give a solution that does all of the following:

- conducts electricity
- tastes sour
- changes the colour of litmus from blue to red
- reacts with active metals such as zinc, liberating hydrogen gas
- reacts with carbonates, releasing carbon dioxide gas

Common Acids Acids occur in both liquid and solid states. Some common acids in the laboratory are sulfuric acid, H_2SO_4; nitric acid, HNO_3; hydrochloric acid, HCl; and acetic acid, CH_3COOH. All of these are dangerous, especially

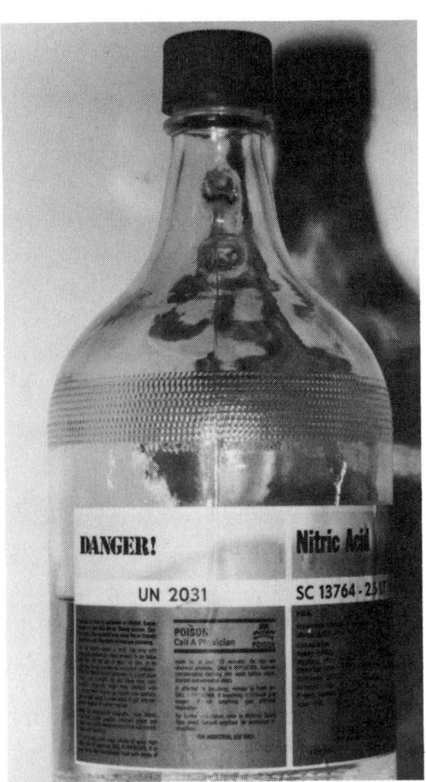

Fig. 19-6 Acids may be dangerous and must be handled with care.

Fig. 19-7 Sodium hydroxide is sold as small white pill-like masses called sodium hydroxide pellets. The pellets dissolve in water and the solution feels slippery. The slippery feel is caused by soap being formed by a reaction between the base and oils on your skin.

when concentrated, but even dilute solutions must be handled with care (Fig. 19-6). Other common acids are acetylsalicylic acid, ascorbic acid, and carbonic acid. Have you ever seen these in your home? Look at the labels on bottles of aspirin, vitamin C, and carbonated soft drinks!

Properties and Definition of Bases

Bases resemble acids in a few ways, but most of their properties contrast sharply with the properties of acids. For example, many compounds in this group resemble acids in that they dissolve in water to form solutions that conduct electricity. On the other hand, bases cause many indicators to assume a colour quite different from that found in acid solutions. For example, bases change red litmus to blue.

If you have ever gotten soap in your mouth, you have noted a bitter taste. Bitter taste is common to compounds classified as bases. Another common property of bases is how they feel. If you rub a small amount of dilute sodium hydroxide solution between your thumb and forefinger, it feels slippery (Fig. 19-7). A similar result is obtained when other bases are used.

When you add a base to an acid, the characteristic properties of both the acid and the base disappear. However, the resulting solution will conduct electricity. This property can be represented by this equation:

Acid + Base → Salt + Water

The salt solution formed does not possess any of the common properties of either acids or bases, except electrical conductivity.

These experimentally observed properties of bases and their solutions provide a definition for this class of compounds. A **base** is a compound that dissolves in water to give a solution that does all of the following:

- conducts electricity
- tastes bitter
- changes the colour of litmus from red to blue
- feels slippery on the skin
- reacts with an acid to destroy its properties

Common Bases Many bases are very caustic or corrosive; that is, they are capable of damaging a number of materials including skin (Fig. 19-8). As a result, sodium hydroxide, NaOH, is called caustic soda and potassium hydroxide, KOH, is called caustic potash. Caustic means burning. Bases require very careful handling. Other common bases are calcium hydroxide, $Ca(OH)_2$; sodium carbonate, Na_2CO_3; sodium hydrogen carbonate, $NaHCO_3$; and ammonia solution, $NH_4OH_{(aq)}$. Bases that are soluble in water are called alkalis and their solutions are called alkaline solutions.

Looking Ahead

1. Indicators and their colours in acidic and basic solutions are explored further in Section 19.4.
2. A theory to explain the common behaviour of acids and bases is presented in Section 19.6.

Fig. 19-8 Bases may be corrosive. Read the label carefully to learn how to handle the contents.

Section Review

1. What classification system is used in Figure 19-3? Name another classification system that can be used to classify compounds.
2. **a)** List the general properties of acids.
   b) List the general properties of bases.
3. **a)** Give three examples of common laboratory acids.
   b) Give three examples of typical bases.
4. In what ways are acids and bases alike? In what ways are they different?
5. Write a general equation for the reaction of an acid with a metal.
6. Write the general equation for the reaction of an acid with a base.

19.3 Activity: Investigating the Properties of Acids and Bases

You learned that every acid has properties in common with other acids. Similarly, each base has properties in common with other bases. In this activity you will check some of the properties of acids and bases presented in the previous section. Then you will use these properties to classify a number of common household substances as acids or bases.

Problem

What are the properties of acids and bases?

Materials

test tubes (3)
glass rod
red and blue litmus paper
zinc pieces
magnesium ribbon
wooden splint
marble chips

dilute acetic acid
dilute hydrochloric acid
dilute sulfuric acid
dilute sodium hydroxide solution
dilute potassium hydroxide solution
sodium hydrogen carbonate solution

household substances such as: lemon juice, vinegar, tea, window cleaner, sour milk, baking soda, toothpaste, shampoo

beaker
nails (2)
wires
switch
ammeter
dry cells (2)
dry cell holders (2)

CAUTION: Wear safety goggles during this activity.

Procedure A Properties of Acids

a. Copy Table 19-1 into your notebook.

Fig. 19-9 Handle all acids with care.

b. Obtain about 40 mL of each of the following solutions: acetic acid, hydrochloric acid, and sulfuric acid.

c. With a clean dry stirring rod, transfer a drop of acetic acid solution to your thumb. Rub the liquid between your thumb and forefinger. Record your observation.

d. Taste the liquid using the tip of your tongue. Don't swallow. Rinse your mouth with water at once. Record your observations.
CAUTION: Do not taste the other acids.

e. Use the stirring rod to place a few drops of acetic acid on a red litmus paper. Then place a few drops on a blue litmus paper. Record your observations. Repeat using hydrochloric acid and sulfuric acid (Fig. 19-9).

f. Half fill a test tube with hydrochloric acid. Drop a small piece of clean magnesium ribbon into the test tube. After about 30 s, bring a burning splint to the mouth of the test tube. Record your observations.

g. Repeat step (f) using sulfuric acid and acetic acid. Note and compare the rates of the three reactions.

h. Repeat step (f) using a small piece of zinc instead of the magnesium ribbon. Record your observations.

i. Set up the apparatus shown in Figure 19-10. Then test the electrical conductivity of the three acids. Compare the results and record your observations.

j. Drop a marble chip (calcium carbonate) into 2 mL of each acid. Record your observations.

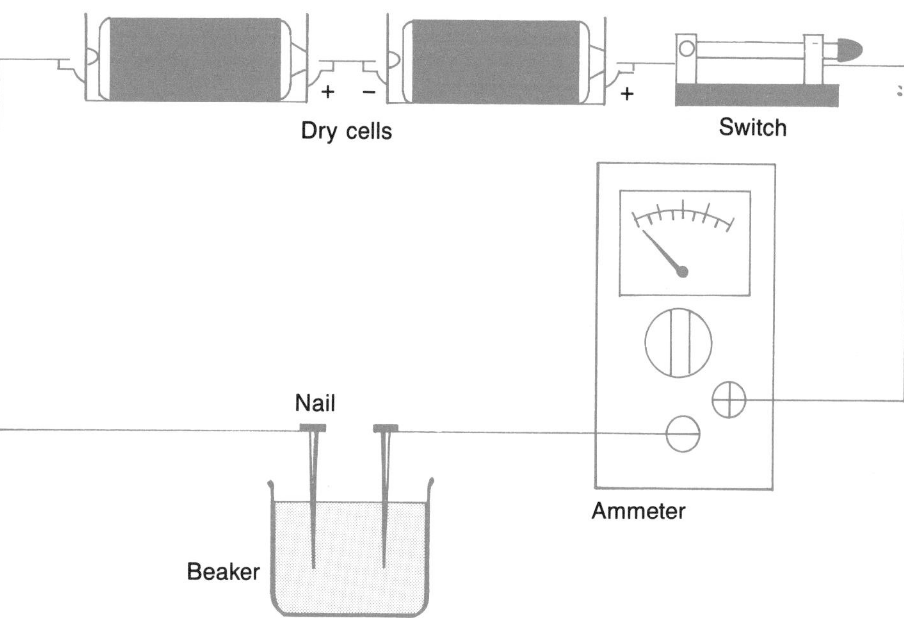

Fig. 19-10 Apparatus for testing liquids and solutions for conductivity

Table 19-1 Properties of Acids

Properties	*Acetic acid*	*Hydrochloric acid*	*Sulfuric acid*
Taste		———	———
Action on red litmus			
Action on blue litmus			
Effect on magnesium			
Effect on zinc			
Conductivity			
Reaction with carbonate			

Discussion A

1. Based on your observations, what are the properties of acids?
2. Do all acids tested have the same strength? How do you know?
3. Write word equations for the reactions of acetic acid, hydrochloric acid, and sulfuric acid with zinc and magnesium.

Procedure B Properties of Bases

Fig. 19-11 Handle all bases with care.

a. Copy Table 19-2 into your notebook.
b. Obtain about 40 mL of each of the following solutions: sodium hydroxide, potassium hydroxide, and sodium hydrogen carbonate (Fig. 19-11).
c. With a clean dry stirring rod, transfer a drop of sodium hydroxide solution to your thumb. Rub the liquid between your thumb and forefinger. Taste the liquid using the tip of your tongue. Don't swallow. Rinse your mouth with water at once. Record your observations. Repeat using potassium hydroxide solution and sodium hydrogen carbonate solution.
d. Use the stirring rod to place a few drops of sodium hydroxide solution on a red litmus paper. Then place a few drops on a blue litmus paper. Record your observations. Repeat using potassium hydroxide solution and sodium hydrogen carbonate solution.
e. Place 5 mL of hydrochloric acid solution in a test tube. Add a small piece of clean magnesium ribbon. Now add 5 mL of sodium hydroxide solution while the reaction between the acid and the magnesium metal is still going on. Record your observations.
f. Test the electrical conductivity of the solutions of the three bases. Compare the results. Record your observations.

Table 19-2 Properties of Bases

Properties	*Sodium hydroxide*	*Potassium hydroxide*	*Sodium hydrogen carbonate*
Taste			
Feel			
Action on red litmus			
Action on blue litmus			
Conductivity			

Discussion B

1. How does the addition of sodium hydroxide solution affect the action of hydrochloric acid on magnesium?
2. List the properties of bases that you investigated in this activity.
3. Do all bases tested have the same strength? How do you know?

Procedure C Classification of Household Substances

a. Obtain samples of each of: lemon juice, vinegar, tea, baking soda, sour cream, window cleaner, shampoo, toothpaste and/or other common household substances. *Avoid substances with warning labels.*

b. Use the litmus paper test and at least one other positive test to classify the substances obtained in (a) as acids or bases.

Discussion C

1. Which of the substances tested are acidic? Which are basic? Give evidence to support your answer in each case.

Extension

Obtain a few pieces of litmus paper from your teacher. Test several substances in your home to see if they are acidic or basic. If the product is a commercial one, read the label. Does the label give sufficient information to ensure that a consumer can use the product safely?

19.4 Indicators: Sources and Uses

Litmus: A Common Indicator

Acids and bases can be recognized by the colour change they cause in certain coloured substances called **indicators**. One of these coloured substances often used in the laboratory is called **litmus**. Litmus is extracted from a lichen. As you already know, this dye has a red colour in acidic solution and a blue colour in basic solution.

What Is an Indicator?

Acids and bases cause colour changes in many other coloured materials like litmus. These coloured materials can be used to *indicate* to us whether a substance is an acid or a base. As a result, they are called **indicators**.

Indicators can be extracted from a wide variety of plants. Flowers, fruits, roots, leaves, and other parts of plants which make good indicators include tea leaves, black currants, beet roots, rose petals of various colours, red cabbage leaves, tumeric, blackberries, and delphinium flowers (Fig. 19-12).

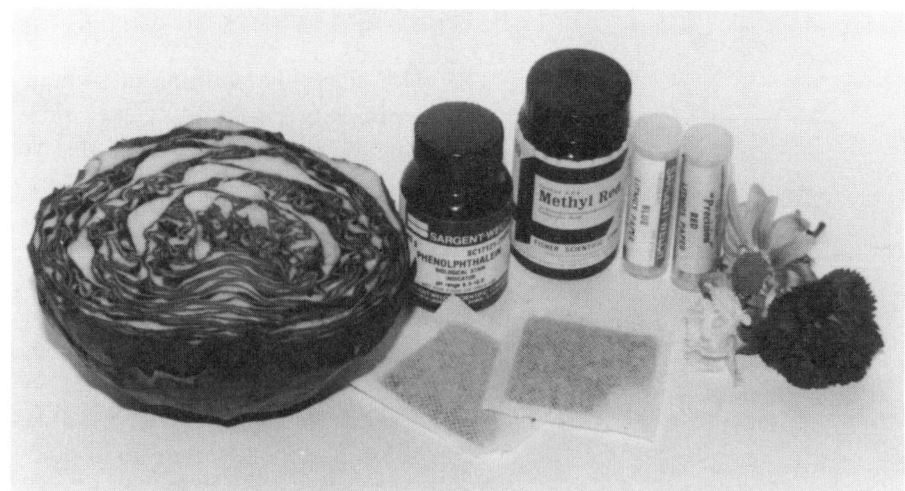

Fig. 19-12 Indicators are extracted from many natural sources.

Indicators and Neutral Substances

Some substances do not cause any colour change in litmus or any other indicator. These substances do not behave chemically in the same way as acids or bases and do not have the general characteristic properties of either group. Their solutions are neither acidic nor basic. These substances are called **neutral** substances and their solutions are called **neutral solutions**. Distilled water and alcohol are neutral liquids. Sodium chloride solution and sugar solution are neutral solutions.

Synthetic Indicators

Synthetic indicators are often used in chemistry laboratories rather than plant extracts. This is because most natural indicators lose their colours and sensitivities when stored for long periods of time. Also, plants suitable for making indicators do not grow in all locations. Where they do grow, they may be available only for short seasons during which indicators can be extracted. Therefore, it would be difficult to have fresh natural indicators all year round. Synthetic indicators, however, can be prepared in large quantities as powders. These can be stored, without losing their properties, for long periods of time (Fig. 19-13). The powder can be dissolved in an appropriate solvent to produce a fresh sample of the indicator when needed.

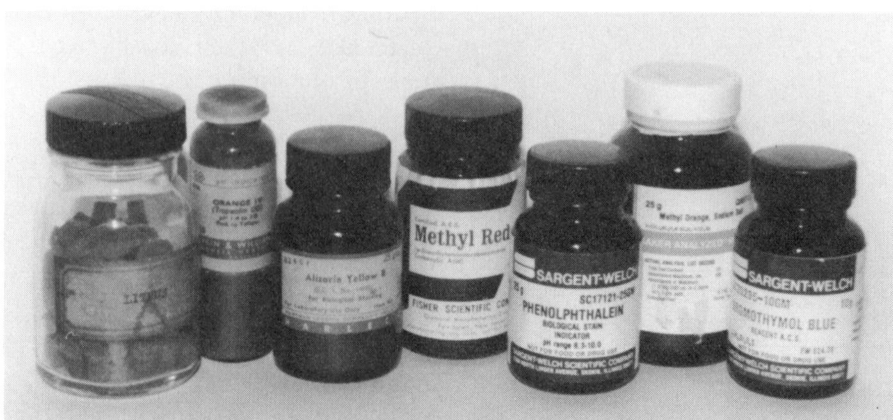

Fig. 19-13 Synthetic indicators can be purchased in powder form and stored for many years.

There are many synthetic indicators which you can find around the science laboratory in your school. Examples of common indicators are bromthymol blue, phenolphthalein, methyl orange, methyl red, methylene blue, alizarine yellow R, and indigo carmine. These indicators show characteristic colour variations in acids, bases, and neutral solutions as shown in Table 19-3.

Table 19-3 Indicator Colours

	Colour of indicator		
Indicator	*Acidic medium*	*Neutral medium*	*Basic medium*
Litmus	red	violet	blue
Phenolphthalein	colourless	colourless	pink
Bromthymol blue	yellow	green	blue
Methyl orange	red	orange	yellow

Extension

Work with a small group of your classmates to prepare a demonstration to support Table 19-3.

Section Review

1. What is an indicator? Give an example to illustrate your answer.
2. Name three examples of plants suitable for making indicators.
3. Define a neutral solution and give two examples.
4. Give two reasons why synthetic indicators are often used rather than plant extracts.
5. Name four common indicators you can find in a chemistry laboratory. What are the colours of each in an acidic, basic, and neutral medium?
6. Suppose you are given four beakers, each containing an unidentified colourless liquid. One is distilled water. The other three are solutions of an acid, a base, and table salt. Describe how you would find out which was which.

19.5 Activity: Extraction of Indicators from Plants

Natural indicators are coloured dyes that are usually obtained from plants. A wide variety of plants can be used for obtaining indicators. The choice depends on the time of the year and on the location of your school. In this activity you will prepare some natural indicators. Then you will find out how their colours change in acidic and basic solutions.

Problem

Can coloured substances extracted from plants act as indicators?

Materials

red cabbage
unsweetened purple grape juice
600 mL beaker
coloured flowers (almost any coloured flower is suitable with the exception of yellow flowers such as dandelions and daffodils)
400 mL beaker
100 mL beakers (3)
250 mL Erlenmeyer flask
ring stand, iron ring, wire gauze, adjustable clamp
filter funnel, filter paper
Bunsen burner
knife
ethanol
dilute sodium hydroxide solution
dilute hydrochloric acid solution
beaker tongs

CAUTION: Wear safety goggles during this entire activity. The heating in Procedure B must be done on a hot plate. Make sure there are no open flames in the laboratory.

Procedure A Preparing a Red Cabbage Juice Indicator

a. Obtain a small section of red cabbage. Chop it into fine pieces.
b. Place the chopped red cabbage in a 400 mL beaker. Add about 300 mL of water.
c. Heat the mixture until it just begins to boil.
d. Remove the beaker from the heat and allow it to cool to room temperature. Filter the juice into another beaker to obtain the indicator.
e. Pour samples of the indicator into three beakers. Add 10 mL of hydrochloric acid solution to one sample and 10 mL of sodium hydroxide solution to another. Compare these with the third sample and note the colour differences.

Procedure B Extracting a Flower Pigment Indicator

a. Chop the flower heads from a colourful flower into fine pieces.
b. Place the flower pieces in the Erlenmeyer flask.
c. Add about 100 mL of ethanol. Heat the mixture gently using a water bath on a hot plate (Fig. 19-14). Heat for about 20 min or until the solid parts of the mixture have become ''white''.
d. Using gloves or tongs, remove the flask from the beaker. Dip the flask into a beaker of tap water to cool it to room temperature. Filter the extract into another beaker to obtain the indicator.
e. Pour samples of the indicator into three beakers. Add 10 mL of hydrochloric acid solution to one sample and 10 mL of sodium hydroxide solution to another sample. Compare these with the third sample and note the colour differences.

Fig. 19-14 Note how the flask containing the chopped flower and ethanol is suspended in a water bath. Why is a water bath needed? Why could the flask not be placed directly on the hot plate?

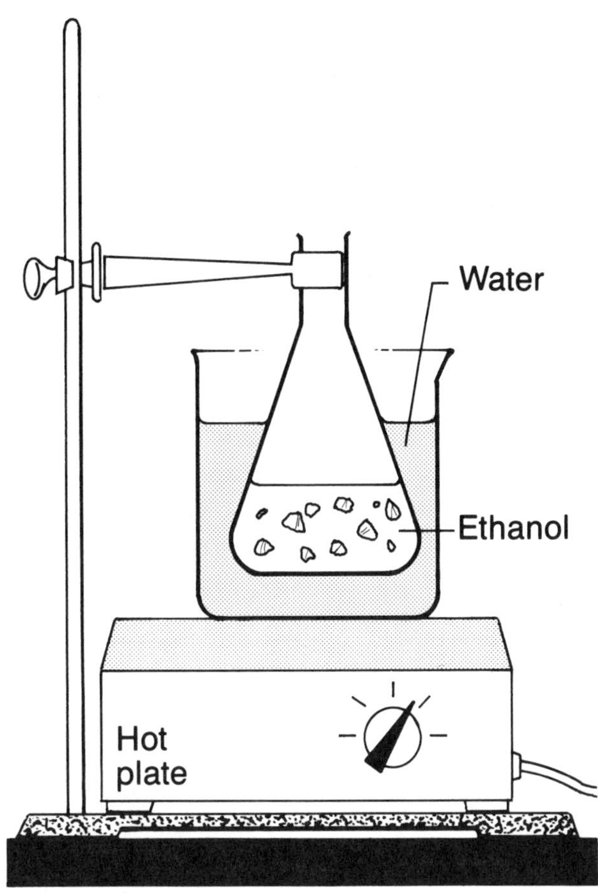

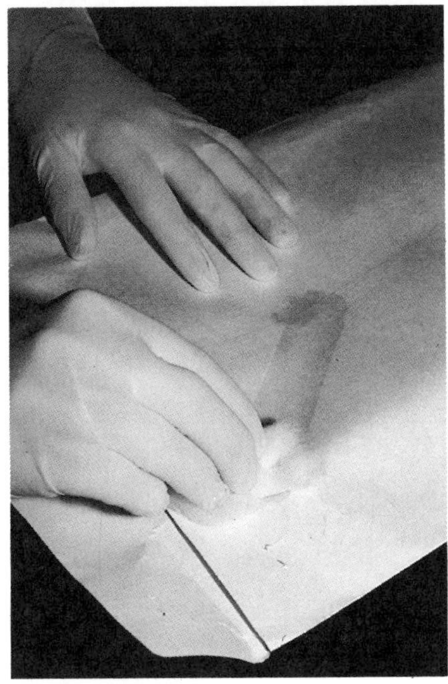

Fig. 19-15 Chemicals in tea and manilla envelopes make good indicators. What happens to tea when lemon is added? What happens to the envelope when it is brushed with ammonium hydroxide? Can you reverse these colour changes? How?

Procedure C Preparing a Grape Juice Indicator

a. Obtain 10 mL of unsweetened purple grape juice in a beaker.

b. Add 40 mL of water to the purple grape juice. Stir the mixture to obtain the indicator.

c. Pour samples of the indicator into three beakers. Add 10 mL of hydrochloric acid solution to one sample and 10 mL of sodium hydroxide solution to another sample. Compare these with the third sample and note the colour differences.

Discussion

1. Organize your observations in a table which includes the original colour of each extract and its colour in acidic and basic solutions.
2. Explain how you could use one of these extracts to test an unknown solution for acidic or basic properties.

Extension

Find out what colours appear when manilla envelopes and tea are tested with acids and bases (Fig. 19-15).

19.6 Strength of Acids and Bases

Ionization: The Source of Strength

You have likely noticed that some acids such as hydrochloric acid attack metals more vigorously than others such as acetic acid. You also know that some acids are edible (aspirin, vitamin C, carbonated soft drinks), whereas others should not be touched, much less consumed (sulfuric acid, nitric acid). Why are acids so different?

When dissolved in water, acids and bases **ionize**. That is, the molecules react with water and break apart into ions. For instance, hydrochloric acid reacts with water according to the following equation:

$$\text{Hydrochloric acid} + \text{Water} \rightarrow \text{Hydronium ion} + \text{Chloride ion}$$
$$HCl + H_2O \rightarrow H_3O^+ + Cl^-$$

H_3O^+ and Cl^- are called ions because they have a charge. Some properties of chemicals like hydrochloric acid depend on the presence of these ions.

The concentration of ions accounts for one common property of acids and bases: the ability to conduct electricity. Substances that form ions in water are called **electrolytes**. If a substance dissolves and forms many ions, it is a **strong electrolyte**. However, if only a few ions are formed, the substance is a **weak electrolyte**. Electricity moves more easily through a strong electrolyte than through a weak one because of the greater concentration of ions (Fig. 19-16).

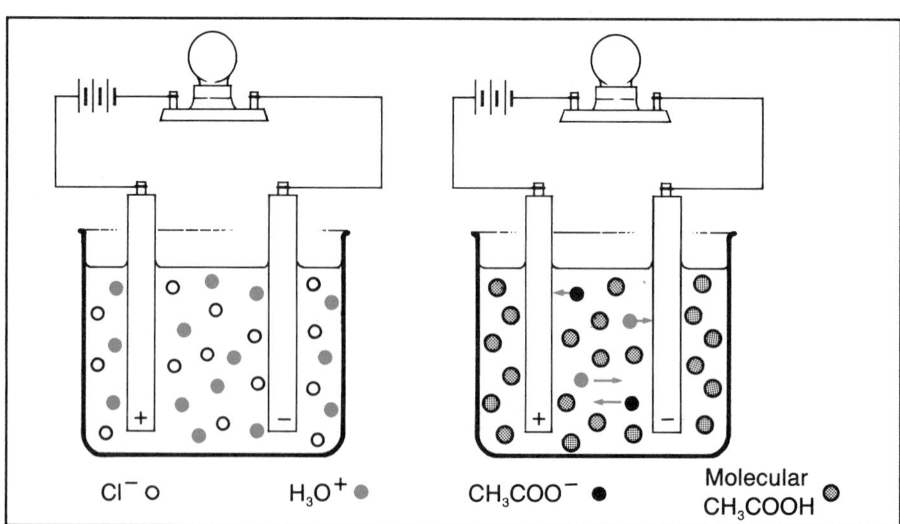

Fig. 19-16 These diagrams represent a model that explains conductivity differences shown by different solutions. Note the difference in the number of ions and the brightness of the bulb in each case.

Strength of Acids

The concentration of hydronium ion, H_3O^+, accounts for the properties of acids. All acids release hydronium ions in water, as you can see from the following sample equations:

$$\text{Acetic acid} + \text{Water} \rightarrow \text{Hydronium ion} + \text{Acetate ion}$$
$$CH_3COOH + H_20 \rightarrow H_30^+ + CH_3COOH^-$$
$$\text{Nitric acid} + \text{Water} \rightarrow \text{Hydronium ion} + \text{Nitrate ion}$$
$$HN0_3 + H_20 \rightarrow H_30^+ + NO_3^-$$

One definition of an acid is: *any substance that releases hydronium ions in an aqueous (water) solution.*

Acids behave in certain ways because of the hydronium ion concentration. Vinegar and vitamin C form acid solutions that have small amounts of hydronium ion in solution. We say that these solutions are weak. However, the liquid in a car battery has large concentrations of hydronium ion. We say that this acid solution is strong.

Acid solutions with high concentrations of hydronium ion react vigorously with certain metals and can chemically "burn" your skin. Acids with low concentrations react slowly with these metals and some are even safe enough to eat or drink! Can you think of a way of measuring the strength or concentration of acid solutions?

Strength of Bases

Just like acids, bases form ions in water:

$$\text{Sodium hydroxide} \rightarrow \text{Sodium ion} + \text{Hydroxide ion}$$
$$NaOH \rightarrow Na^+ + OH^-$$
$$\text{Ammonium hydroxide} \rightarrow \text{Ammonium ion} + \text{Hydroxide ion}$$
$$NH_4OH \rightarrow NH_4^+ + OH^-$$

Since ions are formed, bases are electrolytes. We can also categorize basic solutions as strong or weak electrolytes depending on how concentrated the ions are.

Notice that both bases release hydroxide ions, OH^-, when they dissolve. The behaviour of a base depends on its hydroxide ion concentration. Concentrated bases are dangerous whereas dilute bases are not. How would you define the term "base"? Can you think of a way to measure the concentration of a base?

Fig. 19-17 A neutralization reaction is used to "perm" hair. A base is used to soften the hair. The base is neutralized with an acid and the hair stiffens into its new curled shape. What are the names of these chemicals? How strong are they? You could measure this strength in Activity 19.6.

Neutralization

What happens when an acid and base are mixed together? The hydronium ions react with the hydroxide ions to make water:

$$\text{Hydronium ion} + \text{Hydroxide ion} \rightarrow \text{2 molecules of water}$$
$$H_30^+ + OH^- \rightarrow 2H_20$$

This reaction is called **neutralization**. After neutralization, the solution no longer has high concentrations of either ion (Fig. 19-17). Thus, it no longer has acidic or basic properties. Such solutions are said to be **neutral**. Is tap water neutral? How could you find out?

The pH Scale

So far, we have explained the strength of an acid or base in terms of ion concentrations. We have used qualitative terms like "concentrated", "dilute", "mild", "strong", and "weak". To improve accuracy we prefer to use quantitative terms. Instead of descriptive terms which could be misinterpreted, we use a number scale called the **pH scale** (Fig. 19-18). The pH scale runs from 0 to 14. For acids, pH < 7. For bases, pH > 7. For neutral substances, pH $= 7$.

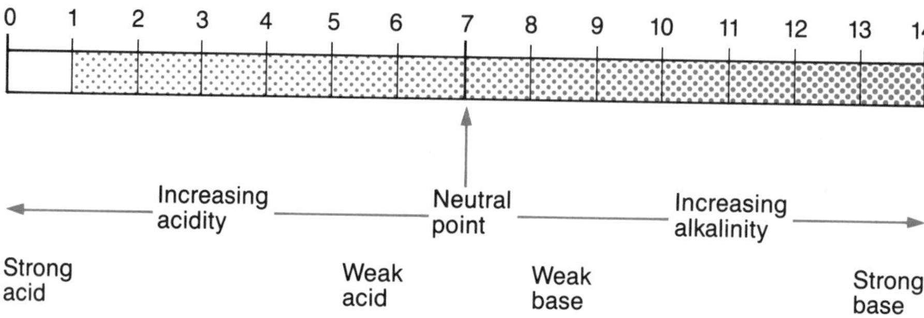

Fig. 19-18 As the pH increases from 0 to 7, the acidity decreases and, as the pH increases from 7 to 14, the basicity (alkalinity) increases.

A change of one pH unit represents a *ten-fold change* in the concentration of hydronium and hydroxide ions. Thus pH 2 is ten times as acidic as pH 3, one hundred times as acidic as pH 4, one thousand times as acidic as pH 5, and so on. Similarly, pH 13 is ten times as basic as pH 12 and so on.

Section Review

1. a) What is ionization?
   b) Write two equations (one for an acid and one for a base) that show ionization.
   c) Identify six ions.
   d) What do all ions have in common?
2. a) What is an electrolyte?
   b) What is the difference between a strong and a weak electrolyte?
3. Which ion is responsible for the properties of acids? of bases?
4. What happens to hydronium and hydroxide ion concentrations when acids and bases are combined? Why?
5. a) What is the pH range of an acid? of a base?
   b) Which is more acidic: pH 3 or pH 5? pH 6 or pH 8?
   c) Which is more basic: pH 14 or pH 7?
6. a) How many times more acidic is pH 1 compared to pH 5? pH 0 compared to pH 6?
   b) How many times more basic is pH 12 compared to pH 7? pH 14 compared to pH 8?

19.7 Activity: Finding the pH with Indicators

In order to find the pH of a solution, you need something which can "indicate" not only whether a solution is acidic or basic, but also how acidic or basic it is. Each indicator you have used so far changes colour at one pH value (Fig. 19-19). A **universal indicator** is a mixture of indicators which gives a series of colour changes over the entire pH range from 0 to 14. This indicator can be used to estimate the pH of any solution by the colour it becomes (Fig. 19-20).

Indicator	Colour of indicator at different pH values	Colour change
Litmus	Red (0–7) / Blue (7–14)	Red↔blue at pH = 7
Methyl orange	Red (0–3.4) / Yellow (3.4–14)	Red↔yellow at pH = 3.4
Phenolphthalein	Colourless (0–9.8) / Pink (9.8–14)	Colourless↔pink at pH = 9.8

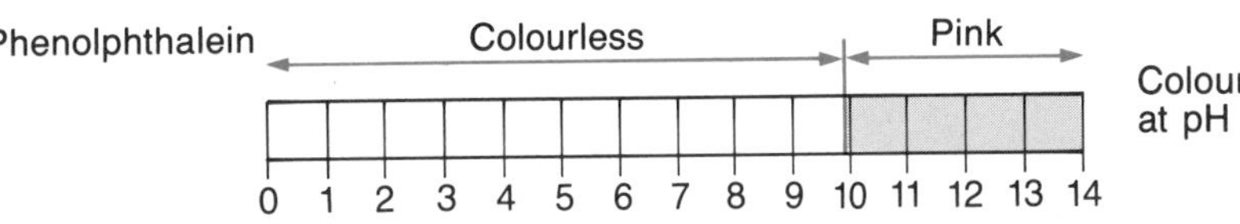

Fig. 19-19 How indicators change colour with pH

In this activity you will use universal pH indicator paper to find the pH of some common household substances.

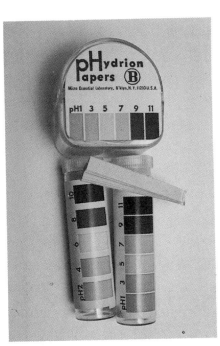

Fig. 19-20 Universal indicator paper and its colour key

Problem

What are the pH values of some common household substances?

Materials

glass stirring rod
test tubes (5)
distilled water
universal indicator paper
lemon juice
orange juice
fruit drinks
vinegar
soft drinks
tomato juice
milk
washing soda
baking soda
window cleaner
drain cleaner
toothpaste
salt
sugar
milk of magnesia
antacid tablets
detergent

Procedure

a. Obtain samples of each of the substances in the list above, one at a time, in a clean test tube.
b. If the sample is a solid, add 5 mL of distilled water and shake to mix. If the sample is a liquid, test it directly.
c. With a clean dry glass rod, transfer a few drops of the first sample to a small piece of universal indicator paper. Wait for 10–20 s. Compare the colour of the universal indicator paper with the colours of the ''key'' on the indicator's box. Estimate and record the pH of the substance tested.
d. Repeat step (c) for each of the other substances.

Discussion

1. Make a large pH chart like the one in Figure 19-18. Along it, write the name of each substance tested with an arrow pointing to its pH.

19.8 Activity: Testing Antacid Tablets

You are probably familiar with television advertising for antacids. These products are used to cure or neutralize ''excess'' stomach acid. They are available in tablet, powder, and liquid forms (Fig. 19-21).

How do antacids work? The fluid in your stomach contains hydrochloric acid. Its pH is between 1 and 3. Too much acidity, however, causes indigestion. Antacids contain bases such as magnesium carbonate and calcium carbonate which, when swallowed, react with hydrochloric acid in the stomach. The reaction is represented by the following equation:

Magnesium carbonate + Hydrochloric acid →
Magnesium chloride + Carbon dioxide + water

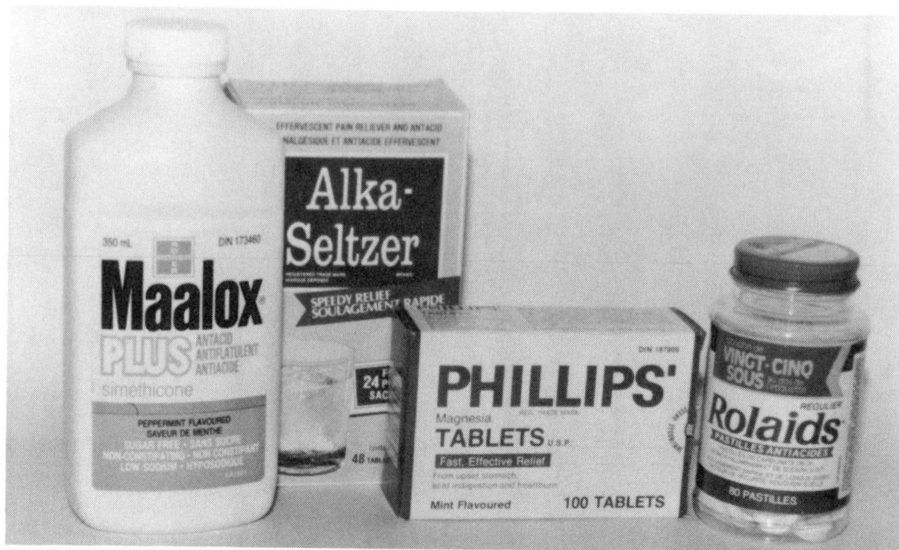

Fig. 19-21 Commercial antacids. Which brand is most effective? How can you find out?

The elimination of excess acid and the familiar burp caused by carbon dioxide gas escaping from the stomach provide some relief.

In this activity you will use the standard procedure for determining the ''acid consuming capacity'' of antacids. Since the normal pH of the stomach is around 3, you will measure the ability of the antacid to bring the pH of an acidic medium to 3. Methyl orange changes colour from red to yellow at a pH value of about 3. Therefore it will be used as the indicator. You will dissolve the antacid in hydrochloric acid. Some of this acid will be neutralized by the antacid and some will remain. The more effective the antacid is, the less acid will remain. The effectiveness of the antacid is measured by the volume of sodium hydroxide solution required to bring the pH of the mixture to 3.

Problem

Which brand of antacid is most effective?

Materials

balance
250 mL Erlenmeyer flask
100 mL graduated cylinder
methyl orange indicator in dropper bottle
hydrochloric acid (0.2 M)
sodium hydroxide solution (0.2 M)
dropper (calibrated in millilitres)
several brands of antacids

CAUTION: Wear safety goggles during this activity. Handle acids and bases with care. Flush immediately with water and call your teacher if you get them on your skin or clothing.

Procedure

a. Obtain one of the antacid tablets. Find its mass. Crush it to a powder. If the antacid is a powder or liquid, find the mass of the recommended dose.

b. Place the antacid sample in a 250 mL Erlenmeyer flask. Add 50 mL of hydrochloric acid and shake until the antacid dissolves as much as possible.

c. Add 5 or 6 drops of methyl orange to the mixture. If the mixture is not red, add more acid until it turns red, keeping track of the volume added. Record the *total* volume of the acid used.

d. Using the dropper, add sodium hydroxide solution one millilitre at a time, swirling constantly. Continue to add the base until the colour changes from red to yellow. Record the volume of base used.

e. Share your results with those of other groups in your class that used different brands of antacid.

Discussion

1. Calculate the acid consuming capacity (ACC) of the antacid as follows: ACC = Volume of hydrochloric acid used − volume of sodium hydroxide solution used.
2. Which antacid is most effective, based on the ACC values?

Extension

Collect and evaluate an advertisement for an antacid. What do the words really mean? Can they be proven experimentally?

19.9 Uses and Abuses of Acids and Bases

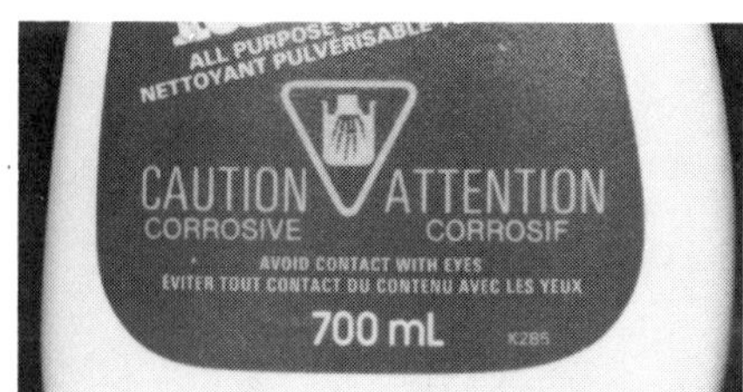

Fig. 19-22 Many household products contain acids and bases. The corrosive nature of these substances means that they must be handled with care.

Acids and bases are important substances in everyday life. The properties and chemical reactions of these two groups of compounds make them very useful around the home (Fig. 19-22).

Acids

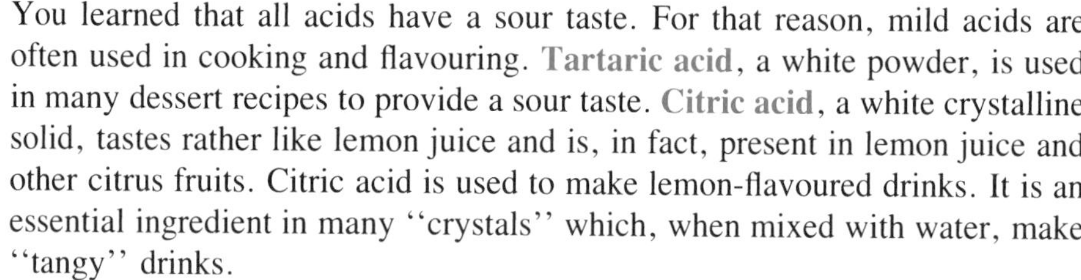

You learned that all acids have a sour taste. For that reason, mild acids are often used in cooking and flavouring. **Tartaric acid**, a white powder, is used in many dessert recipes to provide a sour taste. **Citric acid**, a white crystalline solid, tastes rather like lemon juice and is, in fact, present in lemon juice and other citrus fruits. Citric acid is used to make lemon-flavoured drinks. It is an essential ingredient in many ''crystals'' which, when mixed with water, make ''tangy'' drinks.

Vinegar is widely used in cooking and in salad dressings. Vinegar is a dilute solution of **acetic acid**.

Carbon dioxide dissolves in water to form . A concentrated solution of carbon dioxide is made when this gas is dissolved in water under pressure. The result is **soda water**. ''Fizzy'' drinks like cola and other carbonated soft drinks are made fizzy by having carbon dioxide dissolved under pressure. The tangy taste is due to the presence of carbonic acid. Concentrated sulfuric acid solution is a strong electrolyte. It is the acid used in automobile batteries (Fig. 19-23). Sulfuric acid is the top commercial chemical produced in Canada.

Many acids are used for medical purposes. **Boric acid** is an effective antiseptic used by veterinarians as an eye and ear wash. **Acetylsalicylic acid (ASA)** is commonly known as aspirin. ASA helps lower fevers, relieves headaches and cold symptoms, and eases the pain of arthritis. **Ascorbic acid** is vitamin C. What other household acids have you discovered?

Acid Rain

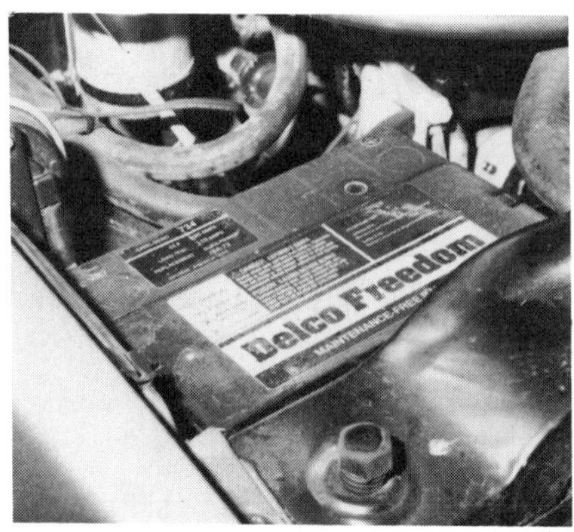

Fig. 19-23 Sulfuric acid is used in automobile batteries.

Sulfuric acid is not only our most valuable industrial chemical, but it also contributes to Canada's top environmental problem—**acid rain**. Through a series of complex chemical reactions, waste gases from smelters, refineries, furnaces, coal-fired generators, incinerators, and automobiles react to make acids. These come down to earth as an acidic solution. The damage is enormous. Steel and limestone structures corrode. Entire lakes become lifeless. The chemistry of soil and water is altered. The total damage amounts to billions of dollars per year.

The pH of "clean" rain is 5.6. Often, however, rain has a pH of 2 or 3 units lower than this. That is, it is an acid that is one hundred to one thousand times as concentrated! What is the pH of rainfall in your area? Where does the acid come from?

Fig. 19-24 Some drain cleaners consist of crystals which contain flakes of aluminum and sodium hydroxide.

Bases

You learned that sodium hydroxide is called caustic soda. This is because it causes chemical burns and destroys many substances. It is these caustic properties that make sodium hydroxide a component of many common household products. Drano® is a commercial **drain cleaner** (Fig. 19-24). It is a mixture of sodium hydroxide and flakes of aluminum. How does sodium hydroxide open your clogged drain? The most common substances that clog drains are fats in the kitchen and hair in the bath or shower. Sodium hydroxide reacts with fats to form soap, which is soluble in water. Aluminum flakes are added to sodium hydroxide in Drano® because aluminum reacts with sodium hydroxide in the presence of water. The reaction produces heat and hydrogen gas. The heat speeds up the reaction between the sodium hydroxide and fats. The hydrogen gas agitates the liquid to break up the clog. As soon as the material in the drain becomes loose, it passes through the pipe as water is flushed down the drain. Hair is made of proteins. Sodium hydroxide reacts with proteins, too. The reaction loosens the clog in the drain and eventually the loosened material passes through the drain as water is flushed down the drain.

Antacid remedies contain insoluble bases, such as calcium carbonate, magnesium carbonate, and magnesium oxide. The use of insoluble bases for that purpose reduces the possibility of the antacid being absorbed into the blood stream, which would produce excess base in the blood.

Ammonia solution, a weak base, is a component of many commercial **window cleaners**.

Fig. 19-25 Baking powder makes baked goods "rise". What chemical reaction causes this?

Section Review

1. a) Name three acids which are used in cooking and flavouring.
   b) Name three acids which are used for medical purposes. Explain their effects.
2. What are the main ingredients in drain cleaners? Explain how drain cleaners open a clogged drain.
3. Why are insoluble bases used in antacids rather than soluble bases?
4. What is the pH of "clean" rain? of acid rain?

Extensions

1. Oven cleaners contain bases. Find out what base is in an oven cleaner and why that base was used.
2. Baking powder contains a dry powdered acid and a dry powdered base called baking soda or sodium hydrogen carbonate, $NaHCO_3$ (Fig. 19-25). They do not neutralize each other until moistened. Write a report explaining why this neutralization is important in baking. Your family studies teacher might be able to help. What gas is produced during neutralization?

Chapter Highlights

1. Acid solutions taste sour, change the colour of litmus to red, conduct electricity, react with carbonates, and react with some metals to liberate hydrogen gas.
2. Basic solutions taste bitter, change the colour of litmus to blue, conduct electricity, feel slippery, and neutralize acid solutions.
3. Indicators are coloured dyes that change colour when the pH is changed.
4. Electrolytes are substances that form ions in water solutions.
5. All acids release hydronium ions in water and their common properties are due to the presence of these ions in their solutions.
6. All bases produce hydroxide ions in water and their common properties are due to the presence of hydroxide ions in their solutions.
7. The pH scale is a special scale of numbers from 0 to 14, which indicates the concentration of hydronium and hydroxide ions.
8. Acids and bases have many applications around the home and in industry.
9. Acid rain is Canada's top environmental problem.

Key Terms

acid
acid rain
antacid
base
electrolyte
hydronium ions
hydroxide ions
indicators
ionization
ions
neutralization
pH scale

Recognizing the Concepts

Each of the following statements or questions is followed by four responses. Choose the correct response in each case. (Do not write in this book.)

1. Solutions of strong acids:
   a) are good conductors of electricity
   b) turn litmus blue
   c) have a pH of 7
   d) feel slippery
2. The pH value of distilled water is:
   a) 4 **b)** 7 **c)** 9 **d)** 12
3. An example of an acid used for medical purposes is:
   a) tartaric acid
   b) sulfuric acid
   c) acetylsalicylic acid
   d) hydrochloric acid
4. Which of the following is a base that is a component of many window cleaners?
   a) vinegar
   b) ammonia solution
   c) caustic soda
   d) sodium hydrogen carbonate
5. Basic solutions:
   a) have pH values less than 7
   b) taste bitter
   c) release hydronium ions in water
   d) turn litmus red

Understanding the Concepts

1. In parallel columns, list the characteristic properties of acids and bases.
2. What gases are produced when an acid reacts with a reactive metal and with sodium carbonate?
3. Why is a vinegar solution at pH 6 not as good a conductor of electricity as vinegar solution at pH 4?
4. Explain the operation of antacids using all of the following terms: acid, base, neutralization, pH.
5. Explain why concentrated bases make good cleaners, particularly when the dirt contains oily materials.

Applying the Concepts

Fig. 19-26 Michelangelo's statue of David was carved from a 4 m tall block of marble (calcium carbonate). It stood outdoors for centuries but is now housed inside. Can you explain why?

1. If concentrated acid is spilled on the floor of your lab, what substance would you add to the spill before you started to clean it up? Why?
2. Valuable marble statues like the one in Figure 19-26 are no longer kept outdoors. Explain why they were safe for centuries outdoors but are not today.
3. Describe a qualitative test that can be used to determine whether:
   a) a substance is an electrolyte or a non-electrolyte
   b) a substance is an acid or a base
   c) an acid is strong or weak
4. What property must a substance have to be suitable for use as an indicator? Why?
5. What colours are produced in litmus, methyl orange, and phenolphthalein by:
   a) rain water whose pH is 6.2
   b) ammonia solution
   c) sugar solution
   d) vinegar
   e) carbonated soft drinks
   f) table salt solution
6. Some scientists have proposed adding marble chips or limestone (both are calcium carbonate) to lakes affected by acid rain. Explain how this could help the lakes.
7. Explain each of the following statements:
   a) Vinegar is an important component of most salad dressings.
   b) Drain cleaners contain a mixture of aluminum flakes and sodium hydroxide.
   c) Tea changes colour when lemon juice is added to it.
   d) Citrus fruits taste sour.
   e) Acid spills are treated with sodium hydrogen carbonate.
   f) Aspirin may upset the stomach.

Investigations

1. Write a research report on one or more aspects of acid rain. Topics could include:
   - sources of acid
   - weather patterns and delivery of acid deposition
   - the chemistry that turns waste gases into acids

Fig. 19-27 Test common drinks like orange juice, tomato juice, and apple juice. How will you test solids like salt and sugar?

- effects of acid rain on plants, northern lakes, soil, and animals
- why acid rain is a political problem

2. Find out from your resource centre what a scrubber is. How might scrubbers help our acid rain problem? Why are scrubbers not being used more frequently?
3. Get some universal indicator paper from your teacher. Then find the pH of each of the foods you eat during one day (Fig. 19-27).
4. Write a research report on one of the following:
   a) the use of acids in fertilizers
   b) the use of nitric acid in the making of explosives
   c) the use of acids in car batteries
   d) the use of bases in the textile industry
5. Find out what chemicals are used in swimming pools and how the concentrations of these chemicals are monitored and controlled. What role does pH play in the water quality of a pool? What happens if the pH is not correct?
6. Build a simple conductivity tester, using a flashlight bulb and two 1.5 volt cells. Use it to test for electrolytes found in your home.
7. Find out how electrical conduction in solutions differs from electrical conduction in metals. Write a report on your findings.

Career: *ENVIRONMENTAL CHEMIST*

HELP WANTED: ENVIRONMENTAL CHEMIST

The Ministry of the Environment requires an environmental chemist to collect and analyze soil, water, and air samples from industrial waste sites, and to prepare reports containing results of analysis.

A career in environmental chemistry is suitable for a person who is looking for a way to combine interest in chemistry and the environment with service to the public. Further, this person should be prepared to travel to the waste sites of different manufacturing facilities to search for toxic materials that may be present in the wastes. Environmental chemists put on protective clothing and use special breathing apparatus while investigating hazardous waste sites. They perform many laboratory tests on the samples collected from these sites using complex equipment. They also write reports containing the results of the analysis, conclusions, and their recommendations for action.

Preparation for a career in environmental chemistry begins in secondary school. You should graduate with good marks in the sciences, calculus, and English. At university, you may obtain your Bachelor of Science (B.Sc.) in chemistry, taking courses in all branches of chemistry and additional courses in mathematics and physics. Job opportunities are very good. You could work for either private industries or for government agencies such as the Ontario Ministry of the Environment.

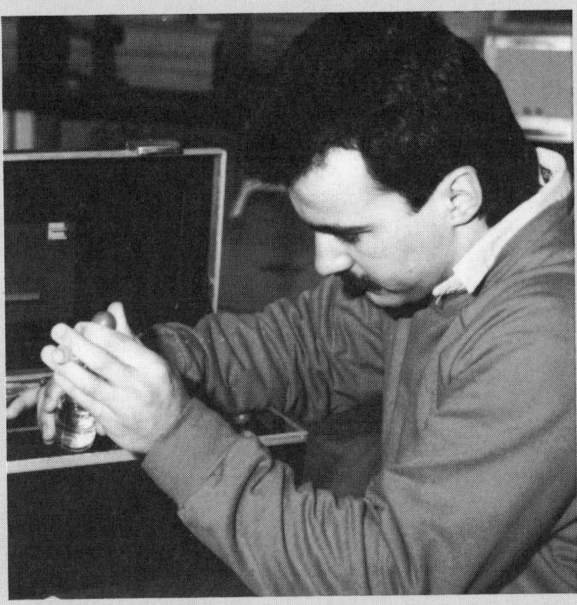

20 Chemistry at Home and at Play

CHAPTER CONTENTS

CHAPTER OBJECTIVES

After completing this chapter you should be able to:

1. Describe how chemistry affects most aspects of our lives.
2. Explain the causes of hardness in hard water.
3. Describe how to soften a sample of hard water.
4. Give examples of natural and synthetic dyes and describe how fabrics are dyed.

Many of the discoveries made by chemists have been put to practical use. For example, many of your activities have been made more pleasant by chemistry (Fig. 20-1). By the time you have finished this chapter, you will become familiar with some of the everyday applications of chemistry. You will study hard and soft water and observe their reactions with soap. You will investigate how hardness is removed from a sample of hard water. You will also study different types of dyes and find out how fabrics are dyed with each type.

Fig. 20-1 What role does chemistry play in the way you look? In what you do for entertainment?

Fig. 20-2 Do you read food labels? Do you pay attention to the expiry dates?

20.1 Living with Chemistry

Almost every activity in your life depends on chemistry. Your food is made of chemicals. So is your medication. The instruments you use at work or at play are products of a chemical age. But do you understand just how much we depend on this science?

Chemistry in Your Food

Everything you eat is made of chemicals (Fig. 20-2). You already know that food is made of chemical groups like proteins, vitamins, carbohydrates, and lipids. From the last chapter, you also know that some food contains acids and bases. But food also contains additives which improve its taste, colour, odour, texture, and nutrient value, or make it last longer.

Esters are compounds that give particular flavours and odours to fruit. Food chemists have learned to synthesize many of these compounds for addition to other foods as flavouring agents. In Section 20.2, you will make some of these esters. Can you recognize the foods that they are in by their smell?

Chemistry in Medicine

Where would you be without medicine? Antibiotics and vaccines have kept many of you alive by preventing infectious diseases.

The first medicines (or pharmaceuticals) came from plants. Acetylsalicylic acid (ASA or aspirin) was chemically extracted from willow trees. The heart drug digoxin is still extracted from foxglove plants. Animals and bacteria have been used to make hormones (insulin and growth hormone) and vaccines.

Chemists attempt to synthesize (artificially produce) medicines in order to make them purer and cheaper. We no longer rely on trees for ASA. But we do rely on natural sources for a host of other medicines that defy our attempts at synthesis. Even with the thousands of pharmaceuticals in use, we know that there are many more waiting to be discovered, purified, tested, and marketed. Perhaps your career will be in the huge pharmaceutical industry.

Chemistry in Baking

Have you ever wondered why baking powder is added to the batter of muffins or cake? This is an application of acid-base chemistry. Baking powder is a mixture of three compounds:

- sodium hydrogen carbonate—a base
- tartaric acid—an acid
- corn starch—an agent that keeps the others dry

When baking powder contacts water in the batter, the acid and the base react. In doing so, carbon dioxide gas is released, creating tiny bubbles all through the batter (Fig. 20-3). This puffs up (leavens) the batter. Heating cooks and solidifies the batter so that it stays in the risen position.

Sodium hydrogen carbonate, or baking soda, can also be used alone. It decomposes into carbon dioxide gas when heated. Thus, the batter rises during baking.

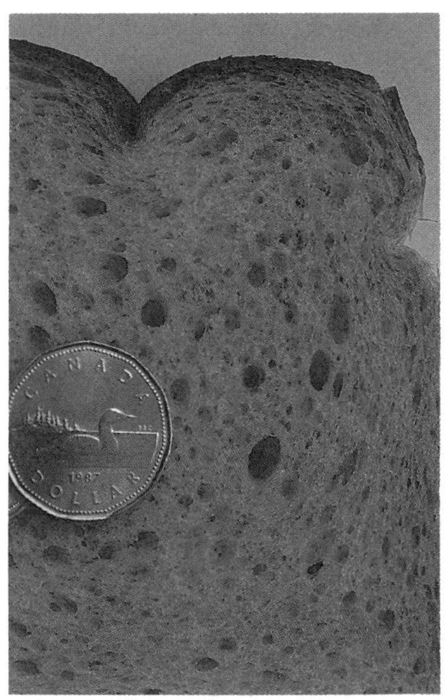
Fig. 20-3 The bubbles created by carbon dioxide become the pores in baked goods.

In Section 20.3 you will carry out a controlled experiment to confirm the effectiveness of baking powder and of baking soda in making batter rise.

Chemistry in Oven Cleaning

Kitchen ovens are often used to roast pork, beef, and poultry. The process involves melting the fats in the meat. This is usually accompanied by splattering and dripping of fats inside the oven. As the oven cools, the fats solidify. With time, layers of fats build up on the ceiling, walls, and floor of the oven. It is very difficult to remove this fatty deposit from the inside of the oven. **Oven cleaners** make this task easier. The main ingredient in oven cleaners is sodium hydroxide. Sodium hydroxide reacts with fats to produce soap (see Section 21.3, page 516). Soap is soluble in water. Therefore, when the oven cleaner is applied to the oven, it slowly reacts with the fat deposit. The deposit loosens and can be wiped off with a damp cloth. Because the reaction is slow, it is usually suggested that the cleaner be applied and left overnight before you attempt to remove the grime. The reaction between sodium hydroxide and fats proceeds faster at a high temperature. This explains why the instructions with oven cleaners suggest that the cleaner will work better if applied to a warm oven.

Chemistry in Photography

Fig. 20-4 How is chemistry used here?

Do you watch television? Do you take pictures with a camera or video recorder (Fig. 20-4)? If you do any of these things, you are using the products of chemistry. The lining of a colour television's picture tube is a marvel of chemical engineering. The back of the screen is printed with rows of three kinds of phosphorescent dots—one for each primary colour. When a beam of electrons hits the dots, they glow. When many dots glow, you see a coloured spot on the screen. The chemical makeup of these dots makes a fascinating research report.

Cameras use film chemistry to permanently record what they ''see''. Film is a solid suspension of various silver compounds which are all sensitive to light. Film developing also involves chemistry. Again, detailing these processes makes for an excellent research report.

Video recorders use videotape. Videotape is also a solid suspension of chemicals. Which chemicals are used? How is information stored? Why can videotape be erased and used again whereas film cannot? Your teacher-librarian or your chemistry teacher may be able to help you find the answers to these questions.

Chemistry in Sport

What hockey player or skier could do well without chemistry (Fig. 20-5)? In every sport, top performances are aided by products that are the result of advanced chemical engineering. For instance, fabric makers design artificial cloth that reduces friction for skiers, skaters, bicyclists, and swimmers. And plastic is better than leather for boots and helmets. Colourful synthetic fabrics are usually less expensive than natural products and far more durable. What would happen to football uniforms if they were not synthetic? How much would all that equipment weigh if it were not made of plastic?

Fig. 20-5 What chemical products do you see here? How do these help the athlete perform better?

What sports do you and your family play? What chemical products do you use in these sports?

Section Review

1. What is an ester?
2. Why do we want to make esters and medicines synthetically?
3. a) Explain how baking soda makes batter rise.
   b) Why do the acid and base in baking powder *not* neutralize each other in the package?
4. Where is chemistry involved in cameras? in video recorders?
5. Identify ten products used in sports that are the products of chemistry.
6. a) What is the main ingredient in oven cleaners?
   b) How does an oven cleaner work?
   c) Why do oven cleaners work better if applied to a warm oven?

20.2 Demonstration: Making Food Additives

The pleasant odours and flavours of fruits are due to a group of chemical compounds known as **esters.** Esters are made naturally by certain plants. Food chemists synthesize these esters and use them as flavouring additives in the preparation of many foods such as ice cream, candy, and syrup. An ester is produced when an organic acid reacts with an alcohol. Because some of the reactants are hazardous, your teacher will demonstrate this activity.

Problem

Can you recognize the odours of esters?

Materials

test tubes (3)
test tube rack
marking pen or pencil
balance
10 mL graduated cylinder
250 mL beaker
hot plate
dropper
masking tape
concentrated sulfuric acid
methanol
ethanol
salicylic acid
benzoic acid
concentrated acetic acid

CAUTION: *Wear safety goggles, gloves, and aprons. If you spill acid on your skin or clothing, flush with water. Methanol and ethanol are flammable and poisonous. Concentrated acetic acid has a strong odour. Salicylic acid may irritate the skin. Do these reactions in a well-ventilated area.*

Procedure

a. Label three test tubes 1 to 3. Place the test tubes in the test tube rack.

b. Into the appropriate test tube, pour the amount of an alcohol and acid as indicated in the table below. (Use the balance to measure the solid salicylic acid and benzoic acid.)

Test tube	Alcohol	Organic acid
1	1 mL ethanol	1 mL acetic acid
2	1 mL methanol	1 g salicylic acid
3	1 mL methanol	3 g benzoic acid

c. Add 4 drops of concentrated sulfuric acid to each test tube.

d. Half fill a 250 mL beaker with water. Heat the water on a hot plate to a temperature of 60°C.

e. Place the test tubes in the hot water bath for 15 min.

f. Allow the test tubes to cool and then add 5 mL of water to each test tube.

g. Carefully note the odour of the contents of the test tubes.

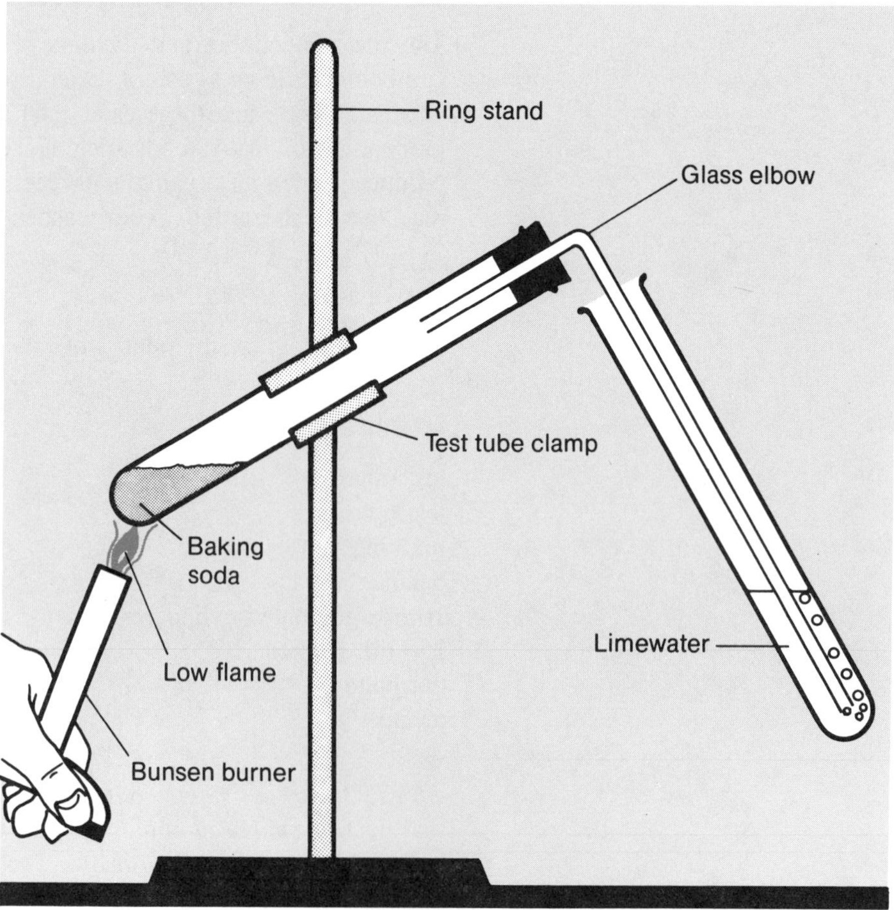

Fig. 20-6 Heating baking soda

CAUTION: Hold the test tube 20 cm away and 10 cm below your nose. Waft the odour toward your nose, sniffing cautiously once or twice.

Discussion

1. What odours can you identify?
2. What familiar products contain these odours?
3. Why would these odours be added to such products?

Extension

Try other combinations of organic acids and alcohols. What odours are produced?

20.3 Activity: Investigating the Chemical Reactions in Baking

In Section 20.1 you read about the roles of baking powder and baking soda in cake and bread making. In this activity you will explore the chemistry behind these baking ingredients.

Problem

What chemical changes take place when baking powder and baking soda are used?

Materials

sodium hydrogen carbonate
baking powder
ring stand
test tube clamp
limewater
vinegar
Bunsen burner
test tubes (4)
test tube rack
delivery tube assembly
250 mL beaker
hot plate (one or two per class)

CAUTION: Wear safety goggles during this activity.

Procedure

a. Place about 2 mL of baking soda (sodium hydrogen carbonate) in a test tube.

b. Clamp the test tube in the ring stand. Then connect the delivery tube assembly so that it leads into another test tube containing limewater as shown in Figure 20-6.

c. Heat the baking soda gently for about 3 min. When no further changes occur, remove the test tube with the limewater. Then stop heating the baking soda. Record your observations.
CAUTION: The limewater will back up into the baking soda if you stop heating before you remove the limewater.

d. Place 2 mL of sodium hydrogen carbonate in a test tube. Add 10 mL of vinegar. *Quickly* connect the delivery tube assembly so that it leads into another test tube containing limewater as you did in step (c). Record your observations.

e. Dissolve 10 mL of baking powder in 50 mL of water. Record your observations.

Discussion

1. What gas is given off when solid sodium hydrogen carbonate is heated? How do you know?
2. What gas is given off when sodium hydrogen carbonate is mixed with an acid such as vinegar? How do you know?
3. What happens when water is added to baking powder? What does that tell you about the composition of baking powder?
4. Write a chemical equation to describe the formation of carbon dioxide from baking powder.
5. Explain the role of baking soda and baking powder in cake and bread making.

20.4 Hard and Soft Water

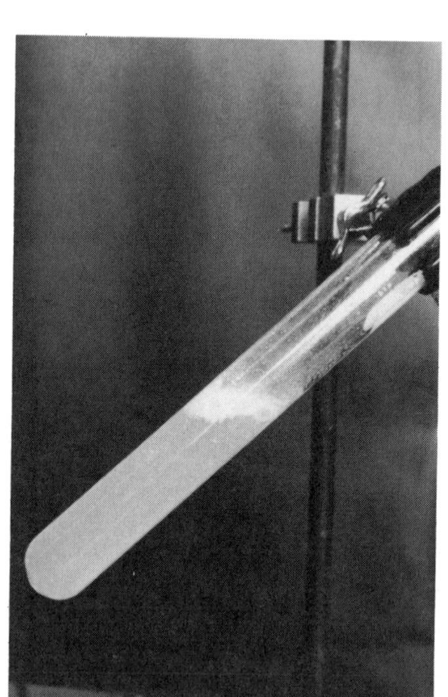

Fig. 20-7 Soap reacts with dissolved substances in hard water to produce an insoluble scum.

If you have ever used soap, not synthetic detergents, for a bath, you have likely seen the scum that deposits on the bathtub. The amount of scum does not depend on the amount of dirt which has been washed off. Instead, it depends on the nature of the water and, as a result, varies from place to place. Where a lot of scum is produced by the soap, the water is said to be **hard**. Where little or none is produced, the water is called **soft**. The scum, sometimes known as **soap curds**, only appears when soap is used. It does not appear with **detergents**. It is actually the product of a chemical reaction between the soap and some dissolved substances in water (Fig. 20-7).

Causes and Sources of Hardness in Water

Some hard waters become soft after being boiled. Other hard waters are unaffected by boiling. Hardness which can be removed by boiling is called **porary hardness**. Hardness which cannot be removed by boiling is called **permanent hardness**.

Hardness is caused by the presence of dissolved calcium and magnesium ions in water. The most important sources of these ions in hard water are calcium hydrogen carbonate, which causes temporary hardness, and calcium sulfate, which causes permanent hardness. Calcium hydrogen carbonate is present because rain water, which contains dissolved carbon dioxide, reacts with limestone in the ground. The reaction produces a dilute solution of calcium hydrogen carbonate. Limestone occurs in large quantities in some soils and in small quantities in practically all soils. Calcium sulfate is present because many rocks and soils contain gypsum (calcium sulfate) which is slightly soluble in water. Some of it dissolves in any water with which it comes in contact.

Disadvantages of Hard Water

Wastage of Soap Soap reacts with calcium and magnesium ions in hard water, producing an insoluble precipitate or scum. This scum clings to sinks, bathtubs, and even to you! When you wash in hard water, a large amount of the soap is used up just to precipitate and remove the calcium and magnesium ions. Only a small extra amount causes the lather (Fig. 20-8). When you wash clothes, further trouble is caused by the scum. If any of it is left stuck to the clothes, discolouration and damage may result.

Scale Formation When calcium hydrogen carbonate is heated, it decomposes into carbon dioxide gas and calcium carbonate:

$$\underset{\text{(soluble)}}{\text{Calcium hydrogen carbonate}} \xrightarrow{\text{heat}} \underset{\text{(insoluble)}}{\text{Calcium carbonate}} + \underset{\text{(gas)}}{\text{Carbon dioxide}} + \text{Water}$$

Calcium carbonate is insoluble. As a result, it deposits in kettles, in pipes, and on the heating elements of electric kettles (Fig. 20-9). The buildup of scale wastes energy and results in loss of efficiency. More energy is needed to heat up the water because of the poor heat conductivity of the layer of scale. **Descaling** should be carried out periodically. This can be done by putting vinegar inside the kettle for several hours.

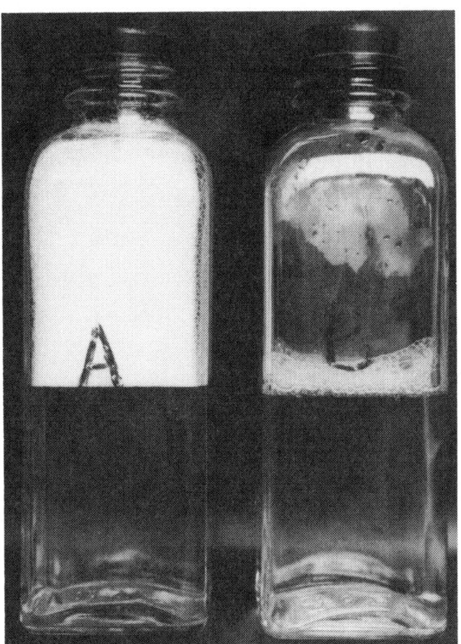

Fig. 20-8 Equal amounts of soap were added to the soft water (A) and to the hard water (B).

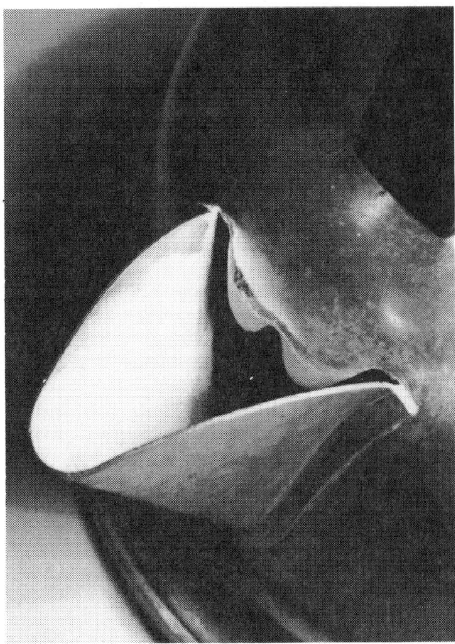

Fig. 20-9 Scale which is deposited on the inside of electric kettles causes wastage of energy. Why is this so?

Hard water has some advantages. First, the calcium and magnesium ions in hard water are essential nutrients for all living things. For example, the magnesium atom is a crucial part of chlorophyll molecules found in all green plants. As a result, hard water tends to have a higher **productivity** (ability to support life) than soft water. Second, people who drink hard water over a long period of time have a lower incidence of cardiovascular diseases (heart attacks and strokes) than people who drink soft water. A third advantage of hard water is that it is more tasteful to drink than soft water.

Section Review

1. **a)** Explain the term ''hard water''.
   b) Define the terms ''temporary hardness'' and ''permanent hardness''.
   c) What is the main chemical that causes temporary hardness in natural water? Explain how it gets there.
   d) Name the chemical that causes permanent hardness in water. Explain how it gets there.
2. Explain how hard water wastes soap and makes cleaning difficult.
3. What is ''scale''? How is it formed in kettles?
4. What are three advantages of hard water?

20.5 The Softening of Hard Water

Hard water wastes soap and energy. As a result, many methods have been developed to soften water. Let us take a look at four of these.

Boiling

Water that has temporary hardness may be softened by heating it to the boiling point. Boiling changes calcium hydrogen carbonate (the temporary hardness) into insoluble calcium carbonate. This material settles or precipitates out. (See page 495 for the equation.) As a result, the calcium ions are no longer in the solution and the water is softer. However, this is an expensive method for normal everyday purposes. Also, it does not soften the water completely because the permanent hardness still remains.

Precipitation Methods

The unwanted calcium and magnesium ions in hard water can be precipitated as insoluble compounds by the addition of other chemicals. A common softening agent used on a household scale is **washing soda** (Fig. 20-10). Washing soda (sodium carbonate) precipitates the soluble calcium and magnesium salts from the water. For example:

$$\underset{\text{(soluble)}}{\text{Calcium sulfate}} + \underset{\text{(soluble)}}{\text{Sodium carbonate}} \rightarrow$$

$$\underset{\text{(insoluble)}}{\text{Calcium carbonate}} + \underset{\text{(soluble)}}{\text{Sodium sulfate}}$$

Since soaps are compounds of sodium, the presence of other compounds of sodium in the water does not interfere with their action. **Bath salts** are often coloured and perfumed crystals of washing soda.

Fig. 20-10 Common softening agents often contain sodium carbonate. How does this soften water?

Another softening agent is **slaked lime**, calcium hydroxide. The addition of slaked lime to water removes all the temporary hardness. It also converts the calcium hydrogen carbonate to insoluble calcium carbonate:

$$\underset{\text{(soluble)}}{\text{Calcium hydrogen carbonate}} + \underset{\text{(soluble)}}{\text{Calcium hydroxide}} \rightarrow \underset{\text{(insoluble)}}{\text{Calcium carbonate}} + \text{Water}$$

Slaked lime is less expensive than washing soda. As a result, it is usually used in industry for softening large quantities of water.

The Ion Exchange Process

Some natural minerals, known as **zeolites**, contain sodium silico-aluminate. When hard water comes in contact with zeolites, the zeolites exchange their sodium ions for the calcium or magnesium ions of the hard water. As a result, the water is softened.

$$\text{Sodium silico-aluminate} + \text{Calcium ions} \rightarrow \text{Calcium silico-aluminate} + \text{Sodium ions}$$

The reaction can be reversed by adding a concentrated solution of sodium chloride (common salt) to the calcium silico-aluminate. The zeolite is thus regenerated and can be used over and over again.

Permutit, sodium aluminum silicate, is an artificial zeolite. It acts more rapidly than natural zeolite. In operation, a tank partly filled with permutit is connected to the water supply as shown in Figure 20-11. As the water flows through the tank, it is softened while the sodium permutit changes to calcium permutit. The permutit is renewed periodically by shutting off the water, draining the tank, and allowing a concentrated solution of common salt to stand overnight in contact with the calcium permutit. The following reaction occurs:

Calcium permutit + Sodium chloride → Sodium permutit + Calcium chloride

The calcium chloride solution is drained off and discarded. After the permutit is rinsed, the unit is ready again for use.

Rather than boiling water or adding precipitators to it, chemistry labs often use an ion exchange column (Fig. 20-12). This device exchanges hydronium or sodium ions for calcium and magnesium ions as the water flows through it.

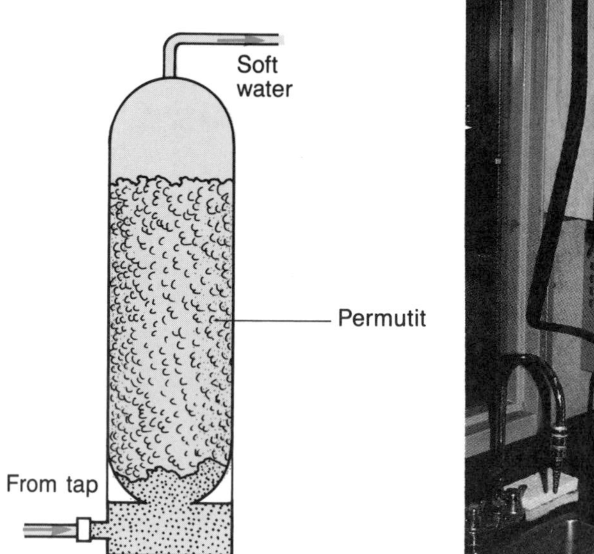

Fig. 20-11 Water softeners like this are widely used in homes. In hard water regions they are often a standard feature connected to the main water supply to every new home.

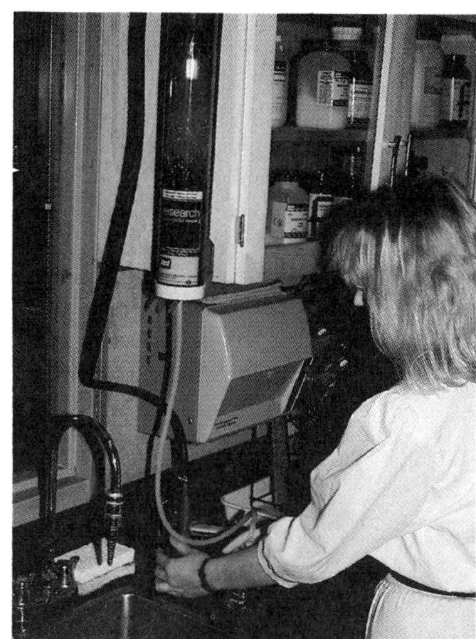

Fig. 20-12 Hardness is removed from tap water as it flows through this ion exchange column. The soft water coming out is essential for many experiments involving chemical reactions. A colour change in the column tells the user when to replace it. Does your lab use one of these?

Section Review

1. Explain why temporary hardness is removed by boiling.
2. Explain how permanent hardness is removed with washing soda.
3. Describe the ion exchange method of softening hard water.
4. a) How do zeolites soften water? Give a word equation for their reaction with calcium sulfate.
   b) How does permutit work?

20.6 Activity: Investigating Hard and Soft Water

Hardness is caused by the presence of calcium and magnesium ions in water. In this activity you will study the reaction of soap with hard water. You will also try different methods of removing temporary and permanent hardness from samples of hard water.

Problem

How does hard water react with soap? How can we remove hardness from hard water?

Materials

distilled water
tap water
calcium chloride solution
magnesium chloride solution
calcium bicarbonate solution
test tubes (5)
test tube rack
liquid soap
washing soda
test tube holder
Bunsen burner
dropper

CAUTION: Wear safety goggles during this activity.

Procedure

a. Copy Table 20-1 into your notebook. Record all your results in it.

Table 20-1 Investigating Hard and Soft Water

	Untreated		*Boiled*		*Washing soda added*	
	Drops of soap	*Observation*	*Drops of soap*	*Observation*	*Drops of soap*	*Observation*
Distilled water						
Tap water						
Calcium chloride solution						
Magnesium chloride solution						
Calcium hydrogen carbonate solution						

b. Add 2 drops of liquid soap to 10 mL of distilled water in a test tube. Shake the test tube. Continue to add liquid soap drop by drop, shaking after every 2 drops, until a 1 cm lather which lasts for 30 s is produced. Record the number of drops of liquid soap used. Also record any change in appearance.

c. Repeat step (b) using 10 mL of each of the following instead of the distilled water: tap water, calcium chloride solution, magnesium chloride solution, and calcium hydrogen carbonate solution.

Fig. 20-13 Hold the test tube at a safe angle. Move it continuously around in the flame. Why is this important?

d. Boil 10 mL of distilled water for 20 s as shown in Figure 20-13. Allow the water to cool to room temperature. Record any change in appearance. Then repeat step (b) using this water.

e. Repeat procedure (d) using 10 mL of each of the following instead of the distilled water: tap water, calcium chloride solution, magnesium chloride solution, and calcium hydrogen carbonate solution.

f. Add 5 mL of washing soda solution to 10 mL of distilled water. Shake the test tube to mix. Record any change in appearance. Then repeat step (b) using this water.

g. Repeat procedure (f) using 10 mL of each of the following instead of the distilled water: tap water, calcium chloride solution, magnesium chloride solution, and calcium hydrogen carbonate solution.

Discussion

1. In steps (b) and (c), which test tube produced lather most readily? Why?
2. How did the presence of calcium chloride in water affect its reaction with soap? What caused the precipitate to form?
3. How did the presence of magnesium chloride in water affect its reaction with soap? What caused the precipitate to form?
4. How did the presence of calcium hydrogen carbonate in water affect its reaction?
5. Is tap water in your school soft or hard? How did you know?
6. Why is hardness caused by calcium hydrogen carbonate called ''temporary'', while hardness caused by calcium chloride and magnesium chloride is called ''permanent''?
7. How does the boiling of temporary hard water remove the cause of hardness? Write a chemical equation for the reaction.
8. How does the addition of washing soda soften temporary and permanent hard water? Write chemical equations to explain your answer.

Extension

Suggest a procedure to test for the *amount* of hardness in water. Use your procedure to compare samples of natural water obtained from different sources.

20.7 Dyes and Dyeing

Why Do We Have Dyes?

The human species has a number of behaviours that are uncommon in the animal kingdom. Among these is the alteration of our natural appearance. For centuries, humans have painted or stained their faces, their hair, and even their entire bodies! Today, we spend countless millions of dollars annually to ''paint'' ourselves with cosmetics, and to dye our hair. Just why we alter our appearance is a complicated matter. Perhaps certain changes indicate status or perhaps they just satisfy some psychological urge for variety.

Fig. 20-14 Where do the colours in our clothes come from?

Ever since humans began wearing clothes, we have had the opportunity to enhance our "body decorating" skills even further. By owning different garments with a variety of patterns and colours, we can change our appearance quickly without the mess of "body paint" (Fig. 20-14). Of course, we must first have the skill to make coloured clothing, and that is where dyes enter the picture. Where would our multi-billion-dollar fashion industry be without these chemicals?

Dyes are different from other pigments such as the coloured molecules in paint. Most pigments do not cling to the object being coloured. Instead, pigments are suspended in a coat of oil or latex which clings to the object being painted. A dye must sink into the object being coloured and stay there by itself.

Natural Dyes

Have you ever stained your fingers or clothes with the juice from blueberries or raspberries? If so, you were using a natural dye! For thousands of years, humans made dyes from coloured molecules found in minerals or in organisms. Plant extracts were favourites: leaves, fruit, bark, and roots yielded an endless variety of coloured products. The root of the Madder plant gave us **turkey red**, the traditional dye of the British Redcoats. In Europe, the Woad plant was grown for centuries because it contained **indigo blue**. This dye can also be extracted from the Indigo plant found in east Asia. A century ago, the economy of India depended heavily on this dye plant.

King George II chose indigo blue as the colour for his navy's uniforms. Ever since, this colour has been called **navy blue**. Today, this dye is manufactured and used as an indicator, as a biological stain (indigo carmine), and as the colour in blue jeans.

Animals also produce colourful, extractable molecules. Cochineal, a cactus-eating insect, produced **cochineal red**. Mediterranean snails yielded **Tyrian purple** (Fig. 20-15). This dye was so expensive that, in Roman times, it was reserved for use by the ruling class. Romans wearing this colour communicated their elevated status with a dye! Can you explain the origin of the expression "born to the purple"?

Fig. 20-15 Crushed and boiled, certain molluscs produce Tyrian purple.

Natural dyes have drawbacks such as availability and expense. Also, natural dyes have to be chemically stable or else the colour will fade. Finally, the dye must stick to the fabric. Many potential natural dyes come out as soon as the cloth is washed! Even worse, some dyes stain the wearer's skin! A good dye has to be **fast**, that is, stuck to the fabric permanently. The dyes named above are among the few natural dyes that are stable and reasonably fast.

Synthetic Dyes

The first synthetic (artificial) dye was produced from coal tar extracts in 1856 by William Perkin, an English chemist. He was trying to synthesize an anti-malarial medicine called quinine. However, he accidentally produced a purple material that made a fast stain on fabric. Recognizing the potential of his discovery, he quit his job, borrowed money, and began making his fortune manufacturing this dye called **mauve**. It soon became the favourite colour of Queen Victoria. Within a short time, dozens of different dyes were produced

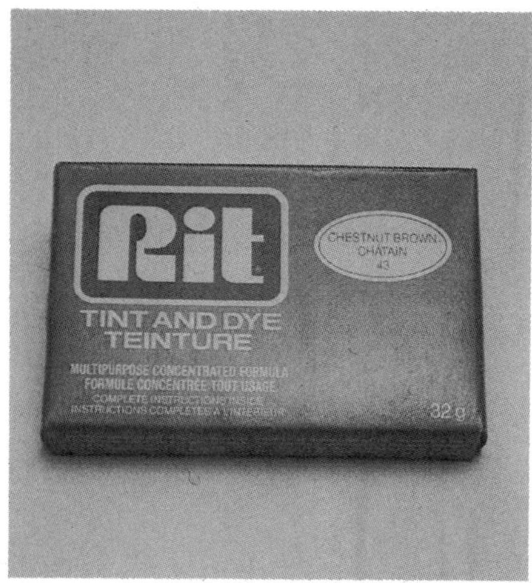

Fig. 20-16 Packaged dyes are delivered to the fabric in water solution.

by Perkin's company and by others. In 1900, the discovery of a synthetic technique for manufacturing indigo blue ruined the economy of India almost overnight.

Today, there are thousands of synthetic dyes available, giving us endless opportunities to alter our natural appearance. Which dyes do you prefer?

Types of Dyes

Direct dyes can be used for all natural fibres. This includes animal proteins like wool and silk as well as plant carbohydrate fibres like cotton. The clean fabric is immersed in a solution of dye until the dye is absorbed. Direct dyes cling so tightly to the fabric that they will not wash or wear out. Packaged dyes for home use are usually direct dyes (Fig. 20-16).

Picric acid is an acid dye that reacts with protein in wool to make a fast yellow colour. Picric acid is too toxic and reactive for you to attempt dyeing wool with it in the lab!

Mordant dyes require a preparatory chemical to make them stick to fabric. The substance used to fasten a dye to fabric is called a **mordant**. Aluminum hydroxide is a commonly-used mordant for dyeing cotton. It fills the tubes of the cotton fibres. When the dye is applied it unites with the mordant, giving the cotton fabric a bright, fast colour. You can investigate mordant dyeing in Activity 20.10.

Vat dyes are fast chemicals manufactured right in the fibres of a fabric. Indigo blue is a good example. The dye is altered to make it soluble and then soaked into the fabric. The fabric is then treated chemically to change the soluble molecules into insoluble, fast molecules. You will be amazed at the gradual appearance of colour when you try vat dyeing in Activity 20.8. You will also enjoy the interesting application of dyes in Activity 20.9.

Section Review

1. What are two differences between dyes and pigments?
2. What industries are dependent on dyes?
3. a) Where do natural dyes come from?
  b) What problems do natural dyes have?
  c) What advantages do synthetic dyes have over natural dyes?
4. Explain the term "fast" as applied to dyes.
5. What is a mordant?
6. How do direct, mordant, and vat dyes differ?

20.8 Activity: Making Blue Jeans Blue

One of our favourite dyes produces the blue colour in denim (Fig. 20-17). In this lab, you will simulate the process of vat dyeing. **Indigo blue** will be used, but if it is not available, **indigo carmine** can be substituted.

Fig. 20-17 How do we get the blue colour into cotton denim? How do we keep it from washing out? How do you suppose the "faded look" is created?

Indigo blue is an insoluble powder. In order to make it soluble, it is reacted with sodium dithionite in a concentrated base. Chemists call this type of reaction **reduction**. Once the dye is soluble, it can be soaked into the fabric. On contact with oxygen in the air, the dye changes back to its insoluble form, and then it is fast. Chemists call this reaction **oxidation**.

Sodium dithionite has a familiar but unpleasant odour until dissolved. To save time and improve safety, your teacher may decide to demonstrate the production of a batch of dye for the whole class (steps (a) through (d)) in the fume hood. This large batch can then be divided up to begin step (e).

CAUTION: Wear safety goggles, gloves, and aprons to keep the dye and base away from eyes, skin, and clothing. Do not drip water into the reagent bottle of sodium hyposulfite.

Problem

How can we dye cotton fabric the colour of blue jeans?

Materials

indigo blue powder (or substitute indigo carmine)
white unsized cotton fabric
125 mL Erlenmeyer flask
sodium dithionite ($Na_2S_2O_4 \cdot 2H_2O$)
spatula
tweezers
paper towel
balance
rubber stopper
sodium hydroxide pellets
graduated cylinder
glass stirring rod

Procedure

a. Put 0.1 g of indigo blue into a clean, dry Erlenmeyer flask.
b. Using the spatula, add 0.5 g of sodium dithionite and two pellets of sodium hydroxide.
c. Add 10 mL of water, stopper the flask, and shake until the contents are yellow. If the solution is not yellow after 3 min, add another 0.5 g of sodium dithionite. Stopper, shake, and proceed with the next step even if the green colour persists.
d. Open the flask and add about 40 mL of water. Swirl gently to mix.
e. Hold the cotton with tweezers and dip it in the dye. Stir with the glass rod for 30 s.
f. Remove the cloth using tweezers, note its colour, and press it between paper towels to remove excess moisture.
g. Place the cloth on a dry paper towel and observe it for 10 min. Record your observations.
h. Test the dye for fastness by rinsing the fabric in water. (Indigo blue works better than indigo carmine in this step.)

Discussion

1. Was the yellow dye soluble? How do you know?
2. Was the blue dye fast? How do you know?
3. If you wanted to remove indigo blue from denim, describe the process that you would use.

20.9 Activity: Air-Sea Rescue: Dyeing Stops Dying

Every year, people have boating accidents. On the Great Lakes and on the oceans, the biggest rescue problem is finding victims before they drown or die from exposure. Rescue operations start with an air search, often under less-than-ideal visibility conditions. Dyes play an important role in these operations. To increase the chance of being spotted, many flotation devices such as inflatable rafts are now equipped with a can of dye which is used to colour the surrounding water. Also, spotter planes drop dye to mark a victim's location.

The hunt for the best dye to use in these circumstances has uncovered fluorescein. Unlike most coloured materials, fluorescein gives off an eerie glow when exposed to small amounts of ultraviolet light. A can of fluorescein powder dropped in the water makes a dye spot visible for several kilometres during daylight. (Daylight contains ultraviolet light.)

In this activity, you will make fluorescein and test its effectiveness in colouring water. Old test tubes should be used because the residue is difficult to clean out. For spectacular results, your teacher may prefer to demonstrate the last step in a dark room.

Problem

How do we dye water in an air-sea rescue?

Materials

resorcinol
phthalic anhydride
concentrated sulfuric acid (1 drop)
Bunsen burner
sodium hydroxide (1 pellet)
balance
test tube (1)
10 mL graduated cylinder
large glass graduated cylinder (as large as possible)
UV light source (optional)

CAUTION: Wear safety goggles, gloves, and aprons. If any of the chemicals contact your skin or clothes, flush with water, and notify your teacher immediately. Avoid looking at the ultraviolet light.

Procedure

a. Put 0.1 g of resorcinol and 0.1 g of phthalic anhydride in a test tube. Add one drop of sulfuric acid.

b. Heat gently with a Bunsen burner for 3 min. Keep the test tube on an angle with the mouth pointed away from people.

c. Let the tube cool for 5 min.

d. When cool, add 5 mL of water and one pellet of sodium hydroxide.

e. Fill the large graduated cylinder with water and put it in a sunny location (where there will be ultraviolet light).

f. Pour the contents of your test tube into the large cylinder and observe.

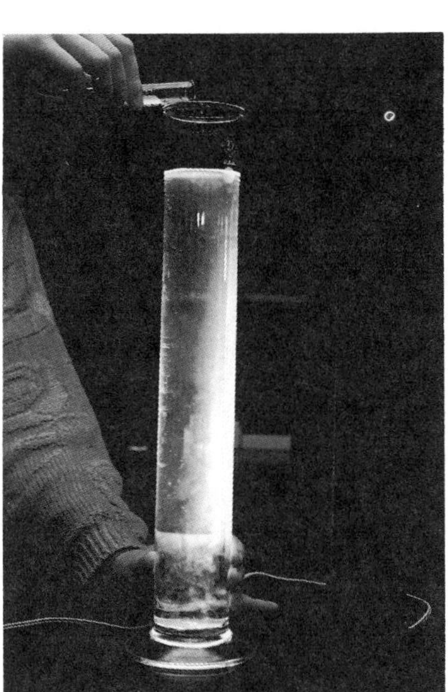
Fig. 20-18 Fluorescein makes an excellent water dye.

g. (Optional) Shine the UV light on a large water-filled graduated cylinder. Darken the classroom and pour your test tube contents into the cylinder (Fig. 20-18).

Discussion

1. What colour is fluorescein in UV light?
2. Could this chemical be used for night rescues? Explain.
3. Explain the title for this activity.

Extension

Fluorescein is an indicator. Design and conduct an experiment to determine what pH values change it to a colourless molecule.

20.10 Activity: Direct and Mordant Dyeing

You have learned that dyes are classified according to how they are used and according to the types of material they are used on. In this activity you will try several dyes on cotton fabric and on synthetic fabrics.

Problem

How do direct and mordant dyes work?

Materials

Congo red solution
Alizarine solution
aluminum sulfate solution
concentrated ammonium hydroxide solution
15 cm × 15 cm white unsized cotton cloth squares (4)
15 cm × 15 cm white synthetic fabric square (1)
100 mL beaker
ring stand, ring, and wire gauze
package of commercial dye

CAUTION: Wear safety goggles, gloves, and aprons during this activity. Do not inhale the fumes from the ammonium hydroxide. Perform this activity in a well-ventilated area.

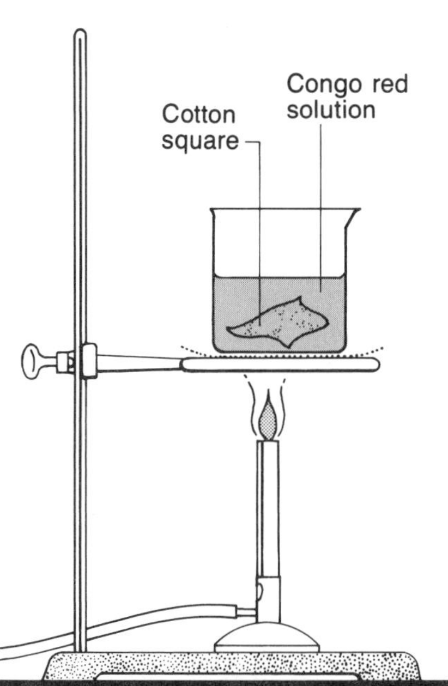

Fig. 20-19 Why is this procedure called direct dyeing?

Procedure A Direct Dyeing

a. Place 20 mL of Congo red solution in a 100 mL beaker. Submerge a square of cotton cloth in the solution. Then boil the solution for several minutes (Fig. 20-19). Pour off the solution, rinse the cotton square, and allow it to dry. Wash the cloth to see if the colour will remain in it. Repeat this step using the synthetic fabric square.

b. Read and follow the directions included in the commercial dye package for "hand dyeing" to dye a second cotton square. Test the cloth to see if the colour will remain in it.

Procedure B Mordant Dyeing

a. Fill a test tube one-third full with aluminum sulfate solution. Add 5 mL of the ammonium hydroxide solution. Record your observations.
b. Add 3 mL of Alizarine solution to the mixture in the test tube. Shake the mixture for one minute. Allow the precipitate to settle. Note the colour of the precipitate and of the liquid above it.
c. Place a square of cotton cloth in a 100 mL beaker. Then cover it with aluminum sulfate solution. Heat the solution for 3 min but do not boil it. Pour off the solution. Then add 15 mL of Alizarine solution and 5 mL of the ammonium hydroxide solution to the beaker. Leave the cloth in the beaker for 3 min. Remove the cloth, rinse it, and press it between paper towels to remove excess moisture.
d. Transfer the mordanted cloth prepared in step (c) to a clean beaker. Cover it with Alizarine solution and boil it for several minutes. Remove the cloth, rinse it thoroughly in water, and allow it to dry.
e. Place another cotton square in a 100 mL beaker. Cover it with Alizarine solution and boil the solution for several minutes. Remove the cloth, rinse it thoroughly in water, and allow it to dry. Compare this square to the one dyed in step (d).

Discussion A

1. Did direct dyeing occur when Congo red was added to cotton or to the synthetic fabric? How do you know?
2. Describe how to "hand dye" a cloth article using a commercial dye.

Discussion B

1. Does Alizarine cling to cotton? Which step in the experiment proved this?
2. What proof do you have that Alizarine clings to the mordant (aluminum sulfate)? Which step proved this?
3. Explain why a mordant is used for Alizarine stain.

Chapter Highlights

1. Chemistry has many applications around the kitchen.
2. Temporary hardness is caused mainly by the presence of calcium hydrogen carbonate in water and can be removed by boiling.
3. Permanent hardness is caused mainly by the presence of calcium sulfate in water. It cannot be removed by boiling.
4. Hard water wastes soap and forms scale.
5. Hard water has ecological and health benefits.
6. Hard water can be softened by removing the calcium and magnesium ions.

7. Dyes may be natural or synthetic.
8. Cotton and linen require different dyes from those used to dye wool and silk.
9. Some dyes are made fast to cloth with the aid of mordants.

Key Terms

demineralized water	permanent hardness	synthetic dye
hard water	permutit	temporary hardness
ion exchange	productivity	washing soda
mordant	soft water	zeolite
natural dye		

Recognizing the Concepts

Each of the following statements or questions is followed by four responses. Choose the correct response in each case. (Do not write in this book.)

1. Which one of the following properties of sodium hydrogen carbonate makes it an important component of baking powder?
   a) It is soluble in water.
   b) It is a solid at room temperature.
   c) It reacts with acid solutions to form carbon dioxide gas.
   d) It is a base.
2. Which one of the following statements applies *only* to temporary hard water?
   a) It reacts with soap to produce a scum.
   b) It contains calcium and magnesium ions.
   c) It wastes soap.
   d) It can be softened by boiling.
3. Which one of the following is an example of a substance used in the ion exchange method for softening hard water?
   a) permutit
   b) slaked lime
   c) washing soda
   d) calcium sulfate
4. A mordant is
   a) a vat dye
   b) a substance used to fasten dyes to fibres
   c) a substance used to dissolve dyes that are insoluble in water
   d) a dye that does not react with natural fibres
5. Picric acid dyes wool yellow because
   a) it is a yellow liquid which acts as a direct dye on the wool
   b) it turns yellow when exposed to air
   c) it reacts with the protein in the wool to form a fast yellow chemical
   d) it acts as mordant that fastens any yellow dye to wool

Understanding the Concepts

1. **a)** What causes temporary hardness in water?
   b) How is temporary hardness in water removed?

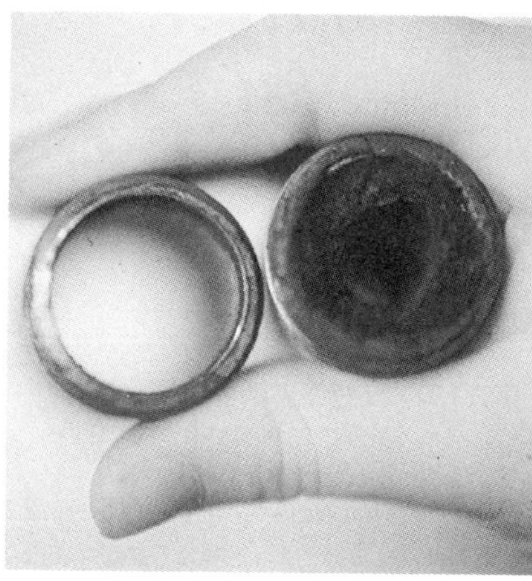

Fig. 20-20 What causes water pipes to become plugged after years of use?

c) Water pipes in homes often become plugged, as shown in Figure 20-20. What causes this?

2. What is the precipitate formed when washing soda reacts with hard water?
3. Distinguish between the way a mordant dye and a vat dye are stuck to fabric.
4. Why are natural dyes seldom used today?

Applying the Concepts

1. **a)** Why does baking powder begin to work only after water is added?
   b) Explain the role of baking powder in cake making.
2. Explain why an oven cleaner is more effective when it is applied to a warm oven than when it is applied and left overnight.
3. **a)** List the main advantages and disadvantages of hard water in a home.
   b) How could the water system of a home be constructed to lessen the disadvantages but retain the advantages?
4. Describe how you could determine which of two samples of water is the harder.
5. **a)** How can certain ion exchange materials be restored? Give one example.
   b) Water that has been softened by ion exchange is not suitable for drinking by people who are on a low salt diet. Why?
6. A "scale remover" is commercially available that removes scale from electric kettles. It contains hydrochloric acid and a corrosion inhibitor. What is the function of each ingredient?
7. Some towns in Ontario get their water from artesian wells. Others get their water from lakes. Generally the water from the wells is much harder than the lake water. Why is this so?

Fig. 20-21 Can you find the ratio of temporary to permanent hardness in water?

Investigations

1. Many direct dyes involve acid-base reactions. Use your resource centre to find out which material (the dye or the fabric) is the acid and which is the base.
2. Research and find out the role that tannic acid plays in the tanning process for treating animal hides.
3. Design a brochure or a poster for a firm that makes water softeners. Your brochure should convince potential customers of the advantages of having soft water.
4. Use the materials in Figure 20-21 to design and try an experiment to find the ratio of temporary to permanent hardness in tap water.
5. Make a chart showing different dyeing methods. Use dyed samples of cloth in your display.
6. Do a tie-dye project of a white T-shirt or similar article. Follow the directions outlined on the package of commercial dye.

Biography

Laura Holmes: Chemical Engineer

Laura Holmes is a chemical engineer with Consumers Gas, a company which distributes natural gas to cities and towns in much of Ontario. Holmes works in the Planning Department where she is responsible for maintaining the computer programs which model all of the gas piping in Toronto. Her department uses the model to make sure customers have an adequate supply of natural gas for their heating, hot water, and processing needs year-round.

In high school, Laura Holmes enjoyed mathematics and science. Engineering provided an opportunity to combine these two interests. After five years in the Coop program at the University of Waterloo, she received her Bachelor of Science degree in Chemical Engineering. The engineering training provided her with the skills required to solve problems in an efficient and effective manner.

Projects, such as coordinating the installation of new pipelines to supply natural gas to Toronto, involve both field and office work. In all her work, good communication skills and the ability to work with other people are important.

Career: *MEDICAL LABORATORY TECHNOLOGIST*

HELP WANTED: MEDICAL LABORATORY TECHNOLOGIST

A large hospital requires a medical laboratory technologist to perform chemical testing of human blood.

A career in clinical chemistry is interesting and challenging. A medical laboratory technologist is an important part of the health team. Physicians depend on the results of the laboratory tests to aid them in the diagnosis of disease and in the selection of appropriate treatment. Because a patient's illness cannot be confined to working hours, emergency duty is an integral part of the responsibilities of a laboratory technologist. Weekend work and on-call night duty are usually handled on a rotation basis by members of the laboratory staff. This calls for the ability to work independently and to exercise individual judgment.

To become a Registered Technologist in medical laboratory technology, you should graduate from high school with good marks in chemistry, mathematics, and biology. Upon completion of a two-year training program at the Toronto Institute of Medical Technology and affiliated hospitals, or a number of community colleges, you can write the registration examinations. Successful candidates become Registered Technologists in medical laboratory technology, which qualifies them to seek employment throughout Canada.

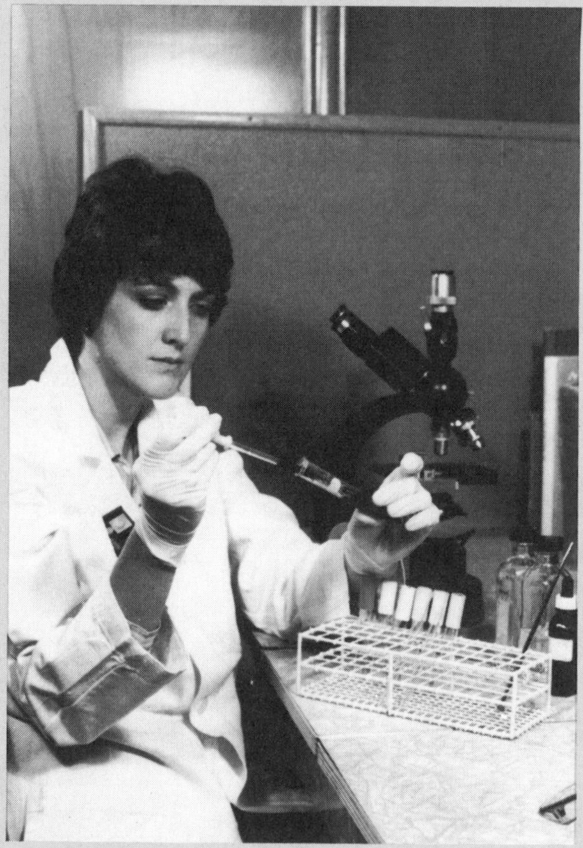

21 Preparing Consumer Products

CHAPTER CONTENTS

CHAPTER OBJECTIVES

After completing this chapter you should be able to:

1. Explain the cleansing action of soap.
2. Describe how soap, synthetic detergents, and nylon are made.
3. Make a soap, a synthetic detergent, and nylon.
4. Distinguish between a synthetic detergent and a soap.
5. Describe the fractional distillation of crude oil.
6. Explain how we are dependent on chemistry for our lifestyles.
7. Explain how chemistry has affected our health and environment.

Chemistry has dramatically altered our lifestyles in the last century. We have created many new kinds of molecules that were unknown a short time ago. In this chapter, you will look at a few of these molecules and how they are made. You will come to understand why we call this the "Plastic Age" and why you are so dependent on chemistry (Fig. 21-1). You will also come to understand some of the problems caused by our chemical discoveries.

Fig. 21-1 Consumer products have changed our lives. By the time you have finished this chapter, you will be able to prepare some of these products.

Monomers

Monomers joined to make a polymer molecule

Fig. 21-2 Polymers are made of small repeating monomers. "Poly" means many, "mono" means one, and "mer" means part. Can you explain why this name makes sense?

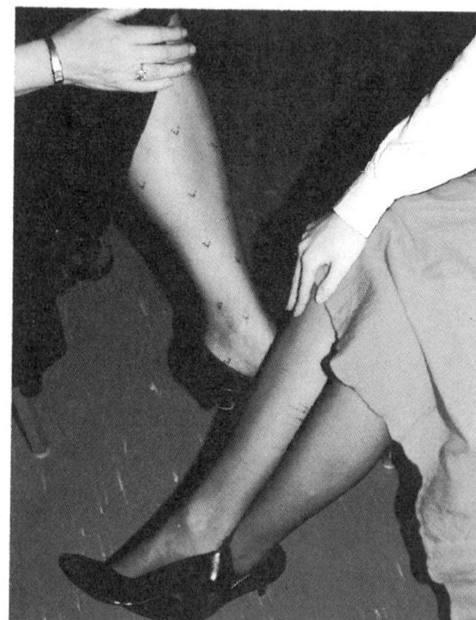

Fig. 21-3 "Nylons", as they soon became known, were an instant commercial success in 1940. Four million pairs sold in four days. Nylons were not available during the rest of the war. They reappeared on the market in 1945 and have been popular ever since. Nylon convinced skeptical consumers that synthetics were good replacements for natural polymers.

21.1 Synthetics: The Good, the Bad, and the Ugly

Just before World War II, the British and American militaries had a chemical nightmare. Military planners knew that if hostilities broke out involving countries in southeast Asia, the trade routes for silk and rubber would be cut off. Both materials were essential to the military: silk for parachutes and rubber for tires and insulating materials. For the planners, the race was on! Find substitutes fast!

The nightmare came true in 1941 when Pearl Harbor was attacked. Within three months, all supplies of silk and rubber were cut off. Partly by luck, there was a silk replacement, but rubber was still on the critical list. No vehicles, planes, or motors could run without it. If no substitute were found, defeat was inevitable.

What are silk and rubber? Both are made of very large, long molecules which, in turn, are made of simpler "building block" molecules joined together. Silk is a protein made of repeating amino acid molecules. Rubber is made of many small neoprene molecules linked in chains. Amino acids and neoprene are examples of **monomers**. The giant molecules they form are called **polymers** (Fig. 21-2). Silk and rubber are, in fact, natural polymers. Other natural polymers include cellulose (wood and paper), leather, and wool.

Natural polymers are essential in our lives. How would your life change without wood, paper, and wool? You might not have a place to live, books to read, or clothes to wear. Even in the Stone Age, people used leather and wood polymers.

By 1930, chemists had developed a few synthetic polymers, but none had the potential to replace the natural ones. Consumers were skeptical about the quality of these products. The first useful synthetic was Bakelite. Introduced in 1907, it is hard, lightweight, strong, and moldable. It is still used to make an endless variety of products like telephones, billiard balls, car parts, buttons, and camera cases. But it could not be used for parachutes or tires.

The Good

The answer to the military's silk problem came when Wallace Carothers produced the first nylon polymer using coal, air, and water as starting materials. Nylon is light, strong, flexible, and elastic (Fig. 21-3). You will make and test nylon in Demonstration 21.2. When war broke out, nylon production was diverted into parachutes, tents, and a host of other war-related fabrics. But it was not until 1942 that synthetic rubber for tires became available.

Carothers was also involved in rubber synthesis. In 1931, he created a neoprene polymer. It was made into life rafts, hoses, and clothing, but was not suitable for tires. However, the invention of this polymer confirmed that the properties of natural rubber could be copied to make a synthetic.

In 1942, desperate for tough rubber, the Americans began manufacturing a German-designed synthetic called Buna-S. The raw materials came from oil and coal. They made 18 000 t that year. The Allied forces in Europe and the

Pacific ran all their machines on this synthetic rubber. By 1945, production exceeded 700 000 t. Natural rubber has not been used for tires ever since.

During and following the war, thousands of new synthetics were developed, tested, and marketed. New varieties of rubber were produced that are vastly superior to natural rubber. Familiar and inexpensive synthetics like vinyl, teflon, orlon, polyethylene, styrofoam, and polyester have brought us into the "Plastic Age" (Fig. 21-4). And more synthetics appear all the time! In fact, organic chemists claim that they can make "custom-tailored" molecules for almost any purpose!

What would your life be like if synthetics suddenly disappeared? Some of you would be wearing only your birthday suits! Your vinyl shoes, nylon jackets, polyester clothes, and spandex underwear would be gone! Your bike tires, sports equipment, music collection, stereo, TV, carpeting, refrigerator, electrical wiring, upholstery, and plumbing would fall apart or disappear! Your vehicles would not run. Many of your parents that make, sell, or use these products would be unemployed. Fortunately for you, your teachers would still be working, but your desks and writing instruments might be gone. Better get a wool suit—it's cold on the floor without any clothes on!

The Bad

What could be wrong with synthetics? They do so much for us; our lifestyles depend on them! One answer is their durability. Unlike the natural polymers, synthetics do not decompose. Bacteria and fungi do not break them down.

Synthetics also have altered our attitudes towards all products. Because synthetics are inexpensive, we have become a "throwaway" society in which we *expect* products to wear out and be thrown away. We even package our garbage in plastic just to throw it out (Fig. 21-5)! What other examples of throwaway products can you think of?

Fig. 21-4 All products in this photograph are synthetic. Many imitate natural products so well that it is difficult to tell them apart. Even the door panel is a synthetic imitation of burnished copper.

Fig. 21-5 How much garbage do you produce each day? How much of it is non-degradeable synthetics?

These two problems of the Plastic Age have put an enormous strain on our resources. We are running out of suitable land for dump sites. And we are running out of oil to make plastics! How can we eliminate these problems? Can we now invent decomposable polymers? You can study the problems caused by synthetics in Chapter 24.

The Ugly

Human-made polymers and other twentieth-century synthetics have created another problem: hazardous wastes. These unusable by-products are produced during the manufacturing of most synthetics. Improper disposal of synthetics produces more. Unfortunately, many of these wastes are also durable. And worse, many are extremely **toxic** (poisonous) or **carcinogenic** (cancer-causing).

Since the invention of nylon and our race into the Plastic Age, we have been careless about these by-products. Some were stored. Others were buried or flushed into lakes. This deadly "inheritance" is coming back to haunt us: synthetic wastes are in our air, food, and water.

How are we to handle such problems? Is it reasonable to stop producing synthetics? Can we make synthetics without wastes? Should the cost of proper waste disposal be included in the price of synthetic products? How do we clean up our environment? You will study issues dealing with these wastes in Chapter 25.

Section Review

1. Explain how World War II stimulated the development of synthetics.
2. What is a monomer? a polymer?
3. What advantages do synthetics have over natural polymers?
4. List ten products that you use which are synthetic.
5. **a)** What attitude problem has the low cost of synthetics caused?
b) What problem has the durability of synthetics caused?
c) What are some possible solutions to these problems?
6. Why are hazardous wastes referred to as a "deadly inheritance"?

21.2 Demonstration: Making Nylon

In this demonstration you will prepare nylon from the reaction of diaminohexane with adipoyl chloride. During the polymerization, hydrochloric acid molecules are released as the two monomers join to form the polymer. The reaction is carried out in the presence of sodium hydroxide (a base) to neutralize the hydrochloric acid produced.

Problem

How is nylon prepared?

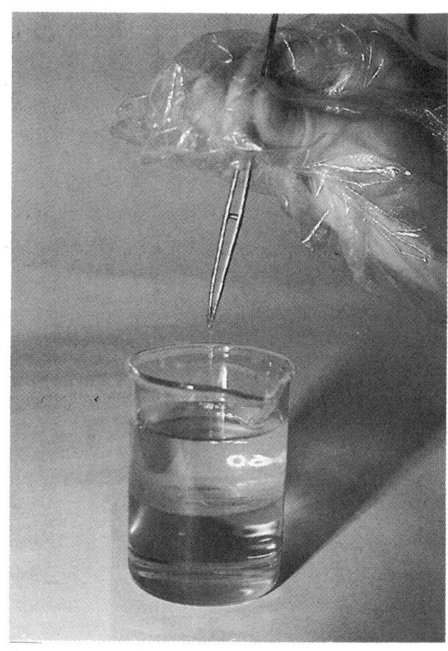

A

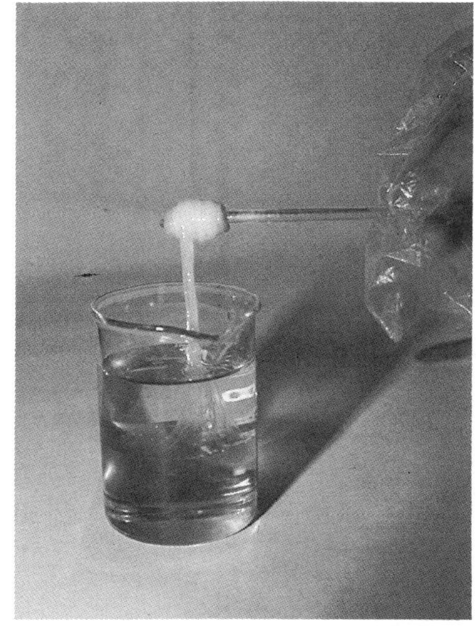

B

Fig. 21-6 Preparing nylon

Materials

adipoyl chloride
1,6 diaminohexane
hexane (50 mL)
sodium hydroxide solution (0.5 M)
250 mL beakers (2)
100 mL graduated cylinder
distilled water
stirring rod
tweezers

CAUTION:
1. *Wear safety goggles, gloves, and aprons during this demonstration.*
2. *Do not get any of the reagents on your hands. Wash immediately with soap and water if contact occurs.*
3. *Handle the nylon with care. Small bubbles sometimes form that can burst and squirt chemicals on you.*

Procedure

a. Dissolve 2 mL of adipoyl chloride in 50 mL of hexane in a clean, dry 250 mL beaker.
b. In a second beaker, warm 3 g of 1,6-diaminohexane until it melts. Then add 50 mL of 0.5 M sodium hydroxide solution.
c. Gently pour the second solution on top of the first so that two layers are formed. It may help to run the second solution down a stirring rod as shown in Figure 21-6, A.
d. With tweezers, grip the centre of the milky ''scum'' layer formed between the two solutions. Pull upwards, slowly forming a nylon ''rope''.
e. When the rope is long enough, reel it up on a glass stirring rod as shown in Figure 21-6, B.
f. Wash the nylon thoroughly with water.
g. Examine the nylon for colour, flexibility, and elasticity. Record your observations.

Discussion

1. Describe the characteristics of the nylon you have prepared.
2. Which characteristics make nylon a desirable textile fabric?
3. Why is nylon classified as a polymer?
4. **a)** What products do you use that are made of nylon? (You may have to read some labels to find out.)
b) Nylon is often used as a blend with other materials like wool. Why?

21.3 Soap: How Is It Made?

Early Soap Making

For many centuries, humans had no soaps, shampoos, or detergents. While ancient humans may have washed regularly, this removed only soluble dirt. The insoluble greases and oils would not wash away from skin, hair, or clothing. In the Middle Ages, Europeans believed that this coating on their hair and skin protected them from disease. By our standards, their body odour must have been outrageous! No wonder the nobility wore scented wigs, carried perfumed hankies, and boiled their clothing to clean it.

Early humans did discover a way to get rid of their body oils. If they rubbed moist wood ashes on their skin and hair before bathing, then the greases rinsed away! Without realizing it, these people were actually making soap right on their skin!

What is soap? It's a combination of a kind of lipid called a **fatty acid** and a base, forming a soluble compound (Fig. 21-7). Lipids are the fats from animals and the oils from plants. The "oil" that your skin produces is a lipid. A concentrated base reacts with the fatty acid part of lipid molecules. The positive ion of the base (e.g. sodium ion) attaches to the fatty acid forming a molecule of soap. The process of soap making is called **saponification**. Wood ashes and water make a good base. Can you explain why moist ashes can clean oily skin?

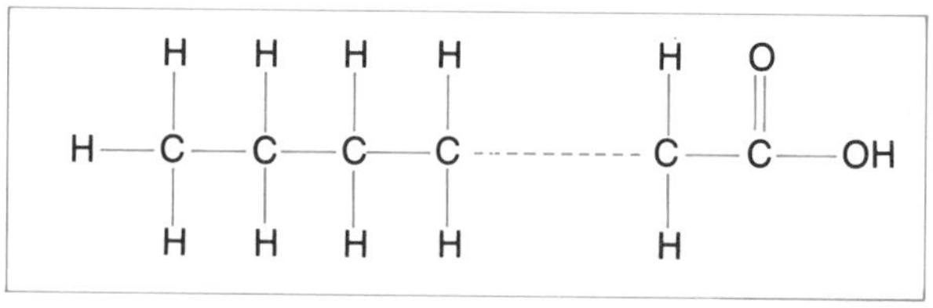

Fig. 21-7 A fatty acid is a long hydrocarbon chain consisting of many carbon and hydrogen atoms chemically bonded in a chain-like arrangement.

```
     H   H   H   H          H   O
     |   |   |   |          |   ||
H —  C — C — C — C -------- C — C — OH
     |   |   |   |          |
     H   H   H   H          H
```

Animal fat (lard) and ashes are still used to make certain kinds of soap. However, these soaps are harsh and irritate the skin. Chemists have discovered that fatty acids from plant oils (e.g. palm oil) combined with other bases make milder soaps and even liquid soaps such as shampoos.

Commercial Preparation of Soap

To make soap commercially, the oils and melted fats are blended in various proportions for various kinds of soap. Then they are put in a large pan. Next, sodium hydroxide is added. Then the mixture is heated to boiling by passing steam into the pan until the saponification is complete. At the end of the process, the soap is in solution. Common salt (sodium chloride) is added to the mixture. Soap is insoluble in sodium chloride solution. Therefore the soap separates out and rises to the top. This process is known as **salting out** the soap. The soap is then drawn off and allowed to cool. Fillers, colouring dyes, perfumes, and antiseptics are added. Finally, the soap is thoroughly rolled. It is then pressed into bars and stamped with its commercial name and design.

The Cleansing Action of Soap

The soap molecule, CH_3CH_2 . . . CH_2COONa, consists of two parts: a long hydrocarbon chain CH_3CH_2 . . . CH_2– and the –COONa part (Fig. 21-8). The –COONa part of the soap molecule is attracted toward water. The hydrocarbon

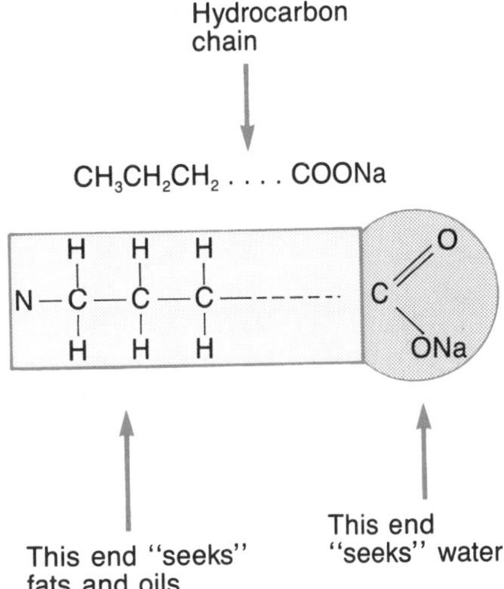

Fig. 21-8 Diagrammatic representation of a soap molecule

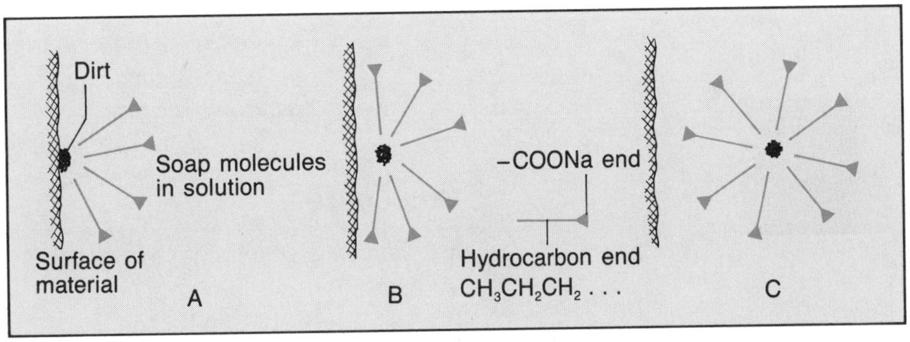

Fig. 21-9 The hydrocarbon ends of the soap molecules are attracted to the "dirt". The -COONa ends remain in the water around the dirt (A). Agitation loosens the dirt (B). Rinsing washes it away (C).

end is attracted toward lipids (fats and oils). Thus, the soap molecule can dissolve in water and lipids at the same time. When oily clothing is placed in the soap solution, the hydrocarbon ends dissolve in the lipid and the –COONa ends remain in the water. With shaking and scrubbing, the dirt is dislodged from the article and held in the solution (Fig. 21-9). Rinsing washes the dirt away.

Section Review

1. Why is lipid dirt difficult to remove from skin, hair, and clothing?
2. Why do wood ashes remove lipid dirt?
3. What is saponification?
4. What is the main difference between soaps made from animal fats and those made from plant oils?
5. Summarize the main stages in the commercial manufacturing of soap.
6. Explain how soap removes grease from "dirty" hands.

21.4 Activity: Preparing Soap

In this activity you will make your own soap. Then you will test your soap's reactions with water and kerosene. Ethyl alcohol is not used in commercial soap making. However, you will use it in this activity to bring the reacting materials into close contact. This will speed up the saponification process.

Problem

How is soap prepared?

Materials

fat, cottonseed oil, or lard
40% sodium hydroxide solution
saturated sodium chloride solution
ethyl alcohol
distilled water
kerosene
50 mL graduated cylinder
250 mL Erlenmeyer flasks (3)
hot plate
scoopula
test tubes (2)
wire gauze
stirring rod
paper towel

CAUTION: 1. *Wear safety goggles, gloves, and aprons during this activity.*
2. *Sodium hydroxide solution is very corrosive. If you get any on your skin or clothing, rinse immediately with water and call your teacher.*
3. *Ethyl alcohol is flammable. Heat gently and carefully. Be sure there are no open flames in the room.*

Procedure

a. Place 10 g of a lipid (lard, or cottonseed oil) in a clean 250 mL Erlenmeyer flask.

b. Add 20 mL of ethyl alcohol and 15 mL of the sodium hydroxide solution to the flask containing the fat or oil.

Fig. 21-10 Heat gently and stir carefully and constantly.

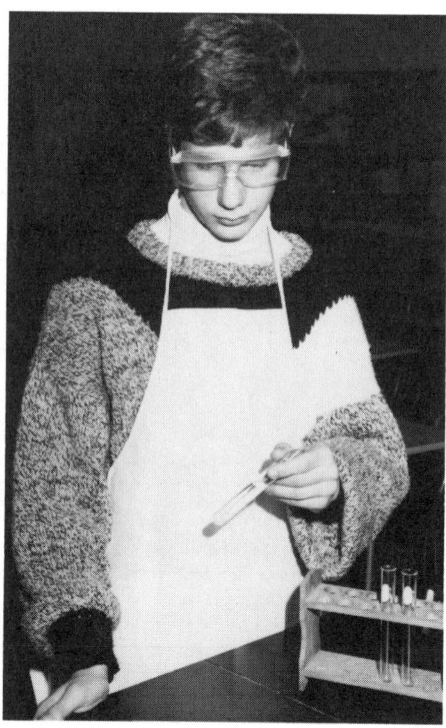

Fig. 21-11 Be careful that you do not get any of these mixtures on your skin or clothing.

c. *Gently* heat the mixture as shown in Figure 21-10, with *constant stirring*. Some of the liquid may be lost due to evaporation. If so, add distilled water to maintain the original volume.

d. While you are waiting for the lipid and base to completely react (about 20 min), prepare and heat the two solutions required for steps (e) and (f) in 250 mL Erlenmeyer flasks.

e. After the fat disappears, allow the mixture to cool. Then add 20 mL of hot distilled water. *CAUTION: Handle hot water carefully.*

f. Allow the mixture to cool again. Then add 50 mL of warm saturated sodium chloride solution. The soap should appear as curds in the solution.

g. Scoop off the soap with the scoopula and discard the liquid. Dry the soap by pressing it between paper towels.

h. Transfer a small amount of your soap to a test tube half full of distilled water. Shake vigorously to dissolve the soap (Fig. 21-11). Record your observations.

i. Add 5 drops of kerosene to a test tube one-third full of distilled water. Shake the mixture and let it stand. Record what happens.

j. Now add a piece of your soap to the kerosene-water mixture. Again, shake vigorously, and let the mixture stand. Record your observations.

CAUTION: Do not use the soap you prepared on your skin.

Discussion

1. Describe the soap you prepared.
2. How did the soap react with distilled water?
3. a) Describe what happened when the kerosene-water mixture was shaken and then allowed to stand.
   b) What was the effect of soap on the kerosene-water mixture? Explain this effect.
4. Why should you not wash your hands with this soap?

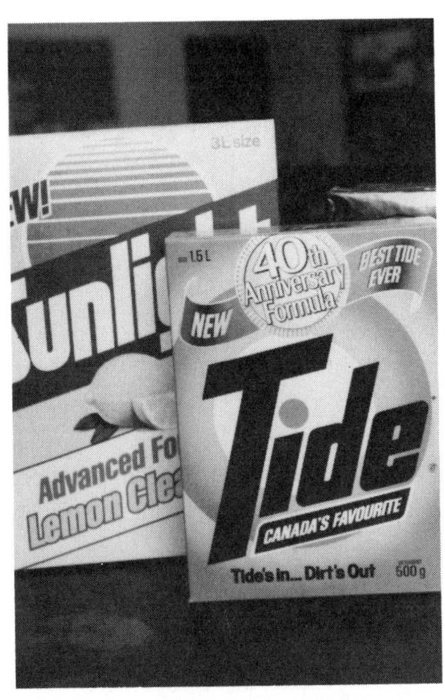

Fig. 21-12 Synthetic detergents like these have some advantages over soap in laundry work. What are those advantages? Can you think of any advantages of soap over synthetic detergents?

21.5 Activity: Preparing a Synthetic Detergent

The term **detergent** is a general name that covers two types of cleaning agents. One of these is ordinary soap. The other type consists of what are called **synthetic detergents** (Fig. 21-12). These are, chemically, very similar to soap. Like soap, their molecules consist of a hydrocarbon chain and a water-attracting group. The hydrocarbon chains in both types of detergents are alike. However, the water-attracting ends of their molecules are different. In soaps, the water-attracting group is $-COONa$. In one type of synthetic detergent, which you will prepare in this activity, the water-attracting group is $-O-SO_3Na$ (a sulfate group).

Synthetic detergents have two main advantages over soap. First, they are more efficient and, as a result, less detergent need be used. Second, their calcium salts are soluble in water. Synthetic detergents, therefore, can be used in hard water without scum being formed.

A number of alcohols are satisfactory for making synthetic detergents. In this activity, you will use lauryl alcohol, $CH_3(CH_2)_{10}CH_2OH$, to prepare the synthetic detergent sodium lauryl sulfate, $CH_3(CH_2)_{10}CH_2{-}O{-}SO_3Na$.

Problem

How are synthetic detergents prepared?

Materials

concentrated sulfuric acid
lauryl alcohol
2 M sodium hydroxide solution
phenolphthalein solution
250 mL beakers (2)
flakes of soap
50 mL graduated cylinder
stirring rod
funnel
filter paper
calcium chloride
test tubes (2)

CAUTION: *1. Wear safety goggles, gloves, and aprons during this activity.*
2. Both sulfuric acid and sodium hydroxide are corrosive. If you spill any on your skin or clothing, flush immediately with lots of water and call your teacher.

Procedure

Fig. 21-13 The mixing of chemicals to produce the synthetic detergent must be done slowly and carefully.

a. Place 20 g of lauryl alcohol in a 250 mL beaker.
b. *Very slowly and cautiously*, add 10 mL of concentrated sulfuric acid. *CAUTION: Handle sulfuric acid with care. See previous caution.*
c. Place 40 mL of the sodium hydroxide solution in a second 250 mL beaker. Add three drops of phenolphthalein solution. Record the colour of the solution.
d. *Carefully and cautiously*, pour the acid solution from step (b) into the sodium hydroxide solution. Do this *slowly* and with *constant stirring*. The phenolphthalein should turn purple, then colourless. If it does not turn colourless, add a small amount of concentrated sulfuric acid, slowly and carefully, until it does. At this point, a white thick precipitate of sodium lauryl sulfate forms (Fig. 21-13).
e. Filter the solution and allow the precipitate to dry.
f. Add a small amount of the dry detergent to a test tube half full of water. Shake the tube and record your observations.
g. Dissolve a pinch of calcium chloride in a test tube half full of water. Add a small amount of the synthetic detergent to the solution. Shake the tube and record your observations. Repeat using a few pieces of soap instead of the synthetic detergent.

Discussion

1. Describe the synthetic detergent you prepared.
2. How did the synthetic detergent react with water?
3. a) What was the purpose of adding calcium chloride?
b) How did the synthetic detergent react with water containing calcium chloride?
c) How did the soap react with water containing calcium chloride?

4. What advantages does a synthetic detergent have over soap? Cite your evidence.
5. Compare the chemical structure of synthetic detergents and soaps.

21.6 Crude Oil

Fig. 21-14 This sample of petroleum from Alberta was pumped out of the ground. The petroleum in some parts of Saskatchewan is so thick that it has to be warmed before it can be pumped up out of the ground.

Did you know that the first commercial oil well in North America was drilled in Ontario? Did you know that a Canadian, James Miller Williams, is called the Father of the North American Oil Industry? Williams hit oil at Oil Springs, Ontario (between London and Sarnia) in 1858 in a well only 18 m down! He made the **crude oil** (**petroleum**) into one of the few products that it was good for at that time: lamp oil.

What is crude oil? It's a mixture of thousands of different compounds, most of which are made of two elements, *hydrogen* and *carbon*. Hence the compounds are called **hydrocarbons**. Crude oil varies in composition from well to well. Some wells such as those in the Alberta tar sands produce a black, sticky (heavy) crude called **tar**. Other wells produce brown, runny (light) crude sometimes resembling muddy water or tea (Fig. 21-14). Sometimes wells hit another hydrocarbon called **natural gas**. It's used to heat our factories and homes.

What was crude oil good for? Not much until the mid-1800s. It seeped to the surface of the ground in places like Alberta, Texas, the Middle East, and southwestern Ontario, but few people put it to use. For North American pioneers, crude oil was often regarded as a curse because it ruined the agricultural quality of their land. But if the "curse" was thick, it could be used for waterproofing a roof or a boat. In western Canada, the Cree Indians used tar for medicines. In Mexico, it was used for chewing gum.

In the mid-1800s, two developments sparked an interest in this "useless" material. The first was the commercial application of **refining**, that is, the separation of crude oil into groups of compounds that were alike. Williams refined his crude oil to get the one part (or **fraction**) that burned cleanly in lamps. Other refiners developed techniques to remove different fractions such as gases like propane, liquids like octane, and solids like wax.

The second development was the **internal combustion engine**. Inventors discovered that refined hydrocarbons were explosive when mixed with air and compressed. With liquid hydrocarbons like octane as fuel, these new engines could be made smaller, lighter, and stronger than the coal-fired steam engines of the day. Almost overnight, the "curse" turned into "Black Gold" and "Texas Tea". The oil boom was on!

Refineries sprang up in southwestern Ontario. In fact, Sarnia still has much of Ontario's refining capacity. Today, Ontario's wells produce only a small volume of oil. We now import much of our crude and refined oil from western Canada.

Refining

Refining crude oil is the key to converting useless crude into valuable hydrocarbons. This is accomplished by heating the crude in a tower as shown in

Figure 21-15. The top of the tower is cooler than the bottom. The compounds in crude oil have different boiling points. Each compound moves as a vapour up to that section of the tower which has this temperature and condenses there. Thus, the various compounds are separated and the hydrocarbons are said to be "refined". Since this distillation process separates the crude oil into its fractions, it is called **fractional distillation**. You may observe this process in Demonstration 21.7.

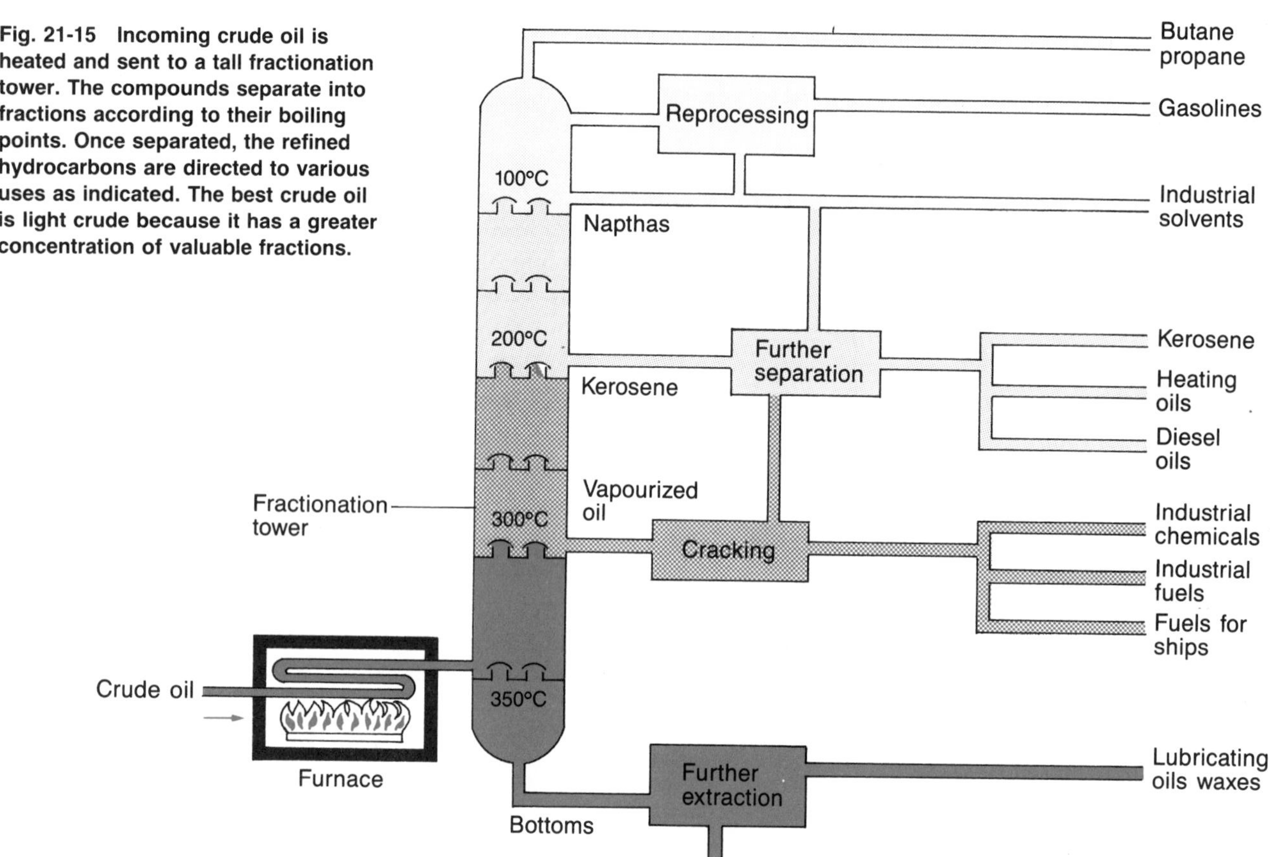

Fig. 21-15 Incoming crude oil is heated and sent to a tall fractionation tower. The compounds separate into fractions according to their boiling points. Once separated, the refined hydrocarbons are directed to various uses as indicated. The best crude oil is light crude because it has a greater concentration of valuable fractions.

Uses of Refined Hydrocarbons

Right now, you are likely wearing an oil product. Sometime today, you will likely eat an oil product. And it's almost certain that plastic plays a role in some of your activities. In short, your lifestyle is dependent on oil. Why? Because *oil is the source of raw materials that we use for synthetics.*

Of course, oil has more obvious uses. We make gasoline, diesel fuel, kerosene (jet fuel), and all lubricants from oil. But we also use it to make medicines, vitamins, fertilizer, pesticides, waxes, and dyes. And we burn oil for heat and electricity.

In the early 1970s, the price of crude oil went up dramatically. It dropped just as dramatically in the 1980s. Can you now explain why we experienced a period of inflation (a rapid rise in prices) for several years after oil prices went up? Can you explain why oil prices dropped again? What will happen to your future if oil becomes scarce?

Section Review

1. What are hydrocarbons?
2. Distinguish between light and heavy crude. Which one is more valuable? Why?
3. What kinds of materials can be refined from crude oil?
4. Why was crude oil once regarded as a useless material?
5. Explain how a fractionating tower works.
6. Explain why our lifestyle is dependent on chemistry.

21.7 Demonstration: The Fractional Distillation of Crude Oil

In this demonstration you will observe the fractional distillation of crude oil. **Distillation** is the process used to separate a mixture of two or more liquids, provided they have different boiling points. When the mixture (crude oil) is heated, the liquid with the lowest boiling point distills off first. When it is nearly all gone, the liquid with the next lowest boiling point distills off, and so on. Each separate liquid that distills off is called a **fraction** (part of the whole). The overall process is called **fractional distillation**. After you have observed this process, read Section 21.6 again.

Problem

What fractions can we get from crude oil?

Materials

crude oil sample
250 mL Erlenmeyer flask
two-hole stopper for Erlenmeyer flask
hot plate
cotton wool
crucible
wood splints (4)
thermometer (0-250°C)
test tubes (4)
stoppers for test tubes (4)
delivery tube (glass)
rubber connecting tube
250 mL beaker

CAUTION: This demonstration should be conducted in a fume hood away from sparks and flames.

Procedure

a. Place 5 mL of crude oil in the Erlenmeyer flask.

b. Set up the apparatus as shown in Figure 21-16. Make sure the thermometer bulb is well above the crude oil.

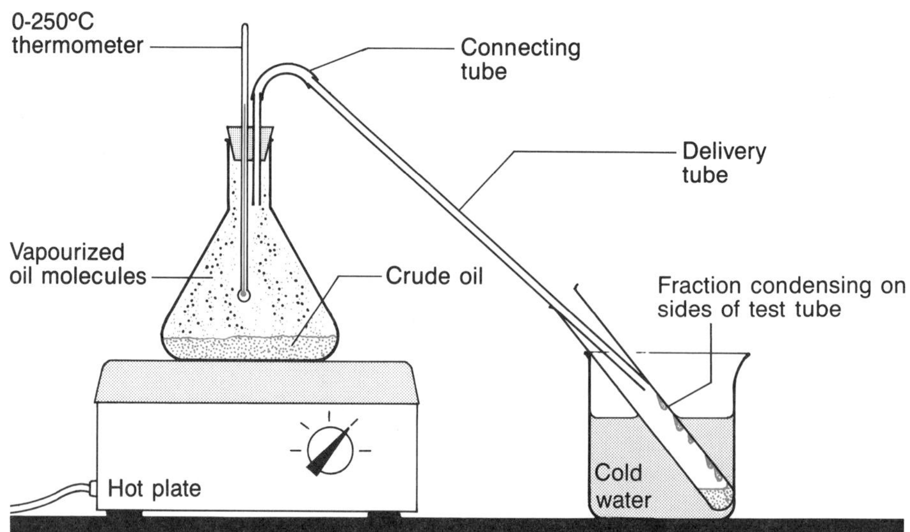

Fig. 21-16 Various crude oil fractions can be separated using this distillation apparatus. The products are combustible. Keep all materials away from sparks of flames.

c. Heat the Erlenmeyer flask *slowly* and *carefully*. Soon, a few drops of liquid will condense in the test tube.

d. Use the four test tubes to collect four fractions within roughly the following temperature ranges:

- Room temperature to 70°C
- 70–110°C
- 110–170°C
- 170–220°C

Stopper each tube after removing it.

e. After reaching 220°C, remove the fourth test tube, turn off the hot plate, and let the apparatus cool. *Keep the delivery tube out of liquids during cooling or fluid will be drawn back into the Erlenmeyer flask.*

f. Examine the residue which remains in the Erlenmeyer flask.

g. Compare the four fractions as to viscosity (how easily they run when the test tube is inverted) and colour. Record your observations.

h. Pour each fraction onto a piece of cotton wool in a crucible in the fume hood. Light the fraction with a wood splint. Compare how easily the fractions burn.

Discussion

1. In what physical property must the liquids in a mixture differ before they can be separated by fractional distillation? Why?

2. Which fraction was the lightest? the heaviest?
3. What use could be made of the residue?
4. Suggest some uses for each fraction collected, based on its properties.

Chapter Highlights

1. Soap is prepared by boiling oil or fat with a concentrated base.
2. Synthetic detergents have some advantages over soap.
3. Synthetic fibres, like nylon, can be prepared by polymerizing monomers.
4. Synthetics have given us problems as well as benefits.
5. Synthetics are used in many aspects of our lives.
6. Crude oil consists of thousands of substances which can be separated by fractional distillation.
7. The components of crude oil are used to make a wide variety of materials.

Key Terms

carcinogenic
crude oil
fraction
fractional distillation
monomer
nylon
polymerization
polymers
saponification
soap
synthetic detergent
synthetic fibre
toxic

Recognizing the Concepts

Each of the following statements or questions is followed by four responses. Choose the correct response in each case. (Do not write in this book.)

1. Nylon is
   - **a)** a natural fibre
   - **b)** a synthetic rubber
   - **c)** a monomer
   - **d)** a long chain polymer
2. Chemically, soap is a
   - **a)** fat or oil
   - **b)** fatty acid
   - **c)** sodium salt of a fatty acid
   - **d)** mixture of glycerine and fat
3. Which of the following is an *incorrect* comparison of synthetic detergent with soap?
   - **a)** Synthetic detergents are more efficient than soaps.
   - **b)** The hydrocarbon chains in the molecules of synthetic detergents and soaps are different, while the water-attracting ends of their molecules are alike.
   - **c)** Molecules of synthetic detergents and soaps consist of hydrocarbon chains and water-attracting groups.
   - **d)** Less synthetic detergent than soap is needed in hard water to produce a lather.

4. If two liquids are to be separated by fractional distillation, they must differ in
   a) melting point
   b) boiling point
   c) solubility in water
   d) density
5. A fractionation tower is used by industries to fractionally distill petroleum. The temperature in the tower is kept high at the bottom and gets gradually lower up the tower. Pentane has a boiling point of 36°C, tridecane a boiling point of 236°C, pentadecane a boiling point of 271°C, and hexadecane a boiling point of 287°C. Which one of these components will condense furthest down the tower?
   a) pentane b) tridecane c) pentadecane d) hexadecane

Understanding the Concepts

1. a) What is a polymerization reaction?
   b) Differentiate between natural and synthetic polymers.
2. a) Why is cotton called a natural fibre?
   b) Why is polyester called a synthetic fibre?
3. How are soaps and synthetic detergents similar? How are they different?
4. Explain the process of saponification.
5. a) Account for the name "fractional distillation".
   b) Explain the principle behind fractional distillation.

Applying the Concepts

1. Why are many shirts 50% cotton and 50% polyester instead of being pure cotton or pure polyester?
2. Explain why homemade soap is usually harsh on the skin.
3. Why is it possible for chemists to make so many different kinds of synthetic fibres?
4. Why are synthetic detergents more commonly used today than soaps are?
5. Our pioneer ancestors made their own soap by heating animal fats with wood ashes. Why does this make soap?
6. Why do petroleum fractionation towers often have a flame burning at the top?
7. Explain why the economy of our country is, in large part, dependent on petroleum.
8. Chemistry played an important role in improving the quality of life in this century. Explain how two consumer products from the chemical industries contributed to this improvement.

Investigations

1. Investigate the difference between hard soap (e.g. soap bar) and soft soap (e.g. a gel in a tube).

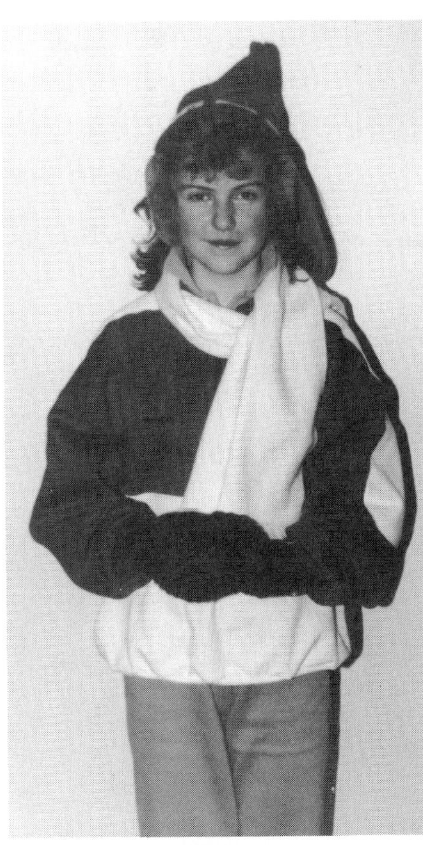

Fig. 21-17 How many kinds of fibres do you wear? You may wish to investigate clothing other than that which you are presently wearing.

2. Find out the chemical makeup of shampoos. Then list the advantages of using a shampoo instead of soap for washing your hair.
3. Design and try an experiment to find out which detergent of the common brands of detergents is most effective in laundry work. Take into account the cost of the detergent and whether it is sufficient by itself or needs other supplements to do the task.
4. Research the life and work of Wallace H. Carothers. Write a report on your findings.
5. Polymerization reactions produce many useful polymers. Choose any one of the following polymers and find out how it is made and why it is an important material in modern life: synthetic rubber, polyethylene plastic, polyvinyl chloride plastic, plexiglas, rayon, polyester, Orlon.
6. Research the extraction of petroleum from Alberta's tar sands.
7. Several topics are listed below that are of concern to environmentalists. For some of these, your teacher will give you further information as well as a resolution to be debated. Select a topic that interests you and decide whether you are for or against the resolution. Your teacher will place you in a team with three or four other students who feel the same way you do. As a team you are to prepare a defence of your position. Then you will conduct a debate with a team that holds the opposite view. Suggested topics are:
   a) the fuel consumption of automobiles
   b) super-tankers and oil spills
   c) rationing of petroleum products
   d) fuel consumption by supersonic passenger jet aircraft
   e) oil exploration in the Arctic
   f) offshore drilling for oil
   g) trans-Arctic pipelines for gas and oil
8. Research how petroleum is formed and how it is obtained from the earth. Write a report on your findings.
9. Find out which synthetic and natural fibres make up your clothing (Fig. 21-17). List the advantages and disadvantages of each fibre.

Biography

James Miller Williams: Oil Pioneer

James Miller Williams is known as the father of the North American oil industry. He was a successful carriage and railcar manufacturer from Hamilton, Ontario. He acquired land at Oil Springs, Ontario in 1856 to settle an unpaid account on a carriage. By 1857, Williams was removing crude oil from shallow hand-dug wells on his land and refining the product to make lamp oil. In the same year, Williams and Charles Tripp began drilling wells, hoping to find larger volumes of oil below bedrock. After a number of unsuccessful attempts, a drilled well hit crude and yielded about 6000 L a day. The Oil Museum of Canada has been built on this site and this first well still operates today.

By 1860 Williams had at least 5 working wells. In November of that year, Williams incorporated the Canadian Oil Company—the first anywhere to produce, refine, and market oil products. His entries in the 1862 International Exhibition in England won 2 gold medals: one for the first commercial production of crude oil and the other for the first Canadian refinery.

The area around Oil Springs went through a boom in the late 1800s as hundreds of new oil wells came into production. A bust followed as the price of oil dropped. Williams left the oil business about the time of Confederation (1867) to become a provincial politician and Hamilton alderman until his death in 1890 at the age of 72. Those who copied Williams' methods created the corporate oil giants of today.

Career: *INDUSTRIAL CHEMIST*

HELP WANTED:
INDUSTRIAL CHEMIST

A large industrial plant involved in synthesis, manufacturing, and marketing of fine chemicals requires an industrial chemist to perform chemical analysis of raw materials and finished products.

The characteristics of a successful industrial chemist include being highly observant, having an analytical mind, taking initiative, and being able to work with others. Industrial chemists carry out careful measurements and chemical analysis to ensure that the industrial products are of the quality required and are free of impurities. They usually supervise the work of several technicians and check their results. They are responsible for checking and adjusting any errors in the instruments used. They write daily reports.

A career in industrial chemistry requires a solid knowledge of chemistry. You should graduate from high school with good marks in chemistry, physics, mathematics, and English. At university you should obtain a degree in chemistry with additional courses in physics, electronics, and computer science. Job opportunities are excellent. For example, you could work for an industrial and consumer product development plant, a nuclear power station, or a petroleum industry.

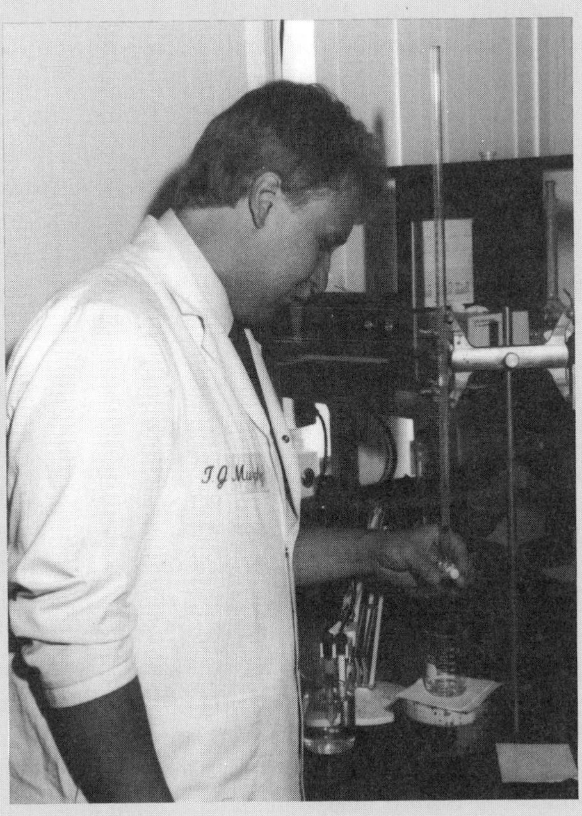

VISTA

LEAD POLLUTION: A SOCIETAL ISSUE

While the products of the chemical industry are usually beneficial, sometimes they are harmful to the environment and human health. Lead is an example.

Lead is a poisonous element. Early symptoms of lead poisoning include weakness, fatigue, stomach pains, and irritability. Chronic lead poisoning causes mental retardation in children, anemia, infertility, and insanity. Most of our lead intake is from lead compounds, not the pure element itself. In Canada, about one million tonnes of lead are used annually. Most of that lead is used in automobile batteries, paints, glass, pottery glazes, and many other consumer products. Lead is also used to make a lead compound known as tetraethyl lead. Tetraethyl lead is added to gasoline to improve the combustion characteristics of the gasoline. Though there are alternative ways of doing this, we continue to market and buy leaded gasoline. Some older cars must use it because their engines were designed for it. However, most cars run just as well or better on non-leaded gasoline. Also, studies have shown that lead decreases the life of engine and exhaust systems.

Most of the lead that enters our bodies comes from automobile exhaust. When we breathe the polluted air, our lungs absorb some of the lead compounds it contains. Also, agricultural crops that are exposed to the polluted air absorb lead compounds which appear in the food made from these crops.

The most significant reductions in lead pollution can be made by banning the use of leaded gasoline. The provincial government has set up a schedule for doing that. For a few more years, however, motorists can choose to pollute the air with this dangerous element. In fact, almost 20% of people with cars designed to run on non-leaded gasoline used leaded gasoline because, until 1988, it was cheaper. In addition to polluting the air, the lead destroys the catalytic converters on these cars. As a result, much higher levels of carbon monoxide, nitrogen dioxide, hydrocarbons, and other pollutants enter the air. Further, engine life is reduced. If you had the power to do something about this issue, what would you do?

VISTA

POLYMERIZATION: THE TECHNOLOGY OF COMFORT AND PROTECTION

Light-weight Outdoor Clothing

The discovery of nylon and other synthetic fibres led to a revolution in outdoor clothing. Strong, relatively non-absorbent and insulating synthetic fabrics were used to make outdoor clothing like ski jackets. A down-filled nylon outer shell and a polyester lining made ski jackets warm and water resistant. However, skiers found that these jackets were bulky and did not allow perspiration wetness to escape. Recently, chemists found the answer to these problems. The absorbency and texture of synthetic fibres were improved by doing such things as "crimping" the yarn to provide air spaces in the fabric. Today, many brands of light-weight ski jackets are available. These jackets are made of a fabric that "breathes". Like your skin, it has billions of microscopic pores. Each pore is much smaller than even the finest raindrop, yet much larger than the water vapour molecules of perspiration. The result: you stay dry inside, even if it is cold and wet outside. Some of these ski jackets are lined with a synthetic polymer with the trade name Thinsulate®. Thinsulate's micro fibres are twice as warm as down, without the bulk. Since the fibres do not absorb water, they continue to insulate even if the fabric is exposed to water.

Bullet-proof Vests

The use of bullet-proof vests by law enforcement officers has saved countless lives and prevented numerous injuries. Modern bullet proof vests are made of a synthetic polymer that is many times as strong as steel. However, these vests are considerably lighter than earlier models which used fabrics reinforced with metallic strands. The lighter vests are more likely to be used by police officers. They are more comfortable to wear and do not restrict the mobility of the users.

UNIT 7 Waste Management

CHAPTERS

All living things make wastes. Our natural environment is designed to clean up such products without pollution. But nature was not designed to treat the huge amounts of waste our large population now produces. Nor was nature designed to handle the synthetic plastics, other polymers, and toxic chemicals that humans have invented.

What wastes do you produce? How much does it cost to clean these up? Is it cheaper to reuse some of these materials again? Which wastes are treated properly? Which ones are not? What responsibilities do you have in managing wastes?

22 What Is Waste?

CHAPTER CONTENTS

CHAPTER OBJECTIVES

After completing this chapter you should be able to:

1. Classify wastes by source and type.
2. Describe what is meant by waste management.
3. Explain why wastes must be managed.
4. Describe techniques for managing waste, including the 4 Rs.

Each Canadian produces almost 3 kg of wastes every day. Yet few people understand what these unwanted materials can do to us or the environment if left untreated (Fig. 22-1). All of us want wastes to be ''gotten rid of''. But we don't realize the difficulties and costs involved. To understand waste management, we must first look at what waste is and what untreated waste can do to the environment.

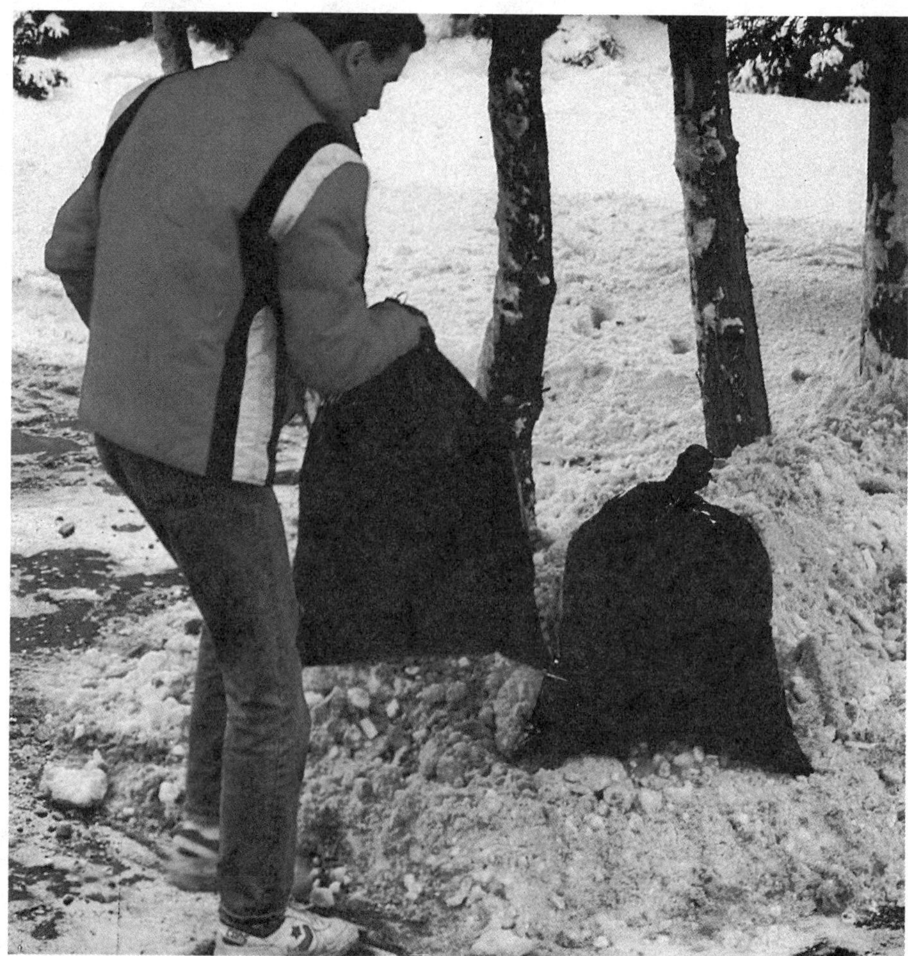

Fig. 22-1 Do you know where your garbage goes? Do you know what treatment it receives? Do you know how it might affect the environment?

22.1 What Is Waste?

Waste is defined as any material that has no further value to its producer. Usually, the producer wishes to get rid of such materials because they take up space, are unattractive, or are unhealthy. For instance, you throw out old newspapers because they take up space. You remove leaves and grass clippings from your lawn because of their untidy appearance. However, the fumes from an oil or natural gas furnace are disposed of because they would poison you if left inside your home.

Wastes come in many forms. Every Canadian produces solids, liquids, and gases that must be disposed of. Some of these wastes are **organic** (contain carbon). Others are **inorganic**. Even energy can be a waste product. What forms of wastes do you produce?

Fig. 22-2 A few week's accumulation of solid waste could look like this.

Solid Wastes

Solid wastes can be classified into groups according to the type of material. Solids are relatively easy to classify: plastic, metal, paper, glass, rubber, food scraps, and so on. In this classification we must include construction wastes such as wood and cement. Our bodies also produce solid wastes called **feces**. What would our environment be like if we did not dispose of all of these solids? Think about all the solid wastes your home produces. Now think about leaving them right where they were produced forever (Fig. 22-2).

Liquid Wastes

Liquid wastes are more difficult to classify. Most of our liquid wastes contain water. These include beverages such as unused milk, wash water, and liquid body waste called **urine**. However, there are a number of liquid wastes that are water-free. These include cleaning solvents, used oil, paint, and glue. Industry produces many chemical wastes in addition to those that are in your homes. What problems do you think all these wastes can cause?

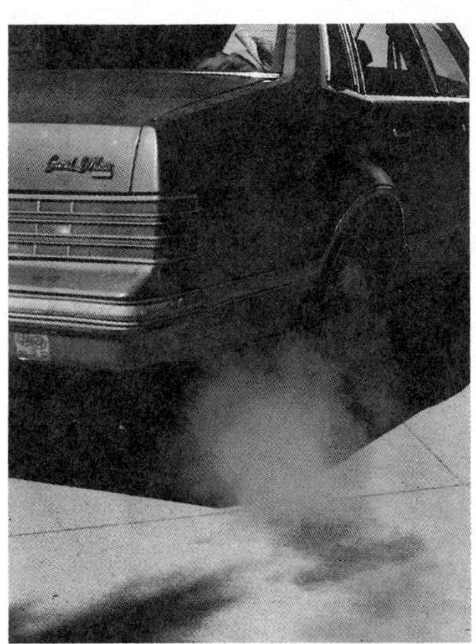

Fig. 22-3 Waste gases such as those which cars emit cause human health problems. They also contribute to environmental damage through acid rain.

Gaseous Wastes

Gaseous wastes are often overlooked when we consider waste management (Fig. 22-3). Our homes and automobiles each produce a tonne (1000 kg) or more of exhaust per year. Many industries also produce exhausts containing numerous chemicals. Individuals also release exotic gaseous wastes. Every time that you use an aerosol can (spray paint, deodorant, hair spray), you release gases into our atmosphere. Scientists believe that some of these gases are harming the environment.

What kinds of wastes do you produce? Are your wastes being handled well? Or are they a problem? What can you do to help?

Section Review

1. What is waste?
2. a) Give five examples of solid waste produced inside your home.
   b) Name two solid wastes produced outside your home.

Fig. 22-4 Which of these wastes are biodegradeable?

3. Name the two human body wastes.
4. Name two liquid wastes that do not contain water.
5. Give three examples of wastes that are released into the atmosphere as gases.

Extension

Form a group with three or four of your classmates. Share ideas regarding ways to reduce the amount of solid waste in your homes and in your community as a whole.

22.2 Activity: Biodegradability

As you learned in Chapter 2, matter is recycled in the natural environment. Our environment is designed to break down waste products so that the atoms in the waste continue through the cycle. Materials that can be broken down by the environment are called **biodegradable**. However, much of the waste we now produce is not biodegradable. Can you predict which wastes in Figure 22-4 are biodegradable and which ones are not? How would you test your prediction?

Problem

What types of wastes are biodegradable?

Materials

plastic tray 25 cm or more deep with cover
moist potting soil to fill the tray
piece of styrofoam cup
leaf
cellophane
orange peel
piece of newspaper
other waste objects of your own choosing
popsicle sticks
cigarette butt
piece of aluminum pop can
piece of cement
piece of glass

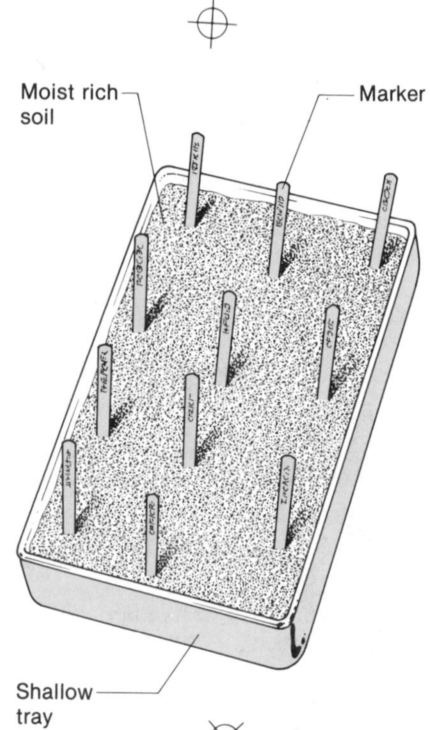

Fig. 22-5 Write the name of each thing you bury on a popsicle stick. Use the sticks as markers.

Procedure

a. Fill the tray with moist soil.
b. Make a list of all objects being tested. Then bury all objects in the soil. Mark the position of each object with a popsicle stick (Fig. 22-5).
c. Cover the tray and store it in a warm location.
d. After a few days, remove all objects from the soil.
e. Examine each object for evidence of decomposition (rotting, changing colour, falling apart).
f. Record all changes in a data chart of your own design.
g. Rebury all objects. Remoisten the soil, if necessary.
h. Repeat steps (c) to (g) for as long as time permits.

Discussion

1. Which objects decomposed completely during the experiment? These objects are **biodegradable**.
2. Some objects did not begin to break down during the experiment. These objects are **non-biodegradable**. List the non-biodegradable objects.
3. Which objects partly decomposed? Do you think that they would decompose completely in time? Are these objects biodegradable or non-biodegradable?

Extension

We use metal cans for food, pop, and other goods. Most of these cans are made of aluminum or steel. Which of these types will rust? What effect does heating this material before burying have on the rate at which rusting occurs? Design and conduct an experiment to investigate these questions.

22.3 Activity: Classification of Solid Waste

What kinds of solid waste do you produce in your home? How much of each kind is produced? Which wastes are biodegradable? Which wastes could be reused? recycled?

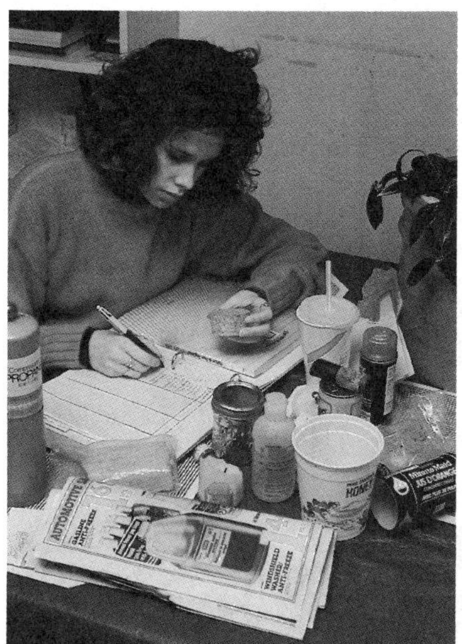

Fig. 22-6 What types of solid wastes does your household throw out? Are any of these difficult to classify? Do any of these require special handling to preserve public health?

Problem

What kinds of solid waste does your household produce?

Materials

samples of solids that you throw out from your home

CAUTION: Wear gloves when you handle wastes.

Procedure

a. Copy Table 22-1 into your notebook. It should occupy an entire page.

Table 22-1 Classification of Solid Waste

Name of waste	Type	Bio-degradable?	Re-usable?	Re-cyclable?	Quantity

b. At home, collect as many kinds of solid waste objects as possible (Fig. 22-6).

c. Record the name of each object in the first column (milk carton, orange peel, soft drink can, newspaper, etc.).

d. In the second column, classify the objects into the following categories: paper, plastic, metal, food scraps, wood, glass, rubber, paint, pesticide, cosmetic, pharmaceutical, or other. Some wastes may fall into more than one category.

e. In the next three columns, indicate with check marks which items you think are biodegradable, reusable, and recyclable. **Reusable** means that the waste item could be used again after cleaning. A glass soft drink bottle is an example. **Recyclable** means that the material in the waste item could be reprocessed into new products. A soft drink can is an example.

f. In the last column, indicate how much of each item is disposed of by your household by using the words "lots", "some", or "rare".

g. Bring five cleaned waste objects to the next science class. These five should include any that you had trouble classifying.

h. As a class or in small groups, discuss the classification of all wastes brought to class.

i. As a class or in small groups, discuss which types (column 2) of garbage make up most of your household waste.

Discussion

1. What types of waste make up most of your solid waste?
2. Could your volume of waste be reduced through reuse or recycling? Explain, using at least three examples.
3. How could your volume of plastic be reduced?
4. How could your volume of paper be reduced?
5. What materials are unnecessarily wasted in your school cafeteria? Describe techniques that could be used to produce less.

Extensions

1. Does your community have a recycling program? If it does not, call your municipal office to find out why your community does not have a recycling program.
2. Find out what products can be made from waste paper. How much is waste paper worth?
3. What uses can be made of waste metal and glass? How much are these wastes worth?
4. Consult officials of your municipality to find out how the volume and type of local industrial waste compares to that from households.

22.4 Why Do We Manage Waste?

Public Health

Our present techniques for handling waste have not been in use for very long. For instance, we take garbage pickup and running water for granted, but these

Fig. 22-7 Commode chairs and chamber pots were in wide use until recent times. Improper disposal of body wastes produces a public health hazard.

are recent developments. Waste disposal a century ago was well described by a Glasgow traveller:

> *". . . lack of lavatories led to the habit of house dwellers filling chamber pots with excreta and after some days, when completely full, and with a shout of, "beware slops", emptying the contents out of the window into the street below."*

Excreta or excrement is made of feces and urine. The "slops" referred to included kitchen scraps and excreta collected in containers such as the chamber pot in Figure 22-7. City dwellers not only had to carry scented handkerchiefs to mask odours, but they had to be nimble, too!

We do not like the appearance and odour of wastes that we produce. These items are unaesthetic. That is, they are not pleasing to our senses. We manage our waste so that it becomes inoffensive. Our environment looks and smells better as a result.

Today, we recognize that dumping wastes on the street is not just unaesthetic, but also unsanitary. The epidemic diseases that swept Europe many decades ago were spread by rats and fleas living on this material. Much of our modern waste management is aimed at **sanitizing** the waste to prevent it from spreading infectious diseases.

Today, we have new wastes that were unknown a century ago. **Radioactive materials** and **hazardous wastes** can cause human diseases as well as environmental destruction. Such wastes must be managed in special ways because they remain toxic for long periods of time. In fact, some of these wastes cannot be destroyed at all. These special wastes will be studied in Chapter 25.

Fig. 22-8 Photographic and X-ray film contains large amounts of silver. This valuable metal can be recovered and used again. Like much of our garbage, old film is a valuable resource.

Resource Recovery

Many wastes are disposed of simply because they are no longer useful. Old appliances, radios, television sets, clothes, bottles, and cars are often thrown out even if they are not defective. Without proper waste disposal, these non-biodegradable items would soon clutter our environment. In addition, however, many of these wastes contain reusable materials such as metal and glass. Proper waste management of such items can save society money and energy. In other words, we should manage wastes to get at the valuable resources that they contain (Fig. 22-8). What other valuable materials are in your wastes? How can we recover these materials?

Environmental Protection

Our environment is our source of life. It provides us with food, air, water, recreation, and other amenities. Some wastes destroy parts of the environment but have little or no direct effect on humans. For example, acid rain does not affect your health directly. However, it is having a profound effect on the environment. It damages forests, food crops, buildings, cars, and aquatic ecosystems. It even releases toxic substances from rocks and soils. Indirectly, then, acid rain does affect your health and your general well-being. Proper waste management considers the environment's health as well as our own. Without a healthy environment, human health will eventually also suffer.

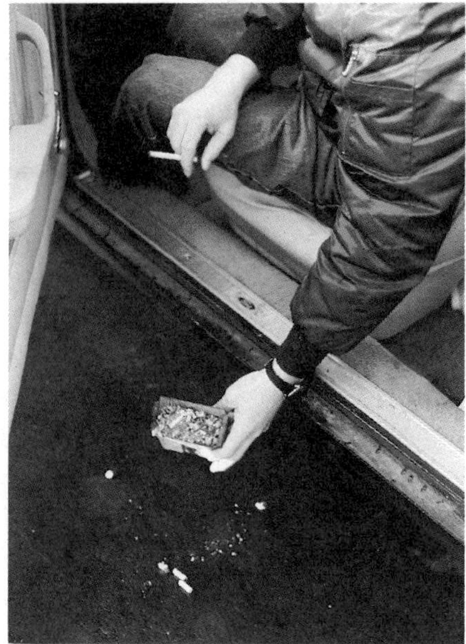

Fig. 22-9 This smoker is "managing" his cigarette wastes during a traffic jam. The butts that escape street cleaners will last in the environment for a long time. Who pays for this cleanup? What alternatives does this polluter have? What do you think of his attitude about waste? Do all smokers share this attitude?

Section Review

1. Explain how humans suffer when household wastes are not properly managed.
2. Explain what is meant by the term aesthetic.
3. a) Give two examples of wastes that humans did not produce a century ago.
   b) Why do these materials require special management?
4. Name three materials that can be recovered from waste.
5. Why must we concern ourselves with the health of our environment?

22.5 How Do We Manage Waste?

In the past, waste management was easy. People just threw the waste away. Winds carried gases away and rivers handled just about anything that was put in them. Solids were dropped just about anywhere—usually away from home! A few people still manage their garbage this way (Fig. 22-9). This **throwaway** option is the main reason that we have pollution.

There are three other things we can do besides throwing waste away. First, we can attempt to produce less. Second, we can treat wastes to make them non-polluting. Third, we can store the wastes in a manner that prevents their escape into the environment. Proper waste management uses combinations of these techniques. **All known wastes can be successfully managed**.

Producing Less with the 4 Rs

The Ontario Ministry of the Environment has been promoting **the 4 Rs of waste management** for years. These techniques—**reuse**, **recycle**, **recover**,

Fig. 22-10 The milk jug is returned to the store. The collected jugs are recycled, or made into, flowerpots and other plastic articles. Several years ago, milk jugs were reused. What are the advantages and disadvantages of reuse over recycling?

Fig. 22-11 A compost heap is an excellent non-polluting waste management system. Table scraps, leaves, and grass clippings quickly decompose, producing humus soil. Both the homeowner and the municipality save money. Can you explain how?

and **reduce**—are all aimed at producing less throwaway waste. **Reuse** involves employing the same waste product over and over. Containers such as egg cartons and glass soft drink bottles are often reused. **Recycling** refers to the use of one industry's waste as a raw material for some other industry. For instance, human sewage can be recycled as fertilizer for certain food crops. Old newspapers can be recycled into cardboard. And plastic milk jugs can be recycled into flower pots (Fig. 22-10). **Recovery** extracts one or more valuable substances from waste and processes these valuables into new products. Metal and glass can be recovered, melted down, and used to make new products. It takes much less energy to produce new containers from recovered metal and glass than it does to produce them from raw materials. **Reduction** is the term applied to any process that results in the production of less waste. **Composting** is a good example (Fig. 22-11).

Which of the 4 Rs do you use? Does your family buy food in refillable containers? Do you separate paper, glass, and metal for garbage pickup? Do you compost kitchen wastes?

Treating Waste

Even after applying the 4 Rs, we will still have leftover materials. These unavoidable wastes usually require treatment to make them aesthetic and safe.

We frequently use burning and burying to treat common garbage. Other materials are digested, detoxified, or sterilized. You will examine some of the techniques used to treat solid and liquid wastes in the next three chapters.

Storing Waste

Certain materials such as radioactive waste and some hazardous wastes are toxic even after treatment. They cannot be allowed into the environment. Such items must be stored for long periods of time in a safe manner. Long-term storage is called **interment**.

Engineers have designed interment facilities that they think will work well. Many people are worried, however, because of potential leakage from the storage sites. Most of us realize the need for these interment facilities, but we don't want one located near us. This conflict between need and location gives rise to the **NIMBY syndrome**—**N**ot **I**n **M**y **B**ack **Y**ard. Should your garbage be "sent away" where it will not affect you but will bother someone else?

Section Review

1. **a)** What four alternatives do we have for managing wastes?
   b) Which of these is unacceptable? Why?
2. **a)** What are the 4 Rs?
   b) Give an example of each.
   c) What do the 4 Rs do to the volume of waste requiring treatment?
3. Name four processes used to treat waste.
4. **a)** What is interment?
   b) Why is interment necessary for certain wastes?
5. **a)** What is the public's concern about waste interment?
   b) What is the NIMBY syndrome?

Chapter Highlights

1. Wastes consist of all solids, liquids, and gases that are no longer useful to their producers.
2. Some wastes are biodegradable; others are not.
3. We must manage our wastes in order to maintain or improve our health and the quality of the environment.
4. All wastes can be successfully treated.
5. We can improve our waste management systems.

Key Terms

aesthetic
biodegradable
composting
feces
inorganic
interment
NIMBY
organic
4 Rs
recover
recycle
reduce
reuse
sanitize
urine
waste

Recognizing the Concepts

Each of the following statements or questions is followed by four responses. Choose the correct response in each case. (Do not write in this book.)

1. Which of the following is *NOT* one of the 4 Rs?
   a) reject **b)** reuse **c)** recycle **d)** reduce
2. Which of the following is the *best* reason for picking up litter alongside a highway?
   a) improve public health
   b) improve aesthetics
   c) improve safety
   d) set a good example
3. Which of the following is the *best* reason for treating human body wastes?
   a) improve aesthetics
   b) improve public health
   c) reduce the rat population
   d) recycle valuable nutrients
4. Which of the following is the *best* reason for treating waste metal and glass?
   a) improve public health
   b) improve aesthetics
   c) reduce costs for new raw materials
   d) these materials are hazardous

Understanding the Concepts

1. **a)** Distinguish among the terms reduce, reuse, recycle, and recover.
   b) What is the overall aim of all of these techniques (the 4 Rs)?
2. **a)** What is the NIMBY syndrome?
   b) How does this syndrome affect our waste management systems?
3. **a)** Why must wastes be managed?
   b) Why do you think that we do not individually manage all of our own wastes?

4. What alternatives do we have for treating non-biodegradable garbage?

Fig. 22-12 Not all recycling and recovery depots are as large or complex as this one in North York, Ontario.

Applying the Concepts

1. Identify as many ways as possible by which your household could reduce its garbage production. Specific application of the 4 Rs would help.
2. Homeowners used to burn leaves in the fall to get rid of them. Explain why municipalities have banned this practice.
3. Explain how composting can convert wastes such as leaves into a valuable resource.
4. Gaseous wastes such as sulfur dioxide cause environmental damage through acid rain. Explain how such environmental damage affects all of us indirectly. You should consider the aesthetic and economic impacts of this damage.
5. Wastes such as scrap lumber, cardboard, and feces are biodegradable, yet can still cause environmental damage. Why is this so?

Investigations

Fig. 22-13 Scrubbers can remove harmful wastes from smokestacks. Do the stacks in your area have scrubbers? If not, why not?

1. Visit a recycling depot in your community (Fig. 22-12). What sorts of materials are handled here? Which recyclable materials are not handled? Why not?
2. Conduct a survey at a local supermarket to determine what fraction of beverages are sold in refillable containers. What reasons do the purchasers of one-time use containers give for their use of such wasteful products?
3. Does your community have a hazardous waste disposal day? If so, what categories of waste are collected? How are they disposed of? If not, your class could try to get such a program established in your community.
4. Investigate the use of scrubbers in smokestacks (Fig. 22-13). How do they remove wastes from exhaust gases? What kinds of wastes are removable? how efficiently? at what cost?

Biography

Catherine Talbot: Municipal Planner

Catherine Talbot is a municipal planner for the City of Burlington. She is responsible for the interpretation and revision of the City's Official Plan. This document is a land-use plan that guides the development of residential, commercial, industrial, agricultural and recreational areas within the city boundary. In any Ontario city, one of the many tasks for planning staff is to determine the need for waste management facilities and to guide the selection of appropriate sites for landfills and treatment plants.

Catherine graduated from the School of Urban and Regional Planning at the University of Waterloo with a degree in Environmental Studies. Planners may also become qualified through Geography courses at other Canadian universities. Educational backgrounds that include math, science, computer skills, or sociology would be an asset. Like most municipal planners, Catherine is a member of the Canadian Institute of Planners (M.C.I.P.) and the Ontario Professional Planning Institute (O.P.P.I.). She has worked for the Province of Alberta, for the City of Edmonton, and for the City of Gloucester near Ottawa.

In the past, Catherine has assisted in the preparation of the waterfront plan for the lakefront in Burlington and Oakville. As a member of Halton waterfront planning team, Catherine represented the interests of the local residents. Municipal planners like Catherine deal with ratepayer committees, politicians, developers, and special interest groups in establishing future policies for their planning areas.

Catherine especially enjoys the diversity of her work. Each year brings new challenges that she is able to work on from start to finish. She also enjoys the team aspect of planning: meeting people, acting as a "clearing house" for ideas, preparing final documents, and speaking to interested community groups, including high school students.

23 Domestic Liquid Waste Management

CHAPTER CONTENTS

CHAPTER OBJECTIVES

After completing this chapter you should be able to:

1. Identify the components of domestic liquid waste.
2. Describe the standard methods of treatment of such wastes.
3. Explain the effects of untreated liquid waste on the environment.
4. Describe the difficulties faced by our sewage management systems.
5. Describe how we can improve our management of liquid wastes.

Water—Canadians' favourite garbage collector. No plastic bags, no smells, no trips to take out the garbage! Just turn on a faucet or flush a toilet and the waste is gone! Or is it?

Where does this waste go? How do we treat it (Fig. 23-1)? Can it get mixed in with our drinking water? Does it spread disease? What effects do these wastes have on the environment? on you?

Fig. 23-1 How does a municipal sewage treatment plant work?

23.1 Our Domestic Liquid Wastes

Almost all the things that we flush away from our homes are both biodegradable and organic. We do not use water to get rid of most inorganic wastes such as metal and glass. In urban areas, water-carried wastes are collected in municipal **sanitary sewers** (underground pipes). These wastes, called **sewage**, are delivered by the sanitary sewers to a **sewage treatment plant** (see Figure 23-1). In rural areas, homes are too far apart to be serviced by sewers. Instead, each home has its own sewage treatment system. This system usually consists of a **septic tank** and **tile bed** (Fig. 23-2). All Ontario homeowners are required by law to use an effective system for handling their liquid wastes.

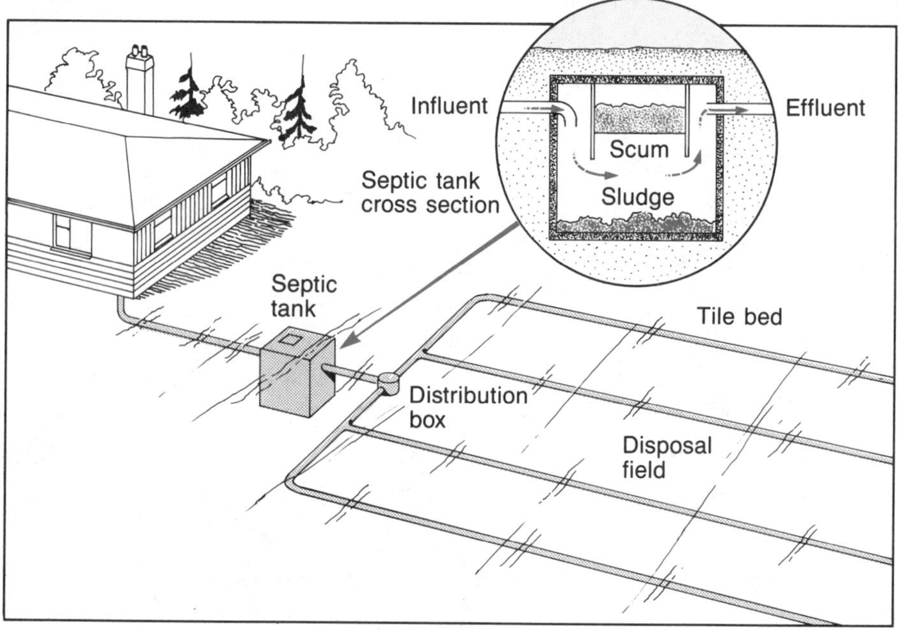

Fig. 23-2 A septic tank and tile bed system treats sewage effectively in areas lacking municipal sewers. Wastes decompose in the tank. By-products trickle out of the tank into the tile bed buried just beneath the surface of the ground. Grass or other vegetation uses the by-product as fertilizer.

What's in Sewage?

The major ingredient in sewage is water. In fact, sewage is more than 99.5% water! The other 0.5% is mainly human body wastes, paper, food scraps, discarded beverages, and soap. Sewage treatment plant operators will tell you that many other items occasionally appear in sewage. From dead pets to diapers, people use the sewers to get rid of an endless variety of objects.

Industries, hotels, hospitals, schools, and commercial buildings also contribute to sewage waste. Of course, organic biodegradable wastes are permitted. Some special wastes can also be put into sewage. However, the producer must have municipal permission and the treatment plant must be capable of dealing with these unusual chemicals. In spite of this, some irresponsible people still add untreatable liquids and solids to our municipal sewage. Large or non-biodegradable items should not be disposed of in sewers. Hazardous substances such as motor oil, cleaning solvents, and poisons should be kept out, too. Have you ever put "illegal" items in the sewer? What problems do they cause?

Section Review

1. **a)** Distinguish between *organic* and *inorganic*.
   b) Give three examples of both organic and inorganic materials.
2. How do urban and rural areas differ in their treatment of sewage?
3. **a)** What are the major ingredients of sewage?
   b) What items should not be put into the sewer? Why?

23.2 Effects of Untreated Liquid Waste

The old practice of dumping sewage just about anywhere, even into waterways, is no longer acceptable. Sewage can spread disease and damage the environment if it is released untreated. Let us look at these two effects of sewage.

Health Effects

Before sewage treatment was introduced, countless millions died of diseases spread by sewage. Diseases such as typhoid fever, cholera, and dysentery are **waterborne**. That is, the disease-causing organisms pass from a sick person's excreta into the drinking water where they can infect healthy people. Clearly, we should kill these **pathogenic** (disease-causing) organisms before they get into our drinking water supplies. In North America, we have been successful in preventing the spread of waterborne diseases. In poorer countries, however, these and other waterborne diseases kill as many as 25 000 people every day!

Testing water for pathogenic organisms is difficult. Therefore we test our water supplies for bacteria found in every human intestine. *Escherichia coli*, or *E. coli*, is a non-pathogenic bacterium that lives in the large intestine of humans. *E. coli* belongs to a group of bacteria called **coliforms**. Most coliforms live in animal intestines. Therefore, if we find coliforms in any water sample, we know that animal sewage is in the water. If we find *E. coli*, we know that untreated human sewage is present. Therefore the water could contain pathogens.

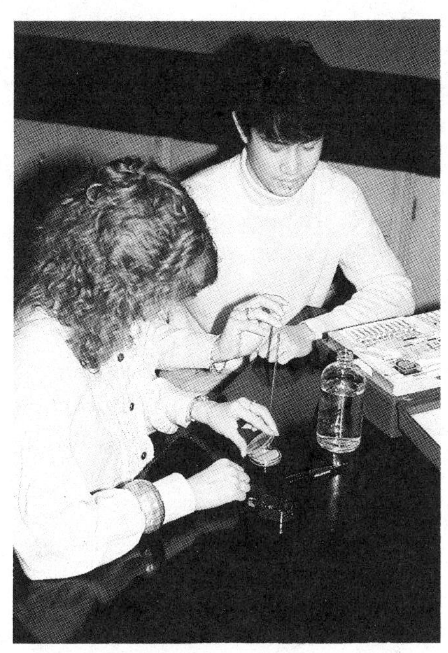

Fig. 23-3 A coliform test kit is used to count the number of bacteria from human excreta in any water sample. A large count indicates the presence of sewage and the possibility of waterborne diseases. Would you want to drink such water? Should you swim in it?

For health reasons, our drinking water must contain no coliforms. If it does, it could also contain pathogens from humans or other animals. In contrast, the water in swimming areas can have a **coliform count** of 1000 per 100 mL before it is deemed unfit for swimming. How do you explain the presence of coliforms in pool water? Why should you not drink pool water?

Public health officials monitor the coliform count of drinking water and swimming areas on a regular basis. Many kits are available that you can use to do the same thing (Fig. 23-3).

You may have noticed that public swimming beaches are sometimes closed for a few days in the summer. This is because sewage has been released into the water and has raised the coliform count above the acceptable level. Closures like these usually happen after a heavy rain. Can you explain why?

Fig. 23-4 This alga, called *Cladophora*, thrives in water that contains sewage. It forms large mats on rocks in streams and along the shores of lakes.

Environmental Effects

Sewage damages the environment in two ways. First, it contains **nutrients** such as carbon, nitrogen, and phosphorus. These nutrients promote the growth of algae. Even a small amount of sewage in a lake can produce a huge population of algae called an **algal bloom** (Fig. 23-4). An algal bloom makes living conditions unacceptable for most other aquatic organisms. For example, some algae release toxins into the water that poison other organisms. Other algae entangle fish in spawning areas. Many algae pile up on beaches and foul swimming areas. But, most important, an algal bloom eventually dies off when it becomes too thick. Then the dead algae decay and rob the water of its oxygen. As you study the second way that sewage harms the environment, you will see how dead algae use up oxygen.

The second way that sewage damages the environment is by decomposition. Aquatic bacteria and other microorganisms use the organic part of the sewage as their food. They react organic compounds with oxygen, just as you do, to get the energy they need for life processes. This type of respiration is called **aerobic** because it uses ''air'' (really just oxygen). In time, these **decomposers** can use up all of the biodegradable organic material. However, the oxygen in the water may also get used up. In the absence of oxygen, other microbes continue to decompose the organic material. This type of decomposition is called **anaerobic** because it occurs in the absence of oxygen. It also creates foul odours.

Fish and other aquatic organisms need oxygen to survive. If decomposing organic material robs the water of its dissolved oxygen, these organisms die. Dead algae from an algal bloom rob water of its oxygen just as sewage does. Further, when the sewage and dead algae decompose, nutrients are released into the water. These nutrients start another algal bloom, and the problems are repeated over and over again.

Sewage plants monitor what is called the **Biochemical Oxygen Demand**, or **BOD**, of their effluents. This is a measure of how much oxygen an effluent will use up from the water into which it is released. BOD is measured in micrograms per gram (μg/g). Untreated sewage has a BOD of about 600 μg/g. That is, the sewage ''demands'', or will eventually use up, 600 μg of oxygen for every gram of sewage. A healthy lake or river normally has an oxygen concentration of around 10 μg/g. Clearly, untreated sewage could soon exhaust a river or lake of its oxygen. A major function of sewage treatment plants is to lower the BOD of the effluent. You will see how this is done in the following section.

Section Review

1. What are the two major effects of untreated sewage?
2. **a)** Explain how a waterborne disease is transmitted from a sick person to a healthy person.
   b) Name three waterborne diseases.
3. **a)** Distinguish between pathogenic and non-pathogenic organisms.
   b) Give an example of a non-pathogenic bacterium.
4. **a)** Distinguish between *E. coli* and coliforms.
   b) What does the presence of coliform bacteria in a water sample tell us?

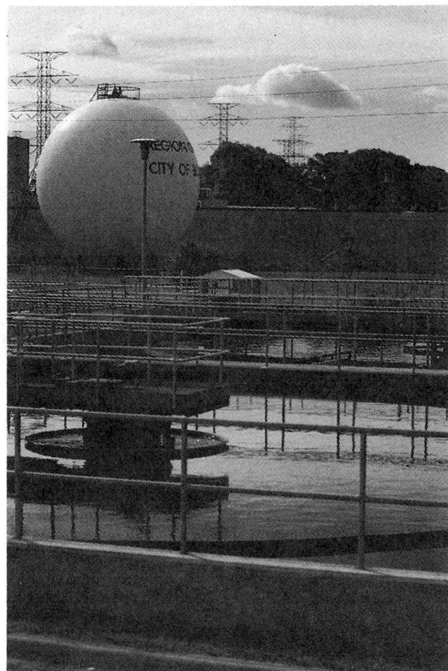

Fig. 23-5 Sewage solids can be stored in a digesting tank. The anaerobic decomposition inside the tank produces methane, or natural gas, which is burned off.

5. Explain how sewage nutrients damage the environment.
6. a) Explain the term BOD.
   b) What harm does sewage effluent with a high BOD do to the organisms living in a river or lake?
7. Distinguish between aerobic and anaerobic decomposition.

23.3 Sewage Treatment

The objective of sewage treatment is to remove those materials that cause health problems or environmental damage. This is accomplished by processes called primary, secondary, and tertiary treatment.

Primary Treatment

Primary treatment of sewage removes the large suspended solids. The sewage is first passed through a series of screens and the trapped material is collected. This trapped waste can be taken to a landfill site, incinerated, or used as fertilizer. It can also be stored temporarily in a "**digesting**" **tank** (Fig. 23-5).

Some suspended solids pass through the screens. Therefore the sewage is allowed to stand undisturbed in a **settling tank**. Much of the remaining solid material settles to the bottom or floats to the surface. Skimmers in the tank remove this **sludge**. It, too, is added to the digesting tank. This removal of solids greatly lowers the BOD of the sewage. The liquid that remains is mostly water. However, it still contains organic matter that gives it a high BOD. It also contains nutrients and pathogenic organisms. The sewage at this stage has a cloudy or turbid appearance.

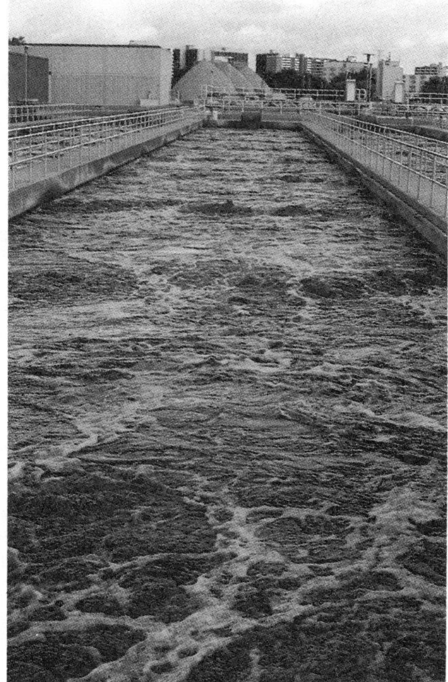

Fig. 23-6 Secondary treatment of sewage. Air is injected into the filtered sewage causing stirring and rapid decomposition of organic materials that raise the BOD.

Secondary Treatment

Secondary treatment is used to lower the BOD as much as possible. Just as in nature, aerobic decomposers such as bacteria are used. Unlike nature, we make sure digestion is rapid and complete by adding large amounts of oxygen. Air is pumped into the sewage (Fig. 23-6). The concentration of organic materials drops rapidly but the bacteria population rises. Paramecia are also used at the secondary stage. They feed on the abundant bacteria.

After aeration the water is passed on to a sedimentation tank, which removes more sludge. A disinfectant such as chlorine gas is added to kill pathogens.

Complete secondary treatment can lower the BOD to nearly 0 μg/g. The sewage can no longer rob a waterway of its oxygen nor can it spread waterborne diseases. But it can still cause algal blooms because it still contains nutrients. In actual practice, secondary treatment is often not done as well as it should be, largely for economic reasons. As a result, the liquid after secondary treatment often has a BOD as high as 30 μg/g.

Tertiary Treatment

Tertiary treatment is a general term for anything that is done to remove nutrients from water. Various chemicals are added to **coagulate** (stick together) the remaining suspended and dissolved particles. This material gradually settles to the bottom. Carbon filters may be used to remove certain chemicals as well. The fully treated sewage water is now safe for release. Any material that we release into our environment is called **effluent**. If it is properly managed, our sewage effluent has little effect on humans or the natural ecosystem. For economic reasons, however, tertiary treatment is often not complete. For example, in Ontario our sewage treatment plants concentrate on the removal of just phosphates during tertiary treatment. Other nutrients are ignored. With one crucial nutrient gone, the chances of the sewage causing an algal bloom are slight. However, the other nutrients are still in the water.

The entire treatment process takes a long time. Primary and tertiary treatment need several hours of settling time. Secondary treatment often requires a day or more. While much of the process is automated, skilled operators are required to ensure the proper operation of the whole process. By the end of the sewage treatment process, the molecules of waste have been collected and transported away for use or broken down into harmless by-products and released into the environment. The transport medium—water—can be released into a river or lake without harm . . . provided, of course, we spend the money to *completely* treat the sewage.

Extension

Electrodialysis or **reverse osmosis** is sometimes used in tertiary treatment to remove dissolved substances. Write a research report describing how this process works and what nutrients it removes from sewage effluent.

Section Review

1. **a)** What materials does primary treatment remove?
   b) What use do we have for these materials?
2. **a)** What does secondary treatment accomplish?
   b) Why is air bubbled through the sewage during secondary treatment?
3. What pollutants are removed in tertiary treatment? How?
4. **a)** Why does treatment require so much time?
   b) Why is sewage treatment often less complete than it should be?

23.4 Activity: Sedimentation and Floc Formation

Very small particles are difficult to remove from sewage. They do not settle out quickly nor can they be easily filtered out. In this activity you will observe how two processes, **sedimentation** and **floc formation**, are used to remove both large and small particles of wastes from sewage water. Instead of real sewage, you will use a mixture of soil and water.

Problem

How can we use sedimentation and floc formation to remove solids from sewage water?

Materials

100 mL graduated cylinders (2)
water
loam soil
alum (aluminum sulfate) solution
lime (calcium hydroxide) solution

Fig. 23-7 Do not disturb the sediment when pouring off the suspension.

CAUTION: Do not get soil particles in the sinks during cleanup.

Procedure

a. Put 100 mL of water in a graduated cylinder.
b. Add 2–3 cm^3 of loam soil to the water.
c. Shake the mixture for 15–20 s. Let it stand for 2–3 min. Then record the appearance of the liquid part (the **suspension**) and of any materials that collect at the bottom (the **sediment**).
d. Let the mixture stand undisturbed for 24 h. Record the appearance of the suspension and the sediment.
e. Pour about half of the suspension into a clean 100 mL cylinder without disturbing the sediment (Fig. 23-7).
f. Record the appearance of the suspension.
g. Add 5–10 mL of alum solution to the suspension.
h. Now add 5–10 mL of lime solution and shake the mixture for 15–20 s. Record the appearance of the suspension.
i. Let the suspension stand for the rest of the class. Record all changes that occur.

Discussion

1. The suspension you produced in step (c) was not unlike raw sewage in appearance. What does simple standing do to the suspension?
2. The material that settled on the bottom of your cylinder is called sediment. What name do we give to the equivalent material in primary sewage treatment?
3. Lime and alum react to form aluminum hydroxide, also known as **floc**. Describe this floc. What effect did floc have on the suspension? Why did it have this effect?
4. Floc can be used during tertiary sewage treatment to remove very tiny particles that do not readily settle out as sludge. Can the water be released into the environment immediately after floc is added? Why or why not?

Extensions

1. Perform experiments to investigate the effects of **filtration**, **distillation**, and **centrifuging** on your suspension in step (e). Does the centrifuge help

sedimentation? Can you explain why? Would any of these processes be practical in a sewage treatment plant? Why or why not?

2. Arrange for a tour of the local sewage treatment plant. Discuss the stages of treatment with the tour guide. What chemicals does the plant use in tertiary treatment? Is the effluent from the plant safe enough to drink? Will it harm the environment in any way?

23.5 Activity: Precipitation

Dissolved materials are difficult to remove from waste water. This activity demonstrates a chemical reaction called **precipitation**. This reaction turns soluble materials into insoluble products. Once formed, insoluble materials can be removed by sedimentation.

Problem

How can we remove dissolved materials from water?

Materials

lead nitrate solution
potassium iodide solution
10–15 mL test tubes (2)

CAUTION: The lead used in this experiment is toxic. Do not pour any wastes down the sink. A waste bottle will be provided by your teacher. Wash your hands thoroughly after the experiment.

Fig. 23-8 Lead is a toxic metal and should not be put into sewage. Store used lead products for transport to a hazardous waste treatment facility.

Procedure

a. Pour about 2 mL of lead nitrate solution into a test tube. Record the appearance of this solution.
b. Pour about 2 mL of potassium iodide solution into the second test tube. Record the appearance of this solution.
c. Carefully pour the second solution into the first solution. Swirl gently to mix the contents. Record the appearance of the mixture.
d. Let the test tube stand undisturbed for 20 min. Record all changes.
e. The test tube used for potassium iodide can be cleaned in the sink. However, the test tube containing the final mixture must be emptied and rinsed into the waste bottle as directed by your teacher (Fig. 23-8).

Discussion

1. The chemical reaction produced a product called lead iodide. Is this chemical soluble? Explain how you know.
2. What types of materials would this precipitation process remove from sewage?
3. At what stage in the treatment process would precipitation be used?

Extension

Copper, iron, and nickel ions can also be removed from water by precipitation. Use chemistry books in your resource centre to find a way to precipitate these ions. With your teacher's permission, conduct an experiment to confirm your findings. What industries should use these processes? Why?

23.6 Problems in Domestic Waste Management

Sewage treatment does not always work perfectly. Several problems can occur. Which of the following two problems can you help correct? Which require action by your municipality?

Sewage Volume

The volume of sewage is remarkably constant from day to day. This is because sewage is produced by people, and people supply a steady volume of wash water and body wastes. However, if the sewer system has been designed improperly, the volume can increase enormously with every rainfall.

Some municipalities use the same sewer line for sewage and rainwater. This extra rainwater does not require treatment. But if it is sent to the sewage treatment plant, the plant is overloaded with diluted sewage. As a result, settling time in the primary and tertiary stages must be cut short. As well, microbial decomposition must be stopped long before the BOD reaches an acceptable minimum. The effluent is released only partially treated. Can you now explain why some swimming areas are closed after a summer storm?

Good municipal engineering uses two sets of sewers (Fig. 23-9). **Sanitary sewers** are used for sewage and **storm sewers** are used for rainwater. Does your municipality have storm sewers? If not, why not?

Fig. 23-9 Rainwater from downspouts, low areas, and roads should be collected by a storm sewer. Why is the storm sewer larger than the sanitary sewer?

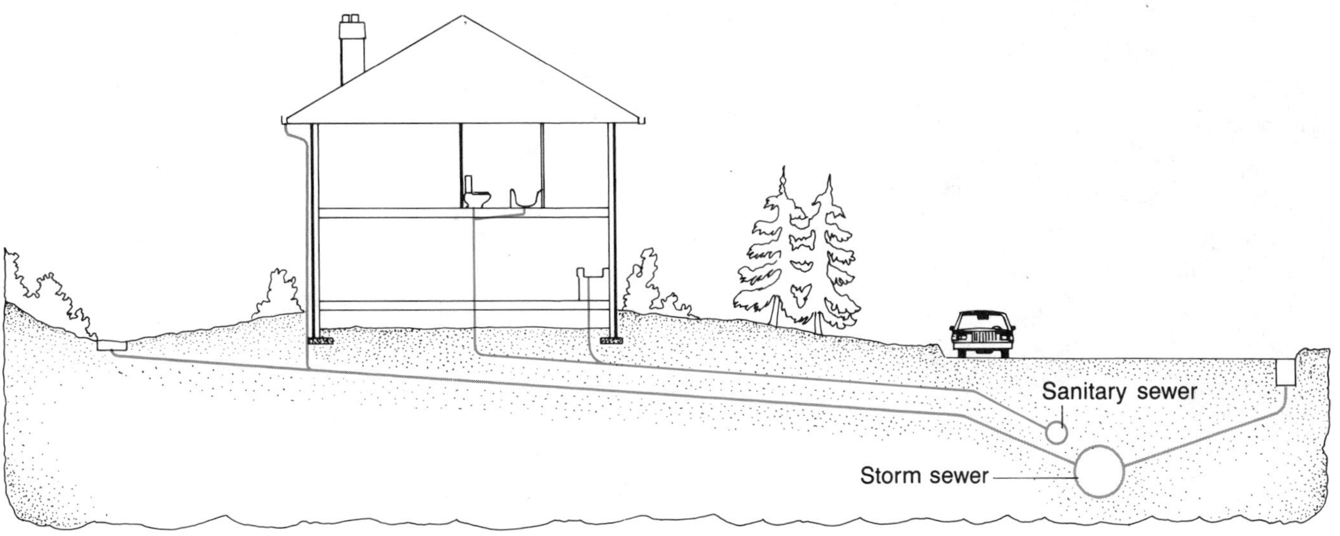

Fig. 23-10 Perhaps you have seen someone dispose of paint or another hazardous waste by pouring it into the storm sewer system. Where does this system end up? What harm could the hazardous waste do?

Some irresponsible homeowners and businesses contribute to the problem as well. These people connect their sump pumps and eavestroughs to the sanitary sewer rather than to the storm sewer. Why do people do this? Does your home have a proper connection?

Hazardous Wastes

Other irresponsible people add hazardous wastes to sewage. These people decide to get rid of cleaning solvent, old paint, oil, or pesticides using the sanitary sewer. The treatment plant was not designed to handle these materials. The microbes used in secondary treatment are particularly susceptible to damage. Many hazardous chemicals can interfere with them or kill them. Secondary treatment is slowed down or even stopped. Does your household dispose of such wastes in the sanitary sewer? How should you properly dispose of these materials (Fig. 23-10)?

Section Review

1. Why is sewage volume fairly constant from day to day?
2. Explain why sewage plants become overloaded when the storm and sanitary sewers use the same pipe.
3. Why does the coliform count of some lakes and rivers go up after a storm?
4. Why should we not dispose of hazardous chemicals in the sanitary sewer?
5. Why should we not dispose of hazardous chemicals in the storm sewer?

Extension

Find out how you are supposed to dispose of hazardous chemicals in your community.

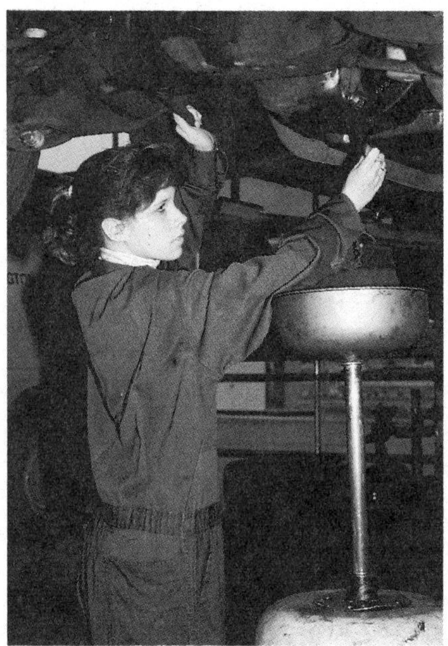

Fig. 23-11 Should used lubricants be added to sewage?

23.7 Activity: Management of Lubricants

Our society uses enormous quantities of oils and greases (Fig. 23-11). These materials, called **lubricants**, decrease friction damage in our machinery. Lubricants like the oil in a car must be replaced periodically. Used lubricants are a waste product. But they are difficult to treat. Microorganisms cannot break them down easily. In this activity you will attempt to find a way to degrade, or break down, lubricants.

Problem

Will lubricants break down in acidic or basic solutions?

Materials

motor oil
lubricating grease
light machine oil
test tubes (9)
test tube stoppers (9)
acidic solution
basic solution
water
marking pen

CAUTION: 1. Wear safety goggles during this activity.
2. Pour all wastes from this activity into the collecting vessel provided by your teacher.
3. If you get any acidic or basic solution on your hands or clothing, flush immediately with water and call your teacher.

Procedure

a. Put about 1 mL of each lubricant in a test tube.
b. Add about 5 mL of acidic solution to each test tube. Stopper and label each test tube.
c. Shake the test tubes vigorously for 10–15 s. Record any changes that you observe.
d. Repeat steps (a) to (c) using water instead of acidic solution.
e. Repeat steps (a) to (c) using the basic solution.
f. Let all nine test tubes stand for 24 h. Then observe any changes.

Discussion

1. a) Compare the densities of the lubricants to the density of water. Explain how you know.
b) What stage in sewage treatment would likely remove lubricants? How do you know?
c) Would a used lubricant such as used motor oil cause problems when mixed with the other wastes removed at that stage? Explain.
2. a) Did the lubricants break down in the presence of acids or bases?
b) What does this tell you about the resistance of lubricants to environmental decomposition?
3. Used lubricants contain valuable components that can be used again. How could they be reclaimed?

Extension

Find out what automotive shops do with used engine oil. What reason(s) do the shop owners provide for handling waste oil this way?

Chapter Highlights

1. Untreated sewage can spread disease and adversely affect the environment.
2. We can successfully manage our sewage with septic systems and sewage treatment plants.
3. Sewage is properly treated in a three-stage process.
4. Physical and chemical processes are used to separate sewage pollutants from water.
5. Hazardous wastes and excessive volume are current problems in our sewage management.

Key Terms

aerobic
algal bloom
anaerobic
biochemical oxygen demand
coagulate
coliform
effluent
floc
lubricant
pathogenic
precipitation
sanitary sewer
sedimentation
septic tank
sewage
sludge
storm sewer
tile bed
turbid
waterborne

Recognizing the Concepts

Each of the following statements or questions is followed by four responses. Choose the correct response in each case. (Do not write in this book.)

1. Which one of the following should *not* be a component of sewage?
   a) lubricants **b)** excreta **c)** water **d)** feces
2. Which one of the following processes removes dissolved nutrients most effectively?
   a) sedimentation **c)** anaerobic digestion
   b) microbial digestion **d)** coagulation
3. Which one of the following is *not* caused by sewage escaping into the environment?
   a) an increased BOD
   b) a lower coliform count
   c) an algal bloom
   d) a lower dissolved oxygen concentration
4. Storm and sanitary sewers using the same pipe will likely:
   a) decrease the BOD of nearby rivers and lakes
   b) decrease the volume of sewage needing treatment
   c) kill aquatic organisms in nearby waterways
   d) reduce the incidence of waterborne disease in the human community

Understanding the Concepts

1. **a)** Distinguish between pathogenic and non-pathogenic organisms.
   b) Give two examples of waterborne pathogens.
2. **a)** Distinguish between aerobic and anaerobic decomposition.
   b) Explain why air is pumped into the holding tanks during secondary sewage treatment.
3. Why do we not use filtration, distillation, or centrifuging to remove suspended solids from sewage?
4. What would happen to the following aspects of our waterways if untreated sewage were dumped into the waterways?
   a) the fish populations
   b) the algal populations
   c) the water quality (colour, smell, taste, oxygen concentration, etc.)

Applying the Concepts

1. Explain how a liquid waste which is toxic to bacteria pollutes the environment if it is disposed of through the sewer system.
2. A number of large communities along the St. Lawrence River do not treat their sewage past the primary stage. What effects will this have on the river? on communities downstream?
3. Swimming pool owners use a variety of chemicals to keep the water in acceptable condition. Among these are a chlorine-releasing agent and a water clarifier. Explain why these two are added and describe how they work. Which stage of sewage treatment is this similar to?
4. Municipal drinking water is treated at a water filtration plant before it is piped to homes. Explain why sand filters, bacteria, and chlorine are used at the plant to treat the drinking water.
5. Outbreaks of cholera and other waterborne diseases often occur in crowded areas after major earthquakes. Explain why this happens.
6. What methods can be used to separate dissolved and suspended materials from sewage?

Fig. 23-12 Garburators place an unnecessary load on domestic sewage systems.

Investigations

1. Visit the water purification plant serving your community. Find out how the preparation of drinking water compares to the treatment of sewage.
2. Some households use **garburators** to get rid of kitchen wastes (Fig. 23-12). Garburators add the wastes to the sewer system. What problems do these extra wastes cause? Explain why garbage pickup and composting are better means for disposing of such wastes.
3. Use a coliform test kit to test for sewage in a variety of water samples. You could try samples from the tap, a river, a lake, and a swimming pool. Stream samples above and below a sewage treatment plant outlet should be interesting.

   CAUTION: Do not go near water that could contain sewage without getting safety precautions from your teacher.
4. Write a report on the operation of a **humus toilet**. How much does one cost? What are its advantages and disadvantages?
5. **Cesspools** and **holding tanks** are alternatives to the treatment systems discussed in this chapter. Find out how these work and why both are illegal in many parts of the province.
6. Find out how a septic system and tile bed work. What maintenance is required on this system?

24 Solid Waste Management

CHAPTER CONTENTS

CHAPTER OBJECTIVES

After completing this chapter you should be able to:

1. Describe the standard techniques for treating solid waste.
2. Explain the advantages and disadvantages of each treatment technique.
3. Identify techniques that you and your family can use to reduce our solid waste disposal problem.

About 1.1 kg of garbage is thrown away every day by each Ontarian. Just like liquid wastes, we want this material to be made aesthetic and safe. We also expect garbage disposal to be cheap and convenient (Fig. 24-1). How is your garbage disposed of? At what cost? How can you reduce the amount of garbage that you produce?

Fig. 24-1 Open dumps are a cheap and convenient way to dispose of solid wastes. However, they are not aesthetic or safe. As a result, they can no longer be used in most areas.

24.1 The Disposal of Solid Waste

Composition of Solid Waste

Solid wastes are also known as **garbage** or **refuse**. Garbage includes materials such as food scraps that degrade quickly. It also includes items that degrade slowly—wood and iron, for instance. Also present are numerous non-degradable materials such as plastics and aluminum. These non-degradable items are sometimes called "new garbage" because they were produced by twentieth century technology.

Disposal Methods

Solid waste disposal is more difficult than liquid waste disposal. It is not as easy to break down these solids into molecules that can be safely released into the environment. Consequently, a variety of disposal techniques are used for garbage.

At one time, garbage was just piled up in an **open dump** as shown in Figure 24-1. Although cheap, this disposal technique is not sanitary. Flies, rats, and birds can transport pathogens far from the dump. Fires in such dumps pollute the air, and wind scatters debris over the surrounding area.

Burying is a common technique for garbage disposal. The refuse is compacted as it is collected by the garbage truck. This reduces the volume of the garbage by squeezing out the air. The garbage is then buried in a **sanitary landfill site**. Layers of garbage are covered with layers of soil as shown in Figure 24-2. What improvements does this technique have over open dumping? Would you want a landfill site near your home? Landfills are not as cheap as open dumps. The location of a landfill must be carefully selected. Due to the massive volume of garbage produced in some communities, nearby landfill sites are used up quickly. Garbage must then be transported a greater distance—perhaps to a neighbouring community. Would you want garbage from another area buried in your community? Also, the biodegradable part of the garbage

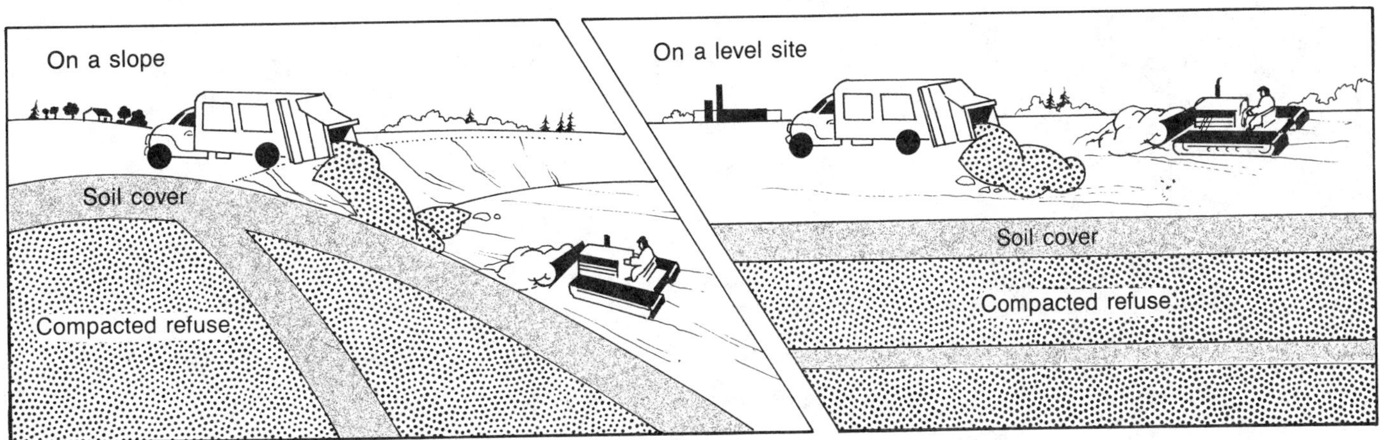

Fig. 24-2 Degradeable garbage slowly decomposes in a sanitary landfill. Some municipalities have made toboggan and ski hills using garbage.

undergoes anaerobic decomposition. This produces methane (natural gas) and other gases. The odours that accompany the production of these gases can foul large neighbourhoods for decades after the garbage has been buried.

Burning is another alternative for solid waste management. The organic parts of the solids are converted largely to carbon dioxide and water. A variety of other gases are produced and released into the atmosphere as well. The remaining residue—a small volume of ash and slag—is buried. This technique is known as **incineration**. It has a number of advantages over burying, but it can cause serious air pollution, particularly when plastics are burned.

Sorting and recycling holds the promise of solving many of the problems of other disposal methods. Each producer of garbage sorts out those materials that can be recycled. In other words, steel cans, aluminum cans, glass, and paper are placed in separate garbage pails. The remaining small volume of garbage can undergo further sorting to remove recoverable materials. Anything left is buried.

In the long run, **reduction** is the key to improved solid waste management. We must develop ways of producing less waste. How is this possible? Are there ways in which you can start now?

Section Review

1. Which components of garbage are biodegradable? Which ones are not?
2. What are the advantages and disadvantages of open dumping?
3. Why is garbage compacted before burial?
4. What can a community do when all of its landfill sites have been used up?
5. What are the advantages and disadvantages of incineration?
6. How can the 4 Rs help solve the solid waste problem?

24.2 Activity: Garbage Reduction

Our consumer society markets many products in individual packages. Some of these packages are unnecessary and some are even double- or triple-wrapped. For instance, cereal is frequently packaged in a wax paper bag inside a box. And toothpaste is sold in a tube inside a box. Some reusable containers are designed to be thrown away after one use. These over-wrapped and throwaway packages contribute to our garbage problem. What products in your home generate excessive garbage? What sorts of unnecessary materials are in this waste? What can you and your family do to produce less waste (Fig. 24-3)?

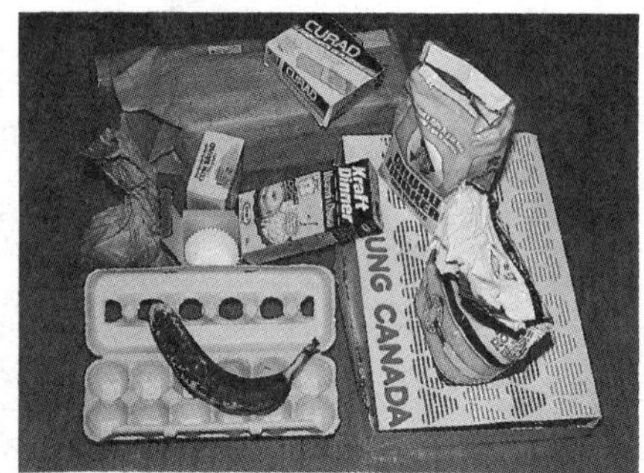

Fig. 24-3 Single-wrapped, degradeable packages do not overburden our waste management systems.

Problem

How can you produce less solid waste?

Materials

packages and containers in your home

Procedure

a. Copy Table 24-1 into your notebook. Allow enough space for 25 entries.

Table 24-1 Overpackaging

Product	*Packaging material*	*Reusable or recyclable?*	*Alternative*

b. At home, examine consumer goods, particularly food, beverage, and cleaning items.

c. List products in the "Product" column that you think produce more waste than they should.

d. Classify this extra waste in the second column as "plastic film", "moulded plastic", "other plastic", "glass", "metal", or "other".

e. In the next class, assemble in small groups. Discuss the following questions:
- What packaging material was most commonly used on overpackaged products?
- Which packages could be recycled or reused?
- What alternatives are there to this unnecessary waste?

f. As a class, discuss:
- How buying products in bulk in your own containers would affect the quantity of waste.
- Whether or not we should allow "No deposit—no return" beverage containers in place of refillable ones.

g. After the discussions, complete the last two columns in your chart.

Discussion

1. What types of package materials were most common in your home? Which ones were least common?
2. What changes will you make to produce less waste in your home?
3. Describe one example of a way to reduce the solid waste at your school.
4. It has been suggested that **reject** be made the fifth "R". Explain how this "R" would work in our waste management. What do you think of this suggestion?

Extension

Conduct a survey to determine what fraction of Canadian households use disposable beverage containers and how many containers are used per week. Measure the mass of typical throwaway bottles and cans. Find out the approximate number of families in your community from your local municipal office. Use the data to determine how many tonnes of such containers are thrown away annually. Contact a local recycling depot to find out the current price of scrap glass and metal. What is the dollar value of your community's beverage container garbage?

24.3 Solid Waste and the Environment

Most people do not like to see our cities or countryside littered with garbage. Our present methods of garbage disposal prevent such unaesthetic waste disposal. However, these methods do not prevent some environmental problems.

How Landfill Sites Affect the Environment

Landfill waste slowly decomposes into a wide range of substances. For example, buried metals corrode. That is, they gradually convert into ions. And food wastes decompose into acids and many other molecules. Many of these molecules and ions are soluble in water. As rain or ground water enters the landfill, these molecules and ions **leach** out of the landfill and into the natural environment (Fig. 24-4). Rivers and lakes, including sources of drinking water, can be affected. Do you want your drinking water to contain these leached materials?

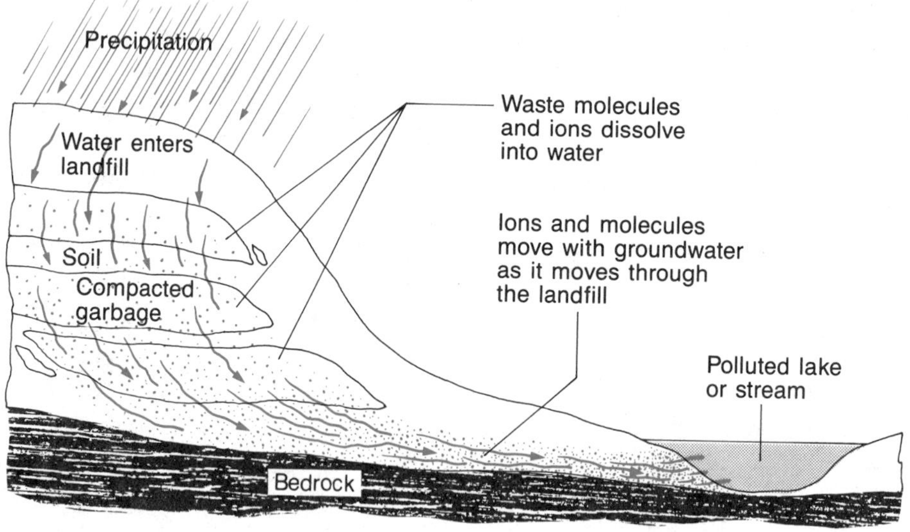

Fig. 24-4 Molecules and ions (shown in colour) move away from a landfill by a process called leaching. Why is it important to prevent hazardous materials from being added to a landfill?

Another problem with landfills is **erosion**. Soil and garbage can be washed away by rain. Once the site is full, erosion can be largely prevented with a vegetation cover. But erosion is difficult to control while garbage is still being added to the site.

Even after a site is covered over and vegetation planted, foul-smelling gases seep up from the buried waste. Nearby residents complain about the odour and worry about unknown health effects. One of the gases released is **natural gas** or **methane**. Engineers are trying to develop a way of converting large volumes of garbage into valuable products like methane. In the future we might rely on these noxious gases to supply some of our energy needs.

Finally, landfills cannot be put just anywhere. The possibilities of leaching and erosion eliminate many potential sites. Nearby residents block the use of others. The politics of garbage disposal will result in ever-increasing costs for new sites. It will also result in increased transportation costs, especially for urban residents. At some time in the future, the excessive financial and environmental costs of burying wastes may force us to look at alternatives.

How Incineration Affects the Environment

Incineration provides some solutions for landfill problems. Site, soil, and transportation costs are low. Leaching and erosion are reduced because only the residual ash is buried. But incineration has a major drawback—air pollution.

Incinerators release many harmful substances into the air. Among these are acids and corrosive particles. Toxins (poisons) such as hydrogen cyanide, furan, and dioxins are also released. Even carcinogens (cancer-causing agents) such as vinyl chloride are released. In some American cities, incinerators are the major source of air pollution.

Cleaning devices called **scrubbers** can be installed on incinerators to reduce their harmful emissions. However, scrubbers are expensive, both to install and to operate.

The Solution?

The 4 Rs offer the best long-term solution to solid waste disposal. The cost in dollars is higher than other methods right now. However, this calculation of cost does not include a calculation of environmental damage, health effects, or resource depletion. These items should be considered if we are to calculate the true value of any waste management method. Would your family be prepared to spend a few more dollars per year to ensure better health and a cleaner environment? Are you prepared to reduce and recycle your wastes for the same objective? Are you prepared to convince others to do the same?

Section Review

1. Explain how water-soluble wastes escape from a sanitary landfill. What is this process called?
2. Explain why the costs of landfilling are constantly increasing.
3. What types of chemicals does incineration put into the atmosphere?
4. How can the 4 Rs help our garbage problem?

24.4 Activity: The Cost of Solid Waste Management

How much does garbage disposal cost in your community? How much does it cost in all of Canada? How much does it cost each Canadian (Fig. 24-5)?

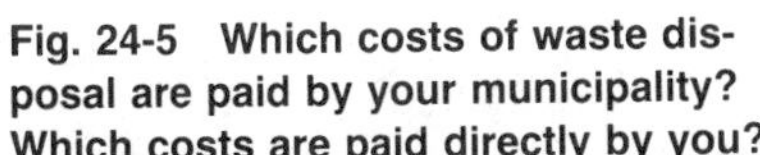

Fig. 24-5 Which costs of waste disposal are paid by your municipality? Which costs are paid directly by you?

Problem

What is the cost of garbage disposal?

Materials

financial statement from your municipality
population data for your municipality and for Canada

Procedure

a. Use the financial statement to determine the total annual cost of garbage disposal in your municipality.
b. Divide this total cost by the number of people living there who use municipal service. (Rural residents may not have service.) This is the annual per person cost for local garbage disposal.
c. Multiply your answer in (b) by the total population of Canada. This is the total Canadian cost for garbage disposal.
d. The average Canadian produces 400 kg (0.4 tonne) of garbage per year. Use your answer in (b) to calculate the cost per tonne of garbage disposal in your municipality.
e. Calculate how many tonnes of garbage are produced annually in Canada.

Discussion

1. How do you think the cost of garbage in your area compares to that in larger and smaller communities? Why?
2. Which of the following costs of garbage are included in your calculation? Which are not?
- labour (drivers, collectors, machinery operators)
- machines (trucks, bulldozers, etc.)
- incinerators (land, building, and operation costs)
- land (new sites for sanitary landfills)
- health costs (treatment of diseases from pollution)
- pollution costs (maintenance or repair of damage caused by pollution)
- aesthetic costs (reduction in value of property located near waste sites)

3. Do you think all of the items in Question 2 should be included in "cost of garbage disposal"? Why or why not?

24.5 Activity: The Disposal of Plastics

Plastics are a miracle product of modern chemistry. We use them just about everywhere: clothing, car parts, artificial bones and blood vessels, electrical insulation, and packages of all kinds. We even package our garbage in plastic! Unfortunately, the properties of plastics that make them so useful also prevent their easy disposal. For safety reasons, your teacher may choose to demonstrate those parts of this activity which use an acid and a base.

Problem

How can we dispose of plastic wastes?

Materials

small pieces of a variety of types of plastic

test tubes (4)	strong acid solution
marking pencil	strong base solution
water	tongs
ethyl alcohol	Bunsen burner

CAUTION: 1. Burning some plastics gives off a toxic gas. Burn plastics only in a fume hood (Fig. 24-6).
2. Wear safety goggles, gloves, and aprons during this activity.
3. If you spill liquids on your skin or clothes, flush thoroughly with water and call your teacher.

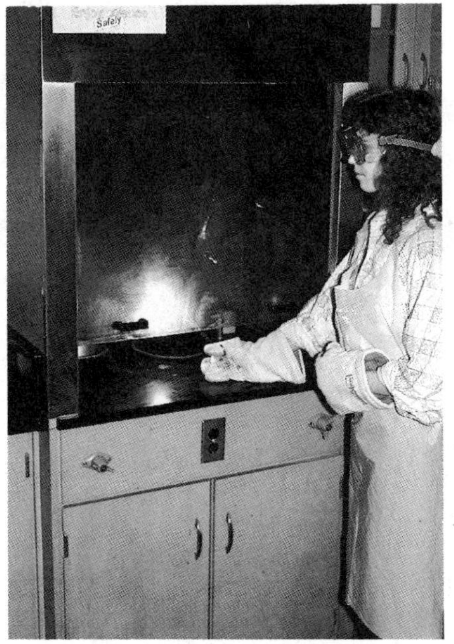

Fig. 24-6 Use a fume hood when testing plastic samples for combustibility.

Procedure

a. Obtain a variety of small pieces of plastic from your home or other places.
b. Prepare a data chart in your notebook with one column for each of the following tests: name of plastic, colour, transparency, hardness, elasticity, flexibility, brittleness, solubility in water, solubility in ethyl alcohol, solubility in a strong base, solubility in a strong acid, and combustibility.
c. Half fill a test tube with each of the following liquids: water, ethyl alcohol, a strong base solution, and a strong acid solution.
d. Label the contents of each test tube using the marking pencil.
e. Select a sample of plastic. Record its name (nylon, cellophane, PVC, green garbage bag, etc.) in the first column.
f. Record the colour of this sample in the second column.
g. Is the sample transparent? hard? elastic? flexible? brittle? Record your answers in the next four columns of your table.
h. Put the sample in the test tube with water. Does it dissolve or react? Record your answers.
i. Repeat step (h) with ethyl alcohol, the base solution, and the acid solution. Use a new sample of plastic each time or rinse the old one well with water before using it again.
j. Observe your teacher attempting to burn a piece of each plastic sample over a Bunsen burner in a fume hood. Is it combustible? Record your result in the last column.

CAUTION: Your teacher may choose to demonstrate or omit this step. A fume hood must be used.

Discussion

1. a) Describe the reactivity of plastics to water, ethyl alcohol, acids, and bases.
b) Why do we use plastics to package so many of our foods?
2. What disposal technique is effective in degrading plastics? Why do we not like to use this method?

3. Are plastics biodegradable? How do you know?
4. If you were a manufacturer of plastic products, what alteration in the chemistry of plastic might you try to make? Why?

Extensions

1. Design an experiment to test the effects of sunlight on your plastic samples. Several months of exposure may be necessary. Be sure to retain matching samples as controls.
2. A chemist at the University of Toronto, Dr. J.E. Guillet, invented a plastic that degrades in a few days when it is exposed to sunlight. Find out more about this plastic. Will it help solve our litter and waste disposal problems?

24.6 The Future of Solid Waste Management

Fig. 24-7 An incinerator. By 1987, construction had begun on what will be the world's largest incinerator. The prevailing wind will carry pollutants from this giant plant in the city of Detroit, Michigan across to Windsor and the best farmland in Canada. The incinerator will not have the best pollution control equipment. What effects will this plant have on your food? On your health? What can you do about this problem? Which levels of government should be involved?

Our solid waste management systems are in trouble. The problems include:

- shortage of suitable land near urban centres for waste burial
- water pollution from leaching
- air pollution from incineration
- increasing costs for land, labour, transportation, equipment, and planning
- political conflict between municipalities over waste disposal sites and disposal techniques (Fig. 24-7)

The NIMBY syndrome summarizes how many citizens feel about solid wastes: **N**ot **I**n **M**y **B**ack **Y**ard. Many of us want an affluent (wealthy) lifestyle. But we do not want garbage—our own or others'—anywhere near us. Our solution to the garbage problem used to be "throw it away". But now, we are running out of "aways".

The 4 Rs appear to be the best solution to solid waste management. Industries, commercial outlets, and individuals will eventually be required to do **source separation**. That is, the producer of the waste will have to sort the material by type (paper, glass, metal, etc.) before pickup. Recovery plants will recycle most of this material. Garbage cans will be used to handle the remaining garbage; plastic bags will be avoided.

The 4 Rs and You How will your lifestyle change in order to solve our solid waste problems? Are you prepared to reject wasteful products? separate your garbage? return empty containers for reuse? Are you prepared to pay more for good waste management? Should people be fined if they don't cooperate?

Section Review

1. What problems do our present disposal techniques have?
2. What is the NIMBY syndrome?
3. a) What is source separation?
   b) Who does this separation?
4. Why will the cost of future garbage disposal increase?

Chapter Highlights

1. We each produce about 1.1 kg of garbage every day.
2. Garbage is managed by burying, incineration, and the use of the 4 Rs.
3. Burying and incineration will become less appropriate for our society because of the environmental and economic problems they cause.
4. The 4 Rs provide the best long-term solution to our solid waste problems.

Key Terms

carcinogen
corrode
erosion
incineration
leaching
NIMBY syndrome
open dump
refuse
sanitary landfill
scrubber
source separation
toxin

Recognizing the Concepts

Fig. 24-8 This automotive manufacturer used to throw away tonnes of cardboard each month. Now, the factory shreds, bundles, and sells this waste for reprocessing into new cardboard. Not only is the former expense of disposal gone, but the company makes a profit from waste!

Each of the following statements or questions is followed by four responses. Choose the correct response in each case. (Do not write in this book.)

1. Figure 24-8 shows the technique of
   a) reduction **b)** recycling **c)** reuse **d)** rejection
2. Which of the following is the *least* suitable waste management technique for individual urban residents?
   a) source separation
   b) rejection
   c) composting
   d) sanitary landfilling
3. Which of the following statements about incineration is *not* correct?
   a) Incineration produces acids, toxins, and carcinogens.
   b) Incineration avoids the need for garbage burial sites.
   c) Air pollution can be reduced with scrubbers.
   d) Organic molecules are converted to gases and released into the air.
4. Approximately how much garbage is produced annually by a Canadian family of four people?
   a) 400 kg **b)** 36.5 kg **c)** 1600 kg **d)** over 10 000 kg
5. What two problems are associated with landfill sites?
   a) leaching and air pollution
   b) waterborne disease and leaching
   c) increasing land and labour costs
   d) leaching and political conflict

Understanding the Concepts

1. What problems of open dumps are corrected by sanitary landfills?
2. Landfill sites cannot be used as a place to erect buildings until many years after their closing. Why is this so?
3. **a)** Distinguish between leaching and corroding.

Fig. 24-9 Landfill sites such as this one in Halton County are constructed to minimize future problems. Due to soil and groundwater conditions, such sites cannot be located on just any unused piece of land.

b) Explain how leaching and corrosion contribute to pollution from landfill sites.

5. Figure 24-9 shows a landfill site prior to filling with garbage and soil. Why is the site bowl-shaped? Why do you think the sides of the site are formed with clay soil? Why is there a "sewer" pipe at the bottom?

Applying the Concepts

1. Explain why landfills are not suitable for building sites but may be used as recreational areas.
2. The type of soil used as a base and cap for landfill sites should be chosen carefully. Should these soils let water through easily, or should they resist water movement? Explain.
3. What changes could you and your family make in your present garbage management to improve it?
4. What changes could your municipality make to reduce the volume and cost of garbage disposal?
5. How could your school cafeteria reduce its garbage volume? What difficulties do the cafeteria employees see in making these changes?

Investigations

1. Visit your local landfill site. How many tonnes are handled by the site each day? How long will the current landfill site last? What action is taken to reduce leaching?
2. People trapped in a burning building or plane die rapidly from toxins in the smoke. Burning plastics and glues give off such chemicals as hydrogen cyanide. It is lethal in three minutes at a concentration of 200 μg/g. Find out what other toxic chemicals are produced in smoke. What building or decorating materials produce these?
3. Landfilling often sterilizes the buried garbage. Find out where the heat comes from that causes this sterilization.
4. Does your community use incineration? If so, visit the incinerator to find out how many tonnes of garbage are burned each day. Does the plant use scrubbers or precipitators? If not, why not?
5. Plastics cause disposal problems because they are not biodegradable. Prepare a report on the development of degradable plastics. What products should these be used in? What products should continue using non-degradable plastic?
6. **Energy From Waste (EFW)** disposal plants were popular a few years ago. Find out what an EFW plant is. What advantages and disadvantages did they have compared to other means of disposal?
7. Find out why the brewing industry altered its containers as shown in Figure 24-10. What fraction of the new containers are reused? recycled?

Fig. 24-10 The Ontario brewing industry used to sell all of its product in a standard bottle shown on the left. Each bottle was reused about 30 times, meaning that little garbage was produced. Now, the containers have changed. Cans may be recycled but not reused. What effect does this change have on our garbage problem? Does this change cost you anything even if you do not buy this product?

Biography

Gerald Bengert: Research Technician

Gerald Bengert is a research technician for the National Water Research Institute at the Canada Centre for Inland Waters (C.C.I.W.) in Burlington, Ontario. He does field work throughout Ontario and chemical analysis at the centre. During his career, he has also worked for the NWRI in British Columbia. The NWRI is Environment Canada's largest research establishment.

We do know that certain hazardous wastes get into our waterways. But we don't always know what will happen to each pollutant or what damage it will cause to the physical and biological components of the environment. The research teams at NWRI concentrate on specific pollutants with three objectives in mind:

- improving methods of analysis for detection of these chemicals (Some substances are difficult to detect, especially in low concentrations.)
- identifying the path the pollutant takes as it moves through the environment
- identifying the "compartment" where the pollutant ends up (for example, in the atmosphere, in solution, absorbed in sediment, in the surface microlayer, or in the food chain)

Much of our knowledge about specific wastes has come from NWRI and other similar research organizations. Ultimately, this knowledge is put to use resolving our environmental problems.

Gerald Bengert's team is involved in the study of alkyl lead compounds in waterways in southwestern Ontario. Because clams bioaccumulate these materials in their soft tissues, Gerald analyzes them. Clam cages are used to maintain research control over the specimens. Control is difficult with fish and birds. Gerald visits each caged group about once per month to record data and to collect samples for chemical analysis. The results of this study will be published after four years of monitoring. The people who work for Environment Canada are giving us the information we need to make choices that affect our future environment.

Career: *SCALE OPERATOR*

HELP WANTED: SCALE OPERATOR
Scale operator required by municipal waste management facility.

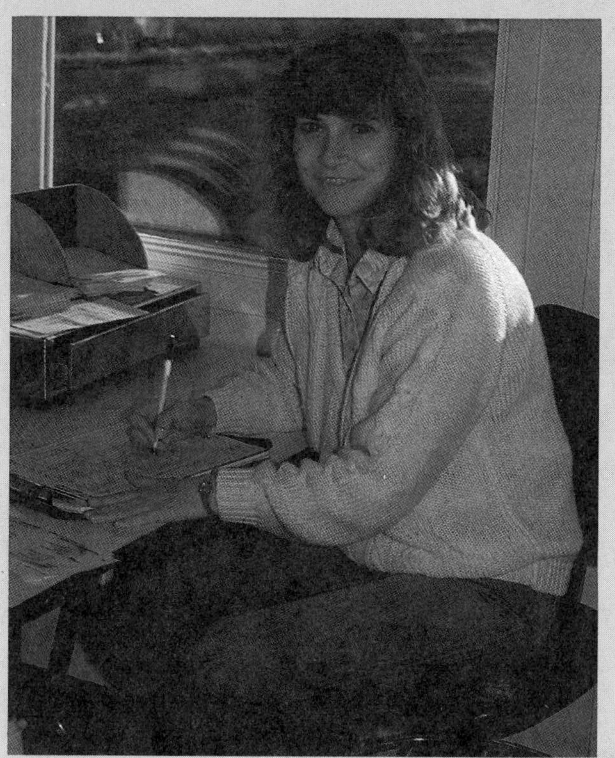

Scale operators are employed by solid waste management facilities to control and record the movement of materials. Some operators assist in the classification of wastes and control the arrival and departure schedules for dangerous products. Good communication skills and a knowledge of secondary school science are important assets. Mathematical and bookkeeping skills are also necessary for accounting and billing procedures. A successful operator has a pleasant personality and enjoys interacting with other people.

To prepare for this career you should obtain your Ontario Secondary School Diploma, including science, mathematics, English, and business courses.

25 Hazardous and Radioactive Wastes

CHAPTER CONTENTS

CHAPTER OBJECTIVES

After completing this chapter you should be able to:

1. Define and give examples of hazardous wastes.
2. Classify such wastes according to how they act.
3. Name the industrial sources for common hazardous and radioactive wastes.
4. Describe how hazardous and radioactive wastes affect us.

We cannot escape! Hazardous chemicals seem to be everywhere—in our air, in our water, and even in our food! Newspapers, radio, and television report many frightening events: dioxins in our drinking water; toxins leaching from Love Canal; pesticides in our food; radioactive soil in a community. What are these chemicals? Where did they come from? Can they really affect us? Is the problem as bad as the media say? What can we do to clean up our environment and keep it clean (Fig. 25-1)?

Fig. 25-1 Many hazardous wastes are found in your own household. Can you identify them? Do you know how to use them safely? Do you know how to dispose of them when they are no longer needed?

25.1 What Are Hazardous Wastes?

A **hazardous waste** is defined this way:

Hazardous waste is any material which no longer serves a purpose and which requires special precautions in its handling to prevent damage to people, property, or the environment.

Included in this definition are useful substances that accidentally get into the environment. A spill of petroleum from a tanker is an example. This useful material becomes a hazardous waste when it escapes. This definition excludes radioactive wastes. Although radioactive materials are indeed dangerous, they are treated differently from those chemicals that meet the definition of hazardous.

What Does "Hazardous" Mean?

Generally, a hazardous chemical interferes with life. The chemical may affect an individual, a population, or the entire biological community in an ecosystem. Hazardous chemicals fit into one or more of the following categories.

Poisonous or Toxic This is any chemical that is capable of causing health damage or death when consumed in small amounts. "Consumption" includes not only eating, but also absorption by the lungs or skin. The restriction of "small amount" is the key to distinguishing poisons from other chemicals. For instance, salt is capable of killing you if you eat several kilograms. Similarly, aspirin can kill if too much is used. But we do not normally think of these chemicals as poisonous. The dose is what distinguishes poisons from other chemicals. A true poison can cause damage in small doses or at low concentration. This category also includes chemicals that can cause cancer, mutations, or birth defects.

Every organism can withstand the poisonous effects of small doses of toxins. The amount of any toxin that is needed to affect an organism is known as the **tolerance** level. Tolerances are often expressed in parts per million (ppm), parts per billion (ppb), or even parts per trillion (ppt).

Corrosive Any chemical that is capable of chemically consuming storage containers or body tissue is called corrosive. Rusting metal is just one example of corrosion. Other materials, including concrete, glass, and human flesh can be corroded by some wastes.

Reactive or Explosive Any unstable material that reacts vigorously is called reactive. Nitric acid is an example. Reactive substances that violently release gases are called explosive. Nitroglycerine and gun powder are examples.

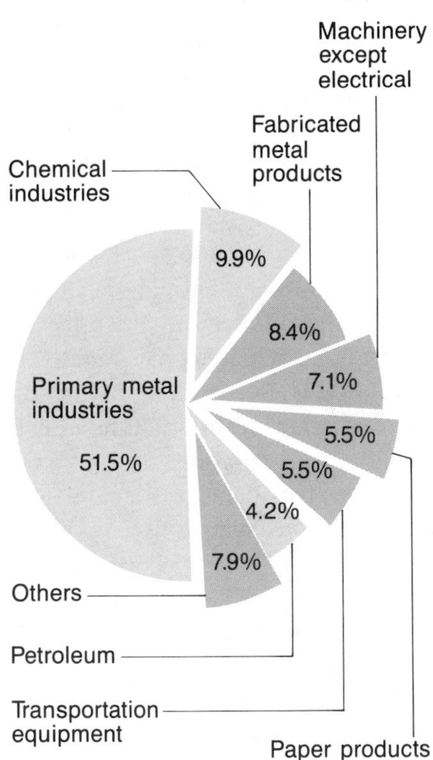

Fig. 25-2 Ontario industries produce about 1 500 000 tonnes of hazardous waste each year. The coloured sectors are primary industries.

Flammable or Ignitable Any chemical that can burn fits into this category. Gasoline and metals like potassium are examples. Some of these substances are capable of starting a fire without a spark or match. Your home likely contains several flammable items. Cleaning solvents, styrofoam packing pellets, and even fertilizers containing ammonium nitrate are flammable.

Sources of Hazardous Wastes

Just about all manufacturing generates hazardous wastes. Over half of this waste in Ontario comes from **primary** metal industries such as steel and nickel producers. Other industrial sources are indicated in Figure 25-2. **Secondary** industries use the products of primary industries to make new goods. For example, a nail manufacturer (secondary) uses metal from a steel maker (primary). A furniture manufacturer using these nails is considered to be a **tertiary** industry.

Homeowners produce hazardous wastes as well. We get rid of toxins such as pesticides and paint. We pour corrosives such as muriatic acid, lye, and drain cleaners into the sewers. And we dispose of flammables such as oils, grease, and cleaning fluids. Even some detergents, glues, pharmaceuticals, and cosmetics (like nail polish remover) are hazardous.

In all, the average Ontarian produces almost 200 kg of hazardous waste each year. And Ontario produces half of the Canadian total. About 70% of this is produced in the industrial "Golden Horseshoe" around the western end of Lake Ontario. As the major Canadian producer of hazardous material, what responsibility does Ontario have in reducing the quantity of waste and in providing suitable disposal systems? Do you think we should treat the wastes here? Or should we ship them to another province or country? What kinds of control systems should be in place to prevent accidental and intentional dumping of these materials? How will you be affected if such controls do not exist?

Section Review

1. **a)** Define "hazardous waste".
   b) What hazardous materials are excluded from this definition?
2. **a)** What are the four categories into which hazardous wastes are classified?
   b) Identify the hazard for each category.
3. What distinguishes poisons from other chemicals?
4. **a)** Distinguish among primary, secondary, and tertiary industries.
   b) Which type produces the largest mass of hazardous waste in Ontario?
5. **a)** What hazardous wastes are produced by homeowners?
   b) How much hazardous waste does each Ontarian produce annually?

25.2 How Do Hazardous Wastes Affect Us?

Improperly managed wastes affect us in three main ways. First, they can have direct health effects by altering the body's metabolism. Second, they can alter

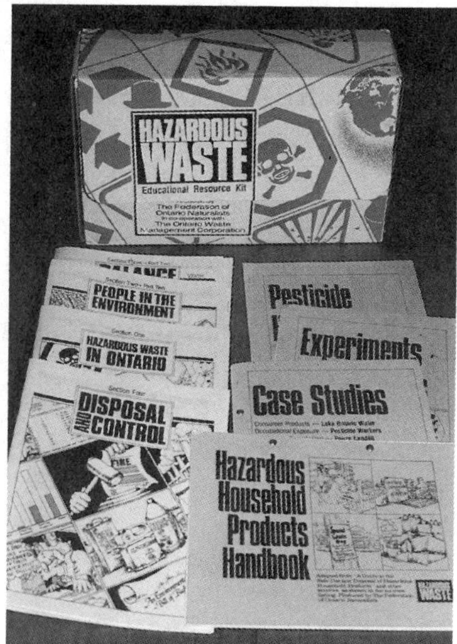

Fig. 25-3 The Federation of Ontario Naturalists has produced a kit to assist students in their study of hazardous wastes.

the metabolisms of other organisms or damage the environment. Finally, wastes affect all of us economically, through taxation and maintenance costs.

This section briefly explores these three categories of effects. Your resource centre probably has the kit shown in Figure 25-3. It gives further information on this topic.

Health Effects

Acute poisoning results from a single exposure to a large dose of a toxin. This single exposure to the hazardous material may kill or injure. For example, fish in a river die when a large volume of toxic solvent is accidentally released into the river. In medicine, the term **acute** means ''reaching a crisis rapidly''.

Chronic poisoning, on the other hand, happens slowly. The hazardous substance is present in the environment over a long period of time. Each individual in that environment is exposed daily to a small dose of the toxin. Each exposure causes a tiny amount of damage. This damage accumulates, meaning that some individuals eventually show serious symptoms.

Chronic poisoning could be occurring in your environment. For instance, the alcohol used in school duplicating machines (ditto machines) can poison chronically as well as acutely. Drinking just a few millilitres of this fluid will cause acute nerve and eye damage. However, breathing the vapours from this alcohol can cause the same damage after many exposures. Unfortunately, chronic poisoning is difficult to verify. How could we prove that a secretary's gradual loss of vision is due to chronic poisoning from duplicating fluid? Similarly, how do we prove that acid rain kills trees in a chronic manner?

Some hazardous wastes are **carcinogens**. That is, they are chemicals that can cause cancer. Cancer seldom starts from a single exposure to a carcinogen. For instance, one cigarette may not produce lung cancer. But chronic exposure to tobacco smoke greatly increases one's chances of getting lung cancer or some other disease. About 10 000 Canadians die each year from carcinogens in their work places. Improperly treated hazardous wastes account for many of these deaths.

Environmental Effects

A process called **bioaccumulation** occurs with some wastes. In this process an individual organism is exposed to very low concentrations or doses of the hazardous chemical. This chemical is absorbed by the individual's body and kept there. The body's cleaning mechanisms simply cannot remove it. The concentration of the chemical builds up inside the individual's tissues. Eventually it reaches dangerous levels.

Bioaccumulation is particularly noticeable in top predators. Figure 25-4 shows how polychlorinated biphenyls, commonly known as PCBs, accumulate in an aquatic environment. Note how the concentration of PCBs in the gulls and their eggs is over 125 000 times higher than that in the water! In effect, the gulls are collecting wastes from the entire food chain and concentrating them in their bodies. This ''collection'' works so well that scientists monitor the tissues of some organisms for wastes rather than monitoring the air or water. Gull eggs are used to detect PCBs. Clams are tested for such accumulated hazardous substances as **dioxins**. Do you think these wastes accumulate in your body?

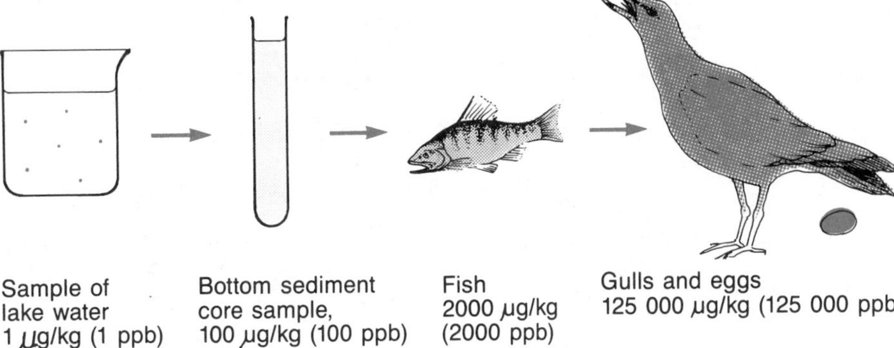

Fig. 25-4 Waste PCBs are concentrated by the food chain. Lake Ontario has PCBs (shown in colour) at a concentration of about 1 µg/kg. PCBs accumulate in bacteria on the bottom, giving the sediment a much higher reading. Scavengers eat the bacteria and are in turn eaten by fish. Top predators like gulls and ospreys eat the fish and end up with very high PCB concentrations in their tissues. Tissue from Lake Ontario gulls has 125 000 times as much PCB as Lake Ontario water!

Hazardous wastes are generally safe at very low concentrations. However, bioaccumulation can increase concentrations to dangerous levels. This is why we are advised not to eat Great Lakes fish over a certain size.

Economic Costs

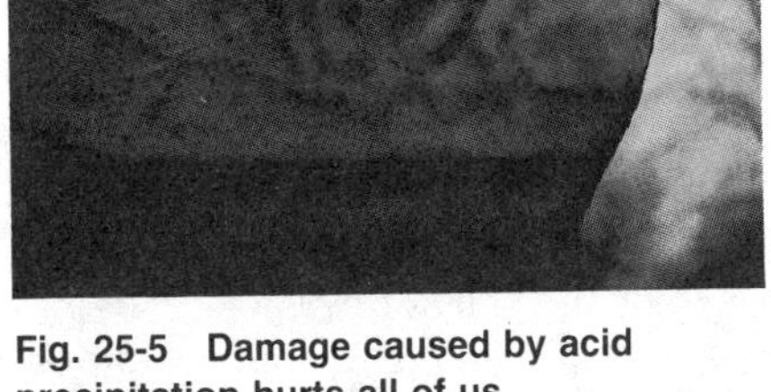

Fig. 25-5 Damage caused by acid precipitation hurts all of us economically.

Economic costs associated with wastes affect all of us. We spend money to repair the damage done to our buildings and environments by chronic corrosives such as acid rain (Fig. 25-5). Our tax dollars are spent fighting irresponsible polluters in court and cleaning up their wastes. Monitoring our environment for hazardous materials is expensive. Medical research and health care for injuries from hazardous waste are also very costly.

Who should pay these costs? Is it cheaper to clean up the waste at the production site or after it escapes into the environment? Which treatment method is most effective? These questions and others are now being dealt with by government, industry, and a very concerned public. With proper management, the health, environmental, and economic effects of hazardous wastes can be reduced or eliminated. **For every known hazardous waste, there is an effective disposal method**.

Many of us want the hazardous waste problem stopped by preventing the production of any new waste. While understandable, this idea may be impractical. Certainly, with effort, the quantity of waste can be reduced. However, many people have jobs and lifestyles that depend on waste-generating products. Therefore we may have to permit the production of hazardous wastes, but provide the facilities and financial incentives to have the wastes neutralized. Then the producer could pay the cost of waste disposal rather than the public having to pay to clean up the damage.

Section Review

1. What are the three main ways by which hazardous wastes affect us?

2. a) Distinguish between acute and chronic poisoning.

b) If a person committed a murder with poison, which type of poisoning would this be?

c) Give two examples of chronic poisoning.

3. a) What does bioaccumulation do to the concentrations of wastes in body tissues?

   b) Why is bioaccumulation particularly dangerous to top predators?
   c) Why should we not eat large predators such as salmon caught in Lake Ontario?
   d) How is bioaccumulation used to measure some environmental toxins?
4. Do carcinogens result in chronic or acute poisoning? Explain.
5. **a)** What are the economic costs of hazardous wastes?
   b) At present, who pays the price for wastes that are carelessly released into the environment?
   c) Who should pay the cost of waste disposal? Why?

Extension

The Ontario Waste Management Corporation (OWMC) has a plan for handling our hazardous wastes. Find out from OWMC what that plan is and at what stage its implementation is. Evaluate this plan.

25.3 Radioactive Wastes

Fig. 25-6 This symbol is used for radioactive materials.

Materials that emit energy in the form of gamma rays, X-rays, alpha particles, or beta particles are called **radioactive** (Fig. 25-6). These forms of energy are called **ionizing radiation**. That's because they have sufficient energy to ionize (make into ions) many atoms. Radioactive materials occur naturally in our environment but at very low concentrations. As a result, we are always exposed to ionizing radiation. In addition, we also get ionizing radiation from the sun and from some electrical devices such as colour television sets. Though we are all exposed to ionizing radiation, the dose we get is normally quite low.

Ionizing radiation is a form of electromagnetic radiation. Other forms include microwaves, TV waves, radio waves, and visible light. However, ionizing radiation is different—it has more energy than the other forms. Because of the extra energy, ionizing radiation can cause tissue damage when it contacts an organism. Those forms of radiation capable of tissue damage are shown in Figure 25-7. The damage to tissues is usually in the cellular chromosomes. Cells are usually able to repair minor damage. This is why low doses of ionizing radiation do little harm. Damage from high doses, however, is generally not

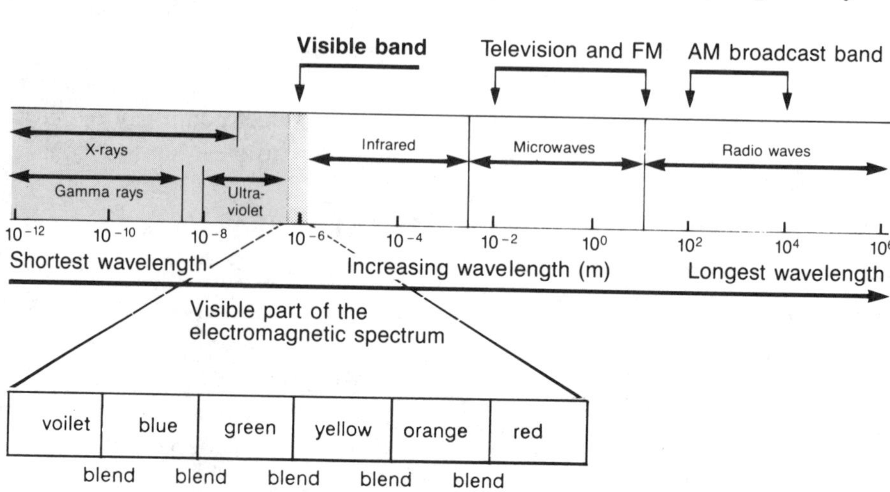

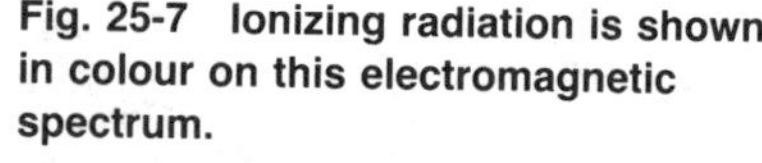

Fig. 25-7 Ionizing radiation is shown in colour on this electromagnetic spectrum.

repairable. Overexposed cells die or are mutilated (deformed). Overexposed cells often become cancerous. The key to radiation safety is to keep the dose low.

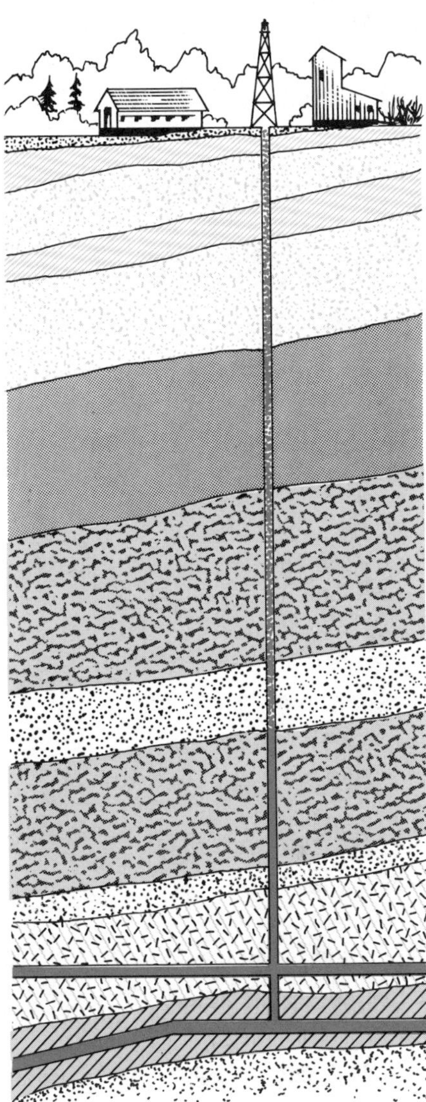

Fig. 25-8 Abandoned hard rock mines may be suitable interment sites for radioactive wastes. The wastes would be deposited in the deep horizontal chambers. When full, the mine shaft can be backfilled with tailings (which are also hazardous) and sealed.

Source of Radioactive Wastes

We are now using and producing large masses of radioactive materials in our nuclear industry. Nuclear reactors generate radioactive wastes which emit an enormous dose of ionizing radiation. For instance, one kilogram of waste plutonium emits enough radiation to start cancer in every human on this planet. The nuclear industry produces many kilograms of plutonium and other radioactive materials each year.

Management of Radioactive Wastes

Unlike ordinary hazardous wastes, radioactive wastes cannot be destroyed. There is no known process that stops radiation from being emitted. Instead, we must wait until the waste gives off most of its radiation and eventually "wears out". This takes a long time—500 000 years for plutonium to become safe! The key to the management of such materials is to store the waste away from organisms until its radiation reaches an acceptable level. This safe storage is called **interment**. At present we can inter these wastes quite safely for a few years. However, how do we inter these for longer periods, such as half a million years?

One proposal for long-term interment is shown in Figure 25-8. Granite rock is preferred over other rock types because radioactive atoms that escape their containers will not leach rapidly through granite. The Canadian Shield underlies much of northern Ontario. Its deep granite layer may be suitable for interment.

Critics of the nuclear industry argue that we should stop using nuclear energy because of our inability to safely handle the waste. Do you think we should stop our reactors until a good disposal system is developed? If granite interment is the answer, should Canada accept radioactive waste from other countries for burial here? What problems do you see with granite interment?

Section Review

1. a) What parts of the electromagnetic spectrum are classified as ionizing radiation?
   b) How does the energy of ionizing radiation compare to the energies of non-ionizing forms of radiation?
2. a) Explain why ionizing radiation causes tissue damage.
   b) Where does such damage occur?
3. a) Why do we seldom suffer from natural radiation?
   b) Why can radioactive waste harm us?
4. a) How must radioactive waste be treated? Why?
   b) What difficulty is posed by treating such wastes as plutonium?
   c) Explain how granite interment might help solve these problems.

Extension

Find out from Atomic Energy of Canada Limited (AECL) or from Ontario Hydro how much radioactive waste is produced in Canada each year. Write a report on how this waste is handled. What proposals have been made for future handling of this waste?

25.4 Activity: Research Report on One Hazardous Waste

We regularly dispose of hundreds of different hazardous chemicals. Unfortunately, not all disposal is done properly. In this individual research report, you will investigate and report on one hazardous substance. Your report will focus on the nature of the waste material and on its proper disposal.

Problem

What are the properties of one hazardous waste and how should it be disposed of?

Resources

newspapers and magazine articles
resource centre
public library
chemical manufacturers
government regulations and guidelines for hazardous materials

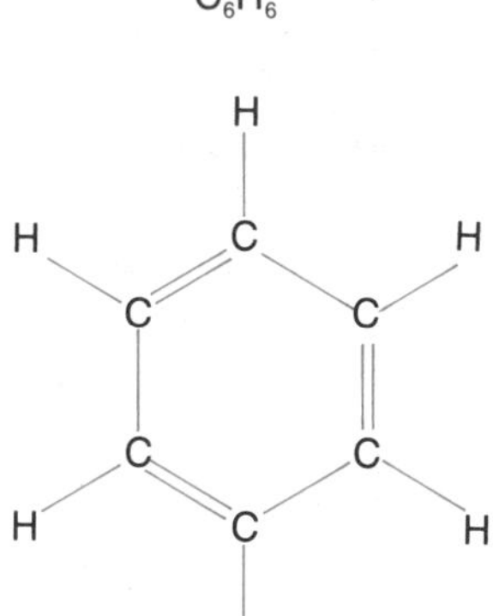

Fig. 25-9 The formula (top) and structure of benzene

Procedure

a. Select one hazardous waste on which to make your report. A partial list includes: polychlorinated biphenyls (PCBs), dioxins, myrex, lead, cadmium, cleaning solvent, sulfur dioxide, DDT, carbon tetrachloride, trichloroethylene, acrylonitrile, benzene, pentachlorophenol, heptachlor, ozone, ethylene glycol, asbestos, chromium, mercury.

b. Find out the following information for your selected hazardous waste:

- Its chemical name, formula, and chemical structure (Fig. 25-9).
- Where, why, and how much of the chemical is produced.
- Its toxicity, that is, how much of the material is required to cause poisoning in test animals. This may be expressed as a **tolerance** or as a **lethal dose** in µg/kg of body mass, or as a toxic concentration in air and water solutions.
- What direct effects it has on organisms, if any (e.g. toxin, carcinogen).
- What environmental effects it has, if any.
- The legal limits, if any, on the amount of this material in air, water, or food.
- How the material is presently disposed of, and how it should be disposed to be properly managed.

c. Write a report on your selected hazardous waste. Use the categories in (b) to organize your report.

Fig. 25-10 Models can be built using styrofoam spheres available from craft and hobby shops.

Discussion

1. At the end of your report, prepare a brief comment on how well this waste is being dealt with. In your opinion, does society handle this material poorly or well? What improvements should and can be made? At what cost?

Extension

Build a model of your selected waste (Fig. 25-10). Colour each type of atom using a standard code. (Oxygen = red, carbon = black, hydrogen = yellow, chlorine = green; your teacher will give you other standard colours if you need them.)

25.5 Activity: Research Report on Hazardous Waste Management

This research activity may be done in small groups or individually. Instead of examining one waste product as described in Section 25.4, this activity focuses on problems and techniques associated with hazardous materials. Some possible topics include:

- The Love Canal—What have we learned?
- Three Mile Island and Chernobyl—Is Canada next?
- McClure Crescent and radioactive soil
- Chemicals in the Great Lakes
- Ontario's designated chemicals
- The waybill system for control of hazardous substances
- Waste management and the law
- Cleaning up lead contamination in Toronto
- Acid precipitation reduction techniques
- Treatment techniques for chlorinated organics such as PCBs
- Disposal techniques for household hazardous wastes
- Home water purifiers—Are they needed and do they work?

Your selected topic could focus on a historical event that has had (or should have had!) an impact on our management of hazardous material. Alternatively, it could focus on one current management aspect of hazardous waste.

Sources of information include the school resource centre, scientific journals, and newspaper reports. Publications produced by the following groups will be useful: The Ontario Waste Management Corporation; The Federation of Ontario Naturalists; Pollution Probe; The Ontario Ministry of the Environment; manufacturers of anti-pollution equipment.

Reports on historical events should clearly indicate what we have learned and how we have changed our procedures as a result of that event. Reports on new procedures and processes should indicate how these have changed our management of hazardous products.

25.6 Activity: Waste Disposal and Soil Type

One solution to the problems of hazardous waste disposal is to treat wastes to make them less harmful. Such treatment can be done using a properly designed, well-operated facility built for just that purpose. Harmful residues left after treatment can be interred at the facility. Obviously, the site for such a facility must be selected very carefully. Some wastes could escape by leaching through the soil. As a result, the soil type is an important consideration when a site is being selected for a hazardous waste disposal facility. What type of soil provides the best barrier against leaching? In this activity, you will simulate the movement of hazardous wastes using water. You will compare several soil types, including sand, loam, clay, and peat.

Problem

What soil type is the best for a hazardous waste disposal facility?

Materials

small juice can with both ends removed
small pail full of each soil being tested (Include clay, sand, loam, and peat.)
500 mL beaker
stopwatch
water

Procedure

a. Compact the soil in each pail by pressing it down firmly.
b. Insert the juice can halfway into one of the pails of soil. Compact the soil around the can.
c. Pour 250 mL of water into the can. Start the stopwatch as soon as all the water is in the can (Fig. 25-11).
d. When the water has drained away or after 10 min has elapsed, stop the stopwatch. Record the "leaching time" for that soil type.
e. Repeat steps (b) to (d) for each of the remaining soil types.

Fig. 25-11 Which soil type is best at preventing leaching?

Discussion

1. Which soil would best prevent the leaching of wastes? Which one would be poorest?
2. Septic tanks digest sewage wastes and then dispose of these harmless by-products through a tile bed. Which soil type should the tile bed be buried in? Why?

Extension

Consult a geology or soils text and find out why one soil was better than the others at preventing leaching.

Chapter Highlights

1. Hazardous wastes and radioactive wastes require special handling to prevent health and environmental problems.
2. Hazardous wastes may be categorized as toxic, corrosive, reactive, and flammable.
3. We annually produce about 200 kg of hazardous waste per person.
4. Damage from hazardous wastes can be to individuals, the environment, and to the economy.
5. Radioactive wastes release large doses of ionizing radiation.
6. Safe disposal of radioactive waste requires long-term interment.

Key Terms

acute
bioaccumulation
carcinogen
chronic
corrosive
flammable
hazardous waste
ignitable
interment
ionizing radiation
radioactive waste
reactive
tolerance
toxic
volatile

Recognizing the Concepts

Each of the following statements or questions is followed by four responses. Choose the correct response in each case. (Do not write in this book.)

1. For many years, the global population of peregrine falcons declined because of the insecticide DDT. The concentration of DDT built up in these top carnivores until the female could no longer lay thick-shelled eggs. This is an example of:
   a) acute poisoning
   b) carcinogenesis
   c) interment
   d) bioaccumulation
2. A chemical that reacts vigorously is called
   a) carcinogenic **b)** flammable **c)** ignitable **d)** reactive
3. Why must radioactive wastes be treated differently from hazardous wastes?
   a) Radioactive wastes do not biodegrade.
   b) Radioactive wastes are very volatile.
   c) Radioactive wastes are among the most toxic substances known.
   d) Radioactive wastes require an interment time in which to make themselves safe.
4. Which type of soil is best suited for a hazardous waste disposal site?
   a) sand **b)** clay **c)** loam **d)** peat

Understanding the Concepts

1. **a)** Distinguish between acute and chronic poisoning.
   b) Give an example of each type.
2. Which type of industry—primary, secondary, or tertiary—is likely to be the largest producer of hazardous materials? Why?

3. On the average, each Ontarian produces 200 kg of hazardous waste annually. Most of us can identify a tiny fraction of this waste (e.g. paint, solvents, used oil, and so on) that we personally produce. Where does the rest come from?
4. a) What is the difference between radiation and *ionizing* radiation?
   b) Give an example of each type.
   c) How does ionizing radiation affect your body?
5. Certain wastes are able to affect us severely, even though they do no damage to our bodies. How is this possible? Give at least one example.

Fig. 25-12 **Barrels such as these can be used to store hazardous waste. What risks do you see in storing wastes this way?**

Applying the Concepts

1. Some producers store their hazardous wastes in steel barrels as shown in Figure 25-12. Sometimes the barrels are left unattended for years. Rusting barrels eventually leak. Explain, step-by-step, how the wastes travel through the environment and end up inside organisms, including you.
2. We have the technology to successfully treat all hazardous wastes. However, we have no treatment for nuclear wastes. Why are nuclear wastes untreatable?
3. Suppose you work in a factory where a toxic gas leaks into the air inside the building. Tests show that its concentration never exceeds one percent of the concentration required for acute poisoning. What information would you want to know before deciding whether or not working conditions were safe?
4. Municipalities encourage businesses to locate within their borders. New businesses create jobs and provide tax revenue. Suppose two industries—one primary and one tertiary—wanted to build on the same site in your municipality. From a hazardous waste standpoint, which one is likely preferable? Why?

Investigations

1. Ionizing radiation doses are measured in **rads** and **rems**. Find out how much radiation a typical Canadian absorbs each year. What are the safe daily and annual exposure levels?
2. Find out how much ionizing radiation is used in dental X-rays. What precautions does a dentist use to protect you from accidental leakage? How is the dental technician protected?
3. DDT is no longer used in North America because of its bioaccumulative properties. Find out what countries still use it. Why do they use it? Where do they buy it? What has replaced DDT in North America? How do the replacements compare in toxic properties?
4. Interment sites for radioactive wastes have been proposed in a number of locations. In Canada, the granite rock of the Canadian Shield is a favoured site. In the United States, scientists have proposed deep burial in underground salt deposits in the western deserts. Find out the pros and cons of each interment location.

5. Find out how Ontario Hydro proposes to handle its nuclear waste from sites such as the Pickering Generating Station (Fig. 25-13). Do you think the public and the environment are adequately protected?
6. Find out why the Ontario Waste Management Corporation selected West Lincoln as the best site for its new hazardous waste treatment facility. Why were potential sites in unpopulated sections of Northern Ontario not considered as good sites?

Fig. 25-13 Nuclear generators such as this one at Pickering produce radioactive waste. How is this waste handled?

ONTARIO'S HAZARDOUS WASTE MANAGEMENT FACILITY

One of the reasons that we have a hazardous waste problem is our lack of treatment facilities for wastes. In the absence of good disposal facilities, individuals and companies may attempt a number of "treatments" which are unacceptable by current standards. In the past, waste has been stored in containers or interred in landfills. We have seen too many leaking barrels and Love Canals to continue these practices.

Perhaps out of frustration or greed, some unscrupulous individuals resorted to illegal dumping of hazardous wastes. Others attempted to treat the waste in a manner that was only partially effective. Some wastes were disposed of very well, such as the combustion of PCBs in Mississauga. However, such disposal became politically unacceptable when the local urban residents protested.

The Ontario Waste Management Corporation was established with the goal of building a high quality waste treatment plant to handle hazardous materials. The probable site is in West Lincoln, southeast of Hamilton. The diagram shows an artist's concept of what this plant will look like. Parts of the facility include test labs, high temperature incinerators, scrubbers, and interment sites. It is hoped that the plant can begin destroying stored hazardous materials in the early 1990s.

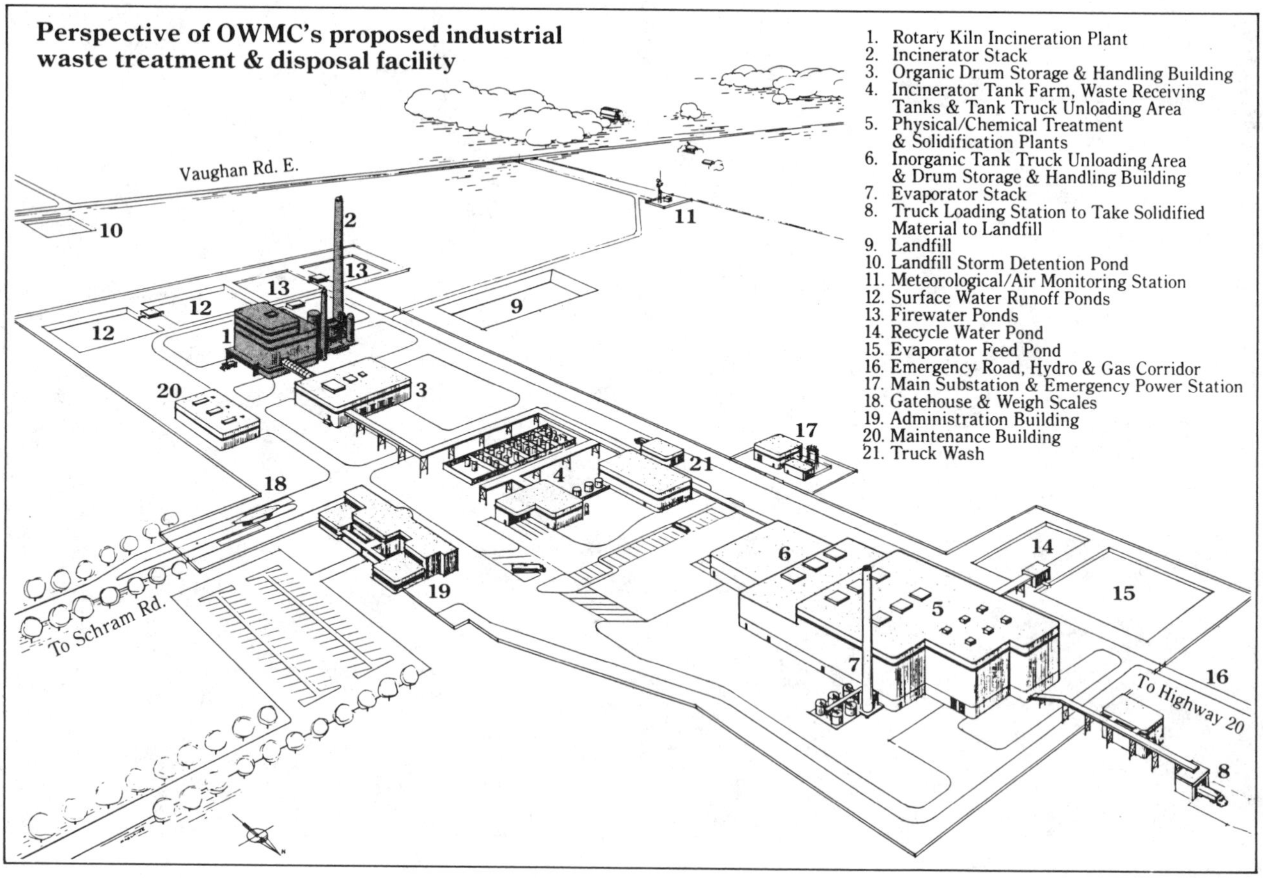

Perspective of OWMC's proposed industrial waste treatment & disposal facility

1. Rotary Kiln Incineration Plant
2. Incinerator Stack
3. Organic Drum Storage & Handling Building
4. Incinerator Tank Farm, Waste Receiving Tanks & Tank Truck Unloading Area
5. Physical/Chemical Treatment & Solidification Plants
6. Inorganic Tank Truck Unloading Area & Drum Storage & Handling Building
7. Evaporator Stack
8. Truck Loading Station to Take Solidified Material to Landfill
9. Landfill
10. Landfill Storm Detention Pond
11. Meteorological/Air Monitoring Station
12. Surface Water Runoff Ponds
13. Firewater Ponds
14. Recycle Water Pond
15. Evaporator Feed Pond
16. Emergency Road, Hydro & Gas Corridor
17. Main Substation & Emergency Power Station
18. Gatehouse & Weigh Scales
19. Administration Building
20. Maintenance Building
21. Truck Wash

UNIT 8 Astronomy

CHAPTERS

Astronomy is the branch of science which deals with the universe beyond the earth's atmosphere. The universe is all matter and energy which exists, so astronomy is the broadest of the sciences. It is also one of the most rapidly-changing. New discoveries in astronomy are constantly being made. That's why you often read about astronomy in the newspaper or see astronomy programs on TV.

The universe is vast, beautiful, and interesting. It excites and sometimes strains our imagination. But we should never feel insignificant when we think about the universe because, as the mathematician Henri Poincare said: "Astronomy shows us how small our bodies, how great our minds."

Astronomy was once important because it was practical. It enabled us to measure time and to keep track of the seasons. It helped us navigate across land and sea. Today, these practical applications are taken for granted. Astronomy now plays a deeper role in our culture. It places our earth in perspective and helps show us our place in the universe.

26 Motions in the Sky

CHAPTER CONTENTS

CHAPTER OBJECTIVES

After completing this chapter, you should be able to:

1. Understand that astronomy is an observational science.
2. Keep an observing log.
3. Observe, measure, and record the positions and motions of objects in the sky.
4. Use a simple sky chart.
5. Understand the motions of objects in the sky.
6. Design, calibrate, and use a simple sundial.
7. Determine direction, using sun by day and stars by night.
8. Observe and explain the cause of phases of the moon.
9. State past and present applications of astronomy.

Astronomers cannot experiment with planets, stars, and galaxies. They must use *observations* of these objects to develop and test their theories. Astronomy is an observational science. "Observations" and "observing" are special words which astronomers use to describe what they do. The ability to make and record observations, and to use them in "the scientific method", is what distinguishes an astronomer from a casual skygazer. In this chapter, you will make the same kinds of systematic observations that astronomers did many centuries ago (Fig. 26-1). You will then explain these in terms of the motions of the earth and moon.

Fig. 26-1 The Jantar Mantar Observatory was built in Delhi by the 18th century Indian astronomer-prince Jai Singh II.

26.1 Activity: Keeping an Observing Log

You have probably looked at the sky many times. But do you remember what you saw? By keeping an **observing log**, you can have a permanent record of what the sky looked like. You can also detect any motions or other changes which take place.

Problem

What is the most effective and convenient way of recording and preserving your observations of the sky?

Materials

loose-leaf binder
ruled and unruled loose-leaf pages
pen and pencil

Procedure

a. On each page on which you record an observation, include the following information:

your name	time	instruments used (if any)
your location	sky conditions	comments (if any)
date		

b. Keep the pages in the loose-leaf binder, in order of date. You may wish to keep different kinds of observations in different parts of the binder. If so, use dividers to separate them.

c. Record your observations on the loose-leaf pages. What you record will depend on the kind of observation. You will meet examples of different kinds of observations in the three chapters in this unit.

Discussion

1. Why must you include your observing location?
2. Astronomers, like all scientists, should express dates in the form 1988 08 14. What does this mean?
3. Time can be expressed as a.m. or p.m. or on the 24 h clock. (The latter is the correct form scientifically.) For instance, 7:30 a.m. is 07:30 on the 24 h clock, and 7:30 p.m. is 19:30. In either case, be sure to record the time system being used—Eastern Standard Time, for instance. Why?
4. Why should you include information about the sky conditions?
5. What comments about your observations might you want to include?
6. A **UFO** (''unidentified flying object'') is an unfamiliar object in the sky. What should you do if you see a UFO?

Extension

Many people think that some UFOs are alien spacecraft. There is no good scientific evidence that this is so. Discuss what you think would be "good scientific evidence" in this case.

26.2 Activity: Designing, Calibrating, and Using a Sundial

A

B

C

Fig. 26-2 Any vertical pole makes a convenient sundial (A). A sundial can be set up on your windowsill (B). A well-constructed sundial is accurate to within a minute or two — as long as the sun is shining (C)!

The sun is the brightest object in the sky. You are probably aware of its regular motion across the sky. This motion regulates our lives—especially if we live or work close to nature.

The sun is not, however, the easiest object to observe! Direct observation of the sun and its motion is difficult and dangerous. However, the sun casts shadows, and the motion of the shadows is much easier to observe—and it directly indicates the motion of the sun.

There are several ways of producing a shadow of the sun, and thus making a **sundial**. You need a shadow-casting device called a **gnomon**. It can be a pole in the schoolyard, a rod mounted on a flat base, or even a spot made on a south-facing window (Fig. 26-2).

Problem

Can you make and use a sundial?

Materials

flat surface on which you can record the position of the shadow
pen or chalk
gnomon

Procedure

The procedure to be used depends on what you use for a gnomon. The gnomon must be in the sunlight. Its shadow must fall on a flat surface on which you can record your observations. This may be the surface of the schoolyard if you are using a pole for a gnomon. It may be a sheet of paper on a table if you are using a windowsill sundial. Note that the gnomon must stay fixed in place throughout the activity!

a. Mark the position of the end of the shadow, and the time at which that position was observed.

b Repeat step (a) 20 or 30 min later.

c. Repeat step (a) at the same times on the next sunny day.

d. If possible, repeat steps (a) and (b) at the same times, each week for a month or two.

Discussion

1. Why does the gnomon cast a shadow?
2. What is the relation between the direction of the sun and the direction of the shadow?
3. What is the relation between the angle of the sun above the horizon and the length of the shadow?
4. Discuss the changes in the position of the end of the shadow from hour to hour, day to day, and week to week. How regular are the changes? Is a sundial a good clock?
5. At what time of day is the shadow shortest? Longest?
6. At what season of the year is the shadow shortest? Longest?

Extensions

1. As a project, construct a permanent, working sundial for your school. It can be mounted on a south-facing wall or on a pedestal in the schoolyard.
2. Determine the angle of the sun above the horizon, by drawing a scale diagram of the gnomon and its shadow. This method can only be used with a vertical gnomon.

26.3 Activity: Finding Direction in the Daytime

The westward motion of the sun provides a convenient way of finding direction in the daytime. The sun must be shining, of course! You will need to find a suitable gnomon. A pole is ideal. The shadow can be cast on a flat surface such as a parking lot, in which case the position of the shadow can be marked with chalk. If the shadow is cast on a grassy surface, the position of the shadow can be marked with a small stone or twig (Fig. 26-3).

Fig. 26-3 These students are using a vertical pole to find direction in the daytime.

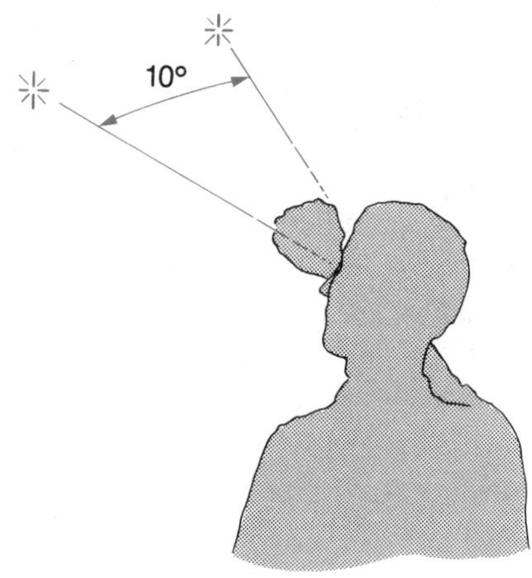

Fig. 26-4 The concept of angles in the sky, and the use of the outstretched hand to measure them

Problem

How can you find direction in the daytime?

Materials

a pole or other suitable gnomon
2 small stones or other markers

Procedure

a. Mark the end of the shadow of the pole.
b. Wait 20 to 30 min.
c. Observe the motion of the end of the shadow of the pole.
d. Mark the end of the shadow of the pole again.
e. Note the line joining the first and second marks. It points from west to east.

Discussion

1. Why was it necessary to use a pole or other gnomon whose shadow had a sharp, well-defined end?
2. Would it be better to use a taller pole? a thinner pole? Why?
3. Would this method work at any time of day at any time of year at any place on earth? Why?
4. How can you improve the effectiveness and accuracy of this method?

Extension

The sun moves in a curved path across the sky, rising in the east, and setting in the west. Why does the end of the shadow of the pole move in a straight line?

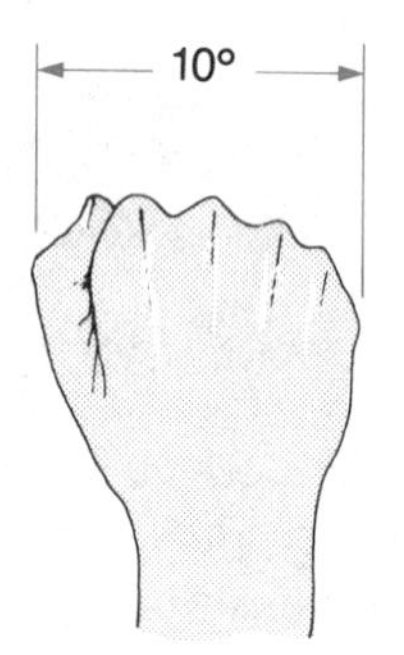

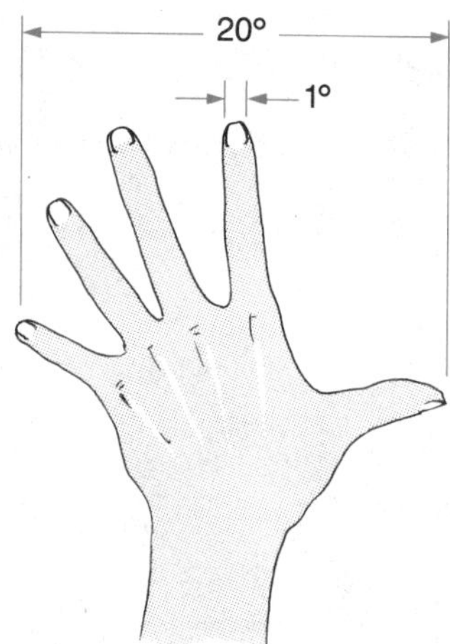

Fig. 26-5 The angles corresponding to different parts of the outstretched hand

26.4 Angles in the Sky

Astronomers often need to give the position of an object in the sky, or the ''distance'' between two objects in the sky. If you think about it, you will realize that it doesn't make sense to talk about the linear distance between two objects in the sky. For instance, we might say that ''the moon is near the star Antares,'' even though Antares is millions of times further away than the moon! We are really talking about the *apparent*, or *angular*, distance between two objects—such as the moon and Antares. Apparent distances in the sky are **angles**, and are measured in **degrees**. This is shown in Figure 26-4. In Activity 26.9, you will use the Big Dipper to visualize angles in the sky. The angle between the horizon and the point directly overhead is 90°. The point directly overhead is called the **zenith**.

A handy way to measure angles in the sky is to use your hand! Figure 26-5 shows the apparent sizes of different parts of your outstretched hand, measured in degrees. You can also use ''fingers'' to measure smaller angles.

Section Review

1. Why does it not make sense to talk about the linear distance between two objects in the sky?
2. How are apparent distances in the sky measured?
3. What is the zenith?
4. Describe a convenient method you can use to measure angles in the sky.

26.5 Activity: Recording Positions in the Sky

Motion is change in position. Therefore, before you can observe motions in the sky, you must be able to observe and record positions in the sky. You can record the position of something in a general way by saying that it is "in the west" or "high in the sky" or "above the school". You will find it more helpful to record the position in a more precise way, using a system of reference points and units of measurements (Fig. 26-6).

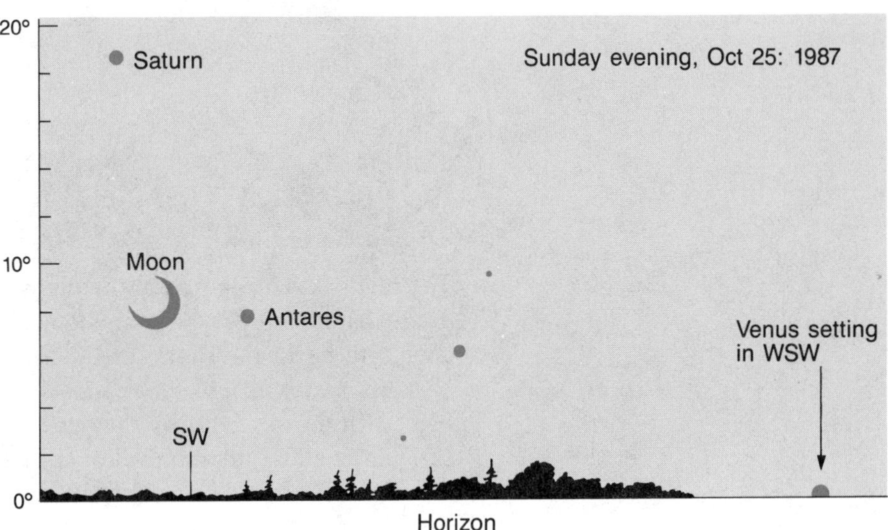

Fig. 26-6 A sample sketch of the horizon, with a scale of angles at the side

Problem

Can you describe the position of an object in the sky?

Materials

observing log pencil two hands

Procedure

a. Find an observing site with a clear view of the sky.

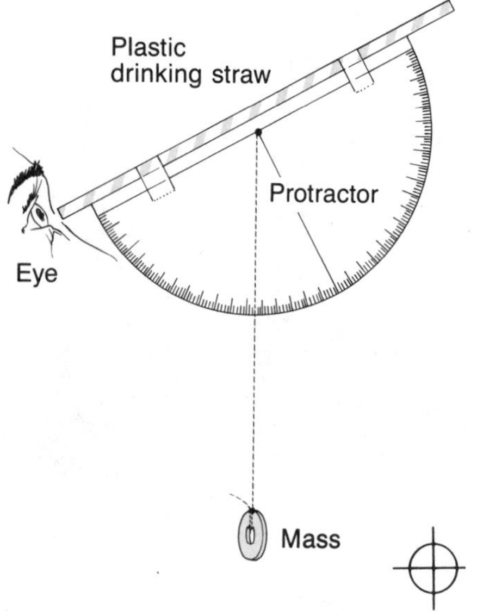

Fig. 26-7 You can construct a simple astrolabe for measuring the altitude of the moon, planets, and stars.

b. Record the location of your observing site in your log, as precisely as possible.
c. Draw the part of the horizon which you are facing in your log, with the true horizon as a horizontal line, and the features on the horizon above it.
d. Draw a scale around the horizon and upward from the horizon using ''hands'' as a convenient unit. Remember that one ''hand'' is 10°.
e. Choose an object in the sky. Estimate its angle above the horizon, using hands and fractions of a hand as a unit. The angle above the horizon is called the **altitude**.
f. Plot the position of the object on your drawing, using its direction around the horizon and its altitude.

Discussion

1. What is the connection between the words ''horizon'' and ''horizontal''?
2. What is the angle in degrees between east and south? East and west?
3. Suppose that you wanted to mark the compass directions on the horizon on your sketch. What are two non-astronomical methods for determining compass direction?
4. What is the number of hands between the horizon and the zenith?

Extension

Build an astrolabe for measuring angles above the horizon. Use Figure 26-7 as a guide.

26.6 Observing the Night Sky

The night sky appears as a moving dome with patterns of stars on the inside. These patterns are called **constellations**. They are made up of stars which appear to be in the same direction as seen from the earth. In the following chapters, we will look more closely at the nature of the stars and the other objects in the sky. In this chapter, we will focus on what the motions in the sky tell us about the motions of the earth. But first, you need some ideas for effective viewing of the night sky.

Hints for Viewing the Night Sky

- It takes up to half an hour for your eyes to get accustomed to the dark, and to reach their maximum sensitivity. Be patient.
- If your eyes are then exposed to bright light, they will lose their sensitivity, and you will have to start again. If you are using a flashlight to read your sky chart and your log, cover it with red cellophane. Red light does not affect the sensitivity of your eyes as much as other colours.
- It takes time to become familiar with the night sky. Learn the constellations one at a time. Use one constellation as a ''stepping stone'' to the next.

Fig. 26-8 This student is well-prepared for a warm evening's stargazing.

- Observing the sky can give you a stiff neck. Get comfortable. A chaise lounge—or even dry grass—can be very convenient for observing the sky. A clipboard is useful for recording your observations (Fig. 26-8).

CAUTION: Many of the activities in this unit are to be done in the evening. It is most practical to do these at your own convenience, in your own backyard, or in some other good observing site. However, you must always be aware of the dangers of being out of doors, in the dark, in a secluded location. It is best to work with one or more other students, within sight of "civilization". Make sure that your parents or guardians know where you are and what you are doing. Follow your teacher's advice on this very important topic!

Light Pollution

Light pollution is the name which astronomers give to unwanted artificial light in the night sky. It comes from bright lights in places like shopping malls and car dealerships. Some comes from lights on roads, shops, and houses (Fig. 26-9). It is wasted light, because it was intended to shine down on the ground, not up in the sky. Light pollution interferes with astronomical research, except at very remote sites. This occurs because light pollution can brighten the sky for 100 km around a city. It also deprives all of us of the pleasure of seeing the sky in its true beauty.

Section Review

1. What is a constellation?
2. Make a summary of the hints for viewing the night sky.
3. a) What is light pollution?
   b) How does it affect the work of astronomers?

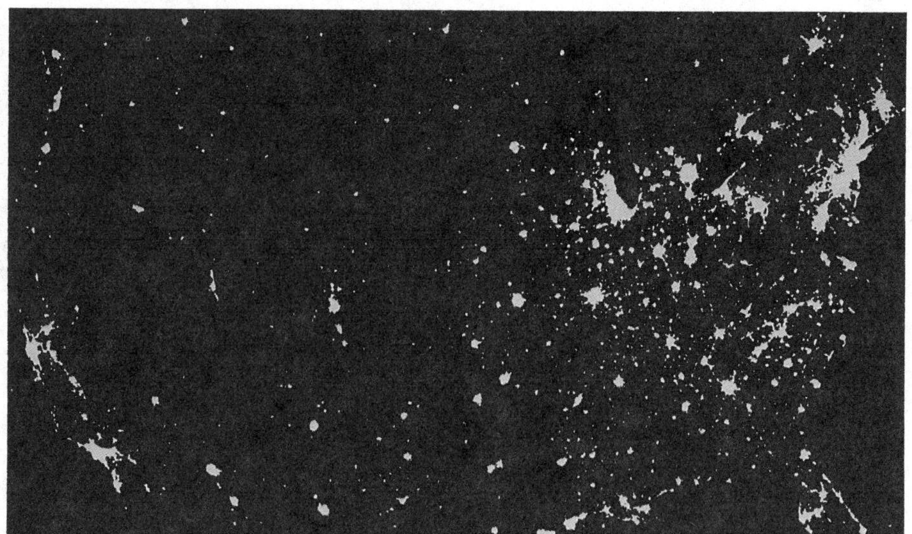

Fig. 26-9 This is what North America looks like from space, at night. Can you find your hometown?

Fig. 26-10 A planisphere is a universal sky chart. It can be set for any hour of any day of the year.

26.7 Activity: Using a Sky Chart

Figure 28–23, page 661, is a sky chart of the winter sky. You can obtain a more complete set of sky charts, which show the appearance of the evening sky in the fall, winter, and spring. The appearance of the sky is constantly changing because of the motions of the earth. It would take an infinite number of different sky charts to show the exact appearance of the sky at any time!

The appearance of the sky depends on your latitude. Make sure that the sky charts you are using are for the correct latitude (within a few degrees). Detailed sets of sky charts can be found in astronomy books and magazines, or can be obtained from planetariums or science museums. These sky charts usually do not show the moon and planets, because these move, relative to the stars, from week to week. A **planisphere** is a universal sky chart. It can be set for any time on any date of the year (Fig. 26–10).

Problem

How can stars and constellations be identified?

Materials

good observing site   sky chart or planisphere   observing log

Procedure

a. Check the times and dates for which the sky chart applies. Be sure to observe the sky at approximately that time.

b. There are several different kinds of sky charts. The one in Figure 28-23, page 661, is called a **horizon map**, because the edge of the chart represents

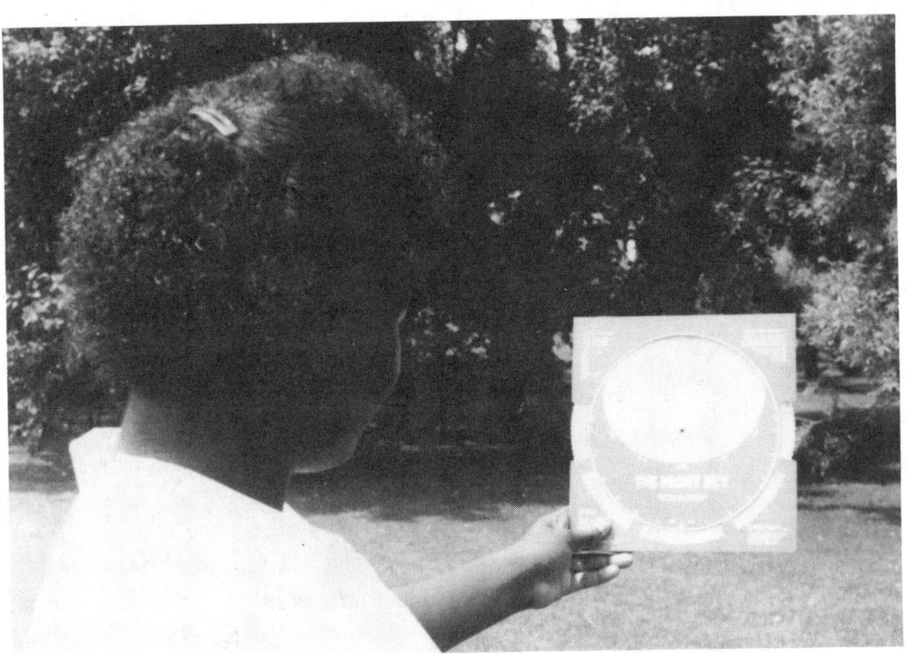

Fig. 26-11 How to hold a "horizon" sky chart, such as the one on page 661.

the observer's horizon. *Hold the chart in front of you so that the part of the horizon which you are facing is down*. For instance, if you are facing south, hold the sky chart so that the part of the horizon marked "south" is down (Fig. 26-11).

c. Compare the appearance of the sky with the chart. Keep in mind that the real stars are approximately white, whereas the stars on most sky charts are black. The size of the star on the chart represents the brightness of the real star: brighter stars are shown as larger. Astronomers use the word **magnitude** to represent the brightness of a star. A first-magnitude star is brighter than a second-magnitude star.

Discussion

1. Why must the sky chart be used at a specified time and date?

2. **a)** What is a horizon map?

b) How is it used?

3. What does "magnitude" mean to an astronomer?

26.8 Activity: Locating Polaris—The North Star

The **North Star** is perhaps the best known of all stars—at least for observers in the northern hemisphere. It cannot be seen by observers in the southern hemisphere! It is not a particularly bright star, but it has the useful property of being almost directly above the north pole of the earth. It is therefore almost exactly due north.

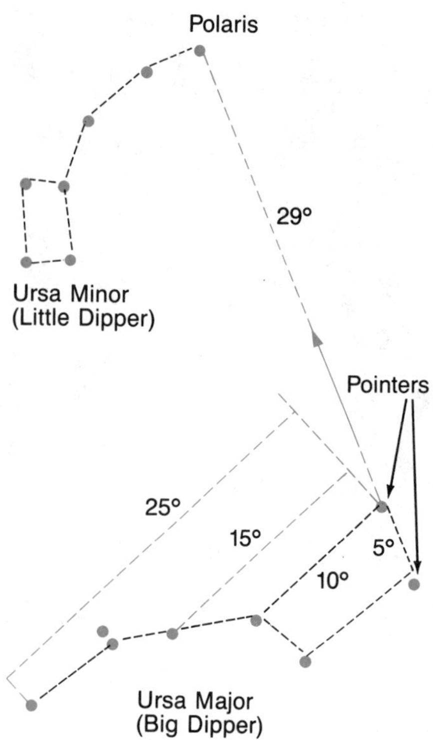

Fig. 26-12 To find Polaris, the North Star, follow the pointers on the end of the bowl of the Big Dipper.

Problem

How can you find the North Star—and hence the direction north?

Materials

good observing site
observing log
sky chart or diagram showing the Big Dipper

Procedure

a. Find an observing site which has a good view of the northern horizon.

b. Look for the **Big Dipper** in the sky. It will be in the northeast, north, or northwest. (Of course, you will not know the direction north until you find the North Star, but you probably know the direction approximately.) Sometimes, the Big Dipper is very low in the sky, and therefore is difficult to see. As you can see in Figure 26-13, most of the stars in the Little Dipper are much fainter than those in the Big Dipper.

c. Use the Pointers—the two end stars on the bowl of the Big Dipper—to locate the **North Star**. Project them out of the bowl, a distance of five times the distance between them (Fig. 26-12).

d. Continue the line from the Pointers, through the North Star, and you will come to the W-shaped (or M-shaped) constellation **Cassiopeia**. The North Star is halfway between the Big Dipper and Cassiopeia. These two constellations are very useful for finding it.

Discussion

1. Why is the Big Dipper easy to recognize?
2. Are all the stars in the Big Dipper the same brightness?
3. Are all the stars in Cassiopeia the same brightness?

Extension

The angle of the North Star above the northern horizon is equal to your latitude on the earth. What is the meaning of **latitude**? What is your latitude, in degrees? If you were at the north pole, what would be your latitude? Where in the sky would the North Star be? If you were at the equator, what would your latitude be? Where in the sky would the North Star be? Measure the angle of the North Star above your northern horizon, using your hands (see Section 26.4) or using an astrolabe, if you have one. Is it equal to your latitude?

26.9 Activity: Measuring Angles in the Sky

Problem

How can you measure apparent sizes and distances between objects in the sky?

Materials

good observing site

observing log

Procedure

a. Locate the Big Dipper in the northeast, north, or northwest sky.
b. Use your hand to measure the distances between the stars in the Big Dipper indicated in Figure 26-12.
c. Sketch the Big Dipper in your observing log. Then mark the distances which you have measured.
d. Compare your results with the distances given on Figure 26-12.

Discussion

1. Why might your measurements be slightly different from the values given on Figure 26-12?
2. If kindergarten students used the "handy" method to measure the same angles in the sky as you did, would they get different results because their arms and hands were smaller? Why?

Extension

Observe the sky by looking through a cardboard cylinder such as the core of a roll of toilet paper or a roll of paper towels. Determine the diameter, in degrees, of the field of view.

26.10 Activity: Westward Motion of the Sky at Night

You probably know that "the stars rise in the east and set in the west". Also, you have probably looked at the sky at night many times. But have you ever observed the stars rise and set? In this activity, you will!

Problem

How can you observe the motion of the sky at night?

Materials

a good observing site
sky chart
pencil, paper, and ruler
observing log

Procedure

a. At the beginning of the evening, select a few bright stars or planets in different parts of the sky. Identify them, if possible. Include Polaris, the North Star, if possible.

b. Make a sketch of the horizon (see Section 26.5).
c. Measure the angle of each star above the horizon, using hands as a unit. (If you have an astrolabe, you can use it in this activity.)
d. For each star, record the position and the angle above the horizon on your sketch.
e. An hour or two later, repeat your observations and measurements.
f. For each star, record the new position and angle above the horizon on your sketch.

Discussion

1. Describe the motion which you observed for the stars in the
   a) east b) south c) west
2. Describe the motion of Polaris, the North Star.

26.11 Activity: The Seasonal Motion of the Stars

Most observers look at the night sky at about the same time each night—shortly after sunset. If you observe the night sky at about this time, week after week, and month after month, you will notice a slow westward motion of the sky—just like the much more rapid westward motion which you observe within each night.

Fig. 26-13 A photograph of the Big and Little Dippers. Can you locate the North Star?

Problem

Over an interval of weeks or months, how does the sky move?

Method A Using Direct Observations

Materials

good observing site sky charts observing log

Procedure

a. On an evening early in the school year, use a sky chart to identify some bright stars and constellations.
b. Record your observations in a sketch of the sky. You might concentrate on the part of the sky above the southern horizon, and the part including the Big and Little Dippers and Cassiopeia in the northern sky (Fig. 26-13).
c. A few weeks later, but at the same time of the evening, use a sky chart again to identify some bright stars and constellations in the same part of the sky.
d. Record these observations in a sketch of the sky. Compare your observations with those made a few weeks earlier.

Discussion

1. How has the sky moved, as seen at the same time at a later date?

Method B Using Sky Charts Only

Materials

sky charts

Procedure

This activity can be carried out indoors, in the daytime, or on a cloudy night!

a. Obtain sky charts which apply to the same time, but different dates. For example, you can use charts for a certain time interval for the evening sky in fall, spring, and winter.

b. Compare the appearance of the same part of the sky as shown on two or more charts. For instance, compare the sky above the southern horizon on the sky charts for fall, winter, and spring.

Discussion

1. Describe the seasonal motion of the stars in
   a) the southern sky **b)** the northern sky

Extensions

1. If you have a planisphere available, use it to carry out Procedure B above. Set the planisphere for the same time in the evening (22:30, for instance) for various dates like mid-September, mid-October, and mid-November.
2. Observe the orientation of the Big Dipper, North Star, and Cassiopeia at the same time in the evening but at different dates in the year. Record your observations in the form of sketches in your observing log.

26.12 The Practical Applications of Astronomy

Thousands of years ago, our ancestors did not understand the workings of the universe as we know it today. They did observe the sky. They recorded the changes in the sky, and hence became aware of the cycles of day and night, and of the seasons. They developed calendars to organize everyday life, and thus to stabilize their economy. They could plan for the seasons, not just react to them. Astronomy became an important part of culture. It brought benefits to the people, and power to the astronomers.

These astronomers—who were more priests than scientists—were aware that the sun affected the earth. They thought that perhaps the planets did also.

They named the planets after their gods: Venus is the Roman goddess of love, and Mars is the Roman god of war. (In fact, many religions still associate God and heaven with the sky.) They named the patterns of stars after the various characters and objects in their myths. They even supposed that the stars and the planets influenced the lives of individual people. Thus the superstition of **astrology** was born. Scientists have shown that the stars and planets do not influence the lives of individual people. Nevertheless, many people enjoy reading their astrological predictions each day.

Astronomers tried for two thousand years to develop a **theory** or **model** which could explain the motions in the sky. Early Greek astronomers developed a model in which the earth rotated on its axis and revolved around the sun. This model was discarded in "The Dark Ages" in favour of the more obvious model in which everything in the sky revolved around the earth. The sun-centred model was rediscovered by Nicolaus Copernicus four centuries ago. It explains the motions in the sky, and has been verified by many other kinds of observations.

The Round, Rotating Earth

We live on a round planet which is about 13 000 km in diameter (see Figure 27-11, page 627). Our planet rotates approximately once each day, about an

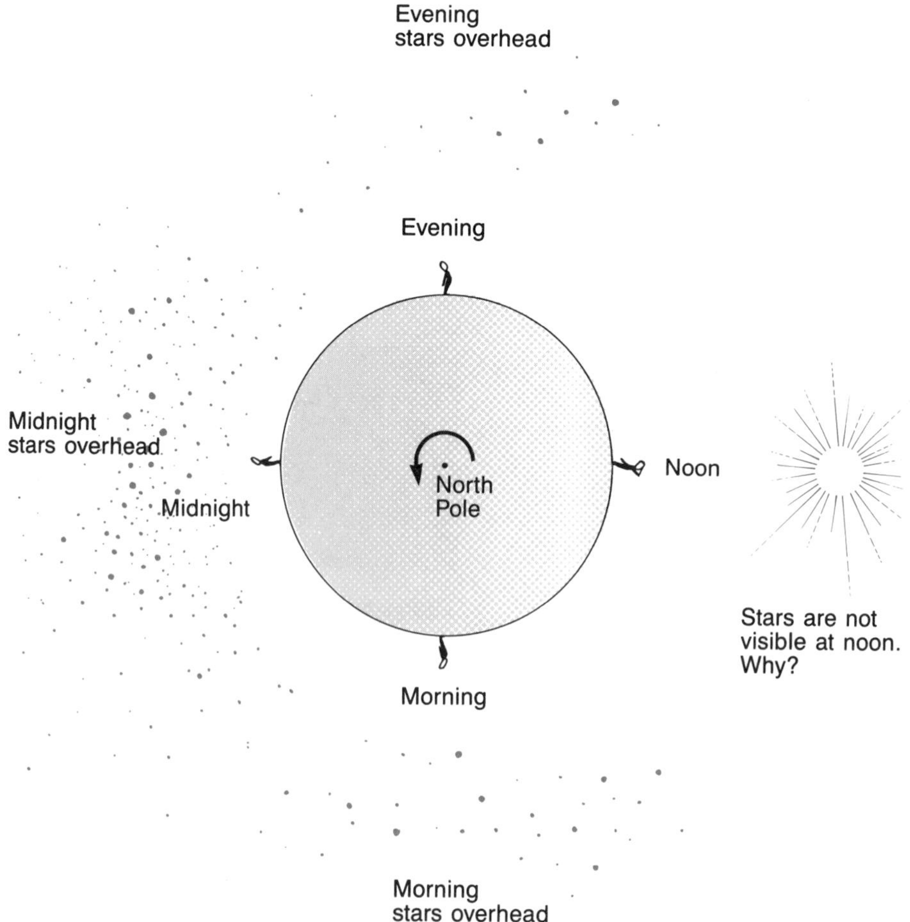

Fig. 26-14 The rotation of the earth constantly carries new constellations into view.

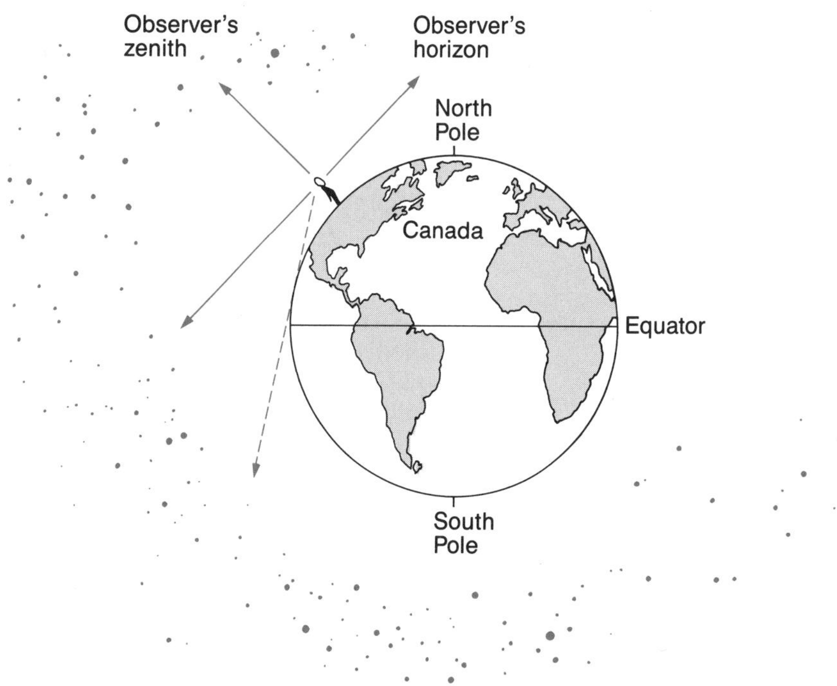

Fig. 26-15 There are constellations which we cannot see from the northern hemisphere.

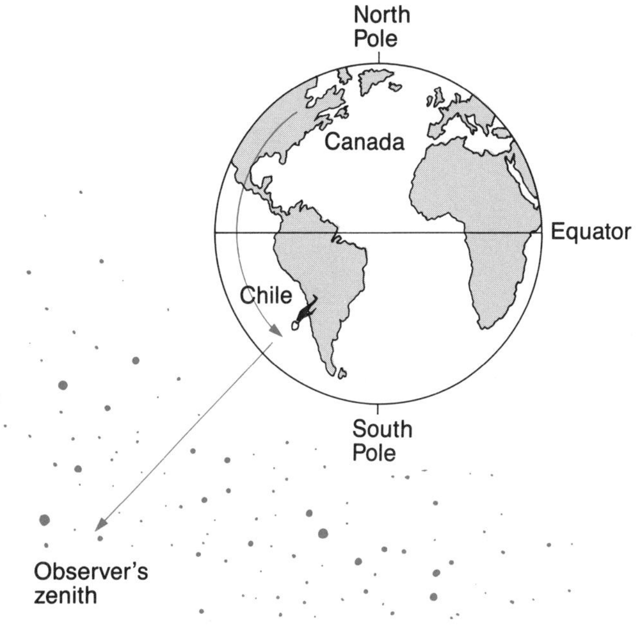

Fig. 26-16 We can see these southern constellations by travelling south.

axis which passes from the north to the south pole. The north and south poles, in fact, are defined as the points of intersection between the rotation axis and the surface of the earth. The shape and rotation of the earth determine which stars are visible to us at any time at any place on earth (Figs. 26-14, 26-15, and 26-16).

Astronavigation

The North Star is almost exactly due north in the sky. Stars which are 90° away from the North Star in the sky rise exactly due east and set exactly due west. These stars therefore serve as direction-finders. Many early civilizations used **astronavigation** to guide them in their travels. The Polynesians, for instance, have used the stars for centuries to navigate between the remote islands of the Pacific.

Various instruments were developed in order to use the stars to determine the travellers' latitude and longitude more precisely. Observatories were established to provide navigators with the astronomical information which they would need. The Royal Greenwich Observatory, which is the reference point for our system of longitude, was established for this purpose.

Sailors now have much more sophisticated methods for navigating. Astronavigation is still an interesting and useful hobby. Many "weekend sailors" still learn and use it.

The Annual Motion of the Sun

Our rotating earth revolves about the sun once each year. The **year** is defined as the time required for the earth to revolve once about the sun. There are two effects of the earth's revolution about the sun. One is the seasonal change in the stars which are visible at any time of the night. This is interesting, but has no important consequences. The other is the seasonal change in climate. This occurs because the earth's axis of rotation is tilted with respect to the earth's orbit. It has many important consequences (Fig. 26-17).

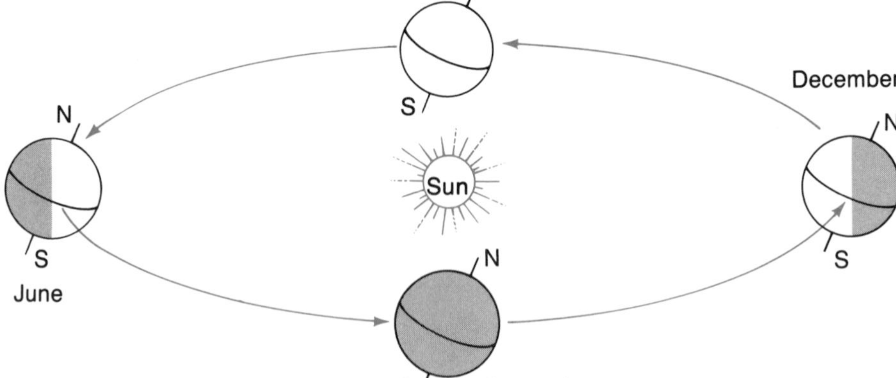

Fig. 26-17 The earth rotates on its tilted axis as it revolves around the sun. How does this cause the seasonal changes in climate?

As the earth revolves about the sun, it rotates on an axis which is tilted at an angle of 23° to the upright. When the northern hemisphere is tilted toward the sun (around June), the sun shines down more directly on the northern hemisphere, and for more hours each day. The weather is warmer at and after this time. When the northern hemisphere is tilted away from the sun (around

December), the sun shines down less directly on the northern hemisphere, and for fewer hours each day. The weather is colder at and after this time.

Calendars

A **calendar** is a device to predict the season or the time of year. This is important for agriculture and for many other human activities. It is also important for setting the date for religious festivals and holidays—many of which celebrate the seasons. The date of Christmas, for instance, was set by the early Christians to coincide with the date of Saturnalia—a Roman celebration of the winter solstice. Based on evidence in the *Bible*, it is unlikely that Christ was born in December. At that season, shepherds were not ''abiding in the fields, keeping watch over their flocks by night''.

The simplest calendar is the sky. The appearance of the sky at a certain time of night changes during the year. The early Egyptians, for instance, used the first appearance of the star Sirius in the morning sky as a way of predicting when the river Nile was about to flood. Even today, there are many bits of folklore about which constellations should be visible when crops are to be sown and harvested.

Other early civilizations observed the annual changes in the motion of the sun in the sky, and used these to predict the seasonal changes in climate. **Stonehenge**, for instance, is one of dozens of structures built by the early Britons (see Vista, this chapter). During the year, there are regular changes in the point on the horizon where the sun rises and sets. The sunrise and sunset points are furthest north on the first day of summer, and furthest south on the first day of winter. Stonehenge is aligned so that it can be used to determine when the sunrise point is furthest north, and therefore when summer begins.

The present calendar is based on ''counting days''. There are 365.2422 d in a year. Therefore, if we count this number of days since the last beginning of spring, we can predict the next beginning of spring. However, it took thousands of years of trial and error to develop our present calendar. Julius Caesar adopted the idea of having a ''leap year'' every 4 years. But this system produced a year 365.25 d long. And the small difference between this and the true length produced an error of almost two weeks by the 16th century. At that time, some further refinements to the calendar were made. Century years were not leap years unless they were divisible by 400 (like the year 2000). In 1752, when England and the Americas adopted the new calendar, 11 d had to be removed from the calendar. Certain eastern European religions still use the old Julian calendar, and therefore celebrate Christmas and New Year 13 d later than others do.

Since the present calendar was developed, it has been relatively easy to specify the exact date on which events occurred. Before that, it was much more difficult. Writers did not always use a numerical system to specify the date. For instance, our calendar uses the date of the birth of Christ as a reference point. But modern research on the *Bible* indicates that Christ was probably born several years BC!

The Month Many early civilizations tried to include the motions of the moon in their calendar. The moon goes through its phases in 29.53 d. This number does not divide evenly into 365.2422. The present calendar uses 12 months with an average length of 30.4 d. Therefore there is no relationship between the time of the month and the phase of the moon.

The Islamic calendar, on the other hand, is strictly based on the phase of the moon. The beginning of each calendar month is based on the first sighting of the new crescent moon. There are 12 such months in the year. The year is therefore $12 \times 29.53 = 354$ d long. The Islamic New Year is also set by the first sighting of the new crescent moon. It moves backward through the present calendar 11 d each year. The Islamic calendar is unusual in that it cannot really be predicted in advance. The month and the new year do not begin until the new crescent moon has actually been sighted.

The Jewish calendar is also based on the phase of the moon. However, 12 and 13-month years are alternated so that the Jewish New Year is always close to the date of the autumnal equinox (late September). Also, the month and the year begin at the "tabular" or predicted time. They do not depend on the new crescent moon being sighted.

The present calendar still has one connection with the phase of the moon. Easter Sunday occurs, not on a fixed day of the year, but on a date which is determined by the following complicated rule: Easter Sunday is celebrated on the first Sunday after the 14th day of the moon (nearly full moon) occurring on or immediately after March 21.

Section Review

1. Distinguish between astronomy and astrology.
2. What is astronavigation?
3. Make a summary that describes the various motions of the earth.
4. Compare the present calendar, the Islamic calendar, and the Jewish calendar.

26.13 Activity: Observing the Phases of the Moon

Which is more useful—the sun or the moon? The moon—because it gives light at night, when it is dark. The sun gives light in the daytime, when it is light anyway.

George Gamow

The moon has provided light for living things for billions of years. Its gravity has raised tides in the oceans, which have influenced life in many ways. Early humans used the moon to regulate their lives, as part of their calendars. The moon is the brightest object in the night sky. Its beauty has inspired artists and writers for centuries. We can now look at the moon and realize that it is the only other world in the universe which humans have yet visited.

This activity provides you with an opportunity to observe and record the phases of the moon. It also lets you work with other students in carrying out a scientific project. It is true that you could carry out all the observations yourself. But it is far more efficient and enjoyable to share the work! And the moon is conveniently visible in the daytime, at least at some phases!

The sequence of phases of the moon begins with **new moon**. The new moon is in almost the same direction as the sun, and is therefore not visible. The sequence progresses through the **crescent phase, first quarter, waxing gibbous, full, waning gibbous, last quarter**, and then **crescent** (Fig. 26-18). You might want to begin your observations at first quarter, when the moon is conveniently visible in the afternoon.

Activity 27.3, page 617, can be carried out at the same time as this one.

Problem

How does the appearance of the moon change with time?

Materials

good observing site unaidedeye observing log

Procedure

a. Consult a calendar and begin this activity on a date near first quarter moon. Note that the moon can be seen in daytime!

b. Locate the moon in the sky.

c. Make a sketch showing the east, south, and west horizon (see Section 26.5, page 591).

d. Measure the angle of the moon above the horizon, using hands as a unit.

e. Show the moon on your sketch, in the correct position. Also show its appearance.

f. Be sure to record the time and date of your observation in your log.

g. Continue your observations on every clear day and night for a month, either by yourself or with the cooperation of your classmates. Where possible, you should observe the moon at the same time of day. From new crescent moon to full moon, for instance, you can observe it in the early evening.

h. At the end of a month, lay out your sketches in the form of a calendar.

Discussion

1. Describe the changing appearance of the moon throughout the month.
2. How does the position of the moon in the sky, relative to the sun, change during the month? When is the moon close to the sun in the sky? Opposite to the sun in the sky?
3. How does the time of moon rise and moon set change during the month? When does the moon rise at noon? In the early evening? In the middle of the night?
4. At new moon, where is the moon in the sky? Why is it not visible?

Extension

Why does the new moon not eclipse the sun every month? Why does the full moon not pass into the earth's shadow, and get eclipsed, every month?

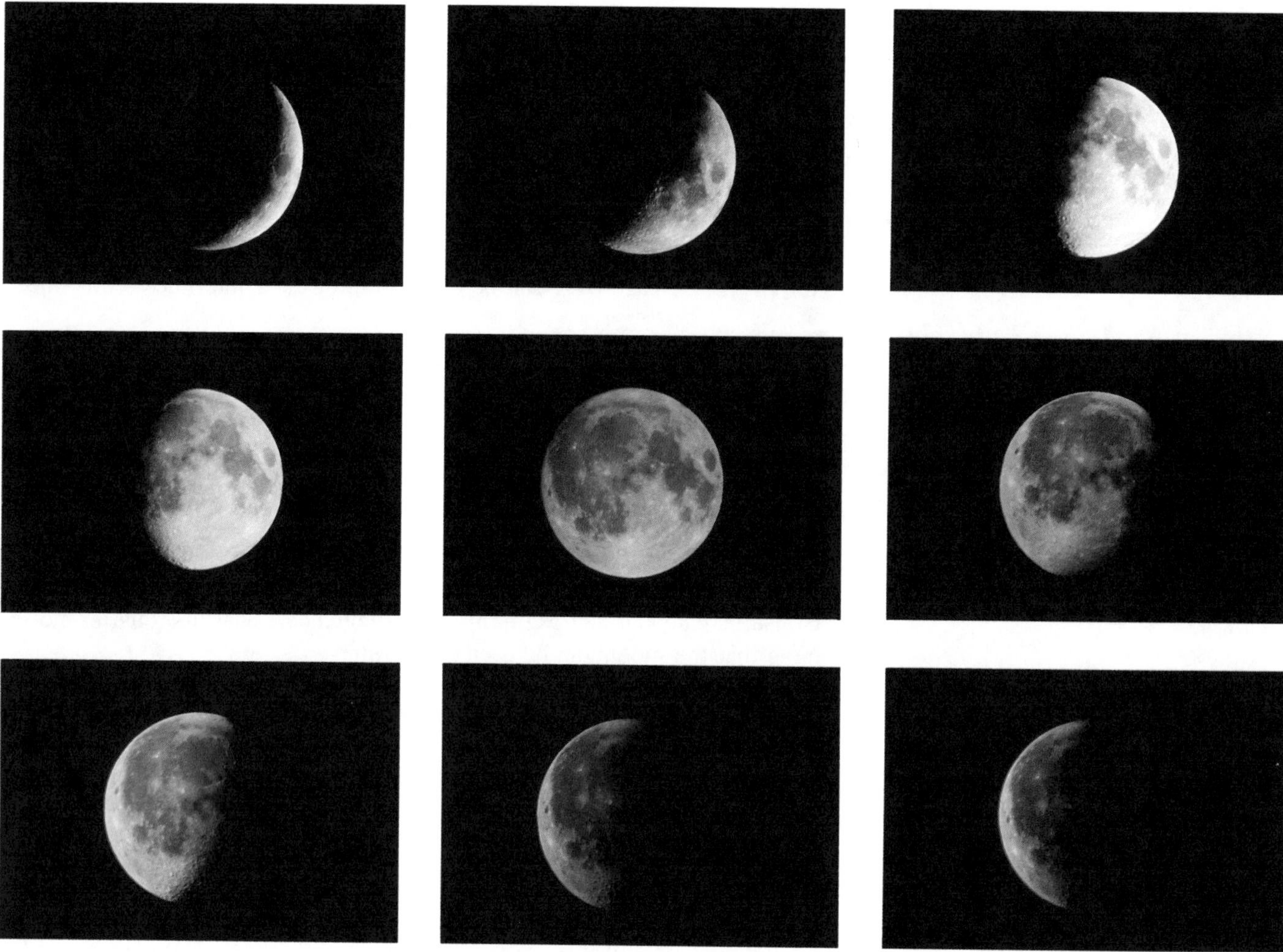

Fig. 26-18 The phases of the moon: waxing crescent through full to waning crescent.

26.14 Activity: Explaining the Phases of the Moon

The Explanation for the Phases of the Moon

The moon, like the other satellites and planets, does not produce its own light. We see it because it is illuminated by the sun. The moon is round, and at any time, one half of the moon is illuminated by the sun and the other half is not. We usually see part of the illuminated half, and part of the unilluminated half. What we see depends on the relative position of the sun, moon, and earth. This changes as the moon revolves about the earth. Figure 26-18 illustrates these changes.

You can also demonstrate the explanation for the phases of the moon by means of a model. You will need a ball, and a source of light in a darkened room. A bright light bulb, or a slide projector, is suitable. Your head represents the earth, and your eyes represent the view of the observer. Set up the model as shown in Figure 26-19. Move the ball representing the moon through the

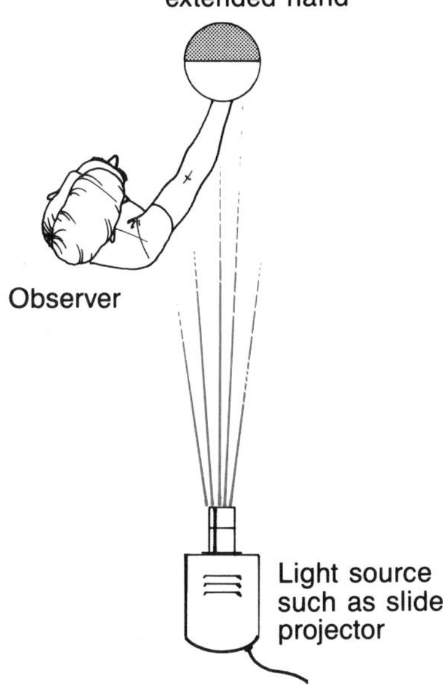

Fig. 26-19 A simple demonstration of what causes the phases of the moon

sequence of positions representing the new crescent, first quarter, waxing gibbous, and full phases. Note the changing appearance of the ''moon''.

Problem

Why does the moon show phases?

Method A An Indoor Study

Materials

ball
darkened room
light source: light bulb or slide projector

Procedure

a. Set up the light source as shown in Figure 26-19. Then darken the room.
b. Move the ball through the sequence of positions shown.
c. Observe the appearance of the ball, as illuminated by the light source, as it is moved through the sequence of positions.

Discussion

1. How does the orientation of the light source, the ball, and the observer represent the orientation of the sun, moon, and earth in each position?
2. Suggest ways of improving the effectiveness of this demonstration.

Method B An Outdoor Study

This activity provides a simpler and more straightforward demonstration of the cause of the phases of the moon. However, it requires a sunny day, and can only be used to demonstrate one phase at any time.

Materials

ball
good observing site

Fig. 26-20 How to set up a demonstration to show how the phases of the moon are caused.

Procedure

a. Choose a date and time when the moon is visible, preferably at first or last quarter.
b. Stand in a sunny location, facing the moon. Hold the ball in one hand. Extend that hand toward the moon as shown in Figure 26-20.
c. Observe the appearance of the ball, as it is illuminated by the sun. Compare its appearance with that of the moon.

Discussion

1. Explain how the orientation of the sun, the ball, and you the observer corresponds to the orientation of the sun, the moon, and you.

Extension

Investigate what kind of ball is most suitable for this demonstration. In what other ways can the demonstration be optimized?

Chapter Highlights

1. Astronomers use observations rather than experiments to study the nature of the universe, and to develop and test their theories.
2. The apparent motions of the sun determine the daily and yearly cycles of our lives. These motions are caused by the rotation and the revolution of the earth.
3. Different cultures have developed and used different kinds of calendars to keep track of the seasons.
4. Navigators have used the North Star and other stars to tell direction, and to determine their position on land or at sea.
5. The phases of the moon are caused by the changing position of the moon, relative to the earth and sun, as it revolves around the earth.
6. Astronomers can successfully predict events such as sunrise, moon phases, and seasons.

Key Terms

altitude
astrology
astronomy
calendar
constellation
gnomon
horizon
light pollution
magnitude
observe
phase (of the moon)
planisphere
revolve
rotate
season
star
UFO
universe
zenith

Recognizing the Concepts

Each of the following statements or questions is followed by four responses. Choose the correct response in each case. (Do not write in this book.)

1. Which of the following statements is correct?
   a) Astronomers in Canada can see some of the constellations at all times of the year.
   b) Astronomers in Canada can see all of the constellations at some time of the year.
   c) Astronomers in Canada can see the same constellations at all times of the year.
   d) Astronomers in Canada can see all the constellations at all times of the year.
2. In astronomy, the altitude of an object is its angle above the
   a) North Star **b)** zodiac **c)** horizon **d)** surface of the earth
3. The moon shows phases because
   a) it rotates on its axis
   b) it revolves about the earth
   c) it is black on one side and white on the other
   d) clouds prevent us from seeing it on about half the days in the month
4. If the moon is rising when the sun is setting, then the phase of the moon is
   a) new moon **b)** first quarter **c)** full moon **d)** last quarter
5. Suppose that you were an astronaut, standing on the surface of the moon, in the middle of the part which faces the earth. If the phase of the earth was first quarter, the phase of the moon, as seen from the earth, would be
   a) new moon **b)** first quarter **c)** full moon **d)** last quarter

Understanding the Concepts

1. State the rule which tells us whether a certain year is a leap year. How was this rule determined? Why is it so complicated? Was last year a leap year? this year? next year?
2. Why was astronomy important to ancient and primitive civilizations?
3. State and briefly describe three different ways in which a civilization can keep track of the time of the year.
4. Why is Antarctic exploration generally done in January and February?
5. Use a simple diagram to show why we see different stars at the same time of night at different times of the year.

Applying the Concepts

1. Determine the date of Easter this year, using the rule given in Section 26.12.

2. Explain why the Arctic is called "The Land of the Midnight Sun".
3. If you saw the phases of the moon from Australia, would they be the same as the phases of the moon seen from Canada? Explain your answer.
4. In what ways (if any) would your observations of the day and night sky be different if the earth's axis of rotation were upright, not tilted at 23°?
5. Why must architects know about the daily and yearly motions of the sun? Give some examples of ways in which they would use this information.
6. Suppose you were a scientist at a permanent research station at the north pole. Describe the daily and yearly motions of the North Star and the Big Dipper.

Investigations

1. Investigate the sources of light pollution in your neighbourhood.
2. When the moon is seen near the horizon, it appears to be larger than when it is seen high in the sky. Try to observe this "moon illusion"—for instance, by observing the full moon rising, and a few hours later when it is high in the sky. Devise a method for measuring the apparent size of the moon. Then use it to verify that the effect is indeed an illusion.
3. Take photographs of the night sky. You will need a camera with a time exposure setting, slide or print film with an ASA rating of 400 or higher, a tripod or other device to hold your camera in place, and an observing site which is not too bright. Place the camera on the tripod; point it at a constellation or other objects; open the camera shutter for 15 to 60 s.
4. List the different kinds of clocks which are used to keep time today. Find out about "atomic clocks" which are used in scientific laboratories to keep time very precisely.
5. Investigate the calendars used by ancient cultures (Egyptian, Mayan . . .) and modern cultures (Chinese, Islamic, Jewish . . .).
6. Find out about the important astronomical discoveries made by one of the following astronomers, and report back to the class: Galileo Galilei, Tycho Brahe, Nicolaus Copernicus, Isaac Newton.
7. Around the time of the autumnal equinox (September 23) or the vernal equinox (March 21), record the time of sunrise and sunset. These times are given in the newspaper and on TV. Are the lengths of the day and night equal on these dates? Does noon (halfway between sunrise and sunset) actually occur at 12:00?

Biography

Mary Grey: Astronomy Educator

Astronomy has a special fascination for people young and old, and there is a great demand for information about the appearance of the sky and the things in it. Planetariums and museums play an important role in providing this information to the public and to schools. Mary Grey is Curator of the Astronomy Division of the National Museum of Science and Technology. She is a leader in producing exhibits, publications, and programs in astronomy for the general public.

Grey received her degree in Civil Engineering from the University of New Brunswick, then joined the Map Compilation Branch of the Department of Energy, Mines, and Resources. When she married, she had to leave this department, because Civil Service regulations at that time said that a married woman could not hold a job if a man was available to fill it! After the birth of her two children, Mary worked first at the Geological Survey of Canada, and then at the Dominion Observatory in Ottawa. There, she became involved with public education as well as research. When the Observatory's 15-inch telescope was "retired" in 1974 and moved to the National Museum, Mary moved with it.

She admits that astronomy has become a dominating force in her life, and her work in the daytime and at night leaves little time for hobbies. Like many astronomy educators, however, she finds that introducing the public to the joys of astronomy is as much fun as any hobby.

Mary Grey was National President of the Royal Astronomical Society of Canada in 1986–88. This organization is a century old, and has thousands of members in its 20 branches across the country. If you are interested in astronomy, no matter what your age or level of knowledge of the subject, you should join this organization. There, you will find many others who share your interest.

VISTA

ARCHAEOASTRONOMY

Archaeoastronomy is the astronomy of civilizations so ancient or primitive that they have left us no written records. Like archaeologists, we must learn about their astronomy from the artifacts which they have left behind. These artifacts seem to suggest that astronomy played an important role in these civilizations. Hunters predicted the phase of the moon by using marks on sticks. Farmers predicted the seasons by watching the changes in the night sky. Sailors navigated from one remote shore to another by using the stars.

The most famous astronomical artifact is Stonehenge. This gigantic structure of standing stones points to where the sun rises on the horizon on the first day of summer. But was it used as an observatory to predict the seasons, or as a "church" in which to hold religious ceremonies that —like many modern religious ceremonies—were connected with the seasons? This illustrates an important difficulty in the study of archaeoastronomy: we cannot prove our theories about how artifacts like Stonehenge were used. Also, we cannot be sure why its users went to the trouble of building it.

There are hundreds of other megalithic (large-stone) sites in the British Isles. Elsewhere there are many other structures with astronomial connections, from Angkor Wat in Cambodia, to the Great Pyramid in Egypt (which was built at about the same time that Stonehenge was begun). The Great Pyramid is aligned in a north-south direction, and one of the passages to the crypt inside points to the North Star. In the New World, there are many Aztec, Inca, and Mayan temples, and hundreds of stone circles called "medicine wheels" in the western United States and Canada, all with suspected astronomical alignments. Most of the medicine wheels are so isolated that they have never been fully investigated or mapped.

Stonehenge was built thousands of years ago by a civilization which left no written records. Was it an observatory?

But we must be careful. Structures like Stonehenge and the Great Pyramid have always inspired fanciful theories—the most fanciful being that they were built by extraterrestrials! Even astronomers have been guilty of seeing much more astronomical significance in Stonehenge than is likely to be there. We must combine the methods and the knowledge of astronomy, archaeology, and the other sciences if we are to understand fully the meaning of these ancient and mysterious monuments.

27 The Solar System

CHAPTER CONTENTS

CHAPTER OBJECTIVES

After completing this chapter, you should be able to:

1. Use a model to visualize the layout of the solar system.
2. Observe and describe the features on the surface of the moon.
3. Describe the major features of each known planet and satellite.
4. Describe the asteroids, comets, and related objects.
5. Describe the methods of exploration of the solar system.

The **solar system** includes the **sun**, nine **planets**, their **satellites**, and smaller objects such as **asteroids** and **comets**. The sun is the most massive object. Its gravity holds the solar system together. A tiny fraction of its energy strikes the planets, making them visible and keeping the nearer ones warm. The planets are much less massive than the sun. And the asteroids and comets are interesting but insignificant in size. Until recently, these objects could only be studied from earth. Now, robot spacecraft have visited a score of other worlds, and humans have walked on the moon (Fig. 27-1). We can compare our world with other worlds, and hence understand all of them better.

Fig. 27-1 Geologist-astronaut Harrison Schmitt explores the surface of the moon.

27.1 The Layout of the Solar System

A General Description

The planets revolve about the sun, all in the same direction (Fig. 27-2). Their orbits are almost circular and almost in the same plane. Each planet is about 1.7 times further from the sun than the next closest planet to the sun. This means that the solar system becomes much more "spaced out" as you get further from the sun. Most of the planets rotate in the same direction as they revolve. Most of the large satellites revolve around their planet in this same direction, in orbits which are almost circular and in the same plane. The solar system is a very orderly place!

The sun is the centre of the solar system. Its gravity holds the rest of the solar system together. If this gravity were suddenly "turned off", the planets would move in straight lines rather than in circles, and would all fly off into space.

The four planets closest to the sun are made mainly of rock. The next two (Jupiter and Saturn) are made mainly of the light gases hydrogen and helium. The outer planets, most of their satellites, and the comet nuclei which lie beyond the outer planets, are made mainly of ice.

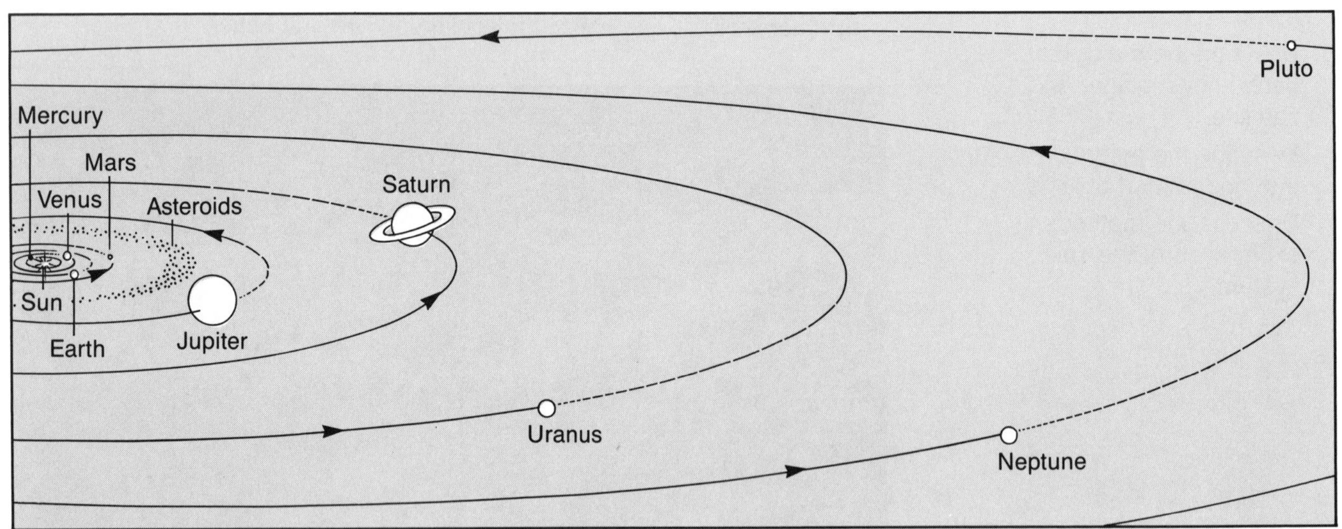

Fig. 27-2 A scale diagram of the orbits of the planets around the sun. Why would it be almost impossible to show the sizes of the planets, using the same scale?

The Scale of the Solar System

It is difficult to appreciate the scale of the solar system, simply because it is so big and so spread out. It might help to imagine that you were a ray of light, travelling outward from the sun at 300 000 km/s. At this speed, you would pass Mercury after 3.2 min, Venus after 6.0 min, and earth after 8.3 min. It would be over an hour before you reached Saturn and over 5 h before you passed the last known planet in the solar system—Pluto. It would then be over 4 years before you reached the nearest star!

Remembering the Order of the Planets

What do you make of the following sentence: ''Man Very Early Made Jars Stand Upright Nearly Perpendicular''? Or this one: ''My Very Educated Mother Just Showed Us Nine Planets''? They are **mnemonics**—memory devices—to help you remember the names of the planets in order from the sun. Can you think of a better mnemonic?

NOTE: On the average, Pluto is the most distant planet from the sun. However, its orbit is quite elongated. Therefore it can, at times, be closer to the sun than Neptune—as it is from 1980 to 1999. This fact complicates some of the things that are said earlier in this section and in Section 27.2.

Section Review

1. Why is the sun the centre of our solar system?
2. In what ways is our solar system an orderly place? In what way(s) is it disorderly?
3. Which planet is presently furthest from the sun? Is it always furthest from the sun?

27.2 Activity: A Scale Model of the Solar System

This is a way of visualizing the scale of the solar system. If you use the same scale for the sizes and the distances of the planets, then you will also see how far apart the planets are, compared with their sizes.

Problem

How can we show the layout of the solar system, the relative sizes of the planets, and their distances apart?

Materials

Table 27-1
the items listed in the last column of Table 27-1
ten sheets of paper, one labelled ''sun'' and each of the others labelled with the name of a planet
lots of space (outdoors)

Table 27-1 A Model of the Solar System

	Actual		Scale		
Object	*Distance from sun (km × 10^6)*	*Diameter (km × 10^3)*	*Distance from sun (m)*	*Diameter (cm)*	*Object*
Sun	0	1392	0	14.0	Grapefruit
Mercury	58	5	6	0.05	Sand grain
Venus	108	12	11	0.1	Pin head
Earth	150	13	15	0.1	Pin head
Mars	228	7	23	0.07	Large sand grain
Jupiter	778	143	78	1.4	Grape
Saturn	1427	120	143	1.2	Cherry
Uranus	2869	51	287	0.5	Small pea
Neptune	4497	49	450	0.5	Small pea
Pluto	5900	3	590	0.03	Small sand grain

At this scale, the MOON would be 0.03 cm in diameter, and would be 4 cm from the EARTH.

The NEAREST STAR would be 14 cm in diameter (a grapefruit) and would be over 4000 km from the SUN!

Procedure

a. Form a group with 9 other students.

b. Assign one student in your group to be the sun, and 9 other students to be the planets.

c. Take the item in the last column of Table 27-1 which represents the size of your sun or planet. Take also the sheet of paper containing the name of your sun or planet. Now walk to a position which represents the distance of that planet from the sun (Fig. 27-3).

Fig. 27-3 These students have set up a scale model of the solar system. The students in the distance are the outer planets. Why are not all the planets shown?

d. Discuss with your group what item would represent the nearest star in this model. How far from the sun should it be?

Discussion

1. Should all 10 students be in a straight line? Explain.
2. If the 9 students representing the planets were to walk in paths which represent the orbits of the planets, what should those paths be like?
3. Does this scale model represent the fact that the orbits of the planets are almost in the same plane?
4. What is the relative position of the sun, earth, and Venus when Venus is (a) closest to the earth? (b) furthest from the earth? Demonstrate these positions using the model.
5. What is the relative position of the sun, earth, and Mars when Mars is (a) closest to the earth? (b) furthest from the earth? Demonstrate these positions using the model.
6. What is the relative position of the sun, earth, and Mercury or Venus, when Mercury or Venus is at its maximum angle from the sun, as seen from the earth? Use the ''handy'' method (see Section 26.4) to determine the maximum angle of (a) Mercury; (b) Venus from the sun.

Extensions

1. Look at the static model, and decide which planets should be visible, and in what part of the sky.
2. Devise instructions for converting this model from a static model into a moving one. How should the nine students representing the planets move in order that their motion represents the actual motion of the planets?
3. Discuss the problems involved in sending spacecraft on long journeys through the solar system.

27.3 Activity: Sketching the Moon

The moon is a **satellite**—an object which revolves about a planet. Satellites are sometimes called **moons**. The moon is the only natural satellite of the earth, though there are now thousands of artificial ones. Like many of the larger satellites in the solar system, the moon is an interesting world—just as interesting as the smaller planets. The moon is also the only other world in the solar system which has been visited in person by humans—yet.

In the previous chapter, you recorded the position and the phase of the moon in the form of a moon calendar. In this activity, you will take a closer look at the moon, and record your view in the form of a sketch. Until the development of astronomical photography a century ago, this was the only way of recording the appearance of an astronomical object. Even as late as the 1960s, visual observations through telescopes were used for mapping the surface of the moon in preparation for the Apollo missions. You will be surprised how much detail you can see with the unaided eye!

You can do this activity at any phase of the moon between first quarter and last quarter. At first quarter, the moon is visible in the late afternoon and evening. At full moon, it is visible all night (but you will probably want to do the activity in the evening after sunset). At last quarter, it is visible in the morning.

Problem

How can you record the details of the appearance of the moon, as seen with the unaided eye? What can you learn from such observations?

Materials

good observing site
white paper and pencil
clipboard
observing log
compasses

Procedure

a. Find a comfortable spot at a good observing site. Use the clipboard as an aid for sketching.

b. Use the compasses or other tool to draw a circle, about 10 to 15 cm in diameter, on a sheet of plain paper. This represents the **limb** or edge of the moon's disc.

c. Carefully draw the **terminator**—the line separating the bright and dark regions of the moon.

d. Observe the illuminated region of the moon carefully. Record what you see in the form of a pencil sketch. Do this as accurately and completely as possible.

e. If possible, repeat this activity at other phases of the moon—first quarter, full moon, and last quarter. Otherwise, you and your classmates can organize the activity so that different students observe and sketch the moon at different phases. You can then compare your sketches.

f. Compare your sketches with a moon map (Fig. 27-4). Identify and label the more conspicuous features.

g. Include your sketch in your observing log.

Discussion

1. Describe the appearance of the surface of the moon, as seen with the unaided eye.
2. How might you classify the features which you have observed and recorded?
3. According to folklore, the features on the surface of the moon resemble a "man in the moon" (or an old woman, or a rabbit . . .). Can you see such a resemblance? These features are best seen around full moon.
4. Compare the detailed appearance of the surface of the moon at first quarter, full moon, and last quarter. Does the moon show the same face to the earth at all phases?

Extensions

1. The full moon is 13 times brighter than the first quarter or last quarter

moon. Is this what you would expect? Why or why not? If not, can you think of an explanation for this observation?

2. If you have access to binoculars or a small telescope, use these to observe the surface of the moon in more detail. Explore some of the features which you have observed with the unaided eye. If possible, observe the moon at different phases.

27.4 Activity: The Surface of the Moon

The most interesting way to become familiar with the surface of the moon (other than to go there) is to observe the moon with binoculars or a small telescope. A more convenient way is to study photographs of the surface (Fig. 27-5). Since the moon keeps the same face turned toward the earth at all times, only about half of the surface of the moon has been photographed from the earth. Almost all of the surface has been photographed by the US Orbiter series of spacecraft, which orbited the moon in the mid-1960s.

Problem

What is the surface of the moon like?

Materials

slides or photographs of the moon
ruler
hand lens (optional)

Procedure and Discussion

a. Begin with Figure 27-6. You may want to look at other slides or photographs later.

b. The interpretation of a photograph of the surface of the moon is based on the shadows which are cast by the different kinds of surface features. From which direction is the sun shining in Figure 27-6?

c. Figure 27-6 shows a large, dark, circular region surrounded by a rugged border. Study and describe this circular region.

d. Identify a mountain in Figure 27-6. A mountain sticks up from the surface. The side of the mountain facing the sun will be bright. The side of the mountain facing away from the sun will be dark. The mountain will cast a shadow on the surface of the moon in a direction pointing away from the sun. How could you determine the height of the mountain?

e. Identify and describe a range of mountains in Figure 27-6.

f. Look carefully at the smaller circular features in Figure 27-6. Study the pattern of brightness and darkness, and try to deduce the nature of the features.

g. Identify a valley in Figure 27-6.

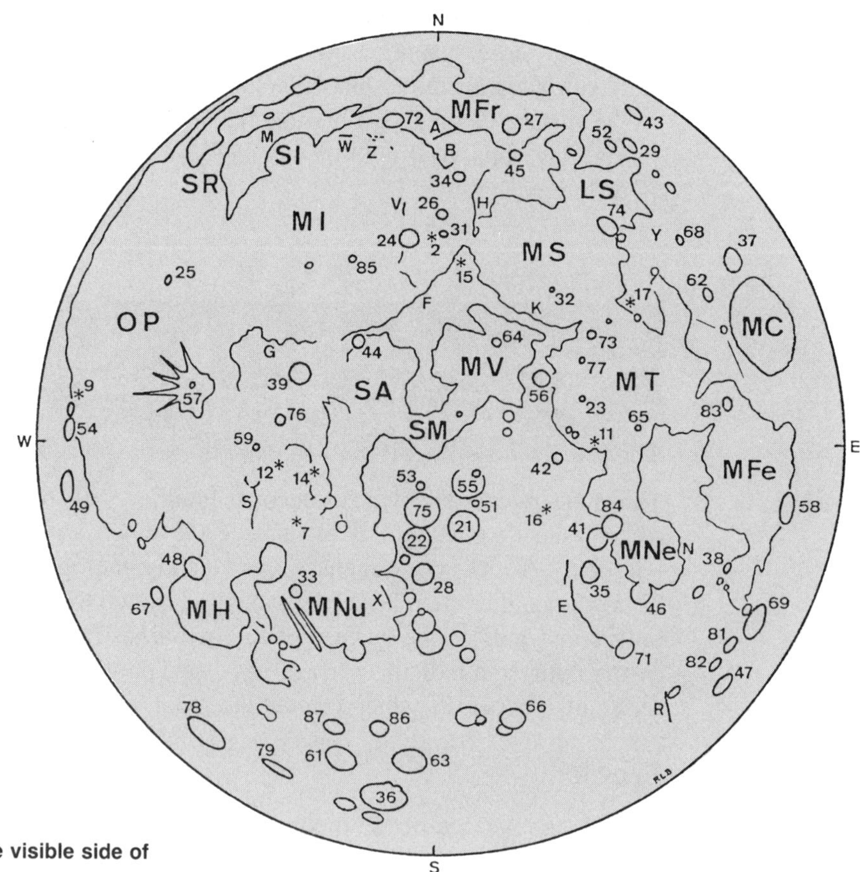

Fig. 27-4 A map of the visible side of the moon

Key to the Map of the Moon

Craters

21 — Albategnius
22 — Alphonsus
23 — Arago
24 — Archimedes
25 — Aristarchus
26 — Aristillus
27 — Aristoteles
28 — Arzachel
29 — Atlas
31 — Autolycus
32 — Bessel
33 — Bullialdus
34 — Cassini
35 — Catharina
36 — Clavius
37 — Cleomedes
38 — Cook
39 — Copernicus
41 — Cyrillus
42 — Delambre
43 — Endymion
44 — Eratosthenes
45 — Eudoxus
46 — Fracastorius
47 — Furnerius
48 — Gassendi
49 — Grimaldi
51 — Halley
52 — Hercules
53 — Herschel
54 — Hevelius
55 — Hipparchus
56 — Julius Caesar
57 — Kepler
58 — Langrenus
59 — Lansberg
61 — Longomontanus
62 — Macrobius
63 — Maginus
64 — Manilius
65 — Maskelyne
66 — Maurolycus
67 — Mersenius
68 — Newcomb
69 — Petavius
71 — Piccolomini
72 — Plato
73 — Plinius
74 — Posidonius
75 — Ptolemaeus
76 — Reinhold
77 — Ross
78 — Schickard
79 — Schiller
81 — Snellius
82 — Stevinus
83 — Taruntius
84 — Theophilus
85 — Timocharis
86 — Tycho
87 — Wilhelm

Mountains

A — Alpine Valley
B — Alps Mts.
E — Altai Mts.
F — Apennine Mts.
G — Carpathian Mts.
H — Caucasus Mts.
K — Haemus Mts.
M — Jura Mts.
N — Pyrenees Mts.
R — Rheita Valley
S — Riphaeus Mts.
V — Spitzbergen
W — Straight Range
X — Straight Wall
Y — Taurus Mts.
Z — Teneriffe Mts.

Maria

LS — Lacus Somniorum (Lake of Dreams)
MC — Mare Crisium (Sea of Crises)
MFe — Mare Fecunditatis (Sea of Fertility)
MFr — Mare Frigoris (Sea of Cold)
MH — Mare Humorum (Sea of Moisture)
MI — Mare Imbrium (Sea of Rains)
MNe — Mare Nectaris (Sea of Nectar)
MNu — Mare Nubium (Sea of Clouds)
MS — Mare Serenitatis (Sea of Serenity)
MT — Mare Tranquillitatis (Sea of Tranquillity)
MV — Mare Vaporum (Sea of Vapours)
OP — Oceanus Procellarum (Ocean of Storms)
SA — Sinus Aestuum (Seething Bay)
SI — Sinus Iridum (Bay of Rainbows)
SM — Sinus Medii (Central Bay)
SR — Sinus Roris (Bay of Dew)

Lunar Probes

2 — Luna 2, first to reach moon (9/13/59)
7 — Ranger 7, first close pictures (7/31/64)
9 — Luna 9, first soft landing (2/3/66)
11 — Apollo 11, first men on moon (7/20/69)
12 — Apollo 12 (11/19/69)
14 — Apollo 14 (2/5/71)
15 — Apollo 15 (7/30/71)
16 — Apollo 16 (4/21/72)
17 — Apollo 17 (12/11/72)

Fig. 27-5 A photograph of the visible side of the moon. Actually, this is two photographs. How can you tell?

h. Look carefully at the pattern of bright streaks in the lower left of Figure 27-6, and around the larger round features in the middle right. Form a hypothesis about the nature of these streaks.

i. Locate any features which interest or puzzle you. Identify them by giving their positions in millimetres from the bottom of the photograph and from the right-hand side of the photograph. Include a short description or sketch of each one.

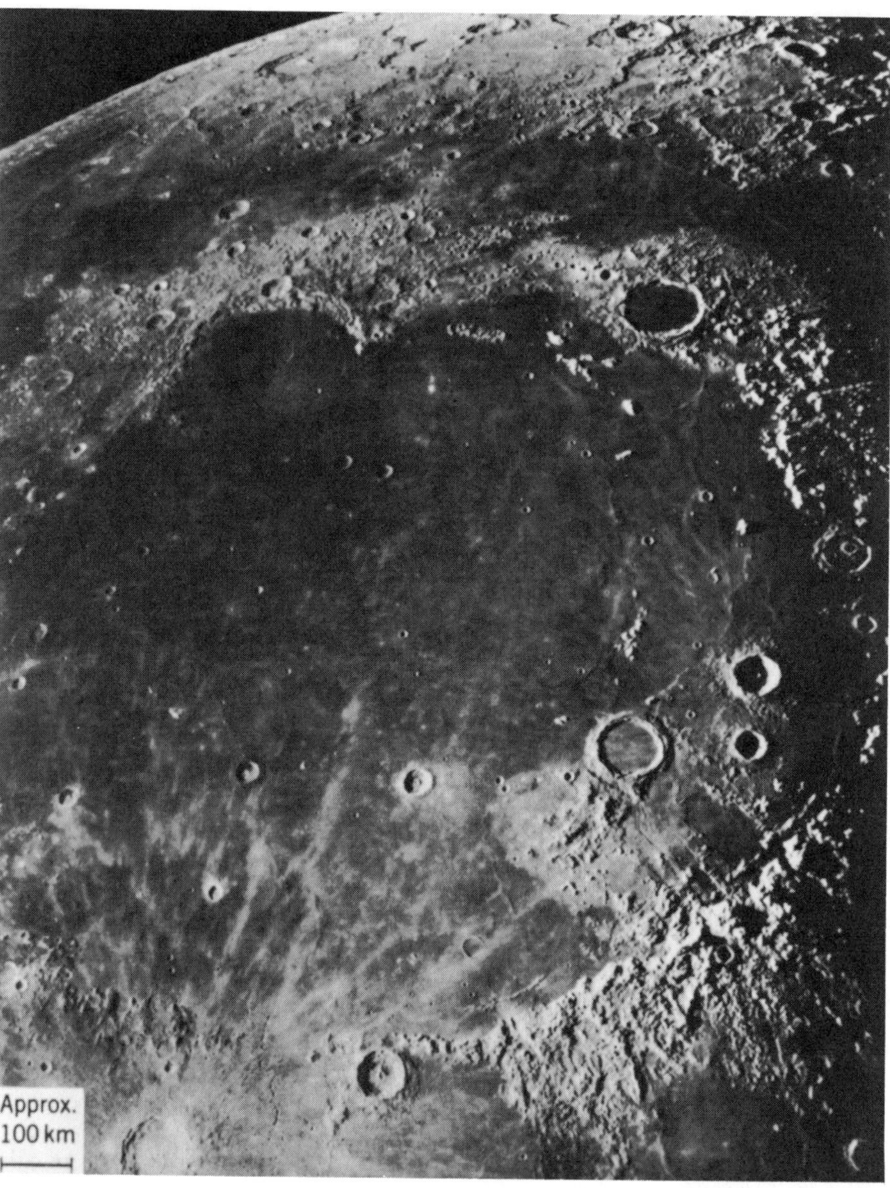

Fig. 27-6 A photograph of Mare Imbrium and vicinity. Why is Mare Imbrium round?

j. Figure 27-6 shows Mare Imbrium—the left ''eye'' of the ''man in the moon''. Compare the photograph with the sketch of the moon which you made in Activity 27.3.

27.5 The Surface Features of the Moon

In Activity 27.3, you already saw two kinds of regions on the surface of the moon: the dark regions and the bright regions. If you compare these regions with Figure 27-5, you will see that the dark regions are vast circular plains with relatively few features on them, whereas the bright regions are rugged areas with many mountains, craters, and other features. The dark regions are called maria—the Latin word for seas—because they looked like seas to the first astronomers who studied them and thought about them seriously. The bright regions are called highlands because they are indeed higher than the maria.

Some Features

- **Maria** are lowland plains of hardened lava. They were formed about 3 000 000 000 years ago when lava flowed out of the moon's interior. They are often round, because they flowed into low, round basins. These basins had been formed earlier by collisions of asteroids with the moon.
- **Highlands** are brighter regions which, being at higher altitude, escaped the lava floods. If you look at them closely, you will see that they are made up of layers of circular features—craters which were already formed when the lava floods took place.
- **Mountain ranges** on the moon are mainly curved rims of the great basins in which the maria formed. On the earth, mountain ranges are mainly straight, and are folded up by slow motions of the continents.
- **Mountains** are sometimes found alone, as well as in ranges. They are most noticeable when they occur on the maria.
- **Craters** are the most numerous features on the moon (Fig. 27-7). They have round, raised rims, with shallow basins inside. There are often hills or mountains in the centre of the basin. A century ago, scientists thought that craters were caused by volcanos. Now scientists know that they were caused by meteorites crashing into the surface. Dozens of meteorite craters have been identified on the earth, including about two dozen in Canada.

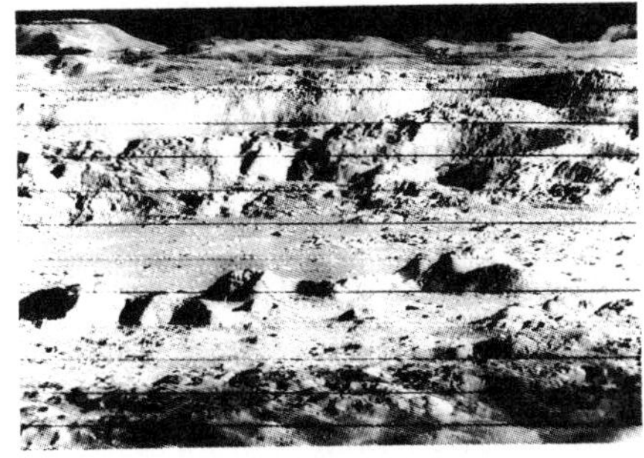

Fig. 27-7 The crater Copernicus, photographed by the Orbiter 2 spacecraft. The horizontal lines are artifacts of the picture-making process.

- **Rays** are bright streaks extending outward from craters, across the surface of the moon. They are caused by a thin powder of lighter-coloured rock, ejected from the crater when it was produced.
- **Rilles** are long, narrow, wandering valleys which are found especially in the maria. They appear to be due to faults (cracks) in the crust of the moon.
- **Rift valleys** are found in several places on the moon. Like the rift valleys on the earth, they appear to be caused by parallel cracks in the crust. The floor of the valley has fallen relative to the sides of the valley.

The Lunar Surface

During the 1960s, scientists learned much about the surface of the moon by sending spacecraft there. The first such spacecraft (Luna and Ranger series) were very primitive. They were designed only to crash-land on the moon. Later, more advanced spacecraft were designed to orbit the moon (Orbiter series) or land gently on its surface (Luna and Surveyor series). The photographs and experiments from these spacecraft laid the basis for the most exciting project of all—the exploration of the moon by astronauts in the Apollo project (Fig. 27-8).

Fig. 27-8 Astronauts exploring the surface of the moon. What is the environment on the moon like? How can the astronauts survive and work in it?

The best way to get a feeling for the surface of the moon is to watch a movie or video of one of the Apollo missions. The second-best way is to study in detail some of the colour photographs taken by the Apollo astronauts.

Section Review

1. List and describe the major kinds of features on the surface of the moon.
2. Describe what you would see if you were standing on the surface of the moon.
3. What is "The Man in the Moon"?
4. What was the Apollo project?

27.6 Observing the Planets

How You Can Tell a Planet from a Star

The most effective way to tell a planet from a star is to wait for several weeks, to see if it moves relative to the background stars. If it does, it is a planet. Planet is derived from the Greek word for *wanderer* (see Figure 27-16, page 631). If you cannot wait for several weeks, there are a few clues which will help you to make an educated guess about which it is. These clues are based on its brightness and colour, and on its position in the sky.

a) The planets are found in a band in the sky called the **zodiac**. This is because the orbits of the planets are all in about the same plane as the orbit of the earth. The constellations around the zodiac are Aries, Taurus, Gemini, Cancer, Leo, Virgo, Libra, Scorpius, Sagittarius, Capricornus, Aquarius, and Pisces. The constellation Ophiuchus is also in the zodiac. But, for some reason, it is not always included in the list.

b) The planets usually shine with a steady light, but the stars often twinkle, especially if they are close to the horizon. Twinkling is due to air currents in the earth's atmosphere.

c) There are some clues about individual planets:

- **Mercury** is as bright as the brightest stars, but it is never more than 25° from the sun. It is only seen in the morning or evening twilight, and is very difficult to see.
- **Venus** is brighter than the brightest stars. It can be as much as 45° from the sun. It can then be seen easily in the morning sky before sunrise, or in the evening sky after sunset.
- **Mars** is reddish, and can be as bright as the brightest stars. The orbits of Mars, Jupiter, and Saturn are outside the orbit of the earth. Therefore these planets can sometimes be seen opposite the sun. Mars could be seen due south at midnight, for instance.
- **Jupiter** is as bright as the brightest stars—sometimes brighter.
- **Saturn** is almost as bright as the brightest stars.

Section Review

Which planet(s) (**a**) are red; (**b**) can never be seen opposite to the sun; (**c**) twinkle; (**d**) is most difficult to see; (**e**) does not move relative to the background stars?

27.7 Activity: Locating and Observing a Planet

If there are planets visible in the night sky when you are studying this unit, you should observe them and record them in your log.

Problem

What planets are visible in the sky? How can they be located and identified? What do they look like?

Materials

sky chart observing site observing log

Procedure and Discussion

a. Consult a sky chart or other source of information to find out what planets are visible in the sky, and where and when they can be seen.

b. Follow the instructions on the sky chart: use it at the time and date indicated, and look in the direction indicated.

c. Compare the pattern of stars and planets on the chart with the pattern of objects in the sky. Thus identify the planet or planets in the sky.
d. Compare the brightness of the planet(s) with that of some of the stars on the chart.
e. Compare the colour of the planet(s) with that of some of the stars on the chart.
f. Estimate the angle of the planet above the horizon, using the ''handy'' method. Also, estimate the angle of the planet from any nearby bright stars.
g. Enter the information in your observing log.

Extension

1. If you have access to binoculars or a telescope, use these to observe and study the planet. Record the appearance of the planet in your observing log.
2. Locate the planet in the sky a few weeks later. Compare the position of the planet relative to the background stars.

27.8 Investigating the Planets

Spacecraft have dramatically improved our ability to observe the planets. To begin with, spacecraft have brought the planets closer. The nearest other planet (Venus) never comes closer than 40 000 000 km. Spacecraft have passed within a few thousand kilometres of a score of planets and satellites, and have landed on the surfaces of three of them.

Spacecraft do not have to look through the murky atmosphere of the earth, as we on the ground do. Air currents smear our view of the planets (and other astronomical objects). Therefore it is difficult to take time-exposure photographs. Light pollution can block out our view of faint objects.

The eye and the telescope can sometimes capture brief moments of better-than-average viewing. But the eye is subject to ''optical illusions''. For instance, if you look at Mars through a telescope, you will sometimes think you see fine lines on its surface. Some astronomers thought that these were human-made canals, and were therefore evidence that Mars was inhabited. The canals later turned out to be an optical illusion.

Mercury

Fig. 27-9 Mercury, photographed by the Mariner 10 spacecraft. In what ways is Mercury like the moon?

Mercury is the planet which is closest to the sun. It is therefore very difficult to see. If you observe it with a telescope, you will see that it shows phases, like the moon. Can you explain why?

Mercury is the smallest planet except for Pluto. As a result, its gravity is very weak—too weak to prevent an atmosphere from drifting away. Mercury has no atmosphere, and probably never had one.

Because Mercury is so close to the sun, it is very hot. The temperature is over 400°C at noon, but drops to about −200°C at midnight. This occurs because there is no atmosphere to moderate the temperature.

Until the space age, virtually nothing was known about the surface of Mercury. Thanks to Mariner 10's fly-by in 1974, we now know that the surface of Mercury is much like that of the moon—covered by thousands of craters (Fig. 27-9).

Venus

Fig. 27-10 The cloud-covered planet Venus, photographed by the Mariner 10 spacecraft

Venus lies closer to the sun than the earth does, but not as close as Mercury. It can be as much as 45° away from the sun. As a result, it is much easier to see. Because of its closeness and its reflective cloud layer, it is extremely bright. If you can observe it with a small telescope, you will see that it shows phases, like the moon and Mercury.

In size, Venus is an almost exact twin of the earth. Its surface is quite similar to the surface of the earth in many ways. We cannot tell that, however, by observing Venus from earth, because Venus is covered by a thick layer of clouds (Fig. 27-10). The most detailed studies of the surface of Venus have been made by the Pioneer Venus spacecraft, in orbit about the planet. It used radar waves to "look" through the clouds, and make maps of the surface. There, it found plateaus (like the earth's continents), lowlands (like the earth's ocean basins), volcanic mountains, and some craters. You may be interested to know that astronomers have decided to name the surface features on Venus after famous women!

Many years ago, astronomers thought that, because Venus was a bit closer to the sun than earth, it would be a bit hotter—like a jungle or desert, perhaps. They were very wrong! The surface temperature on Venus is about 450°C, day and night, all year—almost hot enough to melt lead! This is because Venus has an atmosphere of carbon dioxide, 100 times denser than the atmosphere of the earth. This atmosphere traps heat from the sun, much like a car does if it is left in the summer sun with its windows closed. At the top of this atmosphere is a thick layer of clouds, made up of droplets of sulfuric acid. At the surface of the planet, it is too hot for liquid water to exist. But the temperature in the clouds is much more moderate.

If the earth and Venus are so similar in size, why are they so different in other ways? On earth—but apparently not on Venus—the temperature was low enough for oceans of water to exist. Carbon dioxide from volcanos dissolved in the water and reacted with minerals on the ocean bottom to form carbonate rocks. Some of the carbon dioxide was absorbed by simple life forms which had evolved in the oceans, just as it is absorbed by plant life today.

Earth

Fig. 27-11 The earth photographed from space. What part of the earth is shown?

The **earth** is a planet—the only planet which we knew well until the 1960s. Since then, spacecraft have sent us amazing photographs of our planet and other planets. We can now see the earth from a cosmic perspective (Fig. 27-11).

The earth has a core of iron and nickel. The rotation and flow of the material in the core produces the earth's magnetic field. Above the core is a mantle of hot, non-metallic rock. The continents in the crust of the earth float slowly on the mantle. The slow drift of the continents produces mountains, earthquakes, and many other geological processes and features.

On the crust is a thin layer of water which is essential to life. Above the water and the land is a thin atmosphere, which is also essential. It prevents the oceans from evaporating, and it keeps the earth warm. It provides the air which we and all the other life forms on earth breathe.

Mars

Mars has always fascinated observers on earth, because of its reddish colour, its changing brightness, and its complex motion. Small telescopes reveal its surface features, and its earthlike rotation and seasons.

The orbit of Mars lies outside that of the earth, so Mars can sometimes be seen opposite the sun. At these times, it is closest to us, and brightest.

A good telescope reveals surface features on Mars: white polar caps and greenish features on a reddish background. The greenish features change with the Martian seasons, and were once thought to be vegetation. They are actually types of surface materials which are covered and uncovered by seasonal winds. The reddish features were thought to be deserts of rusty sand, and this hypothesis has turned out to be correct. In addition, there appeared to be narrow linear features, often in pairs, which appeared to be artificial. They were called canals, and were thought by some astronomers to be the work of a dying civilization which was using them for irrigation purposes. This idea led to many popular stories which were the forerunners to today's science fiction. Unfortunately, the canals turned out to be optical illusions. There is no dying—or living—civilization on Mars.

Fig. 27-12 The red deserts of Mars, photographed by the Viking 1 lander spacecraft

The many spacecraft which have visited Mars have revealed a planet which is almost as interesting as the fictional one. There are extinct volcanos, larger than any on earth. There is a canyon which dwarfs the Grand Canyon on earth. There are ancient river beds which must once have carried water. There may still be water frozen under the surface as permafrost. It is visible at the poles of the planet as polar caps of frozen water and carbon dioxide.

The atmosphere of Mars is thin and cold, and consists mainly of carbon dioxide. The winds can be strong. They sometimes cause dust storms which engulf the whole planet. Hostile though the planet is, it could support "life as we know it". As a result, biological life search experiments were an important part of the Viking lander spacecraft which landed on Mars in 1976. No evidence for life—either simple or complex—was found at the sites where the two spacecraft landed (Fig. 27-12).

Jupiter

Jupiter is the largest planet in the solar system—318 times more massive than the earth. It is sometimes called a "gas giant" because it is made up mainly of the two light gases hydrogen and helium. Deep inside the planet, however, the pressure and the temperature are such that these gases change to a liquid and—closer to the centre—to a metal.

A telescope shows bands of light and dark clouds in Jupiter's atmosphere. The longest-lasting feature in the clouds is the Great Red Spot—an immense cyclone. If you watch this feature for a few hours, you will be able to see it move across the disc, due to the planet's rapid rotation. You may also notice that the planet is slightly flattened at the poles—also due to its rapid rotation (Fig. 27-13).

We cannot see beneath the clouds of Jupiter. However, the laws of physics

Fig. 27-13 Jupiter, and two of its Galilean satellites (Io — left; Europa — right), photographed by the Voyager 1 spacecraft. Notice the bands of cloud and the Great Red Spot (behind Io).

give us a good idea of what we would find there. There is no solid surface—only layers of increasing density and temperature, where gases gradually change into a fog and then into an ocean.

Jupiter has numerous satellites, and there are probably many smaller ones waiting to be discovered. The four largest are the Galilean satellites—so called because Galileo discovered them.

1. *Io* is the closest to Jupiter. It has many active volcanos, which cover its surface with colourful layers of sulfur and sulfur compounds. It looks, in a colour photo, like a pizza.
2. *Europa*, the second, has a core which is mainly rock and a crust which is mainly ice. Because the crust is fairly warm, it flows like a glacier. This "wipes out" any surface features like craters. There is a series of cracks in the crust which makes the satellite look something like a cracked egg.
3. *Ganymede* is the largest satellite in the solar system. Its surface is a quilt-like pattern of old and younger continents. On the older continents, there are many craters. Beneath the crust, there may be a layer of ice—or water. Indeed, Europa, Ganymede, or the outer satellite Callisto may have oceans beneath the surface, if the core of the satellite produces enough heat to stop the water from freezing.
4. *Callisto* has an old crust of rock and ice, and many craters. These craters are very bright, because they expose clean ice from beneath the surface. The satellite looks, in photographs, as if it is covered by a multitude of bright lights.

Saturn

Saturn is the most distant planet which can be easily seen with the unaided eye. It moves in slow and stately fashion through the constellations of the zodiac, once every 30 years.

Saturn's "claim to fame" is its rings. These can be seen with a small telescope, and are the most striking thing that the beginning astronomer can

Fig. 27-14 Saturn and its rings, photographed by the Voyager 1 spacecraft. Notice the fine structure of the rings. The rings consist of a vast number of chunks of rock and ice, orbiting the planet.

see with a telescope. The rings are made of a multitude of small chunks of ice and rock. Some of these are the size of sand grains and others are as big as houses. Each chunk moves in orbit about the planet. At some distances from the planet, there is more ring material than at others. This gives the rings a grooved appearance, like a phonograph record. The rings may be the remains of a small satellite—or a stray asteroid—which was ''ground up'' by the tidal forces of the planet (Fig. 27-14).

Saturn itself is similar to Jupiter, but smaller and colder. ***Titan***, the largest satellite of Saturn, is the only satellite in the solar system with an atmosphere. This atmosphere is dense and cold, and consists mainly of nitrogen. The smaller satellites are icy objects with cratered surfaces, but with no atmospheres.

can be seen with the unaided eye if the sky is clear and dark, and if you know where to look. It was probably glimpsed many times through the ages. But it was officially discovered by William Herschel in 1781.

Like Jupiter and Saturn, Uranus has an atmosphere which consists mainly of hydrogen and helium gas, and a few simple compounds of hydrogen, such as ammonia. It has 15 known satellites, 5 of which were discovered from earth between 1787 and 1948. The other 10 were discovered by the Voyager 2 spacecraft which flew by the planet in 1986. The 5 larger ones appear to be icy objects. The innermost one—***Miranda***—has a strange jumbled surface which appears to have been taken apart and reassembled incorrectly!

Uranus also has 9 slender, dark rings which were discovered from earth and studied in detail by Voyager 2 (Fig. 27-15).

Fig. 27-15 The rings of Uranus, photographed by the Voyager 2 spacecraft. Like those of Saturn, the rings of Uranus consist of chunks of material orbiting the planet.

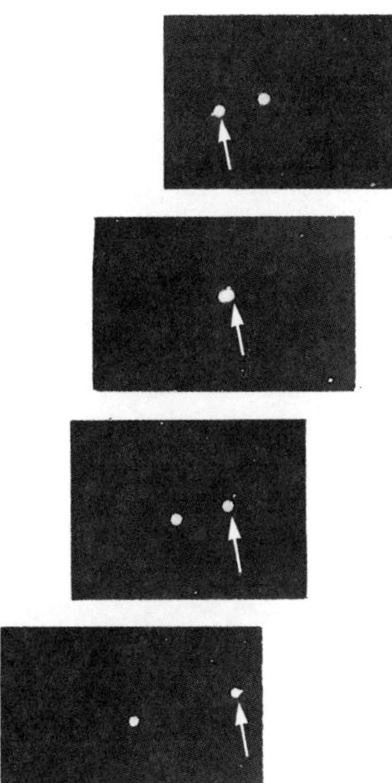

Fig. 27-16 Neptune (arrow), photographed at one-day intervals as it passed in front of a background star. Notice the large satellite Triton, orbiting the planet.

Uranus is unusual because its rotation axis is not upright, but lies in its orbit plane. The orbits of the satellites and the rings are almost perpendicular to the plane of the orbit.

Neptune

Neptune cannot be seen at all with the unaided eye. However, it can be seen with binoculars if the sky is clear and dark. It was discovered through its gravitational pull on Uranus. Actually, it had been seen by astronomers (including Galileo Galilei) several times before, but had been mistaken for a star.

Neptune is probably much like Jupiter, Saturn, and Uranus, but is even colder. Most of the gases, except hydrogen and helium, have probably frozen out of its atmosphere. The Voyager 2 spacecraft is scheduled to pass by Neptune in 1989.

Neptune has a large moon, ***Triton***, which may have glaciers of methane and oceans of liquid nitrogen (Fig. 27-16). This is one example of the many strange environments in the solar system!

Pluto

Pluto was discovered in 1930 after a long and careful search of the sky. It has proven to be the smallest planet in the solar system—even smaller than our moon. It is less dense than the moon, however, and may consist of solid water, methane, and ammonia.

It has one moon—Charon—which is almost as big as the planet (Fig. 27-17). Thus Pluto and Charon form a unique ''double planet'', orbiting about each other every 6 d, only 22 000 km apart.

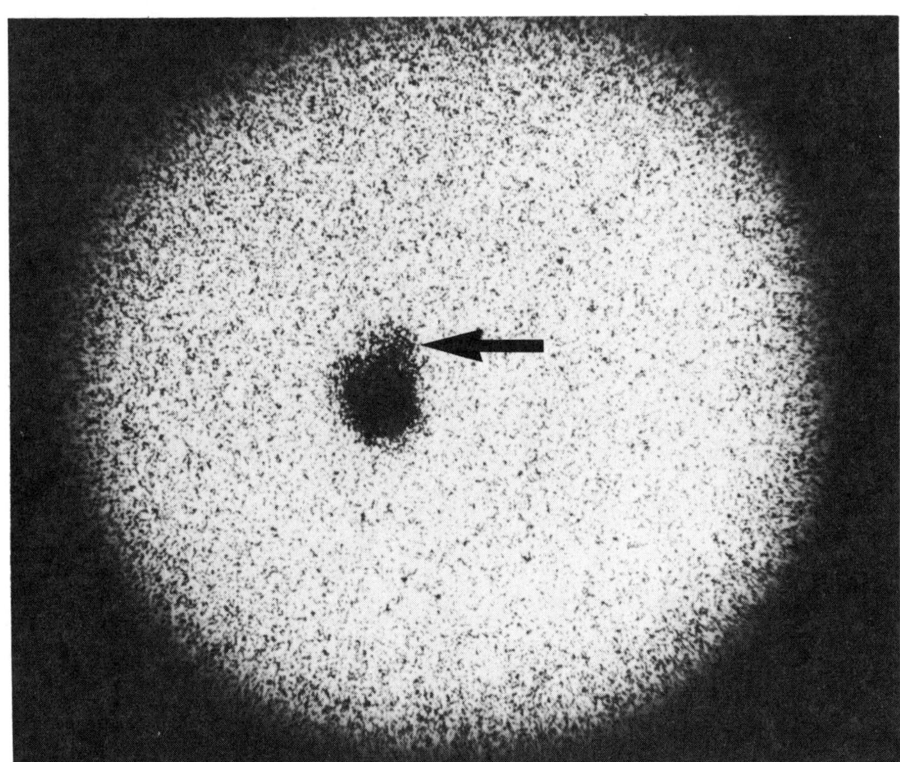

Fig. 27-17 The distant planet Pluto. Its satellite Charon can be seen as a fuzzy blob at the top. The fuzziness is due to the high magnification and the smearing effects of the earth's atmosphere.

Planets Beyond Pluto?

There are many other objects beyond Pluto which revolve about the sun. If there are objects as large as planets, then they must be much further away than Pluto. Otherwise, they would have been discovered already. As you will see in Section 27.10, there are billions of comets out there, only a few kilometres in size. These are certainly not big enough to call planets!

Section Review

1. Make a tabular summary of the information given about the planets in this section. Use these column headings: Name of Planet, Visibility from Earth, Position, Size, Atmosphere, Surface, Major Satellites.

27.9 Activity: Researching the Planets

The preceding section gave you a brief introduction to the planets and some of their satellites. In this section you will explore some of the planets and satellites in more detail.

Problem

Our understanding of the planets and satellites is constantly changing and deepening. What is currently known about these objects? How is the information obtained? Can we understand why these objects are the way they are?

Materials

a good library
photographs, slides, films and/or videos of the planets and satellites

Procedure and Discussion

You can do this activity in groups of 2 or 3 students. Each group can prepare a written or brief oral report on one topic to be shared with the rest of the class.

a. Investigate the methods and problems of sending manned and unmanned spacecraft on expeditions to the other planets.
b. Research the current knowledge and theories about any one of the planets or large satellites, in more detail than is given in Section 27.8. Be sure that your sources of information are up-to-date.
c. Compare any two worlds which have both similarities and differences, by listing these similarities and differences. Examples are the moon and Mercury, the earth and Venus, the earth and Mars.
d. Investigate future planned spacecraft missions to the other planets.
e. Discuss reasons for and against the exploration of the planets using manned or unmanned spacecraft.
f. Invent and discuss different ways to classify the planets.
g. Explain why Mercury and Venus show phases like the moon. Does Mars show phases?

27.10 The Smaller Objects in the Solar System

Asteroids

Asteroids—also known as minor planets—are rocky objects with diameters up to 1000 km. They revolve about the sun, mostly between the orbits of Mars and Jupiter. Only the largest are round. The rest are irregular. To make a model of a typical asteroid, get a potato from home. Stick a knitting needle through it to represent its rotation axis, and spin it slowly.

The asteroids are about 1.7 times further from the sun than Mars, and 1.7 times closer than Jupiter. They therefore occupy a place in the solar system where there should theoretically be a planet. For this reason, astronomers once thought that the asteroids might be the remains of a planet which exploded. This is not likely. There is no reason for a planet to explode. It is more likely that, between the orbits of Mars and Jupiter, there was not enough material to form a single large planet. Several small planets formed there instead.

Comets

Comets are mountain-sized balls of dust and frozen water, ammonia, methane, and other simple chemical compounds. You can think of them as large, dirty snowballs. They usually reside beyond the orbits of Neptune and Pluto, where they are much too small and faint to be seen from the earth.

Sometimes, the comet's slow revolution about the sun is disturbed by the gravity of another comet, a planet, or a passing star. The comet may be thrown out of the solar system, or it may fall inward toward the sun. As it approaches the sun, its surface is warmed. The frozen gases evaporate and form a cloud around the solid nucleus. The light and the wind from the sun push on the

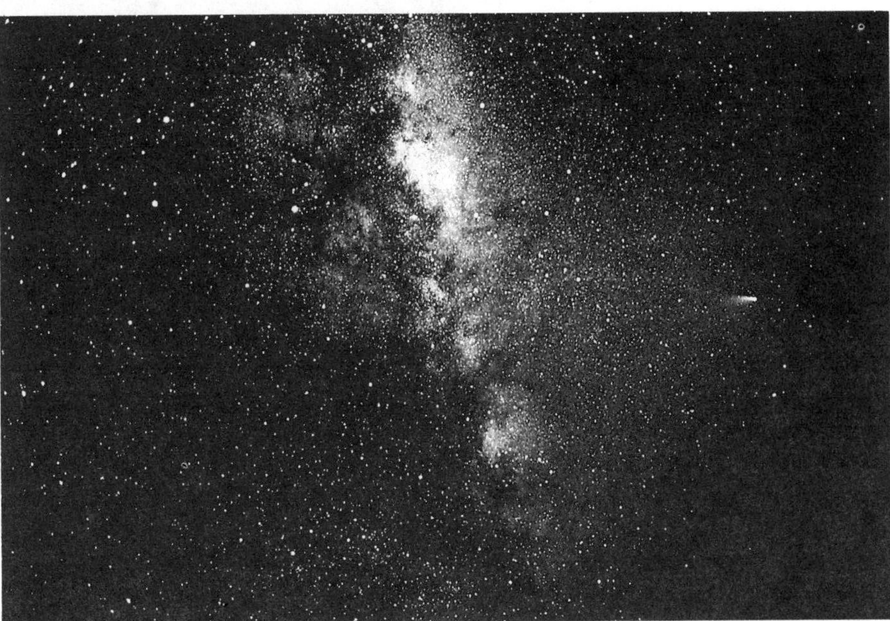

Fig. 27-18 Halley's Comet, photographed as it passed near the earth in 1986. In the background is the Milky Way — the billions of distant stars in our galaxy.

cloud. This forms a tail of gas and dust, which always points away from the sun.

Some comets, like Comet Halley (Fig. 27-18)—return regularly to the sun, and their appearance is predictable. Other comets appear, unpredicted. They are most often discovered by amateur astronomers, patiently and systematically searching for them.

Comet Misconception #1 The tail of a comet does not always trail behind it, but points away from the sun. Can you think of a situation in which the tail points in the same direction as the comet is going?

Comet Misconception #2 Comets do not streak across the sky. They move in slow and stately fashion.

As the earth revolves about the sun, it often encounters small chunks of dust or rock in space. These chunks are called **meteoroids**. They may be the dust from comets whose gases have all evaporated. Or they may be stray fragments of asteroids. The earth collides with these meteoroids, much as the windshield of a moving car collides with raindrops—except that the earth is moving at 30 km/s! The meteoroid takes about a second to pass through the atmosphere. As it does so, it produces a bright streak of light called a **meteor** (Fig. 27-19). Most meteoroids burn up before they reach the ground.

You can see meteors on any clear night. The darker the sky, the more meteors you will see. Because meteoroids are concentrated at certain places around the earth's orbit, meteors will be more frequent at certain times of the year: Jan. 3, Aug. 12, and Dec. 14, for instance.

Fig. 27-19 A meteor is a momentary streak of light in the sky. In what constellation was this meteor seen?

Meteorites

Meteoroids which survive their trip through the atmosphere and land on the ground are called **meteorites**. Most meteorites are fragments of asteroids. Therefore these free samples of cosmic material give us important information about the makeup of the asteroids. Meteorites are of three main kinds: iron, stony-iron, and stony (Fig. 27-20). These come from layers in the asteroid which correspond to the different layers inside the earth: core, mantle, and crust. Carbonaceous chondrites are rare and interesting meteorites which contain natural organic molecules.

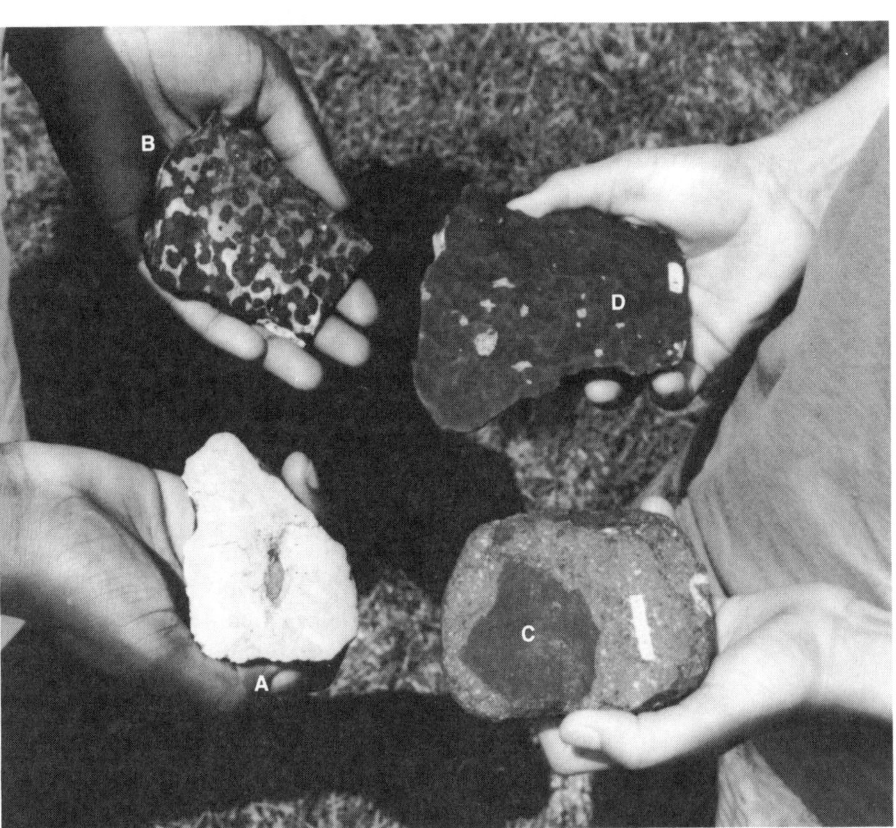

Fig. 27-20 Four meteorites: iron (A); stony iron (B); carbonaceous chondrite (C); stony (D).

Meteorite Craters

A large meteorite is hardly affected by its trip through the earth's atmosphere. It is neither burned up nor slowed down. It hits the ground at enormous speed. When it does so, it produces a **crater**, whose size depends on the size and the speed of the meteoroid. Every few million years, the earth is hit by a meteoroid large enough to produce a crater a kilometre or more in diameter.

There are about two dozen meteorite craters in Canada (Fig. 27-21). The largest and oldest is the Sudbury basin—140 km across and nearly two billion years old. The rocks of the Canadian Shield are particularly good at preserving these craters for hundreds of millions of years.

Section Review

1. a) What are asteroids?

Fig. 27-21 A meteorite crater at Holleford, near Kingston, Ontario. Why is the crater so difficult to see?

b) Where are most of them located?

2. a) What is a comet?
   b) Describe and account for the tail of a comet.
3. a) Distinguish among the terms meteroid, meteor, and meteorite.
   b) What is a meteorite crater?

27.11 Activity: Invent an Alien

Now that you have been introduced to some of the environments in the solar system, you can think of some of the life forms that could conceivably inhabit them! The following activity was devised by Dennis Schatz of the Pacific Science Center, and is now a popular activity across North America.

Problem

If there were life forms on the various planets and satellites in the solar system, what might those forms be like? What would they eat and breathe? How would they move?

Procedure and Discussion

Choose an environment in the solar system—on the surface of a planet or satellite, for instance. Design an alien life form which would be suited to that environment (Fig. 27-22). Describe how the alien life form's breathing, eating, locomotion, and other processes are suited to its environment.

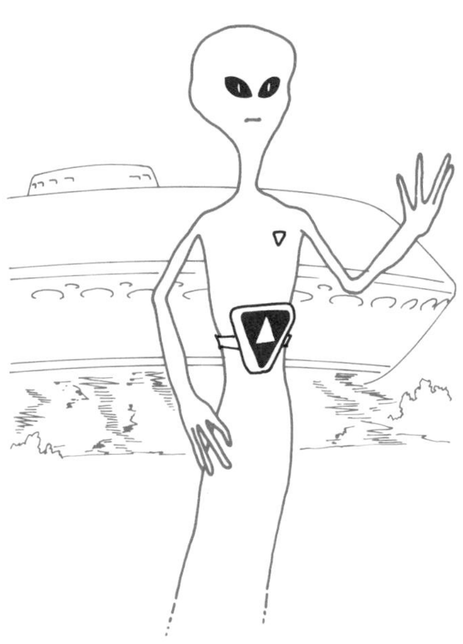

Fig. 27-22 You may even want to include a sketch of your alien.

Chapter Highlights

1. Our knowledge of the moon and planets has increased greatly, as a result of observations from the ground and from space.
2. This knowledge helps scientists to understand the origin and development of the earth.
3. The surface of the moon has been explored in detail, especially by manned and unmanned space missions.
4. The moon and brighter planets can be observed with the unaided eye.
5. There are many regularities in the layout and motions of the solar system.
6. Life may exist on planets beyond our solar system.

Key Terms

asteroid
astronomer
astrophysicist
basin (on the moon)
comet
crater
gravity
highlands (of the moon)
limb (of the moon)
magnetic field
maria
meteor
meteorite
meteoroid
minor planet
planet
ray
rille
ring (of a planet)
satellite
solar system
sun
tail (of a comet)
terminator
zodiac

Recognizing the Concepts

Each of the following statements or questions is followed by four responses. Choose the correct response in each case. (Do not write in this book.)

1. The planets which show phases like the moon are
   a) Venus and Jupiter
   b) Venus and Mercury
   c) Jupiter and Saturn
   d) Venus and Mars
2. The "gas giants" are
   a) earth and Mars
   b) earth and Venus
   c) Jupiter and Saturn
   d) Uranus and Neptune
3. The most common lunar surface features are
   a) canals **b)** craters **c)** volcanos **d)** rings
4. Mars is also known as
   a) the red planet
   b) a gas giant
   c) the ringed planet
   d) the North Star
5. A fuzzy object which moves slowly relative to the background stars in the sky is most likely to be
   a) an asteroid
   b) a comet
   c) an artificial satellite
   d) a meteor

6. Jupiter's Great Red Spot is
a) a volcano
b) a frozen plain of lava
c) an immense cyclone in the atmosphere
d) a dust storm on its surface

Understanding the Concepts

1. State several different ways in which you can tell a planet from a star in the sky **(a)** without a telescope; **(b)** with a telescope.
2. List the planets in order of decreasing size.
3. Suppose that you wanted to make a scale model of the solar system which would fit inside your classroom. What would be the distance from the sun to Pluto? To the earth? What would be the size of the sun?
4. In what ways are Venus and earth similar? In what ways are they different?
5. On which of the other planets would you feel the most ''at home''? Why?
6. Suppose that you sent a spacecraft to explore the planet Pluto. What kind of information would you like it to send back?

Applying the Concepts

1. Why are there fewer craters on the earth than on the moon?
2. On the moon, the gravity is much less than on the earth. What effects would this have on a baseball game on the moon? In what other ways, and for what reasons, would a baseball game on the moon be different from a baseball game on the earth?
3. What would happen if a giant meteorite crashed into the surface of the earth **(a)** on land; **(b)** on water?
4. Suppose that you were an astronomer on Mars. Describe the position and motion of the earth, relative to the sun. Describe the appearance of the earth as seen through binoculars or a small telescope.
5. Describe the difficulties of landing a spacecraft on Venus.
6. Discuss the advantages and disadvantages of sending a manned spacecraft to Mars, and the advantages and disadvantages of sending an unmanned spacecraft.

Investigations

1. Some scientists think that the extinction of dinosaurs and other prehistoric species may have been caused by the collision between the earth and a small asteroid or comet. Investigate and report on this theory.
2. In 1908, a tremendous explosion occurred over a remote area of Siberia. Most scientists think that it was caused by a small comet which collided with the earth. Investigate and report on this event and this theory.
3. Investigate and discuss the history of Comet Halley, and what scientists learned about it when it passed near the earth and sun in 1985–86.

4. Many craters on the moon are named after famous astronomers of the past. Consult a map of the moon. Choose a name of a crater. Investigate the astronomer after which the crater is named and report on his or her contributions to astronomy.
5. Write an essay, or have a debate on the advantages and disadvantages of space exploration—both manned and unmanned.

Biography

Scott Tremaine: Astrophysicist

Scott Tremaine is an astrophysicist—a scientist who uses the laws of physics to simulate and explain astronomical phenomena. He was born in Canada, and studied physics at McMaster University and Princeton University, where he recieved his Ph.D. degree in 1975. During the next decade, he won many awards for his research work, and worked at some of the world's major universities: Cambridge, Princeton, Caltech, and the Massachusetts Institute of Technology. In 1985, he returned to Canada as director of the Canadian Institute for Theoretical Astrophysics, a national research institute located at the University of Toronto.

Computers are the most important piece of astrophysical "hardware". Astrophysicists must also have access to a good library, and to other astronomers, so they can learn more about the astronomical phenomena which their theories must explain. So they frequently have conferences, and visit and collaborate with scientists who have different knowledge and skills than they do.

Much of Scott Tremaine's research deals with the role of gravity in astronomical phenomena. He and two colleagues showed how the structure of the rings of Saturn and Uranus (Figures 27-14 and 27-15) could be explained by the presence of small "shepherd satellites" among the rings. Such satellites were later discovered by Voyager 1 and 2. Tremaine has also investigated the result of collisions between galaxies, by modelling the process on a computer. When a large galaxy collides with a small one, for instance, the stars in the galaxies do not collide—there is too much space between them. Rather, the small galaxy slowly merges with the large one in a process picturesquely called "galactic cannibalism".

VISTA

THE SEARCH FOR EXTRATERRESTRIAL LIFE

As you have observed and thought about the universe, there is one question which you surely have asked: is anyone else out there? In the last century, astronomers have discovered that there are billions of galaxies, each with billions of stars like the sun. Many of these stars are probably accompanied by families of planets. Some of these planets must surely have atmospheres and surfaces like those of the earth.

At the same time, biologists and geologists have studied the nature and development of life on the earth. They have developed a plausible theory of how life began on earth, billions of years ago. For most of that time, life on the earth was as primitive as bacteria or algae, but in the last few hundred million years, it has developed to produce intelligent beings such as ourselves.

There may be life on thousands—or perhaps millions—of planets in our Milky Way galaxy. The nearest of these inhabited planets is probably hundreds of light years away. If the life forms on these planets are primitive, then we will not know of their existence until we can travel to visit them. If the life forms are intelligent, then we may know of their existence from the signals which they emit. These ''aliens'' may even come to visit, though there is no scientific evidence that aliens have ever visited the earth.

This radio telescope, 47 m in diameter, is located at the Algonquin Radio Observatory in Algonquin Park, Ontario. It has been used to search for radio signals from extra-terrestrial intelligence, as well as for radio astronomy.

The most effective method of interstellar communication is by radio signals. Radio signals are inexpensive, travel in many directions at once, and at the maximum possible speed of 300 000 km/s. With present technology, astronomers could now communicate by radio with any civilizations in our galaxy which are as advanced as we are. Powerful radio telescopes are constantly scanning our skies, and may one day receive the first message from beyond the earth. We have sent only one deliberate radio message into interstellar space—a symbolic three-minute message sent in 1975 using a giant radio telescope in Puerto Rico.

But the earth is constantly ''leaking'' radio signals into space. Ironically, the strongest of these are from military radars—hardly a true sign of intelligence! Video carrier signals from TV stations also leak into space, but the signals which carry the information about the TV pictures would be too weak to detect. Considering the quality of some of our TV programs, this may be a good thing!

Four of the spacecraft which have explored the solar system have now escaped from the gravity of the sun and planets, and are on their way to the stars. All of these spacecraft carry messages which tell who launched them, and when. These messages tell us, and any extraterrestrials which find them, that humans have now left their earthly cradle and are about to explore the stars. It may be many million years or more before humans and extraterrestrials ever meet face to face. In the meantime, astronomy and other branches of science are constantly providing us with more information about the chances that extraterrestrial life exists . . . somewhere out there.

28 The Sun and Stars

CHAPTER CONTENTS

CHAPTER OBJECTIVES

After completing this chapter, you should be able to:

1. Understand the role of light, telescopes, and other instruments in providing information about the universe.
2. Observe and describe the appearance of the sun and its spectrum.
3. List the sources of energy used by life on earth, and know which are derived from solar energy.
4. List and describe the types of stars and related objects such as nebulas, star clusters, and galaxies.
5. Use a simple sky chart to identify examples of these.

Virtually all of our information about the sun comes from its **radiant energy**. Radiant energy (light and its relatives) consists of **photons** of energy, which travel at 300 000 km/s. We use the light from the sun to form an image of it, to see what it looks like (Fig. 28-1). We break up its light into a spectrum—rainbow-style—to see how hot the sun is, and what it is made of. We are even more dependent on light to study the more distant stars, because there is no hope of directly sampling the material of which they are made.

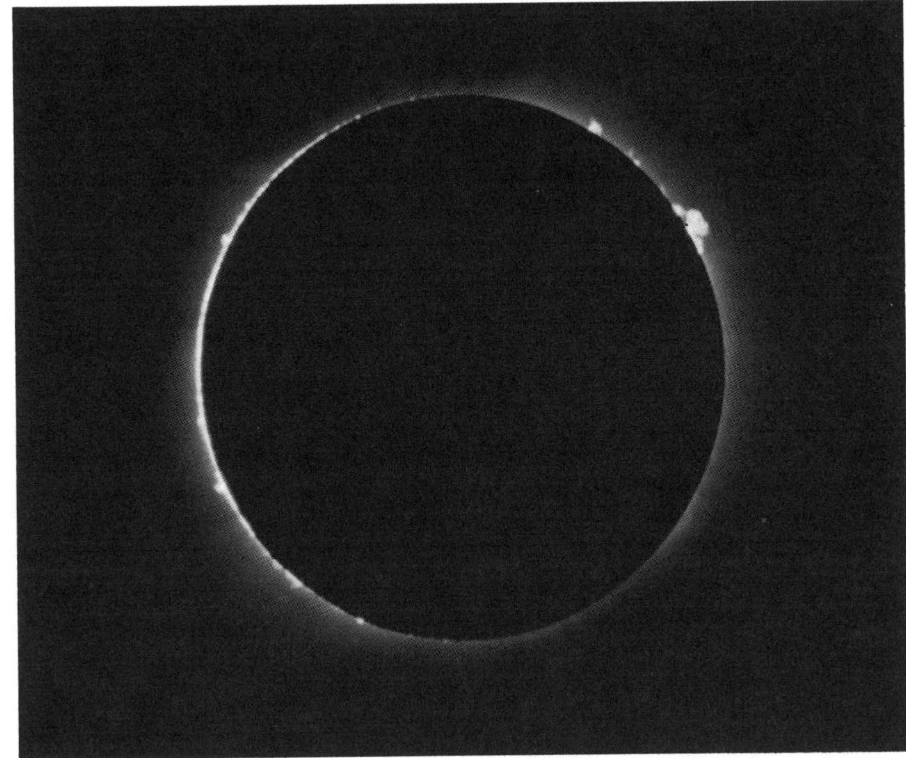

Fig. 28-1 A photograph of the sun in eclipse, showing gas clouds in its atmosphere. The sun does not have a solid surface. It is a gas throughout.

28.1 Activity: Observing the Sun

The sun is the nearest star, and is the only star which we can see in detail. It is conveniently available for observation in the daytime (usually) and—unlike most astronomical objects—is too bright rather than not bright enough!

CAUTION: *Never look directly at the sun, especially when using binoculars, telescopes, or other optical instruments. Direct sunlight can cause permanent eye damage in seconds! Always follow your teacher's instructions when viewing the sun.*

Problem

How can you observe and study the sun effectively and safely? What does it look like?

Method A By Using a Mirror

This method produces an image which is fuzzy, and therefore does not show much detail. However, it shows the shape and size of the sun's disc. Also, it is simple and safe, and it can be used by several people at once to view the sun. It is an ideal method for viewing a partial eclipse of the sun.

You must first find a location where you can stand in the sun and reflect its light onto a shaded wall nearby. The wall could be in a sheltered doorway of your school, for instance. You could even reflect the sunlight into the window of a darkened room, and project an image of the sun on the wall. Once you have found a suitable location, the rest of this activity is quite easy.

CAUTION: *Do not reflect sunlight into your eyes or into the eyes of your classmates!*

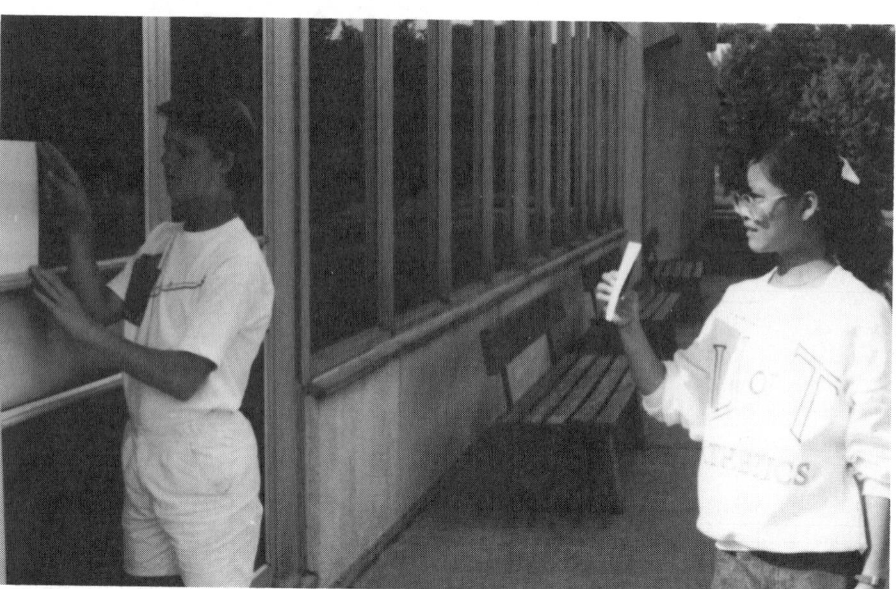

Fig. 28-2 These students are using the "mirror" method to project an image of the sun onto a shaded wall.

Materials

pocket or hand mirror
sheet of cardboard slightly larger than the mirror
sheet of white paper or cardboard

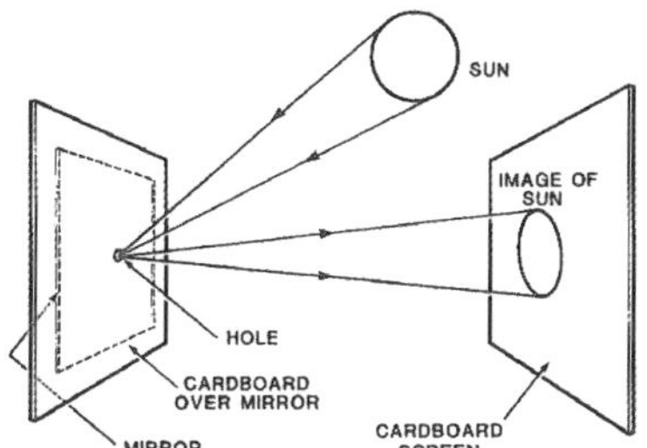

Fig. 28-3 How to use a small mirror to project an image of the sun onto a shaded wall

Procedure

a. Cut the cardboard so that it fits over the mirror (Fig. 28-2).
b. Cut or punch a hole, a few millimetres in diameter, in the middle of the cardboard.
c. Catch the sunlight with the mirror and reflect it onto a shaded wall (Fig. 28-3). It sometimes helps to catch and reflect the sunlight without the cardboard over the mirror. Then put the cardboard over the mirror. It is easier this way to direct the image into the right location.
d. Put the white paper or cardboard on the shaded wall. Use it as a screen to show the image of the sun.
e. Observe the appearance of the image of the sun.
f. Record your observations in your log.

Discussion

1. What shape is the image of the sun? Why?
2. Describe the appearance of the image. Are there any features on it?
3. Slowly move the mirror away from the screen. What happens to the appearance of the image as the distance from the mirror to the image is increased?
4. How would you improve this demonstration?

Extensions

1. Cut a new piece of cardboard to fit over the mirror. This time, cut or punch a hole in it which is not a circle. Try a square or triangle. Repeat the activity. What shape is the disc of the sun this time? Explain this observation.
2. Measure the diameter of the image of the disc of the sun. Then measure the distance of the image from the hole in front of the mirror. The ratio of the diameter to the distance is the same as the ratio of the diameter of the sun to its distance from the hole.
3. Explain how these demonstrations work, remembering that light travels in a straight line.

Method B By Using Binoculars or a Telescope

This method requires binoculars or a telescope. It produces a sharp image of the sun. Therefore it shows details such as sunspots on the sun's disc. It can be used by several people at once to view the sun. *Be sure to follow the safety warning*!

This method requires a bit of patience and practice. But once you have got the hang of it, you can set up the materials and make the observations quickly and easily.

Materials

binoculars or a telescope
sheet of white cardboard (a sheet of white paper can be used instead, but it should be attached to a flat surface such as a clipboard)

Procedure

a. Make a collar of cardboard to fit around the top of the binoculars or telescope. This cuts out the glare of the sun, and in the case of the binoculars stops the light from coming down the side of the binoculars which you are not using.

b. Focus the binoculars or telescope on infinity by using them to look at a distant object (*not the sun!*) in the normal way. If using a telescope, use a low-magnification eyepiece.

c. Point the binoculars or telescope at the sun (Fig. 28-4). Then adjust the direction of pointing until the image of the sun appears on the screen. This may take a minute or two. You may want to hold the binoculars in place with a ring stand and clamp. Or you could use a camera tripod or other arrangement.

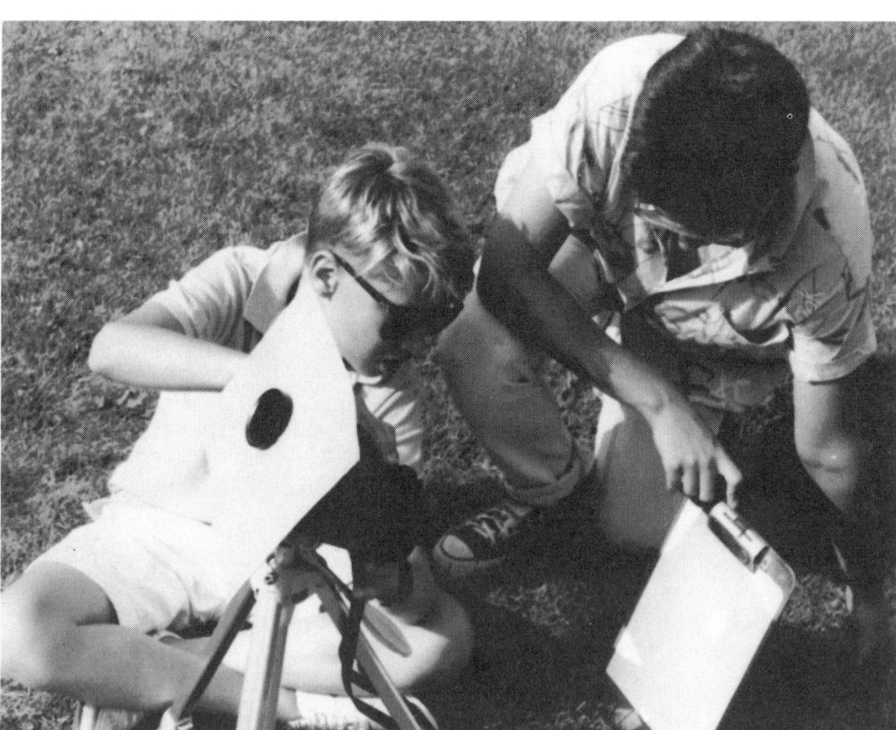

Fig. 28-4 These students are using binoculars to project an image of the sun onto a screen.

d. Hold the white cardboard or paper behind the eyepiece of the binoculars or telescope until the image of the sun fits neatly in the middle of the screen. You can hold the screen in your hand, or invent a way to rest it in place.

e. Jiggle the binoculars or telescope very slightly. Any specks on the image of the sun which move are in the binoculars or telescope, and not on the sun. Jiggle the screen very slightly. Any specks which move are on the screen, and not on the sun.

f. Examine and describe the image of the sun.

g. Record your observations in your log.

Discussion

1. How would you improve this demonstration?

Extensions

1. If there are sunspots on the disc of the sun, record their appearance and position. Do this by placing a sheet of plain white paper on the screen. Then use a pencil to mark the position and appearance of the sunspots, as well as the position of the edge of the disc of the sun. How can you determine which sides of the disc are north, south, east, and west?

2. Observe the image of the sun on several days in succession. Note any changes in the position and appearance of the sunspots.

28.2 Activity: Observing the Spectrum of the Sun

The Spectrum of Sunlight

In Activity 28.1 you used sunlight to form an image of the sun. The image appeared to be white or pale yellow in colour. In the following activity, you will see that there is a whole new dimension to sunlight. Each ray of light can be divided up into light of different colours. All of these colours carry information for the astronomer—much more information than the ''plain'' sunlight alone!

This method is particularly important for studying the more distant stars. They are so far away that we cannot form images of them. Even with our most powerful telescopes, they appear as points of light.

The best way to observe the spectrum of the sun is with a device called a **spectroscope**. You may be able to borrow one of these from a science teacher at your school, and get him or her to help you to set it up. Working with sunlight can be dangerous. Therefore, if you do use a spectroscope, you must be sure to follow the necessary safety precautions. Here is a simpler way to observe the spectrum of the sun. It uses a **transmission diffraction grating**.

Materials

transmission diffraction grating

CAUTION: Do not look at the sun directly using a transmission diffraction grating. Use the procedure below.

Procedure

It helps to construct a holder for the transmission diffraction grating, as shown in Figure 28-5. Cut a deep, V-shaped notch in a cardboard cylinder (such as the core of a roll of paper towels or aluminum foil). Cover one end of the cylinder with tape or aluminum foil. This prevents you from looking directly at the sun. Place the transmission diffraction grating in the notch as shown in Figure 28-5.

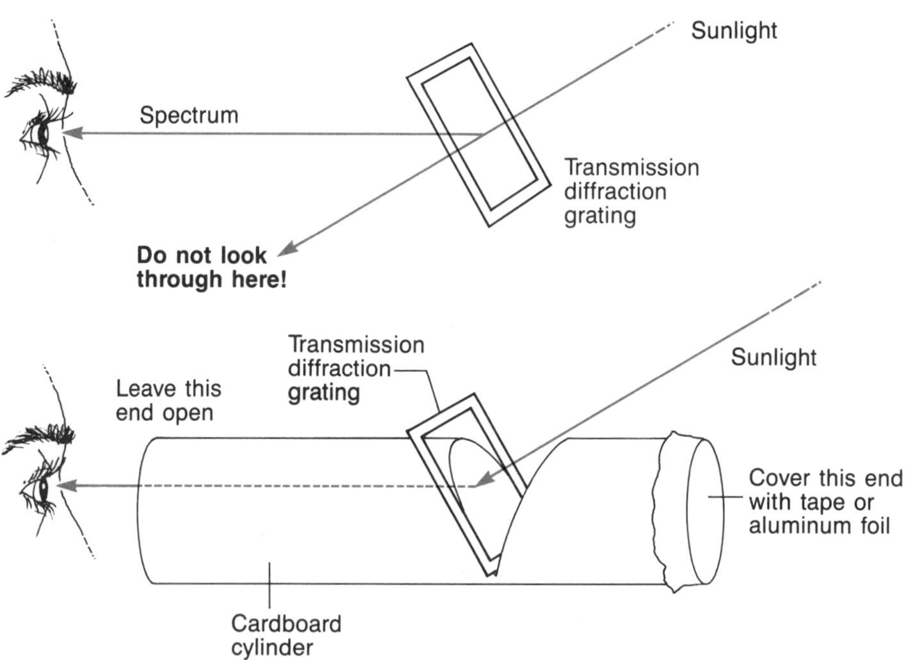

Fig. 28-5 How to use a transmission diffraction grating to view the spectrum of the sun

a. Face the sun, and hold the transmission diffraction grating at eye level, so that it is facing the sun (see Figure 28-5). The (invisible) lines on the grating should be horizontal. However, since you cannot see them, you will have to experiment to get the grating in the right orientation.

b. Look into the transmission diffraction grating at an angle of approximately 30° to the direction of the sunlight.

c. Describe the appearance of the spectrum, and the order of the colours.

Discussion

1. What is the order of the colours in the spectrum?
2. Why do you think that the spectrum stops at red on one end and at violet on the other?
3. What changes could you make to improve this demonstration?

Extensions

1. Investigate the tools which astronomers use to study the spectra of the sun and stars.
2. Investigate the spectra of light sources other than the sun. For instance, you can use a transmission diffraction grating to study the spectra of different kinds of street lamps—mercury vapour, sodium vapour, and incandescent.

28.3 Beyond the Visible Spectrum

When you observed the spectrum of sunlight, you may have wondered why the spectrum went only from red to violet. And how is light related to the other kinds of radiant energy: radio, microwave, infrared, ultraviolet, X-ray, and gamma-ray radiation?

All these are types of energy; all are carried by photons; all travel at 300 000 km/s. They differ only in the energy of the photons. Radio photons have the least energy, gamma-ray photons the most. Light photons have an in-between energy which produces vision by reacting with molecules in the retina of our eye (Fig. 28-6).

Radiant energy also behaves as if it were a wave. Radio radiation has wave lengths from a centimetre to a kilometre or more. We can ''tune in'' different wave lengths of radio radiation by tuning our radio receiver. X-ray radiation has wave lengths of a nanometre or less.

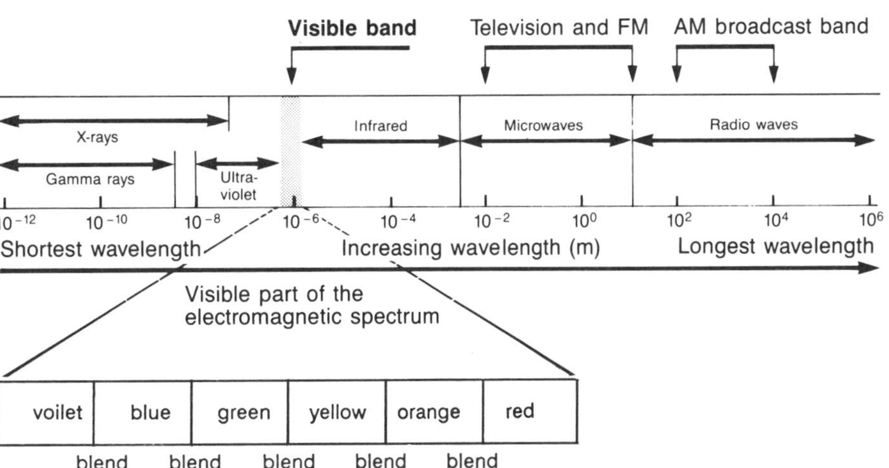

Fig. 28-6 The electromagnetic spectrum of radiant energy goes from the long-wavelength radio waves to the short-wavelength gamma rays, with light in the middle.

Fig. 28-7 Astronomer Dr. Nancy Evans uses a computer to study the spectrum of the ultraviolet light from a star. The spectrum was obtained with the International Ultraviolet Explorer satellite.

Some of these radiations can pass through the earth's atmosphere: light and radio radiation in particular. Infrared radiation is absorbed in the dense, lower layers of the atmosphere, but can be studied at high altitude observatories. Ultraviolet, X-ray, and gamma-ray radiation cannot pass through the atmosphere at all. They can only be studied using balloon-, rocket-, or satellite-borne telescopes above the atmosphere. Since many astronomical objects give out radiant energy other than light, the study of these radiations tells us much about the universe (Fig. 28-7).

Section Review

1. Arrange the different kinds of radiant energy in order of **(a)** increasing energy; **(b)** increasing wavelength.
2. What kinds of radiant energy can be observed from the ground? What kinds can only be observed from space?
3. Why do astronomers use ultraviolet telescopes in space, when there are already telescopes on the ground?

28.4 Activity: Investigating Solar Energy

Solar Energy

The energy of the sun consists mainly of **light**. It also includes a small amount of infrared, ultraviolet, and X-ray energy, most of which is absorbed by the earth's upper atmosphere. The sun also produces a **wind** of hot gas, which blows past the earth at about 500 km/s. This wind blows the tails of comets away from the sun. It also causes the aurora—a glow in the sky which is produced by collisions between the solar wind and the upper atmosphere.

Virtually all the energy which is used by life on the earth is produced directly or indirectly by the sun. Because solar energy is generally safe, clean, and plentiful, scientists and engineers are working hard to harness it in a practical way (Fig. 28-8).

Fig. 28-8 Ecology House in Toronto uses solar energy in many ways. How many can you see?

The Activity

This activity can be done in the library using books and other resource materials. You can work in groups of 2 or 3, and prepare a written or brief oral report on one of these topics to be shared with your classmates.

1. Discuss the role of solar energy in nourishing living plants and animals.
2. Solar energy can be used to heat buildings, produce electricity, and do other useful things. What are some problems of harnessing solar energy in a country such as Canada?
3. Investigate the types of solar energy collectors which are being used in houses and other buildings today.
4. List all the sources of energy which are available to us. Which ones are derived directly or indirectly from the sun? For those that are, investigate how the solar energy is changed into the form which we can use.
5. Dark materials absorb light better than light materials. List and describe several everyday applications of this fact.

Problems

1. The sun provides 1360 W/m^2 of power at the surface of the earth, less a small amount which is absorbed by the atmosphere. How does this power compare with the power used by typical household appliances?
2. Suppose that you had a solar energy collector on your roof which harnessed 10% of all the solar energy falling on it. How big do you think that the collector would have to be to provide the necessary power for your house?

28.5 The Nature of the Sun

The sun is a ball of gas, 100 times larger in diameter than the earth, 1 000 000 times larger in volume, and 300 000 times larger in mass. Like the other stars, it is made up almost entirely of the elements hydrogen and helium.

At the centre of the sun, the temperature is almost 20 000 000°C. The high temperature is caused by the tremendous weight of the material pushing down from above. At this high temperature, hydrogen atoms combine to form helium atoms and energy in a process called **thermonuclear fusion**. The total energy produced—4×10^{24} W—is equivalent to a million hydrogen bombs exploding every second! Still, there is enough hydrogen in the sun to provide radiant energy for 10 000 000 000 years. This energy gradually escapes from the centre of the sun to the "surface", and then to outer space. The sun also loses 4 000 000 t of mass each second!

Although the sun appears to have a solid "surface", it is actually a gas throughout. What we see as the "surface" is the layer where the gas becomes too thick to see any further in. The temperature of this layer is 5500°C. Here, the slow rotation of the sun and the currents of outflowing gas interact to produce a magnetic field. This, in turn, produces dark magnetic areas called **sunspots**, arches of gas called **prominences**, and the hot, glowing outer atmosphere called the **corona**. The corona is so faint that it is only visible to us during a total eclipse of the sun.

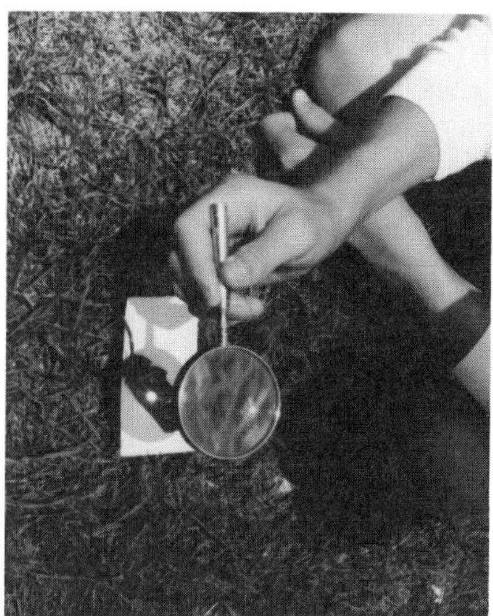

Fig. 28-9 These students are using a magnifying glass to gather and focus sunlight.

Section Review

1. Compare the size and mass of the sun to those of the earth.
2. Describe how the sun produces radiant energy.
3. Describe the surface of the sun.

28.6 Telescopes

Now that you have taken a casual look at the stars, and a detailed look at the sun, you will be aware that the sun is very bright and the stars are very faint. Yet the stars are distant suns, and the sun is our nearest star. To study the faint, distant stars—and other objects beyond our solar system—we must extend our senses. We do this by using a telescope.

The purpose of a telescope is to gather and focus light. It must gather light because most astronomical objects are faint. We must gather as much light from them as possible. We must focus the light in order to study it.

The simplest example of the ''gathering and focussing'' principle is the magnifying glass. You may have performed the activity shown in Figure 28-9. You certainly know what happens.

CAUTION: If you carry out this activity, do it safely. Otherwise you could cause a fire.

Astronomers can use either a lens or a concave mirror to gather and focus light (Fig. 28-10). A lens telescope is called a **refracting** telescope. A mirror telescope is called a **reflecting** telescope. All large astronomical telescopes, and many small ones, are reflecting telescopes. The **light-gathering power** of a telescope depends on how large its collecting lens or mirror is. A telescope is therefore rated according to the diameter of its collecting lens or mirror.

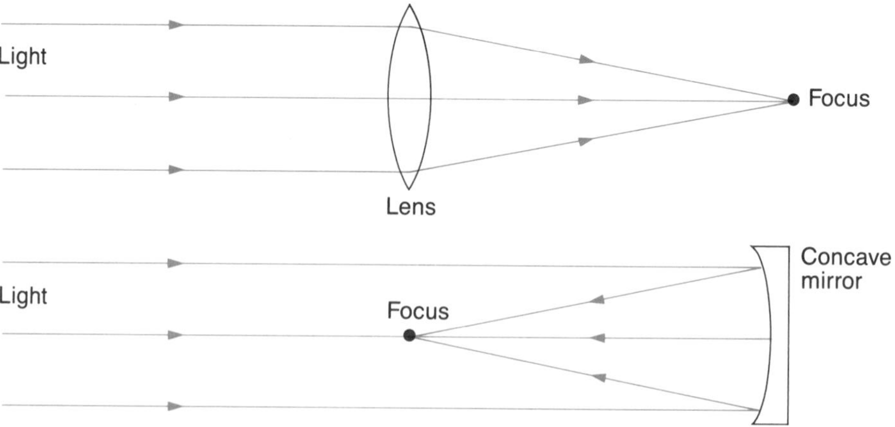

Fig. 28-10 How light is gathered and focused by a refracting telescope (top) and a reflecting telescope (bottom)

Astronomical telescopes are housed in special buildings called **observatories**. They have machinery to point the telescope at its target, and keep the telescope pointed as the target slowly moves westward in the sky (Figs. 28-11 and 28-12).

The lens or concave mirror of the telescope forms an **image** at the focus of the telescope. The image can be viewed using a small lens called an **eyepiece**.

A

B

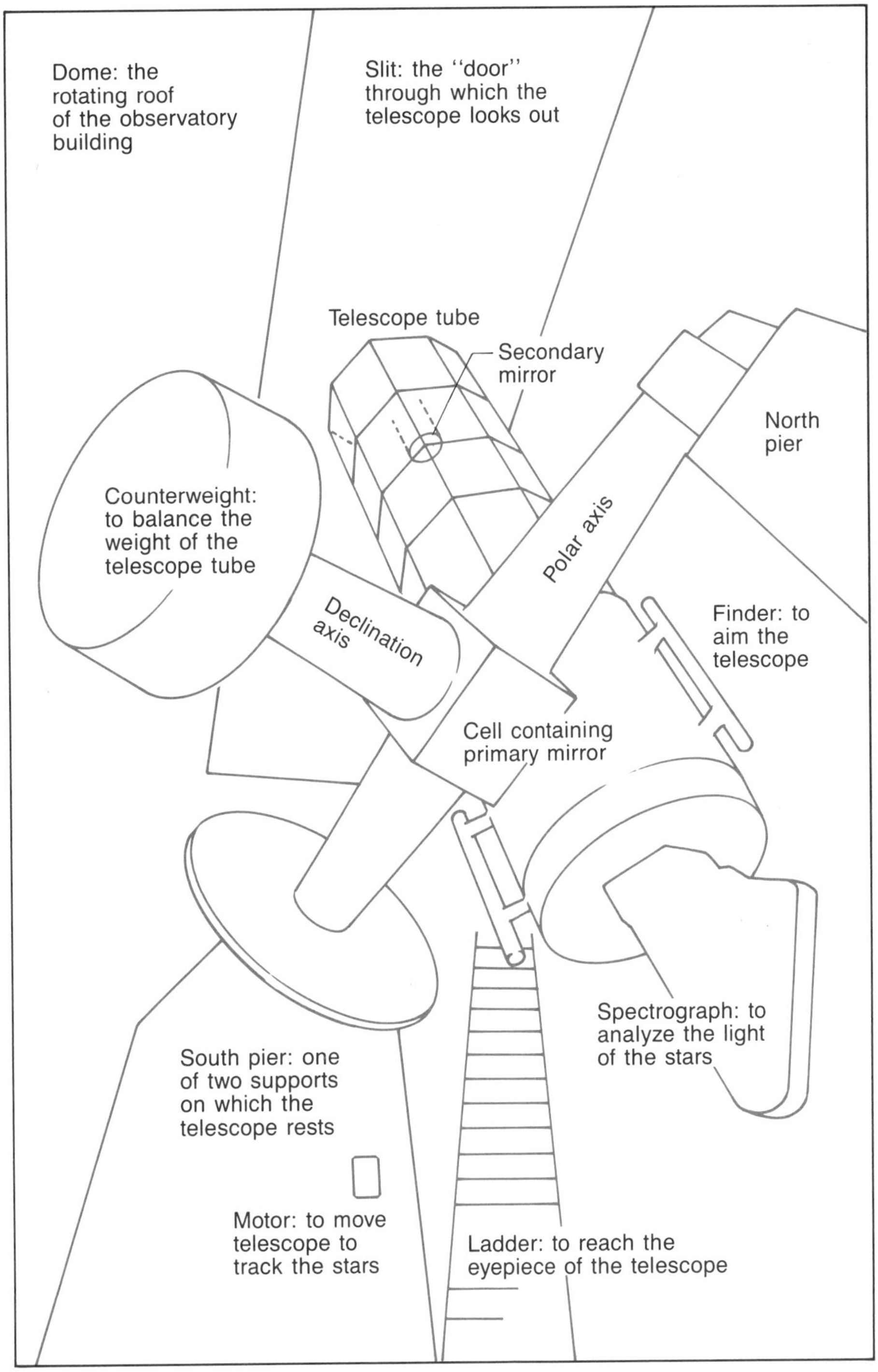

Dome: the rotating roof of the observatory building

Slit: the "door" through which the telescope looks out

Telescope tube

Secondary mirror

North pier

Counterweight: to balance the weight of the telescope tube

Polar axis

Declination axis

Finder: to aim the telescope

Cell containing primary mirror

Spectrograph: to analyze the light of the stars

South pier: one of two supports on which the telescope rests

Motor: to move telescope to track the stars

Ladder: to reach the eyepiece of the telescope

Fig. 28-11 The 1.9 m reflecting telescope (A) at the University of Toronto's David Dunlap Observatory. The diagram (B) shows the function of each part.

Fig. 28-12 The Canada-France-Hawaii telescope on Mauna Kea in Hawaii. Where are the clouds relative to the telescope?

It can be photographed using an ordinary **camera**. It can be recorded on magnetic tape using a sensitive **electronic camera**, something like a TV camera. The brightness of the image can be measured using a **photometer**, like the light meter on a camera. The light can be broken up into colours using a **spectrograph**. All of these instruments help the astronomer to measure and study the light, and hence learn more about the object from which it comes.

Section Review

1. What is the purpose of a telescope?
2. Distinguish between a reflecting and refracting telescope.
3. What are the functions of the following attachments for a telescope: eyepiece, camera, electronic camera, photometer, spectrograph.

28.7 Stars: The Common and the Rare

The Properties of Stars

With telescopes, astronomers can determine the properties of stars, and compare them with the sun. They must first of all determine the **distances** of the stars. The observed properties of the stars—such as their **brightness**—depend on their distance as well as on their true properties—such as their **power**. Therefore we must know the distance before we can determine the power.

Astronomers can measure the distances of the nearer stars by viewing them from opposite sides of the earth's orbit and using the principle of parallax, much as we estimate the distance of a nearby object by our binocular (two-eyed) vision. Even the nearest stars are so far away that their light takes over 4 years to reach us, travelling at 300 000 km/s.

Table 28-1 lists the distances to some of the stars which you may encounter in your exploration of the night sky. **A light year (ly)** is the distance light travels in a year (about 10 000 000 000 000 km).

Table 28-1 The Distances of Stars

Star	*Distance (ly)*	*Star*	*Distance (ly)*
Sirius	9	Aldebaran	68
Procyon	11	Spica	220
Altair	17	Antares	520
Vega	26	Betelgeuse	520
Pollux	35	Rigel	900
Arcturus	36	Deneb	1600
Capella	45		

These numbers also represent the time in years which it would take you to travel from the sun to that star, travelling at the speed of light—300 000 km/s. They are also the time in years which the light has taken to travel from the star to our eyes.

Knowing the distance of each star, astronomers can determine its **power output**. From the colour of the star, astronomers can determine its **temperature**. Cool stars are red and hot stars are blue-white. Astronomers can also determine the **mass** of a star, and its **size**. From these measurements, they can build up a clear picture of the nature of the stars.

The Lives of the Stars

Most stars are like the sun. They shine for billions of years by producing nuclear energy from the hydrogen in their cores. The sun is larger and brighter than 95% of all stars. This is because it formed from a larger-than-average clump of interstellar gas and dust. Stars which have more mass than the sun consume their energy more rapidly. Those which have less mass than the sun consume their energy more slowly. Otherwise, stars are born, live, and die much like the sun does.

There are, however, a small number of stars which are extreme or otherwise bizarre. Most of these are stars which are nearing the end of their life cycle. There are **giant stars**, tens of times larger than the sun, and which are hundreds of times larger. Although these stars are rare, they are also very powerful. As a result, they can be seen even if they are thousands of light years away.

The Deaths of Stars

The death of a star occurs when its supply of nuclear energy is exhausted. The internal pressure which once supported the star against its own weight is reduced. The star begins to contract, or even to collapse.

White dwarfs are the most common ''collapsed stars''. They have a mass like that of the sun, packed into a volume like that of the earth. They, therefore, have a density about 1 000 000 times that of water. The sun will eventually become a white dwarf when it runs out of nuclear fuel, about 5 000 000 000 years from now.

Stars which are much more massive than the sun are very rare. But they end their lives in spectacular fashion by exploding as a **supernova** (see Section 28.10). They leave behind a tiny corpse called a **neutron star**. A neutron star has a mass like that of the sun, packed into a volume only 10 km across—about the size of an average city.

By far the rarest and most exotic stellar corpse is the **black hole**. When a very massive star collapses at the end of its life, no force can stop the collapse. The star becomes so dense, and its gravity so strong, that nothing—not even light—can escape. The material of the star continues to exist, but is no longer visible. But it can still be ''felt''. If the black hole has a companion star, then the two will revolve about each other. The black hole can be detected by the force of its gravity on its companion star.

Section Review

1. How do astronomers measure the distances to the nearer stars?

2. **a)** What is a light year?
b) What does it mean when we say that Sirius is 9 ly away?

3. **a)** What makes a star shine?
b) What are giant and supergiant stars?

4. Give the meanings of these terms: white dwarf, supernova, neutron star, black hole.

Biography

René Racine: Astronomer

René Racine has been interested in astronomy since he was very young, and astronomy was a hobby long before it was a career. He received a B.Sc. degree in physics from Laval University in 1963, and a Ph.D. degree in astronomy from the University of Toronto in 1967. He spent the next 3 years at the famous Mt. Wilson and Palomar Observatories, then returned to Canada to become a professor at the University of Toronto.

One part of his research deals with the globular clusters which surround galaxies such as our own. These clusters were the first objects which formed in these galaxies, so they tell us much about how and when the galaxies formed. However, astronomers need a very powerful telescope to see and study globular clusters in distant galaxies. René Racine has been a leader in designing, building, and using such telescopes. At the University of Toronto, he helped to establish a small observatory at an excellent observing site in Chile. (See Section 28.10.) From 1976 to 1980, he was a professor at the University of Montreal, where he led the construction of a 1.5 m diameter telescope on Mont Mégantic in Québec. From 1980 to 1984, he took on his greatest challenge: to direct the new Canada-France-Hawaii Telescope on the summit of Mauna Kea in Hawaii. Although this telescope is not the largest in the world, it is probably the most effective because of its excellent optical quality and its superb site.

Even now, René Racine is developing new methods to make telescopes better and cheaper, so that telescopes on the ground can rival the very expensive telescopes in space.

Biography

Warren Morrison: Amateur Astronomer

An amateur astronomer is one who has astronomy as a hobby, not as a career. It is a very enjoyable hobby, whether it is done individually or in a group. In addition, amateur astronomers can contribute to the science of astronomy. In fact, astronomy is unique in the way that amateurs can contribute to it. This is because many astronomical events (such as the appearance of new comets and exploding stars) are unpredictable. Professional astronomers do not have the time to search for them. Amateur astronomers can do it well.

Warren Morrison's interest in astronomy began when he was very young, and developed further when he was in high school. There was a 50 mm refracting telescope gathering dust in the science department, and his physics teacher allowed him to take it home to use. He began making measurements of the brightness of variable stars, which is one way in which amateurs can make a particularly important contribution to astronomy. When Morrison graduated from high school, he returned the telescope to the science department, and bought his own 60 mm refractor.

Since then, he has become one of the worlds' leading observers of variable stars. He has discovered two novas—rare, erupting stars. He has made over 25 000 measurements of the brightness of other variable stars. He has also been a coordinator in the International Halley Watch, a project to gather as much information about this famous comet as possible during its 1985–86 return.

Warren lives on a farm in Cavan, near Peterborough, Ontario, away from city lights. His daytime job (at the Quaker Oats Company) is not related to astronomy or any other science. He does his science in the evening, as a hobby, but his contribution to science is every bit as important as if he did his science as a career.

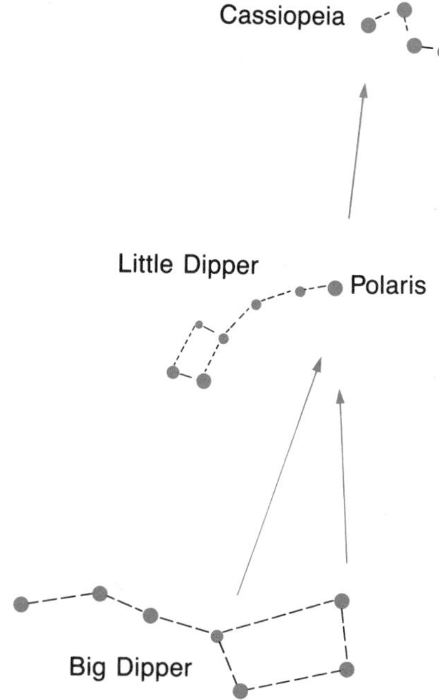

Fig. 28-13 The sky map from the Big Dipper through Polaris (the North Star) to Cassiopeia

28.8 Activity: Exploring the Night Sky

You have examined the sun in some detail. You have also learned about its nature in relation to other stars. Now you are ready to explore the night sky. In Activity 26.7 you viewed the patterns of stars in the night sky, but only to learn something about the motions of the earth. Now, you can understand the nature of the stars, and some of the fainter and more interesting objects in the night sky.

Materials

star charts
good observing site
observing log
binoculars (optional)

Exploration A: The Autumn Sky

a. Find a good observing site, relax, and let your eyes become accustomed to the dark.

b. Begin as always with the **Big Dipper**. It will be rather low in the north. Use it to find the **North Star** and **Cassiopeia** by following the Pointers through the North Star (see Section 28.8 and Fig. 28-13). The North Star is a supergiant star—much bigger than the sun. Like many stars, it is variable in brightness. But the variations are too small to see without a photometer. Observe the seven stars in the Big Dipper. Are there only seven? Look closely at the second star from the end of the handle. Are all of the ''seven'' stars of equal brightness?

Most of the stars in the Big Dipper (and the surrounding area of the sky) belong to a **star cluster** called the **Ursa Major Cluster**. These stars are bound together by gravity, and they move together through space.

c. The brightness of a star depends on its true power (its ''wattage'', in light-bulb terminology) and on its distance. Rank the five brightest stars in Cassiopeia in order of decreasing brightness. Enter your results on a sketch of the constellation in your observing log.

d. East of Cassiopeia is **Perseus**. **Algol**, the second-brightest star in Perseus, is noticeably variable in brightness. This is because it has a large, faint star which revolves about it, and eclipses it every 69 h. If Algol is about the same brightness as the brightest star in Perseus, then it is not in eclipse. If it is much fainter, it is in eclipse. More than half of all stars are actually two or more stars revolving about each other. The bright star below Perseus is **Capella** in the constellation **Auriga**. It is also a pair of stars—each larger than the sun—revolving about each other every 104 d. Algol and Capella are **binary stars**. Algol is also a **variable star**.

e. East of Perseus, you will find a tiny little cluster of stars called the **Pleiades**, or Seven Sisters (Fig. 28-14). Astronomers are not sure where this name came from, because most people can either see only 6 stars or many more than 7. Although the Pleiades looks like a dipper, it is not the Little Dipper.

Fig. 28-14 The Pleiades— an open star cluster in Taurus. This photograph was taken by Canadian amateur astronomer Michael Watson.

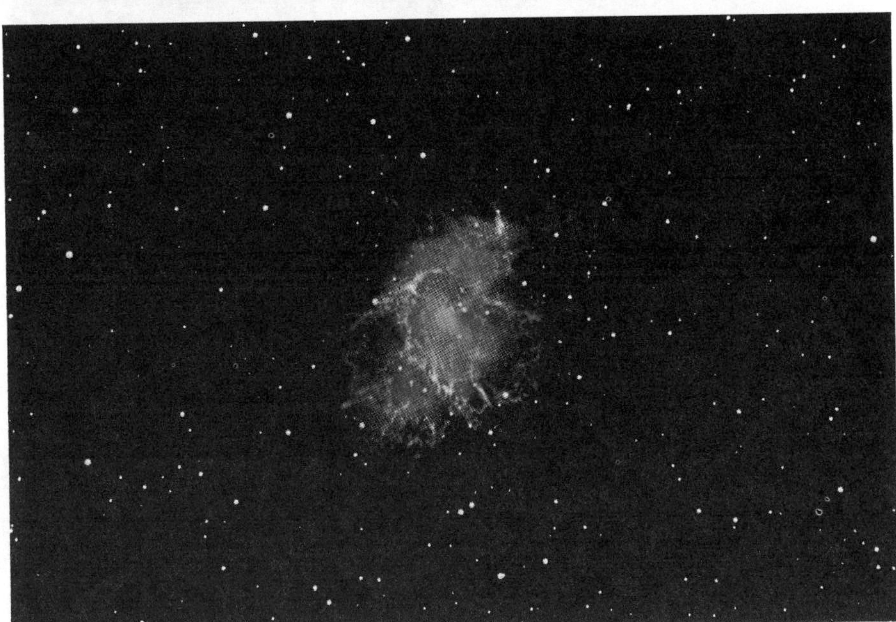

Fig. 28-15 The Crab Nebula, in the constellation Taurus, is the remnant of a star which was observed to explode in 1054 AD.

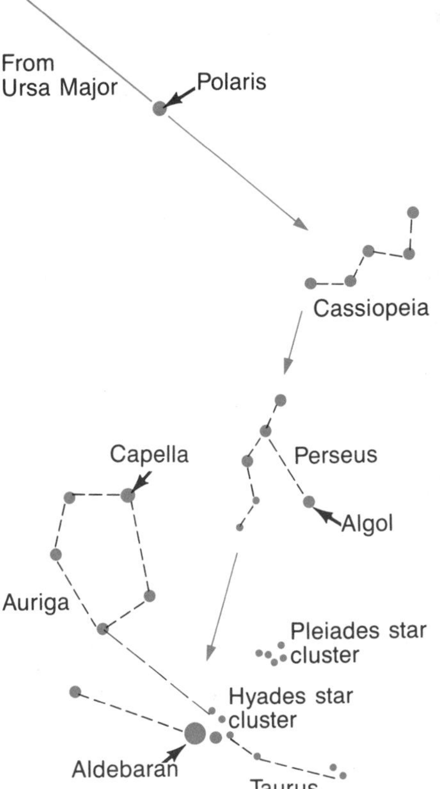

Fig. 28-16 Sky map from Cassiopeia to Perseus to Taurus

Most stars are born in clusters. East of the Pleiades is another larger, less-distinct cluster called the **Hyades**. Both these clusters are in the constellation **Taurus**. They are called **open clusters**, because of their irregular shapes.

The constellation **Taurus** contains another interesting but much fainter object—the **Crab Nebula**. The word *nebula* means *cloud*. At one time, the word was used to mean any fuzzy object (other than a comet) in the sky. Now it refers only to glowing clouds of gas and dust in space. The Crab Nebula is the remains of a star which was observed to explode as a supernova in 1054 AD (Fig. 28-15).

f. On your sky chart, there is a band which runs from the southwest through

Cygnus and Cassiopeia to the northeast (Fig. 28-16). This is the **Milky Way**—a hazy band of light which you can see if the sky is clear and dark, and if you are well away from city lights. It is the light from the hundreds of billions of fainter stars in our **galaxy**—the immense family of stars to which our sun belongs (see Figure 27-18, page 633).

g. Almost directly overhead is the great square of **Pegasus** (Fig. 28-17).

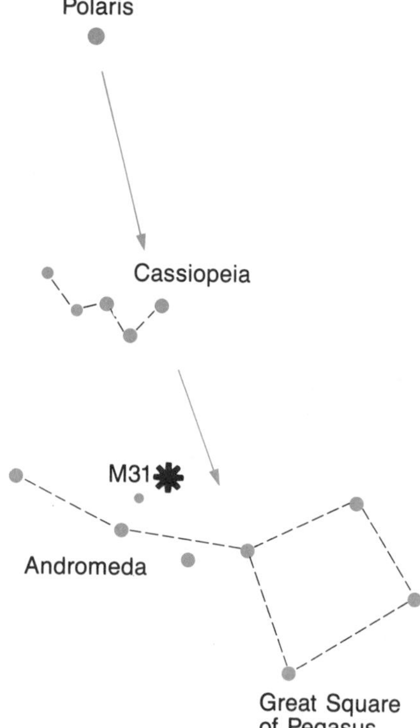

Fig. 28-17 Sky map from Polaris (the North Star) to Cassiopeia to Andromeda and Pegasus—two large constellations of the autumn sky.

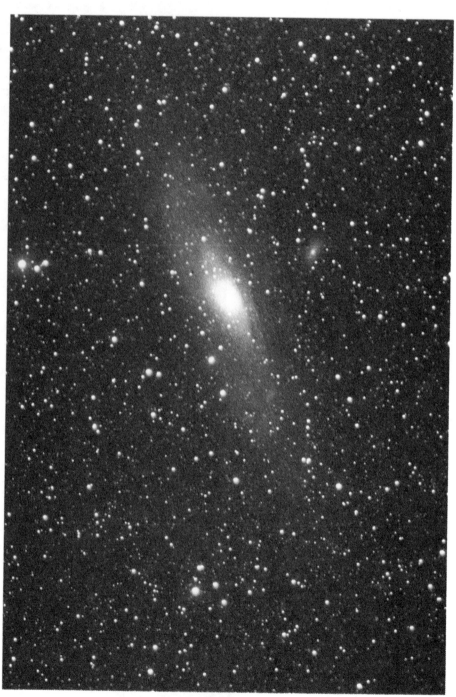

Fig. 28-18 M31 is a galaxy, two million light years away. When did the light which made this photograph leave M31?

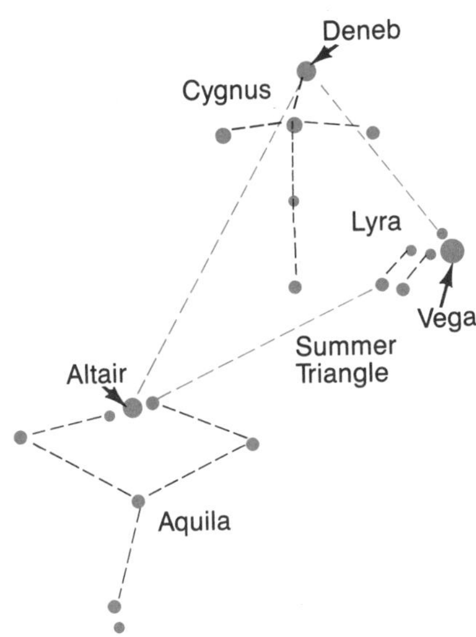

Fig. 28-19 The Summer Triangle is made up of Deneb, Vega, and Altair—three stars in three different constellations.

Pointing from the northeast corner of Pegasus is its "handle" **Andromeda**. On the sky chart, you will see an object labelled " ✱ " in Andromeda. This is M31—the **Andromeda galaxy** (Fig. 28-18). It can be seen as a hazy patch of light if the sky is clear and dark, and if your eyes are good. It is a vast collection of hundreds of billions of stars, like our Milky Way galaxy. But it is so far away that its light takes about 2 000 000 years to reach us. It is the most distant object that can be seen with the unaided eye. M31 was object #31 in a list of fuzzy objects, prepared by the French astronomer Charles Messier two centuries ago.

h. Moving further west, you will see the **Summer Triangle**—a pattern of three bright, widely-spaced stars (Fig. 28-19). They are **Vega** (to the west) in the constellation **Lyra**; **Deneb** (to the east) in the constellation **Cygnus**; and **Altair** (to the south) in the constellation **Aquila**. Vega and Altair are only slightly more powerful than the sun. They are bright because they are relatively nearby. Deneb, on the other hand, is very distant. It appears bright because it is a supergiant star—thousands of times more powerful than the sun. Cygnus (the Swan, in mythology) is sometimes called the **Northern Cross** because of its distinctive and easy-to-recognize shape. Lyra (the Lyre, in mythology) contains an interesting but rather faint object called the **Ring Nebula**. It is a **planetary nebula**—a cloud of gas dust gently ejected by a red giant star as it begins to contract to become a white dwarf (Fig. 28-20).

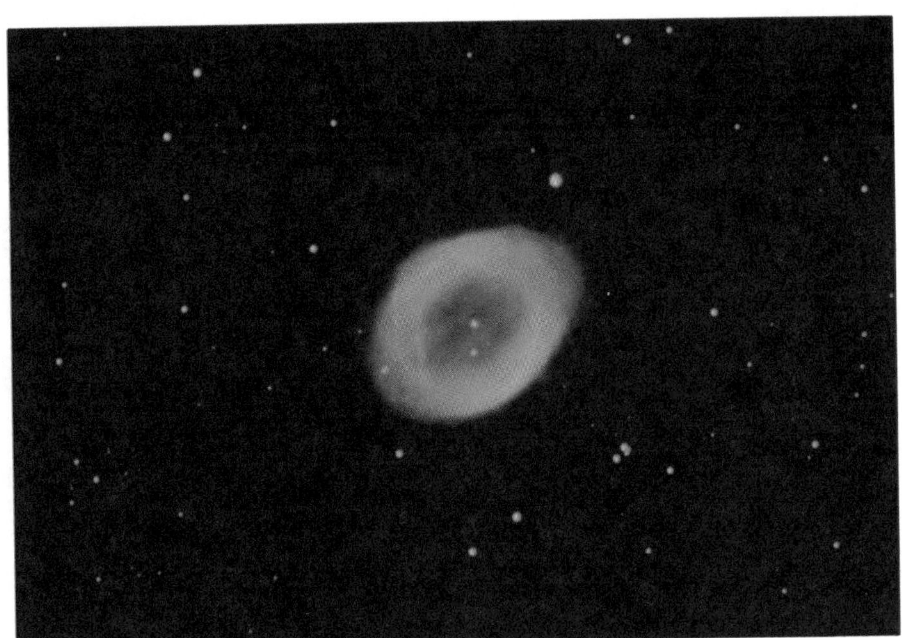

Fig. 28-20 The Ring Nebula, in Lyra, is a planetary nebula—a red giant which has cast off its atmosphere as its core contracts to become a white dwarf.

In 1972, Canadian astronomer Tom Bolton identified the first **black hole** in space. It orbits around a faint star called HDE 224868 in Cygnus (Fig. 28-21).

i. Below Lyra is the constellation **Hercules**, containing no very bright stars. It does contain an interesting star cluster called M13. Unlike the Pleiades

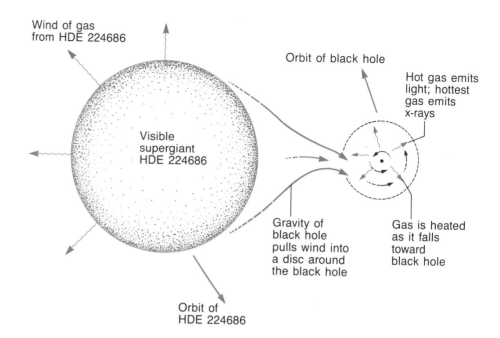

Wind of gas from HDE 224686

Orbit of black hole

Hot gas emits light; hottest gas emits x-rays

Visible supergiant HDE 224686

Gravity of black hole pulls wind into a disc around the black hole

Gas is heated as it falls toward black hole

Orbit of HDE 224686

Fig. 28-21 Cygnus X-1 consists of a black hole in orbit around a normal star. The presence of the black hole was deduced by Canadian astronomer Tom Bolton in 1972.

and the Hyades, it is a faint, distant cluster on the edge of our Milky Way galaxy. Because of its shape, it is called a **globular cluster**. Its hundreds of thousands of stars are among the oldest in our galaxy (Fig. 28-22). Canadian astronomer Helen Sawyer Hogg is known throughout the world for her studies of variable stars in globular clusters.

j. **Cetus** is one of the larger constellations. It should be—it represents a whale. The star **Mira** in Cetus is a red giant star which varies in brightness by a factor of 1000. Sometimes it can easily be seen with the unaided eye. At other times, it can hardly be seen with binoculars.

Fig. 28-22 M13 is a globular cluster of hundreds of thousand of stars, 20 000 ly away in the constellation Hercules.

There are numerous other stars and constellations in the autumn sky which you can identify and study with your sky chart. There are ones with interesting shapes, such as Coronae Borealis (the Northern Crown), Delphinus (the Dolphin), and the Little Dipper. All of these look interesting in binoculars. There are also the constellations of the zodiac: Capricornus, Aquarius, Pisces, Aries, and Taurus.

Exploration B: The Winter Sky

a. If you have already explored the autumn sky in detail, then you have met the stars and constellations in the northern sky: Ursa Major and Minor, Cassiopeia, and Perseus. If not, go back to Exploration A, and work through parts (a) to (e).

b. The path from the Big Dipper through the North Star to Cassiopeia, Perseus, Taurus, and Auriga leads you to the group of constellations around Orion—sometimes called the **Winter Six**. Begin by locating and identifying **Orion** in the southern sky (Fig. 28-23). With four bright stars representing the shoulders and knees of the great hunter, and a row of three bright stars marking his belt, this constellation is one of the easiest to recognize.

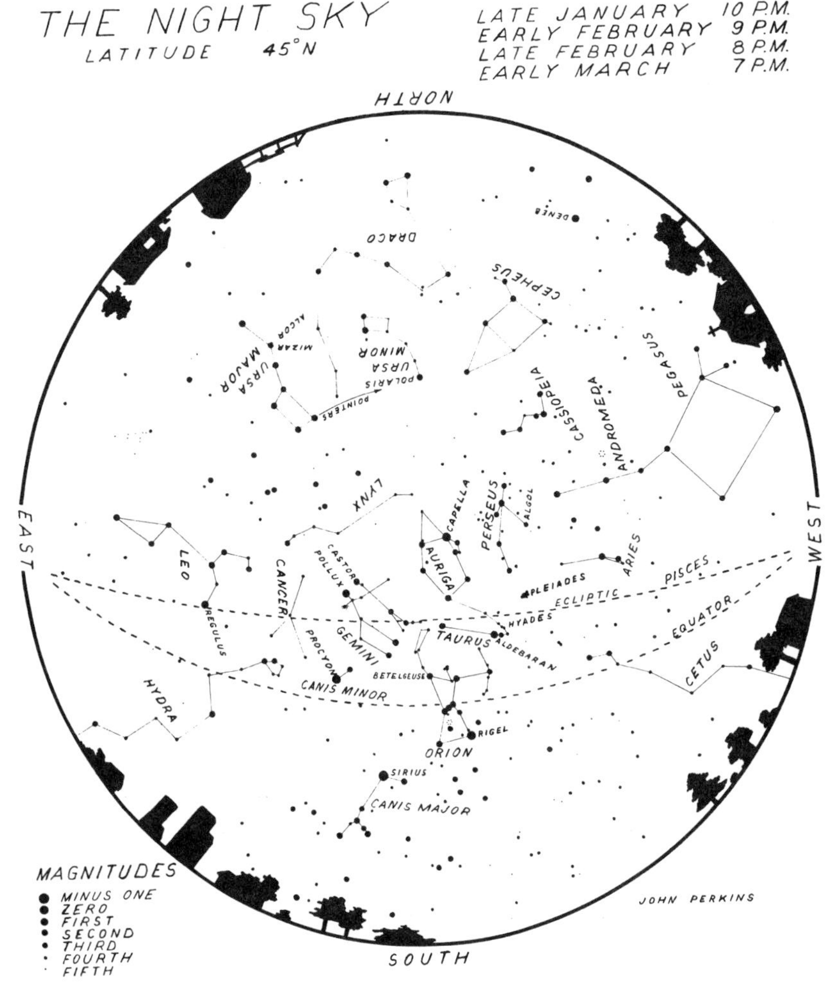

Fig. 28-23 Horizon map of the winter sky. In Activity A you learned how to use maps like this one.

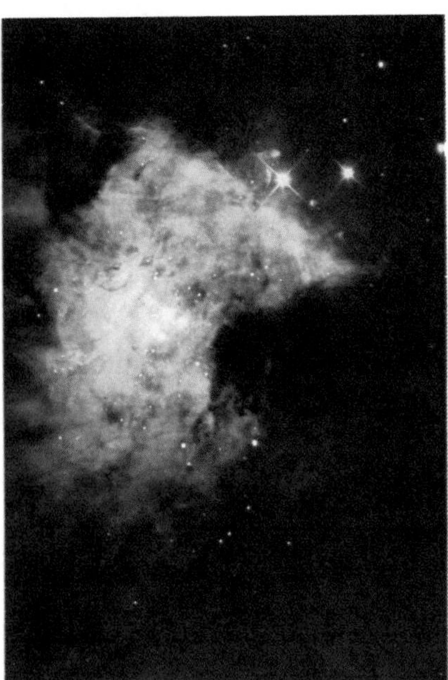

Fig. 28-24 The Orion Nebula is a giant cloud of gas and dust in space, from which stars are forming. The bright stars in this nebula are among the youngest stars known.

c. Compare the stars **Rigel** and **Betelgeuse** with respect to colour. Betelgeuse is an example of a red supergiant. As it approaches the end of its life, it has swelled up hundreds of times the size of the sun. If our sun were as big as Betelgeuse, it would engulf all the inner planets.

Below the belt of Orion is the **Orion Nebula**, a large cloud of gas and dust in space (Fig. 28-24). You can see it with the unaided eye if the sky is clear and dark. It is much easier to see with binoculars, though it still looks only like a faint, fuzzy patch of light. Many stars have formed from the gas and dust in the Orion Nebula. And stars are forming there even today. The ultraviolet light (sometimes called ''black light'') from some of these stars ''lights up'' the Orion Nebula in the same way that an electric current lights up a fluorescent lamp.

d. To the lower left of Orion is **Canis Major** (the Large Dog). The bright star **Sirius** marks the eye of the dog. If your southern sky is clear and dark, you should be able to see the hind quarters of the dog as well. Sirius is the brightest star in the night sky, partly because it is 27 times as powerful as the sun and partly because it is one of the nearest stars to the sun. Sirius is another example of a **double star**. Sirius and a faint **white dwarf** companion revolve about each other every 50 years.

e. Above Canis Major, to the left of Orion, is **Canis Minor** (the Small Dog). It has only one bright star—**Procyon**. This star is much like the sun, except that it, too, is a double star. Like Sirius, it has a faint white dwarf companion. These white dwarfs are the corpses of stars which once shone brightly but have now run out of fuel.

f. Above Canis Minor, to the upper left of Orion, is , the constellation of the twins. The bright stars **Castor** and **Pollux** represent the heads of the twins. Fainter stars make up the rest of their bodies. Castor is not a double star but a sextuple star. It consists of 6 stars arranged in 3 pairs which slowly revolve about each other. At the foot of Gemini is the summer solstice—the position of the sun in the sky on the first day of summer.

g. Above the head of Orion is the constellation **Auriga**, the Charioteer. The Milky Way (Exploration A, part f) passes through Auriga, Perseus, and Cassiopeia. **Capella**, the brightest star in Auriga, is a double star consisting of two almost identical yellow giant stars.

h. To the upper right of Orion is **Taurus**. This is the mythological Bull which Orion is fighting. Orion holds a club in one hand and a shield in the other. Taurus contains the Pleiades and the Hyades, nearby clusters of a few hundred stars. Most of the stars in Taurus belong to the Hyades cluster. An exception is **Aldebaran**, the brightest star. Aldebaran is an example of an orange giant star. In about 5 000 000 000 years, the sun will cool and expand and become a star like Aldebaran.

i. Rising in the east is the constellation **Leo**—one of the few constellations which looks like what it is supposed to represent—in this case, a lion. The bright star in the front paw of the lion is **Regulus**.

Exploration C: The Spring Sky

a. If you have already explored the autumn and/or winter sky, you will have met the constellations of the northern sky. However, the orientation of the

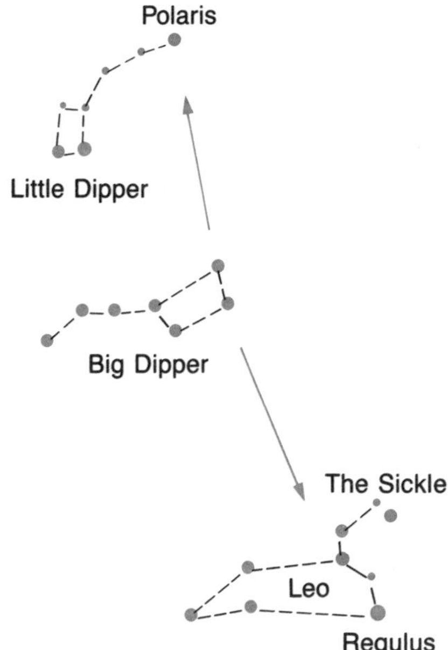

Fig. 28-25 Sky map from the Big Dipper to Polaris (the North Star) in one direction, and to Leo in the other.

constellations with respect to the horizon will have changed, due to the seasonal motion of the sky. To review these constellations, go back to Explorations A and B.

b. The Winter Six constellations are now setting in the early evening. The path from the Big Dipper to Cassiopeia to Perseus will lead you to Taurus and Auriga. You may recognize Orion in the west, from its characteristic shape. To its left, you will see Canis Major, Canis Minor, and Gemini.

c. Leo is now high in the southern sky, almost overhead. The star in the neck of the lion (called **Algeiba** or Gamma Leonis) is a double star which you can see as two stars in a small telescope. You can use the Big Dipper to find Leo by using the Pointers—the two end stars in the bowl—in reverse. Instead of going out of the bowl to the North Star, go backward to Leo (Fig. 28-25).

d. You can use the Big Dipper to find two other spring constellations. Follow the curve of the handle of the Big Dipper away from the bowl to **Arcturus**, the brightest star in the constellation **Bootes** (Fig. 28-26). There is an easy way to remember this: the curve of the handle is an arc, and you follow the arc to Arcturus! Continue in a straight line to **Spica**, the brightest star in **Virgo**. There is an easy way to remember this as well: from Arcturus, make a spike to Spica! Arcturus is an orange giant star. It is very conspicuous, high in the northeast in the evening in the spring, golden in colour. Spica is a pair of much hotter stars revolving about each other every 4 d.

e. To the east of Bootes, you can see the constellations **Hercules** and **Corona Borealis** which were visible in the autumn sky. You may be able to see the globular cluster M13 (Exploration A, part i). You can easily see it with binoculars. **Vega** is rising in the northeast. The Summer Triangle is about to appear!

There are other constellations which have not been mentioned. You can find some of them using your sky chart. There are a total of 88 constellations—the same as the number of keys on a piano.

You should include in your observing log a list of objects which you have seen. Table 28-2 is a checklist of stars and constellations which you might have encountered in your explorations, and also a checklist of the other objects and types of objects which you might have seen.

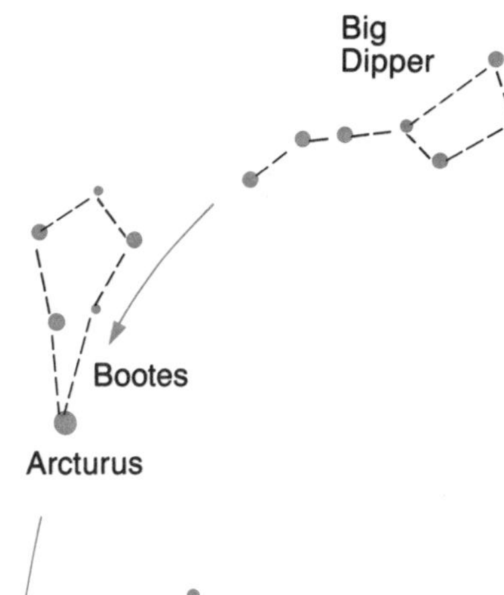

Fig. 28-26 Follow the arc of the handle of the Big Dipper to Arcturus in the constellation Bootes. Then make a spike to Spica in the constellation Virgo.

Table 28-2 A Checklist of Astronomical Objects

Constellation/Star	*Other Object*	*Type of Object*
Andromeda		
	M31: the Andromeda galaxy	galaxy
Aquila		
Altair		
Auriga		
Capella		double star
Bootes		
Arcturus		orange giant

Canis Major		
Sirius		double star with white dwarf
Canis Minor		
Procyon		double star with white dwarf
Cassiopeia		
Cetus		
Mira		variable red giant
Corona Borealis		
Cygnus		
Deneb		supergiant
	Cygnus X-1	double star with black hole
Gemini		
Castor		sextuple star
Pollux		
Hercules		
	M13: Hercules cluster	globular cluster
Leo		
Algeiba		double star
Regulus		
Lyra		
Vega		
	M57: Ring Nebula	planetary nebula
Orion		
Betelgeuse		red supergiant
Rigel		
	M42: Orion Nebula	nebula
Pegasus		
Perseus		
Algol		variable double star
Taurus		
Aldebaran		orange giant
	Hyades	open cluster
	M45: Pleiades	open cluster
	M1: Crab Nebula	supernova nebula
Ursa Major		
Alcor & Mizar		double star
	Ursa Major cluster	open cluster
Ursa Minor		
Polaris (North Star)		variable supergiant
Virgo		
Spica		double star

28.9 Naming Astronomical Objects

The constellation names which we use are derived from Greek and Roman mythology, and are rich in history and meaning. When astronomers first mapped the southern skies, however, Europe was in the midst of the industrial revolution. The astronomers named southern constellations after things like the telescope (Telescopium) and the air pump (Antlia)!

Other civilizations invented completely different constellations. The Chinese, for instance, were observing and recording the appearance of the sky as early as 3000 years ago. They developed a much more detailed set of constellations than the ones that we use today.

Most of the star names which we use are Arabic in origin. The Arabs played an important role in the history of astronomy by preserving astronomical knowledge from the end of the Roman Empire, through the Dark Ages, to the birth of the Renaissance.

Stars also have "Greek letter names"—like Alpha Centauri. The faintest stars have only catalogue numbers, or are designated according to their position in the sky. This would be like naming a town according to its latitude and longitude on earth. There are some companies which will offer to name a star after you—for a price. These names are not official, and are never used by astronomers. So don't waste your money!

The planets and their satellites are named after various gods in Greek and Roman mythology—although, with so many new satellites being discovered by spacecraft, the list of possible names is being used up very rapidly.

Asteroids are named *by* their discoverers. Since several thousand of these minor planets are now known, suitable names are hard to find. The first few dozen were named after characters in mythology. Now, they are named after a variety of things, ranging from countries and cities (such as Toronto) to astronomers both living and dead.

Comets are usually named *after* their discoverer—but there is one famous exception. Comet Halley was not discovered by Halley. Rather, he was the first to realize that it moved in a regular orbit about the sun, and returned to the vicinity of the earth every 76 years. So if you want to have your name in the sky, the best—and most useful—way is to discover a comet!

Mythology is the popular culture of the past. Once, astronomers borrowed names from this popular culture of the past. Today's popular culture is borrowing them back. Think of all the "brand names" which come from astronomy: Mercury cars, Quasar TVs, Pulsar watches, and the Minnesota North Stars hockey team! The three daily papers in Toronto are the *Globe*, the *Star*, and the *Sun*! As a class project, you might collect a complete list of astronomical brand names.

Section Review

1. Prepare a summary of how astronomical objects are named.

2. Make a list of astronomical brand names that includes at least three names not mentioned in this section.

28.10 Supernova Shelton

Nothing illustrates the nature of astronomy as vividly as the discovery of **Supernova Shelton** in 1987. Ian Shelton, a young Canadian astronomer, was using a telescope at the University of Toronto Southern Observatory in Chile to photograph the Large Magellanic Cloud—the nearest other galaxy to our Milky Way. On the night of 1987 02 23–24, he noticed that there was a bright star on his photograph, which had not been visible the night before (Fig. 28-27). He quickly verified his discovery by looking up at the sky. The star—despite its distance of 170 000 ly—was bright enough to see with the unaided eye!

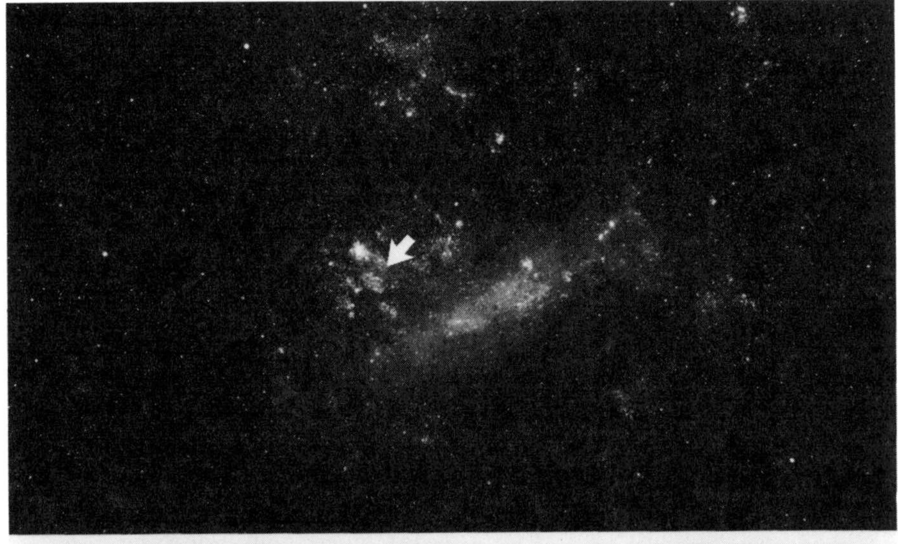

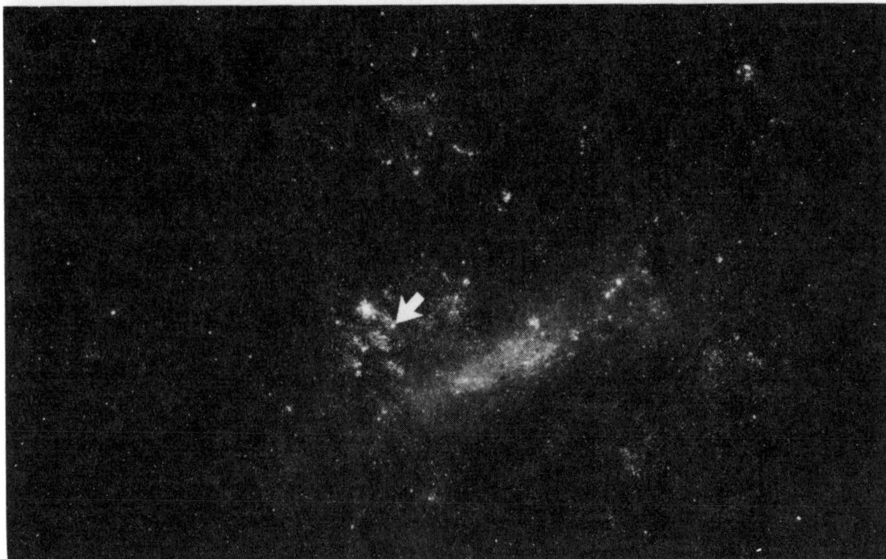

Fig. 28-27 Ian Shelton's photographs of the Large Magellanic Cloud galaxy the night before the supernova appeared (top) and the night the supernova appeared (bottom).

The star was a **supernova**—a massive star whose core had collapsed as its thermonuclear energy supply ran out. The collapse produced a sudden burst of gravitational energy, which exploded the star like a bomb. It swelled at 15 000 km/s, and became a billion times brighter than the sun. The formal name of the supernova is ''1987 A''.

Supernovas are important because they produce chemical elements such as carbon, nitrogen, and oxygen, and spread them into interstellar space where they can form into new stars and planets. The blast waves from supernovas may actually trigger the formation of stars and planets in space. Supernovas are so bright that they are visible even in the most distant galaxies. Therefore astronomers can measure the distance to these galaxies by comparing the apparent brightness of the supernovas with their actual brightness or power at a known distance.

Supernovas remind us that astronomy is an observational science. To understand how a star dies, for instance, astronomers must wait until such an event occurs, then observe it carefully and completely. They can then compare their observations with their theories, to see how well they agree.

Section Review

1. Describe the discovery of Supernova Shelton.
2. **a)** What is a supernova?
   b) Why are supernovas important?

28.11 A Career in Astronomy

Many people think that it would be exciting and romantic to be an astronomer. It is also challenging. It takes 7 or more years at university to become a research astronomer like René Racine or Scott Tremaine, 3 or more years to become an astronomy technician like Ian Shelton or an educator like Mary Grey. No matter what kind or amount of education you have, however, you can become an amateur astronomer like Warren Morrison, and contribute to astronomy in that way. There are only a few hundred people in Canada who make a career of astronomy. But there are tens of thousands who make a hobby of it.

There are two broad classes of astronomers: those who use the mind and the computer to develop theories, and those who use telescopes to make observations to test them. Even ''observational'' astronomers spend most of their time planning and analyzing their observations, and thinking about, discussing, and writing about their results. They spend very little time at the telescope. Those who work in universities have other duties such as teaching and supervising students. Astronomy educators do not generally do research, but spend most of their time preparing articles, displays, lectures, and audio-visual presentations for the public.

Salaries, fringe benefits, and working conditions are quite good. The greatest reward, however, is the joy of exploring the universe, and sharing in astronomical discovery.

Chapter Highlights

1. The sun provides a closeup view of a typical star.
2. The sun's energy has sustained life on earth for billions of years.
3. Astronomers use telescopes and other instruments to study light from distant stars.
4. Astronomers use observations of stars and other objects to develop and test theories of the birth, evolution, and death of stars.
5. Using your unaided eye or binoculars, you can locate stars in various stages of development.
6. The "exploration of the night sky" is an enjoyable activity for anyone, and a useful hobby for many.

Key Terms

amateur astronomer
black hole
double star
galaxy
giant star
globular star cluster
light year
nebula
neutron star
open star cluster
photometer
planetary nebula
reflecting telescope
refracting telescope
solar energy
spectrograph
spectrum
sunspot
supergiant star
supernova
thermonuclear fusion
white dwarf

Recognizing the Concepts

Each of the following statements or questions is followed by four responses. Choose the correct response in each case. (Do not write in this book.)

1. The sun is made mostly of
   a) hydrogen and helium metal, liquid, and gas
   b) the same things as the earth is
   c) hydrogen and helium gas
   d) carbon, nitrogen, and oxygen
2. M31—the fuzzy object in Andromeda—is a
   a) cloud of gas and dust
   b) remnant of a supernova
   c) black hole
   d) galaxy
3. Astronomers expect that, in the future, the sun will become a
   a) white dwarf
   b) comet
   c) tenth planet
   d) supernova
4. Astronomers know what the stars are made of by
   a) direct sampling of their material
   b) photography by spacecraft fly-bys
   c) analysis of their light
   d) assuming that they are the same as the earth
5. The safest way to observe the sun is by
   a) looking at it in a mirror

b) projecting its image on a sheet of white paper
c) looking at it at night
d) looking at it through a telescope

Understanding the Concepts

1. What do we mean when we say that astronomy is an observational science, not an experimental one? How does Supernova Shelton 1987 A illustrate this?
2. Briefly describe the evolution of the sun, from its birth to its death. How do astronomers know this information?
3. What are the advantages and disadvantages of large telescopes?
4. Why do astronomers build telescopes in places like Hawaii and Chile? What would be some advantages of having a telescope near a large city such as Toronto?
5. Why are very few buildings in Canada heated by solar energy?
6. Suppose that the star Betelgeuse were to explode as a supernova. How long would it be before we knew about it? What changes in the star would we expect to observe?

Applying the Concepts

1. If so many of the visible stars are giants and supergiants, why do we say that the sun is an above-average star?
2. What would be the effects on the earth if the sun became **(a)** a red giant; **(b)** a variable star; **(c)** a supernova; **(d)** a white dwarf; **(e)** a black hole?
3. Discuss the problems of communicating by radio with an intelligent civilization in the galaxy M31.
4. Why would it be difficult for astronomers to observe planets around stars other than the sun?
5. Suppose that you lived on a planet (like Venus) that was always cloudy. Would you be able to learn anything about the outside universe? If so, how?
6. Some spacecraft use solar energy and some use other kinds of energy. What other kinds of energy do you think they could use? Give examples of spacecraft which could use solar energy and spacecraft which could not.

Investigations

1. Find out the difference between science fiction and science fantasy. Read a science fiction story about extraterrestrial life, and prepare a written or oral report on it.
2. Find out where the nearest major astronomical observatory is, and what is done there.
3. Research the relationship between astronomers' theories and observations of the birth and death of stars.
4. Investigate the mythological stories connected with the name of a constellation.

THE BIRTH AND DEATH OF THE UNIVERSE

Where did the universe come from? What will be its fate? The laws of physics and the observations of astronomy have enabled scientists to develop a theory which begins to answer these fundamental questions.

The most important observation is that the universe is expanding. Every galaxy is moving away from every other galaxy at a speed which is proportional to the distance between them. How do astronomers know? The waves of light from distant galaxies are stretched by the motion, and so the light becomes redder in colour. This effect is called the **Doppler effect**, and this particular application of it is called the **red shift**.

If the galaxies have been moving away from each other at a constant speed, then we can use the formula *time = distance/speed* to calculate the time since the galaxies were together in space. Since speed is proportional to distance, we get the same time for every pair of galaxies in the universe—about 15 000 000 000 years. This is the same as the age of the oldest stars in the universe, and also the same as the age of the atoms in the universe deduced from their radioactivity. These observations are all consistent with the theory that the universe began 15 000 000 000 years ago, expanding from a dense, hot state called the **big bang**. The "echo" of the radiant energy from the big bang was discovered in 1965 in the form of radio waves which filled all of space. Arno Penzias and Robert Wilson won the Nobel Prize in physics for this discovery because it provides one of the strongest pieces of evidence in favour of the big bang theory.

But will the galaxies continue to expand into a vast loneliness as their stars gradually fade and die? Or will the gravity of each galaxy pull hard enough on every other galaxy so that the expansion will eventually stop, reverse, and pull the universe back together in a **big crunch**? Scientists do not know. For some reason, the universe is very close to the balance point between eternal expansion and eventual crunch.

How and why did the universe come into being? Scientists can probably never answer the "why", because it lies more in the realm of philosophy and religion. But exploring the "how" is one of the most exciting areas of research in modern science. To understand how matter behaved in the heat of the big bang, scientists must use the results of high-energy physics—the branch of physics in which billion-dollar "atom smashers" are used to find out what protons, neutrons, and electrons are made of. At the very highest energies, particles break down into their simple components, and the many forces of nature become one simple, unified force. The universe is reduced to the simplest and most fundamental questions: What is matter? Where did it come from? What are the laws which control it?

Appendices

Appendix A The Metric System of Measurement

Metric Prefixes

The metric system is based upon a system of **primary units**. For example, the primary unit of length is the metre. All other units of length are based on the metre. They are multiples or submultiples of it and are called **secondary units**. For example, a kilometre is a multiple of a metre (one thousand metres). A centimetre is a submultiple of a metre (a hundredth).

The metric system uses prefixes for secondary units. Table A-1 gives the common prefixes you should know from memory. The system is simple to use. **Kilo** means one thousand. If you put ''kilo'' in front of ''metre'' you get **kilometre**. A kilometre is one thousand metres. Or, in symbols, 1 km = 1000 m. **Milli** means a thousandth, or 0.001. If you put ''milli'' in front of ''metre'' you get **millimetre**. A millimetre is a thousandth of a metre. Or, in symbols, 1 mm = 0.001 m.

The same prefixes are used for metric units other than length. Thus one **kilogram** is one thousand grams (1 kg = 1000 g) and one **millilitre** is a thousandth of a litre (1 mL = 0.001 L).

Table A-1 Common Metric Prefixes

Prefix	*Symbol*	*Meaning*
mega	M	1 000 000 (million)
kilo	k	1 000 (thousand)
hecto	h	100 (hundred)
deca	da	10 (ten)
	THE UNIT (e.g. metre)	
deci	d	0.1 (tenth)
centi	c	0.01 (hundredth)
milli	m	0.001 (thousandth)
micro	μ	0.000 001 (millionth)

Some Rules

- Symbols are not followed by periods (except at the end of a sentence).
- Symbols are never pluralized. For example, ''m'' stands for both ''metre'' and ''metres''.

- Commas are not used in numerals. Numerals with 4 or less digits are written this way: 24 280 5285. Numerals with over 4 digits are written this way: 12 045 270 584 3 877 544.

Measuring Length

The main advantage of the metric system is that it uses a decimal system. Each unit is related to the others by factors of 10. Table A-2 shows how this decimal system works for length units. Of the length units shown in this table, only the kilometre (km), metre (m), centimetre (cm), and millimetre (mm) are commonly used.

Table A-2 Measuring Length

1 km = 10 hm		1 km = 1000 m		1 m = 0.001 km	
1 hm = 10 dam		1 hm = 100 m		1 m = 0.01 hm	
1 dam = 10 m	OR	1 dam = 10 m	OR	1 m = 0.1 dam	
1 m = 10 dm		1 dm = 0.1 m		1 m = 10 dm	
1 dm = 10 cm		1 cm = 0.01 m		1 m = 100 cm	
1 cm = 10 mm		1 mm = 0.001 m		1 m = 1000 mm	

Measuring Area

Area is defined as the amount of surface. It is two-dimensional, or flat. That is, it does not extend into the space above. A rectangle, square, triangle, and circle are two-dimensional, and each has an area. For example, the area of a rectangle is calculated using $A = l \times w$, where l = length and w = width (Fig. A-1).

The primary unit of area is the **square metre (m^2)**. Several secondary units are derived from it. Commonly used multiple units are the **square kilometre (km^2)** and the square hectometre (hm^2). The square hectometre is usually called a **hectare (ha)**. A hectare is about the size of two football fields. The **square centimetre (cm^2)** is the only submultiple unit that is commonly used. Table A-3 shows how the common area units are used.

Table A-3 Common Area Units and Uses

Unit	*Symbol*	*Uses*
Square kilometre	km^2	To measure areas of large surfaces such as land masses, oceans, lakes, and forests
Square hectometre or Hectare	hm^2 ha	To measure areas of smaller surfaces such as farms, parks, and playing fields
Square metre	m^2	To measure areas of such things as floors, lawns, small gardens, and offices
Square centimetre	cm^2	To measure areas of small surfaces like the sole of a shoe, a card, a leaf, an animal's footprint

Measuring Volume

Volume is defined as the amount of space an object occupies. It is three-dimensional; it covers an area on a surface and also extends into the space above. A brick, a baseball, and a glass of water all have volume. That is, they take up space.

Volume units are of two types: **cubic units** and **capacity units**. The common cubic units are the cubic metre (m^3), cubic decimetre (dm^3), and cubic centimetre (cm^3). The common capacity units are the kilolitre (kL), litre (L), and millilitre (mL). Table A-4 shows how these units are related. The **cubic metre** is the primary unit of volume.

Table A-4 Volume Units

A. Relationships Among Cubic Units
1 m^3 = 1000 dm^3
1 dm^3 = 1000 cm^3
B. Relationships Among Capacity Units
1 kL = 1000 L
1 L = 1000 mL

Table A-5 Comparison of Cubic and Capacity Units

Cubic unit		Capacity unit
1 m^3	=	1 kL
1 dm^3	=	1 L
1 cm^3	=	1 mL

Generally, cubic units are used for solids and capacity units are used for fluids. However, it is not wrong to speak of 50 mL or 50 cm^3 of water. Nor is it wrong to speak of 50 cm^3 or 50 mL of wood. The two types of units are very closely related, as Table A-5 shows.

Table A-6 shows how the common volume units are used.

Table A-6 Common Volume Units and Uses

Unit	Symbol	Uses
Cubic metre	m^3	To measure large volumes of earth and gravel, the volume of a building, the volume of the hold of a ship
Kilolitre	kL	To measure the volume of water in a reservoir, the volume of gasoline in a tanker truck
Litre	L	To measure volumes of milk, gasoline, paint, ice cream; to measure capacities of pails, kettles, auto gas tanks, refrigerators, freezers
Cubic centimetre	cm^3	To measure volumes of small boxes and other small objects of regular shapes (cuboid, spherical, cylindrical, etc.)
Millilitre	mL	To measure the volume of materials (usually fluid) that come in containers smaller than 1 L; for example, toothpaste, a glass of milk, soft drinks, hair shampoo, shaving lotion

Measuring Mass

The **mass** of an object is the amount of material in it. The primary unit of mass is the **kilogram**. The common mass units are the tonne (t), kilogram (kg), gram (g), and milligram (mg). Table A-7 shows how these are related.

Table A-7 Common Mass Units

1 t	=	1000 kg
1 kg	=	1000 g
1 g	=	1000 mg

Table A-8 shows how the common mass units are used.

Table A-8 Common Mass Units and Uses

Unit	*Symbol*	*Uses*
Tonne or Megagram	t Mg	To measure masses of large objects like trucks, tractors, airplanes, and ships; masses of loads of earth, grain, ore, etc.
Kilogram	kg	To measure masses of sugar, flour, meat, and other grocery items; masses of people, horses, and other animals
Gram	g	To measure masses of smaller grocery items like butter, powdered milk, yogurt, cheese, and meat slices
Milligram	mg	To measure masses of vitamins and minerals in pills, cereal, or bread; masses of ingredients in medical products

Appendix B A Systematic Approach to Problem Solving

A significant amount of effort and time in science is spent solving problems. Many problems appear more difficult than they really are. The use of a systematic approach helps break a problem down into its component parts and facilitates a solution. This appendix illustrates the five basic steps of an approach called the **GRASS method**. This is the method used in this book.

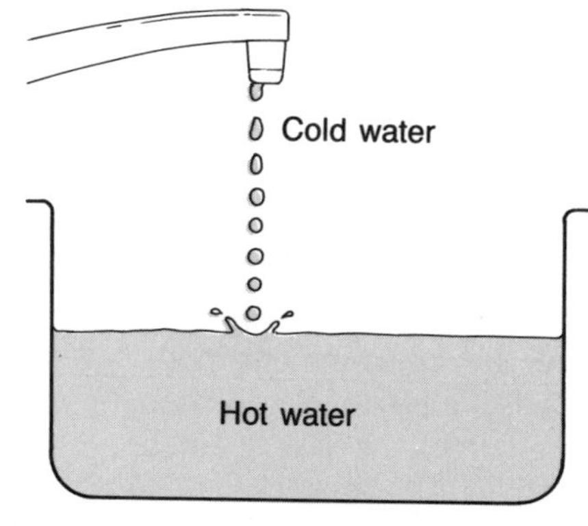

Sample Problem

A wash basin contains 1.2 kg of hot water at a temperature of 75°C. The temperature of the cold water from the tap is 22°C. What mass of cold water in kilograms is needed to adjust the temperature of the hot water to 40°C?

Given

$t_{hot} = 75°C$
$m_{hot} = 1.2$ kg
$t_{cold} = 22°C$
$t_{mixture} = 40°C$

Step 1 List What Is Given

The first step in solving the problem involves answering the question: "What information are we **given?**" To answer this question, read the problem carefully, note the information given, and list it with appropriate symbols and units.

Required

m_c in kg

Step 2 List What You Are Required to Find

The second step involves answering the question: "What am I **required** to find?" To answer this question, identify what the problem is asking you to do. Be sure to include the units requested.

Analysis

- Find the change in temperature of the hot and cold water.
- Use the heat transfer equation $Q = m \cdot \Delta t \cdot c$ for both the hot water and the cool water.
- Use the Principle of Heat Exchange and equate the two equations.
- Solve for the mass of the cold water.

Step 3 Analyze the Problem Carefully

The third step requires a careful analysis of the problem. **Analysis** means to break a problem down into its component parts. If possible, begin by sketching a diagram (Fig. B-1). Many science problems lend themselves to a diagram. A diagram often provides the key to solving the problem. Then write down all the relationships you know involving the given and the unknown. Also write down any assumptions which must be made in order to solve the problem. An assumption is anything that must be taken for granted. Next start with what you are trying to find and ask the question: "What additional information do I need to calculate the unknown?"

Solution

$\Delta t_{hot} = 75°C - 40°C = 35°C$
$\Delta t_{cold} = 40°C - 22°C = 18°C$
$Q_{lost} = m \cdot \Delta t_{hot} \cdot c$
$= 1.2 \text{ kg} \times 35°C \times c$
$Q_{gained} = m \cdot \Delta t_{cold} \cdot c$
$= m \times 18°C \times c$
$Q_{lost} = Q_{gained}$ (Principle of Heat Exchange)
$1.2 \text{ kg} \times 35°C \times c$
$= m \times 18°C \times c$

$$m = \frac{1.2 \text{ kg} \times 35°C \times c}{18°C \times c}$$

$m = 2.3$ kg

Step 4 Synthesize a Solution

The fourth step requires us to synthesize a **solution** to the problem. Synthesis is the reverse of analysis and involves putting together the elements or parts to form a whole. The parts identified during the analysis stage must be put together to form the solution to the problem. In science this often includes substituting the data into an equation, simplifying, and solving for the unknown.

Statement
The mass of cold water that must be added to cool the mixture to 40°C is 2.3 kg.

Step 5 Write a Final Statement
The problem is complete only when a statement is made which answers the original question. Since the original question was a sentence, the answer should be a sentence.

We call this the **GRASS method** of solving problems. The symbols in GRASS correspond to the first letter in the key word of each step: **G**iven, **R**equired, **A**nalysis, **S**olution, **S**tatement. We believe that successful problem solving requires a systematic approach which includes units analysis and the conversion factor method. We will use these components in the sample problems in this text.

Appendix C A Guide for Research and Independent Study

The ''Investigations'' sections which appear at the end of each chapter in this book include many ideas for research and independent study. Research gives you the opportunity to extend your knowledge about a particular area of science. In researching a topic, you find answers to questions and solutions to problems. You also become aware of the social, moral, political, and economic implications of science that scientists face while conducting their studies.

Research is not just experiments done in a laboratory. It involves finding out the results of the work of others on the same and related topics. This makes communication of accurate information vitally important in science. Therefore, scientists continually write and publish research papers and books to document and describe their work and discoveries. These writings become the foundation on which other scientists build and conduct their experimental research. In fact, almost all scientific investigations are preceded by a **literature search**.

How would you conduct a literature search? Where do you start? Research on any topic is easy if you know how to start and where to go for the information. Another important component of research is the **research paper**. What should it contain? How would you put it all together? The information in this appendix will help you find the answers to these questions.

The Research Process

Often, your teacher allows you to choose a topic for independent study. Selecting an appropriate topic and limiting it to a sufficient degree should result in a successful research paper. Selecting a topic impulsively or intuitively may cause you to regret your haste. Here are some of the things you should consider as you choose your topic:

1. Understand the assignment.
2. Select a topic in which you have interest, curiosity, experience, or competency.
3. Select a topic in which appropriate resources are readily available.
4. Select a topic important and significant enough to be researched.
5. Select a topic that can be worked with effectively within the time limits and/or length limits of the assignment.
6. Select a subject that is sufficiently controversial to prompt occasion for discussion.
7. Select a subject that is clearly defined with a beginning, an end, and focal points for discussion.

In conducting your research, you must investigate relevant sources of information. Most of the sources of information are found in your school or public library. You might begin by looking for information in a dictionary, an encyclopedia (look up the title of your topic in the index of the encyclopedia), or other general reference source. An article in a general reference source usually ends with references to books which the writer of the article found useful.

Your next step is to look in the library **subject card catalogue** for some of these books and others written on the subject of your research. Books provide an opportunity for in-depth treatment and analysis of the subject. Books may entice you to investigate more recent or current reports dealing with the specifics of your topic. For that you go to the *Reader's Guide to Periodical Literature* to find magazine articles on your topic.

Keep in mind that the amount of information you can get from a particular source depends on the audience for whom it is written. Some of the magazines and books are intended for practising scientists, some are written for readers who are not scientists but who have a good background in science, and others provide a ''popular'' approach to the topic. If you are looking for information about people in science, you might look in *Who's Who in Science* or other biographical dictionaries, indexes, and directories.

Your research may take you from a dictionary and encyclopedia to books (identified through library card catalogue), to recent magazine articles (identified through *Reader's Guide to Periodical Literature*), to biographical directories. Besides searching in books, you may want to ask specific questions of experts at a university, industrial research centre, or manufacturing plant. You may also want to conduct experiments with the help of your teacher.

Sources of Information

General Reference Sources

General reference sources such as encyclopedias, handbooks, and dictionaries are excellent basic sources of information. They give you an overview of the topic you are researching. These sources should be consulted for

- dates
- people
- narrowing of subject
- background information

Dictionaries
Some of the best-known dictionaries are:

- *The Oxford English Dictionary*, 1933, 12 volumes
- *The Concise Oxford Dictionary*, 1976
- *Webster's Third New International Dictionary*, 1961
- *Webster's New Collegiate Dictionary*, 1977

Special subjects have their own dictionaries. Some useful special dictionaries are the Dictionaries of Biology, Chemistry, Engineering, Medicine, Physics, Geology.

General Encyclopedias
A general encyclopedia summarizes the world's knowledge and provides answers to questions. Three of the better known encyclopedias are:

- *Encyclopedia Britiannica*
- *Encyclopedia Americana*
- *Encyclopedia Canadiana*

Some useful specialized encyclopedias which cover a single field of interest are:

- *How It Works*, an illustrated encyclopedia of science and technology
- *Van Nostrand's Scientific Encyclopedia*
- *McGraw-Hill Encyclopedia of Science and Technology*
- *The New Book of Popular Science*, 6 volumes; Volume 3 on physical science and Volume 6 on technology
- *Science Year*, the World Book Science Annual (contains reviews of major science happenings of the previous year)

Biographies
The life and achievements of individuals are outlined in their biographies. If you are looking for information about a scientist who is dead, consult a biographical dictionary. If the scientist is still alive, consult a biographical index or directory. Some useful biographical dictionaries are:

- *Dictionary of Scientific Biography*
- *Webster's Biographical Dictionary*
- *Encyclopedia of World Biography*

Some biographical indexes and directories are:

- *Who's Who in Science*
- *International Who's Who*, yearly since 1935
- *Current Biography*, monthly since 1939

Handbooks
Handbooks contain facts and specific information about a particular subject. Two useful handbooks are:

- *Guinness Book of World Records*, yearly since 1955
- *Handbook of Chemistry and Physics*, yearly since 1913

Books: The Card Catalogue
In order to find the book you need to consult, you use the **card catalogue**. The card catalogue is an index to all books in the library. Each book may be listed on three kinds of card: a **title** card, an **author** card, and/or a **subject**

card. Looking under the subject is the quickest way to locate books on a specific topic. All the cards are arranged alphabetically and placed in little drawers in a large cabinet. The location of a book in the library is indicated by the **call number** which appears in the upper left-hand corner of the card. Ask the librarian in your school to show you how to use the card catalogue in order to find a book you need.

Periodicals

Periodicals include magazines, journals, and newspapers. They usually provide current information on any topic. Most libraries have a periodical desk where you can check a listing of the magazines and newspapers available. If you want to find out what magazine articles exist on your topic, consult the *Reader's Guide to Periodical Literature* or *Magazine Index* which are located in the "Current Information" section of the library. Other useful periodical indexes are:

- *Applied Science and Technology Index*, monthly since 1964
- *Canadian Periodical Index*, monthly since 1948

If you are interested in a search of newspaper articles, you can use one or more of the following indexes:

- *The New York Times*, yearly since 1851
- *The Times Index* (London), yearly since 1906
- *Christian Science Monitor Index*, yearly since 1960
- *Canadian News Facts*, since 1967

PHOTO CREDITS

Every reasonable effort has been made to find copyright holders of the following material. The publisher would be pleased to have any errors or omissions brought to its attention. For permission to use the following material in this textbook, we thank

Fig. I-6 G. Corbett/Miller Comstock Inc.; Fig. I-8 National Film Board of Canada; Fig. I-18/27-13, 26-0, 27-9, 27-10, 27-12, 27-13, 27-14, 27-15 NASA/Jet Propulsion Laboratory, California Institute of Technology; Fig. 1-17, 5-14B D.K. Moore; Fig. 3-8A J. Taylor/Miller Comstock Inc.; Fig. 3-8B Metropolitan Toronto Zoo; Fig. 3-9B James D. Markou/Miller Comstock Inc.; Fig. 3-16 National Museums of Canada, National Museum of Natural Sciences, Neg. #J9086; Fig. 4-11, 4-12, 13-6 Ontario Ministry of Agriculture and Food; Fig. 4-13, 11-0 Ontario Ministry of Natural Resources; Fig. 5-7A Ontario Ministry of Health Laboratory Services; Fig. 5-7B, 5-8B, 5-14A Dr. Pamela Stokes, Botany Department, University of Toronto; Fig. 5-8A, 9-7 Gilbert L. Twiest, excerpted from Fresh-water Plants and Animals, Sound filmstrip series, Prentice-Hall Media; Fig. 6-1 Al Giddings, Ocean Images Inc.; Fig. 6-12, Vista Ch. 27 National Research Council of Canada; Fig. 6-22 Eric Y.C. Lin, Zoology Department, University of Toronto; Fig. 6-26 Hugh Halliday; Fig. 6-28 Ward's Natural Science Ltd.; Vista Ch. 6 NMRS courtesy Toronto General Hospital; Fig. 7-4, 7-19, 7-26, 7-27, 7-28 H.G. Hedges; Biography Ch. 7 Norah and Fred Urquhart; Vista Ch. 7 Dr. h.c. Lennart Nilsson and "Boehringer Ingelheim International, GMBH"; Fig. 8-1 J. Coleman Fletcher/Miller Comstock Inc.; Fig. 11-0 Ontario Ministry of Municipal Affairs and Housing; Fig. 11-8 Ministry of Energy; Fig. 11-25A Ontario Ministry of Transportation; Fig. 12-17, 12-18, 16-6, 25-13, Biography Ch. 13 Ontario Hydro; Fig. 14-21, 15-1 York University, Toronto Telegram Collection; Fig. 15-21 Binks Manufacturing Co.; Fig. 15-22 CN Tower; Career Ch. 16 Norman Thomas; Fig. 19-0 Imperial Oil Ltd.; Fig. 20-1, 20-5 FMH Canada Ltd.; Biography Ch. 21 Imperial Oil Archives; Fig. 23-1 Ontario Ministry of the Environment; Biography Ch. 24 Gerald Bengert; Fig. 26-9 National Optical Astronomy Observatories and W.J. Sullivan III; Fig. 26-13 Science Graphics Inc.; Fig. 26-18 Len Chester; Vista Ch. 26 Norton Scientific; Fig. 27-1, 27-7, 27-8, 27-11 NASA; Fig. 27-4 Dr. R.L. Bishop/Royal Astronomical Society of Canada; Fig. 27-5, 28-24 Lick Observatory; Fig. 27-6 Mt. Wilson Observatory; Fig. 27-16 Mt. Stromlo and Siding Springs Observatories; Fig. 27-17 U.S. Naval Observatory; Fig. 27-18 University of Toronto Southern Observatory; Fig. 27-19 Thomas B. Kirby and Thomas P. Pope, New Mexico State University; Fig. 27-21 Air photograph A11461-43(c) 1948 Her Majesty the Queen in Right of Canada, reproduced from the collection of the National Air Photo Library with permission of Energy, Mines and Resources Canada; Fig. 28-1, 28-14, 28-18 Michael S.F. Watson; Fig. 28-11 David Dunlap Observatory, University of Toronto; Fig. 28-12 Canada-France-Hawaii Telescope Corp.; Fig. 28-15, 28-20, 28-22 Canada-France-Hawaii Telescope Corp. and Dr. Laird Thompson; Fig. 28-27 Ian Shelton, University of Toronto Southern Observatory.

All other photos were supplied by the authors.

Index

Note: The pages in **boldface** indicate explanations.

R

S

T